TEACHERS' EDITION

# GEOMETRY

**Edwin E. Moise**
Auburn University

**Floyd L. Downs, Jr.**
Hillsdale High School
San Mateo, California

Addison-Wesley Publishing Company
Menlo Park, California • Reading, Massachusetts
London • Don Mills, Ontario • Sydney

Books in the
Addison-Wesley Mathematics Series

ALGEBRA
R. Johnson, L. Lendsey, W. Slesnick

GEOMETRY
E. Moise, F. Downs

ALGEBRA AND TRIGONOMETRY
R. Johnson, L. Lendsey, W. Slesnick, G. Bates

PRE-CALCULUS MATHEMATICS
M. Shanks, C. Flenor, C. Brumfiel

ELEMENTS OF CALCULUS
AND ANALYTIC GEOMETRY
G. Thomas, R. Finney

ISBN 0-201-05029-3
BCDEFGHIJK-VH-8765432

# PREFACE

The *Teachers' Edition* provides a section-by-section commentary on the student text and includes: reproduction of each page of the student text; a general introduction to each chapter; an outline of the chapter to aid teacher lesson planning; mathematical discussions of most sections of the text; proofs of some theorems which were considered too difficult for the student text; suggestions, based on our own classroom experience, on how to teach particular topics and how to handle particular problem sets; quizzes for individual sections; answers to many of the problems; and suggested test questions (in the front of the book). The pages of the student text have been annotated with answers to short-answer and numerical problems. In addition there is a Solution Section at the end of the *Teachers' Edition* which contains all the solutions not given either in the annotations or in the margins of the *Teachers' Edition*. It also contains expansions of some of the answers and discussions of some of the more difficult, interesting problems.

Most of the remarks in the *Teachers' Edition* are intended to furnish practical help in teaching the course. Some of them give the reasons for various novel features of the text. The intent is to make the *Teachers' Edition* complete, in its essentials. At some points, for further explanations of the mathematical background of the course, references are made to *Elementary Geometry from an Advanced Standpoint,* by Edwin Moise (Addison-Wesley, 1963).

# GENERAL INTRODUCTION

As the Preface and the Table of Contents in the text indicate, there is nothing very novel in the choice of material in this book. It is devoted mainly to plane geometry, with shorter introductions to solid geometry, solid mensuration, and plane coordinate geometry.

In its style, however, the book is much less conventional. The reasons for this are explained, as we go along, in the appropriate sections of this *Teachers' Edition*. But the spirit in which the book is written may be clearer if we explain, at the outset, certain general considerations.

## A. THE METRIC POSTULATES

Probably the most novel feature of this book, at first glance, is the postulates. In most elementary books on geometry, the postulates are modifications of those of Euclid. ("When equals are added to equals, the sums are equal," and so on.) By contrast, the postulates used here are the *metric* postulates; they involve the idea of measurement, by real numbers, of distances, and angles, and areas.

One reason commonly given for this change is that it permits a higher level of logical rigor. This is true, and it is important; but in the opinion of the authors, it is not the most important virtue of the metric postulates.

An examination of almost any geometry text in common use will show that the idea of measurement plays a central role. Sides of triangles are marked with numbers, indicating their lengths; angles are marked with numbers, indicating their degree measures; and almost every day the student is asked to solve problems whose answers are numerical. This means that in fact and practice the theory that is being taught is a metric theory, in which there really are such things as the length of a segment and the measure of an angle.

To present one set of ideas in postulates and theorems, undertaking at the same time to teach another set of ideas by extended examples, necessarily involves a certain expository awkwardness. And it has a further weakness which may be less obvious. One of the hazards, in teaching young students, is that so often they regard the theory being presented to them merely as a gesture; they take for granted that their real job is to learn to do each day's homework assignment by acquiring, in the previous class session, the appropriate set of behavior patterns. When this happens, the theory is not serving its purpose, either in communicating skills or in preparing the student for later courses which are supposed to build on it.

To avoid this sort of thing is no easy task. It requires, obviously, that the exposition of the theory be intelligible. It requires also that the ideas presented in the theory be the ideas that the student is going to *use* when he solves problems. This, we believe, is the crucial reason for the use of metric postulates.

The metric theory has other important advantages:

(1) In earlier courses (and in everyday life) measurement is commonplace. Usually the concept of the number line is used, so that geometric intuition can contribute to the understanding of arithmetic and algebra. Thus it is natural, in the introduction to geometry, to use the Ruler Postulate (pages 37–38).

We are saying, in effect, that *any* line can be regarded as a number line. Thus we appeal to the student's earlier experience, and we bring arithmetic and algebra to the aid of formal geometry.

(2) Metric geometry is a better preparation for the courses which will be studied in the following few years. Analytic geometry is automatically metric; and when geometry is used as an intuitive model in the study of advanced algebra and calculus, it appears in a metric form. These considerations apply with special force to the ideas of area and volume. (See the commentary on Chapter 11.)

(3) Geometry is such a complicated subject that any teachable presentation of it in high school must leave logical gaps. In a way it is an evasion of this issue to "presuppose" an understanding of the real numbers, because in fact the student does not have, at this stage, a very thorough understanding of them. But under this scheme, the gaps that we leave are smaller, and they are of such a kind that they will be filled when the student, in later studies, learns more about the number system. (The gaps in a synthetic treatment are such that they would be filled only by a thorough course in the foundations of geometry, which would come many years later, if at all.)

## B. MATHEMATICAL DESCRIPTIONS AND MODELS

It is possible, of course, to think of geometry as an abstract deductive system. But it is also possible—and, at this stage, it is far more important—to think of it as a *concrete* deductive system; that is, as a mathematical model of the physical world, studied by deductive methods.

The standard procedure, in applications of mathematics, is to examine a physical situation and observe that some of its essential features can be described by mathematical conditions. We then pursue, by mathematical methods, the consequences of these conditions, and eventually compare our results with further observations of the physical situation with which we began. Probably the greatest triumph of this method was in the work of Sir Isaac Newton. Newton began with a simple mathematical assumption, the inverse square law of gravitational attraction. He pursued, by mathematical methods, the consequences of this law, and found that the results agreed with the actual behavior of the solar system, with an error so small that even today it is hard to detect and to measure.

The prototype of this method is the deductive geometry developed by the Greeks. This is a description of physical space; and it should still be so regarded even now that we know that the Euclidean description is not the only possible one, and is not necessarily exact. For this reason, geometry offers an excellent opportunity to teach the relation between definitions and the ideas that they are supposed to describe. Nearly all of the ideas of geometry are highly intuitive, and can be conveyed by pictures. Nearly all of them are conveyed first in this way, throughout this book. We then give a definition and invite the student to compare the pictures with the definitions, to make sure that the definition says what it ought to say.

This style of presentation surely makes the definitions easier to understand and to remember, but this is not its sole purpose. The *relation* between intuitive ideas and mathematical definitions is part of the substance of what we are trying to teach. Naturally, the text does not attempt to theorize about this relation; it can only be learned by experience.

## C. CLARITY AND ACCURACY OF LANGUAGE

An extreme attention to accuracy and explicitness in the use of language is often regarded as a burden to the student; and in some cases no doubt it is. But in many cases we believe that an accurate and explicit statement is the easiest to understand and to use. Consider, for example, the familiar statement: *The whole is equal to the sum of its parts.* If this is regarded as a general principle, then we have a fourfold problem, namely, the problem of assigning exact meanings to the words *whole, equal, sum,* and *part.* In practice, the student learns by experience that he is supposed to split the general principle into three specifically geometric statements, as follows:

(1) If $B$ is between $A$ and $C$, on a line, then $AC = AB + BC$ (where $AC$, $AB$, and $BC$ denote distances).

(2) If $D$ is in the interior of $\angle ABC$, as in the figure, then $r + s = t$.

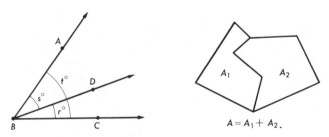

$$A = A_1 + A_2.$$

(3) If a plane region is divided into two nonoverlapping regions, then the area of the whole region is the sum of the areas of the parts.

In this text, statements (1), (2), and (3) are made separately, at the places where they are needed: (1) is conveyed by the definition of *between,* on page 37; (2) is the Angle Addition Postulate, on page 86; and (3) is the Area Addition Postulate, on page 332. Logically speaking, this is preferable, because (1), (2), and (3) cannot really be deduced from any general philosophical principle. And our accuracy is surely no burden on the student, because we have stated our three principles at the points where they are needed, *in the forms in which they are going to be used.*

It is in this spirit, and for this sort of purpose, that we have tried to be exact. It appeared to us that if sufficient care was taken, then most of the supposed conflicts between logic and pedagogy could be resolved, to the benefit of the latter. There were some exceptions to this rule, and in the exceptional cases we used a different style. Thus, for example, on page 69 we attempt to convey a topological idea by talking about maps drawn on sheets of rubber. A formal mathematical treatment of this idea seemed out of the question. The treatment of area and volume, in Chapters 16 and 19, has large logical gaps. (Note the absence of a definition of the word *solid.*) Here again we had no choice: the crucial ideas can be made intuitively intelligible, but a formally accurate treatment would be hopeless.

## D. THE LANGUAGE OF CONGRUENCE

The terminology of this book is, of course, introduced piecemeal as we go along; but in classroom discussions some topics may come up earlier, and so we should explain now some of the ways in which our terminology is novel.

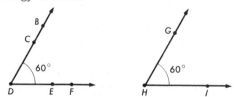

In the first place, we use the symbol "=" and the word "equals" only in the sense in which these are used in algebra; when we write $A = B$ we mean that the symbols $A$ and $B$ denote exactly the same object. Thus, for the angles shown in the figure above, we can write $\angle BDF = \angle CDE$, because $\angle BDF$ and $\angle CDE$ not only have the same measure, but are *exactly* the same angle. The angles $\angle BDF$ and $\angle GHI$ will be called *congruent* (rather than equal), and we shall write $\angle BDF \cong \angle GHI$.

Similarly for segments. If two segments $\overline{AB}$ and $\overline{CD}$ have the same length, then they will be called *congruent.* We shall never say that $\overline{AB}$ and $\overline{CD}$ are "equal" unless they are exactly the same segment. (Thus, for example, we always have $\overline{AB} = \overline{BA}$, although we rarely have any occasion to say so.)

This terminology may seem strange, if it is new to the reader, but it is a considerable simplification. There are two main ideas involved here. One is the logical identity, the relation *is exactly the same as.* The other is the idea of *congruence,* or *geometric equivalence:* two geometric figures, of any kind whatever, are *congruent* if they have exactly the same size and shape. (Thus two segments are congruent if they have the same length, two circles are congruent if they have the same radius, and two equilateral triangles are congruent if their sides have the same length.)

In this book, each of these two fundamental ideas has a word all to itself, and each of them is always described by the same word. This usage gives a much simpler relation between the ideas and the words that refer to them. And it brings the language of geometry into closer accord with the language of the rest of mathematics.

There is, of course, no need to explain the language of congruence to the student until it comes up in the text. But if the subject does arise, it should not be discussed in a terminology which will be replaced by another in later chapters.

## E. PROBLEMS

As everyone knows, problem sequences are the heart of a mathematics course: they are what the student lives with, and any kind of knowledge or skill that is not incorporated in them is unlikely to be learned. Geometry offers a special opportunity—the "originals" that the student is asked to prove are a *part* of the theory, rather than merely an application of it; and this probably is the reason why so many students have gotten for the first time, in a geometry course, some notion of what mathematics means to a mathematician.

The problem sets include a variety of different types of problems of different degrees of difficulty: there are simple exercises in the direct application of definitions and theorems; there are many challenging originals; there are minor theorems which are not included in the text itself; and there are many Honors Problems to challenge the ablest students. Division of problem sets into three levels of difficulty is indicated by single and double rules.

## F. COURSE SCHEDULES

This book is much shorter, for teaching purposes, than the number of pages would suggest. It includes many more problems than a teacher would want to assign to any one class. (It is possible to adjust the problem assignments to suit the needs of a great variety of classes.) Moreover, the text proper is designed to be read, not to be deciphered. For this reason, intuitive explanations are frequent, the exposition is full, figures are used liberally, and excessive use of abbreviations is avoided.

Scattered through the text, at points which seem appropriate, are short biographical sketches of eminent mathematicians. The main emphasis is on their mathematical work, because one of the purposes of the biographical notes is to convey to the student that mathematics is the work of human beings: all of the mathematics that is known today was discovered by some person, at some point in time, to solve a problem. If this is understood, then the student will not be surprised on being told that original mathematics is being done today.

Some sections of the text, while not logically necessary, were included because of the high level of student interest that they usually arouse. These include "The Seven Bridges of Königsberg," "How Eratosthenes Measured the Earth," and "The Impossible Construction Problems of Antiquity."

### 1. General comments on the schedule for an average class

In teaching this text to an average class, you can cover roughly the same topics as you do with a strong class, and you can cover each in approximately the same number of days. There is, however, an important difference in the approach you should take to the subject. The average student is often slow to grasp mathematical ideas; he has difficulty in recalling material covered even a short time ago, he frequently fails to see relationships, and he has difficulty in applying theories to practical situations. Hence, in teaching geometry to the average student, you should concentrate on the rudimentary aspects of the subject. Make sure the student understands the definitions and statements of the theorems, and frequently do prototype problems (especially numerical ones), supplying the student with enough patterns to follow so that he can get off to a good start on his homework.

### 2. Omission of topics

In order to do justice to those topics which you consider most important for your students, you may find it necessary simply to omit certain chapters or sections of the text. We list here, in rough order of preference, those topics which can be omitted:

   (i) Section 6–6 on the proof of the ASA and SSS Postulates and betweenness and separation.
  (ii) A considerable block of time can be saved by omitting or covering only informally Chapters 8, 10, and 19 on the geometry of space and Chapters 17 and 18 on trigonometry, transformations, and vectors.
 (iii) Section 7–7 on the Hinge Theorem and its converse.
  (v) Sections 15–6 through 15–10 on constructions. Logically speaking, the constructions may be omitted, because they will not be needed later; but they arouse so much interest among all students that it would be a pity not to cover them.

[Note: Chapter 13, "Plane Coordinate Geometry," is not included in the list, partly because its place in such a list is controversial, and partly because one of the reasons for omitting other topics is to assure an adequate coverage of coordinate geometry. If you omit Chapter 13, you should also omit Sections 14–8 and 15–2.]

### 3. Sequence of topics

There are, of course, several ways in which the sequence of topics can be rearranged. A few comments are in order: (a) Chapter 8 is needed for Chapters 10 and 19. (b) Chapter 11 must precede Chapter 12, because area theory is used in the proof of the Basic Proportionality Theorem. (c) Chapter 13, "Coordinate Geometry," must come after Chapter 12, "Similarity," because similarity is used in the discussion of slopes of lines. Chapter 13 can, however, be postponed until the end of the course, since the chapters which follow Chapter 13 are not dependent on it, except in Sections 14–8 and 15–2, as noted above.

Note further that all of the theorems of the first eight chapters, and of Sections 9–1 and 9–2 are proved without use of the Parallel Postulate. We suggest that these chapters be taught in the sequence given in the text.

# SUGGESTED TEST QUESTIONS

Note: Answers appear in brackets following each question.

## Chapters 1 and 2 Common Sense and Exact Reasoning; Sets, Real Numbers, and Lines

1. $G$ is between $H$ and $K$ if $G$, $H$, and $K$ are different points on a line and if __?__. [$HG + GK = HK$]
2. According to the Ruler Postulate, the distance between any two points is the __?__ of the corresponding numbers. [absolute value of the difference]
3. (a) The union of $\overrightarrow{RT}$ and $\overrightarrow{TR}$ is __?__. [$\overleftrightarrow{RT}$]
   (b) The intersection of $\overrightarrow{RT}$ and $\overrightarrow{TR}$ is __?__. [$\overline{RT}$]
4. (a) If $x < y$, then $x - y$ is __?__. [negative]
   (b) If $x = y$, then $x - y$ is __?__. [zero]
   (c) If $x > y$, then $x - y$ is __?__. [positive]
5. Three points $A$, $B$, and $C$ are on a line. $AC = 3$ and $AB = 9$. $BC = $__?__, and point __?__ is not between the other two points. [6 or 12 (*both must be given*); $B$]
6. If points $M$, $N$, and $P$ are on a line and $PM = PN$, then $P$ is called the __?__ of $\overline{MN}$. [midpoint]
Supply the missing symbol, if any, over each letter pair.
7. $C$ is an endpoint of $CB$, but $B$ is not. $B$ is an endpoint of $CB$. [$\overrightarrow{CB}$; $\overline{CB}$]
8. If $A$ is a point such that $CA - BA = BC$, then $C$ is a point of $BA$, but not of $BA$ nor of $BA$. [$\overrightarrow{BA}$; $\overrightarrow{BA}$; $\overline{BA}$]
On the number line below show $A$, $B$, and $C$ in the order specified by Question 6.

Given a coordinate system on a line, such that the coordinate of $T$ is $-3$, of $W$ is $9$, of $A$ is $x$, and of $B$ is $y$. Under a new coordinate system, $W$ corresponds to $4$ and $T$ corresponds to $-8$.

9. The new coordinates of $A$ and $B$ are __?__ and __?__, respectively. [$x - 5$; $y - 5$]
10. The new coordinate of the point $K$ such that $TK = WK$ is __?__. [$-2$]
11. Show that the distance $AB$ is the same in both coordinate systems. [In the old system, $AB = |x - y|$. In the new system, $AB = |(x - 5) - (y - 5)| = |x - y|$.]

## Chapter 3 Lines, Planes, and Separation

In the figure for Questions 1–3, points $B$, $C$, $D$, $M$, $N$, $R$, and $S$ all lie in plane $E$.

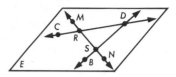

1. Points $C$ and $N$ are in different half-planes formed by __?__, and $C$ and $D$ are in different half-planes formed by __?__. [$\overleftrightarrow{BD}$; $\overleftrightarrow{MN}$]
2. According to Postulate 6, if we know only that points $R$ and $S$ lie in plane $E$, we can conclude that $E$ contains __?__. [$\overleftrightarrow{RS}$]
3. Since $\overleftrightarrow{CR}$ does not intersect $\overleftrightarrow{BD}$, we know that $C$ and $R$ are __?__ of $\overleftrightarrow{BD}$. [on the same side]
4. If a line intersects a plane not containing it, the intersection contains __?__ point(s). [exactly one]
5. If two planes intersect, the intersection contains __?__ points. [infinitely many]
6. The number of planes determined by four noncoplanar points is __?__. [4]
7. Three collinear points are contained in __?__ plane(s). [infinitely many]
8. The number of lines determined by pairs of the six points $R$, $S$, $T$, $X$, $Y$, $Z$, no three of which are collinear, is __?__. [15]

Given the noncoplanar figure in which $B$, $D$, $F$, and $H$ are coplanar and $\overline{AC}$ and $\overline{BD}$ intersect at $R$.

9. Are $F$, $R$, and $H$ coplanar? [Yes]
10. Does $\overleftrightarrow{FC}$ intersect $\overrightarrow{AR}$? [Yes]
11. Does $H$ lie on $\overline{AC}$? [No]
12. Are $A$, $C$, $H$, and $R$ coplanar? [Yes]
13. Does $\overrightarrow{HB}$ intersect $\overline{FC}$? [No]

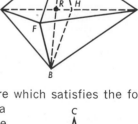

14. Sketch and label a figure which satisfies the following description: $C$ is a point above a horizontal plane $E$. $A$ and $B$ are points in the half-space opposite to that which contains $C$. $\overline{AC}$ and $\overline{BC}$ intersect $E$ in $P$ and $Q$, respectively. Draw $\overline{AQ}$ and $\overline{BP}$.

# Chapter 4  Angles and Triangles

1. In △ABC, M is a point of $\overline{BC}$ between B and C. If $m\angle AMC = 78$, what is $m\angle AMB$?  [102]

2. What is the measure of the complement of an angle whose measure is $90 - x$?  [x]

3. The measure of the supplement of an angle is four times the measure of the complement of the angle. What is the measure of the angle?  [60]

4. Sketch a figure which satisfies the description below and then answer Questions 5–9.

△ABC and △CDE are coplanar and intersect only at C.  Points D and E are on the same side of $\overleftrightarrow{AC}$ as B and also on the same side of $\overleftrightarrow{AB}$ as C.

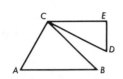

or

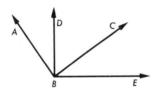

5. Can B be in the interior of ∠D?  [Yes]
6. D is always in the interior of which angle?  [∠A]
7. May E ever be in the interior of △ABC?  [Yes]
8. Must $\overline{DE}$ intersect $\overline{CB}$?  [No]
9. Must $\overleftrightarrow{DE}$ intersect $\overline{CB}$?  [No]
10. Complete the proof by filling in the blanks.
   Given: The figure with

$$m\angle ABC = 90 = m\angle DBE.$$

   Prove: ∠ABD ≅ ∠CBE.

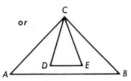

| STATEMENTS | Proof | REASONS |
|---|---|---|
| 1. $m\angle ABC = 90 = m\angle DBE$. | 1. Given |
| 2. ∠ABD is complementary to ∠DBC. | 2. Definition of complementary angles |
| 3. __?__  [∠CBE is complementary to ∠DBC.] | 3. Same as reason 2 |
| 4. ∠DBC ≅ ∠DBC. | 4. __?__  [Every angle is congruent to itself.] |
| 5. __?__  [∠ABD ≅ ∠CBE.] | 5. __?__  [Complements of congruent angles are congruent.] |

# Chapter 5  Congruence

In each pair of triangles below, like markings indicate congruent parts.  In each answer blank labeled (a), complete the appropriate congruence, or write *none*. In each answer blank labeled (b), name the congruence postulate which proves the congruence, or write *none*.

1. (a) △MPR ≅ __?__
      [None]
   (b) __?__  [None]

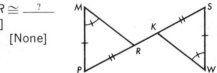

2. (a) △TCP ≅ __?__
      [△XCQ]
   (b) __?__  [SAS]

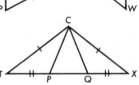

3. (a) △ACE ≅ __?__
      [△DBG]
   (b) __?__  [ASA]

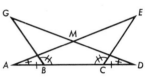

4. (a) △MTG ≅ __?__
      [△NTH]
   (b) __?__  [SSS]

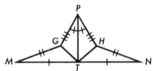

5. Point K is called the __?__ of $\overline{AB}$ if K is between A and B and if $AK = BK$.  [midpoint]
6. $\overrightarrow{MK}$ is the bisector of ∠AMB if K is in __?__ and if __?__.  [the interior of ∠AMB; ∠KMA ≅ ∠KMB]
7. In △MKH, $\overline{MK}$ is said to be the side __?__ by ∠M and ∠K.  [included]
8. In an __?__ triangle every median is also an angle bisector.  [equilateral]
9. Given: The figure with

$\overline{AB} \perp \overline{AD}$, $\overline{DC} \perp \overline{AD}$, $AB = CD$, and E the midpoint of $\overline{AD}$.

Prove: ∠EBC ≅ ∠ECB.

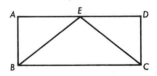

| STATEMENTS | Proof | REASONS |
|---|---|---|
| 1. E is the midpoint of $\overline{AD}$. | 1. __?__  [Given] |
| 2. Therefore __?__  [AE = DE.] | 2. __?__  [Definition of midpoint] |
| 3. $\overline{AB} \perp \overline{AD}$ and $\overline{DC} \perp \overline{AD}$. | 3. __?__  [Given] |

4. ___?___ [∠A and ∠D are right angles.]
5. ∠A ≅ ∠D.

6. AB = CD.
7. ___?___ [△ABE ≅ △DCE.]
8. ___?___ [BE = CE.]

9. Therefore ∠EBC ≅ ∠ECB.

4. Perpendiculars form right angles.
5. ___?___ [All right angles are congruent.]
6. Given
7. ___?___ [SAS]
8. Corresponding parts of congruent triangles
9. ___?___ [The Isosceles Triangle Theorem]

7. AB = CB.

8. ___?___ [△ABD ≅ △CBD.]

7. ___?___ [If two angles of a triangle are congruent, the opposite sides are congruent.]
8. ___?___ [SAS or SSS]

---

# Chapter 6  A Closer Look at Proof

1. In an indirect proof we reason until we reach a ___?___. [contradiction]
2. A point or segment introduced to complete a proof is called an ___?___ [auxiliary set]
3. Which of the following sets are segments? [a, c]
(a) Median  (b) Perpendicular bisector  (c) Angle bisector of a triangle  (d) Bisector of an angle  (e) Side of an angle
4. Which of the following are convex sets?  [a, c, d, e]
(a) Median  (b) Right triangle  (c) Bisector of an angle  (d) Perpendicular bisector  (e) Plane
5. Given: ▱ABCD with ∠DAB ≅ ∠DCB and AD = CD.

Prove: △ABD ≅ △CBD.

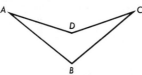

| STATEMENTS | Proof | REASONS |
|---|---|---|
| 1. Introduce ___?___. [$\overline{AC}$ (and $\overline{DB}$)] | 1. ___?___ [The Line Postulate] |
| 2. AD = CD. | 2. ___?___ [Given] |
| 3. ___?___ [∠DAC ≅ ∠DCA.] | 3. The Isosceles Triangle Theorem |
| 4. ___?___ [∠DAB ≅ ∠DCB.] | 4. Given |
| 5. m∠DAB + m∠DAC = m∠DCB + m∠DCA. | 5. ___?___ [The Addition Property of Equality] |
| 6. ___?___ [m∠BAC = m∠BCA.] | 6. The Angle Addition Postulate and the meaning of equality |

6. Given: ∠GHK with bisector $\overrightarrow{HM}$,

GH = KH, and P is the midpoint of $\overline{GK}$.

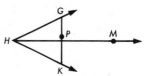

Prove: P lies on $\overrightarrow{HM}$.

| STATEMENTS | Proof | REASONS |
|---|---|---|
| 1. ___?___ [Suppose P is not on $\overrightarrow{HM}$.] | 1. ___?___ [Beginning of indirect proof] |
| 2. Introduce ___?___. [$\overline{HP}$] | 2. ___?___ [The Line Postulate] |
| 3. ___?___ [HP = HP.] | 3. Identity |
| 4. P is the midpoint of $\overline{GK}$. | 4. Given |
| 5. ___?___ [PG = PK.] | 5. Definition of midpoint |
| 6. GH = KH. | 6. Given |
| 7. ___?___ [△PHG ≅ △PHK.] | 7. ___?___ [SSS] |
| 8. ∠PHG ≅ ∠PHK. | 8. Corresponding parts of congruent triangles |
| 9. $\overrightarrow{HP}$ is bisector of ∠GHK. | 9. ___?___ [Definition of angle bisector] |
| 10. But $\overrightarrow{HM}$ bisects ∠GHK. | 10. ___?___ [Given] |
| 11. Steps 9 and 10 are contradictory. Thus our assumption is false and the theorem is proved. | 11. Every angle has exactly one bisector. |

7. Assume you are to prove the following by indirect method.  What is the supposition with which you begin?
If a triangle has no two sides congruent, then it is not isosceles.  [Suppose the triangle is isosceles.]

# Chapter 7   Geometric Inequalities

Questions 1–5 refer to the figure below. For each question name the theorem which justifies the statement.

1. $\angle KAC \cong \angle GAB$. [The Vertical Angle Theorem]
2. $AC < AB$. [The First Minimum Theorem]
3. $AB + AC > BC$. [The Triangle Inequality]
4. $\angle KAC > \angle B$. [The Exterior Angle Theorem]

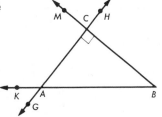

In each pair of triangles below, like markings indicate congruent parts. For each Question 5–10 name the congruence postulate or the congruence theorem which proves the congruence between triangles, or write *none*.

5. [SSS]

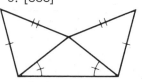

6. [HL]

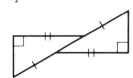

7. [None]

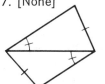

8.   [SAA]

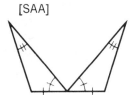

9. [SAS]

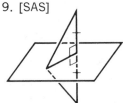

10. [SAA]

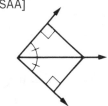

Questions 11–14 refer to the figure below, in which the angles have the indicated measures.

11. Which is greater, *BE* or *EC*? [*EC*]
12. In $\triangle ADE$, what is $\overline{AD}$ called? [hypotenuse]
13. Which is greater, *AE* or *ED*? [*ED*]
14. Which segment of the figure is shortest? Explain. [$\overline{AE}$; $AD > ED > AE$, $DC > EC = ED > AE$, $BC > EC > BE = AB > AE$.]

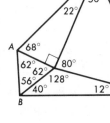

15. Given: The figure with
$HK = HB$ and
$HB > KB$.
Prove: $AK > KB$.

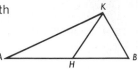

| STATEMENTS | Proof | REASONS |
|---|---|---|
| 1. $HK = HB > KB$. | | 1. Given |
| 2. In $\triangle HBK$, $\angle B >$ ____?____. [$\angle KHB$] | | 2. ____?____ [In a triangle, the larger angle is opposite the longer side.] |
| 3. ____?____ [$\angle KHB > \angle A$.] | | 3. The Exterior Angle Theorem |
| 4. ____?____ [$\angle B > \angle A$.] | | 4. Transitivity |
| 5. Therefore, $AK > KB$. | | 5. ____?____ [In a triangle, the longer side is opposite the larger angle.] |

# Chapter 8   Perpendicular Lines and Planes in Space

1. In this figure $\overrightarrow{PA}$ and $\overrightarrow{PB}$ are each perpendicular to $\overleftrightarrow{CP}$, the line of intersection of planes $E$ and $F$. Which ray and which plane are perpendicular?   [c]

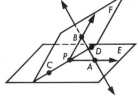

(a). $\overrightarrow{PB}$ and plane $E$   (b) $\overrightarrow{PA}$ and plane $F$
(c) $\overrightarrow{PC}$ and plane $ABP$   (d) $\overrightarrow{BA}$ and plane $F$

2. In this figure, planes $E$ and $F$ intersect at $\overleftrightarrow{PQ}$, $C$ is in $E$, $D$ is in $F$, $\overrightarrow{KA} \perp E$, and $\overrightarrow{KB} \perp F$. Which pairs of rays *must* be perpendicular? [a, b, d]

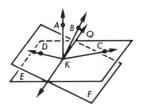

(a) $\overrightarrow{KA}$ and $\overrightarrow{KP}$
(b) $\overrightarrow{KB}$ and $\overrightarrow{KQ}$
(c) $\overrightarrow{KA}$ and $\overrightarrow{KD}$
(d) $\overrightarrow{KA}$ and $\overrightarrow{KC}$

3. The ____?____ of a segment contains all perpendicular bisectors of the segment. [perpendicular bisecting plane]

4. According to the First Minimum Theorem, the shortest segment to a ____?____ from an external point is the ____?____ segment. [line; perpendicular]

5. In this figure, *R* and *D* lie on $\overleftrightarrow{PQ}$, the intersection of planes *E* and *F*; *A* and *C* lie in *E*; and *B* lies in *F*. $\overline{BA} \perp E$. Which angles listed below *must* be right angles? [c, d]

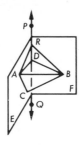

(a) ∠ACB  (b) ∠ADB
(c) ∠DAB  (d) ∠RAB

6. At a given point of a given line there is at most one __?__ perpendicular to the given line. [plane]

7. Given points *A*, *B*, *C*, *D*, and *E*. If *AC = AD*, *CB = BD*, and *ED = CE*, then points __?__ must be coplanar. [*A, B, E*]

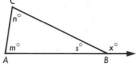

8. If *m* = 80 and *n* = 75, then *x* > __?__. [80]
9. If *s* = 60 and *m* = 100, then *x* __?__. [= 120]
10. If *x* = 85, then *n* __?__. [< 85]
11. If *n* = 90, the longest side of △*ABC* is __?__. [$\overline{AB}$]
12. If *x* = 85, the longest side of △*ABC* is __?__. [$\overline{AC}$]

## Chapter 9  Parallel Lines in a Plane

1. If two angles of a triangle have measures 120 − *a* and 60 + *b*, respectively, what is the measure of the third angle? [*a* − *b*]
2. A transversal intersects two parallel lines at points *A* and *B*. The bisectors of two interior angles on the same side of the transversal intersect each other at *K*. What is *m*∠*AKB*? [90]

In the figure for Questions 3 and 4, $\overline{DC} \parallel \overline{AB}$, $\overrightarrow{AG}$ bisects ∠*A*, $\overrightarrow{BG}$ bisects ∠*B*, $\overline{EF}$ contains *G*, and $\overline{EF} \parallel \overline{AB}$.

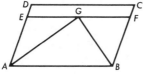

3. If *m*∠*EAB* = 80 and *m*∠*FBA* = 100, what is *m*∠*FGB*? [50]
4. If *m*∠*CDA* = 110, what is *m*∠*EGA*? [35]

Supply the angle measures in Questions 5–14 for the figure to the right.

5. *m*∠*GHK*  [40]
6. *m*∠*BKJ*  [50]
7. *m*∠*BKH*  [40]
8. *m*∠*AHK*  [140]
9. *m*∠*CEJ*  [40]
10. *m*∠*EDC*  [75]

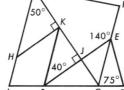

11. *m*∠*DEF*  [150]
12. *m*∠*JCB*  [55]
13. *m*∠*JBC*  [35]
14. *m*∠*KBA*  [105]
15. In △*ABC*, ∠*A* is a right angle and *m*∠*C* = 30. If *AB* = 8, what is *BC*?  [16]
16. In parallelogram □*ABCD*, *m*∠*A* is eight times *m*∠*D*. What is *m*∠*A*?  [160]
17. In △*PQR*, ∠*Q* is a right angle and *A*, *B*, and *C* are the midpoints of $\overline{PQ}$, $\overline{PR}$, and $\overline{QR}$, respectively. If *PR* = 20, *QR* = 12, and *PQ* = 16, how long are the diagonals of □*ABCQ*? [*AC* = 10, *BQ* = 10]
18. In trapezoid □*ABCD*, $\overline{EF}$ is the median. If *AB* = 13, *BC* = 8, *CD* = 9, and *AD* = 5, what is *EF*?  [11]
19. In parallelogram □*ABCD*, *m*∠*B* = 2*x* + 29 and *m*∠*D* = 5*x* − 7. What is the numerical measure of ∠*B*?  [53]
20. Given: The plane figure with $\overrightarrow{PR} \perp \overrightarrow{PQ}$, $\overrightarrow{QS} \perp \overrightarrow{PQ}$, and *CD = CE*.

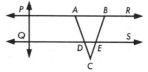

Prove: △*ABC* is isosceles.

| STATEMENTS **Proof** | REASONS |
|---|---|
| 1. $\overrightarrow{PR} \perp \overrightarrow{PQ}$ and $\overleftrightarrow{QS} \perp \overrightarrow{PQ}$. | 1. __?__ [Given] |
| 2. Therefore __?__. [$\overrightarrow{PR} \parallel \overrightarrow{QS}$] | 2. __?__ [In a plane, two lines perpendicular to a third line are parallel.] |
| 3. *CD = CE*. | 3. Given |
| 4. Therefore __?__. [*m*∠*CDE = m*∠*CED*] | 4. __?__ [The Isosceles Triangle Theorem] |
| 5. *m*∠*CDE* = __?__. [*m*∠*CAB*] *m*∠*CED* = __?__. [*m*∠*CBA*] | 5. If two parallels are cut by a transversal, corresponding angles are congruent. |
| 6. __?__ [*m*∠*CAB = m*∠*CBA.*] | 6. Steps 4 and 5 and substitution |
| 7. __?__ [*AC = BC.*] | 7. __?__ [If two angles of a triangle are congruent, the sides opposite the angles are congruent.] |
| 8. △*ABC* is isosceles. | 8. Definition of isosceles triangle |

# Chapter 10  Parallel Lines and Planes

Plane $E$, containing parallel lines $L_1$ and $L_2$, is perpendicular to $\overrightarrow{PQ}$ at $C$. $\overrightarrow{PQ}$ is the edge of right dihedral angle $\angle A\text{-}PQ\text{-}B$. $KC = MC$ and $m\angle A\text{-}PQ\text{-}D = 50$.

1. What is $m\angle B\text{-}PQ\text{-}D$? [40]

2. What is $m\angle CDA$? [65]

3. What is $m\angle ABC$? [25]

4. What is $m\angle CMN$? [115]

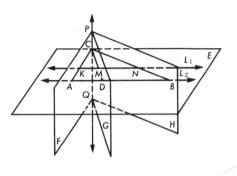

Perpendicular planes $E$ and $F$ intersect in $\overleftrightarrow{AB}$ and plane $CDR$ is the perpendicular bisecting plane of $\overline{AB}$. $C$ is in $F$ and $D$ is in $E$ such that $\overline{AC} \perp \overline{BC}$ and $CR = \frac{1}{2}CD$.

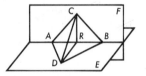

5. What is $m\angle ACR$? [45]
6. What is $m\angle DCR$? [60]
*7. What is $m\angle ADR$? [30]
8. The measure of a dihedral angle is 60. A point $C$ in one face of the dihedral angle is 18 inches from its edge. The projection of $C$ into the other face of the dihedral angle is point $H$. How far is $H$ from the edge of the dihedral angle? [9 in.]
9. One face of a right dihedral angle contains a square. What is the projection of the square into the other face? [A segment]
10. In the figure, $E$ and $F$ are planes, $E \parallel F$, $\overrightarrow{AB} \perp F$, and $\overrightarrow{AG}$ is the perpendicular bisector of $\overline{CD}$. If $m\angle C\text{-}AB\text{-}D = 30$, what is $m\angle BDC$? [75]

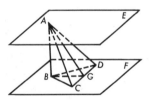

# Chapter 11  Polygonal Regions and Their Areas

1. The hypotenuse of a right triangle is 10 in. long and one leg has length 6 in. What is the area of the triangle? [24 sq. in.]
2. In rhombus $\square ABCD$, $AD = 13$ and the altitude to $\overline{BC}$ is 7. What is $a\square ABCD$? [91]

3. The perimeter of a square is 8 in. How long is a diagonal of the square? [$2\sqrt{2}$ in.]
4. A side of an equilateral triangle is 8 in. long. What is the area of the triangle? [$16\sqrt{3}$ sq. in.]
5. The sides of a triangle have lengths 10, 24, and 26. What is the area of the triangle? [120]
6. A parallelogram has sides of lengths 8 and 18. The altitude to the shorter side is 15. What is the altitude to the longer side? [$6\frac{2}{3}$]
7. The area of an isosceles right triangle is 16. How long is its hypotenuse? [8]
8. In parallelogram $\square ABCD$, $AD = 15$, $DC = 22$, and $m\angle A = 60$. What is $a\square ABCD$? [$165\sqrt{3}$]
9. In the figure on the left below, $D$ and $E$ are midpoints of $\overline{AB}$ and $\overline{AC}$, respectively. If $a\triangle ABC = 36$, what is $a\square BCED$? [27]

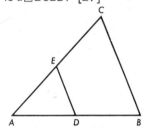
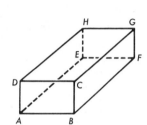

10. In the rectangular solid shown, $BC = 4$, $CG = 10$, and $GH = 4\sqrt{3}$. How long is the diagonal $\overline{CE}$? [$2\sqrt{41}$]

# Chapter 12  Similarity

1. Solve for $x$.

(a) $\dfrac{x + 3}{4x} = \dfrac{14}{35}$ [5]   (b) $\dfrac{15ma}{4xy} = \dfrac{9ab}{2my}$ $\left[\dfrac{5m^2}{6b}\right]$

2. Two similar triangles have a pair of corresponding sides of lengths $3\frac{1}{2}$ and $8\frac{3}{4}$, respectively. What is the ratio of their perimeters? [$\frac{2}{5}$]
3. The hypotenuses of two similar right triangles have lengths 6 and 16. What is the ratio of the areas of the two triangles? [$\frac{9}{64}$]

Given the figure with $\overline{AC} \parallel \overline{PQ}$.

4. If $AT = 5$, $AP = 2$, and $CQ = 3$, what is $TC$? [$7\frac{1}{2}$]
5. If $PT = 33$, $AP = 12$, and $DB = 8$, what is $TD$? [14]

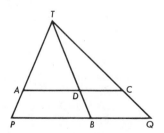

In this plane figure, $\overline{AD} \perp \overline{AB}$ and $\overline{BC} \perp \overline{AB}$. $AB = 3$, $BE = 2$, and $DE = 3$.

6. What is the numerical value of $\dfrac{AD}{BC}$? $[\frac{3}{2}]$

7. What is the numerical value of $\dfrac{a \triangle BCE}{a \triangle DAE}$? $[\frac{4}{9}]$

8. What is the numerical value of $\dfrac{a \triangle ABC}{a \triangle ABD}$? $[\frac{2}{3}]$

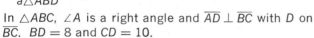

In $\triangle ABC$, $\angle A$ is a right angle and $\overline{AD} \perp \overline{BC}$ with $D$ on $\overline{BC}$. $BD = 8$ and $CD = 10$.

9. What is $AD$? $[4\sqrt{5}]$    10. What is $AB$? $[12]$

11. What is $AC$? $[6\sqrt{5}]$

12. Given: Parallelogram $\square ABCD$, with $\overline{PQ} \parallel \overline{MB}$.

Prove: $AB \cdot CQ = AM \cdot CP$.

| | STATEMENTS **Proof** | REASONS |
|---|---|---|
| 1. | $\square ABCD$ is a parallelogram. | 1. Given |
| 2. | $m\angle A = m\angle C$. | 2. ___?___ [Opposite angles of a parallelogram are congruent.] |
| 3. | $\overline{PQ} \parallel \overline{MB}$. | 3. ___?___ [Given] |
| 4. | ___?___ $[m\angle PQC = m\angle MBQ.]$ | 4. If two lines are parallel, corresponding angles are congruent. |
| 5. | $\overline{AD} \parallel \overline{BC}$. | 5. ___?___ [Definition of a parallelogram] |
| 6. | ___?___ $[m\angle MBQ = m\angle AMB.]$ | 6. ___?___ [PAI Theorem] |
| 7. | Therefore $m\angle PQC = m\angle AMB$. | 7. Steps 4 and 6 and transitivity. |
| 8. | ___?___ $[\triangle ABM \sim \triangle CPQ.]$ | 8. ___?___ [AA Corollary] |
| 9. | ___?___ $\left[\dfrac{AB}{CP} = \dfrac{AM}{CQ}.\right]$ | 9. ___?___ [Definition of similar triangles] |
| 10. | Therefore, $AB \cdot CQ = AM \cdot CP$. | 10. Multiplying both sides of the equation in step 9 by $AM \cdot CQ$ |

# Chapter 13   Plane Coordinate Geometry

1. If two non-vertical lines are perpendicular, the product of their slopes is ___?___. $[-1]$
2. The midpoint of the segment whose end points are $(3, 14)$ and $(13, -4)$ is ___?___. $[8, 5]$
3. Two segments that have equal slopes are either ___?___ or ___?___. [parallel; collinear]
4. Any line which has no slope must be a ___?___ line. [vertical]
5. The vertices of a quadrilateral are the points $(9, 7)$, $(8, -4)$, $(-3, -2)$, and $(0, 11)$. What is the sum of the lengths of its diagonals? $[32]$
6. A triangle has vertices at $(6, 8)$, $(2, -4)$, and $(-3, 8)$. What is its area? $[54]$
7. The vertices of a triangle are the points $(0, 0)$, $(6, 6)$, and $(-8, 8)$. How long is the median to the longest side? $[5\sqrt{2}]$
8. Complete the proof by filling in the blanks.
    Prove: The diagonals of a rhombus are perpendicular and bisect each other.

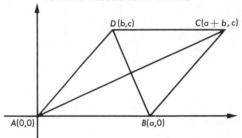

**Proof.** Let the coordinates of $A$, $B$, $C$, and $D$ be as in the figure. We find the coordinates of the midpoints of $\overline{AC}$ and $\overline{BD}$:

Midpoint of $\overline{AC}$: ___?___. $\left[\left(\dfrac{a+b}{2}, \dfrac{c}{2}\right)\right]$

Midpoint of $\overline{BD}$: ___?___. $\left[\left(\dfrac{a+b}{2}, \dfrac{c}{2}\right)\right]$

Since ___?___, the diagonals bisect each other. [the midpoints of both segments are the same]
Next find the slopes of the diagonals.

Slope of $\overline{AC} = $ ___?___. $\left[\dfrac{c}{a+b}\right]$

Slope of $\overline{BD} = $ ___?___. $\left[\dfrac{c}{b-a}\right]$

Since $\square ABCD$ is a rhombus, $AB = AD$, or $a = $ ___?___. $[\sqrt{b^2 + c^2}.]$
Hence, $a^2 = $ ___?___, and $c^2 = $ ___?___. $[b^2 + c^2; a^2 - b^2]$
Thus, the product of the slopes of $\overline{AC}$ and $\overline{BD}$ is ___?___. $[-1]$
Therefore ___?___. $[\overline{AC} \perp \overline{BD}]$

# Chapter 14 Circles and Spheres

1. In a circle whose diameter is 28, a chord of length 14 is drawn. How far is the chord from the center of the circle? [$7\sqrt{3}$]
2. From a point $P$ in the exterior of a circle, secants $\overrightarrow{PB}$ and $\overrightarrow{PD}$ intersect the circle at $A$, $B$ and $C$, $D$, respectively. If $m\angle P = 30$ and $m\widehat{BD} = 5m\widehat{AC}$, what are the measures of the two intercepted arcs? [15; 75]
3. In a circle, $\overline{AB}$ is a diameter and $\overline{AQ}$ is a tangent segment. $\overline{QB}$ intersects the circle at $R$. If $QB = 8$ and $QR = 6$, how long is the tangent segment and what is the radius of the circle? [$4\sqrt{3}$; 2]
4. In the figure on the left below, the two circles are internally tangent at $P$, and $QS = QP$. If $m\widehat{PR} = 140$, what is $m\angle QPS$? [55]

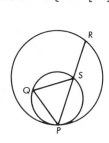 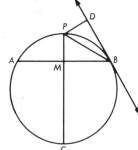

5. Given: A circle with diameter $\overline{CP}$ and chord $\overline{AB}$ such that $\overline{AB} \perp \overline{CP}$ at $M$. $\overline{PD}$ is perpendicular to the tangent at $B$.
   Prove: $PD = PM$.

| STATEMENTS **Proof** | REASONS |
|---|---|
| 1. Diameter $\overline{CP} \perp$ chord $\overline{AB}$. | 1. Given |
| 2. ___?___ [$m\widehat{AP} = m\widehat{BP}$.] | 2. If a diameter is perpendicular to a chord not a diameter, it bisects both arcs of the chord. |
| 3. ___?___ [$m\angle ABP = \frac{1}{2}m\widehat{AP}$.] | 3. ___?___ [The measure of an inscribed angle is $\frac{1}{2}$ the measure of the intercepted arc.] |
| 4. ___?___ [$m\angle DBP = \frac{1}{2}m\widehat{BP}$.] | 4. The measure of an angle formed by a tangent ray and a secant ray is one-half the measure of the intercepted arc. |
| 5. Therefore $m\angle PBD = m\angle PBM$. | 5. Steps 2, 3, and 4 |
| 6. ___?___ [$PB = PB$.] | 6. ___?___. [Identity] |
| 7. ___?___. [$\angle PMP$ is a right angle.] | 7. Perpendiculars form right angles. |
| 8. $\overline{PD} \perp \overleftrightarrow{DB}$. | 8. Given |
| 9. ___?___. [$\angle PDB$ is a right angle.] | 9. Same as reason 7 |
| 10. $\triangle PBD \cong \triangle PBM$. | 10. ___?___. [SAA] |
| 11. ___?___. [$PD = PM$.] | 11. Corresponding parts of congruent triangles are congruent. |

# Chapter 15 Characterizations and Constructions

1. In a plane, the set of all points 4 inches from each of the endpoints of a 3-inch segment is ___?___. [d]
   - (a) a line    (b) a circle    (c) two circles
   - (d) two points    (e) the empty set
2. The set of all points at a given distance from a given point is ___?___. [c]
   - (a) a line    (b) a circle    (c) a sphere
   - (d) a plane    (e) two lines
3. Two circles in the same plane intersect at two points. If their diameters are 8 and 22, the distance between their centers could be ___?___. [b]
   - (a) 4    (b) 12    (c) 16    (d) 20    (e) 24
4. Two altitudes of a triangle intersect at a vertex of the triangle. The triangle must be ___?___. [a]
   - (a) right    (b) isosceles    (c) equilateral
   - (d) obtuse    (e) acute
5. In $\triangle PQR$, $\angle Q$ is a right angle and the medians intersect at $S$. If $PR = 12$ and $PQ = 7$, how long is $\overline{QS}$? [b]
   - (a) $3\frac{1}{2}$    (b) 4    (c) 6    (d) 7    (e) 8
6. $\{(x, y) \mid x^2 - 4 = 0 \text{ and } x + y = 5\}$ equals ___?___. [b]
   - (a) $\{(3, 2)\}$    (b) $\{(2, 3), (-2, 7)\}$
   - (c) $\{(2, 3)\}$    (d) $\{(3, 2), (7, -2)\}$
   - (e) $\{(2, 3), (-2, -3)\}$

In Questions 7 and 8, sketch the set of all points characterized in each item and write a description of the set.

7. In a plane, the set of all points which are centers of circles tangent to line $L$ at point $P$ on $L$.
(A line perpendicular to $L$ at $P$ minus point $P$)

8. Construct a line parallel to a line $L$ through a point $P$ not on $L$. (Use a compass and straightedge only. Show all necessary construction marks.)

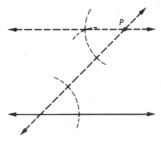

## Chapter 16   Areas of Circles and Sectors

1. A circular region is the __?__ of a circle and its interior.  [union]
2. The sum of the measures of the angles of a convex $n$-gon is __?__.  [$(n - 2)\,180$]
3. A polygon is regular if it is __?__, __?__, and equilateral.  [convex; equilateral]
4. If the perimeter of a regular polygon is three times the diameter of the circumscribed circle, the polygon is called a regular __?__.  [hexagon]
5. An annulus is the region bounded by two __?__.  [concentric circles]
6. A region bounded by a chord of a circle and an arc of the chord is a __?__ of the circle. [segment]
7. What is the measure of each exterior angle of a regular 12-gon?  [30]
8. How many sides has a convex polygon if the sum of the measures of its angles is 2340?  [15]
9. Two circles have circumferences of $4\pi$ and $20\pi$, respectively. What is the ratio of their areas?  [$\frac{1}{25}$]
10. What is the area of the annulus bounded by the inscribed and circumscribed circles of a square whose perimeter is 24?  [$9\pi$]
11. The radius of a sector is 12 and the measure of its arc is 130°. What is the length of the arc and the area of the sector?  $\left[\dfrac{26\pi}{3}\,;\ 52\pi\right]$
12. What is the degree-measure of the arc intercepted by each angle of an inscribed regular pentagon?  [216]
13. A chord at a distance 5 from the center of a circle with a diameter 20 forms a segment (shaded) with its minor arc. What is the area of this segment?
$\left[\dfrac{100\pi}{3} - 25\sqrt{3}\right]$

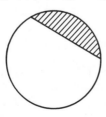

14. Two pipes are bound tightly together with a very thin wire, as in the diagram. The radii of the pipes are 2 in. and 6 in.  Neglecting any practical allowances for securing the wire, etc., determine the minimal length of the wire.
$\left[\dfrac{28\pi}{3} + 8\sqrt{3}\right]$

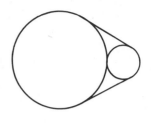

## Chapter 17   Trigonometry

1. In trapezoid $\square ABCD$, $\overline{DC} \parallel \overline{AB}$, $AD = DC = CB = 2$, and $\cos \angle A = .5$.  Find $a\square ABCD$.  $\left[\dfrac{3\sqrt{3}}{4}\right]$
2. In $\triangle ABC$, $m\angle C = 120°$, $m\angle A = m\angle B$, $AC = 2$. Find $a\triangle ABC$.  [$\sqrt{3}$]
3. In a race, instead of following county roads, a crosscountry runner cuts across a field, as shown. If $m\angle A$ is 40° and $AX = 100$ yards, how long, to the nearest yard, is his path across the field?  How much shorter is this path than the prescribed route from $A$ to $B$?  [131 yds; 53 yds]

4. Convert each of the following degree measures to radian measures.
(a) 300  $\left[\dfrac{5\pi}{3}\right]$    (b) $67\frac{1}{2}$  $\left[\dfrac{3\pi}{8}\right]$    (c) 96  $\left[\dfrac{8\pi}{15}\right]$
5. Convert each of the following radian measures to degree measures.
(a) $\dfrac{16\pi}{9}$  [320]    (b) $\dfrac{11\pi}{30}$  [66]    (c) $\dfrac{59\pi}{60}$  [177]
6. $W(\theta)$ is a point on a unit circle. In which quadrant is $W(\theta)$ for the following values of $\theta$?
(a) $\dfrac{9\pi}{8}$  [III]    (b) $\dfrac{-5\pi}{12}$  [IV]    (c) $\dfrac{11\pi}{12}$  [II]
7. For the values of $\theta$ in question 6, in which quadrant is $W(\theta + \pi/2)$?  [IV; I; III]
8. For a point $W(\theta)$ of a unit circle, $\sin \theta = -\frac{7}{25}$ and $\dfrac{3\pi}{2} < \theta < 2\pi$.  Find the following.
(a) $\cos \theta$  $[\frac{24}{25}]$
(b) $\cos (-\theta)$  $[\frac{24}{25}]$
(c) $\sin (-\theta)$  $[\frac{7}{25}]$
(d) $\tan \theta$  $[-\frac{7}{24}]$
(e) $\tan (-\theta)$  $[\frac{7}{24}]$

9. Given that $\sin \theta = \frac{3}{4}$ and $\cos \theta > 0$, find the following.

(a) $\cos \theta$ $\left[\frac{\sqrt{7}}{4}\right]$   (b) $\tan(-\theta)$ $\left[-\frac{3\sqrt{7}}{7}\right]$

(c) $\sin(-\theta)$ $[-\frac{3}{4}]$   (d) $\cos(\theta + \pi/2)$ $[-\frac{3}{4}]$

(e) $\sin(\theta + \pi)$ $[-\frac{3}{4}]$   (f) $\sin(\theta + \pi/2)$ $\left[\frac{\sqrt{7}}{4}\right]$

10. For $\sin \theta_1 = .5$, $\sin \theta_2 = .2$, $\cos \theta_1 > 0$, and $\cos \theta_2 > 0$, find the following.

(a) $\sin(\theta_1 + \theta_2)$ $\left[\frac{\sqrt{6}}{5} + \frac{\sqrt{3}}{10}\right]$

(b) $\sin(\theta_1 - \theta_2)$ $\left[\frac{\sqrt{6}}{5} - \frac{\sqrt{3}}{10}\right]$

(c) $\cos(\theta_1 - \theta_2)$ $\left[\frac{3\sqrt{2}}{5} + \frac{1}{10}\right]$

11. If $\sin \theta = .25$ and $\cos \theta > 0$, find the following.

(a) $\sin 2\theta$ $\left[\frac{\sqrt{15}}{8}\right]$   (b) $\cos 2\theta$ $[\frac{7}{8}]$

12. If $\sin \theta_1 = \frac{\sqrt{2}}{2}$, $\sin \theta_2 = \frac{\sqrt{5}}{3}$, $\cos \theta > 0$, and $\cos \theta_2 > 0$, find the following.

(a) $\tan(\theta_1 + \theta_2)$ $[-9 - 4\sqrt{5}]$
(b) $\tan(\theta_1 - \theta_2)$ $[4\sqrt{5} - 9]$

# Chapter 18   Symmetry, Transformations, and Vectors

1. Given the figure below, give the reflection of the points A, B, and C across

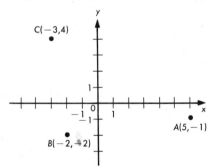

(a) the origin.
   $[(-5, 1); (2, 2);$
   $(3, -4)]$
(b) the x-axis.
   $[(5, 1); (-2, 2);$
   $(-3, -4)]$
(c) the y-axis.
   $[(-5, -12);$
   $(2, -2); (3, 4)]$
(d) the line $x = 2$.
   $[(-1, -1);$
   $(6, -2); (7, 4)]$
(e) the line $y = -3$.
   $[(5, -5);$
   $(-2, -4);$
   $(-3, -10)]$
(f) the line $x + y = 1$.
   $[(2, -4); (3, 3);$
   $(-3, 4)]$

2. Find the image of the points A, B, and C in question 1 under the translation by
   (a) $(3, -2)$   $[(8, -3); (1, -4); (0, 2)]$
   (b) $(-3, -4)$   $[(2, -5); (-5, -6); (-6, 0)]$
3. Find polar coordinates of each of the following points.

(a) $(-2, 0)$   $[2, \pi]$   (b) $(3, -3)$ $\left[3\sqrt{2}, \frac{7\pi}{4}\right]$

(c) $(-5, -5\sqrt{3})$ $\left[10, \frac{4\pi}{3}\right]$

4. Give two other sets of polar coordinates for each of the points in question 3. $[2, -\pi]$, $[2, 3\pi]$; $\Big[3\sqrt{2},$

$-\frac{\pi}{4}\Big]$, $\left[3\sqrt{2}, \frac{23\pi}{4}\right]$; $\left[10, -\frac{2\pi}{3}\right]$, $\left[10, \frac{10\pi}{3}\right]$; other answers possible.

5. Let T be a rotation about the origin under which $[r, \theta] \leftrightarrow [r, \theta - \pi/3]$. Find polar coordinates of the image under T of the points in question 3. $\left[2, \frac{2\pi}{3}\right]$;

$\left[3\sqrt{2}, \frac{17\pi}{12}\right]$; $[10, \pi]$

6. Let Q be a rotation about the origin under which $[r, \theta] \leftrightarrow [r, \theta + \pi/6]$. Find polar coordinates of the pre-image under Q of each of the following points.

(a) $(-3, 0)$ $\left[3, \frac{5\pi}{6}\right]$   (b) $(-4\sqrt{3}, 4)$ $\left[4, \frac{2\pi}{3}\right]$

(c) $(2, -2)$ $\left[2\sqrt{2}, \frac{19\pi}{12}\right]$

7. Find each of the following vector sums.
   (a) $(5, 4) + (4, -3)$   $[(9, 1)]$
   (b) $(3, 6) + (1, 4) + (-3, 7)$   $[(1, 17)]$
   (c) $(5, 9) - (6, 3) + (1, -2)$   $[(0, 4)]$
   (d) $(4, -2) - (3, -1) - (2, -4)$   $[(-1, 3)]$
8. Find each of the following scalar products.
   (a) $3(-5, 0)$   $[(-15, 0)]$
   (b) $-.5(\sqrt{3}, 1)$   $[(-.5\sqrt{3}, -.5)]$
   (c) $-3(-2, 5)$   $[(6, -15)]$
9. Given $\triangle ABC$ with $A(-2, -1)$, $B(-6, 1)$, and $C(-4, -1)$. Under a dilation T from the origin, $A' = T(A) = (-10, -5)$.
   (a) If $B' = T(B)$ and $C' = T(C)$, what are the coordinates of $B'$ and $C'$?   $[B'(-30, 5); C'(-20, -5)]$
   (b) What is the ratio of $a\triangle ABC$ to $a\triangle A'B'C'$?   $[\frac{1}{25}]$
10. Given $\square A'B'C'D'$, the result of a dilation from the origin upon $\square ABCD$. If $A'(-5, -1)$, $B'(-2, -1)$, $C'(-1, 1)$, $D'(-4, 1)$ and $A(-15, -3)$,
   (a) What are the pre-images of $B'$, $C'$, and $D'$?
       $[B(-6, -3); C(-3, 3); D(-12, 3)]$
   (b) What is the ratio of $a\square ABCD$ to $a\square A'B'C'D'$?   $[\frac{1}{9}]$

# Chapter 19  Solids and Their Volumes

1. The diameter of the base of a cylinder is 6 and the altitude of the cylinder is 8.  What is the volume of the cylinder?  [$72\pi$]

2. A square is inscribed in a great circle of a sphere. If the perimeter of the square is 12, what is the volume of the sphere?  [$9\sqrt{2}\,\pi$]

3. The altitude of a right prism is 14.  The base of the prism is a trapezoid whose edges have lengths 7, 13, 19, and 11.  What is the area of the lateral surface of the prism?  [700]

4. A cross section of a pyramid is 4 in. above the base of the pyramid.  If the altitude is 12 in. and the area of the base is 144 sq. in., what is the area of the cross section?  [64 sq in.]

5. A cylindrical pipe has an inside diameter of 10 in. and an outside diameter of 11 in., and the length of the pipe is 12 ft.  If the pipe is made of material weighing 120 pounds per cubic foot, how much does the pipe weigh?  (Use $3\frac{1}{7}$ as an approximation for $\pi$.)  [165 lbs.]

6. A prism has an equilateral triangle as a base.  The length of a side of the triangle is 4 and the altitude of the prism is 7.  What is the volume of the prism?  [$28\sqrt{3}$]

7. A square pyramid and a circular cone have the same altitude and the same volume.  Express the edge, $s$, of the base of the pyramid in terms of $r$, the radius of the base of the cone.  [$s = r\sqrt{\pi}$]

8. A pyramid whose base is a regular hexagon is inscribed in a right circular cylinder, as shown in the figure.  Derive a formula for the volume of the space bounded by the surfaces of the pyramid, the cylinder, and the bases of the cylinder in terms of $r$ and $h$, the radius of the base and the altitude of the cylinder.

$$\left[\left(\pi - \frac{\sqrt{3}}{2}\right)r^2 h\right]$$

9. A sphere is inscribed in a regular square pyramid whose lateral faces are equilateral triangles.  Derive the volume of the sphere in terms of $s$, the length of each edge of the pyramid; then, letting $s = 1 + \sqrt{3}$, obtain the numerical value of the volume of the sphere.

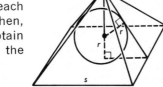

$$\left[V = \frac{s^3 \pi \sqrt{2}}{3(1 + \sqrt{3})^3};\right.$$

$$\left. V = \frac{\sqrt{2}\,\pi}{3} \doteq 1.48\right]$$

# READING SUGGESTIONS

## A. PRIMARILY FOR TEACHERS

Coxeter, H. S. M., *Introduction to Geometry.* New York, John Wiley and Sons, 1961.

Heath, Sir Thomas L., *The Thirteen Books of Euclid's Elements.* Republication of 2nd edition. Volumes I, II, III. New York, Dover Publications, 1956.

Hilbert, David, *The Foundations of Geometry* (translated by E. J. Townsend). LaSalle, Ill., Open Court Publishing Co., 1950.

Hilbert, D., and S. Cohn-Vossen, *Geometry and the Imagination* (translated by P. Nemenyi). New York, Chelsea Publishing Co., 1952.

*The Mathematics Teacher.* Journal of the National Council of Teachers of Mathematics. Washington, D.C.

    Iles, Kim, and Lester J. Wilson, "An Improvement of a Historic Construction," Jan., 1979, pp. 32–34.

    Shin, Joseph, "Are Circumscribable Quadrilaterals Always Inscribable?" May, 1979, pp. 371–372.

    Steen, Lynn Arthur, "Unsolved Problems in Geometry," May, 1979, pp. 366–369.

    Williams, Horace, "Constructing Logic Puzzles," Nov. 1961, pp. 524–527.

Modenov, P. S. and Parkhomenko, A. S., *Geometric Transformations.* New York, Academic Press, 1965.

Moise, Edwin, *Elementary Geometry From an Advanced Standpoint.* Reading, Mass., Addison-Wesley Publishing Co., Inc., 1963.

Polya, G., *How To Solve It.* New York, Doubleday and Co, (Anchor), 1957.

Polya, G., *Mathematics and Plausible Reasoning.* Princeton, Princeton University Press, 1954.

Russell, Bertrand, *Introduction to Mathematical Philosophy.* New York, Humanities Press, 1963.

Whitehead, A. N., *An Introduction to Mathematics.* New York, Oxford University Press, 1958.

Young, J. W., *Lectures on Fundamental Concepts of Algebra and Geometry.* New York, The Macmillan Company, 1959.

## B. FOR STUDENTS AND TEACHERS

[Note: The bracketed numbers in bold-face type refer to the appropriate chapter in this text.]

Abbott, Edwin, *Flatland.* New York, Barnes and Noble, 1963.

Altshiller-Court, Nathan, *College Geometry,* 2nd ed. New York, Barnes and Noble, 1952. Chapter 1, "Geometric Constructions." **[15]**

*Application in School Mathematics.* 1979 Yearbook of the National Council of Teachers of Mathematics. Washington, D.C., 1979.

Asimov, Isaac, *Realm of Measure.* Boston, Houghton Mifflin Co., 1960. **[2]**

Courant, R. and Robbins, H., *What is Mathematics?.* New York, Oxford University Press, 1941.

*Enrichment Mathematics for High Schools.* The Twenty-Eighth Yearbook of the National Council of Teachers of Mathematics. Washington, D.C., 1963.

    Blank, Albert A., "Nets," pp. 76–99.

    Brumfiel, Charles F., "Geometry: Right and/or Left," pp. 100–108.

    Hewitt, Francis, "A New Look at Some Old Geometry Problems," pp. 65–75.

    Kelly, Paul J., "Plane Convex Figures," pp. 251–264.

Eves, Howard, *A Survey of Geometry,* Vol. I. Boston, Allyn and Bacon, 1963. "Non-Euclidean Geometry," pp. 329–336, and "The Foundations of Geometry," pp. 371–436.

*Geometry in the Mathematics Curriculum.* The Thirty-Sixth Yearbook of the National Council of Teachers of Mathematics. Washington, D.C., 1973.

Kazarinoff, Nicholas D., *Geometric Inequalities.* New York, Random House, 1961. **[7]**

Kramer, Edna E., *The Mainstream of Mathematics.* New York, Oxford University Press, 1951.

Newman, James R., editor, *The World of Mathematics.* New York, Simon and Schuster, 1956. 4 vols.

*Problem Solving in School Mathematics.* 1980 Yearbook of the National Council of Teachers of Mathematics. Washington, D.C., 1980.

Rademacher, Hans, and Otto Toeplitz, *The Enjoyment of Mathematics* (translated by H. Zuckerman). Princeton, N.J., Princeton University Press, 1957.

Reid, Constance, *A Long Way from Euclid.* New York, Crowell Co., 1963.

Sanford, Vera, *A Short History of Mathematics.* Boston, Houghton Mifflin Co., 1930. Chapter VII.

Sawyer, W. W., *Mathematician's Delight.* Baltimore, Penguin Books, Inc., 1946.

Steinhaus, H., *Mathematical Snapshots.* New York, Oxford University Press, 1950.

Terry, Leon, *The Mathmen.* New York, McGraw-Hill Book Co., 1964.

Wolfe, Harold E., *Introduction to Non-Euclidean Geometry.* New York, Holt-Rinehart-Winston, 1948.

# GEOMETRY

**Edwin E. Moise**
Auburn University

**Floyd L. Downs, Jr.**
Hillsdale High School
San Mateo, California

Addison-Wesley Publishing Company
Menlo Park, California • Reading, Massachusetts
London • Don Mills, Ontario • Sydney

Books in the
Addison-Wesley Mathematics Series

ALGEBRA
R. Johnson, L. Lendsey, W. Slesnick

GEOMETRY
E. Moise, F. Downs

ALGEBRA AND TRIGONOMETRY
R. Johnson, L. Lendsey, W. Slesnick, G. Bates

PRE-CALCULUS MATHEMATICS
M. Shanks, C. Fleenor, C. Brumfiel

ELEMENTS OF CALCULUS
AND ANALYTIC GEOMETRY
G. Thomas, R. Finney

ISBN 0-201-05028-5
ABCDEFGHIJK-VH-8765432

# PREFACE

As with previous revisions of *Geometry*, this new edition preserves those features once regarded as boldly innovative, but which have proved to be as sound pedagogically as they are logically. We refer in particular to the logical accuracy of the language of the text, to the completeness of the proofs, and to the use of explicit notation to distinguish lines, rays, segments, and lengths. Countless conversations and communications between the authors and practicing classroom teachers, as well as the continuing classroom use of the text by the authors, have reaffirmed the importance of these features in conveying the facts of geometry, as well as the nature of mathematics, to high school students.

Users of the previous edition will find the present edition familiar in its layout and structure. The first four chapters have been extensively rewritten. In all other chapters the changes are comparatively minor and have been made in a way that preserves the pagination of the previous edition. Since most problem sets remain unchanged in all later chapters, continuing users will find the current edition fully compatible with their established lesson plans.

The approaches to teaching geometry from this text are perhaps as numerous as the teachers who use it. Since the first four chapters are introductory and are intended to provide a logical base for the rest of the course, it was natural that the most constructive criticisms from users of the text centered on these chapters. In this revision we have tried to respond to those concerns in the light of extensive classroom experience. The authors have always tried to provide a text fully readable by average students of geometry; in this edition there has been a renewed effort to improve the readability of sections and passages that students have, in practice, found difficult to read and understand. We hope that the expanded section on the beginning of simple proofs, at the end of Chapter 4, will meet with the approval of the many teachers who have asked for more "fill-in" proofs at this stage.

The problems in the earlier editions were carefully designed to help students understand and clarify the ideas of each section of the text, to elicit important insights, and to supply extensions of central concepts. In the present edition nearly all these problems have been retained. In the first four chapters, some harder problems have been replaced by easier, more basic problems. Consequently, students should progress through the first four chapters somewhat more rapidly than before. No student is expected to do every problem, and teachers should select problems discriminately in assigning homework.

The teaching of problem solving has been assigned a prominent role in the mathematics curriculum of the '80's. It has always been a primary goal in the teaching of geometry. The need for a careful reading of the problem, for a review and organization of pertinent facts, for a preliminary analysis leading to a solution strategy, and for a written statement of the solution to the problem remains central to an effective learning process.

Geometry teachers should be quick to recognize their responsibility to improve the problem-solving ability of their students. This ability can only be acquired by extended and varied experiences. In this respect the text provides an abundance of opportunities. Moreover, not all of these are purely geometric. Since the text makes extensive use of the real-number system, many problems provide opportunities to refresh and improve the students' grasp of basic arithmetic and algebraic facts and methods. Thus, students are expected to solve linear equations, square binomials, use the quadratic formula, and simplify radicals. These algebraic skills occur as normal outgrowths of geometric concepts. Teachers should assign these problems and should be prepared to provide classroom discussions of them.

Another important aspect of problem solving is the ability to think in spatial terms. Nearly every chapter of this book deals with relationships in space.

The authors are pleased that there are a significant number of users of Chapters 17 and 18, dealing with analytic trigonometry and with transformations and vectors. These chapters have been retained intact.

The authors wish to acknowledge, with deep gratitude, the assistance of the staff of Addison-Wesley and the contribution of hundreds of teachers and students whose criticisms and suggestions have had substantial impact on the nature of this revision.

Acknowledgment is hereby made for permission to reprint in this volume portions of the SMSG text, *Geometry*, copyright by Yale University. However, this permission must not be construed as an endorsement by the School Mathematics Study Group of the present volume.

Edwin E. Moise

Floyd L. Downs, Jr.

# CONTENTS

ix

**General Remarks on the
First Four Chapters**

The mathematical content of the first four chapters of this book is simple; and these chapters should be covered rather rapidly. The statements of fact are rather obvious, and only toward the end of Chapter 4 do we give an introduction to the idea of formal proof. What we are trying to do, in our first hundred pages or so, is to put some rudimentary facts on record, and introduce the student to the language which we shall be using.

This means that at many points in the early chapters, details should not be insisted upon. This applies, in particular, to Chapter 1. Most of the students who start the introduction to formal geometry have never had experience with a deductive system of any kind. It seems helpful, therefore, to start with a description of the nature of the enterprise. But a really thorough understanding of the way deductive systems work can be acquired only by an extended experience with at least one of them. For this reason, at the start of Chapter 6, after the introduction to congruences in Chapter 5, we refer the student back to Chapter 1. And for this reason, Chapter 1 should not be taught in an insistent spirit—it is better for you to let this chapter serve, as well as it can, its purpose of general orientation, and move on. It is, in our opinion, quite unreasonable to expect a student to acquire a deep understanding of the ideas introduced in Chapter 1 on the basis of a few pages of discussion.

Let us note at this point that the same remarks apply, for reasons of

CHAPTER **1**

# Common Sense and Exact Reasoning

## Objectives . . .

- Introduce the organizational plan of definitions, postulates, and theorems.
- Develop concepts of point, line, and plane.
- Point out the difference between observable facts and mathematical reasoning.
- Realize that intuition is not always trustworthy.

## 1–1 AN ORGANIZED LOGICAL DEVELOPMENT OF GEOMETRY

If you stop to think, you will realize that you already know many facts about geometry. For example, you know the names of many geometric figures such as triangle, square, rectangle, circle, and cube. Also, you probably know how to find the perimeters or circumferences, areas and volumes of some of them.

You also know many facts about geometric figures. Many of these facts seem so obvious that it might never occur to you to put them into words. For example,

*two straight lines cannot cross each other in more than one point.*

Some other facts you know, like the formula for the circumference of a circle ($C = 2\pi r$), are not obvious at all. Nevertheless, all of these facts, whether familiar or not, obvious or not, are important to the effective use of geometry in the learning of mathematics and in the application of mathematics to the world around us.

a quite different sort, to much of the material in Chapters 2, 3, and 4. The Ruler Postulate (p. 33) should be presented as a simple observation; its intuitive meaning is that you can lay down a ruler on any line and measure distances by subtraction. The postulates for angular measure (pp. 85–87) are equally simple observations about the properties and the uses of protractors. If these are presented as though they were earth-shaking and exciting discoveries in themselves, the student is likely to be both confused and alienated. For these reasons, the text tries to put such statements on record in a matter-of-fact way, and we recommend that they be treated in the same style in the classroom.

However, in teaching these chapters you should be aware that the content does, most certainly, form the foundation of the remainder of the text. The importance of these early stated facts (for example, the Point-Plotting Theorem, p. 41) will become apparent as they are used later on. We believe that this very effect is a valuable experience for the student. The implication for both you, the teacher, and your students is that you strengthen your understanding of the first four chapters as you proceed through the course. In other words, *we recommend that you not overteach these chapters in the beginning, but rather that you constantly refer back to them.*

### Planning the Course

Briefly outlined below are the numbers of days the authors estimate will be necessary for each chapter. Those in parentheses are optional chapters. (The midyear examination should follow Chapter 9 for the average class and Chapter 10 for the above-average class.)

Extra classroom days can be used in further study of particularly difficult chapters and the optional chapters, or in individual student work.

**Planning the Chapter**

These two sections can be assigned as reading with class discussion of the problems. Because the first few days of school are sometimes hectic, you may wish to extend the discussion for another day.

In this book we are going to help you organize the facts of geometry in an orderly way, with a few simple statements at the beginning leading up to more complicated ones. We shall see that all the facts of geometry can be derived from a relatively few simple statements. In this organizational structure we shall have three kinds of statements: *definitions*, *postulates*, and *theorems*.

We shall state *definitions* for *geometric ideas* as clearly and exactly as we can, and we shall establish the facts of geometry by giving logical proofs. The statements that we prove will be called *theorems*. Our simplest and most fundamental statements will be given without proof. These will be called *postulates*.

At first thought it may seem best to define every geometric term that we use, and to prove every statement that we make. But it is fairly easy to see that this cannot be done.

Most of the time, when we introduce a new term, we define it, using terms that have already been defined. But the *first* definition that we give cannot work this way, because in this case there aren't any terms that have already been defined. This means that we have to introduce at least one geometric term without defining it. Actually we shall use three of the simplest and most fundamental geometric ideas as *undefined terms*. These *undefined terms* are *point*, *line*, and *plane*.

Though we will not state definitions of point, line, and plane, we can describe in common language the ideas we have in mind.

If you make a dot on a piece of paper, with a pencil, you will get a reasonably good picture of a point. The sharper your pencil is, the better your picture will be. The picture will always be only approximate, because the dot will always cover *some* area, whereas a point covers *no* area at all. But if you think of smaller and smaller dots, made by sharper and sharper pencils, you will get a good idea of what we mean in geometry by the term *point*.

When we use the term *line*, we shall always have in mind the idea of a *straight line*. A straight line extends infinitely far in both directions. Usually we shall indicate this in our illustrations by putting arrowheads at the ends of the part of the line that we draw, like this.

If we do *not* put in the arrowheads, we mean to indicate only a definite part of a line, having end points, called a *line segment*. A thin, tightly stretched string is a physical example of a line segment.

When we use the term *plane*, we have in mind a perfectly flat surface, extending infinitely far in all directions. If you will imagine a sheet of clear window glass that is so huge that you cannot see its edges, you will have a fairly good idea of a geometric plane. A plane has no thickness. Similarly, a line has no width, and a point has no area.

Since points, lines, and planes are geometric ideas, and a picture or a sketch is, at best, a visual representation, the idea of a plane is especially hard to show on paper. The figure at the left below suggests the "infinite extent" of a plane, but is a rather impractical illustration for constant use. Usually we depict a plane as in the figure at the right below.

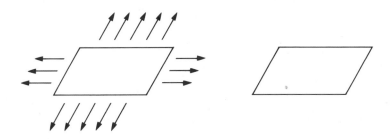

Consider next the question of the theorems. Usually, when we prove a theorem, we show that it follows logically from other theorems that we have already proved. But the *first* theorem that we prove cannot possibly work this way, because there aren't any theorems that we have already proved. This means that we have to accept at least one statement without proof. Actually, we accept several. These unproved statements are the *postulates*.

Postulates, of course, are not made up at random. Postulates describe fundamental properties of space. When we start proving theorems, the only information that we shall claim to have about points, lines, and planes will be the information given in the postulates.

Algebra and the language of sets will be used throughout this course. We shall think of them, however, as things that we are working *with*, rather than things that we are working *on*. Some of our postulates will involve real numbers, and we shall use algebra in proofs. In fact, geometry and algebra are very closely connected, and both are easier to learn if we establish the connection at the outset.

Finally, we give *a couple of warnings*.

*First*, there are limits to what logic can do for us. Logic enables us to check our guesses, but it isn't much help in making guesses in the first

## 1–1 AN ORGANIZED LOGICAL DEVELOPMENT OF GEOMETRY

### Background Material

The distinction between undefined terms and defined terms and the distinction between postulates and theorems will, of course, become more meaningful to students as they begin to work with definitions, postulates, and theorems. It is important at this time simply to clarify the ideas of point, line, and especially, plane.

See Section 27.1 of Moise, *Elementary Geometry from an Advanced Standpoint*, for a discussion of the role of postulates in geometry. Hereafter, this book will be referred to as *EGAS*.

### Classroom Notes

Encourage students to read the text thoroughly and carefully. It is directed to them, and is written so as to be readable.

Ask students to tell what is meant by *point* and *line*. After clarifying these meanings, discuss why these terms are undefined. The concept of a *plane* will require special explanation for most students.

Avoid any involved discussion about what a definition is. We have provided a chance for you to discuss some of the conventions concerning "good" definitions in Problems 5 and 6 of the problem set. Our main concern is that students learn to express their ideas clearly and precisely, and that they not be constrained or confused by adherence to purely formal rules of expression.

The spirit and procedure with which we hope you and your students will study the first few chapters is clearly stated in these two "warnings."

## Quiz

For each item select *all* correct choices.

**1.** Statements accepted without proof are called
    (a) theorems.    (b) postulates.
    (c) ideas.    (d) facts.
    (ans: b)

**2.** The terms point, line, and plane are
    (a) postulates.    (b) theorems.
    (c) defined in the text.
    (d) undefined terms.
    (ans: d)

**3.** A plane
    (a) extends infinitely far in many directions.
    (b) looks like a rectangle.
    (c) has many twists and bumps.
    (d) is perfectly flat.
    (ans: a, d)

**4.** Theorems are statements
    (a) proved by logical reasoning.
    (b) that are accepted without proof.
    (c) that are important to logical reasoning in geometry.
    (d) proved from previous theorems and postulates.
    (ans: a, c, d)

**5.** Algebra is
    (a) not important to geometry.
    (b) closely connected to geometry.
    (c) used in some geometric proofs.
    (d) easier to learn than geometry.
    (ans: b, c)

place. In our study of mathematics, you are always going to need the guidance of the feelings that you have in your bones.

*Second,* the theorems in the next couple of chapters often may seem just as obvious as the postulates. Later, we shall get to some theorems that we shall need to prove, to make sure that they are true. But to do this, we first need to build up some mathematical machinery, and we need to see how proofs work by starting with easy theorems. This will be done in Chapters 2, 3, and 4. The ideas in these early chapters will take on more meaning for you when you use them in solving problems, and when you see how they are used in proving theorems later in the book.

### Problem Set 1–1

1. You are already familiar with many facts about geometry. Make use of things you have learned before to answer the following.

    (a) What is the name of each figure?

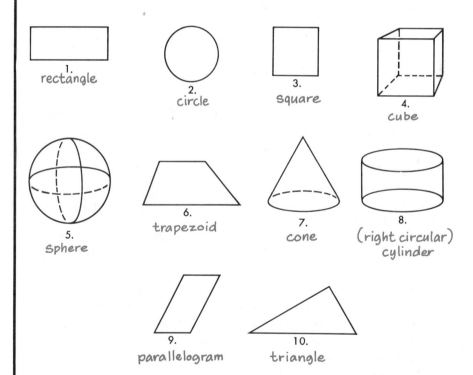

1. rectangle
2. circle
3. square
4. cube
5. Sphere
6. trapezoid
7. cone
8. (right circular) cylinder
9. parallelogram
10. triangle

    (b) If the sides of a triangle are 4 cm, 7 cm, and 6 cm, what is the perimeter of the triangle? 17cm

    (c) If the lengths of two sides of a rectangle are 7 and 10, what is its perimeter? What is its area? 34; 70

(d) The formula for the area of a circle with radius $r$ is $\pi r^2$. If a circle has a diameter of 6 cm, what is its area? (Use 3.14 for $\pi$.) **28.26cm²**

(e) What is the formula for the circumference of a circle with radius $r$? **C = 2πr**

2. A student who wanted to know the meaning of the word "dimension" consulted a dictionary. The dictionary listed as a synonym the word "measurement," whose definition the student in turn looked up. He made the following chart.

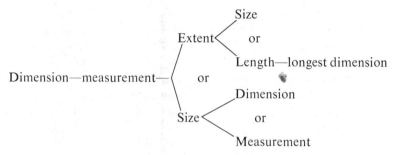

Dimension—measurement—
Extent— Size or Length—longest dimension
or
Size— Dimension or Measurement

(a) Point out from the chart a circular list of three terms, each of which has the term following it as a synonym. (In a circular list, the first term is said to follow the last term.) **Dimension, measurement, size**

(b) Make a circular list having four terms. **Dimension, measurement, extent, size**

3. What are the "undefined terms" of geometry? **Point, line, plane**

4. Make a sketch of a plane. Label it $E$. Mark three points in the plane and label them $A$, $B$, and $C$. Draw the line containing the points $A$ and $C$. Draw the line containing the points $A$ and $B$. Did you remember to use arrowheads?

5. What do you think is wrong with the following faulty "definitions"?

(a) A square is something that is not round.

(b) A right angle is an angle that is right.

(c) A right triangle is a triangle having right angles.

(d) A rectangle has four right angles.

(e) A cone is round with a point.

(f) The circumference of a circle you get when you multiply the diameter by $\pi$.

(g) The perimeter of a rectangle is where you take the sum of the lengths of its sides.

6. Try to write a definition for each term in Problem 5 that accurately describes the term and that is grammatically correct. You may use a dictionary.

---

**Answers to Problems**

**4.** For example:

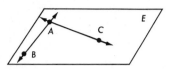

**5.–6.** Some of the faults are merely grammatical errors. Use these to point out the need for good English usage, even in mathematics.

(a) Defining a term usually involves placing it in a class and distinguishing it from other members of the class. The term "something" is an unnecessarily large class into which to place squares. The phrase "that is not round" does not distinguish it from other "somethings." (One satisfactory definition at this point: A square is a rectangle whose sides have the same length.)

(b) Using a term in its own definition is the most trivial case of a circular definition. (A right angle is an angle whose measure is 90°.)

(c) Only one of the angles in a right triangle is a right angle. (A right triangle is a triangle with one right angle.)

(d) Stating what properties a figure "has" does not tell what it "is," which is what a definition should do. (A rectangle is a plane quadrilateral that has four right angles.)

(e) Not sufficiently or accurately descriptive. (A cone is a surface formed by the set of all lines passing through a circle and a point not in the plane of the circle.)

(f) "When" refers to time, not to geometric figures. (The circumference of a circle is the product of $\pi$ and the diameter of the circle.)

(g) "Where" refers to place, not to geometric figures. (The perimeter of a rectangle is the sum of the lengths of its sides.)

## 1-2  TWO KINDS OF PROBLEMS

Consider the following two problems.

PROBLEM 1.   The product of two consecutive positive numbers is 12. What are the numbers?

PROBLEM 2.   The sum of the squares of two consecutive even integers is 340. Find all such integers.

The first of these problems has what you might call a "common sense" solution. Your familiarity with numbers helps you to think of the answer, 3 and 4, because you know that $3 \times 4 = 12$.

The second problem requires more than a "common sense" approach. To solve it requires knowing something about mathematical methods and problem-solving techniques. If we let the integers be $x$ and $x + 2$, then we can write the relationship

$$x^2 + (x + 2)^2 = 340.$$

This gives

$$x^2 + (x^2 + 4x + 4) = 340,$$

or

$$2x^2 + 4x - 336 = 0.$$

Dividing both sides by 2, we get

$$x^2 + 2x - 168 = 0.$$

Factoring,

$$(x - 12)(x + 14) = 0.$$

Now either

$$x - 12 = 0 \quad \text{or} \quad x + 14 = 0.$$

Therefore

$$x = 12 \quad \text{or} \quad x = -14$$

and

$$x + 2 = 14 \quad \text{or} \quad x + 2 = -12.$$

Thus there are two sets of integers that satisfy the conditions of Problem 2: the pair 12, 14 and the pair $-14$, $-12$.

There are cases of this kind in geometry. Consider the next two problems.

PROBLEM 3.   A rectangle measures 6 cm by 8 cm. The area enclosed is cut into two pieces by a line segment. If the area of one piece is 20 cm² (square centimetres), what is the area of the other piece?

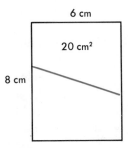

6 cm

20 cm²

8 cm

PROBLEM 4.   A rectangle is 10 cm longer than it is wide. A line segment cuts the area enclosed into two pieces, one of which is a square. The area of the rectangle is 118 more than the area of the square. What is the width of the rectangle?

You should be able to get the answer to Problem 3 without having to think very hard. The answer is 28 cm², because $6 \cdot 8 = 48$ and $48 - 20 = 28$.

Solving Problem 4 becomes easy, too, once you have applied some organized reasoning to stating it in mathematical terms. A figure helps. Let the width be $x$. Then the length will be $x + 10$.

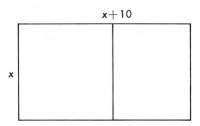

x+10

x

Referring to the problem we can write the equation

$$x(x + 10) = x^2 + 118.$$

Then

$$x^2 + 10x = x^2 + 118,$$
$$10x = 118,$$
$$x = 11.8.$$

Thus the width is 11.8 cm.

For each item select *all* correct choices.

**1.** Simple mathematical problems are most easily solved by
    (a) complicated computations.
    (b) using algebra.
    (c) common sense methods.
    (d) organized knowledge.
    (ans: c)

**2.** Systematized logical reasoning may lead to
    (a) surprising results that no one would guess.
    (b) modern science.
    (c) solutions to hard problems.
    (d) using a protractor.
    (ans: a, c)

**3.** The ancient Greeks
    (a) built the Great Pyramid of Gizeh.
    (b) proved generalizations by logical reasoning.
    (c) came after the ancient Egyptians.
    (d) laid the foundations of modern mathematics.
    (ans: b, c, d)

**4.** Hard mathematical problems
    (a) are not worth trying to solve and should never be stated in the first place.
    (b) can usually be solved by common sense methods.
    (c) always lead to complicated answers.
    (d) usually require organized logical reasoning for their solutions.
    (ans: d)

**5.** This section discusses
    (a) two kinds of problems.
    (b) four kinds of problems.
    (c) some accomplishments of the ancient Egyptians and Greeks.
    (d) two kinds of solutions.
    (ans: a, c, d)

If all problems we had to solve were as easy as Problems 1 and 3 we could be satisfied with only "common sense" solutions. But, as Problems 2 and 4 illustrate, we can solve harder problems if we are willing to apply some logical reasoning, that is, an organized system of knowledge, to their solutions.

Guessing and experimenting play important roles in solving problems. For example, if you take three sticks of length 30 cm, 40 cm, and 50 cm and place them end to end to form a triangle, you might guess that the angle opposite the longest side will be a right angle (90 degrees). Measuring the angle with a protractor would probably convince you that your guess was correct. This fact was known to the ancient Egyptians.

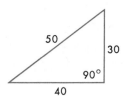

The Egyptians were extremely skillful at making physical measurements. For example, the edges of the base of the Great Pyramid of Gizeh are about 230.4 m long, and the lengths of these four edges agree, with an error of only 1.7 cm. Nobody seems to know how the builders achieved such accuracy.

But the ancient Greeks, who came somewhat after the Egyptians, discovered a vastly more powerful method. They turned their observations and plausible guesses into generalizations which they proved by logical reasoning. Thus they were able to learn some startling facts that nobody would have believed unless they were convinced by logical proof. In this way the Greeks laid the foundations of modern mathematics and hence of modern science.

For example, the Greeks observed that if a right triangle had sides of length $a$, $b$ and $c$, with $c$ the length of the longest side, then

$$a^2 + b^2 = c^2.$$

Furthermore, they proved, logically, that this would always be true. Thus not only did the 30-40-50 combination work, but the Greeks were able to find many other numbers that worked too. Eventually, it was realized that if $a$ and $b$ were each 1, then $c$ would have to be $\sqrt{2}$. This led to the discovery of irrational numbers.

In the chapters that follow you should be looking for patterns that may lead to generalizations. But before you can be certain they are valid, you must be able to prove them, as the Greeks were able to do, by logical reasoning. To this end we will proceed to organize the geometric facts that you already know and many other facts that you will learn into a logical system as described in the previous section.

## Problem Set 1–2

1. The first of the pair of questions below can be answered by "common sense." State only its answer. The second requires some arithmetic or algebraic process for its solution. Show your work for it.

    (a) What is one-sixth of 12? **2**

    (b) What is one-sixth of 5 255 622? **875 937**

2. Follow the directions for Problem 1.

    (a) One-third of the distance between two cities is 10 kilometres. What is the distance between them? $\frac{1}{3}d = 10;\ d = 30\ km$

    (b) The distance between two cities is 10 km more than one-third of the distance between them. What is the distance between them? $d = \frac{1}{3}d + 10;\ \frac{2}{3}d = 10;\ d = 15km$

3. An important part of learning mathematics is learning to recognize patterns which suggest general truths. For example, looking at the statements,

$$3 + 5 = 8, \qquad 9 + 5 = 14, \qquad 11 + 17 = 28,$$

you might guess that the sum of two odd numbers is an even number. Can you think of two odd numbers whose sum is an odd number? Does your answer prove that two such odd numbers do not exist? **No, No**

4. Consider the following figures and the pattern suggested.

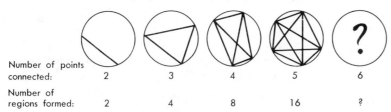

| Number of points connected: | 2 | 3 | 4 | 5 | 6 |
|---|---|---|---|---|---|
| Number of regions formed: | 2 | 4 | 8 | 16 | ? |

    (a) Replace the question mark under the 6 by the number you think belongs there.

    (b) Draw a circle and connect any six points on it in all possible ways. Count the regions thus formed. Does the result agree with your answer to part (a)?

    (c) What does this problem indicate about showing whether a generalization is true or false?

**Explanation for Problems**

Nothing in the text tells students *how* to do these problems. The object of this problem set is to show that a mathematical approach to problem solving is usually better than an uncalculated guess.

Problems 1 and 2 illustrate the theme of Section 1–2. Problems 3 and 4 point out the importance of pattern seeking, and also one of its dangers.

Problem 9 presents an impossible situation. The lack of a positive answer may make some students uncomfortable, but should keep them alert to this type of problem.

Problem 10 is a good challenge problem that students may take home to the family. The fact that the result is independent of the radius of the band is surprising and hard to believe. This problem raises the question, "If a fact is proved mathematically, must we believe it?"

**Answers to Problems**

**3.** The fact that we cannot readily think of two odd numbers whose sum is an odd number does not prove that two such odd numbers do not exist.

**4.** (a) 32 is a natural guess from observing the pattern.

   (b) In general, there will be 31 regions formed, never 32. If the six points are equally spaced around the circle there will be 30 regions formed.

   (c) A single counterexample is sufficient to prove that the generalization is false.

5. How good are you at guessing? Try this experiment. Take a piece of string about 1 m long, and place it on the floor in a loop with the ends free:

Then pull the ends of the string, gradually making the loop smaller, and stop when you think the loop is the size of your waist. Mark the string where it crosses itself, and check your guess by putting the string around your waist. *After* you have made this check, read the remarks on Problem 5 at the end of this set of problems.

6. This is also a problem in guessing.

A page of a newspaper is not very thick, about 0.076 mm, and you often have seen a stack of newspapers. Suppose you were to place one sheet of newspaper on the floor. Next you place another sheet on top of the first, then two more sheets, then four, and so on, building up a pile of newspaper. Each time you add to the pile as many sheets as are already there. After the tenth time you would have a pile about 76.2 mm high. If you were able to continue until you had added to the pile for the fiftieth time, how high would the pile be?

One of the answers (a) through (d) below is the correct one. All you have to do is guess, or calculate, which one it is.

(a) About as high as your classroom

(b) About as high as a four-story building

(c) About as high as the tallest building

(d) More than twice as high as the tallest building

*After* you have made your choice, read the remarks on Problem 6 at the end of this set of problems.

7. The following optical illusions show that you cannot always trust appearances to decide upon a fact.

(a) Is this a circle? Test your answer with a dime. Yes

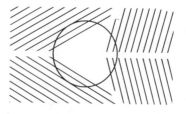

(b) Are *XY* and *YZ* the same length? Compare the lengths with your ruler or compass. **Yes**

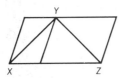

(c) Are *MN* and *PQ* straight line segments? **Yes**

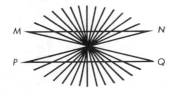

(d) Which line at the right of the rectangle is the continuation of the line at the left? **The bottom line**

(e) Which is longer, *AB* or *CD*? **They are equal.**

8. As in Problems 1 and 2 above, the first of the pair of questions below can be answered by common sense reasoning. State only its answer. The second question requires some arithmetic or algebraic process. Show your work for it.

(a) If a 5-cm piece of wire is cut into two parts so that one part is four times as long as the other, what is the length of the longer part? **4cm**

(b) If a 5-cm piece of wire is cut into two parts such that a square formed by bending one part will have four times the area of a square formed by bending the other part, what is the length of the longer part?

**8.** (b) Designate the length of the longer part by $x$ and the length of the shorter part by $5 - x$. Then the area of the larger square is $x^2$ and the area of the smaller square is $(5 - x)^2$. Then, $x^2 = 4(5 - x)^2$; $3x^2 - 40x + 100 = 0$; $(x - 10)(3x - 10) = 0$; $x - 10 = 0$, or $3x - 10 = 0$; hence $x = 10$ or $x = \frac{10}{3}$. Obviously neither part is 10. Therefore the length of the longer part is $3\frac{1}{3}$ cm and the sides of the squares are respectively $\frac{5}{6}$ cm and $\frac{5}{12}$ cm.

**9.** In order to cover the 1000 km course at an average speed of 1000 kph the pilot must reach the destination in exactly one hour. Since this hour is used by traveling the first 800 km at 800 kph, it is impossible to achieve an average speed of 1000 kph.

**10.** Let $r$ be the radius of the earth; the circumference of the iron band is then $c = 2\pi r$. Let $r'$ designate the radius of the enlarged iron band; its circumference is $c' = 2\pi r'$. The difference of these circumferences is 2 m: $c' - c = 2$ m. But $c' - c = 2\pi r' - 2\pi r = 2\pi(r' - r)$. Therefore $r' - r = \frac{2}{2\pi} = \frac{1}{\pi}$. Since $\pi$ is approximately 3, $\frac{1}{\pi}$ is approximately equal to $\frac{1}{3}$. Therefore the enlarged band is approximately $\frac{1}{3}$ m from the sphere. Note that the numerical value of the radius of the band was never used in the calculations; consequently, the answer is valid for a band of any radius.

**9.** A jet pilot plans to cover a 1000-km course at an average speed of 1000 km/h. For the first 800 km the speed is 800 km/h. At what rate must the remaining distance be covered?

**10.** Suppose you were able to wrap an iron band tightly around a very large sphere, say the earth at its equator. The band would be about 40 000 km in circumference. Suppose that you inserted into the band an additional iron strip 2 m long so that the band would no longer fit tightly around the sphere. The enlarged iron band would stand out from the sphere, and would have a radius slightly greater than the radius of the original band. About how far from the sphere would the enlarged iron band be?

REMARKS ON PROBLEM 5. Almost everybody makes a loop about twice as big as it should be. You can get very satisfactory results if you think somewhat as follows. The circumference of a circle is $\pi$ times the diameter, and $\pi$ is approximately equal to 3. Therefore, the diameter is about one-third of the circumference. Hence, if you know that your waist measure is, say, 60 cm, the loop should have a diameter of about 20 cm. This may seem unbelievably small, but if you have analyzed the problem mathematically, you will know that your careful logic is reliable.

REMARKS ON PROBLEM 6. Since each time you double the number of pages, after 50 times you would have $2^{50}$ or 1 125 899 906 842 624 sheets. This pile would be well over 85 million kilometres high; that is, more than one-half the distance from the earth to the sun.

Even if you reasoned that (d) was the right choice, you probably did not realize it represented so much of an understatement.

Euclid (Third Century B.C.)

Euclid was one of the most famous of the Greek mathematicians and was probably the most successful scientific author who ever lived. His book, the *Elements*, was a treatise on geometry and the theory of numbers. For well over two thousand years, every student who learned geometry learned it from Euclid's book. And in all that time the *Elements* served as a model of logical reasoning for everybody.

Nobody knows, today, how much of the geometry in the *Elements* was original with Euclid. Some of it may have been based on earlier books, and some of the most important ideas in it are supposed to be due to Eudoxus, who lived at about the same time. In any case, of the books which have come down to us, the *Elements* is the first one which presents geometry in an organized, logical fashion, starting with a few simple assumptions and building on them by logical reasoning.

This has been the basic method in mathematics ever since. The remarkable thing is that it was discovered so early and used so well. Logic plays the same part in mathematics that experiments do in physics. In mathematics and physics, you may get an idea that you think is right. But in physics, you had better go to the laboratory and try it and in mathematics, you had better think a little further and try to get a proof.

While Euclid's general method is here to stay, his postulates and the theory based on them are no longer very widely used. Since the development of algebra, the use of numbers to measure things has become fundamental. This method does not appear in the *Elements*, because in Euclid's time algebra was almost unknown.

### Sets, Real Numbers, and Lines

In Chapter 2 we state the metric postulates for a line. As we noted in the general comments for Chapters 1–4, the material in this chapter is rudimentary and it should be covered rather rapidly. For a thorough discussion of the idea of distance, see Chapter 3 of *EGAS*.

#### Planning the Chapter

For the average class Section 2–6 will be the most difficult. The authors suggest three days on this section and approximatoly $1\frac{1}{2}$ days on the first three sections of the chapter. Sections 2–4 and 2–5 may be studied for $1\frac{1}{2}$ days.

An above-average class will also require $1\frac{1}{2}$ days for the first three sections. Four or five days can then be spent on Sections 2–4, 2–5, and 2–6.

CHAPTER **2**

# Sets, Real Numbers, and Lines

## Objectives . . .

- Review the ideas of sets, and apply them to geometric elements.
- Review the nature of the real numbers and their fundamental properties.
- Review properties of inequalities and absolute value.
- See that the Distance Postulate conveys our basic understanding of the relation between numbers and points.
- Relate our notions of distance between points to the Ruler Postulate.
- Apply the betweenness concept to a set of three points on a line.
- Develop the basic vocabulary of lines, segments, and rays.

**The use of the language of sets.** This section is not an exposition of the mathematical theory of sets, but simply an explanation of the language used in the text. There are only two set-theoretic concepts which it is essential to understand and distinguish: intersection and union. These terms are used continually; for example, an angle will be defined as the union of two non-collinear rays, and the interior of an angle will be defined as the intersection of two half-planes.

This text uses the language of sets for the sake of clarity and for the sake of convenience. Likewise, standard symbols of the language of sets are used only when it is convenient or advantageous to do so. These symbols are used sparingly because (1) they generally do little to clarify concepts being taught and (2) surprisingly few instances occur in elementary geometry where set notation appears to be used to advantage. For most students taking geometry this material will be a general review. We suggest you teach it as such, with appropriate attention to clarification.

## 2–1   SETS

In mathematics we use the language of sets frequently. In the next few paragraphs we review and clarify the terms with which you should be familiar. Since geometric figures are sets of points, this terminology will turn out to be useful in our ability to describe figures accurately.

The idea of a *set* is easy to understand. Your family is a set of people, consisting of you, your parents, and your brothers and sisters (if any). These people are the *members* of the set. The members of a set are also called *elements* of the set. These two terms, *members* and *elements*, mean the same thing.

A member of a set is said to *belong to* the set. A set is said to *contain* its members. If one set contains every element of another set, then we say that the second set is a *subset* of the first. We say that the subset *lies in* the set that contains it. Note that every set is a subset of itself.

When we write

$$A = \{a, b, c, \ldots\}$$

we mean that $A$ is the set whose elements are listed between the braces. Thus if

$$I = \{1, 2, 3, \ldots\},$$

then $I$ is the set of all positive integers. Similarly, if

$$E = \{2, 4, 6, \ldots\}$$

and

$$T = \{3, 6, 9, \ldots\},$$

15

**The use of formal logic in geometry.**
Although we use the language of sets, we do not employ the terminology or the notation of formal logic. Our basic assumption is that a style of thinking is best grasped informally at first, and should be formalized only at a later stage.

Formal geometry builds on everyday perceptions and extends them. But the student's experience with logic is, at this level, limited. We believe that the best way to begin the study of logic is to use it in a study which requires it. This geometry course will provide the field of experience which will allow better understanding of formally stated principles of logic at some later stage of the student's education.

We want the development of geometry to proceed naturally as an interpretation of a student's experiences, not as a detached subject dependent upon a rigid set of rules of formal logic.

then $E$ is the set of all even integers, and $T$ is the set of all multiples of 3. Notice that $E$ is a subset of $I$. We abbreviate this by writing

$$E \subset I.$$

Similarly, $T \subset I$. On the other hand, $I$ is *not* a subset of $E$. (Why?) We abbreviate this by writing $I \not\subset E$.

If the object $a$ belongs to the set $A$ then we write

$$a \in A.$$

Thus, in the above examples, $1 \in I$, $4 \in E$, and $9 \in T$. The expression $a \in A$ can be read in any way that conveys its meaning: "$a$ belongs to $A$," or "$a$ is an element of $A$," and so on.

If the object $a$ does *not* belong to the set $A$, then we write $a \notin A$. Thus, in the above examples, $0 \notin I$, $1 \notin E$, and $2 \notin T$.

When we say that two sets are *equal*, or write an equality $A = B$ between two sets $A$ and $B$, we mean merely that the two sets have exactly the same elements. Suppose, for example, that $A$ is the set of all whole numbers between $9\frac{1}{3}$ and $14\frac{1}{10}$, and $B$ is the set of all whole numbers between $9\frac{1}{10}$ and $14\frac{1}{3}$. Then $A = B$, because each of the sets $A$ and $B$ contains precisely the elements 10, 11, 12, 13, and 14. Nearly always, in fact, the same set can be described in many different ways. The expressions $3 \cdot 17$ and $39 + 12$ look different, but they describe the same number; and this is what we mean when we write $3 \cdot 17 = 39 + 12$. If $A$ and $B$ are not the same set, then we write $A \neq B$. In general, the symbol $\neq$ means "is not equal to," no matter what sort of objects we are talking about.

In geometry the ideas of *union* and *intersection* are used fairly often when referring to geometric figures.

### Definitions

The *union* of two sets is the set of all elements that belong to one or both sets. The *intersection* of two or more sets is the set of all elements common to the sets.

For the sets

$$E = \{2, 4, 6, \ldots\} \qquad \text{and} \qquad T = \{3, 6, 9, \ldots\},$$

the union is $\{2, 3, 4, 6, 8, 9, 10, 12, 14, \ldots\}$ and the intersection is $\{6, 12, 18, \ldots\}$.

In the figure below we see two rectangular regions lying in two different planes. The union of the two regions is the set of all points in the figure. The intersection of the two regions is merely a line segment.

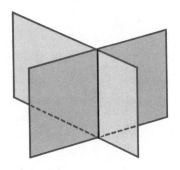

The union of two sets $A$ and $B$ is denoted by

$$A \cup B,$$

and the intersection is denoted by

$$A \cap B.$$

(The symbols $\cup$ and $\cap$ are read "union" and "intersection.")

Sometimes the intersection of two sets contains no elements at all. In this case we say that the intersection is empty, or is the empty set. That is, the *empty set* is the set that contains no elements. For example, the intersection of the set of all odd numbers and the set of all even numbers is the empty set.

Thus when we speak of the *intersection* of two sets, we allow the possibility that the intersection is empty, but when we say that two sets *intersect*, we always mean that their intersection contains at least one member. We make this clear in the following definition.

**Definition**

Two sets *intersect* if there are one or more elements that are common to the sets.

The empty set is a subset of every set. This follows from the definition of subset, since every set contains every element of the empty set. The empty set is denoted by $\emptyset$.

The symbol for the empty set, Ø, is a letter of the Danish alphabet, not a Greek letter as many think. A more descriptive symbol is {}. But note that {Ø} is *not* a correct symbol for the empty set since this set has one element; namely, the empty set.

**Quiz**

Complete each sentence with the word(s) or symbol(s) that will make it true.

**1.** If two sets do not intersect, their intersection is _____.
(ans: Ø)

**2.** Every element of a set is said to _____ to the set or to be _____ in the set.
(ans: belong; contained)

**3.** $A \subset B$ means that set $A$ is a _____ of set $B$, or that $B$ _____ every element of $A$.
(ans: subset; contains)

**4.** If $K = \{x, y, z\}$, then $y$ _____ $K$.
(ans: ∈ or is an element of)

**5.** If $R = \{-1, 0, 1\}$ and $S$ is the set of all integers between $-1\frac{1}{2}$ and $1\frac{1}{2}$, then $R$ _____ $S$.
(ans: = or equals)

*Word of warning:* Zero and the empty set are not the same thing. For example, the equation $x + 3 = 3$ has 0 as its only root, and so the set of roots is $\{0\}$; the set of roots has exactly one element, namely 0. On the other hand, the equation $x + 1 = x + 2$ has no roots at all. Therefore its set of roots is Ø.

**Problem Set 2–1**

**1.** For which of the following pairs of sets, $A$ and $B$, is $A = B$?

(a) $A$ is the set of all whole numbers between $\frac{3}{2}$ and $\frac{25}{3}$. $B = \{2, 3, 4, 5, 6, 7, 8\}$.

(b) $A$ is the set of all girls' names beginning with J. $B = \{$Jane, Jean, Joan, June, Jackie, Judy$\}$.

(c) $A = \{-4\}$. $B =$ the set of all roots of $x + 4 = 0$.

(d) $A$ is the set of all students in your geometry class who are less than 10 years old. $B$ is the set of all months of the year whose names begin with R.

(e) $A =$ the set of all roots of $x + 7 = 12$. $B =$ the set of all roots of $x^2 = 25$.

**2.** In the figures below, consider the lines and the circles as two sets of points. $A$, $P$, and $Q$ are points. In each case, name the set which is the intersection of the line and the circle.

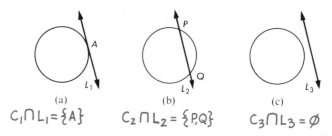

(a)              (b)              (c)

$C_1 \cap L_1 = \{A\}$     $C_2 \cap L_2 = \{P, Q\}$     $C_3 \cap L_3 = \emptyset$

**3.** Let $P = \{2, 5, 7, 10, 14, 17\}$ and $Q = \{2, 4, 6, 8, 10, 12\}$. What is $P \cap Q$? What is $P \cup Q$? $\{2, 10\}$; $\{2, 4, 5, 6, 7, 8, 10, 12, 14, 17\}$

**4.** Consider each of the following questions carefully.

(a) How many elements are in $\{1\}$? 1

(b) How many elements are in $\{0, 1\}$? 2

(c) How many elements are in $\{0\}$? 1

(d) How many elements are in $\{ \}$? 0

(e) Which of the symbols in (a)–(d) would be a suitable representation of the empty set? (d)

**5.** Use the figure below.

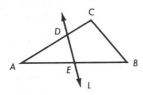

(a) What is the intersection of the line $L$ and the triangle $ABC$? $\{D, E\}$

(b) What is the intersection of the line $L$ and the triangular region $ABC$? $\overline{DE}$

(c) What is the intersection of the triangle $ABC$ and the segment $\overline{BC}$? $\overline{BC}$

**6.** Consider the set $E$ of all positive even integers and the set $O$ of all positive odd integers.

(a) Describe $E \cup O$. The set of all integers

(b) Describe $E \cap O$. $\emptyset$

**7.** Let $A$ = the set of all positive multiples of 3 and let $B$ = the set of all positive multiples of 4.

(a) Describe $A \cup B$. $\{3, 4, 6, 8, 9, 12, 15, 16, \ldots\}$

(b) Describe $A \cap B$. $\{12, 24, 36, \ldots\}$

**8.** Think of a point, $A$, on the blackboard or on a piece of paper. How many lines (straight lines) in the plane of the blackboard or paper are there which contain $A$?. The lines containing $A$ form a set. The lines are the elements of the set. How many elements does this set have? Infinitely many; Infinitely many

**9.** (a) Given two different points $A$ and $B$, how many elements are in the set of all lines (straight lines) that contain both $A$ and $B$? We often phrase this question differently and ask: How many lines can be drawn through two points, $A$ and $B$? One

(b) Given three points, $A$, $B$, and $C$, which do not all lie in a line, how many lines are there each of which contains a pair of the three points? Three

• B

A •

• C

**Classroom Notes**

It is not to be expected, at this stage, that the students will have a thorough understanding of the real number system. It is therefore misleading to say that this text "presupposes" an understanding of the real numbers. At this maturity level, all mathematical understanding is partial. But by bringing out early the relations between geometry and algebra, we enable partial understanding of geometry and partial understanding of algebra to reinforce each other.

Remember, in particular, that most tenth-grade students are not accustomed to thinking of the real number system in its completeness. They think of numbers as integers and "fractions"; they know very little about irrational numbers. Try to give them a feeling for the completeness of the real number system by appealing to the geometric idea that lines have no holes in them.

It should also be understood that when we use the Ruler Postulate, we are making a long step forward from the use of the number line in algebra. The Ruler Postulate tells us that any line at all may be regarded as a number line.

**The idea of correspondence.** The material in this section, like that in the preceding section, is informally presented. This intuitive development is intended to convince the student that a correspondence can be set up between the points of a line and the real numbers in such a way that (1) to each point on a line there corresponds a real number, and (2) to each real number there corresponds a point on the line. A feeling for the arrangement of the real numbers on a line is important to the student at this time.

(c) Given four points, $A$, $B$, $C$, and $D$, such that no three of them lie in a line, how many lines are there each of which contains a pair of the points? If a fifth point is given under the same conditions, how many lines are there? **six ; ten**

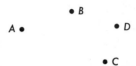

(d) In (a), (b), and (c) the same question is asked for different numbers of points. Answer this question if $n$ points are given. $\frac{1}{2}n(n-1)$

10. The set $\{a, b\}$ has the following subsets: $\{a, b\}, \{a\}, \{b\}, \emptyset$. Thus, a set with two elements has four subsets.

(a) List all the subsets of $\{a, b, c\}$.

(b) How many subsets does a set of four elements have? **16**

(c) How many subsets does a set of five elements have? **32**

(d) How many subsets does a set of $n$ elements have? $2^n$

## 2-2   ORDER ON THE NUMBER LINE

The first numbers that you learned about were the "*counting numbers*," or the "*natural numbers*," namely

$$1,2,3,4,5, \ldots$$

We may think of the counting numbers as arranged on a line, from left to right:

To the left of 1, we put the number 0:

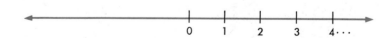

We now have the *whole numbers*. Next we enter the corresponding negative numbers.

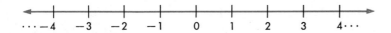

The numbers that we have so far are the *integers* (positive, negative, and zero). The counting numbers are the positive integers, and are often referred to by this name.

Note that there are many points of the line that have no numbers attached to them so far. We need, at least, to put in the fractions $\frac{1}{2}$, $\frac{1}{3}$, $\frac{2}{3}$, $-\frac{1}{2}$, $-\frac{1}{3}$, $-\frac{2}{3}$, and so on. There are infinitely many of these between every two integers. In a figure, therefore, all we can do is to indicate some of them, as samples:

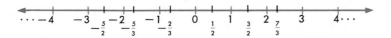

What we have mentioned so far are the rational numbers. *Rational numbers* are numbers of the form $p/q$, where $p$ and $q$ are integers and $q \neq 0$. This name refers to the fact that the rational numbers are *ratios* of integers.

The rational numbers do not fill up the number line completely. There are many numbers that cannot be expressed as ratios of integers. For example, $\sqrt{2}$ is not rational. Neither are $\sqrt{3}$, $\sqrt{5}$, or $\pi$. These are *irrational numbers*.

If we insert all the irrational numbers, then every point of our line has a number corresponding to it. We then have the complete set of *real numbers*, which form the *number line*. This is sometimes called the *real number line*. (You should check that the irrational numbers shown in the figure appear in approximately the places where they belong.)

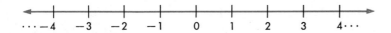

We believe that it is easier in teaching to first establish that to each *integer* there corresponds a point on the line. Then select an interval (say from 3.0 to 4.0) and "locate" the points corresponding to other rational numbers, such as 3.5, 3.75, and so on. The points corresponding to irrational numbers are easily "located" by using the decimal approximations of these numbers. If students need to be convinced that to each point on the line there corresponds a real number, you should select a point $P$ on the line and explain that we can find (to any desired degree of accuracy) the real number $r$ corresponding to $P$ by observing that this real number $r$ must satisfy an inequality, for example, $3.7 < r < 3.8$, then that $r$ satisfies the inequality $3.72 < r < 3.73$, and so on. By this technique of successively more accurate approximations you can "zero in on" the real number corresponding to $P$.

**The Properties of Equality.** Addition and multiplication are operations performed on *numbers*, not operations performed on symbols. And we have agreed that $a = b$ means that the symbols $a$ and $b$ are merely two names for the same number. Therefore the "Addition Property of Equality" merely reminds us that the sum of two numbers depends only on the numbers; it does not change if we denote the numbers by different symbols. Analogously, if a man named Smith weighs 180 lb, and he changes his name to Jones, then Jones weighs 180 lb; weight is a property of the man and not of the name.

In practice, students find these properties convenient to refer to. Since they are true statements, this surely does no harm. But if a student should happen to ask whether we have to take them as postulates, it should be explained that we do not.

In writing statement and reason proofs we shall use "Addition Property of Equality" (rather than the archaic formation "If equals are added to equals, then the sums are equal") as the reason for a statement obtained by addition.

In your study of algebra you have by now learned a great deal about the behavior of real numbers under the operations of addition and multiplication. The fundamental properties of these operations are:

**Commutative Property of Addition**

$$a + b = b + a$$

**Commutative Property of Multiplication**

$$ab = ba$$

**Associative Property of Addition**

$$(a + b) + c = a + (b + c)$$

**Associative Property of Multiplication**

$$(ab)c = a(bc)$$

**Distributive Property**

$$a(b + c) = ab + ac$$

Each of these fundamental properties holds for all real numbers $a$, $b$, and $c$. Ordinarily we shall use them with little or no comment. You will also find the following statements convenient to refer to as reasons for steps you take later in writing proofs.

**Addition Property of Equality**

If $a = b$ and $c = d$, then $a + c = b + d$.

**Subtraction Property of Equality**

If $a = b$ and $c = d$, then $a - c = b - d$.

**Multiplication Property of Equality**

If $a = b$ and $c = d$, then $ac = bd$.

**Division Property of Equality**

If $a = b$ and $c \neq 0$, then $\dfrac{a}{c} = \dfrac{b}{c}$.

A number $x$ is *less than* a number $y$ if $x$ lies to the left of $y$ on the number line:

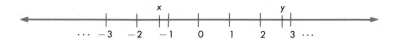

We indicate this fact by writing $x < y$. If $x < y$, then *y is greater than x*, and so we may also write $y > x$. The expressions $x < y$ and $y > x$ mean exactly the same thing.

Every negative number lies to the left of every positive number. Therefore every negative number is less than every positive number.

The expression $x \leq y$, which is read "*x* is less than or equal to *y*," means that either $x < y$ or $x = y$. Similarly, the expression $x \geq y$ is read "*x* is greater than or equal to *y*." Thus $-2 \leq 1$, because $-2 < 1$; and $2 \leq 2$, because $2 = 2$.

Expressions using $<$, $>$, $\leq$, and $\geq$ are called *inequalities* or *order relations*. The fundamental properties of inequalities are:

**Trichotomy Property**

> For every $x$ and $y$, one and only one of the following conditions holds:
> $$x < y, x = y, x > y.$$

**Transitive Property of Inequalities**

> If $x < y$ and $y < z$, then $x < z$.

**Addition Property of Inequalities**

> If $a < b$ and $x \leq y$, then $a + x < b + y$.

**Multiplication Property of Inequalities**

> If $x < y$ and $a > 0$, then $ax < ay$.

The other rules of inequalities that we need to know can be derived from these properties. We state two of these as our first theorems.

## Quiz

For each item select *all* correct choices.

**1.** Which of the following are sets of real numbers?
   (a) The counting numbers
   (b) The integers
   (c) The rational numbers
   (d) The irrational numbers
   (ans: a, b, c, d)

**2.** The rational numbers
   (a) fill up the number line.
   (b) Include the numbers $-\frac{5}{7}$, $1\frac{2}{3}$, $\frac{12}{4}$, 5, and 0.
   (c) are numbers of the form $p/q$, where $p$ and $q$ are integers and $q \neq 0$.
   (d) are only positive numbers.
   (ans: b, c)

**3.** The order relation $x > y$ means
   (a) the same as $y < x$.
   (b) that $x$ and $y$ are positive numbers.
   (c) that $x$ lies to the left of $y$ on the number line.
   (d) that $x$ lies to the right of $y$ on the number line.
   (ans: a, d)

**4.** Which of the following are true statements?
   (a) $\sqrt{25} = -5$
   (b) $-5$ is a square root of 25.
   (c) $\sqrt{25} = \pm 5$
   (d) $(\sqrt{7})^2 = 7$
   (ans: b, d)

**5.** All the numbers $\sqrt{3}$, $\sqrt{5}$, and $-\sqrt{7}$
   (a) are real numbers.
   (b) are rational numbers.
   (c) are irrational numbers.
   (d) have squares that are rational numbers.
   (ans: a, c, d)

### Theorem 2–1

If $a - b > 0$, then $a > b$.

**Proof.** We are given that $a - b > 0$. Therefore we have $a - b + b > 0 + b$, by the Addition Property of Inequalities. Simplifying this by the usual rules of algebra, we get $a > b$.

### Theorem 2–2

If $a = b + c$ and $c > 0$, then $a > b$.

**Proof.** We are given that $a = b + c$. Applying the Subtraction Property of Equality we get $a - b = b + c - b$. Simplifying this we get $a - b = c$. Since we were given also that $c > 0$, this means that $a - b > 0$. Now applying Theorem 2–1, we get the desired result, $a > b$.

Finally, we shall need the following:

### Existence of Square Roots

Every positive number has exactly one positive square root.

There is a rather tricky point in connection with square roots. When we say, in words, that *x is a square root of a*, we mean merely that $x^2 = a$. For example, 3 is a square root of 9, because $3^2 = 9$. But $-3$ is also a square root of 9, because $(-3)^2 = 9$. Thus 9 has two square roots, 3 and $-3$.

But when we write, in symbols, that $x = \sqrt{a}$, we mean that $x$ is the *positive* square root of $a$. Thus $-\sqrt{a}$ is the *negative* square root of $a$. For example, $\sqrt{7}$ is the positive square root of 7, and $-\sqrt{7}$ is the negative square root of 7.

Consider these three statements:

$$(1) \quad -3 \text{ is a square root of } 9 \quad \text{(True)}$$
$$(2) \quad -3 = \sqrt{9} \quad \text{(False)}$$
$$(3) \quad -3 = -\sqrt{9} \quad \text{(True)}$$

The first statement is true because $(-3)^2 = 9$. The second is false because $\sqrt{9}$ is the *positive* square root of 9, and $-3$ is not positive. The third is true because $-3$ is the negative square root of 9.

A common mistake is to think that putting a plus sign in front of the symbol for square root somehow makes it "more positive." But a plus sign never changes the value of any expression. Thus we reemphasize that $\sqrt{a}$ always denotes the *positive* square root of $a$; and that $-\sqrt{a}$ always denotes the *negative* square root of $a$. We define $\sqrt{0}$ to be 0.

## Problem Set 2–2

1. Fill each blank with one of the symbols $=$, $<$, or $>$ to make each completed statement true.

   (a) $5 \times (6 + 13)$ __<__ 100.

   (b) $(9 + 6) \div 3$ __=__ 5.

   (c) $(4)(7)$ __<__ $(5)(7)$ and $(4)(-7)$ __>__ $(5)(-7)$.

   (d) $6 - 13 + 5 \times 3 + 4 - 6$ __>__ 0.

   (e) $18 + 12 \div 2 + 16 - 4 \times 3 + 9 \div 3$ __>__ 30.

2. Name the property which is a reason for each statement.

   (a) If $a < 0$ and $b > 0$, then $a < b$. **Transitive**

   (b) If $x > 7$, then $x \neq 7$. **Trichotomy**

   (c) If $5 < 9$ and $2 < 3$, then $7 < 12$. **Add. Prop. of Inequalities**

   (d) If $m = 10$ and $n = 6$, then $m + n = 16$. **Add. Prop. of Equality**

   (e) If $\sqrt{a} = 5$ is true, then $\sqrt{a} = 4$ is false. **Existence of Sq. Roots**

3. Name the property which is a reason for each statement. **Distributive Property**

   (a) $6(3x + 5y) = 18x + 30y$

   (b) $5a + 10b = 5(a + 2b)$

   (c) $7x + 8x = (7 + 8)x$

4. Along a number line marked at unit intervals of 1 cm, correctly place the following symbols.

$$0, \quad 1, \quad \sqrt{4}, \quad -\sqrt{4}, \quad \sqrt{9}, \quad -\sqrt{9}, \quad \sqrt{16}, \quad -\sqrt{25}$$

5. Fill each blank with one of the symbols $=$, $<$, $>$, $\leq$, or $\geq$ to make each completed statement true.

   (a) If $p$ is a positive number, then $p$ __>__ 0.

   (b) If $q$ is a negative number, then $q$ __<__ 0.

   (c) If $r$ is non-negative, then $r$ __$\geq$__ 0.

   (d) If $s$ is both non-negative and nonpositive, then $s$ __=__ 0.

### Explanation for Problems

The last two parts of Problem 1 give you a chance to remind students of the convention of performing indicated multiplication and division before addition and subtraction. We assume this is one of many understandings they bring from elementary algebra. Preferably this point will arise from student discussion of the problems.

In general, this problem set provides a review of many arithmetic and algebraic facts which should be familiar to the students. While Problems 1–10 should be within the scope of all students, full understanding of the nature of the real numbers is neither expected nor implied.

Problem 4 is particularly helpful in explaining the meaning of the symbol for the negative square root.

### Answers to Problems

4.

# Answers to Problems

**7.**

| Real Numbers | Rational Numbers | Integers | Irrational Numbers |
|---|---|---|---|
| 7 | 7 | 7 | |
| $\frac{2}{3}$ | $\frac{2}{3}$ | | |
| $\sqrt{11}$ | | | $\sqrt{11}$ |
| 0.02 | 0.02 | | |
| $\sqrt{4}$ | $\sqrt{4}$ | $\sqrt{4}$ | |
| $1\frac{3}{4}$ | $1\frac{3}{4}$ | | |
| 14.003 | 14.003 | | |
| $-3$ | $-3$ | $-3$ | |
| $\frac{\sqrt{2}}{5}$ | | | $\frac{\sqrt{2}}{5}$ |
| $-\sqrt{\frac{3}{8}}$ | | | $-\sqrt{\frac{3}{8}}$ |
| 0 | 0 | 0 | |
| 1.414 | 1.414 | | |
| $-\sqrt{\frac{9}{16}}$ | $-\sqrt{\frac{9}{16}}$ | | |
| $\pi$ | | | $\pi$ |

## Quiz

**1.** What term names numbers of the form $a/b$, where $a$ and $b$ are integers and $b \neq 0$?
(ans: rational numbers)
**2.** Name the two square roots of 64.
(ans: 8 and $-8$)
**3.** Name the two square roots of 19.
(ans: $\sqrt{19}$ and $-\sqrt{19}$)
**4.** Is it true or false that $\sqrt{16} = -4$?
(ans: false)
**5.** If $x = 3$ and $y = 8$, which property justifies the statement $x + y = 11$?
(ans: Addition Property of Equality)
**6.** Is it true or false that for all real numbers $x$, $-x$ is a negative number?
(ans: false)
**7.** Which property justifies this statement? If $a < 5$ and $b > 5$, then $b > a$.
(ans: Transitive Property)
**8.** Write the following using symbols only: $x$ is a negative number.
(ans: $x < 0$)
**9.** Is it true or false that $\sqrt{\frac{9}{25}}$ is a rational number?
(ans: true)
**10.** Which property justifies this statement? $2a + 7a = (2 + 7)a$.
(ans: Distributive Property)

---

**6.** For the statement "$a$ is between 3 and 12" Karen wrote "$3 > a > 12$," Mary wrote "$12 > a > 3$," and Sally wrote "$a < 12$ and $a > 3$." Which of the girls wrote the statement correctly? **Mary and Sally**

**7.** Prepare a table with the following column headings: "Real numbers," "Rational numbers," "Integers," "Irrational numbers." Under the heading "Real numbers" list the following:

$$7, \quad \tfrac{2}{3}, \quad \sqrt{11}, \quad 0.02, \quad \sqrt{4}, \quad 1\tfrac{3}{4}, \quad 14.003, \quad -3$$

$$\frac{\sqrt{2}}{5}, \quad -\sqrt{\frac{3}{8}}, \quad 0, \quad 1.414, \quad -\sqrt{\frac{9}{16}}, \quad \pi.$$

Complete the table by putting each number under the name of each subset of the real numbers to which it belongs.

**8.** Tell whether each of the following statements is true or false.
(a) Negative numbers are real numbers. **T**
(b) The real number line has at least one end point. **F**
(c) $-x$ is a negative number for every $x$. **F**
(d) If $x$ is a negative number, then $\sqrt{x^2} = -x$. **T**

**9.** Tell whether each of the following statements is true or false.
(a) There is a point on the real number line that corresponds to $\sqrt{2}$ and is different from the point corresponding to 1.414. **T**
(b) If $x$ is a negative number, then $-x$ is a positive number. **T**
(c) If $x > y$, then $x - y > 0$. **T**
(d) If $ax < ay$, then $x < y$. **F**

**10.** Write a definition of a positive number; of a negative number.
    $x > 0; \quad x < 0$

---

**11.** Which of the following are true?
(a) $\sqrt{16} = 4$. **T**      (b) $\sqrt{25} = -5$. **F**
(c) $-\sqrt{64} = -8$. **T**      (d) $-\sqrt{0.36} = -0.6$. **T**
(e) $-\sqrt{0.04} = 0.2$. **F**      (f) $\sqrt{1.21} = 1.1$. **T**

**12.** Under which of the following conditions is it true that $\sqrt{x^2} = x$?
(a) $x = 3$.      (b) $x = -3$.      (c) $x = 0$.
(d) $x = 1$.      (e) $x = -1$.      (f) $x < 0$.
(g) $x \geq 0$.      (h) $\frac{1}{x} > 0$.      (i) $-x > 0$.

## 2–3   ABSOLUTE VALUE

The *absolute value* of a number $x$ is denoted by $|x|$. The meaning of the symbol $|x|$ is readily understood from a few examples:

$$|0| = 0, \qquad |-8| = 8,$$
$$|2| = 2, \qquad |87| = 87,$$
$$|-2| = 2, \qquad |-95| = 95,$$
$$|7| = 7, \qquad |-\sqrt{13}| = \sqrt{13},$$

and so on. Here we are using the following rules:

(1) If $x \geq 0$, then $|x| = x$.

(2) If $x < 0$, then $|x|$ is the corresponding positive number.

If a particular number is written arithmetically, it is easy to see how to write its absolute value. If there is no minus sign in front, we leave the number unchanged. If there is a minus sign in front, we omit the minus sign to get the absolute value.

But when we work algebraically with expressions like $|x|$ and $|a - b|$ it is convenient to have an algebraic form of condition (2). Thus, given a negative number $x$, we wish to have an algebraic way of describing the corresponding positive number. If the negative number is denoted by $x$, then we cannot "omit the minus sign," because there isn't any minus sign to omit. We can get around this difficulty by a simple trick: *if $x < 0$, then the corresponding positive number is $-x$.* This is illustrated by the following figure:

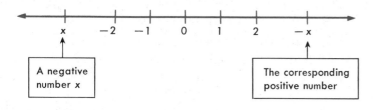

Here are some examples:

(1)   If $x = -2$, then $-x = -(-2) = 2$,

(2)   If $x = -3$, then $-x = -(-3) = 3$.

### Classroom Notes

The concept of the absolute value of a real number will be used in the Ruler Postulate (Postulate 2).

Experience indicates that the definition of the absolute value involves a serious teaching difficulty: the definition says that for $x < 0$, $|x| = -x$; and this looks utterly wrong to many students, because $|x|$ is supposed to be positive, and $-x$ looks as though it ought to be negative. The root of this trouble is the notion that letters used as variables always denote positive numbers. Indeed, many textbook authors have willfully propagated this misconception by mentioning "the positive number $+a$" and "the negative number $-a$." The discussion of the text is designed to reveal and uproot the notion that all variables are positive.

We are interested in absolute values as a means to an end: a concise, mathematically accurate statement of how to compute the distance between two points on the number line. We perform essentially only one type of computation: the evaluation of $|a - b|$, where $a$ and $b$ are real numbers. It is important for the student to be proficient at evaluating $|a - b|$ for different combinations of positive and negative numbers, $a$ and $b$; for example, $|5 - 2|$, $|5 - (-2)|$, $|(-5) - 2|$, and $|(-5) - (-2)|$. Stress that one "performs operations inside absolute value signs" first, and then "takes absolute values." Students are inclined to think that the absolute value function is an additive function, that is, that $|a + b| = |a| + |b|$. If students appear to have this idea, it should be corrected.

If students understand the arithmetical properties of absolute value, it will be much easier for them to understand the use we make of absolute value in the Ruler Postulate.

This leads us to a second way of describing $|x|$.

## Definition

$$|x| = \begin{cases} x \text{ if } x \geq 0 \\ -x \text{ if } x < 0 \end{cases}$$

Note that this definition is in two parts, corresponding to rules (1) and (2) above.

## Quiz

For each item select *all* correct choices.

**1.** $x \geq 0$ means
  (a) $x$ is a number greater than or equal to zero.
  (b) $x$ is not a negative number.
  (c) $x$ is either zero or a positive number.
  (d) $x$ is a non-negative number.
  (ans: a, b, c, d)

**2.** $x < 0$ means
  (a) $x$ is a number less than zero.
  (b) $x$ is a negative number.
  (c) $-x$ is a negative number.
  (d) $-x$ is a positive number.
  (ans: a, b, d)

**3.** If $x = -4$, then
  (a) $|x|$ is a positive number.
  (b) $|x| = -4$.
  (c) $|x| = 4$.
  (d) $|x| = x$.
  (ans: a, c)

**4.** $|23| - |-7|$ equals
  (a) $|23 + 7|$.
  (b) $|23 - 7|$.
  (c) 16.
  (d) 30.
  (ans: b, c)

**5.** If $|x + 7| = 13$, then
  (a) $x = 6$ only.
  (b) $x = 6$ or $x = -6$.
  (c) $x = 6$ or $x = 20$.
  (d) $x = 6$ or $x = -20$.
  (ans: d)

**6.** For all real numbers $x$ and $y$, $|x| + |y|$ equals
  (a) $x + y$.
  (b) $|x + y|$.
  (c) $|x| + |-y|$.
  (d) $|-x| + |-y|$.
  (ans: c, d)

## Problem Set 2–3

**1.** Evaluate each of the following.

  (a) $|5|$   5      (b) $|-6|$   6
  (c) $-|-6|$   -6      (d) $|2| + (-2)$   0
  (e) $|2| + |-2|$   4      (f) $|5 - 8|$   3
  (g) $|5| - |8|$   -3      (h) $|-8 - 5|$   13

**2.** Which of the following are true?

  (a) $|-3| = 3$.      (b) $|3| = -3$.
  (c) $|-3| < 3$.      (d) $|3| > -3$.
  (e) $7 - 9 < 9 - 7$.      (f) $7 - 9 = 9 - 7$.
  (g) $|7 - 9| < |9 - 7|$.      (h) $|7 - 9| = |9 - 7|$.

**3.** Solve for the variable.

  (a) $|x| + 5 = 8$.   $\{3, -3\}$      (b) $|x + 5| = 8$.   $\{3, -13\}$
  (c) $|y| - |7| = 8$.   $\{15, -15\}$      (d) $|y - 7| = 8$.   $\{15, -1\}$
  (e) $|z| - 6 = 4$.   $\{10, -10\}$      (f) $|z - 6| = 4$.   $\{2, 10\}$

**4.** Indicate whether each statement is true or false.

  (a) If $b > 0$, then $b$ is a positive number.   T
  (b) If $-b > 0$, then $b$ is a negative number.   T
  (c) If $-b < 0$, then $b$ is a positive number.   T
  (d) If $b < 0$, then $-b$ is a positive number.   T

**5.** For each pair of values of $h$ and $k$ evaluate

$$\text{(i)} \quad |h + k|, \quad \text{(ii)} \quad |h - k|, \quad \text{(iii)} \quad |h| - |k|$$

  (a) $h = 7, k = 4$   11; 3; 3      (b) $h = -7, k = 4$   3; 11; 3
  (c) $h = -6, k = -3$   9; 3; 3      (d) $h = 3, k = -6$   3; 9; -3
  (e) $h = 5, k = -5$   0; 10; 0      (f) $h = 0, k = 7$   7; 7; -7

## 2–4   RULERS AND UNITS OF DISTANCE

When you use a ruler to measure the distance between two points $P$ and $Q$, the number that you get depends on the unit that is used on the ruler.

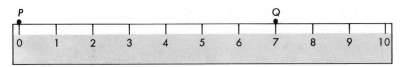

In the figure, the ruler is marked in centimetres, and the answer that we get is 7 cm. If we used a ruler marked in millimetres, the picture would look like this:

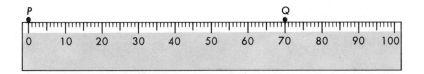

This gives the answer 70 mm. Thus the number that we get for the distance between two points depends on the unit of measure.

Logically speaking, one unit works just as well as another. However, using various units in the same problem would cause needless trouble. Let us therefore choose a unit, and agree to use this unit in all our theorems. (It will do no harm to think of this chosen unit as being anything we like. *All our theorems will hold true for all units.*)

Thus, once we have chosen a unit, to every pair of points $P$, $Q$ there will correspond a number which tells us how far $P$ is from $Q$. This number is called the *distance* between $P$ and $Q$.

We make these ideas official by stating a postulate and a definition.

**POSTULATE 1.**   The Distance Postulate

*To every pair of different points there corresponds a unique positive number.*

### Definition

The *distance* between two points is the number given by the Distance Postulate. If the points are $P$ and $Q$, then the distance is denoted by $PQ$.

**Classroom Notes**

The Distance Postulate may be approached inductively, by marking several pairs of points, $P$ and $Q$, $R$ and $S$, and so on, on the board and computing the distance between $P$ and $Q$ with a metre stick. The following observations are then natural: (1) The distance between two points is a *real number*; (2) it is a *positive* real number; (3) it is a *unique* positive real number. These observations are formalized in the Distance Postulate.

We allow the possibility that $P = Q$, that is, that $P$ and $Q$ are the same point. In this case, $PQ = 0$. The distance is defined simply for a pair of points, and does not depend on the order in which the points are mentioned. Therefore we always have $PQ = QP$.

If two distances $PQ$ and $RS$ are the same in one unit, then they are the same in all other units. And the *ratio* $PQ/RS$ is the same in all units. This is why so many geometric statements are independent of the choice of a unit.

Some of the problems you will be asked to solve will involve various units, centimetres, metres, and so on. As we have already noted, all our theorems will apply to these units, providing that you *consistently use one unit each time you apply a theorem.*

### Problem Set 2–4

1. Allen, Bruce, and Charles measured the distance between two points, $P$ and $Q$, marked on a blackboard. Allen said $PQ = 27$, Bruce said $PQ = 27.5$, and Charles said $PQ = 26.75$. How many of the boys could be right? Why? Were any of the boys necessarily right? Discuss.

2. If the distance $MN$ is 200 cm, what is $MN$ measured in metres? measured in millimetres?  **2; 2000**

3. If the distance $RS$ is 1500 m, what is $RS$ measured in centimetres? measured in kilometres?  **150000; 1.5**

4. If the distance $RT$ is $x$ metres, what is $RT$ measured in centimetres? measured in millimetres? Check your answer by letting $x = 2$.  **100x; 1000x**

5. If the distance $CD$ is $k$ centimetres, what is $CD$ measured in metres? Check your answer by letting $k = 500$.  **0.01k**

6. If the distance $RS$ is $x$ millimetres, what is $RS$ measured in centimetres? measured in metres?  **0.1x; 0.001x**

7. If the distance $PM$ is 150 cm, what is $PM$ measured in metres? measured in millimetres?  **1.5; 1500**

8. If the distance $AD$ is 750 mm, what is $AD$ measured in centimetres? measured in metres?  **75; 0.75**

9. If the distance $RA$ is $c$ metres, what is $RA$ measured in centimetres? measured in millimetres?  **100c; 1000c**

10. Edward and Frank measured the distances between the same points $A$, $B$, and $C$. Edward said, "$AB = 1$, and $BC = 2.5$." Frank said, "$AB = 100$, and $BC = 250$." In fact, both boys were right.

 (a) Why did they get different numbers?

 (b) Both of them said that the *ratio* of $BC$ to $AB$ was 2.5. Why did they get the same answer for the ratio?

## 2-5  AN INFINITE RULER

The real number line that we discussed in Section 2–2 can be used as an "infinite ruler" to measure the distance between any two points, no matter how far apart they may be. Before we can use the number line for this purpose, however, we need to be certain that it will satisfy the condition we agreed to in the Distance Postulate. That is, we must be certain that for any two points we will always get the same positive number for the distance, even if we happen to place the number line onto the points in many different ways.

First let us note that the integers are spaced consecutively at unit intervals along the number line. In the figure, the number 0 corresponds to the point $Q$.

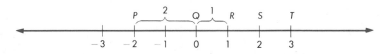

Point $R$, corresponding to 1, is to lie at a distance 1 from point $Q$; point $P$, corresponding to $-2$, is to lie at a distance 2 from $Q$; and so on. From the figure we can read off the distances

$$QR = 1, \qquad QP = 2, \qquad QS = 2, \qquad QT = 3.$$

The same should be true for all points of the number line, even when we include all the remaining rational and irrational numbers.

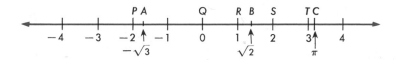

Again from the figure we can read the distances

$$QA = \sqrt{3}, \qquad QB = \sqrt{2}, \qquad QC = \pi.$$

## 2-5 AN INFINITE RULER

**The Ruler Postulate as a description of the geometry of a line.** The Ruler Postulate was arrived at by generalizing from specific examples. You should observe that the three conditions in the Ruler Postulate are necessary to describe any line as a number line. Condition (1) guarantees that no point on the line is without a coordinate and that no point has two different coordinates. Condition (2) guarantees that each real number is represented uniquely by a point on the line. But note that conditions (1) and (2) are not by themselves sufficient to guarantee that the coordinates are related to distance in the way that we want them to be. The coordinates might be distributed nonuniformly.

Or the numbering might be as usual, except for the fact that the coordinates of two points have been interchanged.

Neither of these numbering schemes is a coordinate system. The reason is that when we try to calculate the distance between two points by substituting the "coordinates" in the distance formula, we get wrong answers.

Observe that the Ruler Postulate does not say that it is possible to establish only one coordinate system for a line. For a good reason: we can, in fact, establish many different coordinate systems for the same line. If we are given a coordinate system for a line we can obtain new coordinate systems by: (1) reversing the direction of the given coordinate system, (2) shifting the coordinates to the left or right (see Problem 6 of Problem Set 2–5), (3) performing a sequence of the above two transformations.

**1.** Is this statement true or false? The distance between two points is always the difference of their corresponding numbers on the number line.
(ans: false)

**2.** Is this statement true or false? A coordinate system can be used to find the distance between two points that are millions of kilometres apart.
(ans: true)

On the second number line on page 31,

**3.** what is the distance *SA*?
(ans: $2 + \sqrt{3}$)

**4.** what is the distance *RC*?
(ans: $\pi - 1$)

**5.** what is *QC*? *QB*? *QA*?
(ans: $\pi$, $\sqrt{2}$, $\sqrt{3}$)

**6.** what is *PC*? *AR*? *AB*?
(ans: $\pi + 2$, $1 + \sqrt{3}$, $\sqrt{2} + \sqrt{3}$)

Why do each of the following two figures not show coordinate systems?

**7.**

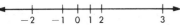

(ans: The coordinates are not distributed uniformly. When we try to calculate the distance between two points by substituting the "coordinates" in the distance formula, we get wrong answers.)

**8.**

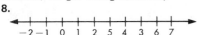

(ans: The coordinates of two points have been interchanged. When we try to calculate the distance between two points by substituting the "coordinates" in the distance formula, we get wrong answers.)

**9.** What is the distance formula?
(ans: $|x - y|$, where $x$ and $y$ are the coordinates of two points.)

**10.**

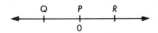

(a) If $PQ = 7$ and the Ruler Placement Postulate is applied, what will be the coordinate of $Q$?
(ans: 7)

(b) If $PR = PQ$, what will be the coordinate of $R$?
(ans: $-7$)

Also from the figure it is obvious that $ST = 1$, $RT = 2$, and $PR = 3$. It is obvious because we can count the unit intervals. But what about $RB$, $BC$, or $AC$? Here we cannot count the unit intervals because there are none.

To get an idea about what to do, consider what happens when we subtract the numbers corresponding to the points $S$, $T$, and $P$:

$$ST = 3 - 2 = 1,$$
$$RT = 3 - 1 = 2,$$
$$PR = 1 - (-2) = 3,$$

and these are correct distances. Similarly, for the points $A$, $B$, $C$, and $R$, by subtraction we get

$$RB = \sqrt{2} - 1$$
$$BC = \pi - \sqrt{2}$$
$$AC = \pi - (-\sqrt{3}) = \pi + \sqrt{3},$$

and these are correct. It looks as if we can always find the distance between two points by taking the difference of the corresponding numbers on our "infinite ruler."

But this is not quite correct. If we should subtract the numbers in reverse order we get the *negative* of the correct distance:

$$ST = 2 - 3 = -1,$$
$$RT = 1 - 3 = -2,$$
$$PR = -2 - 1 = -3,$$

and these are *wrong*.

It is easy, however, to get around the difficulty: we take the *absolute value* of the difference of the corresponding numbers. Thus

$$ST = |3 - 2| = |1| = 1$$

and

$$ST = |2 - 3| = |-1| = 1,$$

as it should be.

Finally, we note that the real numbers fill up the number line such that every point of the line has one, and only one, real number. Also, there are no real numbers left over; that is, there is exactly one point for every real number.

We make this common sense official by summing it up in a postulate.

**POSTULATE 2.**   The Ruler Postulate

*The points of a line can be placed in correspondence with the real numbers in such a way that*

*(1) to every point of the line there corresponds exactly one real number;*

*(2) to every real number there corresponds exactly one point of the line; and*

*(3) the distance between any two points is the absolute value of the difference of the corresponding numbers.*

### Definitions

A correspondence of the sort described in the Ruler Postulate is called a *coordinate system*. The number corresponding to a given point is called the *coordinate* of the point.

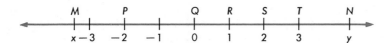

In the figure above, the coordinate of $P$ is $-2$, the coordinate of $Q$ is 0, the coordinate of $R$ is 1, and so on. If the coordinate of $M$ is $x$ and the coordinate of $N$ is $y$, then the Ruler Postulate tells us that $MN = |x - y|$. This is called the *distance formula*.

The Ruler Postulate tells us that on any line we can set up a coordinate system. This can be done in many different ways. For example, given any point $P$ of the line, we can make $P$ the zero point and then lay off the rest of the scale in either direction:

Therefore, if $Q$ is any other point of the line, we can lay off the scale in such a way that the coordinate of $Q$ is positive:

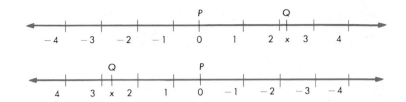

In each case, the scale is laid off so that $x > 0$.

We make this observation official by stating it as a postulate.

**POSTULATE 3.**   The Ruler Placement Postulate

> *Given two points P and Q of a line, the coordinate system can be chosen in such a way that the coordinate of P is zero and the coordinate of Q is positive.*

**Problem Set 2–5**

1. Use this number line to answer each question.

(a) What is the coordinate of $D$? −1

(b) Which point has coordinate 3? H

(c) What is the coordinate of $J$? 5

(d) Which point has coordinate −3? B

(e) Which points are distance 3 from the point whose coordinate is 1?

I, C

2. Simplify:

(a) $|6 - 2|$ 4                            (b) $|2 - 6|$ 4

(c) $|5 - 0|$ 5                            (d) $|0 - 5|$ 5

(e) $|0 - (-5)|$ 5                         (f) $|4 - (-4)|$ 8

(g) $|x|$ x if x ≥ 0, −x if x<0            (h) $|x - 0|$ |x|

(i) $|x - (-x)|$ |2x|                       (j) $|x| - |-x|$ 0

3. Copy this figure of a coordinate system and complete it by labeling each indicated point not named with a capital letter according to the clues given in parts (a)–(i).

(a) The coordinate of $B$ is 3.

(b) The coordinate of $P$ is both nonnegative and nonpositive.

(c) $ST = BT$ and $S \neq B$.

(d) The coordinate of $R$ is the negative of the coordinate of $C$.

(e) The point $H$ corresponds to $\sqrt{12}$.

(f) The point $D$ corresponds to $-\sqrt{12}$.

(g) $PL = 5$.

(h) The coordinate of $Q$ is $-\frac{5}{2}$.

(i) $ET + TM = 7$ and $E$ lies to the left of $T$.

4. In the figure a coordinate system, with 0 at $A$ and 1 at $C$, has been established on a line. For clarity of reading, some nonintegral coordinates are written one space lower than the integers.

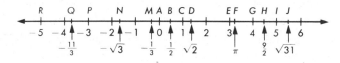

Find the following distances.

(a) $AC = 1$       (b) $AD = \sqrt{2}$       (c) $EI = 2$

(d) $PR = 2$       (e) $RI = 10$       (f) $AN = \sqrt{3}$

(g) $BH = 4$       (h) $QM = \frac{10}{3}$       (i) $AF = \pi$

(j) $DJ = \sqrt{31} - \sqrt{2}$       (k) $ND \; \sqrt{3} + \sqrt{2}$       (l) $PF = 3 + \pi$

5. Using the Ruler Postulate find the distance for each pair of points having the following coordinates.

(a) 0 and 8   8       (b) 8 and 0   8

(c) 0 and $-8$   8       (d) $-5$ and $-7$   2

(e) $-\frac{2}{3}$ and $\frac{1}{3}$   1       (f) $\sqrt{2}$ and $\sqrt{5}$   $\sqrt{5} - \sqrt{2}$

(g) $\sqrt{3}$ and $-\sqrt{5}$   $\sqrt{5} + \sqrt{3}$       (h) $x$ and $y$   $|y - x|$

(i) $2a$ and $-a$   $3|a|$       (j) $x$ and $-x$   $2|x|$

# Explanations for Problems

The procedure developed in Problems 7–10 is important for students to know. Do not assign all four problems together, but save one or two for a follow-up assignment.

## Answers to Problems

**7.** (a) $R$ has the coordinate 1; $P$ the coordinate $x - 4$; $Q$, $y - 4$.

(b) On the $B$-scale, $RQ = |5 - y|$.
On the $A$-scale,
$RQ = |1 - (y - 4)| = |5 - y|$.

(c) On the $A$-scale,
$PQ = |(x - 4) - (y - 4)|$
$= |x - y|$.
On the $B$-scale, $PQ = |x - y|$.

**8.** (d) If the coordinates of the points in the original coordinate system are designated by $a$ and $b$, then their new numbers will be $a + 3$ and $b + 3$ respectively. Then,
|(New number for one point)
− (new number for other point)|
$= |(a + 3) - (b + 3)|$
$= |a - b|$.
Since $|a - b|$ is, in the original coordinate system, the distance between the points, the formula does give the distance between the points.

(e) Since the new correspondence between points and numbers satisfies each of the conditions of the Ruler Postulate (see parts c and d of this problem) this correspondence is a coordinate system, and each new number for a point can be called the coordinate of the point, by definition.

**10.** Let $x$, $y$ be the coordinates of $P$, $Q$ in scale $A$ and $x'$, $y'$ be the coordinates of $P$, $Q$ in scale $B$. Then $x' = x - 4$ and $y' = y - 4$. So in scale $B$, $PQ = |(x - 4) - (y - 4)| = |x - 4 - y + 4| = |x - y|$. In scale $A$, $PQ = |x - y|$.

**6.** Consider a coordinate system on a line. The points $R$ and $S$ have coordinates $x$ and $y$, respectively. The Ruler Placement Postulate is applied, that is, the scale is shifted, so that the coordinate of $R$ is 0 and the coordinate of $S$ is a positive number. What will this positive number be, given that $x$ and $y$ are:

(a) $x = -3$, $y = 4$.    7      (b) $x = -4$, $y = -10$.   6

(c) $x = 8$, $y = -2$.   10      (d) $x = \frac{9}{2}$, $y = -4$.   8.5

(e) $x = 5.2$, $y = 6.1$.   0.9      (f) $x = a$, $y = b$.   $|a-b|$

**7.** In the figure, scale A and scale B use the same unit but assign numbers in a different way. $P$ and $Q$ are any points of the line.

(a) What are the coordinates of $R$, $P$, and $Q$ on a scale A?

(b) Show how to find the distance $RQ$, using scale B; using scale A.

(c) What is the distance $PQ$ on the A-scale? on the B-scale?

**8.** Consider a coordinate system on a line. Suppose that 3 is added to the coordinate of each point and each new sum becomes the new number assigned to each point.

(a) If $P$ had coordinate 5, what will be its new number? If $Q$ had coordinate $-2$, what will be its new number?   8; 1

(b) If two points of the line had coordinates $a$ and $b$, what will be their new numbers?   $a+3$; $b+3$

(c) Will each point of the line correspond to a new number? Will each new number correspond to a point of the line?   Yes; Yes

(d) Show that the formula
|(New number for one point) − (New number for other point)|
gives the distance between the two points.

(e) Does the new correspondence between points and numbers satisfy each of the three conditions of the Ruler Postulate? Can each new number be called the coordinate of a point? Why?

**9.** In the figure scale A and scale B use the same unit but assign numbers in a different way.

(a) What is the coordinate of $K$ in scale A?   $-2$

(b) What are the coordinates of $M$ and $N$ in scale B?   $-x$ and $-y$

(c) If $x = -6$, what is the coordinate of $M$ in scale B? **6**

(d) If the coordinate of $N$ in the B-scale is $9\frac{1}{2}$, what would $y$ equal? **$-9\frac{1}{2}$**

(e) What is the distance $KM$? the distance $MN$? **$|x+2|$; $|x-y|$**

10. In the figure scale A and scale B use the same unit but assign numbers in a different way. $P$ and $Q$ are any points of the line. Prove that $PQ$ on scale B equals $PQ$ on scale A by evaluating $PQ$ in each scale.

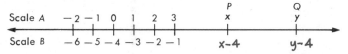

## 2–6 BETWEENNESS, SEGMENTS AND RAYS. THE POINT-PLOTTING THEOREM

We now need to discuss an important geometric idea of the more obvious sort. Suppose that on a line the point $B$ is between the points $A$ and $C$, like this:

or like this:

If we know the distances $AB$ and $BC$, then we can calculate the distance $AC$, because $AB + BC = AC$. This also works the other way around: if $B$ is not between $A$ and $C$, then $AB + BC \neq AC$. For example, in this figure, $AB + BC > AC$.

These ideas enable us to describe the idea of *betweenness for points on a line* in terms of *line* and *distance*. And we should do this, because we promised in Chapter 1 that all our geometric terms were going to be defined, except for the terms *point*, *line*, and *plane*.

### Definition

$B$ is *between* $A$ and $C$ if (1) $A$, $B$, and $C$ are different points of the same line, and (2) $AB + BC = AC$. When $B$ is between $A$ and $C$, we write $A$–$B$–$C$ or $C$–$B$–$A$.

We have defined ''between.'' Traditional texts, following Euclid, left the term undefined; they often tacitly employed betweenness considerations, and even when they employed them explicitly they used them without comment or justification. A few comments are in order:

(1) In a purely synthetic treatment of geometry, *between* must be taken as an undefined term. But when distance is given, betweenness *can* be defined in terms of it; and the number of undefined terms should not be increased beyond necessity.

(2) The definition given on this page is based on an idea that everybody continually uses: when we use the fact that $B$ is between $A$ and $C$, this is nearly always because we want to calculate $AC$ by adding $AB$ and $BC$ (or calculate $AB$ by subtracting $BC$ from $AC$). Thus the definition is a *working* definition; it is not a mere gesture.

(3) One of the most important of mathematical skills is the process of formulating ideas in mathematical terms. In elementary algebra, this appears mainly as the art of reading a word problem, analyzing its meaning, and then rewriting the problem in the form of an equation. This is just as important, and is harder to learn, than the art of solving an equation which is given.

In geometry, similarly, we have the art of describing geometric ideas in mathematical terms. This is the way in which we arrive at formal definitions. The idea in each case should be explained intuitively by figures and informal discussion; the definition should be presented as a *description* of the idea; and the student should be invited to check the definition against the intuitive idea, to make sure that it really says what it is supposed to say. Nearly every definition in this book is presented in this style.

The skill we are trying to teach in these discussions is fundamental in both pure and applied mathematics, and is most crucial in the latter. This skill appeared first in the study of physical space by mathematical methods, in ancient Greece. The mathematical study of space geometry remains, to this day, the best introduction to it. For this reason, if we ignore definitions or teach them by rote, we have missed a good opportunity to teach the relation between descriptions and the ideas that they describe.

(4) By comparison with these considerations, the use of the definition of *between* in the development of the foundations of geometry is of secondary importance. In fact, the definition can be used to show that betweenness has the properties we expect. The *facts* about betweenness are important, and students should know them, but they need not know the proofs, though they should be able to read and understand them.

The ideas of segment and ray are easily understood by reference to pictures. Asked to define these terms, students often respond to the effect that both are "parts" of a line. Point out that this terminology is not precise enough and does not use words whose meanings we have agreed on. By considering the conditions which the points of a segment or a ray must satisfy, the definitions of the text develop quite naturally. This is what a definition is supposed to do: describe the idea that we have in mind.

In using the idea of betweenness to help us prove theorems and solve problems it is helpful to know the following two theorems:

### Theorem 2–3

Let $A$, $B$, and $C$ be points of a line, with coordinates $x$, $y$, and $z$ respectively. If $x < y < z$, then $A$–$B$–$C$.

### Theorem 2–4

If $A$, $B$, and $C$ are three different points of the same line, then exactly one of them is between the other two.

To apply Theorem 2–3, consider the following: Given a coordinate system on a line containing points $R$, $S$, and $T$. If the coordinates of $R$, $S$, and $T$ are 5, $-7$, and 9 respectively, then we can conclude that $S$–$R$–$T$ because $-7 < 5 < 9$.

To apply Theorem 2–4, note that if we know that $A$–$B$–$C$, then we can conclude that it is not possible for $B$–$A$–$C$ or $A$–$B$–$C$.

While these two theorems can be proved, it is not important that we do so here. Their truth seems obvious enough, and we will use them without further justification.

In the next figure the two curved lines each contain the two points $A$ and $B$.

But we agreed earlier that line, by itself, would always mean "straight line." Therefore the following postulate makes sense. It is often restated in the form: "Two points determine a line."

### POSTULATE 4. The Line Postulate

*For every two different points there is exactly one line that contains both points.*

The line that contains $A$ and $B$ is denoted by $\overleftrightarrow{AB}$. Here the double-headed arrow over the letters $A$ and $B$ is supposed to remind us of our pictures of lines. The notation suggests that the line is determined when the points $A$ and $B$ are named, and this is exactly what the Line Postulate has just told us. Sometimes, of course, it is simpler to denote a line by one letter such as $L$, $W$, or any other.

The two points $A$ and $B$ also determine a segment.

The definition of *between* provides us with a simple definition of a segment.

### Definitions

For any two points $A$ and $B$, the *segment* $\overline{AB}$ is the union of $A$ and $B$, and all points that are between $A$ and $B$. The points $A$ and $B$ are called the *end points* of $\overline{AB}$.

In the symbol $\overline{AB}$, the horizontal bar on top is supposed to remind us of a picture of a segment. Note that there is a big difference between the segment $\overline{AB}$ and the distance $AB$: $\overline{AB}$ is a *geometric figure*, that is, a set of points, while $AB$ is a *number* which measures the distance between the end points.

### Definition

The number $AB$ is called the *length* of the segment $\overline{AB}$.

Each of the following figures is a ray.

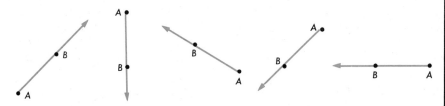

In each case the ray starts at $A$, proceeds through $B$ along a straight line, and then goes on forever in the same direction. In the notation for a ray, we always draw the arrow above the letters from left to right, regardless of the direction in which the ray points. For example, each of the rays above is denoted by $\overrightarrow{AB}$.

**1.** *A*, *B*, and *C* are three points on a line with coordinates 7, 3, and 12 respectively. Which point is between the other two?
(ans: *A* is between *B* and *C*.)

**2.** If $\overrightarrow{RS}$ and $\overrightarrow{RT}$ are opposite rays, which one of the points *R*, *S*, or *T* is between the other two?
(ans: *R* is between *S* and *T*.)

**3.** *G*, *H*, and *K* are three points on a line. Which of the following can be true?
  (a) *K* is between *G* and *H*, and *H* is between *G* and *K*.
  (b) *H* is between *K* and *G*, and *H* is between *G* and *K*.
  (c) *K* is between *H* and *G*, and *G* is between *K* and *H*.
  (d) *G* is between *K* and *H*, and *G* is between *H* and *K*.
    (ans: b, d)

**4.** Is $\overline{AB} = AB$? Why? What is $\overline{AB}$ called?
(ans: No. $\overline{AB}$ is a segment. *AB* is a number. *AB* is the length of $\overline{AB}$.)

**5.** (a) Is $\overleftrightarrow{AB} = \overleftrightarrow{BA}$?
  (b) Is $\overrightarrow{AB} = \overrightarrow{BA}$?
  (c) Is $\overline{AB} = \overline{BA}$?
  (d) Is $AB = BA$?
  (ans: yes, no, yes, yes)

**6.** (a) How many midpoints may a segment have?
  (ans: Only one)
  (b) How many bisectors may a segment have?
  (ans: Infinitely many)

**7.** What conditions are necessary for *B* to be between *A* and *C*?
(ans: (1) *A*, *B*, and *C* lie on the same line. (2) $AB + BC = AC$)

**8.** Which postulate means "two points determine a line"?
(ans: Postulate 4, The Line Postulate)

Having explained informally what a ray is, we now give a mathematical definition.

### Definitions

Let *A* and *B* be points. The *ray* $\overrightarrow{AB}$ is the union of (1) $\overline{AB}$ and (2) the set of all points *C* for which *A–B–C*. The point *A* is called the *end point* of $\overrightarrow{AB}$.

Thus, the two parts of the ray described in the definition look like this:

In the next figure *A* is between *B* and *C* on *L*, and the two rays $\overrightarrow{AB}$ and $\overrightarrow{AC}$ "point in opposite directions":

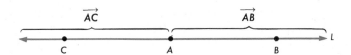

### Definition

If *A* is between *B* and *C*, then $\overrightarrow{AB}$ and $\overrightarrow{AC}$ are called *opposite rays*.

Note that a pair of points *A*, *B* determines at least six geometric figures and one number. The six geometric figures are:

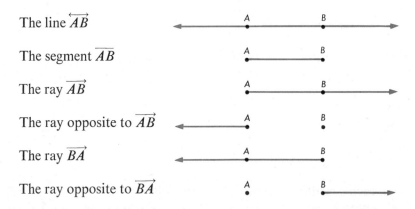

The line $\overleftrightarrow{AB}$

The segment $\overline{AB}$

The ray $\overrightarrow{AB}$

The ray opposite to $\overrightarrow{AB}$

The ray $\overrightarrow{BA}$

The ray opposite to $\overrightarrow{BA}$

The number determined by *A* and *B* is, of course, the distance *AB*.
  The following theorem will be useful in proving other theorems in later chapters.

**Theorem 2–5.**   The Point-Plotting Theorem

*Let $\overrightarrow{AB}$ be a ray, and let $x$ be a positive number. Then there is exactly one point $P$ of $\overrightarrow{AB}$ such that $AP = x$.*

**Proof.** By the Ruler Placement Postulate, we can choose a coordinate system for the line $\overleftrightarrow{AB}$ in such a way that the coordinate of $A$ is 0 and the coordinate of $B$ is a positive number $r$.

Let $P$ be the point whose coordinate is the given number $x$. Then $P$ lies on $\overrightarrow{AB}$, because $x > 0$; and, by the Ruler Postulate, $AP = |x - 0| = |x| = x$. (By the definition of absolute value, $|x| = x$ when $x > 0$.) Therefore (by the Ruler Postulate), only one point of the line corresponds to $x$. Only one point of the ray lies at a distance $x$ from $A$.

**Definition**

A point $B$ is called a *midpoint* of a segment $\overline{AC}$ if $B$ is between $A$ and $C$ and $AB = BC$.

**Theorem 2–6.**   The Midpoint Theorem

*Every segment has exactly one midpoint.*

**Proof.** We want a point satisfying the two conditions (1) $B$ is between $A$ and $C$, and (2) $AB = BC$. By the definition of *between*, $AB + BC = AC$. Since $AB = BC$ this gives $AB + AB = AC$. Therefore $2AB = AC$, so that $AB = \frac{1}{2}AC$. By the Point-Plotting Theorem, there is exactly one point $B$ of the ray $\overrightarrow{AC}$ that lies at a distance $\frac{1}{2}AC$ from $A$. Therefore $\overline{AC}$ has exactly one midpoint.

**Definitions**

The midpoint of a segment is said to *bisect* the segment. The midpoint of a segment $\overline{AB}$, or any line, plane, ray, or segment which contains the midpoint and does not contain $\overline{AB}$, is called a *bisector* of $\overline{AB}$.

The Point-Plotting Theorem is a straightforward observation, and should be presented in this spirit, for later reference. Students should not be asked to regard either the theorem or its proof as profound.

There is a good reason for stating trivial theorems such as this one. Soon students are going to be writing proofs of their own, in double-column form, with a reason given for every statement. It seldom (if ever) happens that all of the "reasons" in a double-column proof are deep theorems; often they are trivialities; but students still need to refer to them, and it is hard to do this if they have not been placed on record. Thus the main purpose in stating the Point-Plotting Theorem and similar theorems is not to achieve an extreme of logical thoroughness, but rather to enable students to do their homework in an orderly way. Learning to write proofs is a difficult task at best, and most students need all of the help orderliness can give them; they need an adequate set of blocks with which proofs can be built.

Theorem 2-6 is obvious. Do not overteach the proof.

**10.** Three points $P$, $Q$, $R$ determine three segments $\overline{PQ}$, $\overline{PR}$, $\overline{QR}$ regardless of whether the points are collinear or non-collinear. However, three *noncollinear* points $P$, $Q$, $R$ determine three lines $\overleftrightarrow{PQ}$, $\overleftrightarrow{PR}$, $\overleftrightarrow{QR}$ whereas three *collinear* points $P$, $Q$, $R$ determine only one line.

**Problem Set 2–6**

1. Suppose $R$, $S$, $T$ are three points of a line. If $S$–$R$–$T$, what relation involving $RS$, $ST$, and $RT$ must be true? SR + RT = ST

2. $P$, $Q$, $R$ are three points of a line. If $PQ = 12$, $PR = 7$, and $QR = 5$, which point is between the other two? Which postulate or definition is a reason for your answer? R is between P and Q; definition of betweenness

3. $G$, $H$, $K$ are three points of a line. The coordinates of $G$ and $H$ are 4 and $-3$, respectively. If $H$ is between $G$ and $K$ and $GK = 13$, what is the coordinate of $K$? -9

4. $J$, $K$, $L$ are three points of a line with coordinates $-3$, $-8$, and $\frac{5}{2}$, respectively. Which point is between the other two? J

5. $D$, $E$, $F$ are three points of a line with coordinates $3$, $\sqrt{6}$, and $4\frac{1}{2}$ respectively. Which point is between the other two? D

6. $P$, $Q$, $R$ are three points on a line with coordinates $-5$, $-\sqrt{4}$, and $-\sqrt{12}$, respectively. Which point is between the other two? R

7. If three points are on a line, how many of them are not between the other two? Two

8. $D$, $E$, $F$ are three points not all on a line. How many lines do they determine? Name them. Three; $\overleftrightarrow{DE}$, $\overleftrightarrow{DF}$, $\overleftrightarrow{EF}$

9. $D$, $E$, $F$, $G$ are four points no three of which are on a line. How many lines do they determine? Name them. Six; $\overleftrightarrow{DE}$, $\overleftrightarrow{DF}$, $\overleftrightarrow{DG}$, $\overleftrightarrow{EF}$, $\overleftrightarrow{EG}$, $\overleftrightarrow{FG}$

10. $P$, $Q$, $R$ are three points. How many segments do they determine? Name them. How many lines do $P$, $Q$, $R$ determine?

11. What is the intersection of $\overrightarrow{CD}$ and $\overrightarrow{DC}$? of $\overleftrightarrow{CD}$ and $\overrightarrow{DC}$? $\overline{CD}$; $\overrightarrow{DC}$

12. On $\overrightarrow{ST}$, $S$, $T$, and $V$ are distinct points. Can $ST = SV$? Which postulate, theorem, or definition is a reason for your answer? No; Theorem 2-5

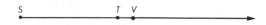

13. $P$ is a point on a line, and $n$ is a positive number. How many points of the line are a distance $n$ from $P$? Which definitions or theorems provide reasons for your answer? Two; Theorem 2-5

14. Define the midpoint $K$ of a segment $\overline{MN}$. K lies on $\overline{MN}$ and MK = KN.

15. Can you define a midpoint of a line? No, only of a segment

16. $A$, $B$, $C$ are three points of a line. $AC = BC = 5$. The coordinate of $C$ is 8, and the coordinate of $A$ is greater than the coordinate of $B$. What are the coordinates of $A$ and $B$? 13 and 3

17. $A$, $B$, $C$ are three points of a line. $AC = BC = 10$. The coordinate of $C$ is 8, and the coordinate of $A$ is greater than the coordinate of $B$. What are the coordinates of $A$ and $B$? 18 and -2

18. $A$, $B$, $C$ are three points of a line. The coordinates of $A$ and $B$ are $-2$ and 8, respectively. If $C$ bisects $\overline{AB}$, what is the coordinate of $C$? 3

19. $B$, the midpoint of $\overline{AC}$, has coordinate 5. If the coordinate of $A$ is greater than the coordinate of $C$, and if $BC = 9$, what are the coordinates of $A$ and $C$? 14 and -4

20. Explain how the definition of between and the Subtraction Property of Equality can be used to show the following:

If $A\text{–}B\text{–}C$, then $AB = AC - BC$ and $BC = AC - AB$.

21. Why is the following statement not a correct definition of a midpoint of a segment? B must lie on $\overline{AC}$.

A point $B$ is called a midpoint of a segment $\overline{AC}$ if $AB = BC$.

22. (a) If the coordinates of $P$ and $Q$ are 4 and 10, respectively, and $M$ bisects $\overline{PQ}$, what is the coordinate of $M$? 7

(b) If the coordinates of $R$ and $S$ are $x$ and $y$, respectively, what is the coordinate of $T$, the midpoint of $\overline{RS}$? $\frac{x+y}{2}$

(c) What word (or words) completes the following sentence?

If $M$ is the midpoint of $\overline{PQ}$, then the coordinate of $M$ is the _average_ of the coordinates of $P$ and $Q$.

23. $A$, $E$, $K$ are three points of a line. The coordinates of $A$ and $K$ are $\sqrt{2}$ and $-\sqrt{18}$. If $AE = EK$, what is the coordinate of $E$? $-\sqrt{2}$

24. If $A$, $B$, $C$ are three points of a line such that $AC + BC = AB$, what is the intersection of $\overrightarrow{CB}$ and $\overrightarrow{BA}$? of $\overrightarrow{AC}$ and $\overrightarrow{AB}$? of $\overrightarrow{CA}$ and $\overrightarrow{CB}$? $\overline{CB}$; $\overrightarrow{AC}$; $\{C\}$

25. (a) Copy the following paragraph, supplying the appropriate symbol, if any, over each letter pair.

$\overleftrightarrow{XZ}$ contains points $Y$ and $V$, but $\overline{XZ}$ contains neither $Y$ nor $V$. $V$ belongs to $\overrightarrow{XZ}$ but $Y$ does not. $YZ + ZV = YV$.

(b) Make a sketch showing the relative position of the four points in (a). The points are in the order Y-X-Z-V.

Answers to Problems

**20.** $A\text{–}B\text{–}C$ means that $AB + BC = AC$ by the definition of between. By the Subtraction Property of Equality, $AB = AC - BC$ and $BC = AC - AB$.

**Quiz**

**1.** If $A\text{–}C\text{–}B$, what is the intersection of
  (a) $\overrightarrow{CA}$ and $\overrightarrow{AB}$?
  (b) $\overrightarrow{AC}$ and $\overrightarrow{BC}$?
  (ans: $\overline{AC}$, $\overline{AB}$)

**2.** $K$ is the midpoint of $\overline{MN}$. What is the coordinate of $K$ if the coordinates of $M$ and $N$ are, respectively,
  (a) 3 and 12?
  (b) $-14$ and 4?
  (ans: 7.5, $-5$)

**3.** Points $A$, $B$, and $C$ lie on a line. Their coordinates are 5, $-4$, and $-1$, respectively.
  (a) Which point is between the other two?
  (b) What is the length $AB$?
  (ans: $C$, 9)

**4.** (a) Can a line be a bisector?
  (b) Can a line be bisected?
  (ans: yes, no)

**5.** $P$, $Q$, and $R$ lie on a line, with $PQ = 6$, $QR = 9$, and $PR = 3$. The coordinate of $P$ is 1. What are the coordinates of $Q$ and $R$ if the coordinate of $Q$ is
  (a) less than that of $R$?
  (b) greater than that of $R$?
  (ans: $Q = -5$, $R = 4$; $Q = 7$, $R = -2$)

## CHAPTER REVIEW—CHAPTERS 1 and 2

1. Name the undefined terms of geometry. Point, line, plane

2. Who wrote the *Elements*, and when did he live? Euclid, 3rd cent. B.C.

3. Complete each statement.

    (a) A member of a set is said to ___belong___ to the set, and a set is said to ___contain___ its members.

    (b) An easier way to write the sentence "Five is an element of the set whose members are the numbers from one to nine" is _____.
    $5 \in \{1,2,3,4,5,6,7,8,9\}$

    (c) Given two sets, the set of all elements that belong to one or both sets is called the ___union___.

    (d) The relations $<$ and $>$ are called ___order___ relations.

    (e) If $x$ and $y$ are numbers and $x < y$, we know that $x \neq y$ because of the ___trichotomy___ property.

    (f) For every two points, the distance between them is a ___positive___ unique number.

    (g) On a number line, the number ___corresponding___ to a given point is called the ___coordinate___ of the point.

    (h) "The point $K$ is between the points $S$ and $P$" is written briefly as ___S-K-P___.

4. (a) State the Distance Postulate. See page 29.

    (b) State the Ruler Postulate. See page 33.

5. Let $A$ be the set of all months whose names begin with J. ={Jan., Jun., Jul.}
   Let $B$ be the set of all months with exactly 30 days. ={Sept., Apr., Jun., Nov.}
   Let $C$ be the set of all months whose names begin with F. = {February}

    (a) What is $A \cap B$? {June}

    (b) What is $A \cup C$? {January, February, June, July}

    (c) What is $B \cup C$? {February, September, April, June, November}

    (d) Which statements are true? $C \subset A$.  $C \subset B$.  $\boxed{C \subset C.}$

6. For this figure, name each set specified below.

    (a) $\overline{FD} \cap \overline{BE}$. {G}

    (b) $\overline{AE} \cap \triangle FGE$. $\overline{FE}$

    (c) $\overline{ED} \cup \overline{DC}$. $\overline{EC}$

    (d) $\overline{BG} \cup \overline{BE}$. $\overline{BE}$

    (e) $\overline{AB} \cap \overline{EG}$. $\varnothing$

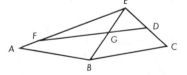

**11.** (a) *AB* is greater than *CD*.
   (b) *m* is less than or equal to *n*.
   (c) 5 is between −11 and 8.
   (d) *k* is between −2 and 2.
   (e) *x* is negative.
   (f) *y* is nonnegative.

7. Write a definition for each term: between (for points on a line), segment, ray, $|x|$, opposite rays, bisector.

8. (a) How many squares does a given positive number have? One
   (b) What is the square of 4? 16
   (c) How many square roots does a given positive number have? Two
   (d) Is $\sqrt{4}$ negative? No

9. (a) If $a < b$, then $a - b$ is __negative__
   (b) If $a = b$, then $a - b$ is __zero__ .
   (c) If $a > b$, then $a - b$ is __positive__.

10. Write the following using the symbols of order (that is, $<$, $\geq$, and so forth).
    (a) $x$ is greater than 0. $x > 0$
    (b) $y$ is between $-1$ and 2. $-1 < y < 2$
    (c) $w$ is between 5 and 2. $2 < w < 5$
    (d) $k$ is positive. $k > 0$
    (e) $m$ is negative. $m < 0$
    (f) $n$ is nonnegative. $n \geq 0$

11. Restate the following in words:
    (a) $AB > CD$.              (b) $m \leq n$.
    (c) $-11 < 5 < 8$.          (d) $-2 \leq k \leq 2$.
    (e) $x < 0$.               (f) $y \geq 0$.

12. Express the following without absolute value bars.
    (a) $|-6|$ 6              (b) $|5 - 7|$ 2
    (c) $|5| - |7|$ -2        (d) $|-5| - 7$ -2
    (e) $|n|$ $n$ if $n \geq 0$, $-n$ if $n < 0$     (f) $|-n|$ $|n|$
    (g) $|n + (-n)|$ 0        (h) $|n| + |-n|$ $2|n|$

13. (a) What equation defines the relative positions of points $P$, $M$, and $Q$? $PM + MQ = PQ$
    (b) Under what conditions would $M$ be the midpoint of $\overline{RS}$?
        $M$ is between $R$ and $S$, and $RM = MS$.

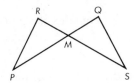

**18.** In scale $B$, the coordinate of $P$ is $6-x$ and the coordinate of $Q$ is $6-y$. Thus in scale $B$, $PQ = |(6-x)-(6-y)| = |6-x-6+y| = |y-x|$. In scale $A$, $PQ = |y-x|$.

**14.** (a) What is the coordinate of $W$? of $S$? $3; -1$

(b) What is the name of the point whose coordinate is $0$? $-3$? $5$? $T; Q; Y$

(c) Evaluate $RT, VZ, TW, TQ, RW, PZ, XS, YQ.$ $2 \quad 4 \quad 3 \quad 3 \quad 5 \quad 10 \quad 5 \quad 8$

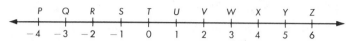

**15.** Given a coordinate system on a line. The coordinate of $A$ is 7 and the coordinate of $C$ is $-12$. What is the coordinate of $B$ if $BA = BC$? $-2.5$

**16.** $M, N, P$ are three points of a line. $MN = 7$, $NP = 9$, and $MP = 2$. The coordinate of $M$ is 3. What are the coordinates of $N$ and $P$ if

(a) the coordinate of $M$ is less than that of $N$? $10$ and $1$, respectively

(b) the coordinate of $M$ is greater than that of $N$? $-4$ and $5$, respectively

**17.** Indicate whether each statement is true or false.

(a) $-5$ is an integer. $T$

(b) $\frac{4}{7}$ is a real number. $T$

(c) $0$ is a rational number. $T$

(d) $\sqrt{8}$ is a rational number. $F$

(e) $\sqrt{9}$ is an integer. $T$

(f) $-\dfrac{31}{6}$ is a rational number. $T$

(g) $\dfrac{\sqrt{2}}{4}$ is a rational number. $F$

(h) $-x$ is a negative number for every real $x$. $F$

(i) $-\sqrt{\dfrac{4}{9}}$ is a rational number. $T$    (j) $|x| = x.$ $F$

**18.** In the figure scale A and scale B use the same unit but assign numbers in a different way. $P$ and $Q$ are any points of the line. Prove that $PQ$ on scale $B$ equals $PQ$ on scale $A$ by evaluating $PQ$ in each scale.

**19.** If the distance from $A$ to $B$ measured in centimetres is $k$, what is $AB$ measured in metres? How can you check your answer? $0.01k$

**20.** The letter pairs in the following paragraph indicate either numbers, lines, line segments, or rays. Copy the paragraph, putting in the proper symbols where they belong.

$AB + BC = AC.$ $\overleftrightarrow{DB}$ contains the points $A$ and $C$, but $\overline{DB}$ contains neither the point $A$ nor the point $C$. $A$ belongs to $\overrightarrow{DB}$ but $C$ does not.

Make a sketch showing the relative position of the four points. The points are in the order A-B-D-C.

David Hilbert (1862-1943)

David Hilbert was one of the great mathematicians of his generation. He deserves special mention in this book because of his work on the foundations of geometry, done in 1898–99. The treatment of geometry in Euclid's *Elements* was much more logical and exact than we had any right to expect, considering the times in which he wrote; and for over two thousand years it was rightly regarded as a model of logical thinking. It was recognized, however, about a hundred years ago, that Euclid's treatment of geometry was not up to modern standards. In a famous book, *The Foundations of Geometry*, Hilbert showed how the flaws in Euclid could be removed.

In Hilbert's time, and ever since, mathematics has been highly specialized, and most mathematicians—even the best—have worked in one branch of the subject or perhaps two. Hilbert was a notable exception to this rule. Every few years, he would turn his attention to some new branch of mathematics; and the variety of his total achievement was extraordinary. At the International Congress of Mathematicians, in Paris in 1900, he delivered a lecture entitled *The Problems of Mathematics*. In this lecture, he tried to identify the most important of the unsolved problems in *all* of mathematics. In the breadth of knowledge and understanding that it showed, this lecture was one of a kind, with no forerunner and no successor. Many of the problems that Hilbert discussed have been solved, but many others have not been, in spite of the efforts of the best mathematicians in the world.

## Lines, Planes, and Separation

The General Remarks on the first four chapters at the beginning of Chapter 1 apply with special force to Chapter 3: the ideas are easy, and the main hazard in teaching it is to fall into the position of belaboring trivialities. The presentation of this chapter should not be inflated, and the chapter should not be given more time than it needs.

In this chapter we begin to develop student awareness of spatial figures by introducing them in natural ways. Help students identify and describe their intuitive feelings about lines and planes. The incidence postulates, relating properties of points, lines, and planes and the separation postulates, dependent upon the idea of convexity, will gain in familiarity and degree of understanding as they are used later in the text.

### Planning the Chapter

For both average and better-than-average classes one day on each section should be sufficient in this chapter with the exception of Section 3-4. Two days will probably be required on this section. Section 3-5 is optional and may be discussed later in the year or omitted if students need extra time on Section 3-4.

---

CHAPTER **3**

# Lines, Planes, and Separation

## Objectives . . .

- State postulates describing how points, lines and planes are related.
- Develop familiarity with basic concepts of points, lines and planes in space.
- Develop concepts of convex set and separation.
- Provide experience in interpreting sketches of three-dimensional figures.

## 3–1  DRAWING SKETCHES OF FIGURES IN SPACE

In the last chapter we were dealing mostly with lines, segments and rays, and with the measurement of distances along a line. In this chapter we begin the study of lines and planes in space. We recall that our basic, undefined terms are *point*, *line*, and *plane*. Lines and planes are, of course, sets of points. The set of all points is called *space*.

### Definition

*Space* is the set of all points.

In the following two sections we shall explain some of the terms we use in discussing points, lines and planes in space, and we shall state some basic facts about them. Most of these facts will be stated as postulates, but a few will be stated as theorems. Later, in Chapter 6, we shall see how to prove the theorems on the basis of the postulates. But first you need to learn to visualize geometric figures in space from sketches drawn on paper. And you need to learn how to draw your own sketches of spatial figures so that they "look right" and can convey the correct understandings.

Here is a sketch of a cube. It is correct, because it shows all the edges and faces of the cube that we see from a usual perspective. All three of the faces that we see are really squares in space, although only one of them is drawn as a square. The other two are drawn as parallelograms.

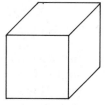

Problems 1–5 are designed to get the student to reflect on ideas involved in Postulates 4, 5, 6, 7, and 8.

Problem 12 illustrates the vague way in which we often use language, appealing to general experience and understanding. In common usage the term "half" does not always have a strict quantitative meaning, but in mathematics we tend to feel it should. The fact that the union of two half-pieces does not equal a whole piece seems contradictory until one realizes that the use of "half" in this way—such as in "you take the bigger half"—is merely a way of naming sets. Realizing this helps students better accept the terms *half-plane, half-space,* and *half-line* when they appear in Section 3-4.

The sketch of a cube below is also correct, for exactly the same reasons. But it is more useful as a diagram, because the edges that we would not ordinarily see are drawn in as dotted segments. This gives us, at a glance, a clearer picture of the actual shape and outline of the cube.

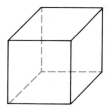

The next two figures depict a plane, *E*, in space, pierced by a segment, $\overline{AB}$.

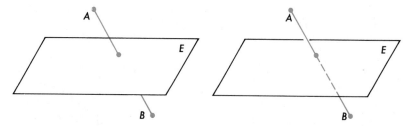

In the sketch on the left, part of $\overline{AB}$ is obscured by the plane, and we can't see it. In the sketch on the right, all of $\overline{AB}$ has been drawn. The part that we "can't see" is dotted. This sketch is more useful, because it tells us the whole story instead of making us guess. Note also, in the sketch on the right, that there is a small gap in the top "edge" of the plane. How does this help to make the sketch appear more realistic?

During this time when you are learning to think about the relationships that exist among points, lines, and planes in space, you may find it helpful to use pieces of cardboard to illustrate planes, and a pencil or a piece of stiff wire to illustrate a line. Making an actual three-dimensional model is often a good way to get to understand the real figure that a sketch represents.

## Problem Set 3–1

1. Hold your arm straight out in front of you. Consider a point *A*, at the tip of your forefinger, and a point, *B*, at the upper right front corner of your room. How many lines contain both points *A* and *B*? What postulate supports your answer? *Exactly one; the Line Postulate*

**2.** Take your book or a piece of stiff cardboard. Can you support it in a fixed position on the sharpened ends of two pencils? What is the minimum number of pencils needed to support it in this manner? No; three

**3.** Can three points lie on one line? Must three points lie on one line? No
Yes

**4.** Let a corner of your desk represent a point *P*, the light switch on the wall a point *Q*, and a corner of the room a point *R*. Is there a plane containing points *P*, *Q*, and *R*? Yes

**5.** What is the minimum number of points necessary to determine a plane? Will three points always determine a plane? Three; No, not unless three points are noncollinear.

**6.** In this sketch of a pup tent, what line segments must you imagine in order to complete the outline of the tent? What is the intersection of the planes that contain the two sides of the tent? A line

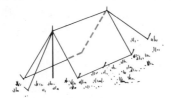

**7.** The tent in this sketch has a square floor. What line segments will complete the outline of the tent?

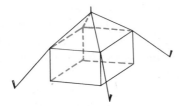

**8.** Hold two pencils together by their sharpened ends between your thumb and forefinger. If the pencils represent two intersecting lines, how many planes will contain both these lines? Exactly one plane

**9.** Which sketch do you consider to be a more meaningful picture of a book? How would you have to hold a book so that it would appear as in sketch (a)? as in sketch (b)?
Sketch (b) is more meaningful to most people.

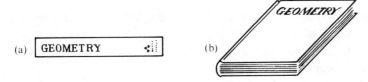

(a) GEOMETRY    (b)

**10.** Perspective pictures from an angle are generally more easily recognized even though there is some distortion, so that circles, for example, appear as ellipses.

**12.** The sawing removes a piece approximately 0.3 cm wide from the board. If the board were cut exactly at its midpoint, the resulting "halves" would be 0.9985 m long, and their combined length would be 1.997 m.

## 3-2 AND 3-3 LINES, PLANES, AND PICTURES

### Classroom Notes

Sections 3-2 and 3-3 establish the fundamental properties of lines and planes. While teaching these sections it should be borne in mind that students have their own intuitive ideas of lines and planes. We state, with little explanation, rather abstract postulates which seem to students to be rather far removed from their ideas; it is advisable to bridge this gap.

Here and hereafter, in talking about lines and planes, one of the main hazards is that the language of geometry is different from the language of common speech. In geometry, lines extend infinitely far, both ways; and planes extend infinitely far in infinitely many directions. We use the terms *line* and *plane* for these infinite figures because in common speech there *isn't* any word for either of them. Thus, in the language of geometry, segments have end points, but lines do not. *One of the things that we are trying to teach in this course is a consistent and exact use of mathematical language.* By this standard, the traditional language of geometry books is quite loose. For example, it is not uncommon for authors to speak of "extending a line." Here they mean *segment*: we

**10.** Which sketch is more easily recognized as a picture of a cup? Compare the top of the cup in Figure (a) with that in Figure (b). Which looks most like a circle? What does this suggest about the way you look at, or draw, pictures of three-dimensional objects?

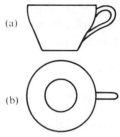

(a)

(b)

**11.** Take a familiar object, such as a sharpened pencil. Close, or cover, one eye, and look at the object from at least three different perspectives. Sketch what you see.

**12.** A board 4 m long is marked at its middle, that is, 2 m from either end. The board is carefully sawed at the mark, yet neither resulting half is 2 m long. Moreover, the combined lengths of the two half-pieces does not equal the original length of the whole board. How can you explain this?

## 3-2   LINES, PLANES, AND PICTURES

The figure on the left below is a picture of a triangular pyramid. The segments, $\overline{AB}$, $\overline{AC}$, $\overline{AD}$, $\overline{BC}$, $\overline{BD}$, and $\overline{CD}$ are called its *edges*. Note that the edge $\overline{BD}$ is dashed, because you couldn't see it if the pyramid were solid. If the figure had been drawn as shown on the right, it would look like a set of points lying on a plane.

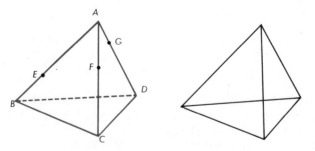

The points $A$, $E$, and $B$ all lie on a single line, namely, the line $\overleftrightarrow{AB}$. Such a set of points is called *collinear*. Of course, the points $A$, $B$, and $C$ do not form a collinear set. Similarly, $A$, $F$, and $C$ form a collinear set, but $A$, $F$, and $G$ do not.

The points $A$, $E$, $B$, $C$, and $F$ all lie in a single plane, namely, the plane that contains the upper front face of the pyramid. Such a set of points is called *coplanar*. Of course, the points $A$, $B$, $C$, and $D$ are not coplanar.

We now make these definitions formally.

### Definition

A set of points is *collinear* if there is a line which contains all the points of the set.

### Definition

A set of points is *coplanar* if there is a plane which contains all points of the set.

[*Query*: In the figure on page 52, the points $E$, $F$, and $G$ are not in any one face of the pyramid. Does it follow that $E$, $F$, and $G$ are not coplanar?]

To do geometry under the scheme described in Chapter 1, we need postulates that convey the real meanings of our undefined terms: *point*, *line*, and *plane*. For lines, we have already done this. The Ruler Postulate is a good description of what lines look like when you view them one at a time. We also said that any two points determine a line, when we first stated Postulate 4 on p. 38.

### POSTULATE 4. The Line Postulate

> *For every two different points there is exactly one line that contains both points.*

Earlier, on p. 38, we noted that the Line Postulate describes the picture on the left below, but not the one on the right.

Thus the figure on the right is impossible. This is the idea expressed in the following theorem. Its proof will be given in Chapter 6.

can extend a segment, by drawing a longer one which contains it, but we cannot extend a line, because a line is already extended as far as it can be, that is, infinitely far. This sort of thing causes no trouble to people versed in the literature of geometry, just as the French irregular verbs cause no trouble to the French. But if we are learning a language from scratch, a simple and consistent language is easier. Moreover, one of the greatest troubles that students have in advanced courses is in realizing that mathematicians really mean what they say. Probably this is due in part to the unnecessary looseness with which people often talk to young students about simple matters.

Note that the postulates really do convey the idea that lines and planes are infinite in extent. If we do not distinguish between lines and segments, then the Line Postulate is not only false but absurd: surely every two points lie on infinitely many segments. Similarly, if planes were regions of finite extent, then Postulate 6, page 57, would become false: no region of finite extent contains all of an infinite line, or even all of the segments that contain two of its points.

Class discussions should bring out the way in which the postulates describe the fundamental properties of lines and planes, and the relations between them. The Ruler Postulate has already told us that a line is ''infinitely long'' and ''continuous,'' and the Line Postulate guarantees that a line is straight: the only ''curve'' with the property that for every two points there is exactly one such ''curve'' that contains those points is a ''straight line.''

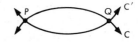

The characteristic features of a "plane" are that it is (1) obviously "wider" than a line, but "smaller" than space, (2) that it is "flat" (the most characteristic feature of all), and (3) that it is "continuous" and "infinite in extent." If you solicit the students' concepts of a plane before stating the postulates about planes, you can then present the postulates to them, one by one, as mathematical formulations of their ideas.

(1) Postulate 5(a) incorporates the idea that a "plane" is wider than a "line." and Postulate 5(b) incorporates the idea that a "plane" is "smaller" than space.

(2) The incidence property that describes the flatness of planes is the fact that if two points lie in a plane, then the line containing them lies in that plane. A "spherical surface" does not possess this property. A "cylindrical surface" is trickier: for *some* pairs of points on the surface of a cylinder, the line determined by those points lies in that surface; however, not *all* pairs of points satisfy this requirement. Postulate 6 incorporates the idea that a plane is "flat."

(3) Once we have Postulate 6 we do not need to state another postulate to incorporate the idea that a plane is "infinite in extent." We can argue that a "plane" has these properties by virtue of Postulate 5(a), the Line Postulate, Postulate 6, and the Ruler Postulate: By Postulate 5(a) a plane contains at least three noncollinear points $A$, $B$, and $C$. By the Line Postulate there is a line $L$ determined by $B$ and $C$. By Postulate 6, line $L$ lies in the given plane. By the Ruler Postulate there are infinitely many points on line $L$. Point $A$, in conjunction with each of these points, individually determines infinitely many lines. Each of these lines and the infinitely many points on each line lie in the plane, by Postulate 6.

**Theorem 3–1**

*If two different lines intersect, their intersection contains only one point.*

We now wish to write postulates that will describe planes and space. Our next postulate says that figures of the kind that we pictured at the beginning of this section really do occur in our geometry.

**POSTULATE 5.** The Plane-Space Postulate

(a) *Every plane contains at least three different noncollinear points.*

(b) *Space contains at least four different noncoplanar points.*

This is merely another way of saying that planes are wide and space is not flat.

*Note*: Beginning with the next section, whenever we speak of *two* lines, or *two* planes, we shall mean that the lines or planes are different. That is, when we speak of *two* things, or *three* things, or *four* things, and so on, we mean that they are, indeed, separate items. But if we say merely that $P$ and $Q$ are points, we mean to allow the possibility that $P = Q$.

**Problem Set 3–2**

In problems 1–7, complete each sentence with the word(s) or symbol(s) that will make it true.

1. If all points of a set lie on one line, the set is called a _collinear_ set.

2. If all points of a set lie in one plane, the set is called a _coplanar_ set.

3. Every plane contains _at least three different noncollinear_ points.

4. Space is the set of _all points_.

5. Space contains _at least four different noncoplanar_ points.

6. If we say that $A$, $B$, and $C$ are three points, we mean that $A$, $B$, and $C$ must be _different_ points.

7. If we say that $L_1$ and $L_2$ are lines, we allow the possibility that $L_1$ and $L_2$ are the _same_ line.

8. In this drawing of a three-dimensional figure, the points $B$, $C$, $D$, and $E$ are coplanar. Decide whether each of the following sets of points is collinear, coplanar, or neither.

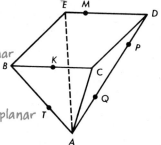

   (a) $\{T, P, E\}$ Coplanar

   (b) $\{A, B, D, M\}$ Neither

   (c) $\{B, K, C\}$ Collinear, coplanar

   (d) $\{A, K, E\}$ Coplanar

   (e) $\{M, K, T\}$ Coplanar

   (f) $\{A, Q, P, D\}$ Collinear, Coplanar

9. Decide by looking at this drawing of a three-dimensional figure whether each of the following sets of points is collinear, coplanar, or neither.

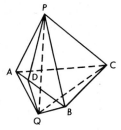

   (a) $\{A, B, C, D\}$ Coplanar

   (b) $\{A, D, B\}$ Collinear, Coplanar

   (c) $\{P, D, Q\}$ Coplanar

   (d) $\{P, B, C\}$ Coplanar

   (e) $\{A, B, C, Q\}$ Neither

10. How many lines may contain one given point? two given points? any three given points?

11. Given: $P$ and $Q$ are different points. The line $L_1$ contains both $P$ and $Q$. The line $L_2$ contains both $P$ and $Q$.
What must be true of $L_1$ and $L_2$? What postulate or theorem supports your conclusion? $L_1 = L_2$. The Line Postulate

12. Given: $L_1$ and $L_2$ are different lines. The point $P$ lies on $L_1$ and on $L_2$. The point $Q$ lies on $L_1$ and on $L_2$.
What must be true of $P$ and $Q$? What postulate or theorem supports your conclusions? $P = Q$. Theorem 3-1

13. If $L_1$ and $L_2$ are two lines that intersect in points $M$ and $N$, what is the distance $MN$? 0

14. Which of the following statements are true?

   (a) Any set of two points is collinear. T

   (b) If three points are collinear, then they are coplanar. T

   (c) If three points are coplanar, then they are collinear. F

15. May two points be noncollinear? three points? five points? Yes
                    No              Yes

Finally, a word about the spirit in which such arguments are to be taken: they are strictly informal; no mathematical validity is to be attributed to them. Their purpose is merely to suggest to students that the mathematical formulations in our postulates are descriptions of the intuitive ideas of ''line'' and ''plane.''

It is best not to get overly concerned with teaching students to *prove* Theorem 3-1, or to try to discuss methods of proof. See the student text of Section 6-3.

You may wish to call attention to the agreement about the use of the word ''two'' stated in the paragraph preceding Problem Set 3-2.

**Explanation for Problems**

Problem 19 is a familiar optical illusion that helps to develop students' perceptual abilities.

**Answers to Problems**

**10.** There are infinitely many lines containing one given point. There is exactly one line containing two given points. If the three given points are collinear, there is exactly one line containing them; but if the three given points are noncollinear there is no one line containing all three points.

19.

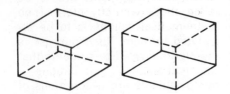

## Background Material

Before introducing the postulates on separation (in Section 3-4) it may be well to reexamine the postulates we already have. Postulates 4, 5, 6, 7, and 8 are similar in that they are purely geometric and describe how points, lines, and planes lie on or are "incident with" each other. They are called *incidence* postulates. On the other hand, Postulates 1, 2, and 3 involve the real numbers; they are concerned with properties of measurement, and so are called *metric* postulates.

The incidence postulates are simple ones that logically form a natural unit with which to begin the course. However, this does not seem attractive, for two reasons. First, the incidence postulates confront students with space geometry in their first approach to a new subject. Second, the proofs of the basic incidence theorems (Theorems 3–1 through 3–4) involve the indirect method; and at the beginning of the course this would cause difficulty for many students.

Postulates 1, 2, and 3 form the basis of an introductory unit on measurement in Chapter 2. This makes use of students' knowledge of algebra, and involves, geometrically, only sets of points contained in a line. Chapter 3 then discusses the incidence properties of points, lines, and planes and separation properties. These are nonmetrical in character.

The discussion in the preceding three paragraphs suggests a rather basic point, namely, the restrictive

16. *R*, *S*, *T*, and *V* are four distinct points that are not all on the same line. What geometric term can be applied to the set $\{R, S, T, V\}$?
     Noncollinear

17. Given a line *L*, how many planes in space may contain *L*?
     Infinitely many

---

18. How many lines can be drawn through pairs of the different points *A*, *B*, *C*, and *D* if
    (a) *A*, *B*, and *C* are collinear. One line or four lines
    (b) no three of the points are collinear. Six lines
    (c) the points are noncoplanar. Six lines

19. Stare directly at this figure of a cube for a few moments, until it appears to shift position. Redraw the figure twice, showing each position separately. In each case, use dashed segments for "hidden" segments, and slightly darker segments for those which should appear closest to you.

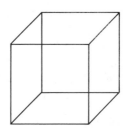

## 3–3 LINES, PLANES, AND PICTURES (CONTINUED)

The following postulate describes the flatness of planes. Planes are like the figure on the left below, and not like the figure on the right.

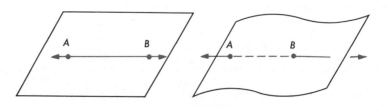

**POSTULATE 6.**   The Flat Plane Postulate

*If two points of a line lie in a plane, then the line lies in the same plane.*

Our next theorem describes the way in which lines and planes intersect each other.

**Theorem 3–2**

*If a line intersects a plane not containing it, then the intersection contains only one point.*

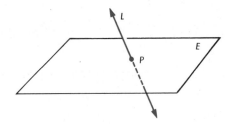

In the figure, we see a line $L$ intersecting a plane $E$ in the way that Theorem 3–2 says it ought to. You will see many figures of this kind, and you should examine them carefully so that you can learn to draw them yourself. To draw a line, of course, we first draw a segment of the line and then put arrowheads at the ends to indicate that the line isn't supposed to stop. Usually we indicate a plane by drawing a rectangle in the plane. When we look at a rectangle edgewise, as we are supposed to in the figure above, the rectangle looks like a parallelogram. If our eyes were in the plane of the rectangle, the rectangle would merely look like a segment, as in the figure below, and the drawing would be logically correct, but not instructive.

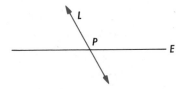

effect of introducing new postulates into a mathematical theory. Consider the Incidence Postulates 4, 5, 6, 7, and 8. Evidently they are satisfied in ordinary Euclidean space, in which lines and planes contain infinitely many points, and are infinite in extent. But the incidence postulates, in themselves, describe very few of the basic properties of space. The easiest way to see this is to observe that Postulates 4, 5, 6, 7, and 8 are satisfied by a "miniature geometry," defined as follows.

Consider the following definitions: *M-space* is a set whose only elements are four noncoplanar points, $A$, $B$, $C$, $D$. A *line* is any pair of points belonging to *M*-space. A *plane* is any triplet of points belonging to *M*-space. Our postulates are no longer statements involving undefined or uninterpreted terms, but become definite statements (true or false) about the "points," "lines," and "planes" of *M*-space. Thus Postulate 4 now says: any two of the objects $A$, $B$, $C$, $D$ are contained in a unique pair of them. This is trivially true. Similarly, Postulate 6 says that if a triplet of the objects contains two of them, then it contains the pair composed of these two. This is also a trivial truth. It can also be shown that each of the Postulates 4, 5, 6, 7, and 8 is satisfied when point, line, and plane are interpreted in the given way. By virtue of this, the system composed of the four "points" $A$, $B$, $C$, $D$, the six "lines" $\{A, B\}$, $\{A, C\}$, $\{A, D\}$, $\{B, C\}$, $\{B, D\}$, $\{C, D\}$, and the four "planes" $\{A, B, C\}$, $\{A, B, D\}$, $\{A, C, D\}$, $\{B, C, D\}$ is called a *model* for Postulates 4 through 8.

Since the model satisfies Postulates 4 through 8, it must satisfy the theorems which are deduced from these postulates (using no others), for example, Theorems 3–1, 3–2, 3–3, and 3–4. This is easily verified. The principle that a line contains infinitely many points can obviously not be deduced as a theorem from Postulates 4 through 8. For if this could be done, our model would have to have this property—and it does not, because each of its lines contains exactly two points.

This shows the effect of introducing the metric postulates, in particular the Ruler Postulate. This guarantees that a line is dense, and that its infinitely many points are arranged on the line and determine distances in just the way we want for the kind of geometric theory we are constructing. The introduction of the metric postulates excludes finite models, of the type we have discussed, which do satisfy the incidence postulates. And in general, as new postulates are added in a mathematical theory, the scope of its application, that is, the family of models which satisfy the postulates, is reduced.

Similarly, a circle seen in perspective looks like an ellipse. If our eyes were in the plane of the circle, the circle would also look like a segment, and would be indistinguishable from a rectangle.

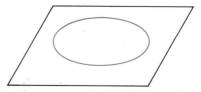

Postulate 4 told us that two points determine a line. To determine a plane, we need three noncollinear points.

**POSTULATE 7.**    The Plane Postulate

*Any three points lie in at least one plane, and any three noncollinear points lie in exactly one plane.*

More briefly, *any three points are coplanar, and any three noncollinear points determine a plane.*

Theorem 3–3

**Given a line and a point not on the line, there is exactly one plane containing both.**

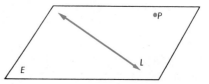

Theorem 3–4

**Given two intersecting lines, there is exactly one plane containing both.**

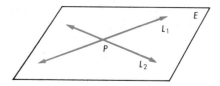

More briefly, *a line and a point not on it determine a plane*, and *two intersecting lines determine a plane.*

Finally, we state the following postulate.

**POSTULATE 8.**   Intersection of Planes Postulate

*If two different planes intersect, then their intersection is a line.*

It may look as if we will continue indefinitely, writing down an endless series of postulates to describe our common-sense ideas about space. It turns out, however, that we do not need to do this. In this book, we shall study the geometry of space on the basis of only twenty-four fundamental statements. Everything else can be derived from these if you know how. In this book, you will learn how.

Twenty-four should not be regarded as a large number. It is really so small that it makes geometry completely different from a science such as biology for example. In biology, twenty-four facts would get us nowhere; to obtain the thousands of other facts that we need to know, we have to go on working in the laboratory, examining the actual plants and animals. In place of a laboratory, geometry uses logical reasoning, starting with a relatively small number of fundamental facts.

## Problem Set 3–3

1. The plane $E$ contains the points $R$ and $T$. What can you conclude about $\overleftrightarrow{RT}$? What postulate or theorem supports your answer?
   E contains $\overleftrightarrow{RT}$. Postulate 6

2. A line $L$ does not lie in a plane $E$. Must the intersection of $L$ and $E$ be exactly one point? No, the intersection may be ∅.

3. A line may be named by naming two of its points. How many points of a plane must be named, to name the plane? Three points of the plane, and they must be noncollinear.

4. Which postulate does this figure illustrate? Postulate 8

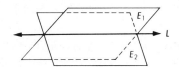

**Quiz**

For each item select *all* correct choices.
1. Three different points
   (a) always determine a plane.
   (b) can be collinear.
   (c) can be noncollinear.
   (d) always lie in at least one plane.
   (ans: b, c, d)
2. If two points of a line lie in a plane, then
   (a) all points of the line lie in the plane.
   (b) the line pierces the plane in exactly two points.
   (c) the plane contains all points of the line.
   (d) the intersection contains only two points.
   (ans: a, c)
3. A plane is determined by
   (a) a line and a point.
   (b) two intersecting lines.
   (c) any three points.
   (d) a line and a point not on it.
   (ans: b, d)
4. The intersection of two planes may be
   (a) a line segment.
   (b) another plane.
   (c) a line.
   (d) the empty set.
   (ans: c, d)
5. If $P$, $Q$, $R$, and $S$ are four points, then
   (a) they are noncoplanar.
   (b) they determine four lines.
   (c) they determine six lines.
   (d) they are different points.
   (ans: d)

**6.** Infinitely many. Infinitely many. One if the points are noncollinear; infinitely many if the points are collinear.

**7.**

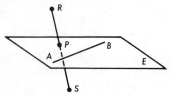

**9.** The ends of the three legs are coplanar. The end of the fourth leg may or may not lie in the plane containing the other three ends.

**10.** A tripod. See the answer to Problem 9.

**13.** No. Planes E and F could intersect in a line, and points A, B, and C could lie on this line. If we had also been told that A, B, and C were noncollinear, then we could conclude by Postulate 7 that planes E and F are the same.

**15.**

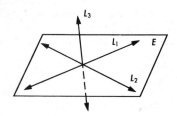

---

**5.** State three conditions that determine a plane.
Postulate 7, Theorem 3-3, Theorem 3-4

**6.** How many planes can contain one given point? two given points? three given points?

**7.** Draw a plane $E$, using a parallelogram to indicate the plane. Draw a line segment which lies in $E$. Draw a line segment which intersects $E$ in only one point, but which does not intersect the other segment.

**8.** If $\overleftrightarrow{AB}$ and the plane $F$ have two points $K$ and $M$ in common, what can you conclude about $\overleftrightarrow{AB}$ and $F$? Why?  $\overleftrightarrow{AB}$ lies in F. Postulate 6

**9.** On a level floor, a four-legged table will sometimes rock, while a three-legged table is always steady. Explain.

**10.** What device, often used by surveyors and by photographers, makes use of the principle of the Plane Postulate? Explain.
A tripod. See Problem 9

**11.** Examine this figure of a rectangular solid until you see how it is drawn to look like a three-dimensional figure. Then close the book and draw a figure like this from memory. Practice until you are satisfied with the results.

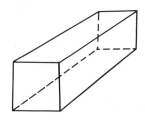

**12.** After doing Problem 11, draw a figure of a cube.

**13.** Given: The points $A$, $B$, $C$ lie in the plane $E$. The points $A$, $B$, $C$ lie in the plane $F$. Can you conclude that the plane $E$ is the same as the plane $F$? Explain.

**14.** If our eyes were in the plane of a circle, how would the circle appear?
As a segment

**15.** Draw a plane $E$ and draw two intersecting lines, $L_1$ and $L_2$, that lie in $E$. Draw line $L_3$ that intersects both $L_1$ and $L_2$ but that does not lie in $E$.

**16.** Three lines, $L_1$, $L_2$, and $L_3$ all intersect at point $P$, as in the figure, but do not all lie in the same plane. How many planes do they determine? What postulate or theorem did you use? Copy, or trace, the figure. Then sketch in the planes determined by the lines.
**Three; Theorem 3-4**

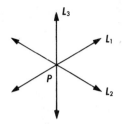

**17.** The figure formed by all the segments that have four noncoplanar points as their end points is called a triangular pyramid, or a *tetrahedron*. The four points are the vertices of the tetrahedron.

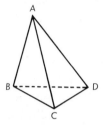

(a) State a definition of an edge of a tetrahedron.

(b) How many edges does the tetrahedron have? Name them.

(c) Are there any pairs of edges that do not intersect?

(d) A *face* is the triangular region determined by any three vertices. Name the four faces. Are there any pairs of faces that do not intersect?

**18.** This figure is a square pyramid whose base, a square, is supposed to be closest to you. Name the planes determined by its vertices. (You should find seven planes.)

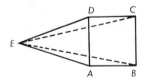

---

**19.** Given: $L_1$ and $L_2$ are different lines. $L_1$ lies in the plane $E$. $L_2$ lies in the plane $F$. $L_1$ and $L_2$ intersect at the point P. The point $Q$, different from $P$, lies on $L_1$ and is in $F$. The point $R$, different from $P$, lies on $L_2$ and is in $E$.    **They are identical.**
What can you conclude about plane $E$ and plane $F$? What postulates or theorems support your answer? **See Solution Section.**

**16.**

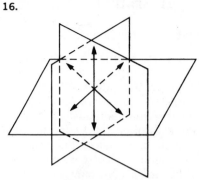

**17.** (a) An *edge* of a tetrahedron is a segment whose end points are two vertices of the tetrahedron.

(b) Six edges: $\overline{AB}$, $\overline{AC}$, $\overline{AD}$, $\overline{BC}$, $\overline{BD}$, $\overline{CD}$

(c) Yes, three pairs: $\overline{AB}$ and $\overline{CD}$, $\overline{AC}$ and $\overline{BD}$, $\overline{AD}$ and $\overline{BC}$

(d) The four faces are: $ABC$, $ABD$, $ACD$, $BCD$; no, each pair of faces intersects in an edge of the tetrahedron.

**18.** There are five planes which contain the faces of the square pyramid: $EAB$, $EBC$, $ECD$, $EDA$, $ABCD$. There are two planes which do not contain any face of the pyramid: $EAC$, $EBD$.

**19.** The planes $E$ and $F$ are identical. $L_1$ lies in $E$. Since the points $P$ and $R$ which are on $L_2$ both lie in $E$, $L_2$ lies in $E$ by Postulate 6. Similarly the two intersecting lines $L_1$ and $L_2$ are contained in plane $F$. But by Theorem 3–4, given two intersecting lines, there is exactly one plane containing them. Therefore $E$ and $F$ are identical.

# 3–4 CONVEX SETS AND SEPARATION

## Classroom Notes

This section provides a good illustration of the practice of the authors in presenting ideas informally at first, and then more formally in a precise mathematical definition. Students often fail to see this distinction, or to realize this is the way they themselves discuss new ideas.

The idea of convexity is presented partly because of its intrinsic interest and partly to shorten the statements of the two separation postulates. See the alternative statements (1) and (2) at the bottom of page 63. The properties of convex sets have been extensively investigated by mathematicians. Mathematical journals frequently contain articles on convexity.

Note that a half-plane does not contain its edge. ("The points of the plane that do *not* lie on the line form two sets . . .")

## Background Material

Considering that we have a Plane Separation Postulate and a Space Separation Postulate, it might seem natural to state the following:

**The Line Separation Postulate.** Given a point and a line containing it, the points of the line, other than the given point, form two sets such that

(1) each of the sets is convex, and
(2) if P is in one of the sets and Q is in the other, then $\overline{PQ}$ contains the given point.

There are two reasons why no such postulate was included.

(1) As a practical matter, we already have a way of describing how a point separates a line; we can express a line as the union of two opposite rays $\overrightarrow{AB}$ and $\overrightarrow{AC}$.

# 3–4   CONVEX SETS AND SEPARATION

Each of the sets of points shown below is a *convex set*.

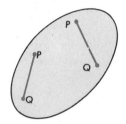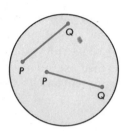

Each of these sets is a whole region in the plane, not just the boundary. In these sets, you can get from any point P to any other point Q, moving along a straight line, without leaving the set.

On the other hand, none of the following sets is convex.

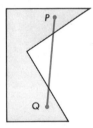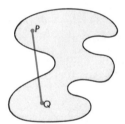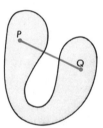

We have indicated why these sets are not convex by giving examples of points P and Q which cannot be joined by segments lying in the set.

Stating this more mathematically, we make the following definition.

## Definition

A set M is called *convex* if for every two points P and Q of the set, the entire segment $\overline{PQ}$ lies in M.

The sets that we have been talking about so far are "small," but a convex set may easily be large. For example, every plane is a convex set; and a line in a plane cuts the plane into two sets, each of which is convex and is infinite in extent. These two sets are called *half-planes* or *sides* of the line L, and L is called the *edge* of each of them.

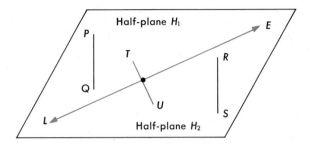

Half-plane $H_1$

Half-plane $H_2$

Half-planes are convex because if two points are on the same side of the line, the segment joining them never crosses the line.

On the other hand, if $T$ and $U$ are points on *opposite sides* of the line, the segment $\overline{TU}$ *always* intersects the line.

We now summarize the preceding statements in a postulate and some definitions.

### POSTULATE 9.   The Plane Separation Postulate

*Given a line and a plane containing it. The points of the plane that do not lie on the line form two sets such that*

*(1) each of the sets is convex, and*

*(2) if P is in one of the sets and Q is in the other, then the segment $\overline{PQ}$ intersects the line.*

### Definitions

Given a line $L$ and a plane $E$ containing it, the two sets described in the Plane Separation Postulate are called *half-planes* or *sides* of $L$, and $L$ is called the *edge* of each of them. If $P$ lies in one of the half-planes and $Q$ lies in the other, then we say that $P$ and $Q$ *lie on opposite sides of L.*

Our postulate tells us two things about the way in which a line separates a plane into two half-planes.

(1) If two points lie in the same half-plane, then the segment joining them lies in the same half-plane, and so *never* intersects the line.

(2) If two points lie in opposite half-planes, then the segment joining them *always* intersects the line.

And if we want to convey the idea that "B and C are on opposite sides of A," we merely say that A is between B and C.

(2) Logically, it is unnecessary. On the given line $L$, we set up a coordinate system in such a way that the given point has coordinate zero. Let $H^+$ be the set of all points of $L$ with positive coordinates, and let $H^-$ be the set of all points of $L$ with negative coordinates. It can then be verified that $H^-$ and $H^+$ satisfy the conditions of the "Line Separation Postulate."

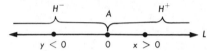

Let $P$ and $Q$ be any points of $H^+$, with coordinates $x$ and $y$. It is a matter of notation to suppose that $x < y$. Thus $0 < x < y$. It follows that $P$ is between $A$ and $Q$.

(See the comments on Section 2–6.) Therefore $A$ is not between $P$ and $Q$, and $A$ is not in $\overline{PQ}$. Therefore $H^+$ is convex.

Similarly, we verify that $H^-$ is convex. Here $x < y < 0$, $Q$ is between $P$ and $A$, $A$ is not between $P$ and $Q$, and $A$ does not lie in $\overline{PQ}$.

If $P$ is in $H^-$ and $Q$ is in $H^+$, then $x < 0 < y$, and $A$ is between $P$ and $Q$.

**1.** In a plane what is the union of a line and the two half-planes determined by that line?

(ans: a plane)

**2.** What is the maximum number of regions into which two planes can separate space?

(ans: four)

**3.** Indicate whether each statement is true or false.

(a) Every half-plane contains its edge.
(b) The union of two half-planes is a plane.
(c) A circle is a convex set.
(d) A ray is a convex set.
(e) A half-plane is a convex set.

(ans: F, F, F, T, T)

**4.** What is the maximum number of regions into which three lines can separate a plane?

(ans: seven)

**5.** The line $L$ is the edge of two coplanar half-planes. The points $M$ and $K$ are on opposite sides of $L$. What must be true of $\overleftrightarrow{MK}$ and $L$? What postulate or theorem supports your answer?

(ans: $\overleftrightarrow{MK}$ intersects $L$, by Postulate 9.)

While a line has only two sides in any given plane, every line has infinitely many sides in space. In the next figure, we see five of the infinitely many half-planes in space that have the line $L$ as an edge.

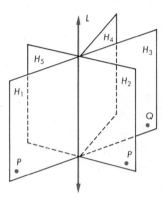

[*Query*: Is there a difference between the following two statements?

(1) $P$ and $Q$ lie on different sides of $L$.

(2) $P$ and $Q$ lie on opposite sides of $L$.]

A plane separates space in exactly the same manner in which a line separates a plane.

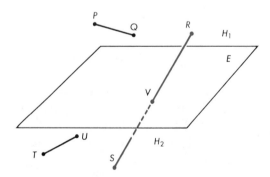

The two sets into which a plane separates space are called *half-spaces*, or *sides* of the plane. In the figure, these are $H_1$ (above the plane) and $H_2$ (below). Each of the two half-spaces is convex. But if $R$ is in of them and $S$ is in the other, the segment $\overline{RS}$ always intersects the plane.

Again we sum up with a postulate and some definitions.

## POSTULATE 10.   The Space Separation Postulate

*The points of space that do not lie in a given plane form two sets, such that*

*(1) each of the sets is convex, and*

*(2) If P is in one of the sets and Q is in the other, then the segment PQ intersects the plane.*

## Definitions

The two sets described in the Space Separation Postulate are called *half-spaces*, and the given plane is called the *face* of each of them.

Note that while every line in space is the edge of infinitely many half-planes, every plane in space is a face of only two half-spaces.

### Problem Set 3–4

[*Note*: In answering the problems of this set use your intuitive understanding in situations not covered by our postulational structure.]

1. Discuss the following questions.
    (a) Is a line a convex set? Yes
    (b) Is a set consisting of only two points convex? No
    (c) Is a circle a convex set? No
    (d) Is the region enclosed by a circle a convex set? Yes
    (e) Does a point separate a plane? space? a line? No; No; Yes

2. Discuss the following questions.
    (a) If a single point is removed from a line, do the remaining points form a convex set? No
    (b) Is a sphere a convex set? No
    (c) Is the space enclosed by a sphere a convex set? Yes
    (d) Does a ray separate a plane? does a line? does a segment?
        No          Yes          No
    (e) Can two lines in a plane separate the plane into two regions? three regions? four regions? five regions? No; Yes; Yes; No

3. If one point is removed from a plane, is the resulting set convex? No

### Explanation for Problems

Problem 12 is the first of several problems scattered throughout Chapters 3–9 that contain ideas that can challenge students' "intuitive" feelings about parallelism, specifically the uniqueness feature of the Parallel Postulate, page 272. In the hands of a teacher knowledgeable about this topic, these problems can be used to motivate students to appreciate the real role of postulates in a logical system, and, perhaps, to investigate some non-euclidean geometry.

The other problems are:
Problem 11 on page 221
Problems 16, 17, and 20 on page 241
Problems 11 and 15 on page 268. You may wish to refer to additional comments for each problem.

The part of Problem 12 which is controversial is that of getting five regions with three coplanar lines. Without benefit of the Euclidean Parallel Postulate the following diagram, in which lines $L_1$ and $L_2$ are both parallel to $L$, is possible.

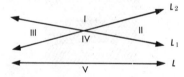

At this point, what seems "logical" to students is what fits in with their frame of reference; namely, *all* of their past experience. Yet, speaking mathematically, we have no logical reason to reject the solution indicated by the diagram above.

Whether you use this in your classes depends entirely on you and on your assessment of your students. *Do not* underrate their ability to consider such ideas exciting.

The Background Material, page 62, discusses the ideas presented in Problem 16. The meaning of the term "half-line," while not formally stated, seems clear enough to allow its inclusion in this problem. In this way students can take part in developing mathematical ideas.

**Answers to Problems**

**8.**

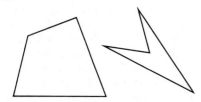

**9.**

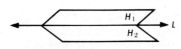

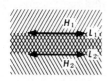

**10.** Here are three possibilities:

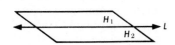

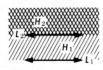

**11.** (a) No; since a half-plane does not contain its edge, the common edge is not contained in the union of $H_1$ and $H_2$. Hence the union of the two half-planes is not the whole plane.

(b) No; as shown in the figure, a region of the plane is not included in their union.

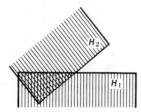

**4.** The interiors, $C$ and $D$, of the two circles are each convex sets.

(a) Is $C \cap D$ a convex set? Yes

(b) Is $C \cup D$ a convex set? No

**5.** If $L$ is a line in the plane $E$, is the set of all points of $E$ on one side of $L$ a convex set? Yes

**6.** Is the set of points consisting of all points of a sphere and all points in the interior of the sphere a convex set? Yes

**7.** Is a torus (a doughnut-shaped figure) a convex set? No

**8.** Draw a plane quadrilateral (a figure with four sides) whose interior is a convex set. Draw one whose interior is not a convex set.

**9.** Draw two half-planes which have a common edge and are coplanar. Draw two which have a common edge but are not coplanar.

**10.** Draw two half-planes which are coplanar but do not have a common edge.

**11.** $H_1$ and $H_2$ are two coplanar half-planes. Is the union of $H_1$ and $H_2$ the whole plane if

(a) $H_1$ and $H_2$ have the same edge? Explain.

(b) the edge of $H_1$ intersects the edge of $H_2$ in exactly one point? Explain.

(c) the edge of $H_2$ lies entirely in $H_1$?

**12.** Can three lines in a plane ever separate the plane into three regions? four regions? five regions? six regions? seven regions?
Yes    No    Yes    Yes    No

**13.** Into how many sets do two intersecting planes separate space? two non-intersecting planes? Three    Four

14. Three planes intersect in pairs as in the figure. Into how many regions do they separate space? *Seven*

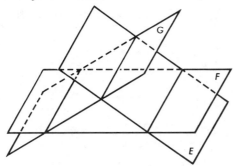

15. What is the greatest number of sets into which space can be separated by three different planes? What is the least number? *Four*

*Eight*

16. (a) Into how many sets does a point on a line separate the line? What name would you suggest giving to each of these sets? *Half-line* *Two*

(b) Using the terminology you developed in (a), write a Line Separation Statement similar to Postulates 9 and 10.

(c) How does a ray differ from a half-line? *A ray has an end point, but a half-line has no end point.*

## 3–5　THE SEVEN BRIDGES OF KÖNIGSBERG

You might think there isn't much to the idea of crossing streets, bridges, and so on, but as a matter of fact there is a famous problem in mathematics that involves the idea of "crossing" and hardly any other idea at all.

The city of Königsberg is on the coast of the Baltic Sea, at the mouth of the Pregel River. (The *ö* in Königsberg is pronounced like the *ur* in the English word b*ur*n.) In the river there are two islands, linked to the mainland and to each other by seven bridges, as shown below.

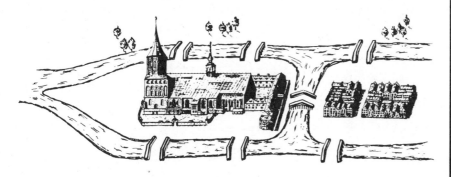

(c) No, if like the second figure in the answer to Problem 10. Yes, if like the following figure:

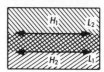

16. (b) The Line Separation Statement: Given a point and a line containing it. The points of the line different from the given point form two sets such that (1) each of the sets is convex and (2) if $P$ is in one set and $Q$ is in the other, then the segment $\overline{PQ}$ contains the given point.

## 3–5　THE SEVEN BRIDGES OF KÖNIGSBERG

**Classroom Notes**

This supplementary section is an introduction to a fascinating branch of mathematics called topology.

*Caution*: In an effort to make the solution as simple as possible, we have simplified the problem itself, by requiring that the walker start on the south bank of the river. This was not a condition of the original problem. Euler showed that the "Königsberg Walk" is impossible, no matter where you start.

Proof. (1) An odd number of bridges lead to the south bank. Therefore the walk must either *begin* or *end* on the south bank.

(2) For the same reason, the walk must either begin or end on the western island.

(3) For the same reason, the walk must either begin or end on the eastern island.

This means that the problem is impossible, because there can be only one starting point and one stopping point.

The people who strolled around on these islands found that if they started on the south bank of the river, they could not plan their walk so as to cross each of the bridges exactly once. It seemed that they had to skip at least one bridge:

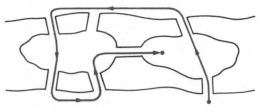

or cross some bridge twice:

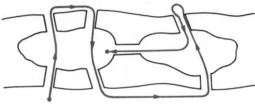

People were convinced that they couldn't cross each bridge exactly once, but nobody was sure. Finally in the year 1735, somebody submitted the problem to the great Swiss mathematician Leonard Euler (pronounced Oiler). Euler discovered that people might as well quit trying. He came up with the following analysis of the problem.

First consider the island on the east:

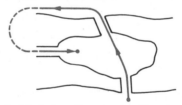

There are three bridges leading to it. Since you started on the south bank, as the problem requires, you must have started somewhere *off* the eastern island. Since you make each of the three crossings exactly once, you end up *on* the eastern island. (Similarly, if the lights are *off*, and you flip the switch three times, then the lights are *on*.)

Next consider the western island.

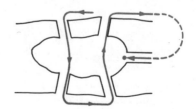

There are five bridges leading to it, and five is an odd number. Therefore, since you started *off* the western island, you must end up *on* the western island. (This is like flipping a light switch five times: if the light was off at the start, it is on at the end.)

But this means that the "Königsberg Walk" is impossible, because you can't end up in two places at once.

Euler's solution of this problem was a very important event because it was the first time that anybody had solved this *kind* of problem. Note that if you draw the map of the islands on a sheet of rubber, you can stretch the rubber any way you like without changing the problem at all.

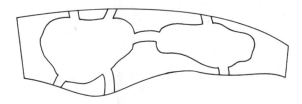

From Euler's analysis of the "Königsberg Walk" developed a whole branch of mathematics, dealing with problems of this kind. This is called *topology*.

## Problem Set

1. In this problem, you "win" if you can cross each segment of the figure exactly once without lifting your pencil from the paper. Copy the figures on a piece of paper and see whether you can discover in which two of the five figures it is possible for you to "win." Is there a way to make up figures for which you must always "lose"?

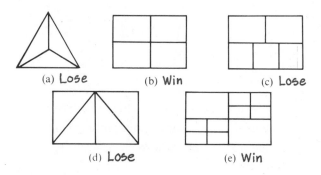

(a) Lose    (b) Win    (c) Lose

(d) Lose    (e) Win

1. Definition: A region is odd (even) if its boundary consists of an odd (even) number of segments. The exterior of a figure is also considered a "region of the figure." Figure (d), for example, separates the plane into four regions of order 3 and one region (the exterior of the figure) of order 6; hence Figure (d) separates the plane into four odd regions and one even region.

There are two theorems underlying the problem of crossing each of the segments of a particular figure exactly once:

Theorem 1. If the number of odd regions is greater than two, then it is not possible to construct a path which crosses each segment exactly once. The proof is easy. The path can only have two ends, and each odd region must contain an end point of the path.

Theorem 2. If the number of odd regions is 0 or 2, then it is possible to construct a path which crosses each of the segments exactly once. Note, however, that Theorem 2 is not needed in the solution of this problem. It suffices to sketch paths for Figures (b) and (e) which cross each segment exactly once.

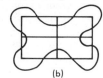

(b)

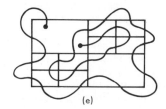

(e)

**2.** The first and third networks can be traversed by proceeding sequentially through the vertices as numbered in the diagrams.

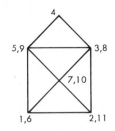

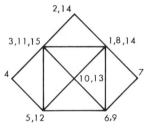

It is impossible to traverse the second network continuously without retracing a segment.

Before discussing briefly two theorems underlying the problem of traversing these networks, we must first define an odd vertex.

Definition: A vertex is odd if it is the end point of an odd number of simple arcs.

Theorem A. If the number of odd vertices is greater than two, then the network cannot be traversed by a path without retracing a segment. The proof is easy: the path can have only two ends, and each odd vertex must be an end point of the path.

Theorem B. If the number of odd vertices is not greater than 2, then the network can be traversed without retracing a segment. The proof of this theorem is very hard. Note, however, that Theorem B is not needed in the solution of this problem. If a path can be traversed we can prove this simply by traversing it, as indicated in the above figures.

**2.** Of the three figures shown, two can be drawn without lifting your pencil or retracing a line segment, while the third one cannot. Which two can be drawn in this manner? Try to reproduce each figure on your paper without lifting your pencil or retracing a segment. Is there an easier way of arriving at a conclusion?

Possible          Impossible          Possible

**3.** Which figures can be drawn without retracing any line segment?

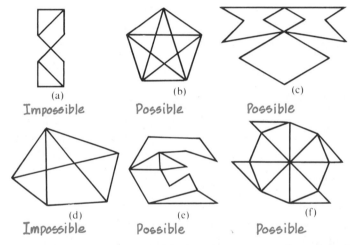

(a)          (b)          (c)

Impossible          Possible          Possible

(d)          (e)          (f)

Impossible          Possible          Possible

**4.** A figure of the sort shown below is called a *network*, and each point indicated by a heavy dot is called a *vertex*. A vertex is said to be odd or even according to the number of segments leading from it.

  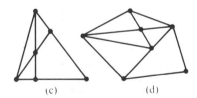

(a)          (b)          (c)          (d)

(a) How many odd vertices does each figure have?  0; 2; 4; 2

(b) Which figures can be drawn without retracing any segment?
(a), (b), (d)

(c) Do you have a better idea how to tell easily? Try it out in Problems 1–3 again!  See comments for Problem 2.

5. *The Möbius Strip.* (Here *ö* is pronounced as *ur*, as in *Königsberg.*) You may already have seen a Möbius strip, which is a piece of paper having only one side and one edge. It is easy to make one. Cut a fairly long strip of paper, about 8 cm wide, from a standard sheet of paper. Better yet, take a piece of adding machine tape about 60 cm long. Next, glue the ends of the strip together, first giving the tape a half-twist, as illustrated below.

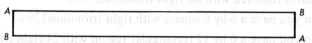

You can investigate many of the peculiar properties of the Möbius strip. For instance, a pencil mark down the center, lengthwise, will return to its starting point without ever crossing an edge or retracing itself. Call this mark the midline.

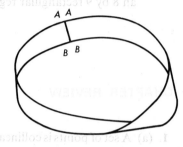

(a) With scissors, cut the Möbius strip along its midline. What happens?

(b) Take the strip (or strips), and cut again, along the midline (or midlines). What do you get?

(c) Now perform the same operation a third time, and observe the results.

6. *The Domino Problem.* The figure on the left below consists of 20 squares. If each square were half the size of a domino, then you could exactly cover, or "pave," the figure with 10 dominos.

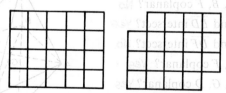

But suppose we remove two squares (equivalent to one domino), and get the figure on the right above. Can this figure be paved with nine dominos? Yes

7. Can a 5 by 5 square be paved with dominos? If one small corner square is removed, can the resulting figure be paved by dominos? No; Yes

8. If you take a standard 8 by 8 checkerboard and remove or eliminate a pair of squares at opposite corners (as in Problem 6), can the resulting figure be paved with dominos? (You should make a figure, or better yet, use a real checkerboard and dominos.) No

**Answers to Problems**

5. (a) One strip is formed.
   (b) Two interlocking strips are formed.
   (c) Four strips are formed, any two of which are interlocking.
7. No, if a board can be covered by dominos, then the number of squares must be even.
8. Each domino would cover one red and one black square, but the squares removed at opposite corners would have the same color.

**9.** (a) No, the number of squares must be a multiple of three.

(b) Yes

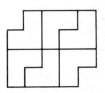

(c) Yes, a 2 x 3 region can be formed by two triominos, and a 6 x 6 region can be built up by six such regions.

**9.** Just as a domino is formed by two adjacent squares, a triomino is formed by three adjacent squares. In particular, a right triomino looks like the figure on the right.

(a) Can you pave a 5 by 4 rectangular region with right triominos? No

(b) Can you pave a 5 by 4 rectangular region having a pair of opposite squares removed with six right triominos? Yes

(c) Can you pave a 6 by 6 square with right triominos? Yes

(d) Can you pave a 6 by 12 rectangular region with 24 right triominos? an 8 by 9 rectangular region? Yes, as in (c)

## CHAPTER REVIEW

**1.** (a) A set of points is collinear if _there is a line that contains all the points of the set_ .

(b) A set of points is coplanar if _there is a plane that contains all the points of the set_ .

(c) May 3 points be collinear? Yes (d) Must 2 points be collinear? Yes

(e) Must 3 points be collinear? No (f) May 10 points be collinear? Yes

(g) Must 3 points be coplanar? Yes (h) May 10 points be coplanar? Yes

**2.** Study the three-dimensional figure given (in which $A$, $B$, $C$, $D$ are coplanar) and answer the following questions.

(a) Are $E$, $D$, $F$ collinear? No

(b) Are $E$, $C$, $B$, $F$ coplanar? No

(c) Do $\overline{AC}$ and $\overline{BD}$ intersect? Yes

(d) Do $\overline{AC}$ and $\overline{DF}$ intersect? No

(e) Are $E$, $B$, $F$ coplanar? Yes

(f) Are $F$, $B$, $G$, $D$ coplanar? Yes

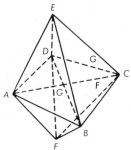

**3.** Given three points not on the same line, how many planes contain them? One

**4.** Each of the planes $E$, $F$, $G$ intersects the other two as shown in the figure. Into how many convex regions do they separate space? Eight

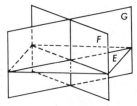

**Answers to Problems**

7. In order for a set $K$ to be convex it must be true that for every two points $P$ and $Q$ in $K$ the entire segment $\overline{PQ}$ lies in $K$.

5. What is the least number of points necessary to determine
   (a) a line? Two
   (b) a plane? Three
   (c) space? Four

6. State *in full* the postulate or theorem suggested by each figure:

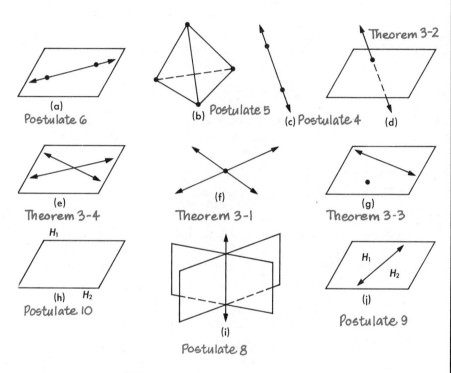

(a)
Postulate 6

(b) Postulate 5

(c) Postulate 4

(d) Theorem 3-2

(e)
Theorem 3-4

(f)
Theorem 3-1

(g)
Theorem 3-3

(h)
Postulate 10

(i)
Postulate 8

(j)
Postulate 9

7. Every point on $\overline{AB}$ is contained in the set $K$. Does this mean that $K$ is a convex set? Explain. No

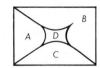

8. Is every plane a convex set? Explain. Which postulate is essential to your explanation? Yes. Postulate 6

9. Which of the regions named by capital letters are convex sets? A and C

**13.**

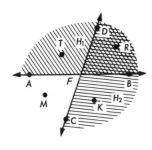

**14.**

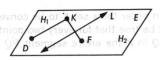

**15.** No. If $L_1$ is to intersect $L_2$, it must do so in plane $E$ since $L_2$ lies entirely in $E$. But the *only* point (Theorem 3–2) at which $L_1$ intersects $E$ is point $P$, and $P$ does not lie on $L_2$.

**16.** Yes. Since $P$ lies in plane $E$ and in plane $F$, it lies in the intersection of $E$ and $F$, which is line $\overleftrightarrow{AB}$. Therefore $P$ lies in $\overleftrightarrow{AB}$. Similarly $Q$ lies on $\overleftrightarrow{AB}$.

**10.** Complete: Every line in space is the edge of ___infinitely many___ half-planes, but every plane in space is the ___face___ of only ___two___ half-spaces.

**11.** In this figure all points lie in the plane $E$. Complete each sentence.

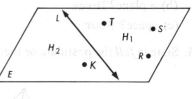

   (a) $H_1$ and $H_2$ are called ___half-planes___

   (b) The points $S$ and $K$ lie on ___opposite___ sides of the line ___$L$___.

   (c) $L$ is called the ___edge___ of both $H_1$ and $H_2$.

   (d) $E = $ ___$H_1$___ $\cup$ ___$H_2$___ $\cup$ ___$L$___.

**12.** Does a half-plane contain its edge? ___No___

**13.** Draw a line $L$ separating a plane into two half-planes. Label the half-planes $H_1$ and $H_2$. $D$, $K$, and $F$ are points such that $D \in H_1$, $K \in H_1$, and $F \in H_2$.

   (a) What is $\overline{DK} \cap L$? Why? ___$\emptyset$. $\overline{DK}$ is contained in $H_1$.___

   (b) What is $\overline{KF} \cap L$? Why? ___A point on $L$. $K$ and $F$ are on opposite sides of $L$.___

**14.** Draw a figure according to the following directions. $\overleftrightarrow{AB} \cap \overleftrightarrow{CD} = F$, and $A$-$F$-$B$ and $C$-$F$-$D$. Shade in $H_1$, the half-plane of $\overleftrightarrow{AB}$ containing $D$. Shade, in a different manner, $H_2$, the half-plane of $\overleftrightarrow{CD}$ containing $B$. Let $R$ be any point in $H_1 \cap H_2$. Let $M$ be any point neither in $H_1$ nor in $H_2$. Let $K$ be any point in $H_2$ but not in $H_1$. Let $T$ be any point in $H_1$ but not in $H_2$.

   (a) May $M$ lie on $\overleftrightarrow{AB}$? ___Yes___

   (b) $T$ and $R$ *must* lie on opposite sides of the line ___$\overleftrightarrow{CD}$___.

   (c) $K$ and $R$ *must* lie on ___opposite sides___ of $\overleftrightarrow{AB}$.

   (d) Must $\overleftrightarrow{TR}$ intersect $\overleftrightarrow{KF}$? ___No___

**15.** The line $L_1$ intersects the plane $E$ in $P$, but does not lie in $E$. The line $L_2$ lies in the plane $E$, but does not contain the point $P$. Is it possible for $L_1$ to intersect $L_2$? Explain.

**16.** Two planes $E$ and $F$ intersect in $\overleftrightarrow{AB}$. Each of the points $P$ and $Q$ lies in both of the planes $E$ and $F$. Must $P$ and $Q$ lie on $\overleftrightarrow{AB}$? Explain.

Leonhard Euler (1707–1783)

Euler's solution of the problem of the seven bridges of Königsberg was typical of his insight and ingenuity. Before his time, it had not occurred to anybody that this sort of problem belonged to mathematics at all. Since then, mathematics has grown fast, in many unexpected directions. Euler's analysis of the Königsberg bridge problem was the first hint of a new branch of mathematics, now known as topology, which has reached its highest development in the twentieth century and is still growing.

Euler was not only very clever but hard working; he produced original mathematics at a rate which has hardly been equaled. His collected mathematical works fill over sixty large volumes. At twenty-eight he lost the sight in one eye; and at fifty he became almost totally blind. But his memory was fabulous—he knew all of Vergil's *Aeneid* by heart—and he had always been able to carry out long calculations in his head. Thus he was able to go on working, at the same rate as before, for the rest of his life.

## CHAPTER 4

## Angles and Triangles

In Chapter 4 we state the postulates on angular measure, we prove the elementary theorems on angles, and we introduce students to the problem of writing a simple proof.

In studying this chapter, students should begin to learn definitions, postulates, and theorems with more thoroughness than was necessary in the first three chapters. Careful attention to the problem sets will help.

### Planning the Chapter

Section 4–3 can be combined with Section 4–4 as a reading assignment. For the above-average class one day may be spent on each of the remaining sections with teaching emphasis placed on Sections 4–2 and 4–9. For the average class two days should be spent on these two sections and one day on each of the other sections.

CHAPTER

# 4

# Angles and Triangles

## Objectives . . .

- Define the basic terms: angle, triangle, interior, exterior, angle measure, and perpendicular.
- State the postulates for measuring angles.
- State and prove theorems about how angles are related: right, congruent, complementary, supplementary, vertical.
- Describe the hypothesis-conclusion form for theorems and postulates.
- Begin to practice writing mathematical proofs.

## 4–1 THE BASIC TERMS

An *angle* is a figure like one of these:

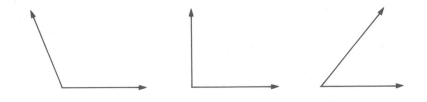

### Definitions

If two rays have the same end point, but do not lie on the same line, then their union is an *angle*. The two rays are called its *sides*, and their common end point is called its *vertex*. If the rays are $\overrightarrow{AB}$ and $\overrightarrow{AC}$, then the angle is denoted by $\angle BAC$ or $\angle CAB$.

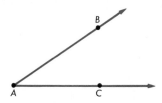

It makes no difference which side is mentioned first. In fact, it doesn't matter which point you name on each of the two sides, as long as the name of the vertex appears between the names of the other two points.

**Classroom Notes**

Angles are defined as geometric figures, that is, as sets of points. Note that the sides of an angle are required to be noncollinear rays. If ''zero angles'' were allowed, they would merely be rays; and if ''straight angles'' were allowed, they would merely be lines. It turns out not to be useful to regard rays and lines as angles, for the purposes of elementary geometry; furthermore, it leads to a certain amount of trouble. If rays are angles, then not every angle has an interior. If lines are angles, then each of the sides of the line can equally well be regarded as the interior. A further discussion of this is given in Section 4–3.

Note that when we draw a triangle, we have not necessarily drawn its angles because the triangle does not contain its angles. (There is nothing peculiar about this; in fact, the use of the possessive very seldom means that one thing contains another. Thus a city does not contain its suburbs, and a sword does not contain its sheath.) If we wish to draw the angles, we have to extend the sides and use arrowheads as shown in the figure below. Usually there is no need to do this, because it is obvious what the angles are supposed to be.

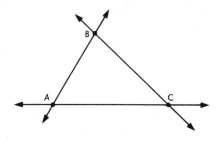

The definition of the *interior of an angle* should be formulated carefully. Consider a point *P* which is (obviously) in the interior of ∠*BAC*.

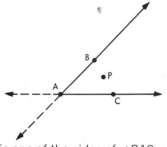

$\overrightarrow{AC}$ is one of the sides of ∠*BAC*, and $\overrightarrow{AC}$ is contained in $\overleftrightarrow{AC}$. By the Plane Separation Postulate, $\overleftrightarrow{AC}$ separates the plane of ∠*BAC* into two half-planes which can be distinguished as the side of $\overleftrightarrow{AC}$ that contains *B* and the side of $\overleftrightarrow{AC}$ that does not contain *B*. Observe that any point *P* in the interior of ∠*BAC* lies on the side of $\overleftrightarrow{AC}$ that contains *B*. Similarly any such point *P* also lies on the *C*-side of $\overleftrightarrow{AB}$. These two observations suggest the definition. Note that a point *P* which is *not* in the interior of ∠*BAC* does not satisfy the conditions of the definition.

This definition is not difficult; but it represents a degree of preciseness of expression that most students are not used to. See the paragraph that follows the definition of the interior of a triangle.

The angle in the figure on the left below could be described equally well as ∠*BAC*, ∠*DAE*, ∠*BAE*, and so on. However ∠*BCA* does *not* describe this angle, since the vertex of ∠*BCA* must be the point *C*. For ∠*BAC* we may, for short, write simply ∠*A*, if it is plain what the sides are supposed to be.

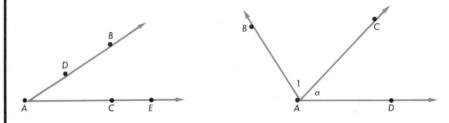

In figures such as the one on the right above, we may write numbers and letters inside angles, so that we can write ∠1 for ∠*BAC*, ∠*a* for ∠*CAD*, and so on.

Note that the sides of an angle are rays, not segments. Thus the figure on the left below is an angle, but the figure on the right is not.

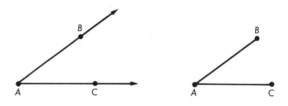

Of course, the figure on the right *determines* an angle, but that doesn't mean that it *is* one. (In the same way, a segment *determines* a line without *being* a line.)

The *interior* and the *exterior* of an angle are as indicated in the figure below.

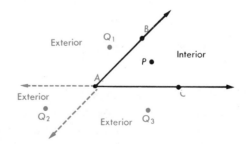

You should check the following definition against the figure to make sure that it really says what we have in mind.

## Definitions

The *interior* of ∠ *BAC* is the set of all points *P* in the plane of ∠ *BAC* such that (1) *P* and *B* are on the same side of $\overleftrightarrow{AC}$, and (2) *P* and *C* are on the same side of $\overleftrightarrow{AB}$. The *exterior* of ∠ *BAC* is the set of all points of the plane of ∠ *BAC* that lie neither on the angle nor in its interior.

This checks with the figure. For example, *P* is in the interior because it satisfies both (1) and (2). $Q_1$ is not in the interior; it satisfies (1) but not (2). $Q_2$ is not in the interior; it satisfies neither (1) nor (2). $Q_3$ satisfies (2) but not (1).

Note that we have defined the interior of an angle as the intersection of two half-planes. One of these is the side of $\overleftrightarrow{AC}$ that contains *B* and the other is the side of $\overleftrightarrow{AB}$ that contains *C*.

Note also that an angle separates all the points of the plane that are not on the angle into two sets, only one of which is convex. [*Query:* Which one is convex?]

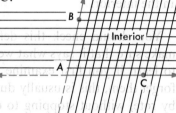

A *triangle* is a figure like one of these:

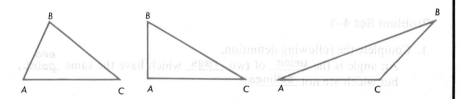

## Definitions

If *A*, *B*, and *C* are any three noncollinear points, then the union of the segments $\overline{AB}$, $\overline{AC}$, and $\overline{BC}$ is called a *triangle*, and is denoted by △ *ABC*. The points *A*, *B*, and *C* are called its *vertices*, and the segments $\overline{AB}$, $\overline{AC}$, and $\overline{BC}$ are called its *sides*. Every triangle △ *ABC* determines three angles, namely, ∠ *BAC*, ∠ *ABC*, and ∠ *ACB*. These are called the *angles* of △ *ABC*. The *perimeter* of a triangle is the sum of the lengths of its sides.

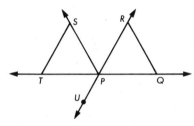

The *interior* and *exterior* of a triangle are as shown in the figure.

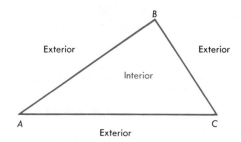

## Definitions

A point lies in the *interior* of a triangle if it lies in the interior of each of the angles of the triangle. A point lies in the *exterior* of a triangle if it lies in the plane of the triangle but does not lie on the triangle or in the interior.

You should check this definition against the figure, as before, to make sure that it says what we really mean. Definitions are much easier to learn if you first examine them in this manner. In fact, when you forget them, this is usually due to the fact that you tried to learn them by rote, without stopping to consider how they express the ideas that they are supposed to express.

### Problem Set 4–1

1. Complete the following definition.
   An angle is the __union__ of two __rays__ which have the same __point__, end
   but which are not __collinear__

2. Which of the following are correct names for the angle shown at the right?
   (a) ∠ACD      (b) ∠DAC
   (c) ∠C        (d) BCE
   (e) ∠BCE      (f) ∠ECB
   (g) ∠AEC      (h) DCA
   (i) ∠BDE

3. Are $\overrightarrow{GF}$ and $\overrightarrow{HG}$ the sides of ∠FGH? Explain.
   No, GF and GH are the sides of ∠FGH.

**4.** In the figure, points $K$, $P$, and $H$ are collinear. Name all five angles. ∠MPH, ∠HPG, ∠GPK, ∠KPM, ∠MPG

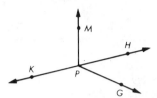

**5.** Given △$ABC$, are $\overline{AC}$ and $\overline{AB}$ the sides of ∠$A$? Explain. No, the sides of ∠A are $\overrightarrow{AC}$ and $\overrightarrow{AB}$, the rays containing the segments.

**6.** How many angles are determined by this figure? Name them. Which of them may be named by using the vertex letter?

**7.** Can two angles of a triangle ever have a common side? Explain. No

**8.** How many angles are in this figure? (There are more than six.) Twelve

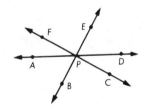

**9.** For the figure of Problem 8, describe

  (a) ∠$APB$ ∩ ∠$APE$. $\overrightarrow{PA}$

  (b) ∠$FPD$ ∩ ∠$APE$. {P}

  (c) ∠$APF$ ∩ ∠$DPE$. {P}

  (d) ∠$APC$ ∩ ∠$BPC$. $\overrightarrow{PC}$

**10.** Which points of the figure are in

  (a) the interior of ∠$CBA$? H,K,P

  (b) the exterior of ∠$EBC$? M,Q,S,T,R

  (c) the interior of ∠$ABD$? H,K,P

  (d) the interior of ∠$ABQ$? M

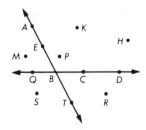

**11.** Is the vertex of an angle in the interior of the angle? in the exterior?
                                     No              No

**15.** No. $\angle CAB \cup \angle CBA$ includes the line $\overleftrightarrow{AB}$ and the rays $\overrightarrow{AC}$ and $\overrightarrow{BC}$, and $\triangle ABC$ is the union of three segments.

**22.** The sides of the angle determine two intersecting lines, which determine exactly one plane, by Theorem 3-4.

**25.** (a) Yes. Point $P$ is in the exterior of $\triangle ABC$ but in the interior of $\angle A$.

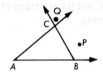

(b) Yes. Point $Q$ is in the exterior of $\triangle ABC$ and not in the interior of either $\angle A$, $\angle B$, or $\angle C$.

**26.** (a) Yes; $\angle AED$, $\angle BED$, and $\angle CED$ have a common side $\overrightarrow{ED}$.

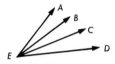

(b) Yes; as in (a).

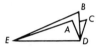

**28.** 12 triangles. [Note that there are $_6C_3 = \dfrac{6 \cdot 5 \cdot 4}{1 \cdot 2 \cdot 3} = 20$ different triplets of points which can be formed from the six points $P$, $R$, $H$, $M$, $D$, $K$, but four of these triplets ($PHM$, $PRK$, $MDR$, $HDK$) contain points which are collinear and four others ($PRD$, $PHD$, $PMD$, $PDK$) need $PD$ as a side.]

**31.** To show that $G$ is in the interior of $\triangle ABC$ it is necessary to show that $G$ is in the interior of each of the angles of $\triangle ABC$. Details are contained in the Solution Section.

---

12. For the figure on the right describe the intersection of

(a) the interior of $\angle SKV$ and the interior of $\angle TKP$. Interior of $\angle TKV$

(b) the interior of $\angle PKV$ and the interior of $\angle RKQ$. $\emptyset$

(c) the exterior of $\angle TKP$ and the exterior of $\angle SKQ$. Interiors of $\angle SKT$ and $\angle PKQ$

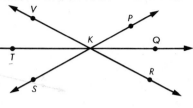

13. Is the following statement true for all points $A$, $B$, and $C$? $\triangle ABC = \overline{AB} \cup \overline{AC} \cup \overline{BC}$. Why? No. Only if $A, B,$ and $C$ are noncollinear

14. Name all the triangles in this figure. (There are more than four.) There are eight triangles.

| | |
|---|---|
| $\triangle ABE$ | $\triangle ACD$ |
| $\triangle ABC$ | $\triangle BCE$ |
| $\triangle ABD$ | $\triangle BCD$ |
| $\triangle AED$ | $\triangle CDE$ |

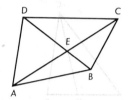

15. Is the following statement true? $\triangle ABC = \angle CAB \cup \angle CBA$. Why? NO

16. Into how many sets does a line separate a plane? Which postulate supports your answer? Two. Plane Separation Postulate

17. Into how many sets does an angle separate the plane that contains it? How many of them are convex sets? Two; one

18. Into how many regions does a triangle separate the plane of the triangle? How many are convex sets? Two; one

19. Into how many regions do the angles of a triangle separate the plane of the triangle? How many are convex sets? Seven; seven

20. Is a triangle a convex set? No

21. Is the interior of a triangle a convex set? is the exterior? Yes; No

---

22. Explain why the following statement is true.

Given an angle, there is exactly one plane that contains it.

23. Given $\overleftrightarrow{KA} \cap \overleftrightarrow{RM} = \{D\}$ and $K$-$D$-$A$ and $R$-$D$-$M$ in a plane $E$; a point $P$ is on the $M$-side of $\overleftrightarrow{KA}$ and on the $A$-side of $\overleftrightarrow{RM}$. $\overleftrightarrow{KA} \cup \overleftrightarrow{RM}$ separates $E$ into four regions. Which region contains the point $P$? The interior of $\angle MDA$

24. Given $\triangle ABC$ and a point $P$ in the interior of $\angle A$ and also in the interior of $\angle C$. What can you conclude about $P$? *P is in the interior of △ABC*

25. (a) Can a point be in the exterior of a triangle and in the interior of an angle of the triangle? Illustrate.

    (b) Can a point be in the exterior of a triangle and not in the interior of any angle of the triangle? Illustrate.

26. (a) Can three coplanar angles have a common side? Illustrate.

    (b) Can three noncoplanar angles have a common side? Illustrate.

27. For the figure on the left below describe
    (a) $\triangle ADE \cap \triangle BDE$. *DE*        (b) $\triangle EHK \cap \triangle HBE$. *EH, HK*
    (c) $\triangle EHB \cap \triangle EBD$. *EB, K*        (d) $\triangle CHB \cap \triangle ABE$. *EH, B*

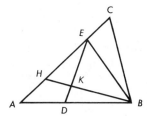
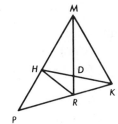

28. How many triangles are in the figure on the right above? (One way of attacking this problem is to write $PRHMDK$, then write all possible combinations of three letters, and check each combination with the figure.) *There are twelve triangles.*

---

29. Given $\triangle ABC$ and a point $P$; $P$ and $A$ are on the same side of $\overleftrightarrow{BC}$. $P$ and $B$ are on the same side of $\overleftrightarrow{AC}$.

    (a) Is $P$ in the interior of $\angle ACB$? *Yes*

    (b) Is $P$ in the interior of $\triangle ACB$? *Not necessarily*

30. Given $\triangle ABC$. A-D-B, B-E-C, C-D-F, and D-G-E.

    (a) Is $G$ in the interior or exterior of $\triangle ABC$? *Interior*

    (b) Does $\overrightarrow{BG}$ intersect $\overline{AC}$? *Yes*

    (c) $G$ and $F$ are on opposite sides of ___*$\overleftrightarrow{AB}$*___?

31. How can you justify your answer to part (a) of Problem 30?
                    *See Solution Section.*

## Preparation for Section 4-2

While a natural feature of this text is its frequent reference to concepts previously discussed whenever they are about to be used again, in a few instances we have suggested a more extensive review of ideas by including these ''Preparation Sections.''

### Answers to Preparation Problems

1. The three conditions necessary for the Ruler Postulate are the following:
   (1) To every point of the line there corresponds exactly one real number.
   (2) To every real number there corresponds exactly one point of the line.
   (3) The distance between any two points is the absolute value of the difference of the corresponding numbers.

## 4-2 MEASURING ANGLES

### Classroom Notes

Note that we distinguish, in the notation, between an angle and its measure. An angle and its measure are objects of quite different kinds: one is a set of points and the other is a real number.

   In teaching this section we suggest that you present each postulate as a formulation of a familiar and natural idea and show that the postulate is phrased so as to say what we want it to say accurately, but as briefly as possible. We recommend that you take two days to cover Section 4-2.

   **The Angle Measurement Postulate.** This postulate is analogous to the Distance Postulate; it tells us that angles can be measured with numbers, and that the measure is uniquely determined when the angle is named.

   There is, however, an important difference. Our postulates for distance are satisfied no matter what

---

## Preparation for Section 4-2

Before studying the next section you should answer these questions or review each topic mentioned.

1. What are the three conditions of the Ruler Postulate?

2. In a plane, how many sides does every line have? **Two**

3. Which property is a reason for the following:

   If $x = y + z$, then $x - y = z$? **Subtraction Property of Equality**

4. Must a point in the interior of an angle be coplanar with the angle? **Yes**

## 4-2 MEASURING ANGLES

Just as we measure segments with a ruler, so we measure angles with a protractor. Protractors commonly in use have the whole numbers from 0 to 180 arranged uniformly as in the figure below.

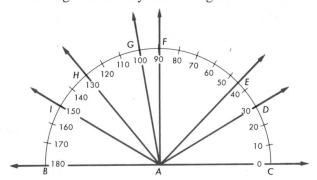

The unit of measure is called a *degree*. The number of degrees in an angle is called its *measure*. If there are $r$ degrees ($r°$) in $\angle PQR$, then we write

$$m\angle PQR = r.$$

This is pronounced "the measure of $\angle PQR = r$." From the markings on the protractor, we see that

$$m\angle CAD = 30, \qquad m\angle CAF = 90,$$
$$m\angle CAE = 45, \qquad m\angle CAG = 100,$$

and so on.

   Note that we don't need to use the degree sign when we write 30, 45, and so on, because the $m$ takes care of this: $m\angle PQR$ is the *number of degrees* in the angle.

Just as we found distances by subtraction, with a ruler, we can use subtraction to find the measures of angles. For example, we must have $m\angle DAE = 15$ because $15 = 45 - 30 = m\angle CAE - m\angle CAD$. The same device gives us $m\angle GAD = 100 - 30 = 70$.

Note that 180 is not the measure of any angle in the figure. (There is no such thing as $\angle BAC$, because $\overrightarrow{AB}$ and $\overrightarrow{AC}$ are collinear.) We can still subtract from 180, however, to get $m\angle BAI = 180 - 150 = 30$, $m\angle BAH = 180 - 130 = 50$, and so on.

The following postulates sum up the facts about protractors that we have just been using. In the figures illustrating these facts, we write $r°$, $s°$, and so on, to remind ourselves that these numbers are degree measures of angles.

**POSTULATE 11.**    The Angle Measurement Postulate

*To every angle  $\angle BAC$ there corresponds a real number between 0 and 180.*

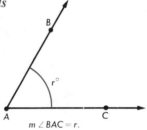

$m \angle BAC = r.$

**Definition**

The number given by the Angle Measurement Postulate is called the *measure* of $\angle BAC$, and is written $m\angle BAC$.

Anywhere we like, we can construct an angle with any measure between 0 and 180. Of course, if we start with a ray in a plane and a number $r$, we can construct our angle on either side of the line containing the ray.

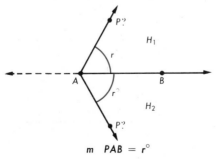

$m\ PAB = r°$

Hence we have the conditions of the following postulate.

unit we choose to use, because if all distances are multiplied by a positive constant, the Ruler Postulate continues to hold. But if the measures of all angles are multiplied by a constant greater than 1, then Postulate 11 no longer holds; and if they are multiplied by any positive constant *different from* 1, then Postulate 14 surely does not hold.

This means that these postulates are sufficient to determine that the unit of measurement is the degree. Thus to get radian measure we would have to change the statement of Postulate 11 and also change the definition of ''supplementary,'' replacing 180 by $\pi$ in each case.

In calculus, of course, degrees are useless and radians are obligatory. But in elementary geometry, one unit is as good as another, and it seemed preferable to use the unit which was already familiar.

Once it is agreed that the unit of measure is the degree, it may appear that the use of the degree sign is superfluous. But for some purposes it is useful. In the figure on the left, the degree sign tells us that $a$ is the *measure* of the angle, while on the right, the label tells us that the *angle itself* will be referred to as $\angle a$.

In the text, we speak of ''a 60° angle,'' ''a 90° angle,'' and so on. This is to avoid a needless departure from common speech.

**The Angle Construction Postulate.** All students know how to use a protractor to construct an angle with a specified measure; the Angle Construction Postulate incorporates this idea into our geometry.

**The Angle Addition Postulate.** Using a specific angle and measures such as 70, 30, and 40, observe for your class that if $D$ is in the interior of $\angle BAC$, then $m\angle BAC = m\angle BAD + m\angle DAC$. This is a fundamental property of angle measure and we formalize this observation as the Angle Addition Postulate.

It is important for the students to know that the Angle Addition Postulate can be used, without further explanation, to justify the computation of the measure of an angle by subtraction. For, if $D$ is in the interior of $\angle BAC$, then $m\angle BAC = m\angle BAD + m\angle DAC$, and consequently, $m\angle DAC = m\angle BAC - m\angle BAD$. Note finally that the Angle Addition Postulate makes essential use of the idea of the interior of an angle. However, we seldom give a formal proof that a point is in the interior of an angle before using the Angle Addition Postulate.

**POSTULATE 12.**   The Angle Construction Postulate

*Let $\overrightarrow{AB}$ be a ray on the edge of the half-plane $H$. For every number $r$ between 0 and 180 there is exactly one ray $\overrightarrow{AP}$, with $P$ in $H$, such that $m\angle PAB = r$.*

We can calculate measures of angles by addition and subtraction, using the following postulate.

**POSTULATE 13.**   The Angle Addition Postulate

*If $D$ is in the interior of $\angle BAC$, then*
$$m\angle BAC = m\angle BAD + m\angle DAC.$$

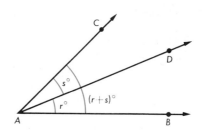

Note that Postulate 13 says that only *measures* of angles are added. Angles themselves, which are sets of points, can *not* be added; but their measures, which are numbers, can be added and subtracted.

By applying the Subtraction Property of Equality to the equation in Postulate 13, we get $m\angle DAC = m\angle BAC - m\angle BAD$.

Two angles form a *linear pair* if they look like this:

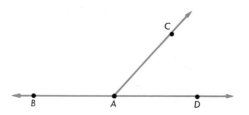

More precisely, we have the following definition.

### Definition

If $\overrightarrow{AB}$ and $\overrightarrow{AD}$ are opposite rays, and $\overrightarrow{AC}$ is any other ray, then $\angle BAC$ and $\angle CAD$ form a *linear pair*.

The following definition deals purely with angular measure. It says nothing at all about where the angles are.

### Definition

If the sum of the measures of two angles is 180, then the angles are called *supplementary*, and each is called a *supplement* of the other.

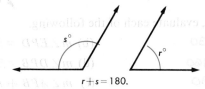

$$r + s = 180.$$

The angles are *allowed*, however, to form a linear pair, and in this case they are always supplementary.

**POSTULATE 14.**   The Supplement Postulate

*If two angles form a linear pair, then they are supplementary.*

### Problem Set 4–2

1. If $m\angle A = 63$ and $m\angle B = 117$, then $\angle A$ and $\angle B$ are said to be ____. *Supplementary*

2. If, in the figure on the left below, $m\angle QPS = 41$ and $m\angle QPM = 37$, what is $m\angle MPS$? What postulate supports your conclusion?
   $m\angle MPS = 78;\ AAP$

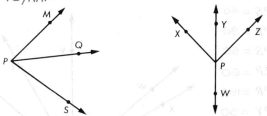

3. Given the figure to the right above with the points $Y$, $P$, $W$ collinear and $m\angle XPY = m\angle ZPY$.

   (a) Name two linear pairs.  $\angle WPX$ and $\angle XPY$; $\angle WPZ$ and $\angle ZPY$

   (b) Name three sets of supplementary angles.  $\angle WPX$ and $\angle XPY$; $\angle WPZ$ and $\angle ZPY$; $\angle WPX$ and $\angle ZPY$; $\angle WPZ$ and $\angle XPY$

---

**The Supplement Postulate.** It is important to clarify the distinction between a linear pair and a pair of supplementary angles. The definition of two supplementary angles depends solely on their measures, that is, the sum of their measures is 180. Two such angles may not intersect each other at all. In contrast, the angles forming a linear pair always have a common side, and contain a pair of opposite rays.

The Supplement Postulate states the obvious connection between these two concepts. Note that while the angles of a linear pair are always supplementary, two angles which are supplementary do not necessarily form a linear pair.

These postulates may be referred to, for short, as AMP, ACP, AAP, and SP. These are, of course, abbreviations of Angle Measurement Postulate, Angle Construction Postulate, Angle Addition Postulate, and Supplement Postulate.

4. Complete each sentence and state a definition or postulate to justify each answer. Given that *A-K-F* and *D* is a point not on $\overleftrightarrow{AF}$,

   (a) $\angle AKD$ and $\angle FKD$ form a ___linear pair___ .

   (b) $\angle AKD$ and $\angle FKD$ are ___supplementary___

   (c) $m \angle AKD + m \angle FKD =$ ___180___ .

5. In the figure, $\overleftrightarrow{GH}$ and $\overleftrightarrow{PQ}$ intersect, forming four angles.

   (a) If $b = 52$, what is $a$? 128

   (b) If $a = 110$, what are $b$, $c$, and $d$?
       b = 70, C = 110, d = 70

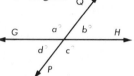

6. Using the figure, evaluate each of the following.

   (a) $m \angle APC$ = 30                  (b) $m \angle EPD$ = 30

   (c) $m \angle GPA$ = 160                 (d) $m \angle DPB$ = 35

   (e) $m \angle FPC$ = 90                  (f) $m \angle APB + m \angle BPE$ = 75

   (g) $m \angle HPG + m \angle FPC$ = 110  (h) $m \angle APC + m \angle CPH$ = 180

   (i) $m \angle FPA - m \angle DPA$ = 75   (j) $m \angle FPH - m \angle FPG$ = 20

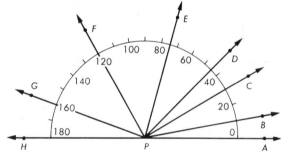

7. Use a protractor to evaluate each of the following.

   (a) $m \angle RPS$ = 40

   (b) $m \angle VPR$ = 90

   (c) $m \angle VPS$ = 50

   (d) $m \angle TRP$ = 60

   (e) $m \angle XPR$ = 150

   (f) $m \angle XPY$ = 30

   (g) $m \angle WPS$ = 100

   (h) $m \angle XPW$ = 10

   (i) $m \angle XPS$ = 110

   (j) $m \angle TPR + m \angle SPW$ = 60 + 100 = 160

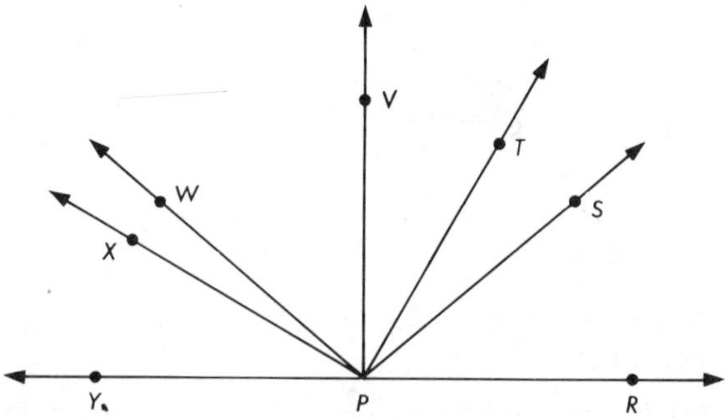

8. With practice you should be able to estimate the size of angles fairly accurately *without* using a protractor. Do *not* use a protractor to decide which angles shown have measures within the indicated ranges. Match the angles on the right with the appropriate range in the left column.

(a) $80 < x < 95$.

(b) $55 < x < 70$.

(c) $40 < x < 60$.

(d) $90 < x < 105$.

(e) $20 < x < 45$.

(f) $110 < x < 125$.

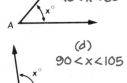

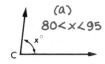

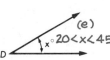

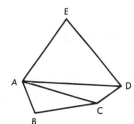

9. Using a straightedge and a protractor, construct angles having degree measures of 30, 60, 15, 90, 100, and 135.

10. Using only a straightedge and *not* a protractor, sketch angles whose measures are approximately 10, 30, 45, 60, 90, 120, 135, and 150. Then use a protractor to check your sketches.

11. In the plane figure,

(a) $m\angle CAB + m\angle DAC = m\angle$ __DAB__ .

(b) $m\angle EAD + m\angle DAC = m\angle$ __EAC__ .

(c) $m\angle EAD + m\angle DAB = m\angle$ __EAB__ .

(d) $m\angle EAC - m\angle DAC = m\angle$ __EAD__ .

12. In the figure for Problem 11,

(a) $m\angle EDA + m\angle CDA = m\angle$ __EDC__ .

(b) $m\angle EDA = m\angle$ __EDC__ $- m\angle CDA$.

(c) $m\angle ACD = m\angle$ __BCD__ $- m\angle$ __BCA__ .

(d) $m\angle EAD + m\angle DAC + m\angle CAB = m\angle$ __EAB__ .

13. If two supplementary angles have equal measures, what is the measure of each angle? 90

14. Determine the measure of the supplement of angles with the following measures.

(a) 80 100

(b) 48 132

(c) 144 36

(d) 25.5 154.5

(e) $n$ 180-n

(f) $n + k$ 180-(n+k) =180-n-k

(g) $180 - n$ n

(h) $90 - n$ 90+n

# Answers to Problems

**16.** $x = 3(180 - x)$
$4x = 3 \cdot 180$
$x = 135$

**17.** $x = (180 - x) + 24$
$2x = 204$
$x = 102$

**18.** (a) Definition of a linear pair
(b) Supplement Postulate
(c) Definition of supplementary angles
(d) To establish (d) we must repeat the argument for steps (a), (b), and (c).

**21.** If $C$ is in the interior of $\angle DAB$, then $m\angle CAB = m\angle DAB - m\angle DAC = 65 - 32 = 33$. If $D$ is in the interior of $\angle CAB$, then $m\angle CAB = m\angle CAD + m\angle DAB = 65 + 32 = 97$.

**24.** $2x = 5(180 - x) - 30$
$7x = 870$
$x = 124\frac{2}{7}$

**25.** $4x = 3(180 - x) + 7$
$7x = 547$
$x = 78\frac{1}{7}$

---

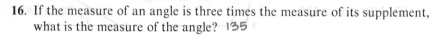

**15.** In the figure,

(a) $m\angle SPR + m\angle QPO = m\angle$ ___SPQ___.

(b) $m\angle RSQ + m\angle$ ___QSP___ $= m\angle RSP$.

(c) $m\angle POQ + m\angle POS =$ ___180___.

(d) $m\angle SRQ - m\angle SRO = m\angle$ ___ORQ___.

(e) $m\angle ROQ = 180 - m\angle$ ___SOR or 180−m∠POQ___.

(f) $SO + OQ =$ ___SQ___.

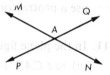

**16.** If the measure of an angle is three times the measure of its supplement, what is the measure of the angle? **135**

**17.** The measure of an angle is 24 more than the measure of its supplement. Find the measures of both angles. **102,78**

**18.** Given the figure, with $\overleftrightarrow{MN}$ and $\overleftrightarrow{PQ}$ intersecting at $A$, what postulates or definitions support each of the following statements?

(a) $\angle PAM$ and $\angle QAM$ form a linear pair.

(b) $\angle PAM$ and $\angle QAM$ are supplementary.

(c) $m\angle PAM + m\angle QAM = 180$.

(d) $m\angle QAM + m\angle QAN = 180$.

**19.** Given the figure with $A$-$B$-$D$, what properties, postulates, or definitions support each of the following statements?

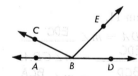

(a) $m\angle CBD = m\angle CBE + m\angle EBD$.  **AAP**

(b) $m\angle ABC + m\angle CBD = m\angle ABC + m\angle CBE + m\angle EBD$.  **AAP**

(c) $m\angle ABC + m\angle CBD = 180$.  **SP**

(d) $m\angle ABC + m\angle CBE + m\angle EBD = 180$.  **AAP, SP**

**20.** On the edge of a half-plane take points $M$, $K$, $A$ such that $M$-$A$-$K$. Take $\overrightarrow{AT}$ so that $m\angle TAK = 35$. In the same half-plane take $\overrightarrow{AV}$ such that $m\angle MAV = 85$. Measure $\angle TAV$ with a protractor. Does your finding agree with correct calculation? **m∠TAV= 60**

**21.** If, in a plane, $m\angle BAD = 65$ and $m\angle DAC = 32$, what is $m\angle CAB$? **33 or 97**

22. Artillery men in military service learn to use a unit of angle measure called a *mil*. A protractor based upon mils has angle measures between 0 and 3200, as indicated in the figure in which the inner scale is marked in degrees. Copy this figure and mark the number in mils, to the nearest mil, that corresponds to each 15 degree interval.

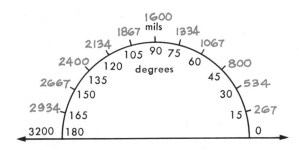

23. In certain mathematics courses it is convenient to use a unit of angle measure called a *radian*. A protractor like ours, but using radian measure, would have a scale running from 0 to $\pi$. Thus $\frac{1}{2}\pi$ radians would correspond to 90°. What would correspond to 30°? to 45°? to 60°? to 120°? to 135°? to 150°? $\frac{\pi}{6}, \frac{\pi}{4}, \frac{\pi}{3}, \frac{2\pi}{3}, \frac{3\pi}{4}, \frac{5\pi}{6}$

24. Twice the measure of an angle is 30 less than five times the measure of its supplement. What is the measure of the angle? $124\frac{2}{7}$

25. Four times the measure of an angle is 7 more than three times the measure of its supplement. What is the measure of the angle? $78\frac{1}{7}$

## HONORS PROBLEM

Why is the following statement true?

If a line $L$ intersects two sides of $\triangle ABC$ at $D$ and $E$ (and $D$ and $E$ are distinct from $A$, $B$, and $C$), then $L$ does not intersect the third side.

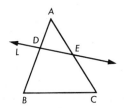

[*Hint*: Refer to Section 3–4, and show that $B$ and $C$ are on the same side of $L$.]

**Quiz**

Complete each of the following:

1. If $\overrightarrow{RS}$ and $\overrightarrow{RT}$ are opposite rays and $\overrightarrow{RQ}$ is any other ray then _____ form a linear pair.
　　(ans: $\angle SRQ$ and $\angle QRT$)
2. If the measure of an angle is $x$, then the measure of its supplement is _____ .
　　(ans: $180 - x$)
In this figure, $\overrightarrow{BA}$ and $\overrightarrow{BD}$ are opposite rays.

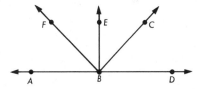

3. $m\angle ABE = m\angle ABF +$ _____
　　(ans: $m\angle FBE$)
4. $m\angle EBD - m\angle CBD =$ _____
　　(ans: $m\angle EBC$)
5. $180 - m\angle CBD =$ _____
　　(ans: $m\angle CBA$)

This section is merely looking ahead to some of the ideas presented in Chapter 17 on trigonometry. Students need to read this section for information only.

## 4–3   SOME REMARKS ON ANGLES

Angles, as we have defined them in this chapter, are simply sets of points, as shown in the figure. The order in which the sides of an angle are named makes absolutely no difference.

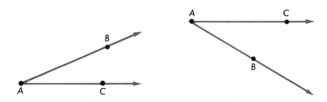

This is the simplest form of the idea of an angle. It is the idea that is needed for the purposes of this course. Later on, however, when you study trigonometry, the idea of an angle will appear in a different form. In trigonometry, it will make a difference which side of an angle is mentioned first:

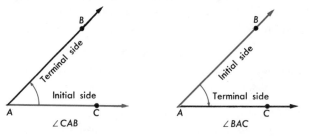

That is, in trigonometry, we distinguish between $\angle CAB$ and $\angle BAC$. In $\angle CAB$, $\overrightarrow{AC}$ is the *initial side* and $\overrightarrow{AB}$ is the *terminal side*. In $\angle BAC$, $\overrightarrow{AB}$ is initial and $\overrightarrow{AC}$ is terminal. Angles such as these are called *directed* angles. When we use directed angles, we allow "zero angles" and "straight angles."

We may think of a directed angle as the result of a rotation; we rotate the initial side until it falls on the terminal side. Rotations going counterclockwise are counted positively, and rotations going clockwise are counted negatively. Hence the indicated measures in the figures below.

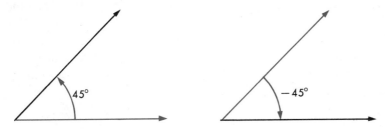

Because we can rotate in either direction as much as we want, numbers greater than 360 or less than −360 may arise as measures, like this:

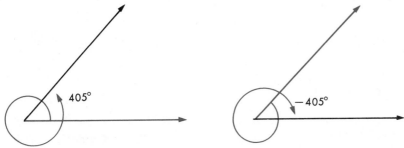

Note that this leads to a further complication: if a directed angle is known, then its measure is not determined. (If the measure is increased or decreased by 360, then the position of the terminal side is unchanged.)

In the study of directed angles, we very seldom use the degree as a unit of measure. Instead, we use the *radian*. To get an angle of radian measure 1, we draw a circle of radius 1, and measure off an arc of length 1. The circumference of this circle is $2\pi$. Thus a right angle has radian measure $\pi/2$, because it cuts off one-fourth of the circumference of the circle. A 45° angle has radian measure $\pi/4$, and so on.

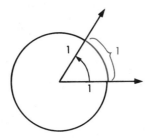

In this course, directed angles will not be used until Chapter 17, because they are not needed in elementary geometry. For example, the

## 4-4 PERPENDICULARS, RIGHT ANGLES AND RELATED ANGLES, CONGRUENT ANGLES

### Classroom Notes

At this point postulates and definitions seem, to students, to be accumulating at a staggering rate. Try to show the natural connections between ideas that make them easier to remember.

Note that we first define right angle and then perpendicularity; it is possible to define them in the opposite order.

We have chosen to define perpendicularity in the way it is commonly understood and used. Two relatively short segments that are a very great distance apart would not ordinarily be considered perpendicular even though the lines containing them were perpendicular. Thus condition (2) that the sets intersect, is included in the definition.

You may wish to read again the remarks in Section D, The Language of Congruence, on page T3 of the General Introduction.

It is important to use correctly the notation for measures of angles and for congruence. Random variations may easily arise: $\angle ABC$ for $m\angle ABC$, $ABC$ for $\angle ABC$, $\angle ABC = \angle DEF$ for $\angle ABC \cong \angle DEF$, $m\angle ABC \cong m\angle DEF$, and so on. Occasional errors are natural; but if they occur wholesale, the impression is conveyed that our symbolism merely alludes, in a vague sort of way, to what we have in mind, without ever meaning anything in particular. Obviously notation is a matter of convention. But unless we adopt *some* convention, and then follow it, we have no language in which to write briefly and clearly. A reasonable insistence that students adhere to these conventions will pay dividends in increased understanding.

angles of a triangle are never zero angles or straight angles, and there is no reasonable way of deciding in which direction they should go. To assign directions to them, we would have to proceed at random; and the random directions of the angles would be of no use to us, because they would be unrelated to the problems that we were working on. Similarly, in elementary geometry there is no advantage in using radian measure, and so we use degrees, which are more convenient and more familiar.

### 4-4 PERPENDICULARS, RIGHT ANGLES AND RELATED ANGLES, CONGRUENT ANGLES

The following definitions deal only with *measures* of the angles, and do not depend on their positions.

### Definitions

A *right angle* is an angle having measure 90. An angle with measure less than 90 is called *acute*. An angle with measure greater than 90 is called *obtuse*.

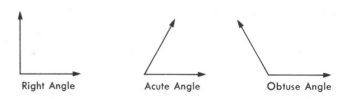

Right Angle          Acute Angle          Obtuse Angle

Thus a 38° angle is acute, and a 97° angle is obtuse.

### Definition

If the sum of the measures of two angles is 90, then they are called *complementary*, and each of them is called a *complement* of the other.

If $m\angle A = 43$ and $m\angle B = 47$, then $\angle A$ and $\angle B$ would be called complementary angles because $m\angle A + m\angle B = 90$. [*Queries*: What is the complement of a 52° angle? What is the supplement of a 52° angle?]

## Definition

Two angles with the same measure are called *congruent*.

Thus, if

$$m\angle ABC = m\angle DEF,$$

then $\angle ABC$ and $\angle DEF$ are congruent; and we write

$$\angle ABC \cong \angle DEF.$$

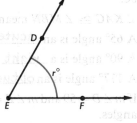

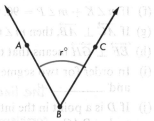

The symbol $\cong$ is pronounced
"is congruent to."

Note that the equation $m\angle ABC = m\angle DEF$ and the congruence
$\angle ABC \cong \angle DEF$ mean exactly the same thing. We can replace either
one of these by the other any time we want.

The following definitions deal with the relative positions of lines, rays,
and segments.

## Definition

Two *rays* are *perpendicular* if they are the sides of a right angle. Two
*lines* are *perpendicular* if they contain a pair of perpendicular rays.

If $\overrightarrow{AB}$ and $\overrightarrow{AC}$ are the sides of a right angle $\angle BAC$, then they are
called *perpendicular rays*, and we write $\overrightarrow{AB} \perp \overrightarrow{AC}$. We use the same term
and the same notation for any combination of lines, rays, or segments.
Thus, if

$$\overrightarrow{AB} \perp \overrightarrow{AC}, \quad \text{then} \quad \overline{AB} \perp \overrightarrow{AC}, \quad \overline{AB} \perp \overleftrightarrow{AC}, \quad \overleftrightarrow{AB} \perp \overline{AC},$$

and so on.

## Definition

Two sets are *perpendicular* if (1) each of them is a line, a ray, or a segment,
(2) they intersect, and (3) the lines containing them are perpendicular.

The definitions above are sometimes referred to as "Perpendiculars
form right angles."

Complete each sentence:

1. An angle whose measure is less than 90 is called an _____ angle.
   (ans: acute)
2. A right angle has measure _____ .
   (ans: 90)
3. The measure of an _____ angle is greater than 90.
   (ans: obtuse)
4. Two angles whose measures are equal are called _____ .
   (ans: congruent)
5. Two angles are complementary if _____ .
   (ans: the sum of their measures is 90)

**Problem Set 4-4**

1. Complete each sentence with the word(s) or symbol(s) that will make it true.

   (a) $\angle KAG \cong \angle MBN$ means the same as ___$m\angle KAG = m\angle MBN$___

   (b) A 65° angle is an __acute__ angle.

   (c) A 90° angle is a __right__ angle.

   (d) A 117° angle is an __obtuse__ angle.

   (e) If $m\angle D = 59$ and $m\angle E = 121$, then $\angle D$ and $\angle E$ are called __supplementary__ angles.

   (f) If $m\angle K + m\angle P = 90$, then $\angle K$ and $\angle P$ are called __complementary__ angles.

   (g) If $\overrightarrow{AC} \perp \overrightarrow{AB}$, then $m\angle CAB = $ __90__ .

   (h) $\overleftrightarrow{EF} \perp \overleftrightarrow{GH}$ means that the lines $\overleftrightarrow{EF}$ and $\overrightarrow{GH}$ are __Perpendicular__

   (i) In order for two segments to be perpendicular they must __intersect__ and _____ . __the lines containing them must be perpendicular__

   (j) If $D$ is a point in the interior of $\angle BAC$ and $\overrightarrow{AB} \perp \overrightarrow{AC}$, then $\angle DAB$ and $\angle DAC$ are __complementary__ angles.

2. In this problem, line segments are meant to be perpendicular if they look perpendicular. Pick out the pairs of perpendicular segments. If you believe that a pair is not perpendicular, state why. __In (c) and (f) the segments do not intersect.__

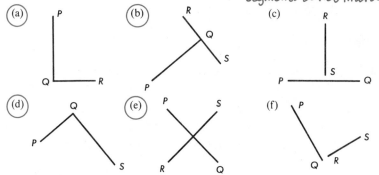

3. In this figure the angles have the indicated measures.

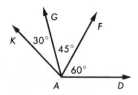

   (a) Name a pair of complementary angles. __∠KAG and ∠FAD__

   (b) Which postulate makes it possible to assert that $m\angle DAG = 105$? __Angle Addition Postulate__

4. Given the figure, with the vertex $M$ of right angle $\angle SMT$ on $\overleftrightarrow{AB}$, and $m\angle TMB = 50$, name a pair of

(a) perpendicular rays, if any occur. $\overrightarrow{MS}$ and $\overrightarrow{MT}$

(b) complementary angles, if there are any.
$\angle AMS$ and $\angle BMT$

(c) congruent angles, if any occur. None

(d) supplementary angles, if any occur.
$\angle AMS$ and $\angle SMB$,
$\angle AMT$ and $\angle TMB$

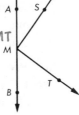

5. Complete each sentence to make it true.

(a) If $m\angle MPS = 39$ and $m\angle THN = 39$, then $\angle MPS$ is _congruent_ to $\angle THN$.

(b) The supplement of an acute angle is an _obtuse_ angle.

(c) The complement of an acute angle is an _acute_ angle.

(d) If $\angle ADK \cong \angle BEH$, the measures of the angles are _equal_.

6. Can an obtuse angle have a complement? No

7. If the measure of an angle is twice the measure of its complement, what is the measure of each angle? 60,30

8. Determine the measure of the complement of an angle whose measure is as follows.

(a) 20    (b) 68    (c) 46.5    (d) $n$ $\quad$ 90-n for 0<n<90    (e) $90 - n$ $\quad$ 45-n for 0<n<45    (f) $45 + n$
70        22         43.5                                n for 0<n<90

9. In a plane, $m\angle BAC = 58$ and $m\angle CAD = 32$. Is it true that $\angle BAC$ and $\angle CAD$ are complementary? Is it true that $\overrightarrow{AD} \perp \overrightarrow{AB}$? Yes ; No

10. Point $A$ is the end point of two perpendicular rays, $\overrightarrow{AB}$ and $\overrightarrow{AC}$. $D$ is a point in the interior of $\angle BAC$ and $E$ is a point in the exterior of $\angle BAC$ such that $\overrightarrow{AD} \perp \overrightarrow{AE}$.

(a) Name a pair of complementary angles, if any occur.
$\angle EAC$ and $\angle CAD$ or $\angle EAB$ and $\angle BAD$, $\angle BAD$ and $\angle DAC$

(b) Name a pair of supplementary angles, if there are any.
$\angle BAE$ and $\angle DAC$ or $\angle EAC$ and $\angle DAB$, $\angle BAC$ and $\angle DAE$

(c) Name a pair of congruent angles, if any occur.
$\angle EAC$ and $\angle BAD$ or $\angle EAB$ and $\angle CAD$, $\angle BAC$ and $\angle DAE$

11. What is the measure of an angle if the measure of its supplement is 39 more than twice the measure of its complement? 39

12. What is the measure of an acute angle if twice the measure of its supplement is 24 more than five times the measure of its complement? 38

13. The sum of the measures of an acute angle and an obtuse angle is 140. The sum of twice the supplement of the obtuse angle and three times the complement of the acute angle is 340. What are the measures of the angles? 130,10

Answers to Problems

10. Note that there are two cases to consider, as shown below.

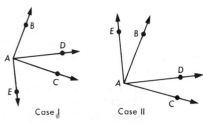

Case I          Case II

The first answer is for Case I and the second for Case II. The third answer is true in either case.

11. $(180 - x) - 2(90 - x) = 39$
$\qquad\qquad\qquad x = 39$

12. $2(180 - x) = 5(90 - x) + 24$
$\qquad\qquad 3x = 114$
$\qquad\qquad\;\; x = 38$

13. $\qquad\qquad\qquad x + y = 140$
$2(180 - x) + 3(90 - y) = 340$
$\qquad\quad -2x - 3y = -290$
$\qquad\qquad\qquad\quad x = 130$
$\qquad\qquad\qquad\quad y = 10$

## Classroom Notes

The ideas in this section are suggested by the properties of equality for real numbers. For most students these ideas are not difficult. You may wish to discuss the following:

If the meaning of congruence for segments is analogous to the meaning of congruence for angles, how would you define congruence for segments? Is it an equivalence relation? Why?

## Explanation for Problems

Problems 7, 8, and 9 in particular begin to build student awareness of a dependent sequence of steps as we move closer to student construction of logical proofs.

## 4–5   EQUIVALENCE RELATIONS

Angles may be congruent, of course, without being the same angle. Nevertheless, congruence is like equality in certain ways which are useful to note. Equality between numbers has the following properties:

(1) Reflexive Property: $a = a$, for every $a$.
(2) Symmetric Property: If $a = b$, then $b = a$.
(3) Transitive Property: If $a = b$ and $b = c$, then $a = c$.

The relation of congruence between angles has the same properties.

(1) Reflexive Property: $\angle A \cong \angle A$, for every $\angle A$.
(2) Symmetric Property: If $\angle A \cong \angle B$, then $\angle B \cong \angle A$.
(3) Transitive Property: If $\angle A \cong \angle B$ and $\angle B \cong \angle C$,
    then $\angle A \cong \angle C$.

To see this, all we need to do is to translate each of these statements into the language of angular measure: (1) says that $m\angle A = m\angle A$. (2) says that if $m\angle A = m\angle B$, then $m\angle B = m\angle A$. (3) says that if $m\angle A = m\angle B$ and $m\angle B = m\angle C$, then $m\angle A = m\angle C$.

A relation that is reflexive, symmetric, and transitive is called an equivalence relation. Thus we have found that the following is true:

### Theorem 4–1

**Congruence between angles is an equivalence relation.**

### Problem Set 4–5

**1.** Name the properties of equality illustrated by each example below.

(a) If $r = s$ and $s = t$, then $r = t$. Transitive
(b) If $KM = PQ$, then $PQ = KM$. Symmetric
(c) If $a + b = 180$ and $m + n = 180$, then $a + b = m + n$. and Symmetric Transitive
(d) $CD = CD$. Reflexive
(e) If $AB + BC = AC$, then $AC = AB + BC$. Symmetric
(f) $m \angle GHK = m \angle KHG$. Reflexive

**2.** Name the property of congruence illustrated by each geometric example below.

(a) If $\angle BAC \cong \angle DEG$, then $\angle DEG \cong \angle BAC$. Symmetric
(b) If $\angle DBC \cong \angle DBC$ and $\angle RST \cong \angle RST$. Reflexive
(c) If $\angle GIM \cong \angle OUR$, then $\angle OUR \cong \angle GIM$. Symmetric
(d) If $\angle D \cong \angle K$ and $\angle M \cong \angle K$, then $\angle D \cong \angle M$.
     Symmetric and Transitive

3. In this figure it is given that $\angle a \cong \angle c$ and $\angle c \cong \angle e$. Why is $\angle a \cong \angle e$?
By the Transitive Property

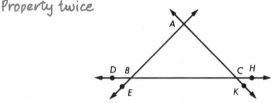

4. In this figure, given that $\angle ACH \cong \angle BCK$ and $\angle CBE \cong \angle BCK$ and $\angle CBE \cong \angle ABD$, why is $\angle ACH \cong \angle ABD$?
By the Symmetric Property once and the Transitive Property twice

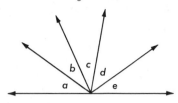

5. Is the relation "$<$" for numbers an equivalence relation? Why?
No. It is neither symmetric nor reflexive.

6. Is every angle congruent to itself? Why? Yes, $m\angle A = m\angle A$, so $\angle A \cong \angle A$ for every $\angle A$.

7. In the figure $\overleftrightarrow{AB} \cap \overleftrightarrow{CD} = \{P\}$. Justify each statement below with the appropriate definition, postulate, property, or theorem. These statements form a dependent sequence of steps.

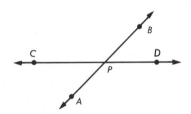

  (a) $\angle APC$ and $\angle BPC$ form a linear pair and $\angle BPD$ and $\angle BPC$ form a linear pair. Definition of linear pair

  (b) $\angle APC$ and $\angle BPC$ are supplementary and $\angle BPD$ and $\angle BPC$ are supplementary. Supplement Postulate

  (c) $m\angle APC + m\angle BPC = 180$ and $m\angle BPD + m\angle BPC = 180$. Def. of Supp. angles

  (d) $m\angle APC + m\angle BPC = m\angle BPD + m\angle BPC$. Trans. and Symm. Properties

  (e) $m\angle APC = m\angle BPD$. Subtr. Prop. of Equality

  (f) $\angle APC \cong \angle BPD$. Definition of congruence

8. In the figure, $\angle 3$ and $\angle 4$ form a linear pair, $\angle 1 \cong \angle 5$, and $\angle 2 \cong \angle 6$. Give a reason for each statement in the sequence below.

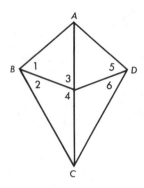

(a) $m\angle 1 = m\angle 5$ and $m\angle 2 = m\angle 6$.  Def. of congruent angles
(b) $m\angle ADC = m\angle 5 + m\angle 6$.  AAP
(c) $m\angle 5 + m\angle 6 = m\angle 1 + m\angle 2$.  APE
(d) $m\angle ADC = m\angle 1 + m\angle 2$.  Transitivity
(e) $m\angle 1 + m\angle 2 = m\angle ABC$.  AAP
(f) $m\angle ADC = m\angle ABC$.  Transitivity
(g) $\angle ADC \cong \angle ABC$.  Def. of congruent angles

9. In the figure, $\angle RPQ \cong \angle TPS$. Give a reason for each statement in the sequence below.

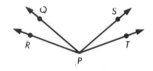

(a) $m\angle RPQ = m\angle TPS$.  Def. of congruent angles
(b) $m\angle QPS = m\angle QPS$.  Reflexive Property
(c) $m\angle RPQ + m\angle QPS = m\angle TPS + m\angle QPS$.  APE
(d) $m\angle RPQ + m\angle QPS = m\angle RPS$.  AAP
(e) $m\angle RPS = m\angle TPS + m\angle QPS$.  Transitivity
(f) $m\angle TPS + m\angle QPS = m\angle QPT$.  AAP
(g) $m\angle RPS = m\angle QPT$.  Transitivity
(h) $\angle RPS \cong \angle QPT$.  Def. of congruent angles

## 4–6　SOME THEOREMS ABOUT ANGLES

It is easy to see that the following four theorems are true by recalling the definitions of the terms that are used.

### Theorem 4–2

*If the angles in a linear pair are congruent, then each of them is a right angle.*

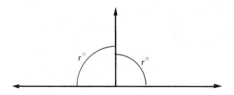

[*Hint*: If they are congruent, they have the same measure *r*. Now show that *r* must be 90.]

### Theorem 4–3

*If two angles are complementary, then both are acute.*

We know that $90 = m\angle B + m\angle C$ (Why?) and that $m\angle B > 0$ and $m\angle C > 0$ (Why?). Now apply Theorem 2–2.

### Theorem 4–4

*Any two right angles are congruent.*

### Theorem 4–5

*If two angles are both congruent and supplementary, then each is a right angle.*

[*Query*: How is Theorem 4–5 different from Theorem 4–2?]

Up to now we have said very little about how you should begin writing out proofs. We present the next theorem in such a style that you can use it as a pattern in writing proofs of your own. If you use this two-column form, it is easier to organize your work, and it is easier to remember that every time you make a statement in a proof, you are

---

### 4–6 SOME THEOREMS ABOUT ANGLES

**Classroom Notes**

Theorems 4–2, 4–3, 4–4, and 4–5 are mostly trivial consequences of the definitions. It is in this section and the next section, however, after approximately four weeks of preliminary work, that students encounter the first theorems in geometry for which they should be responsible:

**Theorem 4–6.** Supplements of congruent angles are congruent.

**Theorem 4–7.** Complements of congruent angles are congruent.

**Theorem 4–8.** Vertical angles are congruent.

These theorems are extremely useful and their proofs, while simple, are not trivial. Remember that up to this point we have simply been establishing the raw material of geometry and while we have sometimes offered reasoned arguments to support our assertions, we have not asked students to deal seriously with the idea of proof. We recommend that you have the students learn the proofs of Theorems 4–6, 4–7, and 4–8. Note that in Section 4–6 we discuss some conventions about proof and establish some elementary facts about angles. The matter of writing a proof will be elaborated on in Section 4–9. Throughout the rest of Chapter 4, however, we are more concerned with introducing the subject to students than with their complete mastery of technique.

## Questions for Discussion

**1.** Is the Supplement Theorem used for proving two angles
  (a) supplementary,
  (b) complementary, or
  (c) congruent?

**2.** Is the Complement Theorem used for proving two angles
  (a) supplementary,
  (b) complementary, or
  (c) congruent?

supposed to cite a reason. You should study this proof to try to see the logical order in the sequence of statements. We use the term "given" to refer to facts from the "if" clause of the theorem on which we can base our reasoning process. The symbol $\therefore$ means "therefore."

**Theorem 4–6.**  The Supplement Theorem

*Supplements of congruent angles are congruent.*

**Restatement.** If (1) $\angle A \cong \angle B$, (2) $\angle A$ and $\angle C$ are supplementary, and (3) $\angle B$ and $\angle D$ are supplementary, then (4) $\angle C \cong \angle D$.

### Proof

| Statements | Reasons |
|---|---|
| 1. $\angle C$ is supplementary to $\angle A$. | 1. Given |
| 2. $m\angle C + m\angle A = 180.$ | 2. Definition of supplementary |
| 3. $\angle D$ is supplementary to $\angle B$. | 3. Given |
| 4. $m\angle D + m\angle B = 180.$ | 4. Definition of supplementary |
| 5. $\therefore m\angle C + m\angle A = m\angle D + m\angle B.$ | 5. Transitive Property of Equality |
| 6. But $m\angle A = m\angle B.$ | 6. Given, Definition of congruent angles |
| 7. $\therefore m\angle C = m\angle D.$ | 7. Subtraction Property of Equality |
| 8. $\angle C \cong \angle D.$ | 8. Definition of congruent angles |

Note that before we started proving this theorem, we first restated it. This is a device which will often be useful later. Whenever we can, we shall state theorems in words, using very little notation or none at all. The theorems are then easier to read and easier to remember. In the restatement, we introduce the notation that will be used in the proof.

The figure given for Theorem 4–6 shows a very special case. Two angles may be supplementary without being lined up in such a way as to make it obvious to the eye that they are supplementary, like this:

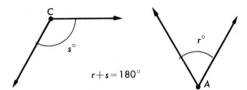

$r + s = 180°$

Usually a figure is only an illustration of a theorem or a problem. You should not get the idea that the figures given in this book are in each case the *only* correct ones.

The proof of Theorem 4–7 is very much like the proof of Theorem 4–6, and you ought to be able to write it out yourself, using the preceding proof as a pattern. In fact you will be asked to do this in Problem 6 of the following problem set. Let the figure help you. Make your own restatement of the theorem.

**Theorem 4–7.**    The Complement Theorem

### *Complements of congruent angles are congruent.*

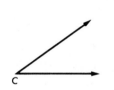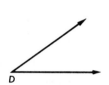

### Problem Set 4–6

1. $\angle 1 \cong \angle 2$ and $\angle 1$ is supplementary to $\angle 2$. What conclusion follows? ∠1 and ∠2 are right angles
What postulate, definition, or theorem supports this conclusion? Theorem 4-5

2. $\angle A$ and $\angle B$ are complementary. What else do you know about $\angle A$ and $\angle B$? What is your reason? Both are acute. Theorem 4-3

3. Complete each sentence.
   (a) If $\angle P$ and $\angle Q$ are complementary, then $m\angle P + m\angle Q = $ __90__.
   (b) If $\angle T$ and $\angle R$ are right angles, then $\angle T \underline{\ \cong\ } \angle R$.
   (c) If $\angle A \cong \angle H$ and $\angle D \cong \angle H$, then __∠A ≅ ∠D__

4. If $\angle M$ is supplementary to $\angle K$, $\angle P$ is supplementary to $\angle Q$, and $\angle Q \cong \angle M$, what is true of $\angle K$ and $\angle P$? What statement supports your conclusion? ∠K ≅ ∠P. Theorem 4-6

## Answers to Problems

**6.**

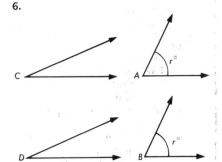

**Restatement.** If (1) $\angle A \cong \angle B$, (2) $\angle A$ and $\angle C$ are complementary, and (3) $\angle B$ and $\angle D$ are complementary, then (4) $\angle C \cong \angle D$.

**Proof.**

1. $\angle C$ is complementary to $\angle A$. (Given)
2. $m\angle C + m\angle A = 90$. (Definition of complementary)
3. $\angle D$ is complementary to $\angle B$. (Given)
4. $m\angle D + m\angle B = 90$. (Definition of complementary)
5. $\therefore m\angle C + m\angle A = m\angle D + m\angle B$. (Transitive Property)
6. But $m\angle A = m\angle B$. (Given, definition of congruent angles)
7. $\therefore m\angle C = m\angle D$. (Subtraction Property of Equality)
8. $\angle C \cong \angle D$. (Definition of congruent angles)

**7. Restatement.** If (1) $\angle A$ is a right angle and (2) $\angle B$ is a right angle, then (3) $\angle A \cong \angle B$.

**Proof.**

1. $m\angle A = 90$. (Given, definition of right angle)
2. $m\angle B = 90$. (Given, definition of right angle)
3. $m\angle A = m\angle B$. (Transitivity of Equality)
4. $\angle A \cong \angle B$. (Definition of congruent angles)

**8.** By the Supplement Theorem, angles supplementary to congruent angles are congruent. But any angle is congruent to itself by the Reflexive Property of Congruence, and so angles supplementary to the same angle are congruent.

---

**5.** If $\angle PAM$ and $\angle MAJ$ are complementary and $\angle KAJ$ and $\angle MAJ$ are complementary, why is $\angle KAJ \cong \angle PAM$?
Theorem 4-7 and Reflexive property

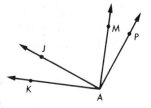

**6.** Write a two-column proof of Theorem 4–7, copying the statement of the theorem and the figure, and making a restatement.

**7.** Prove Theorem 4–4.

**8.** Explain how the Reflexive Property of Congruence and the Supplement Theorem can be used to prove that two angles supplementary to the same angle are congruent.

**9.** Provide a reason for each step in the proof of this problem. Given: The plane figure has $\overrightarrow{BE} \perp \overrightarrow{AC}$ and $\angle ABG \cong \angle CBD$.
Prove: $\angle GBE \cong \angle DBE$.

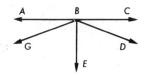

### Proof

| STATEMENTS | REASONS |
|---|---|
| 1. $\overrightarrow{BE} \perp \overrightarrow{AC}$. | 1. Given |
| 2. $\angle ABE$ and $\angle CBE$ are right angles. | 2. Def. of perpendicular |
| 3. $m\angle ABE = 90 = m\angle CBE$. | 3. Def. of right angle |
| 4. $m\angle ABG + m\angle GBE = m\angle ABE$. $m\angle CBD + m\angle DBE = m\angle CBE$. | 4. Angle Add. Postulate |
| 5. $m\angle ABG + m\angle GBE = 90$. $m\angle CBD + m\angle DBE = 90$. | 5. Transitive and Symmetric Properties |
| 6. $\angle GBE$ is complementary to $\angle ABG$. $\angle DBE$ is complementary to $\angle CBD$. | 6. Def. of complementary |
| 7. $\angle ABG \cong \angle CBD$. | 7. Given |
| 8. $\therefore \angle GBE \cong \angle DBE$. | 8. Theorem 4-7 |

**10.** In this figure, $\overrightarrow{BA}$ and $\overrightarrow{BE}$ are opposite rays, $\angle ABG \cong \angle KBG$, and $\angle KBD \cong \angle DBE$. Find $m\angle GBD$. [*Hint:* Let $m\angle ABG = x$ and $m\angle DBE = y$.]
$x + x + y + y = 180$
$m\angle GBD = x + y = 90$

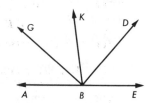

# 4–7  VERTICAL ANGLES

When two lines intersect, they form four angles. In the figure, $\angle 1$ and $\angle 3$ are called *vertical angles*, and $\angle 2$ and $\angle 4$ are called *vertical angles*. That is:

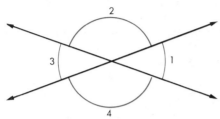

### Definition

Two angles are *vertical angles* if their sides form two pairs of opposite rays.

In the figure, it looks as though the vertical angles are congruent, and in fact this is always the case, as is shown in the next theorem.

**Theorem 4–8.**   The Vertical Angle Theorem

***Vertical angles are congruent.***

**Restatement.**   If $\angle 1$ and $\angle 2$ are vertical angles, then $\angle 1 \cong \angle 2$.

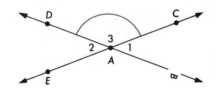

### Proof

| STATEMENTS | REASONS |
|---|---|
| 1. $\angle 1$ and $\angle 2$ are vertical angles. | 1. Given |
| 2. $\overrightarrow{AC}$ and $\overrightarrow{AE}$ are opposite rays, and $\overrightarrow{AB}$ and $\overrightarrow{AD}$ are opposite rays. | 2. Definition of vertical angles |
| 3. $\angle 1$ and $\angle 3$ form a linear pair, and $\angle 2$ and $\angle 3$ form a linear pair. | 3. Definition of linear pair |
| 4. $\angle 1$ is supplementary to $\angle 3$, and $\angle 2$ is supplementary to $\angle 3$. | 4. Supplement Postulate |
| 5. $\angle 3 \cong \angle 3$. | 5. Reflexive Property |
| 6. $\angle 1 \cong \angle 2$. | 6. Supplement Theorem |

## Quiz

**1.** If two lines intersect and the measure of one of the angles formed is 32, what are the measures of the other angles?
(ans: 148, 32, 148)

**2.** In the figure ∠2 is complementary to ∠4 and $m\angle 1 = 132$. Find the measures of the other angles.

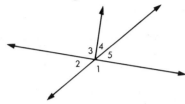

(ans: $m\angle 2 = 48$, $m\angle 3 = 90$, $m\angle 4 = 42$, $m\angle 5 = 48$)

**3.** Three coplanar lines intersect at a single point forming ∠1, ∠2, ∠3, ∠4, ∠5, and ∠6 consecutively. Let $m\angle 1 = 37$ and $m\angle 5 = 98$.

(a) What are the measures of the other angles?
(ans: $m\angle 2 = 98$, $m\angle 3 = 45$, $m\angle 4 = 37$, $m\angle 6 = 45$)

(b) Name a pair of complementary angles, if any.
(ans: ∠3 and ∠6)

(c) Name two pairs of congruent angles.
(ans: ∠1 and ∠4, ∠2 and ∠5, ∠3 and ∠6)

In the figure for the next theorem, the little square at the vertex of ∠1 indicates that ∠1 is a right angle, that is, that the lines are perpendicular. This is given. You ought to be able to give the reason for each step of the proof.

### Theorem 4–9

*If two lines are perpendicular, they form four right angles.*

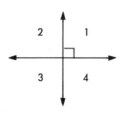

### Proof

| STATEMENTS | REASONS |
|---|---|
| 1. $L_1 \perp L_2$. | 1. Given |
| 2. ∠1 is a right angle. | 2. Definition of perpendicular |
| 3. $m\angle 1 = 90$. | 3. Def. of right angle |
| 4. ∠2 is supplementary to ∠1. | 4. Supplement Postulate |
| 5. $m\angle 2 + 90 = 180$. | 5. Definition of supplementary |
| 6. $m\angle 2 = 90$. | 6. Subtraction Property of Equality |
| 7. ∠2 is a right angle. | 7. Def. of right angle |
| 8. ∠3 is a right angle. | 8. Vertical Angle Theorem |
| 9. ∠4 is a right angle. | 9. Vertical Angle Theorem |

### Problem Set 4–7

**1.** (a) If two lines intersect, how many pairs of vertical angles are formed? Two

(b) If the measure of any one of the angles in (a) is 62, what are the measures of the other angles? 118, 62, 118

(c) If all four angles in (a) are congruent, what is the measure of each? 90

**2.** How many pairs of opposite rays are shown in this figure? How many pairs of vertical angles? Name them. Three. Six, ∠1 and ∠4, ∠2 and ∠5, ∠3 and ∠6, ∠AGE and ∠BGD, ∠AGC and ∠FGD, ∠FGB and ∠EGC.

3. In a figure, what symbol is used to indicate that two lines are perpendicular? A small square at the vertex of a right angle

4. What previous theorem is important to the proof of the Vertical Angle Theorem? The Supplement Theorem (Theorem 4-6)

5. In the figure on the left below, three coplanar lines intersect at the same point. Given that $a = 85$ and $e = 30$, find $b, c, d,$ and $f$.
$b \approx 30, c = f = 65, d = 85$

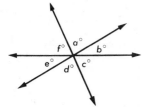 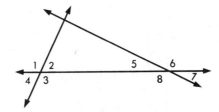

6. Given the figure on the right above with $\angle 2$ complementary to $\angle 5$, and $m \angle 1 = 126$, find the measure of each numbered angle $m \angle 1 = m \angle 3 = 126, m \angle 2 = m \angle 4 = 54, m \angle 5 = m \angle 7 = 36, m \angle 6 = m \angle 8 = 144$

7. In the figure on the left below, if $A$-$D$-$B$, $m \angle ADE = 55$ and $m \angle BCD = 33$, what is $m \angle CDE$? What justifies your answer? $m \angle CDE = 92$.
Angle Addition Postulate and definition of linear pair

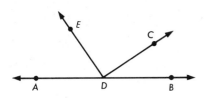 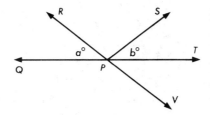

8. Given the figure on the right above as marked, find $m \angle RPS, m \angle QPV, m \angle SPV,$ and $m \angle RPT.$ $180 - (a+b); 180-a; a+b; 180-a$

9. Supply the missing reasons in the proof of Theorem 4–9.

10. Given a line $\overleftrightarrow{AB}$, separating a plane into two half-planes $H_1$ and $H_2$; $P$ is a point of $H_1$ such that $m \angle PAB = 30$. If $Q$ is a point of $H_2$ such that $\angle QAB \cong \angle PAB$, then $B$ lies in the ___interior___ of $\angle PAQ$ and $m \angle PAQ = $ ___60___. If $\overrightarrow{AQ}$ is opposite to $\overrightarrow{AP}$, then $\angle PAB$ is ___supplementary___ to $\angle QAB$ and $m \angle QAB = $ ___150___.

---

10. Case I. If $Q$ is a point of $H_2$ such that $\angle QAB \cong \angle PAB$, then $B$ lies in the interior of $\angle PAQ$ and $m \angle PAQ = $ <u>60</u>.

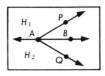

Case II. If $\overrightarrow{AQ}$ is opposite to $\overrightarrow{AP}$, then $\angle PAB$ is <u>supplementary</u> to $\angle QAB$ and $m \angle QAB = $ <u>150</u>.

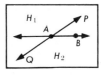

11. In the figure, the planes $E$ and $F$ intersect in $\overleftrightarrow{AB}$. $\overleftrightarrow{GH}$ and $\overleftrightarrow{KM}$ lie in $F$ and intersect $\overleftrightarrow{AB}$ at $P$.

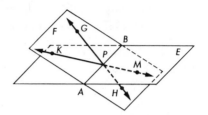

(a) Name two pairs of vertical angles. *∠GPK and ∠HPM, ∠GPB and ∠HPA, etc.*

(b) Name two pairs of supplementary angles. *∠KPA and ∠APM, ∠KPB and ∠BPM, etc.*

(c) If $\overrightarrow{GH} \perp \overrightarrow{AB}$, name two pairs of complementary angles. *∠APK and ∠HPM, ∠BPM and ∠GPK, etc.*

## 4–8 THEOREMS IN THE FORM OF HYPOTHESIS AND CONCLUSION

Every theorem is a statement that *if* a certain thing is true, *then* something else is also true. For example, Theorem 4–3 says that if two angles are complementary, then they both are acute. The *if* part of a theorem is called the *hypothesis*; it states what is *given*. The *then* part is called the *conclusion*; it states what is to be *proved* on the basis of what is given. We can write Theorem 4–3 in the following way.

**Theorem 4–3**

> *Hypothesis: two angles are complementary.*
> *Conclusion: they both are acute.*

Similarly, we can write Theorem 4–4 as follows.

**Theorem 4–4**

> *Hypothesis: two angles are right angles.*
> *Conclusion: they are congruent.*

Postulates are like theorems, except that they will not be proved. Most of the postulates can be put in the same *if . . . then* form as theorems. For example, the Angle Addition Postulate can be written as follows.

## POSTULATE 13.   The Angle Addition Postulate

*Hypothesis: D is in the interior of ∠BAC.*
*Conclusion: m ∠BAC = m ∠BAD + m ∠DAC.*

In some cases, the hypothesis-conclusion form is not natural or useful, as, for example, in the Ruler Postulate.

It is not necessary, of course, that all theorems be stated in the hypothesis-conclusion form. Regardless of the form in which the theorem is written; it ought to be clear what is given and what is to be proved. Most of the time, however, we ought to be *able* to state a theorem in the hypothesis-conclusion form if we want to, because if we can't, the chances are that we don't understand exactly what the theorem says.

*A word of warning:* The word *if* is often used in stating definitions, but this should not be confused with the use of *if* in if-then statements of postulates and theorems. In definitions the word *if* is being used in a special way. In any definition, when two statements are connected by the word *if*, then the two statements are considered to be completely equivalent. Thus, if we know that two angles are vertical angles, we can conclude that their sides form two pairs of opposite rays; and if we know that the sides of two angles form two pairs of opposite rays, we can conclude they are vertical angles. The word *if* is not used in this way in postulates and theorems. Only in definitions does the word *if* mean *is equivalent to*.

**Problem Set 4–8**

1. Identify the hypothesis and the conclusion for each of the following statements.

   (a) If [two planes intersect,] then [their intersection is a line]
   (b) If [$a = b$ and $b = c$] then [$a = c$.]
   (c) [$a + c = b + c$] if [$a = b$]

2. Write each of the following statements as an "If . . . then" statement.

   (a) Any three noncollinear points lie in exactly one plane.

   (b) Two angles which form a linear pair are supplementary.

   (c) Supplements of congruent angles are congruent.

Answers to Problems

2. (a) If three points are noncollinear, then they lie in exactly one plane.
   (b) If two angles form a linear pair, then they are supplementary.
   (c) If two angles are supplements of congruent angles, then they are congruent.

## 4-9 WRITING UP PROOFS

### Background Material

There are several reasons for discussing proof at this point in our development of geometry:

(1) In Sections 4-6 and 4-7 students encountered the first important theorems in geometry; having several models at our disposal, we are now in a position to examine a proof: (i) we can draw the distinction between hypotheses and conclusion; (ii) we can explain that a proof is a chain of assertions leading from our hypotheses to our conclusion; (iii) we can insist that for each of these assertions we must give a reason which is either a definition, postulate, theorem, or an assertion established earlier in the course of the proof; and (iv) we can establish the format for writing a proof.

(2) We felt that having covered the basic theorems on angles it would be good to give students some practice in the application of these theorems. There are many interesting facts we can establish here, using simply the basic theorems on angles. Their proofs do not depend on congruence of triangles, and so there is no reason to postpone them until after the discussion of congruent triangles.

(3) Students have to learn how to *use* the elementary theorems on angles. In discussing the proofs of Examples 1 and 2 of this section and Problems 7 through 18 of the problem set the teacher can establish the correct use of these theorems:

(i) Example 1 and Problem 9 show how to use the Angle Addition Postulate to add and subtract the measures of angles.

### Preparation for Section 4-9

Before studying the next section you should answer these questions or review each topic mentioned.

**1.** State the Addition Property of Equality. *See page 22.*

**2.** State the Angle Addition Postulate. *See page 86.*

**3.** What definition does this sentence illustrate:

$$AB + BC = AC?$$ *B is between A and C.*

**4.** Define perpendicularity for rays. *If $\overrightarrow{AB}$ and $\overrightarrow{AC}$ form a right angle, then they are perpendicular.*

**5.** What are the properties of an equivalence relation? *Reflexivity, Symmetry, and transitivity*

**6.** Distinguish between the terms *complementary* and *supplementary*.

### 4-9  WRITING UP PROOFS

Very soon, writing your own proofs will be a fairly large part of your problem work. There is no one best way to write up a proof. The important thing is that you make your reasoning clear, as well as correct. Learning to do this is not always easy, and so we offer here a few suggestions that experience has shown are helpful.

(1) Copying the figure and copying the full hypothesis and conclusion can help you in understanding the problem and may provide some insight into how you can solve it.

(2) Using the two-column form for the proof makes it easier to organize your work when you are first learning.

(3) Make the figure large enough so you can see clearly how its parts are related. The straight edge of a ruler or the edge of a file card can help you make the figures more meaningful. Neatness is often an aid to clearer thinking.

The examples which follow, and many of the problems in the problem set, state simple geometric facts that can be proved using the postulates, theorems, and definitions we now have. Some of these simple facts will occur as minor steps in later problems. Giving careful attention to them here will make your work that much easier later on.

In these examples and problems you may assume the figures are coplanar unless otherwise stated. You may also use the figures to indicate collinearity of points, the order of points on a line, and the location of points in the interior of angles.

Since one learns how to write up proofs by practicing first on simple problems, you should study these examples and then try to make your proofs of the problems look like these.

*Example 1*

*Given*: $\triangle ABC$ and $\triangle ABD$, as in the figure below, with $\angle DAB \cong \angle DBA$ and $\angle CAD \cong \angle CBD$.

*Prove*: $\angle CAB \cong \angle CBA$.

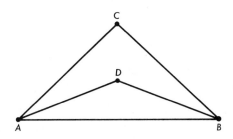

**Proof**

| STATEMENTS | REASONS |
|---|---|
| 1. $m\angle DAB = m\angle DBA$. | 1. Given, Definition of congruent angles |
| 2. $m\angle CAD = m\angle CBD$. | 2. Given, Definition of congruent angles |
| 3. $m\angle DAB + m\angle CAD = m\angle DBA + m\angle CBD$. | 3. Addition property of equality |
| 4. $\therefore m\angle CAB = m\angle CBA$. | 4. Angle Addition Postulate |
| 5. $\therefore \angle CAB \cong \angle CBA$. | 5. Definition of congruent angles |

Part of learning to write up proofs is learning how much detail to include to make the reasoning clear. It is neither reasonable nor possible to set any hard and fast rule that can provide reliable guidance. In Example 1 you may have noticed that we combined some steps in going from Statement 3 to Statement 4. You are asked to examine this reasoning in closer detail in Problems 2 and 3 of the Problem Set.

(ii) Example 2 and Problem 8 show how to use the definition of "between" to add and subtract distances.

(iii) Problem 7 shows how to use the definition of a right angle and the definition of perpendicular.

(iv) Problems 10 and 11 show how to use the Supplement Postulate and the Supplement Theorem.

(v) Problems 13 and 16 show how to use the Vertical Angle Theorem.

(vi) Problem 15 suggests how to use the Complement Theorem.

In the Solution Section we suggest some conventions for the use of the elementary theorems on angles. There is a great deal of variation possible in the application of these theorems, especially in respect to the telescoping of statements and reasons. You should establish the form you want your students to follow. The rules ought to depend on the maturity level of the class (or of the individual student) and on the style in which you prefer to work. For these reasons, the text avoids stating rules for the form in which proofs should be written. The proofs given in the text are written in a variety of styles, partly to suit the context and partly to furnish a variety of models.

*Example 2*

*Given*: The collinear points $A$, $B$, $C$, $D$, as in the figure below, with $AD = CB$.

*Prove*: $AC = DB$.

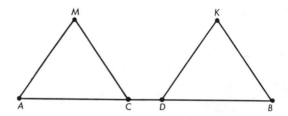

## Proof

| STATEMENTS | REASONS |
|---|---|
| 1. $A$, $B$, $C$, $D$ are collinear points. | 1. Given |
| 2. $AC + CD = AD$. | 2. Definition of between |
| 3. $CD + DB = CB$. | 3. Definition of between |
| 4. $AD = CB$. | 4. Given |
| 5. $\therefore AC + CD = CD + DB$. | 5. Transitive property of equality |
| 6. $\therefore AC = DB$. | 6. Subtraction property of equality |

**Problem Set 4–9**

**1.** Copy all of the following and complete the proof.

Given: $m \angle A = 38$, and $m \angle B = 52$.

Prove. $\angle A$ is complementary to $\angle B$.

## Proof

| STATEMENTS | REASONS |
|---|---|
| 1. $m \angle A = \underline{\ 38\ }$. | 1. Given |
| 2. $m \angle B = \underline{\ 52\ }$. | 2. Given |
| 3. $m \angle A + m \angle B = \underline{\ 90\ }$. | 3. Add. Prop. of Equality |
| 4. $\angle A$ is complementary to $\angle B$. | 4. Def. of complementary |

2. The proof in Example 1 of this section can be written in greater detail as shown below. Supply a reason for each step.

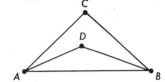

1. $\angle DAB \cong \angle DBA.$ Given

2. $\angle CAD \cong \angle CBD.$ Given

3. $m \angle DAB = m \angle DBA.$ Definition of congruent angles

4. $m \angle CAD = m \angle CBD.$ Definition of congruent angles

5. $m \angle DAB + m \angle CAD = m \angle DBA + m \angle CBD.$ Addition property of Equality

6. $m \angle DAB + m \angle CAD = m \angle CAB.$ Angle Addition Postulate

7. $m \angle DBA + m \angle CBD = m \angle CBA.$ Angle Addition Postulate

8. $m \angle CAB = m \angle CBA.$ Transitivity and Symmetry

9. $\angle CAB \cong \angle CBA.$ Definition of congruent angles

3. In the proof of Example 1 the use of the Angle Addition Postulate depends upon an observable, but unstated, condition of the figure. What is this condition? D is in the interior of ∠CAB.

4. In Example 2, what unstated fact from the figure is used in the proof?
   A-C-D and C-D-B

5. In Example 2, what is subtracted in going from Step 5 to Step 6?
   CD is subtracted.

6. The statement "$x = y = z$" can be called a *continued equality*. Write a continued equality to show how the transitive property of an equivalence relation applies in Example 2. AC+CD = AD=CB=CD+DB

7. Copy *all* of the following and complete the proof by supplying the missing reasons.

Given: Rays $\overrightarrow{AB}$, $\overrightarrow{AC}$, and $\overrightarrow{AD}$, with $C$ in the interior of $\angle BAD$, and with $m \angle BAC + m \angle CAD = 90$.
Prove: $\overrightarrow{AB} \perp \overrightarrow{AD}$.

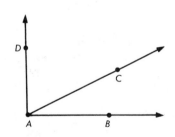

**Proof**

| STATEMENTS | REASONS |
|---|---|
| 1. $C$ is in the interior of $\angle BAD$. | 1. Given |
| 2. $m \angle BAD = m \angle BAC + m \angle CAD$. | 2. Angle Add. Postulate |
| 3. $m \angle BAC + m \angle CAD = 90$. | 3. Given |
| 4. $\therefore m \angle BAD = 90$. | 4. Transitivity |
| 5. $\therefore \angle BAD$ is a right angle. | 5. Def. of right angle |
| 6. $\therefore \overrightarrow{AB} \perp \overrightarrow{AD}$. | 6. Def. of perpendicular |

8. Copy *all* of the following and complete the proof.

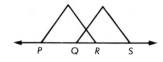

Given: The figure with $PQ = RS$.
Prove: $PR = QS$.

**Proof**

| STATEMENTS | REASONS |
|---|---|
| 1. $PQ = RS$. | 1. Given |
| 2. $PQ + QR = QR + RS$. | 2. Add. Prop. of Equality |
| 3. ∴ $PR = QS$ | 3. Definition of between and Transitive property of equality. |

9. Copy *all* of the following and complete the proof.

Given: The figure with
$m \angle CAB = m \angle CBA$ and
$m \angle p = m \angle q$.
Prove: $\angle x \cong \angle y$.

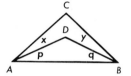

**Proof**

| STATEMENTS | REASONS |
|---|---|
| 1. $m \angle CAB = m \angle CBA$. | 1. Given |
| 2. ∴ $m \angle x + m \angle p = m \angle y + m \angle q$. | 2. The Angle Addition Postulate and Transitivity |
| 3. $m \angle p = m \angle q$. | 3. Given |
| 4. ∴ $m \angle x = m \angle y$. | 4. Subtr. Prop. of Equality |
| 5. ∴ $\angle x \cong \angle y$. | 5. Def. of congruence |

10. Copy and complete the proof.
Given: The figure with $\angle PMN \cong \angle PNM$.
Prove: $\angle CMP \cong \angle DNP$.

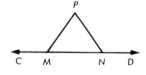

**Proof**

| STATEMENTS | REASONS |
|---|---|
| 1. $\angle CMP$ is supplementary to $\angle PMN$. | 1. Two angles forming a linear pair are supplementary. |
| 2. $\angle DNP$ is supp. to $\angle PNM$ | 2. Same as reason 1 |
| 3. $\angle PMN \cong \angle PNM$ | 3. Given |
| 4. $\angle CMP \cong \angle DNP$. | 4. Supplement Theorem |

**11.** Copy and complete the proof.

Given: The figure with $\angle DBC \cong \angle ECB$.

Prove: $\angle ABC \cong \angle ACB$.

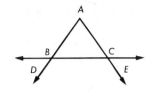

**Proof**

| STATEMENTS | REASONS |
|---|---|
| 1. $\angle ABC$ is supp. to $\angle DBC$. | 1. Supplement Postulate |
| 2. $\angle ACB$ is supp. to $\angle ECB$ | 2. Supplement Postulate |
| 3. $\angle DBC \cong \angle ECB$. | 3. Given |
| 4. $\therefore$ $\angle ABC \cong \angle ACB$ | 4. Supplement Theorem |

**12.** Copy and complete the proof.

Given the figure with $\angle 2 \cong \angle 3$.

Prove that $\angle 1 \cong \angle 4$.

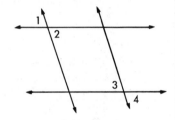

**Proof**

| STATEMENTS | REASONS |
|---|---|
| 1. $\angle 1 \cong \angle 2$. | 1. Vertical Angle Theorem |
| 2. $\angle 2 \cong \angle 3$. | 2. Given |
| 3. $\angle 3 \cong \angle 4$ | 3. Vertical Angle Theorem |
| 4. $\therefore \angle 1 \cong \angle 4$. | 4. Transitivity |

**13.** Copy and supply the reasons.

Given: $\overleftrightarrow{AB}$, $\overleftrightarrow{CD}$, and $\overleftrightarrow{EF}$ intersect at $K$; $a = c$.

Prove: $b = c$.

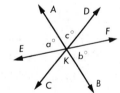

**Proof**

| STATEMENTS | REASONS |
|---|---|
| 1. $\overleftrightarrow{AB}$ and $\overleftrightarrow{EF}$ intersect at $K$. | 1. Given |
| 2. $\angle AKE \cong \angle BKF$. | 2. Vertical Angle Theorem |
| 3. $a = b$. | 3. Def. of congruent angles |
| 4. $a = c$. | 4. Given |
| 5. $b = c$. | 5. Transitivity |

Complete the proof by filling in the blanks:

**1.** Given the figure with $\angle c \cong \angle m$. Prove that $\angle a \cong \angle p$.

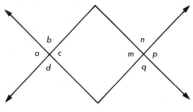

*Proof*

| | |
|---|---|
| 1. _____ | 1. _____ |
| 2. $\angle c \cong \angle m$ | 2. _____ |
| 3. _____ | 3. _____ |
| 4. $\therefore \angle a \cong \angle p$ | 4. _____ |

(ans: 1. $\angle a \cong \angle c$    1. Vertical Angle Theorem

    2. $\angle c \cong \angle m$    2. Given

    3. $\angle m \cong \angle p$    3. Vertical Angle Theorem

    4. $\therefore \angle a \cong \angle p$    4. Transitivity)

**2.** Supply a proof:

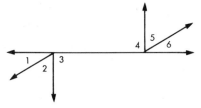

Given the figure with
   $\angle 1$ complementary to $\angle 2$,
   $\angle 5$ complementary to $\angle 6$,
  and $\angle 2 \cong \angle 5$.
Prove that $\angle 1 \cong \angle 6$.
(ans: 1. $\angle 1$ is complementary to $\angle 2$.
    (Given)
    2. $\angle 5$ is complementary to $\angle 6$.
    (Given)
    3. $\angle 2 \cong \angle 5$ (Given)
    4. $\therefore \angle 1 \cong \angle 6$ (The Complement Theorem)

**14.** Copy and complete the proof.

Given: $\overrightarrow{AD} \perp \overrightarrow{FB}$ and $\angle BAC \cong \angle DAE$.

Prove: $\angle DAC \cong \angle FAE$.

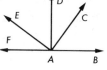

**Proof**

| STATEMENTS | REASONS |
|---|---|
| 1. $\overrightarrow{AD} \perp \overrightarrow{FB}$. | 1. Given |
| 2. $\angle DAF$ and $\angle DAB$ are right angles. | 2. Def. of Perpendicular |
| 3. $m\angle DAF = \underline{90}$ and $m\angle DAB = \underline{90}$. | 3. Definition of right angle |
| 4. $m\angle DAF = m\angle DAE + \underline{m\angle EAF}$. $m\angle DAB = \underline{m\angle DAC} + \underline{m\angle CAB}$. | 4. Angle Addition Postulate |
| 5. $\therefore m\angle DAE + m\angle EAF = 90$. $m\angle DAC + m\angle CAB = 90$. | 5. Transitivity and Symmetry |
| 6. $\angle DAE$ and $\angle EAF$ are complementary, $\angle DAC$ and $\angle CAB$ are complementary. | 6. Definition of complementary angles |
| 7. $\underline{\angle CAB \cong \angle DAE}$ | 7. Given |
| 8. $\therefore \angle DAC \cong \angle EAF$. | 8. Complement Theorem |

**15.** Copy and complete the proof.

Given the figure with $\angle w$ complementary to $\angle z$ and $\angle x$ a right angle.

Prove that $\angle t \cong \angle y$.

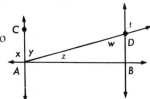

**Proof**

| STATEMENTS | REASONS |
|---|---|
| 1. $\angle x$ is a right angle. | 1. Given |
| 2. $\therefore \angle BAC$ is a $\underline{right\ angle}$. | 2. Theorem $\underline{4\text{-}9}$ |
| 3. $m\angle BAC = 90$. | 3. Def. of right angle |
| 4. $m\angle BAC = m\angle y + m\angle z$. | 4. Angle Addition Postulate |
| 5. $\therefore m\angle y + m\angle z = \underline{90}$. | 5. Transitivity |
| 6. $\therefore \angle y$ is $\underline{complementary\ to\ \angle z}$ | 6. Definition of complementary angles |
| 7. But $\angle w$ is complementary to $\angle z$. | 7. Given |
| 8. $\therefore \angle w \cong \angle y$. | 8. Complement Theorem |
| 9. $\underline{\angle w \cong \angle t}$ | 9. Vertical Angle Theorem |
| 10. $\therefore \angle t \cong \angle y$. | 10. Transitivity |

**16.** Copy and supply a proof.

Given: The figure with $\angle ABC \cong \angle ACB$.

Prove: $\angle DBF \cong \angle ECG$.

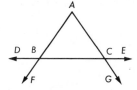

**17.** Copy and supply a proof.

Given the figure with $\overrightarrow{MC} \perp \overrightarrow{AB}$, $\overrightarrow{ND} \perp \overrightarrow{AB}$, and $\angle x \cong \angle y$.

Prove that $\angle w \cong \angle z$.

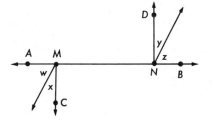

**18.** $\overleftrightarrow{CD}$ and $\overleftrightarrow{EF}$ intersect $\overleftrightarrow{AB}$ at points $P$ and $Q$, respectively, such that $A$–$P$–$Q$, $P$–$Q$–$B$, $C$–$P$–$D$, and $E$–$Q$–$P$. $C$ and $E$ are on the same side of $\overleftrightarrow{AB}$. If $\angle CPQ \cong \angle PQF$, prove that $\angle APD \cong \angle BQE$. (Here you must draw your own figure, write out the "given" and "to prove," and supply a full proof.)

## CHAPTER REVIEW

In items 1 through 15, complete each of the statements given.

**1.** To every angle there corresponds a real number between ____0____ and ____180____, called the measure of the angle.

**2.** The instrument used to measure angles is a _protractor_

**3.** If the sum of the measures of two angles is 90, then each angle is a _complement_ of the other.

**4.** An angle with measure less than 90 is called _acute_.

**5.** An angle with measure greater than 90 is called _obtuse_.

**6.** Two angles formed by the union of two opposite rays and a third ray having the same end point are called a _linear pair_

**7.** Angles whose measures are equal are called _congruent_ angles.

**8.** Two angles which are complementary must each be _acute_.

---

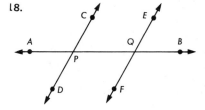

9. If two angles are congruent, their supplements are _congruent_.

10. Two angles which are both congruent and supplementary must each be _right angles_

11. Every triangle has _three_ sides and _three_ angles; a triangle contains its _sides_, but does not contain its _angles_.

12. The sum of the measures of two complementary angles is _90_, and the sum of the measures of two supplementary angles is _180_.

13. The sum of the measures of two _acute_ angles is always less than 180, and the sum of the measures of two _obtuse_ angles is always less than 360.

14. If the sides of two angles are opposite rays, the angles are called _vertical angles_.

15. A point $M$ is in the interior of $\angle GHK$ if $M$ and _G_ lie on the same side of $\overleftrightarrow{HK}$ and if $M$ and _K_ lie on the same side of $\overleftrightarrow{GH}$.

Items 16 through 25 refer to the figure below. (Points that look collinear are meant to be collinear.)

16. How many triangles are in this figure? 8

17. Is $m\angle BFC = m\angle BFD$? Yes

18. Is $\angle BFC = \angle BFD$? Yes

19. Is $\angle FDB \cong \angle EDC$? Yes

20. Name the angle supplementary to $\angle ABF$. $\angle FBC$

21. $m\angle AGB + m\angle BGF =$ _m$\angle AGF$_.

22. $m\angle GFC + m\angle DFE =$ _180_.

23. Name a set of vertical angles. $\angle FDE$ and $\angle BDC$, $\angle FDB$ and $\angle EDC$

24. If $\angle GBF$ is complementary to $\angle FBE$, then $\overline{GB}$ and $\overline{BE}$ must be _Perpendicular_.

25. How many angles are indicated in the figure? 24

26. Name the three properties of an equivalence relation.
    Reflexive, Symmetric, Transitive

27. If $\angle A \cong \angle B$ and $\angle B \cong \angle C$, then $\angle A \cong \angle C$. This is an example of the _transitive_ property of congruence.

**28.** For $\triangle ABC$, $\angle ACB \cong \angle BCA$. Which property of congruence is a reason for this statement? *Reflexive*

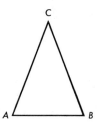

**29.** For $\triangle ABC$, if $\angle A \cong \angle B$, then $\angle B \cong \angle A$. This is an illustration of which property of congruence? *Symmetric*

**30.** The fact that congruence between angles is an equivalence relation is proved by using the fact that *equality* between *real numbers* is an equivalence relation.

**31.** State the theorem which is the basis for proving the Vertical Angle Theorem. *Supplements of congruent angles are congruent.*

**32.** Given the figure with $\overrightarrow{GA}$ opposite to $\overrightarrow{GE}$ and $\overrightarrow{GB} \perp \overrightarrow{GC}$, complete the proof that $\angle AGB$ is complementary to $\angle EGC$.

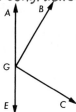

### Proof

| STATEMENTS | REASONS |
|---|---|
| 1. $\overrightarrow{GA}$ is opposite to $\overrightarrow{GE}$. | 1. *Given* |
| 2. $\angle AGB$ is supplementary to $\angle BGE$. | 2. Supplement Postulate |
| 3. $m\angle AGB + m\angle BGE = 180$. | 3. *Def. of supp. angles* |
| 4. $\overrightarrow{GB} \perp \overrightarrow{GC}$. | 4. *Given* |
| 5. $m\angle BGC = 90$. | 5. Definitions of perpendicular and right angle |
| 6. $m\angle BGE = m\angle EGC + 90$. | 6. *Angle Addition Postulate* |
| 7. $m\angle AGB + m\angle EGC + 90 = 180$. | 7. *Additive, Transitive and Symmetric properties of Equality* |
| 8. $m\angle AGB + m\angle EGC = 90$. | 8. *Subtra. Prop. of Equality* |
| 9. $\angle AGB$ is complementary to $\angle EGC$. | 9. *Def. of complementary angles* |

**33.** Is the following a correct restatement of the Angle Construction Postulate? No

> Given a ray $\overrightarrow{RS}$ and a number $k$ between 0 and 180, there is exactly one ray $\overrightarrow{RP}$ such that $m \angle SRP = k$.

**34.** Given the figure with $\angle 2$ and $\angle 3$ supplementary, prove that $\angle 1 \cong \angle 4$.

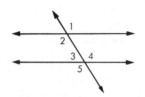

**Proof**

| STATEMENTS | REASONS |
|---|---|
| 1. $\angle 1 \cong \angle 2$. | 1. Vertical Angle Theorem |
| 2. $\angle 2$ is supp. to $\angle 3$. | 2. Given |
| 3. $\angle 4$ is supp. to $\angle 3$. | 3. Supplement Postulate |
| 4. $\angle 2 \cong \angle 4$. | 4. Supplement Theorem |
| 5. $\therefore \underline{\angle 1 \cong \angle 4}$. | 5. Transitivity |

**35.** If, in the figure, $\angle b \cong \angle c$, prove that $\angle a \cong \angle d$.

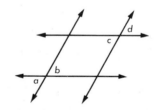

**Proof**

| STATEMENTS | REASONS |
|---|---|
| 1. $\angle a \underline{\cong \angle b}$. | 1. Vertical Angle Theorem |
| 2. $\angle b \cong \angle c$ | 2. Given |
| 3. $\angle c \underline{\cong \angle d}$. | 3. Vertical Angle Theorem |
| 4. $\therefore \underline{\angle a \cong \angle d}$ | 4. Transitivity |

**George David Birkhoff (1884–1944)**

G. D. Birkhoff was one of the most versatile and productive mathematicians of his generation. In his lifetime he wrote one hundred and ninety research papers, in various branches of pure and applied mathematics. His collected works fill three large volumes. He also wrote several books, on mathematics and the theory of relativity.

The postulates for geometry used in this book are modifications of a set of postulates due to Birkhoff. For several centuries, the idea of measurement, for both segments and angles, has been a central idea in geometry. Birkhoff's postulates introduce this idea at the outset; they describe the methods which in fact everybody uses. Thus, while Birkhoff's postulates were not among his great original ideas, they nonetheless greatly contributed to clarity.

The treatment of congruence in this book is rather different from the conventional ones. It is designed to bring the underlying ideas to the surface and make them explicit.

In practice, when we say that two triangles are congruent, this is nearly always because we want to infer that a pair of corresponding sides (or a pair of corresponding angles) is congruent. To draw such conclusions, it is not enough to know that the triangles are congruent. We also need to know what corresponds to what.

Moreover, if we want to prove that two triangles are congruent, we need to set up a matching scheme between the vertices of the first triangle and those of the second, and observe that the matching scheme "works," by using SAS, ASA, or SSS. Thus the idea of a correspondence is crucial both in establishing triangle congruences and in using them. In Chapter 5, this crucial idea is made explicit. See page 130 for the definition of the statement, $\triangle ABC \cong \triangle DEF$: it means that the triangles are congruent *under the correspondence*

$$A \leftrightarrow D,$$
$$B \leftrightarrow E,$$
$$C \leftrightarrow F.$$

There is no need to repeat here the discussion in Section 5–2 of the text. But a few observations are in order.

(1) Under the convention that we have just described, the formula gives full information: we can read off the pairs of corresponding sides and angles, without further reference to a figure.

(2) The task of writing the formula $\triangle ABC \cong \triangle DEF$ correctly, under our convention, is never an additional task: in practice, if you

# CHAPTER 5

# Congruence

## Objectives...

- Use the congruence postulates for triangles in proofs.
- Learn properties of isosceles triangles and equilateral triangles.
- Learn the meaning of converse theorems.
- Learn how to write proofs.

## 5–1 THE IDEA OF A CONGRUENCE

Roughly speaking, two geometric figures are congruent if they have exactly the same size and shape. For example, in the figure below, all three triangles are congruent.

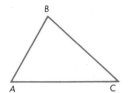 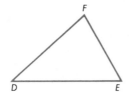 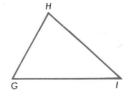

One way of describing the situation is to say that any one of these triangles can be moved onto any other one in such a way that it fits exactly. Thus, to show what we mean by saying that two triangles are congruent, we have to explain which points are supposed to go where. For example, to move $\triangle ABC$ onto $\triangle DFE$, we should put $A$ on $E$, $B$ on $F$, and $C$ on $D$. We can write the pairs of corresponding vertices as follows.

$$A \leftrightarrow E \quad B \leftrightarrow F \quad C \leftrightarrow D.$$

To describe the congruence of the first triangle and the third, we should match up the vertices like this:

$$A \leftrightarrow G \quad B \leftrightarrow H \quad C \leftrightarrow I.$$

How would you match up the vertices to describe the congruence of the second triangle with the third?

(3) A clear understanding of congruences as correspondences permits us to use the simplest possible proof of the Isosceles Triangle Theorem (page 154).

### Planning the Chapter

Because this chapter is the most important of the text, a chart is shown below to help you plan the chapter more efficiently. A review and test is planned following Section 5–6 to divide the long chapter and to help the student assimilate the difficult ideas of proof.

| Section | Average Class | Above-average Class |
|---|---|---|
| 5–1 | 1 | 1 |
| 5–2 | 2 | 1 |
| 5–3 | 1 | 1 |
| 5–4 | 2 | $1\frac{1}{2}$ |
| 5–5 | 2 | $1\frac{1}{2}$ |
| 5–6 | 1 | 1 |
| Review/Test | 1 | 1 |
| 5–7 | 2 | 2 |
| 5–8 | 1 | 1 |
| 5–9 | 3 | 2 |
| 5–10 | 2 | 1 |
| Supplementary Problems | 1 | 2 |
| Review/Test | 1 | 1 |

### 5–1 THE IDEA OF A CONGRUENCE

#### Classroom Notes

Section 5–1 is designed to teach the idea of congruences as correspondences on an intuitive level, apart from all problems of technique. Here the student learns to examine figures, and to look for correspondences by which one figure can be superimposed on another without changing its size or shape. Exact definitions and techniques come later.

In this chapter the student gets his first extended experience in discovering his own geometric proofs and writing them. By now the statements that the student will need to use as reasons in his proofs are all on record; and this means that the question of what is a proof and what is not is much less a matter of convention and conformity than is normally the case. There remains, of course, the problem of deciding when a proof has been properly written and, in particular, the question of how many details the student should furnish. The decision on this, at each stage of the course, is up to the teacher. The main hazards, in the opinion of the authors, are (1) allowing a student to be slipshod at the beginning, so that he never learns how a proof is supposed to fit together, and (2) enforcing a tedious formality after it has become plain that the student knows what he is doing and that he can furnish details on demand. These equal and opposite hazards are what the authors had in mind when they wrote the last paragraph on page 142.

**The idea of a one-to-one correspondence.** Note that in this section, the idea of a one-to-one correspondence is not formally defined. To be exact, the correspondence

$$A \leftrightarrow A',$$
$$B \leftrightarrow B',$$
$$C \leftrightarrow C'$$

is the following set of ordered pairs:

$$\{(A, A'), (B, B'), (C, C')\}.$$

One-to-one correspondences between two sets, in general, are defined as collections of ordered

A matching-up scheme of this kind is called a *one-to-one correspondence* between the vertices of the two triangles. If the matching-up scheme can be made to work, that is, if the triangles can be made to fit when the vertices are matched up in the prescribed way, then the one-to-one correspondence is called a *congruence* between the two triangles. For example, the correspondences that we have just given are congruences. On the other hand, writing

$$A \leftrightarrow F$$
$$B \leftrightarrow D$$
$$C \leftrightarrow E$$

does give us a one-to-one correspondence, but *not* a congruence, because the first and second triangles cannot be made to coincide by this particular matching-up scheme. This correspondence leads to many difficulties. $\overline{AB}$ is too short to be fitted onto $\overline{FD}$, $\overline{AC}$ is too long to be fitted onto $\overline{FE}$, and so on.

We can write one-to-one correspondences more briefly, in one line. For example, the correspondence

$$A \leftrightarrow E \quad B \leftrightarrow F \quad C \leftrightarrow D$$

which is the first example that we gave, can be written in one line:

$$ABC \leftrightarrow EFD.$$

Here it should be understood that the first letter on the left corresponds to the first letter on the right, the second corresponds to

the second, and the third corresponds to the third. Let us take one more example. The two figures below are of the same size and shape.

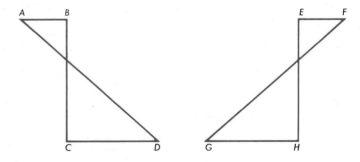

To show how one can be moved onto the other, we should match up the vertices like this:

$$A \leftrightarrow F \qquad C \leftrightarrow H$$
$$B \leftrightarrow E \qquad D \leftrightarrow G.$$

This correspondence is a congruence; that is, the figures can be made to fit if the vertices are matched in the given way. For short, we can write the congruence in one line:

$$ABCD \leftrightarrow FEHG.$$

Note that the order in which the matching *pairs* are written does not matter. We could have written our list of matching pairs in this way:

$$D \leftrightarrow G \qquad C \leftrightarrow H$$
$$B \leftrightarrow E \qquad A \leftrightarrow F;$$

and we could have described our one-to-one correspondence in one line:

$$DBCA \leftrightarrow GEHF.$$

All that matters is which points are matched with each other.

It is quite possible for two figures to be congruent in more than one way. Here the correspondence

$$ABC \leftrightarrow FDE$$

is a congruence, and the correspondence

$$ABC \leftrightarrow FED$$

is a different congruence between the same two figures.

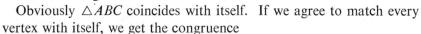

Obviously $\triangle ABC$ coincides with itself. If we agree to match every vertex with itself, we get the congruence

$$ABC \leftrightarrow ABC.$$

This is called the *identity* congruence. However, there is another way of matching up the vertices of this triangle. We can use the correspondence

$$ABC \leftrightarrow ACB.$$

Under this correspondence, the figure is made to coincide with itself, with the vertices $B$ and $C$ interchanged. This is not, by any means, possible for all triangles; it won't work unless at least two sides of the triangle are of the same length.

pairs, in a logically exact and thorough treatment.

At this stage, however, we believe that this degree of formalism is unnecessary and premature. The intuitive idea of a one-to-one matching scheme is plain enough, and in Section 5-1 it is motivated in a matter-of-fact way; you *use* it, to explain how one figure is to be fitted onto another, and the correspondences appear as answers to significant questions. Geometric ideas can be and should be formalized at this level, because the student has had a variety of intuitive experiences with them. When the same is true of one-to-one correspondences, it will be time to formalize them too; hence the definition of a function, page 574.

The one-to-one correspondences that the student writes down as answers to problems will all be congruences. But it should be emphasized that not all one-to-one correspondences have this property.

If classroom discussion appears to suggest it, it may be a good idea to point out that one-to-one correspondences are often used for a purpose totally different from the purposes of Section 5-1. When we count a pack of cards, and get the answer 52, what we have done is to set up a one-to-one correspondence between the cards in the pack and the positive integers from 1 to 52. In this sense, correspondences make their first appearance in the first grade. Note also that correspondences can be used to show that two sets have the *same* number of elements, in some cases where we do not know what the actual numbers are. Thus, in a shoe store, the number of left shoes is the same as the number of right shoes; and to draw this conclusion we do not need to know how many pairs of shoes the store has in stock.

## Background Material

It is often possible to establish more than one congruence between two figures. Since this fact is obvious even on an intuitive level, it should be dealt with now. Observe that if there is one congruence between the vertices of two isosceles triangles, then there is always another correspondence between them.

It is often possible to establish more than one congruence between a figure and itself. We recommend that you restrict your observations to the case of an isosceles triangle; these observations become the basis of our proof of the Isosceles Triangle Theorem in Section 5–7. [Note: The analogous problems for an equilateral triangle (Problem 10), a square, a regular pentagon (Problem 9) are best dealt with by considering those physical transformations, that is, reflections and rotations, which map the figure into itself. These problems are an excellent introduction to the elementary theory of groups, but this should not be taken up at this time.]

### Explanation for Problems

In teaching Section 5–1 it is particularly important to emphasize that a congruence is a particular type of correspondence. The mere fact that two figures *appear* congruent is not enough; we must specify the particular correspondence under which they *are* congruent. We describe a congruence by stating how the vertices of the two figures are matched up. We have a convenient compact notation for correspondences, and it is particularly important to adhere to it. It is essential that the student become proficient at establishing congruences; Problems 1 through 7 of Problem Set 5–1 are designed to drive home the idea and give the student lots of practice in using it.

### Problem Set 5–1

In some of the problems of this problem set you are to decide upon congruences by inspection. That is, correspondences which *look* like congruences if the figures are measured with reasonable care may be called congruences. (No trick effects are involved in the drawings.)

**1.** Which of the following pairs of figures are congruent? Write a congruence between the congruent figures.

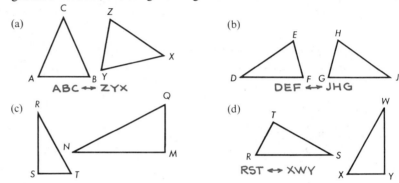

**2.** Which of the figures below do not have a matching counterpart?

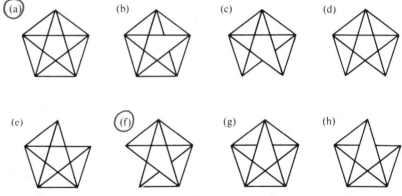

**3.** (a) Is a figure congruent to itself? Yes

(b) If each of two figures is congruent to a third, are they congruent to each other? Yes

(c) Are the sides of a square congruent? Yes

(d) Are the sides of a rectangle congruent? No

(e) Are two opposite faces of a cube congruent? Yes

(f) Are two adjacent faces of a cube congruent? Yes

(g) Are two opposite faces of a rectangular block, such as a brick, congruent? Yes

(h) Are two adjacent faces of a brick congruent? No

4. Look at the figures below. Write as many congruences as you can between these figures. You should get six congruences. (You may ignore the identity congruence for all the figures, but you should count the congruence, which is not an identity, between a triangle and itself if the triangle has two congruent sides. One congruence is $ACB \leftrightarrow LMN$.)

ACB $\leftrightarrow$ NML
BCA $\leftrightarrow$ NML
ACB $\leftrightarrow$ BCA
LMN $\leftrightarrow$ NML

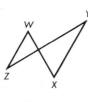
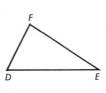

ACB $\leftrightarrow$ LMN
BCA $\leftrightarrow$ LMN
RTS $\leftrightarrow$ EFD
HIJK $\leftrightarrow$ XYZW

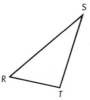
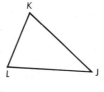

5. Follow the directions of Problem 4 for the following figures.

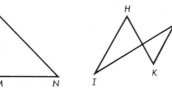

GIH $\leftrightarrow$ LJK
HIG $\leftrightarrow$ LJK
ABCDEF $\leftrightarrow$ WXYZUV
MNP $\leftrightarrow$ STR
GIH $\leftrightarrow$ HIG
LJK $\leftrightarrow$ KJL
GIH $\leftrightarrow$ KJL
HIG $\leftrightarrow$ KJL

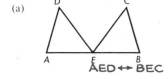

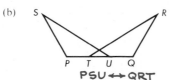

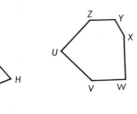

6. The triangles in each of the following pairs are congruent. Write the congruences for each pair. (The first one is $AED \leftrightarrow BEC$.)

(a)
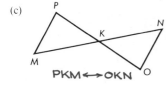
AED $\leftrightarrow$ BEC

(b)
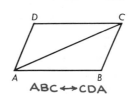
PSU $\leftrightarrow$ QRT

(c)
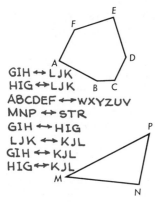
PKM $\leftrightarrow$ OKN

(d)

ABC $\leftrightarrow$ CDA

**Quiz**

The figures in each pair are congruent.
Write the congruences for each pair.

1.
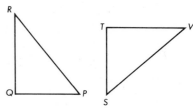

(ans: $PQR \leftrightarrow STV$)

2.
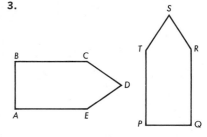

(ans: $ABC \leftrightarrow EDF$ or $ABC \leftrightarrow EFD$)

3.

(ans: $ABCDE \leftrightarrow QPTSR$)

**8.** (a) Two segments are congruent if they have the same length.

(b) Two lines are always congruent.

(c) Two angles are congruent if they have the same measure.

(d) Two circles are congruent if they have equal radii.

(e) Two squares are congruent if a side of one is congruent to a side of the other.

(f) Two triangles are congruent if their corresponding sides and angles are congruent.

**10.** $ABC \leftrightarrow ABC$     $ABC \leftrightarrow ACB$

$ABC \leftrightarrow BAC$     $ABC \leftrightarrow BCA$

$ABC \leftrightarrow CAB$     $ABC \leftrightarrow CBA$

**7.** The triangles in each of the following pairs are congruent. Write the congruence for each pair.

(a)

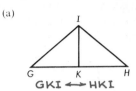

GKI ⟷ HKI

(b)

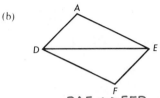

DAE ⟷ EFD

(c)

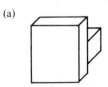

XYZ ⟷ YXW

(d)

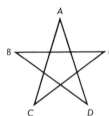

PKS ⟷ NMR

**8.** Under what conditions would the following pairs of figures be congruent?

(a) Two segments    (b) Two lines    (c) Two angles

(d) Two circles    (e) Two squares    (f) Two triangles

---

**9.** Consider the five-pointed star *ABCDE*. Write all the congruences between the star and itself, beginning with $ABCDE \leftrightarrow ABCDE$.

ABCDE ⟷ ABCDE
ABCDE ⟷ BCDEA
ABCDE ⟷ CDEAB
ABCDE ⟷ DEABC
ABCDE ⟷ EABCD

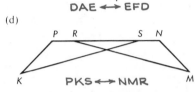

ABCDE ⟷ AEDCB
ABCDE ⟷ EDCBA
ABCDE ⟷ DCBAE
ABCDE ⟷ CBAED
ABCDE ⟷ BAEDC

**10.** $\triangle ABC$ is equilateral, that is $AB = BC = AC$. Write all congruences between the triangle and itself, starting with the identity congruence $ABC \leftrightarrow ABC$. (There are more than four.)

**11.** Which of these three-dimensional figures are congruent? *(a) and (f)*
*(b) and (d)*

(a)

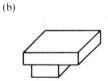

(b)

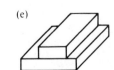

(c)

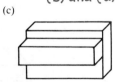

(d)

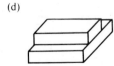

(e)

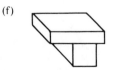

(f)

12. Which of the following plane figures can be fitted onto each other? Some matched pairs can be made to coincide by sliding the figures around in the same plane. But in some cases we need to turn one of the figures over in space to get it to coincide with the second. For each matched pair that you find, indicate whether turning over is needed.

(a) and (e) turn over and slide.

(a)   (b)   (c)

(b) and (c) rotate and slide.

(d)   (e)   (f)

(d) and (f) rotate and slide.

## 5-2  CONGRUENCES BETWEEN TRIANGLES

In the preceding section, we explained informally the idea of a congruence. Let us now give some mathematical definitions so that we can handle the idea mathematically.

For angles and segments, it is easy to say exactly what we mean.

### Definitions

Angles are *congruent* if they have the same measure. Segments are *congruent* if they have the same length.

Of course, the first of these definitions is a repetition from Section 4-4.

Just as we write $\angle A \cong \angle B$ to indicate that $\angle A$ and $\angle B$ are congruent, so we write

$$\overline{AB} \cong \overline{CD},$$

to indicate that $\overline{AB}$ and $\overline{CD}$ are congruent. Thus,

$$\overline{AB} \cong \overline{CD} \qquad \text{means that} \qquad AB = CD.$$
$$\angle A \cong \angle B \qquad \text{means that} \qquad m\angle A = m\angle B.$$

Each of the *equations* on the right is an *equation between numbers*. Each of the *congruences* on the left is a *congruence* between geometric figures.

### Classroom Notes

In this section we formally define a *congruence between two triangles*. This section should be easy to teach: the student acquired an intuitive understanding of congruence in the previous section, and so the formal definition should be easy to learn and use. Problems 1 through 4 of Problem Set 5-2 are exercises in the use of the definition.

We use "equality" as the equivalence relation when discussing the measures of segments and the measures of angles, but since we distinguish between a segment and the measure of that segment and between an angle and the measure of that angle we use another equivalence concept, *congruence*, when discussing segments and angles.

Since any definition is an agreement that one expression is an abbreviation for another, the sentence "$\angle A \cong \angle B$" may be replaced by the sentence "$m\angle A = m\angle B$" and the sentence "$m\angle A = m\angle B$" may be replaced by the sentence "$\angle A \cong \angle B$." A similar observation holds for segments.

Note, however, that although we can use the expressions "$\overline{AB} \cong \overline{CD}$" and "$AB = CD$" interchangeably, we cannot use the symbols "$\cong$" and "$=$" interchangeably. The statement $\overline{AB} = \overline{CD}$ means something different from the statement $\overline{AB} \cong \overline{CD}$, and the statement $AB \cong CD$ is meaningless.

### Background Material

The question may very well arise as to why we have two different ways of writing exactly the same thing. If $\overline{AB} \cong \overline{CD}$ means that $AB = CD$, why bother to introduce the notation $\overline{AB} \cong \overline{CD}$?

A first reason is that we are obliged to distinguish concepts which are, in fact, distinct. There is a difference between a segment and its length and a difference between an angle and its measure. Measures are real numbers, and when discussing measures, we use the idea of *equality*. But since segments and angles are point sets, we introduce another idea, *congruence*, in terms of which we discuss the equivalence of segments and the equivalence of angles.

The statements "$\overline{AB} \cong \overline{CD}$" and $AB = CD$ are interchangeable, and the objection that it is redundant to use two languages to describe the same ideas would be valid if we were talking only about congruence of segments and congruence of angles. However, we will also be talking about congruence of triangles, and here the situation is different. There is a measure (called the *area*) associated with each triangular region just as there is a measure associated with each segment and each angle. But while the statement "If $\triangle ADC \cong \triangle DEF$, then $a\triangle ABC = a\triangle DEF$" is true, the statement "If $a\triangle ABC = a\triangle DEF$, then $\triangle ABC \cong \triangle DEF$" is not true. In short, when talking about triangles, the concept of congruence is indispensable. And since we want uniformity in our discourse about congruence, we find it valuable to define and discuss congruent segments and congruent angles. Finally, remember that while the formal definitions of congruence of segments, angles, and triangles are different, the basic intuitive idea is the same: two figures are congruent if one can be moved so as to coincide with the other. Since the underlying idea is the same, it is valuable to be able to use the same terminology and notation in reference to segments, angles, and triangles.

We do not write $=$ between two names of geometric figures unless we mean that the figures are exactly the same, and occasions of this sort are quite rare. One example is shown at the right. Here it is correct to write

$$\angle BAC = \angle EAD$$

because $\angle BAC$ and $\angle EAD$ are not merely congruent, they are *exactly the same angle*. Similarly, $\overline{AB}$ and $\overline{BA}$ are always exactly the same segment, and so it is correct to write not only $\overline{AB} \cong \overline{BA}$ but also $\overline{AB} = \overline{BA}$.

Consider now a correspondence

$$ABC \leftrightarrow DEF$$

between the vertices of two triangles $\triangle ABC$ and $\triangle DEF$. This automatically gives us a correspondence between the sides of the triangles:

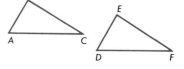

$$\overline{AB} \leftrightarrow \overline{DE}$$
$$\overline{AC} \leftrightarrow \overline{DF}$$
$$\overline{BC} \leftrightarrow \overline{EF}$$

and it also gives us a correspondence between the angles of the two triangles:

$$\angle A \leftrightarrow \angle D$$
$$\angle B \leftrightarrow \angle E$$
$$\angle C \leftrightarrow \angle F.$$

We can now state the definition of a congruence between two triangles.

**Definition**

Given a correspondence

$$ABC \leftrightarrow DEF$$

between the vertices of two triangles. If every pair of corresponding sides are congruent, and every pair of corresponding angles are congruent, then the correspondence $ABC \leftrightarrow DEF$ is called a *congruence between the two triangles*.

When we write $\triangle ABC \cong \triangle DEF$, we mean that the correspondence $ABC \leftrightarrow DEF$ is a congruence. This is a very efficient shorthand: the single expression $\triangle ABC \cong \triangle DEF$ tells us *six* things at once, namely,

$$\overline{AB} \cong \overline{DE}, \quad \text{or} \quad AB = DE,$$
$$\overline{AC} \cong \overline{DF}, \quad \text{or} \quad AC = DF,$$
$$\overline{BC} \cong \overline{EF}, \quad \text{or} \quad BC = EF,$$
$$\angle A \cong \angle D, \quad \text{or} \quad m\angle A = m\angle D,$$
$$\angle B \cong \angle E, \quad \text{or} \quad m\angle B = m\angle E,$$
$$\angle C \cong \angle F, \quad \text{or} \quad m\angle C = m\angle F.$$

In each of these six lines, the congruence on the left means the same thing as the equation on the right. We can therefore use either notation, according to convenience. Usually, we shall write $AB = DE$ instead of $\overline{AB} \cong \overline{DE}$, because it is easier to write. And for the same reason, we shall usually write $\angle A \cong \angle D$ instead of $m\angle A = m\angle D$. The six facts of the definition above are often referred to by the statement, "Corresponding parts of congruent triangles are congruent."

In figures, it is convenient to indicate congruences between segments and angles by marking the figure as shown below.

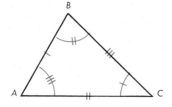 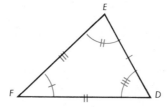

In this case, the six congruences indicated by the marks tell us that

$$\triangle ABC \cong \triangle DEF.$$

In the following figure, the marks tell us less:

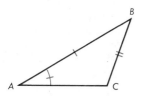 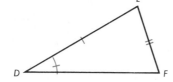

In fact, it is rather easy to see that these two triangles are not congruent under any correspondence whatever.

**The definition of a congruence between two triangles.** Obviously the definition at the bottom of page 130 is fundamental. Every student should learn it and be able to reproduce it accurately. While a weak student may feel safer if he learns it *verbatim*, a logically accurate paraphrase should really be regarded as better: it is evidence that the student understands what he is saying.

Note that we could equally well have defined a congruence between two triangles as a one-to-one correspondence between their vertices such that every pair of corresponding sides have the same length and every pair of corresponding angles have the same measure.

**Looking Ahead**

The text suggests here that we do not actually need all six pieces of information,

$$\overline{AB} \cong \overline{DE}, \quad \angle A \cong \angle D,$$
$$\overline{AC} \cong \overline{DF}, \quad \angle B \cong \angle E,$$
$$\overline{BC} \cong \overline{EF}, \quad \angle C \cong \angle F,$$

to be able to conclude that the correspondence $ABC \leftrightarrow DEF$ is a congruence. In fact, we can get along with considerably less information. In Problems 7 through 12 of this problem set the student discovers for himself the classical minimal sets of conditions under which he can conclude that a correspondence between two triangles is a congruence. These problems are essential, and we feel that it is very important to assign them.

In some cases, we may be given only partial information, and may still be able to infer that a certain correspondence is a congruence.

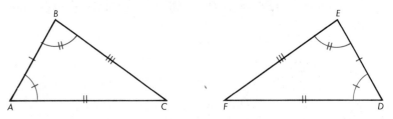

Under the correspondence $ABC \leftrightarrow DEF$, we are told that all three pairs of corresponding sides, and two out of three pairs of corresponding angles, are congruent. It surely ought to follow that $\angle C \cong \angle F$, so that $\triangle ABC \cong \triangle DEF$. And in fact, we ought to be able to get by with even less information. In the Preparation for Section 5–3, you will discover for yourself the conditions under which we can conclude that a correspondence between two triangles is a congruence. The facts of this matter are not difficult to figure out, as you will see.

### Definitions

A *side* of a triangle is said to be *included* by the angles whose vertices are the end points of the segment.

An *angle* of a triangle is said to be *included* by the sides of the triangle which lie in the sides of the angle.

For example, in $\triangle ABC$ above, $\overline{AC}$ is included by $\angle A$ and $\angle C$. And $\angle A$ is included by $\overline{AB}$ and $\overline{AC}$.

The following theorems will be useful when we need to cite the reflexive, symmetric, and transitive properties of congruence as reasons in proofs.

### Theorem 5–1

*Congruence for segments is an equivalence relation.*

**Proof.** The proof is exactly the same as the proof of Theorem 4–2, which states that congruence for angles is an equivalence relation. That is, we translate all the statements about congruence into the language of lengths.

### Theorem 5–2

*Congruence for triangles is an equivalence relation.*

**Proof.** We need to show that congruence of triangles has the following properties.

(1) (Reflexive Property) $\triangle ABC \cong \triangle ABC$.

(2) (Symmetric Property) If $\triangle ABC \cong \triangle DEF$, then $\triangle DEF \cong \triangle ABC$.

(3) (Transitive Property) If $\triangle ABC \cong \triangle DEF$ and $\triangle DEF \cong \triangle GHI$, then $\triangle ABC \cong \triangle GHI$.

Because congruence of triangles is defined in terms of the congruence of the three pairs of corresponding sides and the three pairs of corresponding angles, each of the statements above follows from the corresponding statement about segments and angles. Thus (1) holds because congruence is *reflexive* for segments and angles, (2) holds because congruence is *symmetric* for segments and angles, and (3) holds because congruence is *transitive* for segments and angles.

A common way of referring to the reflexive property of congruence is by the term *identity*.

## Problem Set 5–2

**1.** Given that $\triangle ABE \cong \triangle DCF$, complete the following statements by supplying the missing symbols. The correspondence $A\ \underline{BE} \leftrightarrow \underline{D}\ CF$ is a congruence.

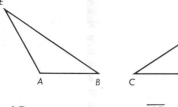

$\angle A \cong \angle D$.            $\overline{AB} \cong \underline{\overline{CD}}$.

$\angle B \cong \underline{\angle C}$.            $\overline{AE} \cong \underline{\overline{DF}}$.

$\angle E \cong \underline{\angle F}$.            $\overline{BE} \cong \underline{\overline{CF}}$.

**2.** Given that $\triangle MQP \cong \triangle NQP$. List the six pairs of corresponding, congruent parts of these two triangles.

$\angle M \cong \angle N$      $\overline{MQ} \cong \overline{NQ}$

$\overline{MP} \cong \overline{NP}$      $\angle MQP \cong \angle NQP$

$\angle MPQ \cong \angle NPQ$      $\overline{PQ} \cong \overline{PQ}$

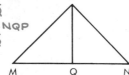

10. $\angle P \cong \angle A$      $\overline{PR} \cong \overline{AB}$
    $\angle R \cong \angle B$      $\overline{RQ} \cong \overline{BC}$
    $\angle Q \cong \angle C$      $\overline{QP} \cong \overline{CA}$

11. 1. $\triangle ABC \cong \triangle DEF$. (Given)
    2. $\angle A \cong \angle D$, $\angle B \cong \angle E$, $\angle C \cong \angle F$, $\overline{AB} \cong \overline{DE}$, $\overline{BC} \cong \overline{EF}$, $\overline{CA} \cong \overline{FD}$. (Definition of congruent triangles)
    3. $\angle D \cong \angle A$, $\angle E \cong \angle B$, $\angle F \cong \angle C$, $\overline{DE} = \overline{AB}$, $\overline{FD} = \overline{CA}$. (Symmetry of congruence for angles and segments)
    4. $\triangle DEF \cong \triangle ABC$. (Definition of congruent triangles)

13. Since $\overleftrightarrow{PC} \perp \overleftrightarrow{KM}$, $\angle KPC$ and $\angle MPC$ are right angles. Since $A$ is on the same side of $\overleftrightarrow{KM}$ as $C$, and $A$ is on the same side of $\overleftrightarrow{PC}$ as $K$, $A$ is in the interior of $\angle KPC$, and hence by the Angle Addition Postulate $m\angle KPA + m\angle APC = m\angle CPK = 90$. Therefore, $\angle KPA$ and $\angle APC$ are complementary. Similarly, $\angle MPB$ and $\angle BPC$ are complementary. From the given information $\triangle ACP \cong \triangle BCP$ and consequently $\angle APC \cong \angle BPC$. Therefore, $\angle KPA \cong \angle MPB$ because complements of congruent angles are congruent by Theorem 4–7.

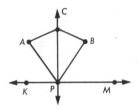

14. $\triangle ABC$ is an equilateral triangle; that is, all three sides and all three angles are congruent. Proof: $\triangle ABC \cong \triangle BAC$ tells us that $\overline{BC} \cong \overline{AC}$ and $\angle A \cong \angle B$. $\triangle ABC \cong \triangle ACB$ tells us that $\overline{AC} \cong \overline{AB}$ and $\angle B \cong \angle C$. Putting these together, we get $\overline{BC} \cong \overline{AC} \cong \overline{AB}$ and $\angle A \cong \angle B \cong \angle C$.

---

3. For each of the congruences list the six pairs of corresponding, congruent parts.
   (a) $\triangle RQF \cong \triangle ABX$. You may make a sketch of the triangles if you wish.
   (b) $\triangle FHW \cong \triangle MRK$. Do not use a figure.
   (c) $\triangle AZW \cong \triangle BWZ$. Do not use a figure.

4. Write the congruence for the two triangles which is determined by these six pairs of congruent parts: $\triangle AKT \cong \triangle BWR$

$$\overline{AK} \cong \overline{BW}, \qquad \angle A \cong \angle B.$$
$$\overline{KT} \cong \overline{WR}, \qquad \angle K \cong \angle W.$$
$$\overline{AT} \cong \overline{BR}, \qquad \angle T \cong \angle R.$$

5. (a) In $\triangle ABC$, which is the included angle of the sides $\overline{BC}$ and $\overline{AB}$? **∠B**
   (b) Which is the included side of $\angle A$ and $\angle C$? **$\overline{AC}$**
   (c) Which sides include $\angle C$? **$\overline{AC}$ and $\overline{BC}$**
   (d) Which angles include $\overline{BC}$? **∠B and ∠C**

6. Consider $\triangle GHK$. Without drawing a figure, can you discover an easy method of deciding which sides and angles are included sides and included angles?
   (a) Does $\overline{GH}$ and $\overline{HK}$ include $\angle H$? **Yes**
   (b) Does $\angle G$ and $\angle K$ include $\overline{GK}$? **Yes**
   (c) What is the included angle of $\overline{GH}$ and $\overline{GK}$? **∠G**
   (d) What is the included side of $\angle G$ and $\angle H$? **$\overline{GH}$**

7. (a) $\triangle ABC$ and $\triangle DEF$ do not intersect and $M$ is a point between $B$ and $C$. Which of the two symbols $=$ and $\cong$ could be used to fill the blanks to make each of the following a true statement?
   (i) $\triangle ABC \underline{\ \cong\ } \triangle DEF$.
   (ii) $m\angle B \underline{\ =\ } m\angle E$.
   (iii) $BC \underline{\ =\ } EF$.
   (iv) $\overline{AB} \underline{\ \cong\ } \overline{DE}$.
   (v) $\angle E \underline{\ \cong\ } \angle F$.
   (vi) $\angle ABM \underline{\ \cong\ } \angle ABC$. **or, ∠ABM = ∠ABC**
   (vii) $m\angle ABM \underline{\ =\ } m\angle DEF$.
   (viii) $AB \underline{\ =\ } DE$.

   (b) In which blank would both symbols work? **(vi)**
   (c) If $\overline{AB}$ had been the same segment as $\overline{DE}$ but $C$ and $F$ were different points, in which blank would $\cong$ change to $=$? **(iv)**

8. If
$$\triangle ABC \cong \triangle DEF \quad \text{and} \quad \triangle DEF \cong \triangle GHK,$$
**△ABC ≅ △GHK (Transitive Property)**
what can you conclude about $\triangle ABC$ and $\triangle GHK$? Why? **Theorem 5–2**

**6.**

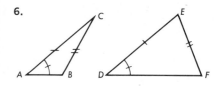

9. The pairs of triangles shown below are purposely drawn so as not to look congruent. You should rely only on the markings to determine which pairs of triangles are congruent.

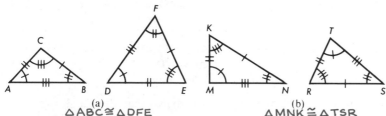

(a)
△ABC ≅ △DFE

(b)
△MNK ≅ △TSR

**7.** If we assign lengths $AB = 1$, $BC = 2$, $AC = 4$, then no triangle is determined.

**8.** (e) $\angle M$ and $\angle O$ are supplementary angles. "The sum of the angles of a triangle is 180."

(f) "The sum of two sides of a triangle is greater than the third side." $EF + DF = 7$ which is not greater than $DE = 8$.

10. Since the definition of congruent triangles is our only means so far of proving two triangles congruent, what facts must be known in order to conclude that $\triangle PRQ \cong \triangle ABC$?

11. Prove Theorem 5–1.

12. What conclusion follows from this hypothesis? $\triangle ABC \cong \triangle DEF$ and $\triangle EDF \cong \triangle RST$. What theorem supports your conclusion?
   △ABC ≅ △SRT, Theorem 5-2

13. Given $\overleftrightarrow{PC} \perp \overleftrightarrow{KM}$, with $K\text{-}P\text{-}M$. $A$ and $B$ are points on the same side of $\overleftrightarrow{KM}$ as $C$, but $A$ and $B$ are on opposite sides of $\overleftrightarrow{PC}$. $A$ is on the same side of $\overleftrightarrow{PC}$ as $K$. $\triangle ACP \cong \triangle BCP$. Prove that $\angle KPA \cong \angle MPB$.

14. Given $\triangle ABC$. If $\triangle ABC \cong \triangle BAC$ and $\triangle ABC \cong \triangle ACB$, what conclusions can be drawn about $\triangle ABC$? How do you prove that your conclusions hold?

### Preparation for Section 5–3

You may use a protractor, a ruler, or a compass to complete these constructions.

1. Construct a triangle $\triangle RST$ in which $RS = 7$ cm, $RT = 4$ cm, and $m\angle R = 35$.

2. Construct a triangle $\triangle ABC$ in which $AB = 5$ cm, $m\angle A = 45$, and $m\angle B = 60$. If you construct several triangles $\triangle ABC$ having the given measures, what common characteristic do the triangles share?
   The triangles are all congruent.

3. Construct a triangle $\triangle MNP$ in which $MN = 7.5$ cm, $NP = 5$ cm, and $PM = 9$ cm. You may find that you will need a compass to complete this construction.

4. Using only your ruler, construct any triangle which has no two sides congruent. Next construct a second triangle congruent to the first triangle and describe the steps you take.

## 5-3 THE CONGRUENCE POSTULATES FOR TRIANGLES

### Classroom Notes

In this brief but important section we state three basic congruence postulates for triangles. It is conventional to state an SAS Postulate, and then, on the basis of the SAS Postulate, prove an ASA Theorem and a SSS Theorem. We introduce these three congruence statements simultaneously, and we give them each, *at this time,* the same status, that is, the status of postulates. There are good reasons for doing so:

(1) To state an SAS Postulate and then prove an ASA Theorem and a SSS Theorem gives the student the impression that the SAS Postulate enjoys a natural, logical priority. This impression runs contrary to his intuitive notions. A triangle is, even intuitively, a union of three segments, and two triangles are congruent, intuitively, if their corresponding sides are congruent. Thus the student is likely to feel that "SSS" is the most natural set of conditions to guarantee congruence, and so he expects to postulate that every SSS correspondence is a congruence. To present each of these techniques as postulates has the advantage that it does not give an unmotivated priority to the SAS Postulate at this time.

(2) But there is a more important reason: the student has only recently encountered proof, and he is certainly not proficient at devising proofs or even at reading them. At this stage, the proofs of the ASA Theorem and SSS Theorem are difficult. And since the student has not yet gotten a feeling for the postulational structure of geometry, it is of little value to develop our geometry with the minimum number of postulates. At this stage, it

**136**

5. Refer to your work in Problem 4. Is there more than one way of obtaining the second triangle from the first? **Yes** How many of the six parts of the first triangle did you use in forming the second triangle? What is the least number of congruent parts necessary to ensure that the two triangles are congruent? **Three**

6. Construct $\triangle ABC$ in which $m\angle A = 40$, $AC = 7.5$ cm, and $CB = 5$ cm. Then construct $\triangle DEF$ in which $m\angle D = 40$, $DF = 7.5$ cm, and $FE = 5$ cm. Must $\triangle ABC$ and $\triangle DEF$ be congruent? **No**

7. In Problem 2 you should have concluded that all triangles $\triangle ABC$ whose parts have the measures given are congruent; that is, all the corresponding parts are congruent. When this is true, we say that the three given parts *determine* a triangle. In Problem 6 you should have found two triangles which were not congruent but which satisfied the given measures. Does Problem 1 allow for one or more triangles? does Problem 3? Is it possible to assign measures to angles or segments so that no triangle is determined? **Problem 1 and Problem 3 allow for only one triangle; Yes**

8. Construct the triangle determined by each set of measures given below. If the information allows two triangles, construct both. If more than two triangles or if no triangle may be constructed, explain why.
   (a) $m\angle M = 30$, $MO = 2$, $m\angle O = 90$. **1**
   (b) $m\angle B = 55$, $AB = 5$, $BC = 3$. **1**
   (c) $m\angle G = 35$, $GH = 6$, $HI = 4$. **2 ($\angle I$ may be acute or obtuse.)**
   (d) $AB = 5$, $BC = 3$, $AC = 4$. **1**
   (e) $m\angle M = 80$, $MO = 2$, $m\angle O = 120$. **0**
   (f) $DE = 8$, $EF = 3$, $DF = 4$. **0**

### 5-3   THE CONGRUENCE POSTULATES FOR TRIANGLES

As you have probably realized, there are at least three situations in which we can conclude that a correspondence between two triangles is a congruence.

In the first case, $ABC \leftrightarrow DEF$ is called an *SAS correspondence;* by this we mean that two sides and the included angle of the first triangle are congruent to the corresponding parts of the second. ("SAS" stands for "Side Angle Side.") In this case it follows that $\triangle ABC \cong \triangle DEF$.

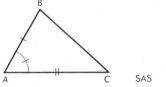
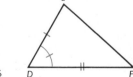

In the second case, $ABC \leftrightarrow DEF$ is called an *ASA correspondence;* by this we mean that two angles and the included side of the first triangle are congruent to the corresponding parts of the second. ("ASA" stands for "Angle Side Angle.") In this case also, it follows that $\triangle ABC \cong \triangle DEF$.

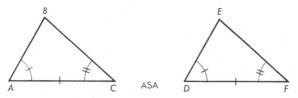

Finally, in the third case, $ABC \leftrightarrow DEF$ is called an *SSS correspondence;* by this we mean that all three sides of the first triangle are congruent to the corresponding sides of the second. ("SSS" stands for "Side Side Side.") Here we must have $\triangle ABC \cong \triangle DEF$.

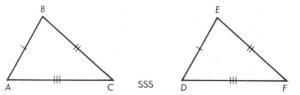

We make these observations official in the following postulates.

**POSTULATE 15.**   The SAS Postulate

*Every SAS correspondence is a congruence.*

**POSTULATE 16.**   The ASA Postulate

*Every ASA correspondence is a congruence.*

**POSTULATE 17.**   The SSS Postulate

*Every SSS correspondence is a congruence.*

In most instances, we shall apply these postulates to correspondences between two different triangles. We have seen, however, that in some cases we can set up a correspondence between a triangle and itself; and the above three postulates apply in such cases. Thus an SAS correspondence could be illustrated like this.

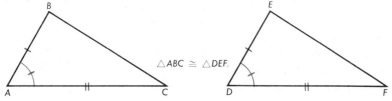

is much more valuable to teach the student to *use* the basic congruence postulates. The next three sections of the text are designed to do this.

(3) Chapter 6 is devoted, in part, to a closer examination of some ideas which were used earlier either intuitively, or as postulates, or, at any rate, without proof. In Section 6–6 of the text, we give proofs of the ASA Theorem and the SSS Theorem; by this time the student has had enough experience with proofs to understand the proofs of these two theorems.

Note that each of the postulates is very short. This is because we have already explained what we mean by an SAS correspondence:

An *SAS correspondence* is a correspondence between the vertices of two triangles under which two sides and the included angle of one triangle are congruent to the corresponding parts of the second triangle.

If we had not given this preliminary explanation, we would have had to state the SAS Postulate in a rather cumbersome form; it would have had to include the definition of an SAS correspondence. Note also that since the SAS, ASA, and SSS Postulates are so short, it is easy to quote them *verbatim*.

It could also be illustrated as in the figure below.  Here the marks tell
us that $ABC \leftrightarrow ACB$ is an *SAS* correspondence.  We can then apply
the SAS Postulate and conclude that $\triangle ABC \cong \triangle ACB$.

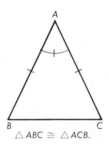

$\triangle ABC \cong \triangle ACB.$

*Warning:* There is no such thing as an SSA Postulate! In this figure,
$ABC \leftrightarrow DEF$ is an "SSA correspondence"; two sides and a *non*included
angle of $\triangle ABC$ are congruent to the corresponding parts of $\triangle DEF$.

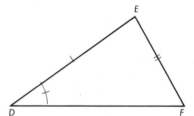

But the correspondence is obviously not a congruence; in fact, $\overline{DF}$ is
too long, $\angle E$ is too big, and $\angle F$ is too small.

*Warning:* There is no such thing as an AAA Postulate! If corresponding angles are congruent, it follows merely that the two triangles have
the same *shape*; they do not necessarily have the same size.

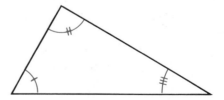

Triangles related in this way are called *similar*.

Hereafter, for short, we shall often refer to our three congruence
postulates simply as SAS, ASA, and SSS.

## Problem Set 5–3

**1.** In each of the pairs of triangles sketched below, like markings indicate congruent parts. Which triangles are congruent by the SAS Postulate?

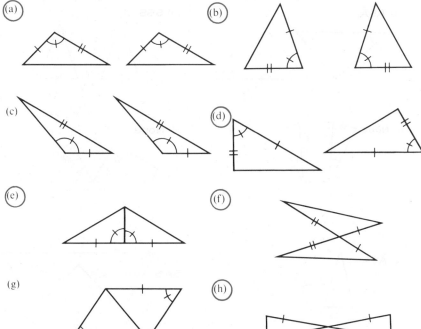

(a)

(b)

(c)

(d)

(e)

(f)

(g)

(h)

**2.** Each pair of triangles below has two corresponding sides or angles marked as congruent. Indicate the additional information needed to enable us to apply the specified congruence postulate.

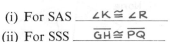

(i) For ASA  $\angle B \cong \angle D$
(ii) For SAS  $\overline{AC} \cong \overline{FE}$    (a)

(i) For SAS  $\angle K \cong \angle R$
(ii) For SSS  $\overline{GH} \cong \overline{PQ}$    (b)

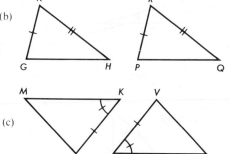

(i) For SAS  $\overline{MK} \cong \overline{TU}$
(ii) For ASA  $\angle N \cong \angle V$    (c)

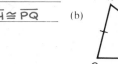
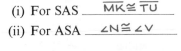

**3.** For each of the pairs of triangles sketched below, like markings indicate congruent parts. Name the congruence postulate (SAS, ASA, SSS), if any, that will prove the triangles congruent.

(a) ASA

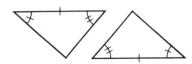

(b) SSS

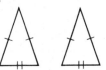

(c) None

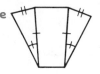

(d) None

(e) ASA

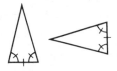

(f) SAS

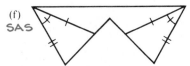

(g) ASA

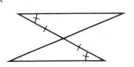

(h) None

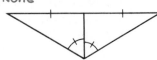

(i) None

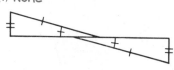

(j) None

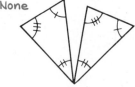

(k) SSS

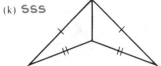

(l) None

## 5–4  THINKING UP YOUR OWN PROOFS

You now have enough basic material to be able to write real geometric proofs of your own.  From now on, writing your own proofs will be a very important part of your work, and the chances are that it will be more fun than reading other people's proofs.

Let us take a couple of examples, to suggest how we go about finding proofs and writing them up.

### Example 1

If two segments bisect each other, then the segments joining the ends of the given segments are congruent.

To work a problem like this, we first draw a figure and label it, using a capital letter for each vertex.  Then, we state the hypothesis and conclusion in terms of the lettering of the figure.

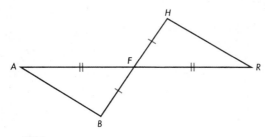

*Given:* $\overline{AR}$ and $\overline{BH}$ bisect each other at $F$.

*To prove:* $\overline{AB} \cong \overline{RH}$.

We mark the figure to indicate the congruences that are given.

Since our object is to prove that two segments are congruent, we must recall what we know about congruent segments.  The marks on the figure indicate that $\overline{FB} \cong \overline{FH}$, and this is right, by definition of the midpoint.  For the same reason, $\overline{AF} \cong \overline{RF}$.  If we want to show that $\overline{AB} \cong \overline{RH}$, our best chance is to show that they are corresponding parts of congruent triangles.  To do this, we must set up a correspondence between the triangles in the figure, and then show that we have an SAS correspondence, an ASA correspondence, or an SSS correspondence.  From the figure, it looks as though the correspondence ought to be

$$AFB \leftrightarrow RFH.$$

Two pairs of sides are congruent, because

$$\overline{AF} \cong \overline{RF} \quad \text{and} \quad \overline{FB} \cong \overline{FH}.$$

### Background Material

Section 5–4 deals with the practical problem of training the student to write a simple proof.  The difficulty is that the student does not yet understand the idea of proof.  (Geometry in junior high school is descriptive rather than deductive.)

We have to understand the student's frame of mind at this stage: a statement either is diagrammatically obvious (in which case it hardly needs to be proved), or it is not.  One statement does not have any natural priority over another statement.  That we should grant certain statements the status of postulates or hypotheses is rather puzzling; that it is actually necessary to substantiate an assertion is an idea which is foreign.  The student has had little experience in constructing a chain of reasoning leading from a given set of hypotheses to a conclusion, and he has little idea as to what type of reasons can and cannot be used to justify statements.  In short, when the student arrives at Section 5–4, he has encountered proofs, but he has not learned how to think them up and present them.  He begins to learn how in Section 5–4; it is perhaps the most important section in the text.

### Classroom Notes

The student learns how to write a proof by imitation.  We suggest that the teacher present a sample proof, and then establish some of the conventions he wants the student to observe in his own proofs.  We recommend the following conventions:

(1) Draw a figure and state the hypotheses or "Given" and the conclusion or "To Prove" in terms of the notation of the figure.  (This is,

of course, *absolutely* essential when the problem is stated without reference to a particular figure.)

(2) Insist on the two-column, statement-and-reason form. Number both the statements and the reasons.

(3) Insist that students state their reasons in full, and tell them what they can legitimately use as reasons: definitions, postulates, theorems, basic facts of algebra and logic, the incidence properties of the given figures, and results established earlier in the problem.

(4) Ask them, in writing a congruence proof, to align their statements; that is, keep the parts of △ABC on the left of the congruence signs and the corresponding parts of △DEF on the right of the congruence signs. Also ask them, in writing an SAS congruence proof, for example, to establish a pair of congruent sides, a pair of congruent angles, and a pair of congruent sides in that order (see Example 2).

We recommend that you insist on these conventions *at least initially.* When and how to amend them is up to you. An amendment which considerably reduces the student's labor is to allow the use of certain abbreviations:

| | |
|---|---|
| AAP | Angle Addition Postulate |
| ACP | Angle Construction Postulate |
| AMP | Angle Measurement Postulate |
| SCAC | Supplements of Congruent Angles are Congruent |
| SAS | Side-Angle-Side Postulate |
| CPCTC | Corresponding Parts of Congruent Triangles are Congruent |
| ITT | Isosceles Triangle Theorem |

It is, however, up to the individual teacher to decide what abbreviations the students will be permitted to use.

How about the included angles? If they are congruent too, then we can apply the SAS Postulate. And they *are* congruent, because they are vertical angles. Therefore, by the SAS Postulate, our correspondence is a congruence. The sides $\overline{AB}$ and $\overline{RH}$ are corresponding sides, and so they are congruent. This is what we wanted to prove.

Written in the double-column form, our proof would look like this:

*Given:* $\overline{AR}$ and $\overline{BH}$ bisect each other at *F.*

*To prove:* $\overline{AB} \cong \overline{RH}.$

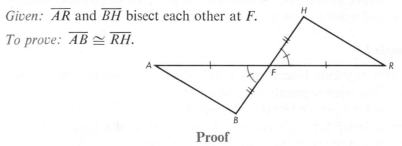

**Proof**

| STATEMENTS | REASONS |
|---|---|
| 1. $\overline{AR}$ and $\overline{BH}$ bisect each other. | 1. Given |
| 2. $AF = RF.$ | 2. Definition of bisect |
| 3. $FB = FH.$ | 3. Definition of bisect |
| 4. $\angle AFB \cong \angle RFH.$ | 4. Vertical angles are congruent |
| 5. $\triangle AFB \cong \triangle RFH.$ | 5. The SAS Postulate |
| 6. $\overline{AB} \cong \overline{RH}.$ | 6. Definition of a congruence between triangles |

This proof is given merely as a sample of how your work might look. There is a limit to how "standard" we can expect the form of a proof to be. For example, in steps 2 and 3 we have indicated congruences between segments by writing

$$AF = RF \quad \text{and} \quad FB = FH.$$

We might just as well have written

$$\overline{AF} \cong \overline{RF} \quad \text{and} \quad \overline{FB} \cong \overline{HF},$$

because in each case the congruence between the segments and the equation between their lengths mean the same thing.

We also have a good deal of choice in deciding how many details to give in a proof. As your knowledge and skill increase, you can write proofs containing fewer details. Your teacher is the best judge of when you have earned the right to do this, and of how much you may omit.

By now, you should have the idea, and so we give our second example in an incomplete form. Your problem is to fill in the blank spaces in such a way as to get a proof.

*Example 2*

*Given:* $\overline{AH} \cong \overline{FH}$, $\angle AHB \cong \angle FHB$.

*To prove:* $\angle A \cong \angle F$.

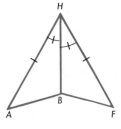

**Proof**

| Statements | Reasons |
|---|---|
| 1. $\overline{AH} \cong \overline{FH}$. | 1. Given |
| 2. $\angle AHB \cong \angle FHB$. | 2. Given |
| 3. $\overline{HB} \cong \overline{HB}$. | 3. Reflexive Property (Theorem 5–1) |
| 4. $\triangle AHB \cong \triangle FHB$. | 4. SAS Postulate |
| 5. $\angle A \cong \angle F$. | 5. Definition of Congruent Triangles |

**Problem Set 5–4**

**1.** Copy this problem on your paper and fill in the missing information.

Given: The figure with
$\overline{CD} \perp \overline{AB}$ and $\overline{AD} \cong \overline{BD}$.
Prove: $\triangle ADC \cong \triangle BDC$.

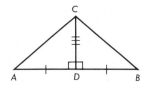

**Proof**

| Statements | Reasons |
|---|---|
| 1. $\overline{AD} \cong \overline{BD}$. | 1. Given |
| 2. $\overline{CD} \perp \overline{AB}$. | 2. Given |
| 3. $\angle ADC \cong \angle BDC$. | 3. Definition of perpendicular and Theorem 4-4 |
| 4. $\overline{CD} \cong \overline{CD}$. | 4. Reflexive Property (Theorem 5–1) |
| 5. $\triangle ADC \cong \triangle BDC$. | 5. SAS |

You must also decide when to switch to "paragraph proofs." Honors students can make the change at the end of Chapter 5; good students somewhere in Chapter 9; average students should probably be held to double-column, statement-and-reason proofs throughout the course.

There remains, however, the creative problem of getting the student to think of a proof to write. The proofs at this stage are very simple; they are "one-step" verifications of congruence. You can, however, suggest that the students work both "forward" and "backward." Get them to ask, "What use can we make of the given information?" and "What techniques do we have at our disposal that might be useful in establishing the desired result?"

**Quiz**

Given: The figure with $\angle A \cong \angle F$, $\overline{AC} \cong \overline{DF}$, $\angle EDA \cong \angle BCF$.

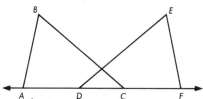

Prove: $\triangle ABC \cong \triangle FED$.
Proof: 1. $\angle A \cong \angle F$, $\overline{AC} \cong \overline{DF}$, $\angle EDA \cong \angle BCF$. (Given)
2. $\angle EDA$ and $\angle EDF$ are supplementary.
$\angle BCF$ and $\angle BCA$ are supplementary. (Linear pair of angles are supplementary.)
3. $\angle BCA \cong \angle EDF$. (Theorem 4–6)
4. $\triangle ABC \cong \triangle FED$. (ASA)

**4.** 1. $AB = CD$.  (Given)
2. $m\angle x = m\angle y$.  (Given)
3. $AC = CA$.  (Reflexive Property of Equality)
4. $\triangle ACB \cong \triangle CAD$.  (ASA)
5. $m\angle ACB = m\angle CAD$.  (CPCTC)

**2.** Copy this problem on your paper and fill in the missing information.
Given: $\triangle MKP$ and $\triangle XYZ$ such that $\angle M \cong \angle Y$, $\angle MKP \cong \angle YXZ$, and $MK = XY$.
Prove: $\overline{PK} \cong \overline{ZX}$.

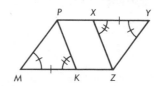

**Proof**

| STATEMENTS | REASONS |
|---|---|
| 1. $\angle M \cong \angle Y$.<br>$MK = XY$.<br>$\angle MKP \cong \angle YXZ$. | 1. <u>Given</u> |
| 2. $\triangle MKP \cong$ <u>$\triangle YXZ$</u> | 2. <u>ASA</u> |
| 3. <u>$\overline{PK} \cong \overline{ZX}$</u>. | 3. Corresponding parts of congruent triangles are congruent (from the definition of a congruence between triangles). |

**3.** In the figure, $\overline{AE}$ intersects $\overline{BD}$ at $C$ so that $AC = DC$ and $BC = EC$. Show that $\angle A \cong \angle D$, by copying the following proof. Supply the missing reasons.

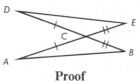

**Proof**

| STATEMENTS | REASONS |
|---|---|
| 1. $AC = DC$. | 1. Given |
| 2. $\angle ACB \cong \angle DCE$. | 2. <u>Vertical angles are congruent</u> |
| 3. $BC = EC$. | 3. <u>Given</u> |
| 4. $\triangle ACB \cong \triangle DCE$. | 4. <u>SAS</u> |
| 5. $\angle A \cong \angle D$. | 5. Corresponding parts of congruent triangles are congruent. |

(Note: Although Statements 2 and 4 above look very much alike, one deals with angles and the other with triangles.  Consider this in stating Reasons 2 and 4.)

**4.** In this figure, $AB = CD$ and $m\angle x = m\angle y$.
Prove that $m\angle ACB = m\angle DAC$.

**5.** Copy the problem and complete the proof.  Prove that if in the figure,

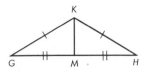

$GK = HK$ and $M$ is the midpoint of $\overline{GH}$, then $\angle G \cong \angle H$.

**Proof**

| STATEMENTS | REASONS |
|---|---|
| 1. $GK = HK$. | 1. Given |
| 2. $M$ is the midpoint of $\overline{GH}$. | 2. Given |
| 3. $GM = MH$ | 3. Definition of midpoint |
| 4. $\overline{KM} \cong \overline{KM}$ | 4. Reflexive Property |
| 5. $\triangle GMK \cong \triangle HMK$. | 5. SSS |
| 6. $\angle G \cong \angle H$ | 6. CPCTC |

**6.** Given:  The figure with
$CE = CB$ and $\angle E \cong \angle B$.

Prove:  $\angle D \cong \angle A$.

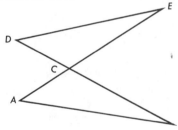

**7.** In this three-dimensional figure, points $Q$, $R$, and $S$ are in plane $E$; $QS = QR$ and $\angle PQS \cong \angle PQR$.  Prove that $PR = PS$.

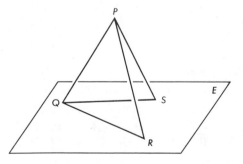

**8.** Given that segments $\overline{AE}$ and $\overline{DF}$ bisect each other at $P$.  Prove that $\triangle PDA \cong \triangle PFE$.  (Here you must construct your own figure.)

**Answers to Problems**

**6.** 1. $CE = EB$ and $\angle E = \angle B$.  (Given)
2. $\angle DCE \cong \angle ACB$.  (Vertical Angle Theorem)
3. $\triangle DCE \cong \triangle ACB$.  (ASA)
4. $\angle D \cong \angle A$.  (CPCTC)
**7.** 1. $QS = QR$, $\angle PQS \cong \angle PQR$.  (Given)
2. $PQ = PQ$.  (Reflexive Property of Equality)
3. $\triangle PQS \cong \triangle PQR$.  (SAS)
4. $PS = PR$.  (CPCTC)
**8.** 1. $\overline{AE}$ and $\overline{DF}$ bisect each other at point $P$.  (Given)
2. $AP = PE$; $DP = PF$.  (Definition of bisect)
3. $\angle APD \cong \angle EPF$.  (Vertical angles are congruent.)
4. $\triangle PDA \cong \triangle PFE$.  (SAS)

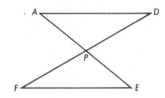

**9.** 1. $GK = HK$. (Given)
2. $\angle GKM \cong \angle HKM$. (Given)
3. $KM = KM$. (Reflexive Property)
4. $\triangle GKM \cong \triangle HKM$. (SAS)
5. $GM = MH$. (CPCTC)
6. $G\text{-}M\text{-}H$. (Given)
7. $M$ is the midpoint of $\overline{GH}$. (Definition of midpoint)

**10.** 1. $TR = UR$; $TS = US$. (Given)
2. $RS = RS$. (Reflexive Property)
3. $\triangle RST \cong \triangle RSU$. (SSS)
4. $\angle T \cong \angle U$. (CPCTC)
5. $m\angle T = m\angle U$. (Definition of congruent angles)

**11.** 1. $\angle D \cong \angle C$. (Given)
2. $DG = CH$. (Given)
3. $\overline{AG} \perp \overline{DK}$; $\overline{BH} \perp \overline{CK}$. (Given)
4. $\angle AGD$, $\angle BHC$ are right angles. (Definition of perpendicular)
5. $\angle AGD \cong \angle BHC$. (Definition of right angle; Definition of congruent angles)
6. $\triangle AGD \cong \triangle BHC$. (ASA, Steps 1, 2 and 5)
7. $AD = BC$. (CPCTC)

**12.** Sketch the figure and observe that $\triangle ABE \cong \triangle CBD$ by the SSS Postulate, and that consequently $\angle ABE \cong \angle CBD$.

**13.** 1. $\angle SRK \cong \angle K$, $\angle VRT \cong \angle T$. (Given)
2. $\angle SRK \cong \angle VRT$. (Vertical Angle Theorem)
3. $\angle K \cong \angle T$. (Transitivity and symmetry of congruence for angles)
4. $KR = TR$. (Given)
5. $\triangle SRK \cong \triangle VRT$. (ASA)
6. $SK = VT$. (CPCTC)
The hypothesis $\angle M \cong \angle N$ is not needed.

---

**9.** In $\triangle GHK$, $GK = HK$, $G\text{-}M\text{-}H$, and $\angle GKM \cong \angle HKM$. Prove that $M$ is the midpoint of $\overline{GH}$.

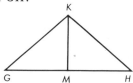

**10.** Given: A segment $\overline{RS}$ and points $T$ and $U$ on opposite sides of $\overleftrightarrow{RS}$ such that $TR = UR$, $TS = US$, and $UR < US$. Note UR<US unnecessary to proof.
Prove: $m\angle T = m\angle U$.

**11.** Given: $DG = CH$, $\angle D \cong \angle C$, $\overline{AG} \perp \overline{DK}$, $\overline{BH} \perp \overline{CK}$.

Prove: $AD = BC$.

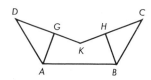

---

**12.** Given: The points $A$, $C$, $D$, and $E$ are collinear, with $A\text{-}E\text{-}D$ and $A\text{-}D\text{-}C$. $B$ is a point not on $\overleftrightarrow{AC}$ such that $AB = CB$, $EB = DB$, and $AE = CD$. Prove: $\angle ABE \cong \angle DBC$.

**13.** Given the figure with $\angle SRK \cong \angle K$, $\angle VRT \cong \angle T$, $KR = TR$, and $\angle M \cong \angle N$. Prove that $SK = VT$. What part of the hypothesis is not useful?

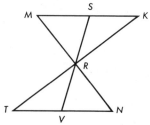

---

14–15. See Solution Section.

**14.** Given that $\overline{BQ}$ bisects $\overline{PA}$ at $R$, but $BQ \neq PA$. $B$ and $Q$ are on opposite sides of $\overleftrightarrow{PA}$. $S$ and $C$ are points on $\overline{PR}$ and $\overline{AR}$, respectively, such that $RS = RC$, $\overline{BC} \perp \overline{PA}$, and $\overline{QS} \perp \overline{PA}$. Also, $\angle BAR \cong \angle QPR$. Prove that $\overline{PA}$ bisects $\overline{BQ}$ and that $\angle ABC \cong \angle PQS$.

**15.** Given: $\angle HRE$ with $RH = RE$. $M$ and $K$ are points on the sides of $\angle HRE$ such that $R\text{-}H\text{-}M$ and $R\text{-}E\text{-}K$. $\overline{EM}$ and $\overline{HK}$ intersect at $T$. $\angle HRT \cong \angle ERT$. Prove that $\triangle MTH \cong \triangle KTE$.

## 5–5  USING MARKS ON FIGURES

Sometimes in a proof, you will find that you can make the figure more instructive by putting marks on it.

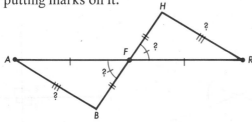

The above figure illustrates Example 1 of Section 5–4. The marks on $\overline{AF}$ and $\overline{FR}$ and on $\overline{FH}$ and $\overline{FB}$ indicate the congruences that derive from the *given* information. These congruences are needed in the proof. The marks on $\angle AFB$ and $\angle RFH$ indicate that these angles, which are congruent by the Vertical Angle Theorem, are also needed in the proof. And the marks on $\overline{AB}$ and $\overline{RH}$, including the question marks (?), show what is *to be proved* in this problem.

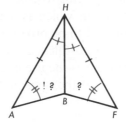

Similarly, the marks on the figure at the right tell us what was *given* and what was *to be proved* in Example 2 of the previous section.

Likewise, the three congruence postulates, SAS, ASA, and SSS, are fully illustrated by the marks in the following figures.

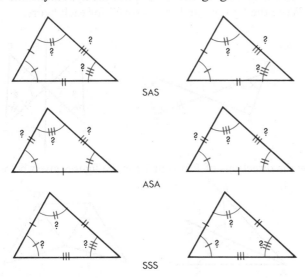

SAS

ASA

SSS

## 5–5 USING MARKS ON FIGURES

**Classroom Notes**

This section is mainly an extension of the previous section, with another problem set of relatively simple proofs which allows the student to gain confidence in his own ability to devise a complete proof. The use of marks on the figures helps the student to remember exactly what is given and what is to be proved while he is studying the figure. At this point it may not seem necessary since the proofs are simple; however, as the proofs become more complicated the student sometimes loses sight of his objective in the maze of the statements of the proof. The marks should help to remind him of his goal.

**Quiz**

1. For the figures below, write the "given" and the "prove."

(a)

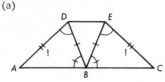

(ans: Given: ∠ADB ≅ ∠CEB,
∠DBA ≅ ∠CBE, $\overline{DB} \cong \overline{EB}$.
Prove: DA = EC.)

(b)

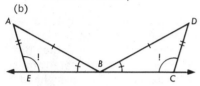

(ans: Given: ∠ABE ≅ ∠DBC,
$\overline{AE} \cong \overline{DC}$, $\overline{AB} \cong \overline{DB}$.
Prove: ∠AEB ≅ ∠DCE.)

2.

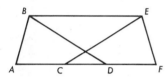

Given: ∠A ≅ ∠F, ∠ECA ≅ ∠BDF, C the midpoint of $\overline{AD}$ and D the midpoint of $\overline{CF}$.
Prove: $\overline{AB} \cong \overline{EF}$.
Proof: 1. ∠ECA ≅ ∠BDF. (Given)
2. ∠ECA is supplementary to ∠ECF.
∠BDF is supplementary to ∠BDA. (Supplement Postulate)
3. ∠ECF ≅ ∠BDA. (Theorem 4–6)
4. $AC = CD = \frac{1}{2}AD$.
$DF = CD = \frac{1}{2}CF$. (Definition of midpoint)
5. AD = CF. (Addition Property of Equality)
6. ∠A ≅ ∠F. (Given)
7. △ABD ≅ △FEC. (ASA)
8. $\overline{AB} \cong \overline{EF}$. (Definition of congruent triangles)

3. Can problem 1(b) above be proved? Explain.
(ans: No, triangles cannot be proved congruent using an SSA correspondence.)

**148**

148

**5–5 | USING MARKS ON FIGURES**

In general, it is a good idea to mark figures in such a way that they will convey as much information as possible. Sometimes we may be able to draw a figure that is a complete picture of a theorem. For example, the following figures are pictures of theorems that appeared in Chapter 4. Which theorems are they?

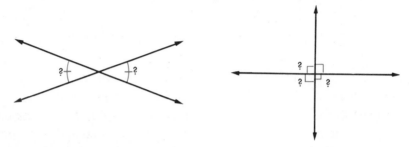

A frequent mistake in proofs is to *assume* as true the very thing you are trying to *prove*. Another common mistake is to use as a reason a theorem which is actually a *consequence* of the statement you are supposed to be proving. Such arguments are called *circular arguments* and are worthless as logical proofs. A particularly bad kind of circular argument is the use of the theorem you are trying to prove as a reason for one of the steps in "proof."

**Problem Set 5–5**

1. Each figure is marked so that it specifies the hypothesis and the conclusion. Write the "given" and the "prove" for each figure.

(a)   (b)

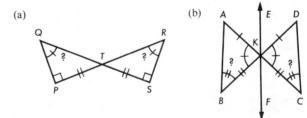

2. Follow the directions of Problem 1 for the figures given below.

(a)   (b)

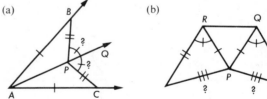

3. Complete the proof of the following problem.  Given the figure with $AC = BC$, $DC = EC$.  $G$ is the midpoint of $\overline{DC}$, $H$ is the midpoint of $\overline{EC}$, and $\angle ACE \cong \angle BCD$.  Prove that $AG = BH$.

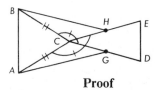

**Proof**

| STATEMENTS | REASONS |
|---|---|
| 1. $AC = BC$. | 1. _Given_ |
| 2. $DC = EC$. | 2. _Given_ |
| 3. $\frac{1}{2}DC = \frac{1}{2}EC$. | 3. Multiplication Property of Equality |
| 4. $G$ is the midpoint of $\overline{DC}$.  _H_ is the _midpoint of EC_. | 4. _Given_ |
| 5. $DG = GC = \frac{1}{2}DC$. | 5. Definition of midpoint |
| 6. $EH = HC = \frac{1}{2}EC$. | 6. _Definition of midpoint_ |
| 7. $GC = HC$. | 7. Steps 3, 5, 6 and transitivity |
| 8. $m\angle ACE = m\angle BCD$. | 8. Given and definition of congruent angles |
| 9. $m\angle ACG + m\angle GCH = m\angle BCH + \underline{m\angle GCH}$. | 9. Step 8 and Angle Addition Postulate |
| 10. $m\angle GCH = m\angle GCH$. | 10. _Reflexive Property_ |
| 11. $m\angle ACG = \underline{m\angle BCH}$. | 11. Subtraction Property of Equality |
| 12. $\triangle AGC \cong \triangle BHC$. | 12. Steps 1, 7, 11 and the _SAS_ Postulate |
| 13. $AG = BH$. | 13. _Definition of congruent triangles_ |

4. In the figure, $AE = BC$, $AD = BD$, and $DE = DC$.  Prove that $\angle E \cong \angle C$.

5. In the figure, $AE = BC$, $AD = BD$, and $\angle EAD \cong \angle CBD$.  Prove that $\angle BDE \cong \angle ADC$.

6. In the figure, $AE = BC$, $AD = BD$, and $\angle E \cong \angle C$.  Can you prove that $ED = CD$?  If so, do so.  If not, explain why not.

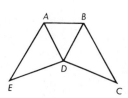

7. In the figure, $\angle E \cong \angle C$, $ED = CD$, and $\angle BDE \cong \angle ADC$.  Can you prove that $AE = BC$?  If so, do so.  If not, explain why not.

---

**Answers to Problems**

**1.** (a) Given: $\overline{QP} \perp \overline{PR}$, $\overline{RS} \perp \overline{QS}$, $PT = TS$.  Prove: $\angle Q \cong \angle R$.

(b) Given: $AK = KD$, $BK = CK$, $\angle AKB \cong \angle DKC$.  Prove: $\angle B \cong \angle C$.

**2.** (a) Given: $AB = AC$, $PB = PC$.  Prove: $\angle BPQ \cong \angle QPC$.

(b) Given: $MR = KQ$, $PR = PQ$, $\angle MRP \cong \angle KQP$.  Prove: $MP = KP$.

**4.** Use the SSS Postulate and the definition of congruent triangles.

**5.** Use the SAS Postulate to show $\triangle EAD \cong \triangle CBD$.  By the definition of congruent triangles, $m\angle EDA = m\angle CDB$, and hence $m\angle EDA + m\angle ADB = m\angle CDB + m\angle ADB$, so that by the AAP we have $m\angle EDB = m\angle CDA$.

**6.** No.  In each triangle the angles which are congruent are not the angles included between the congruent sides.

**7.** If we can show that $\angle EDA \cong \angle CDB$, then the triangles must be congruent by the ASA Postulate.  Begin as follows:

1. $m\angle EDB = m\angle CDA$.  (Given)
2. $m\angle EDB = m\angle EDA + m\angle ADB$.  $m\angle CDA = m\angle CDB + m\angle ADB$. (AAP)
3. $m\angle EDA + m\angle ADB = m\angle CDB + m\angle ADB$. (Substitution)
4. $m\angle EDA = m\angle CDB$.  (Subtracting property)

**8.** $\triangle ABM \cong \triangle ABK$ by the SAS Postulate, and so $\angle AMB \cong \angle AKB$. Therefore $\angle x \cong \angle y$, since supplements of congruent angles are congruent.

**9.** 1. $\angle RPQ \cong \angle SPQ$. (Given)
   2. $\angle PQR$ and $\angle PQS$ are right angles. (Definition of perpendicular)
   3. $\angle PQR \cong \angle PQS$. (Theorem 4–4)
   4. $\overline{PQ} \cong \overline{PQ}$. (Reflexivity of congruence of segments)
   5. $\triangle PQR \cong \triangle PQS$. (ASA)
   6. $RQ = SQ$. (CPCTC)

**10.** 1. $BC = DE$, $AB = EF$. (Given)
   2. $\overline{BC} \cong \overline{DE}$, $\overline{AB} \cong \overline{EF}$. (Definition of congruent segments)
   3. $\angle B \cong \angle E$. (Given)
   4. $\triangle ABC \cong \triangle FED$. (SAS)
   5. $AC = DF$. (CPCTC)

**11.** 1. $\angle 2 \cong \angle 5$, $\angle 3 \cong \angle 4$. (Given)
   2. $\overline{CD} \cong \overline{DC}$. (Reflexivity of congruence of segments)
   3. $\triangle ACD \cong \triangle FDC$. (ASA)
   4. $AD = CF$. (CPCTC)

**13.** 1. $MR = KR$, $MG = KG$. (Given)
   2. $\overline{MR} \cong \overline{KR}$, $\overline{MG} \cong \overline{KG}$. (Definition of congruent segments)
   3. $\angle M \cong \angle K$. (Given)
   4. $\triangle MRG \cong \triangle KRG$. (SAS)
   5. $\angle GRM \cong \angle GRK$. (CPCTC)
   6. $\angle GRM$ and $\angle GRK$ form a linear pair. (Definition of linear pair)
   7. $\angle GRM$ and $\angle GRK$ are right angles. (Theorem 4–5)
   8. $\overline{GR} \perp \overline{MK}$. (Definition of perpendicular)

**14.** $\triangle ARB \cong \triangle ARK$ by the SSS Postulate and hence $\angle ARB \cong \angle ARK$, which means that $\overrightarrow{AE} \perp \overline{BK}$.

**15.** Since $\angle 1 \cong \angle 2$, $\angle CFD \cong \angle CMD$ (vertical angles are congruent), and therefore $\triangle CFD \cong \triangle CMD$ by the ASA Postulate. Hence $\angle 5 \cong \angle 6$ by the definition of congruent triangles. Note, incidentally, that this means that $\overline{CD} \perp \overline{FM}$.

**16.** Since $B$-$P$-$Q$ and $P$-$Q$-$C$, $BQ = BP + PQ$ and $PC = PQ + QC$; and since $BP = CQ$ is given, $BQ = PC$ by the Addition Property of Equality. Since $AB = DC$ and $AQ = DP$ are given, $\triangle ABQ \cong \triangle DCP$ by the SSS Postulate, and $\angle A \cong \angle D$ by CPCTC.

---

**8.** Given: The figure with $\overline{AB} \perp \overleftrightarrow{MK}$. $B$ is the midpoint of $\overline{MK}$.

Prove: $\angle x \cong \angle y$.

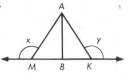

**9.** Two lines, $L_1$ and $L_2$, are perpendicular at a point $Q$. From a point $P$ on $L_2$ segments are drawn to the points $R$ and $S$ of $L_1$ such that $\angle RPQ \cong \angle SPQ$. Prove that $RQ = SQ$.

**10.** In the figure, $BC = DE$, $\angle B \cong \angle E$, and $AB = EF$.

Prove that $AC = DF$.

**11.** In the figure, $\angle 1 \cong \angle 6$, $\angle 2 \cong \angle 5$, and $\angle 3 \cong \angle 4$.

Prove that $AD = CF$. What part of the hypothesis is not necessary for your proof? $\angle 1 \cong \angle 6$

**12.** In the figure, $\angle B \cong \angle E$, $DB = CE$, and $AD = CF$. Can you prove that $\triangle ABD \cong \triangle FEC$? No If so, do so. If not, explain why not. **The corresponding angles are not included between corresponding sides.**

**13.** In this figure, $M$-$R$-$K$, $MR = KR$, $MG = KG$, and $\angle M \cong \angle K$. Prove that $\overline{GR} \perp \overline{MK}$.

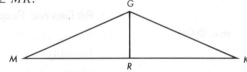

**14.** Given that $\overrightarrow{AE}$ bisects $\overline{BK}$ at $R$ such that $AB = AK$. Prove that $\overrightarrow{AE} \perp \overline{BK}$.

**15.** In the figure, $CF = CM$, $\angle 1 \cong \angle 2$, and $\angle 3 \cong \angle 4$.

Prove that $\angle 5 \cong \angle 6$.

**16.** Given the figure with $AB = DC$, $BP = CQ$, and

$$AQ = DP.$$

Prove that $\angle A \cong \angle D$.

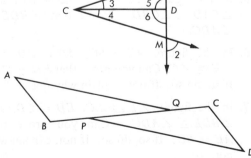

17. Given that $\overline{PQ}$ and $\overline{RS}$ intersect at $T$, with $P$-$T$-$Q$ and $R$-$T$-$S$, such that $RT = QT$, $\overline{PR} \perp \overline{RS}$, and $\overline{SQ} \perp \overline{PQ}$. Prove that $\angle P \cong \angle S$.

18. Prove that if in the figure, $PS = QS$, $PV = QV$, and $\angle x \cong \angle y$, then $\overline{SV} \perp \overline{PQ}$.

19. In the figure, $AB = CB$, $\angle MAE \cong \angle NCD$, and $AE = CD$. Prove that $\triangle ABE \cong \triangle CBD$.

20. In the figure, $\angle EAB \cong \angle DCB$, $\angle EBA \cong \angle DBC$, and $\angle E \cong \angle D$. Can you prove that $\triangle ABE \cong \triangle CBD$? Explain. There are no pairs of No congruent sides.

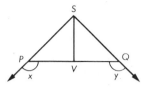

21. In the figure, $AB = CB$, $m\angle MAE = m\angle NCD$, and $m\angle ABD = m\angle CBE$. Does it follow that $BE = BD$? If your answer is yes, supply the proof.

22. In the figure on the left below, $A$, $B$, $C$, and $D$ are noncoplanar points with $B$, $C$, and $D$ in the plane $E$. Show that if $\overline{AB} \perp \overline{BC}$, $\overline{AB} \perp \overline{BD}$, and $BC = BD$, then $AC = AD$.

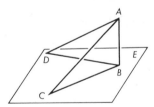
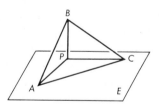

23. In the figure on the right above, $\angle ABP \cong \angle CBP$, $\overline{BP} \perp \overline{AP}$, and $\overline{BP} \perp \overline{CP}$. Prove that $AB = CB$. $\triangle ABP \cong \triangle CBP$ by the ASA Postulate and consequently, AB = CB by CPCTC.

24. Given the figure with $\angle BAE \cong \angle ABC$, $AE = BC$, $DE = DC$, and $BD = AD$. Prove that $\triangle ADC \cong \triangle BDE$.

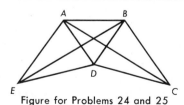

Figure for Problems 24 and 25

25. In the figure above let $\overline{AD} \cap \overline{BE} = \{P\}$ and let $\overline{BD} \cap \overline{AC} = \{Q\}$. Show that if $\triangle APB \cong \triangle BQA$ and $AC = BE$, then $AE = BC$.

# 5-6 BISECTORS OF ANGLES

## Classroom Notes

Every angle has a bisector. This fact is useful, but may hardly seem to require proof. The proof is an existence and uniqueness proof, and since we do not discuss such proofs until Section 6-3, we recommend that you not emphasize the proof of the Angle Bisector Theorem. Concentrate on the use of the definition in the problems.

The proof of the Angle Bisector Theorem is incomplete: we have not shown that the midpoint $D$ of $\overline{BC}$ is in the interior of $\angle BAC$. It is possible to complete the proof, using Theorems 6-5 and 6-6, page 204. Since the result is obvious and the proof is tedious, it seemed better on this page to leave well enough alone, and postpone the question to Section 6-6.

An exact study of such incidence properties as this is difficult, and only the strongest students can handle it. For examples, see Problems 5-7 in Problem Set 6-6.

## Quiz

Given: Opposite rays $\overrightarrow{AB}$ and $\overrightarrow{AC}$ and any ray $\overrightarrow{AD}$
Prove: The bisectors of $\angle BAD$ and $\angle CAD$ are perpendicular.
Proof: $\angle BAD$ and $\angle CAD$ are supplementary since they form a linear pair, $m\angle BAD + m\angle CAD = 180$. If $\overrightarrow{AQ}$ bisects $\angle BAD$ and $\overrightarrow{AR}$ bisects $\angle CAD$, then $m\angle QAD = (\frac{1}{2})m\angle BAD$ and $m\angle DAR = (\frac{1}{2})m\angle CAD$ by definition of angle bisector. Hence, $m\angle QAD + m\angle DAR = (\frac{1}{2})180 = 90$, and $\overrightarrow{AQ}$ and $\overrightarrow{AR}$ form a 90° angle. Thus $\overrightarrow{AQ} \perp \overrightarrow{AR}$.

## Answers to Problems

1. (a) False. All points on the bisector of an angle, with the exception of the end point of the bisector, lie in the interior of the angle. The end point of the bisector is the vertex of the angle and thus lies on the angle, not in its interior.

---

## 5-6   BISECTORS OF ANGLES

The markings on this figure indicate that $\overrightarrow{AD}$ bisects $\angle BAC$. But $\overrightarrow{AE}$ does *not* bisect $\angle BAC$ because it points in the wrong direction.

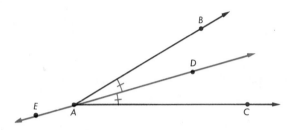

Thus we arrive at the following definition.

### Definition

If $D$ is in the interior of $\angle BAC$, and $\angle BAD \cong \angle DAC$, then $\overrightarrow{AD}$ bisects $\angle BAC$, and $\overrightarrow{AD}$ is called the *bisector* of $\angle BAC$.

**Theorem 5-3.**   The Angle Bisector Theorem

*Every angle has one and only one bisector.*

**Proof.**   (1) On the sides of $\angle A$ choose points $B$ and $C$ (by the Point-Plotting Theorem) so that $AB = AC$. $\overline{BC}$ exists (by the Line Postulate). Let $D$ be the midpoint of $\overline{BC}$ (See the marks on the figure.). Let $\overrightarrow{AD}$ be the ray through $D$ (by Postulate 4). By SSS, $\triangle ADB \cong \triangle ADC$. Therefore, $\angle BAD \cong \angle CAD$. This makes $\overrightarrow{AD}$ a bisector of $\angle A$ by the definition of a bisector of an angle.

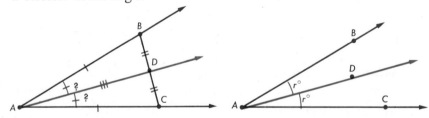

(2) To show that $\overrightarrow{AD}$ is the *only* bisector of $\angle A$, let $m\angle CAD = r$. Since $\angle BAD \cong \angle CAD$, we know that $m\angle BAD = r$. Thus, by the Angle Addition Postulate, $m\angle BAC = r + r = 2r$. By the Division Property we get $\frac{1}{2} m\angle BAC = r$. Since $D$ is on the $B$-side of $\overrightarrow{AC}$, the Angle Construction Postulate assures us that there is *only one* ray, $\overrightarrow{AD}$, that gives us an angle with the measure $r$.

## Problem Set 5–6

**1.** Are the following statements true or false? Explain your answers.

(a) The bisector of an angle lies entirely in the interior of the angle. F

(b) The bisector of an angle forms two acute angles with the sides of the angle. T

**2.** Given that $\overrightarrow{AP}$ bisects $\angle BAC$ and $AC = AB$. Prove that $PC = PB$.
Observe that $\triangle CAP \cong \triangle BAP$ by the SAS Postulate and consequently, $PC = PB$ by CPCTC.

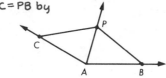

**3.** $A$ and $B$ are points on opposite sides of $\overleftrightarrow{CY}$, $C$ is in the interior of $\angle AXB$, and $C$-$X$-$Y$. If $\angle AXY \cong \angle BXY$, prove that $\overrightarrow{XC}$ bisects $\angle AXB$.

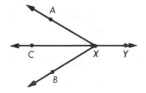

**4.** Given two angles that form a linear pair. Prove that their bisectors are perpendicular.

**5.** Given: $\overleftrightarrow{AD}$, $\overleftrightarrow{BE}$, and $\overleftrightarrow{CF}$ intersect one another at $K$, and $\overrightarrow{KC}$ bisects $\angle DKB$.

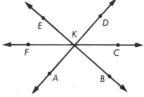

Prove: $\overrightarrow{KF}$ bisects $\angle AKE$.

---

**6.** Given $\overrightarrow{AB} \perp \overrightarrow{AC}$; $D$, $E$, and $G$ are points in the interior of $\angle BAC$ such that $\overrightarrow{AE}$ bisects $\angle DAC$ and $\overrightarrow{AG}$ bisects $\angle DAB$. Prove that $m\angle EAG = 45$.

**7.** In the figure, the planes $E$ and $F$ intersect in $\overleftrightarrow{AB}$. $\overrightarrow{PK}$ is in the plane $F$ and intersects $\overleftrightarrow{AB}$ at $D$. $PA = PB$, $\angle PAB \cong \angle PBA$, and $D$ is the midpoint of $\overline{AB}$. Prove that $\overrightarrow{PK}$ bisects $\angle APB$.

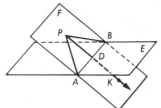

**1.** (b) True. Since the measure of an angle is a real number $r$, $0 < r < 180$, the measure of each angle whose sides are one of the sides of the given angle and the bisector of the given angle is therefore a real number $r/2$, $0 < r/2 < 90$. Therefore, each of these angles is acute.

**3.** Since $C$, $X$, and $Y$ are collinear, with $X$ between $C$ and $Y$, $\angle CXA$ and $\angle AXY$ form a linear pair and are consequently, by the Supplement Postulate, supplementary. Similarly, $\angle CXB$ and $\angle BXY$ are supplementary. But $\angle AXY \cong \angle BXY$, and since supplements of congruent angles are congruent this implies that $\angle CXA \cong \angle CXB$. But by the definition of the bisector of an angle this means that $\overrightarrow{XC}$ bisects $\angle AXB$.

**4.** Suppose that $A$-$C$-$B$ and that $D$ is not on $\overrightarrow{AB}$. Then $\angle ACD$ and $\angle DCB$ form a linear pair, and are consequently supplementary. Let $\overrightarrow{CE}$ be the bisector of $\angle ACD$, and $\overrightarrow{CF}$ be the bisector of $\angle DCB$. Then $m\angle ECF = m\angle ECD + m\angle DCF = \frac{1}{2}m\angle ACD + \frac{1}{2}m\angle DCB = \frac{1}{2}(m\angle ACD + m\angle DCB) = \frac{1}{2}(180) = 90$. Therefore, $\overrightarrow{CE} \perp \overrightarrow{CF}$.

**5.** Since $\overrightarrow{KC}$ bisects $\angle DKB$, $m\angle DKC = m\angle CKB$. Since vertical angles are congruent, $m\angle DKC = m\angle AKF$ and $m\angle CKB = m\angle FKE$. Therefore $m\angle AKF = m\angle FKE$, which means that $\overrightarrow{KF}$ bisects $\angle AKE$.

**6.** By the definition of bisector, $m\angle EAD = \frac{1}{2}m\angle DAC$ and $m\angle DAG = \frac{1}{2}m\angle BAD$, so $m\angle EAG = m\angle EAD + m\angle DAG = \frac{1}{2}m\angle DAC + \frac{1}{2}m\angle BAD = \frac{1}{2}m\angle BAC$ by the AAP and the Addition Property of Equality. But $m\angle BAC = 90$ so $m\angle EAG = 45$.

**7.** Observe that $\triangle PAD \cong \triangle PBD$ by the SAS Postulate, and that consequently $\angle APD \cong \angle BPD$. This means that $\overrightarrow{PD}$, which is the same ray as $\overrightarrow{PK}$, bisects $\angle APB$.

**8.** Part (1). Since $S$ is in the interior of $\angle QON$ and $\angle SOQ \cong \angle SON$, $\overrightarrow{OS}$ bisects $\angle QON$. Similarly $\overrightarrow{OT}$ bisects $\angle QON$. But by Theorem 5–3 an angle has only one bisector. Therefore $\overrightarrow{OS} = \overrightarrow{OT}$, which means that $O$, $S$, and $T$ are collinear. Part (2). Consider the ray $\overrightarrow{OA}$ which is opposite to $\overrightarrow{OS}$. Since $\angle MOA \cong \angle SON$ and $\angle POA \cong \angle QOS$ (Vertical angles), and since $\angle SON \cong \angle QOS$ we have $\angle MOA \cong \angle POA$. This means that the ray opposite to $\overrightarrow{OS}$ is the bisector of $\angle MOP$. But $\overrightarrow{OR}$ is the bisector of $\angle MOP$. Since an angle has only one bisector, this means that $\overrightarrow{OR}$ is the ray opposite to $\overrightarrow{OS}$. Therefore, points $R$, $O$, $S$, and $T$ are collinear.

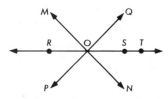

**9.** Since (1) $AB = AC$, (2) $\overrightarrow{AD}$ bisects $\angle BAC$, and (3) $AD = AD$, $\triangle ABD \cong \triangle ACD$ by SAS, and consequently $BD = DC$. Secondly, $\triangle BPD \cong \triangle CPD$ by SSS, and therefore $\angle BPD \cong \angle CPD$. This means that $\overrightarrow{PD}$ bisects $\angle BPC$. (See Solution Section for two-column proof.)

## 5–7 ISOSCELES AND EQUILATERAL TRIANGLES

### Classroom Notes

The Isosceles Triangle Theorem is a striking example of the use of a particular correspondence to establish a congruence. We merely show that an isosceles triangle is congruent to itself under a correspondence which interchanges the vertices at the ends of the base. To establish a correspondence between a triangle and itself is at this stage a rather subtle device, and it is advisable to discuss the theorem in detail in class. We suggest that you prove it, after preliminary discussion, in two-column form, following the conventions given in the comments on Section 5–4 concerning the sequence and alignment of the congruences. Note that the discussion at the bottom of page 125 and Problems 4, 5, 9, and 10 of Problem Set 5–1 are designed to prepare the student for the proof of the Isosceles Triangle Theorem. It may be worthwhile to refer back to them in class.

**8.** $\overleftrightarrow{MN}$ and $\overleftrightarrow{PQ}$ intersect at $O$, with $M\text{-}O\text{-}N$ and $P\text{-}O\text{-}Q$. $S$ and $T$ are points in the interior of $\angle QON$ such that $\angle TOQ \cong \angle TON$ and $\angle SOQ \cong \angle SON$. $\overrightarrow{OR}$ bisects $\angle POM$. Prove that $R$, $S$, and $T$ are collinear.

**9.** In the figure, $P$, $B$, $D$, and $C$ are points in plane $E$, and $A$ is not in $E$. $\triangle ABC$ and $\triangle PBC$ are isosceles, with $AB = AC$ and $PB = PC$, respectively. Prove that if $\overrightarrow{AD}$ bisects $\angle BAC$, then $\overrightarrow{PD}$ bisects $\angle BPC$.

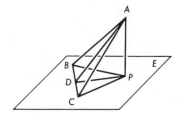

## 5–7 ISOSCELES AND EQUILATERAL TRIANGLES

At the end of Section 5–1 we mentioned the correspondence between a triangle and itself which is possible when two or more sides of the triangle have the same length. A correspondence of this kind is used in the following congruence theorem.

**Theorem 5–4.**    The Isosceles Triangle Theorem

> **If two sides of a triangle are congruent, then the angles opposite these sides are congruent.**

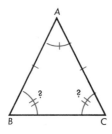

**Restatement.** Given $\triangle ABC$. If $\overline{AB} \cong \overline{AC}$, then $\angle B \cong \angle C$.

**Proof.** Consider the correspondence

$$ABC \leftrightarrow ACB$$

between $\triangle ABC$ and itself. Under this correspondence, we see that

$$\overline{AB} \leftrightarrow \overline{AC}$$
$$\overline{AC} \leftrightarrow \overline{AB}$$
$$\angle A \leftrightarrow \angle A.$$

Since this is an SAS correspondence, it follows by the SAS Postulate that

$$\triangle ABC \cong \triangle ACB,$$

that is, the correspondence $ABC \leftrightarrow ACB$ is a congruence. By the definition of a congruence between triangles all pairs of corresponding parts are congruent. Therefore $\angle B \cong \angle C$ because these angles are corresponding parts.

We now show how the above proof looks in two-column form. The same restatement and figure are used.

### Proof

| STATEMENTS | REASONS |
| --- | --- |
| 1. $\overline{AB} \cong \overline{AC}$. $\overline{AC} \cong \overline{AB}$. | 1. Given |
| 2. $\angle A \cong \angle A$. | 2. Reflexive Property |
| 3. $\triangle ABC \cong \triangle ACB$. | 3. Steps 1 and 2 and SAS |
| 4. $\angle B \cong \angle C$. | 4. Definition of a congruence between triangles |

### Definitions

A triangle with two congruent sides is called *isosceles*. The remaining side is the *base*. The two angles that include the base are *base angles*. The angle opposite the base is the *vertex angle*.

In these terms, we can state Theorem 5–4 in the following form: "The base angles of an isosceles triangle are congruent."

### Definitions

A triangle whose three sides are congruent is called *equilateral*.

A triangle no two of whose sides are congruent is called *scalene*.

A triangle is *equiangular* if all three of its angles are congruent.

Using the terms *equilateral* and *equiangular*, we state a theorem which readily follows from Theorem 5–4. We denote this theorem as Corollary 5–4.1. A *corollary* is a theorem which is an immediate consequence of another theorem.

### Background Material

Although a good proof of the Isosceles Triangle Theorem was known in antiquity, a rather unsatisfactory proof became conventional. This "conventional" proof says to bisect $\angle BAC$, letting $D$ be the point at which the bisecting ray $\overrightarrow{AF}$ intersects the base, and then show that $\triangle ADB$ and $\triangle ADC$ are congruent. This proof is longer than the proof in the text, and also, it is incomplete. From a rigorous point of view it is necessary to show that $\overrightarrow{AF}$ intersects $\overline{BC}$. This follows from the Crossbar Theorem (Problem 7 of Problem Set 6–6), but the latter theorem is extremely difficult, and its difficulties are foreign to the problem before us. The proof of the Isosceles Triangle Theorem in the text is simple, in keeping with the simplicity of the theorem itself, and is free from logical gaps.

### Note of Interest

Euclid's own proof of the Isosceles Triangle Theorem (Problem 32 on page 173) is rather difficult.* The proof given in the text is due, essentially, to Pappus, although Pappus naturally did not use the sort of formulation for the congruence postulates that we have been using here. Not many years ago—or so the story goes—an electronic computing machine was programmed to look for proofs of elementary geometric theorems. When the *pons asinorum* theorem was fed into the machine, it promptly printed Pappus' proof on the tape. This is said to have been a surprise to the people who had coded the problem; Pappus' proof was new to them. What had happened, of course, was

---

*Euclid's proof was a stumbling block to some students in the Middle Ages, and the theorem consequently acquired the name *pons asinorum* or "The Bridge of Asses."

that the SAS postulate had been coded in some form such as this:

"If (1) *A*, *B*, and *C* are noncollinear; (2) *D*, *E*, and *F* are noncollinear; (3) $\overline{AB} \cong \overline{DE}$; (4) $\overline{BC} \cong \overline{EF}$; and (5) $\angle ABC \cong \angle DEF$, then (6) $\overline{AC} \cong \overline{DF}$; (7) $\angle ACB \cong \angle DFE$; and (8) $\angle BAC \cong \angle EDF$."

This is the sort of austere language in which people commonly talk to transistors; you can't indoctrinate them with vague preconceptions. Since nothing in the coded statement of the SAS Postulate says there must be *two* triangles, the machine did not operate on that assumption. It did not occur to anybody to code, explicitly, two triangles, so the machine proceeded, in its simple-minded way, to produce the simplest and most elegant proof.

**Classroom Notes**

It is, of course, necessary to distinguish between the Isosceles Triangle Theorem and its converse. (The idea of *converse* is discussed in the next section.) It is advisable to use the two-column form of proof and carefully establish that the correspondence used in this proof is a congruence.

**Corollary 5–4.1**

*Every equilateral triangle is equiangular.*

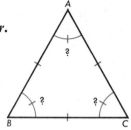

**Restatement.** Given $\triangle ABC$. If $BC = AC = AB$, then $\angle A \cong \angle B \cong \angle C$.

To prove this, we apply Theorem 5–4 twice. The details are left to you.

The following theorem may look like Theorem 5–4, but in fact it is different. A look at the restatements shows this quite clearly. Notice also the difference in the markings of the figures.

**Theorem 5–5**

*If two angles of a triangle are congruent, then the sides opposite them are congruent.*

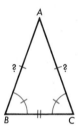

**Restatement.** Given $\triangle ABC$. If $\angle B \cong \angle C$, then $AB = AC$.

**Proof.** Since $\angle B \cong \angle C$, $\overline{BC} \cong \overline{CB}$, and $\angle C \cong \angle B$, the correspondence

$$ABC \leftrightarrow ACB$$

is an ASA correspondence. Therefore it is a congruence, and

$$\triangle ABC \cong \triangle ACB.$$

Therefore $AB = AC$, because corresponding sides are congruent.

**Corollary 5–5.1**

*Every equiangular triangle is equilateral.*

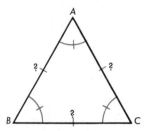

You should be able to write a restatement and a proof.

## Problem Set 5–7

**1.** Select the choice which correctly completes each sentence.

(a) An angle bisector is a

  (i) segment.      (ii) ray.      (iii) plane.

(b) An equilateral triangle is

  (i) isosceles.      (ii) scalene.      (iii) not isosceles.

(c) A corollary is a

  (i) definition.      (ii) postulate.      (iii) theorem.

(d) If two angles of a triangle are congruent, we can conclude that it has two congruent sides according to a

  (i) definition.      (ii) corollary.      (iii) theorem.

**2.** In the figure, $\triangle PRS$ is isosceles, with $PR = PS$. Prove that $\angle x \cong \angle y$.
∠PRS ≅ ∠PSR (Theorem 5-4)
∠PRS and ∠x are supplements
∠PSR and ∠y are supplements
(The Supplement Postulate)
∠x ≅ ∠y (Theorem 4-6)

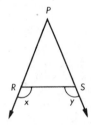

**3.** In the figure, $\angle m \cong \angle n$. Prove that $\triangle GHK$ is isosceles.
∠GHK ≅ ∠GKH (Theorem 4-6)
△GHK is isosceles (Theorem 5-5)

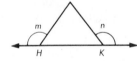

**4.** Which one of the theorems, Theorem 5–4 or Theorem 5–5, is used to prove that a triangle is isosceles?

**5.** Why is the following "proof" an example of circular reasoning?

**Theorem:** The base angles of an isosceles triangle are congruent.

**Restatement:** Given $\triangle ABC$. If $AC = BC$, then $\angle A \cong \angle B$.
Note that the theorem to be proved
is the Isosceles Triangle Theorem.
The "proof" uses the theorem as a
reason thereby assuming
it is true.

**Proof**

| STATEMENTS | REASONS |
|---|---|
| 1. $AC = BC$. | 1. Given |
| 2. $\angle A \cong \angle B$. | 2. The Isosceles Triangle Theorem |

## Explanation for Problems

Rather curiously, in Problem 7 on page 158 we cannot omit the hypothesis that the figure lies in a plane; without it, the theorem is false. Consider the following situation.

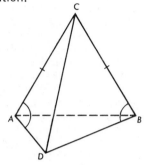

In the figure $CA = CB$ and $m\angle CAD = m\angle CBD$, even though $\angle CAD$ is in the plane determined by these points and $\angle CBD$ is in a different plane. There is insufficient information to prove that $\triangle ADB$ is isosceles.

**Quiz**

Given: $\triangle ABC$ is isosceles with $AB = BC$ and $AD = EC$.
Prove: $\triangle BDE$ is isosceles.

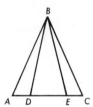

Proof: $\angle A \cong \angle C$ (Theorem 5–4), $AB = BC$ (definition of isosceles) and $AD = EC$ (given) so $\triangle ADB \cong \triangle CEB$ by SAS. Then $BD = BE$ (CPCTC) and $\triangle BDE$ is isosceles by Theorem 5–5.

**6.** Since $AC = BC$, $m\angle CAB = m\angle CBA$. Similarly, since $AD = BD$, $m\angle DAB = m\angle DBA$. Therefore $m\angle CAB + m\angle DAB$ $m\angle CBA + m\angle DBA$. But, by the AAP, $m\angle CAB + m\angle DAB = m\angle CAD$ and $m\angle CBA + m\angle DBA = m\angle CBD$. Therefore, $m\angle CAD = m\angle CBD$.

**7.** It is given that $m\angle CAD = m\angle CBD$. Since $AC = BC$, $m\angle CAB = m\angle CBA$ by Theorem 5–4. Hence, by subtraction, $m\angle BAD = m\angle ABD$. But by Theorem 5–5 this implies that $AD = BD$.

**8.** The proofs given for Problems 6 and 7 employ the AAP, and to use the AAP we must know that points $A$, $B$, $C$, and $D$ are coplanar. It is easy to give a proof of Problem 6 which does not use the AAP and which is valid even if the points $A$, $B$, $C$, and $D$ are noncoplanar. (Simply introduce $\overline{CD}$ and use the SSS Postulate.) It is not possible to prove Problem 7 without the AAP and so in this problem it is necessary to assume that $A$, $B$, $C$, and $D$ are coplanar.

**9.** Given $\triangle ABC$. If $\angle A \cong \angle B \cong \angle C$, then $BC = AC = AB$. Since $\angle A \cong \angle B$, $BC = AC$ by Theorem 5–5. Since $\angle B = \angle C$, $AC = AB$. Therefore $BC = AC = AB$.

**10.** (1) Since $\angle KPQ \cong \angle KQP$, $KP = KQ$ by Theorem 5–5. (2) Also $\angle MPK \cong \angle NQK$ since supplements of congruent angles are congruent. (3) $MP = QN$. Therefore $\triangle MPK \cong \triangle NQK$ by SAS and consequently $MK = KN$.

**13.** Given: $\triangle ABC$ in which $AB = BC$. $D$ is the point at which the bisector of $\angle B$ intersects $\overline{AC}$. Prove: (1) $AD = DC$, (2) $\overline{BD} \perp \overline{AC}$. Proof: Use either the SAS Postulate or the ASA Postulate.

**14.** Since $AC = CB$, $\angle A \cong \angle B$. But $\angle A \cong \angle x$, and $\angle B \cong \angle y$. Therefore, $\angle x \cong \angle y$ and by Theorem 5–5, $CD = CE$ so that $\triangle CDE$ is isosceles.

**16.** $\triangle PMQ \cong \triangle PNQ$ by SAS and $PM = PN$ by CPCTC. Thus, $\triangle MNP$ is isosceles by Theorem 5–5.

---

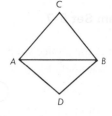

**6.** Given: The plane figure $ADBC$ with $AD = BD$ and $AC = BC$.

Prove: $\angle CAD \cong \angle CBD$.

**7.** Given: The plane figure $ADBC$ with $AC = BC$ and $\angle CAD \cong \angle CBD$.

Prove: $AD = BD$.

**8.** In Problems 6 and 7, does the hypothesis have to specify that the figure is a plane figure? Explain.

**9.** Prove Corollary 5-5.1:

Every equiangular triangle is equilateral.

**10.** Given the figure as marked, prove that $\triangle MNK$ is isosceles.

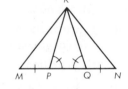

**11.** Given $\triangle ABC$ for which the correspondence $ABC \leftrightarrow ACB$ is a congruence. We can conclude that $\triangle ABC$ is

    (a) scalene.     (b) isosceles.     (c) equilateral.

**12.** Given $\triangle ABC$ for which the correspondence $ABC \leftrightarrow CAB$ is a congruence. We can conclude that $\triangle ABC$ is

    (a) scalene.     (b) isosceles.     (c) equilateral.

---

**13.** Prove: The bisector of the angle opposite the base of an isosceles triangle bisects the base and is perpendicular to the base.

**14.** In the figure, $AC = BC$, $\angle A \cong \angle y$, and $\angle B \cong \angle x$. Prove that $\triangle CDE$ is isosceles.

**15.** In a plane, $C$ and $D$ are points on opposite sides of $\overleftrightarrow{AB}$ such that $\triangle ABC$ is an equilateral triangle and $\triangle ABD$ is an equiangular triangle. Prove that $\angle C \cong \angle D$. **See Solution Section.**

**16.** Given that in the figure $\overline{PQ} \perp \overline{MQ}$, $\overline{PQ} \perp \overline{NQ}$, and $MQ = NQ$, prove that $\triangle MNP$ is isosceles.

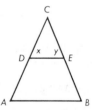

**17.** In the figure, $\angle PMN \cong \angle PNM$ and $\angle MPQ \cong \angle NPQ$. Prove that $\angle PMQ \cong \angle PNQ$. **See Solution Section.**

## 5–8 CONVERSES

Theorems 5–4 and 5–5 are related in a special way; they are called *converses* of each other. The relation between them is more readily seen if we restate them as follows.

**Theorem 5–4**

> *Given $\triangle ABC$. If $AB = AC$, then $\angle C \cong \angle B$.*

**Theorem 5–5**

> *Given $\triangle ABC$. If $\angle C \cong \angle B$, then $AB = AC$.*

Similarly, Corollaries 5–4.1 and 5–5.1 are converses of each other. Here also, the relation between them becomes clearer if we restate them.

**Corollary 5–4.1**

> *Given $\triangle ABC$. If $\triangle ABC$ is equilateral, then $\triangle ABC$ is equiangular.*

**Corollary 5–5.1**

> *Given $\triangle ABC$. If $\triangle ABC$ is equiangular, then $\triangle ABC$ is equilateral.*

When we have proved a theorem which has a simple *if . . . , then . . .* form, it is usually a good idea to investigate the converse. We *need* to make a separate investigation in each case, because it can easily happen that the converse of a true theorem is not true at all. For example, we know that if two angles form a vertical pair, then they are congruent. The converse would say that if two angles are congruent, then they form a vertical pair; and this is not only false, but ridiculous. Similarly, if $x = y$, then $x^2 = y^2$. The converse would say that if $x^2 = y^2$, then $x = y$. Thus the converse is false: it fails to allow for the possibility that $x = -y$.

If it happens that a theorem and its converse are both true, then we can combine them into a single theorem, using the phrase *if and only if*. For example, we can combine Theorems 5–4 and 5–5 like this.

**Theorem**

> *Given $\triangle ABC$. $\angle C \cong \angle B$ if and only if $AB = AC$.*

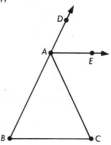

**Answers to Problems**

1. (a) If you cannot see the moon, then clouds cover the sky.
  Both statement and converse are false.
 (b) If you see lions and elephants, then you are in Africa.
  Both the statement and its converse are false.
 (c) If you are seriously ill, then you have scarlet fever.
  The statement is true; the converse is false.

2. (a) If two angles are right angles, they are congruent.
  The statement is false; the converse is true.
 (b) If two angles are supplementary, they form a linear pair.
  The statement is true; the converse is false.
 (c) Any point equidistant from the end points of a segment is on the perpendicular bisector of the segment.
  The statement is true; the converse is true.
 (d) If two angles are each acute, then they are complementary.
  The statement is true; the converse is false.

3. No. John has repeated his original statement only interchanging the <u>order</u> of the phrases. The correct converse is: If I will be burned, then I hold a lighted match too long.

5. A triangle is isosceles if and only if it is equilateral. No, a triangle may have two sides congruent without having three sides congruent.

6. If in △*ABC*, (1) and (3), then (2). If in △*ABC*, (3) and (2), then (1).

---

Similarly we can combine Corollaries 5–4.1 and 5–5.1.

**Theorem**

*A triangle is equiangular if and only if it is equilateral.*

**Problem Set 5–8**

1. Write the converse of each statement. Try to decide whether each statement, and each converse, is true or false.

 (a) If clouds cover the sky, you cannot see the moon.

 (b) You see lions and elephants if you are in Africa.

 (c) Anyone who has scarlet fever is seriously ill.

2. Follow the directions of Problem 1.

 (a) If two angles are congruent, they are right angles.

 (b) If two angles form a linear pair, then they are supplementary.

 (c) A point on the perpendicular bisector of a segment is equidistant from the ends of the segment.

 (d) Two angles are each acute if they are complementary.

3. When asked to give the converse of the statement, "If I hold a lighted match too long, I will be burned," John said, "I will be burned if I hold a lighted match too long." Was John's sentence the converse of the original statement? Discuss.
  **No**

4. (a) Is a converse of every true statement true? Justify your answer.   **No, see 1(c), 2(b), 2(d)**

 (b) May a converse of a false statement be true? Justify your answer.
  **Yes, see 1(a), 2(a)**

5. Combine the following into one statement, using *if and only if.*

  If a triangle is equilateral, it is isosceles.

  If a triangle is isosceles, it is equilateral.

 Is the resulting statement true? Explain.
  **NO**

---

6. Some statements may have several parts to the hypothesis; we may get a converse by interchanging a *part* of the hypothesis with a *part* of the conclusion. For example, the statement

  If in △*ABC*, *D* is the midpoint of $\overline{AB}$ and *AC = BC*, then $\overrightarrow{CD}$ bisects ∠*ACB*.

 has the following two converses.

  If in △*ABC*, *D* is the midpoint of $\overline{AB}$ and $\overrightarrow{CD}$ bisects ∠*ACB*, then *AC = BC*.

  If in △*ABC*, $\overrightarrow{CD}$ bisects ∠*ACB* with *D* on $\overline{AB}$ and *AC = BC*, then *D* is the midpoint of $\overline{AB}$.

Diagram these statements using the notation (1) for "$D$ is the midpoint of $\overline{AB}$," (2) for "$AC = BC$," and (3) for "$\overrightarrow{CD}$ bisects $\angle ACB$." Thus the first statement becomes

In $\triangle ABC$, if (1) and (2), then (3).

**7.** Write all of the converses of the following statement.

If $\angle A$ and $\angle B$ are both congruent and complementary, then $m\angle A = m\angle B = 45$.

Are all of the converses true?

**8.** Write all of the converses of the following statement.

If $C$ and $D$ are points on opposite sides of $\overleftrightarrow{AB}$, $AC = BC$, and $AD = BD$, then $\triangle ACD \cong \triangle BCD$.

Are all of the converses true?

## 5–9 OVERLAPPING TRIANGLES. USE OF FIGURES TO CONVEY INFORMATION

Frequently in geometric figures, the congruent triangles that we work with are not entirely separate but overlap, like $\triangle AFM$ and $\triangle FAH$ in the figure below.

To avoid confusion and mistakes in dealing with such cases, it is especially important to write our congruences correctly:

$$\triangle AFM \cong \triangle FAH.$$

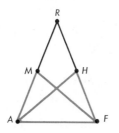

Looking only at the congruence $\triangle AFM \cong \triangle FAH$, and *not* at the figure, we know that

$$AF = FA, \quad FM = AH, \quad AM = FH$$

because these are corresponding sides, under the correspondence

**Answers to Problems**

**7.** Let (1) stand for "$\angle A \cong \angle B$," (2) stand for "$\angle A$ and $\angle B$ are complementary," and (3) stand for "$m\angle A = 45 = m\angle B$." Converses are "If (2) and (3), then (1)" and "If (3) and (1), then (2)." Both are true.

**8.** Let (1) stand for "$C$ and $D$ are points on opposite sides of $\overleftrightarrow{AB}$," (2) stand for "$AC = BC$," (3) stand for "$AD = BD$," and (4) stand for "$\triangle ACD \cong \triangle BCD$." Converses are "If (2), (3), and (4), then (1)," "If (3), (4), and (1), then (2)," and "If (4), (1), and (2), then (3)." The second and third are true but the first is not, as the following example shows.

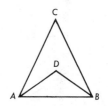

**5–9 OVERLAPPING TRIANGLES. USE OF FIGURES TO CONVEY INFORMATION**

**Overlapping triangles.** Once the student has acquired the technique of proving simple "one-step" congruences, we ask him to extend this technique in two ways: (1) to establish the congruences of pairs of overlapping triangles, and (2) to do "two-step" congruence proofs, that is, to establish the congruence of a pair of triangles which cannot be proved congruent until a preliminary pair of triangles have first been proved congruent.

Recommend to the student that in working on a problem involving overlapping triangles he follow this procedure:

(1) He should observe which pairs of triangles might be proved congruent, and then decide which pair of triangles, if he *could* prove

them congruent, would yield the desired result. The student may find it valuable to indicate this crucial pair of triangles with colored pencils.

(2) He should prove this crucial pair of triangles congruent. This is frequently no easy task; however, (because the triangles are overlapping) there is often an opportunity to use the identity congruence for segments and for angles, the definition of "between," the Angle Addition Postulate, and Theorem 4–6.

**Quiz**

Given: $AB = EF$, $AC = DE$, $BD = CF$.

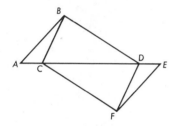

Prove: $\angle BCD \cong \angle FDC$.
Proof: $AC + CD = CD + DE$ (Addition Property of Equality) and $AD = CE$ (definition of between). Since $AB = EF$ and $BD = CF$ then $\triangle ABD \cong \triangle EFC$ by SSS so that $\angle BDA \cong \angle FCE$. Then $\triangle BCD \cong \triangle FDC$ by SAS and $\angle BCD \cong \angle FDC$ by CPCTC.

Let us now consider a case in which this problem comes up in the proof of a theorem.

*Given:* $HA = HF$; $HM = HQ$.

*To prove:* $FM = AQ$.

We shall prove that the two segments are corresponding sides of congruent triangles. To use this method, we must locate the triangles which contain $\overline{FM}$ and $\overline{AQ}$. These are $\triangle HMF$ and $\triangle HQA$, and these triangles overlap quite a bit. But we can show that they are congruent. The proof, written in the double-column form, is given below.

**Proof**

| STATEMENTS | REASONS |
|---|---|
| 1. $HA = HF$. | 1. Given |
| 2. $\angle H \cong \angle H$. | 2. Reflexive Property |
| 3. $HM = HQ$. | 3. Why? Given |
| 4. $\triangle HMF \cong \triangle HQA$. | 4. Why? SAS |
| 5. $FM = AQ$. | 5. Why? CPCTC |

A strictly logical proof must not depend on a figure but must follow from the postulates, the definitions, and the previously proved theorems. But geometers use figures very freely as a shorthand in explaining what the problem was in the first place. In this spirit, we stated Example 1 at the beginning of Section 5–4 as follows.

*Given:* $\overline{AR}$ and $\overline{BH}$ bisect each other at $F$.

*To prove:* $\overline{AB} \cong \overline{RH}$.

We explained in Section 5–5 that the whole theorem could be conveyed by additional marks on the figure, without using words at all, like the figure at the top of the next page.

To get along without a figure, we would have to restate Example 1 in the following form.

### Example 1

Let $A$, $B$, $F$, $H$, and $R$ be five noncollinear points lying in a plane. If (1) $F$ is between $A$ and $R$, (2) $F$ is between $B$ and $H$, (3) $AF = FR$, and (4) $BF = FH$, then (5) $AB = RH$.

The first two statements of the example, using figures, are surely easier to read than the third statement, and they are just as exact, once you understand how figures are used as shorthand. We shall use figures to indicate collinearity of points, the order of points on a line, the location of points in the interiors of angles, and, in general, the relative positions of points, lines, and planes. On the other hand, you should *not* infer that segments are congruent, or that angles are congruent, merely because they look as if they were. To convey this kind of information by a figure, we have to *mark* the figure in the usual way.

For example, the figure on the right tells us that $\overline{DE} \cong \overline{EF}$, but the figure on the left does not tell us that $\overline{AB} \cong \overline{BC}$, even though careful measurement suggests that this ought to be the case

Similarly, the figure on the left tells us that $\overline{AB} \perp \overline{CD}$, but the figure on the right does not.

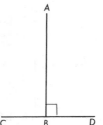

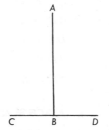

# Answers to Problems

2. Since $\overline{KG} \perp \overline{GH}$ and $\overline{LH} \perp \overline{GH}$, $\angle KGH$ and $\angle LHG$ are right angles and consequently $\angle KGH \cong \angle LHG$. Therefore, $\triangle KGH \cong \triangle LHG$ by the ASA Postulate, and consequently $\overline{KH} \cong \overline{LG}$.

3. Observe that $\angle ACE \cong \angle BCD$ by the identity congruence, and therefore $\triangle ACE \cong \triangle BCD$ by the ASA Postulate.

5. Since $MR = NS$, $MR + RS = NS + RS$. But since $R$ is between $M$ and $S$, $MR + RS = MS$, and similarly $NS + RS = RN$. Therefore, $\triangle PSM \cong \triangle QRN$ by the SSS Postulate, and consequently $\angle PSM \cong \angle QRN$. $\angle PSN \cong \angle QRM$ because they are supplements of congruent angles.

7. (1) $\angle A \cong \angle B$. (2) Since $AD = BE$, $AD + DE = BE + DE$; and this means that $AE = DB$. (3) Since $\angle ADG \cong \angle BEF$, and since supplements of congruent angles are congruent, $\angle GDB \cong \angle AEF$. Therefore, $\triangle AFE \cong \triangle BGD$ by the ASA Postulate, and consequently $\angle AFE \cong \angle BGD$. But since supplements of congruent angles are congruent, we can now conclude that $\angle CFE \cong \angle CGD$.

8. (1) Since $m\angle VRT = m\angle TSV$ and $m\angle TRS = m\angle VSR$, we can conclude that $m\angle VRT + m\angle TRS = m\angle TSV + m\angle VSR$. But by the Angle Addition Postulate, $m\angle VRT + m\angle TRS = m\angle VRS$, and $m\angle TSV + m\angle VSR = m\angle TSR$. Therefore, $m\angle VRS = m\angle TSR$. (2) $RS = SR$. (3) $m\angle RSV = m\angle SRT$. Therefore, $\triangle VRS \cong \triangle TSR$ by the ASA Postulate, and consequently $RV = ST$. Note that we cannot use the Angle Addition Postulate unless we assume that the points $V$, $R$, $S$, and $T$ are coplanar.

10. (1) Since $m\angle x = m\angle y$ and $m\angle m = m\angle n$, we can conclude that $m\angle x + m\angle m = m\angle y + m\angle n$. But by the Angle Addition Postulate $m\angle x + m\angle m = m\angle CDB$, and $m\angle y + m\angle n = m\angle CEA$. Therefore, $m\angle CDB = m\angle CEA$. (2) Since $m\angle y = m\angle x$, $CD = CE$. (3) $m\angle C = m\angle C$. Therefore, $\triangle CDB \cong \triangle CEA$ by the ASA Postulate, and consequently $BC = AC$.

---

## Problem Set 5–9

1. In the figure, $RV = ST$, $RQ = SP$, and $\angle VRQ \cong \angle TSP$. Complete the proof that $QV = PT$.

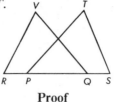

**Proof**

| STATEMENTS | REASONS |
|---|---|
| 1. $RV = ST$. | 1. _Given_ |
| 2. $\angle VRQ \cong \angle TSP$. | 2. _Given_ |
| 3. _$RQ = SP$_. | 3. Given |
| 4. $\triangle RQV \cong$ _$\triangle SPT$_. | 4. _SAS Postulate_ |
| 5. _$QV = PT$_. | 5. _CPCTC_ |

2. In the figure on the left below, $\overline{KG} \perp \overline{GH}$, $\overline{LH} \perp \overline{GH}$, and $\angle KHG \cong \angle LGH$. Prove that $\overline{KH} \cong \overline{LG}$.

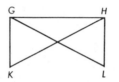

3. Given $AC = BC$ and $\angle CAE \cong \angle CBD$ in the figure on the right above, prove that $\triangle ACE \cong \triangle BCD$.

4. In the figure, $AC = BC$, $DC = EC$, and $AD = BE$. Complete the proof that
$$\angle ACE \cong \angle BCD.$$

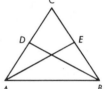

**Proof**

| STATEMENTS | REASONS |
|---|---|
| 1. $AC = BC$. $DC = EC$. | 1. Given |
| 2. $AD = BE$. | 2. _Given_ |
| 3. $DE = DE$. | 3. _Reflexive Property of Equality_ |
| 4. $AD + DE = BE + DE$. | 4. Addition Property of Equality |
| 5. $AE = BD$. | 5. Definition of between, and Step 4 |
| 6. _$\triangle ACE \cong \triangle BCD$_ | 6. _SSS Postulate_ |
| 7. $\angle ACE \cong \angle BCD$. | 7. _CPCTC_ |

5. In the figure, $PM = QN$, $PS = QR$, and $MR = NS$. Prove that $\angle PSN \cong \angle QRM$.

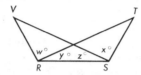

6. In the figure, $AF = BG$, $\angle A \cong \angle B$, and $AE = BD$. Prove that $EF = DG$. $\triangle AEF \cong \triangle BDG$ (SSS) and thus $EF = DG$.

7. In the figure, $\angle A \cong \angle B$, $AD = BE$, and $\angle ADG \cong \angle BEF$. Prove that $\angle CFE \cong \angle CGD$.

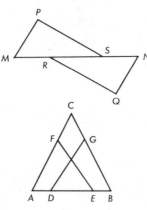

Figure for Problems 6 and 7

8. Given the plane figure with $w = x$ and $y = z$, prove that $RV = ST$.

9. On the sides of $\angle A$ the points $B$ and $C$ are taken such that $AB = AC$. A line through $B$ is perpendicular to $\overrightarrow{AC}$ at $D$. Similarly, a line through $C$ is perpendicular to $\overrightarrow{AB}$ at $E$. Given $AD = AE$, prove that $BD = CE$. Observe that $\triangle ABD \cong \triangle AEC$ (ASA) and thus $BD = CE$.

10. Given that in the figure $\angle x \cong \angle y$ and $\angle m \cong \angle n$, prove that $AC = BC$.

11. In the figure, $DF = EF$ and $\angle x \cong \angle y$. Prove that $\triangle AFB$ is isosceles.

12. In the figure, $AC = BC$ and $DC = EC$. Prove that $DF = EF$.

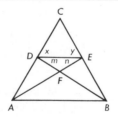

Figure for Problems 10, 11, 12

13. In the figure, $MK = MQ$, $ML = MP$, and $KL = QP$. Find the angle congruent to $\angle KML$. Prove your answer. $\triangle KML \cong \triangle QMP$ (SSS) $\angle KML \cong \angle QMP$ (CPCTC)

14. In the figure, $MK = MQ$, $\angle K \cong \angle Q$, $\overline{PM} \perp \overline{MK}$, and $\overline{LM} \perp \overline{MQ}$. Prove that $\angle L \cong \angle P$.

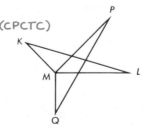

Figure for Problems 13 and 14

11. (1) $\angle C \cong \angle C$. (2) Since $\angle x \cong \angle y$, $CD \cong CE$. (3) Since $DF = EF$, $m\angle m = m\angle n$, and since it is given that $m\angle x = m\angle y$, we can conclude that $m\angle x + m\angle m = m\angle y + m\angle n$. But by the AAP, $m\angle x + m\angle m = m\angle CDB$, and $m\angle y + m\angle n = m\angle CEA$. Therefore $m\angle CDB = m\angle CEA$. Hence $\triangle CDB \cong \triangle CEA$ by the ASA Postulate and consequently $DB = EA$. But by hypothesis $DF = EF$, and so by subtraction $FB = FA$, which means that $\triangle AFB$ is isosceles.

12. (1) Since $BC = AC$, $\angle C \cong \angle C$, and $DC = EC$, we can conclude that $\triangle CDB \cong \triangle CEA$ by the SAS Postulate, and consequently that $m\angle CDB = m\angle CEA$. (2) But since $DC = EC$, $m\angle x = m\angle y$; and hence by subtraction $m\angle m = m\angle n$. (3) Therefore $DF = EF$ by Theorem 5-5.

14. (1) $MK = MQ$. (2) $\angle K \cong \angle Q$. (3) Since $PM \perp \overline{MK}$ and $\overline{LM} \perp \overline{MQ}$, $\angle KMP$ and $\angle QML$ are each right angles, and consequently $m\angle KMP = m\angle QML$. Therefore, $m\angle KMP + m\angle PML = m\angle QML + m\angle PML$, and hence by the Angle Addition Postulate $m\angle KML = m\angle QMP$. Therefore, $\triangle KML \cong \triangle QMP$ by the ASA Postulate, and consequently, $\angle L \cong \angle P$.

15. (1) $\triangle ABD \cong \triangle BAC$ by the SSS Postulate, and consequently $\angle ABD \cong \angle BAC$. (2) Since it is given that $AK = BN$ and $AG = BH$, we can now conclude that $\triangle AKG \cong \triangle BNH$ by SAS, and consequently that $KG = NH$.

**17.** Given: $L$ is a perpendicular bisector of $\overline{XY}$ at $S$, $R$ is the midpoint of $\overline{XS}$, $T$ is the midpoint of $\overline{YS}$, $AX = BY$, $AT = BR$.
Prove: $AS = BS$.

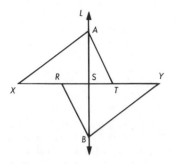

Proof:
1. $S$ is the midpoint of $\overline{XY}$, $R$ is the midpoint of $\overline{XS}$, $T$ is the midpoint of $\overline{YS}$. (Given)
2. $XS = YS$, $XR = RS = ST = TY$. (Definition of midpoint and transitivity)
3. $XT = YR$. (Addition Property of Equality)
4. $AX = BY$, $AT = BR$. (Given)
5. $\triangle AXT \cong \triangle BYR$. (SSS)
6. $\angle ATX \cong \angle BRY$. (CPCTC)
7. $\triangle BRS \cong \triangle ATS$. (SAS)
8. $AS = BS$. (CPCTC)

**18.** Since $\angle D \cong \angle DKM$, we can conclude that $KM = DM$ by the converse of the Isosceles Triangle Theorem. Then since (1) $KM = TM$, (2) $\angle KMD \cong \angle TMC$, and (3) $DM = CM$, $\triangle KMD \cong \triangle TMC$ by the SAS Postulate, and consequently $\angle D \cong \angle C$. Now, since (1) $\angle D \cong \angle C$, (2) $DM = CM$, and (3) $\angle DMA \cong \angle CMB$, we can conclude that $\triangle DMA \cong \triangle CMB$ by the ASA Postulate, and that consequently $AD = BC$.

**20.** (a) $\angle MXY$ and $\angle YXN$ are supplementary. $\angle NXZ$ and $\angle ZXM$ are supplementary. Since supplements of congruent angles are congruent, we can conclude that $\angle YXN \cong \angle ZXM$. Therefore $\triangle YXN \cong \triangle ZXM$ by the ASA Postulate and consequently $\angle Y \cong \angle Z$.

(b) No. We can assert that $\angle MXY$ and $\angle YXN$ are supplementary provided we know that they form a linear pair. In order for these angles to form a linear pair,

**15.** In the figure below, $AD = BC$, $AC = BD$, $AK = BN$, and $AG = BH$. Prove that $KG = NH$.

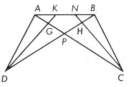

**16.** In the figure, $B$, $D$, $H$ are in the plane $E$, and $A$ and $C$ are not in $E$. $\overline{AB} \perp \overline{BD}$, $\overline{CD} \perp \overline{HD}$, $AB = HD$, and $CD = BD$.

Prove that $AD = HC$.
$\triangle ABD \cong \triangle HDC\ (\text{SAS})$

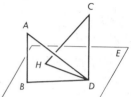

**17.** The line $L$ is perpendicular to $\overline{XY}$ and bisects $\overline{XY}$ at $S$. $R$ and $T$ are the midpoints of $\overline{XS}$ and $\overline{YS}$, respectively. $A$ and $B$ are points of $L$, on opposite sides of $\overleftrightarrow{XY}$, such that $AX = BY$ and $AT = BR$. Prove that $AS = BS$.

**18.** Prove that if $\angle D \cong \angle DKM$ and $KM = CM = TM$, then $AD = BC$.

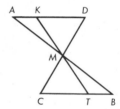

**19.** (a) Prove that if, in the figure, $X$ is the midpoint of $\overline{MN}$, $MZ = NY$, and $XZ = XY$, then $\angle Y \cong \angle Z$. $\triangle MXZ \cong \triangle NXY\ (\text{SSS})$ and $\angle Y \cong \angle Z\ (\text{CPCTC})$

(b) Under the conditions of this problem, must $M$, $N$, $X$, $Y$, and $Z$ be coplanar? **No**

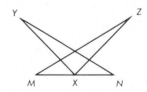

Figure for Problems 19 and 20

**20.** (a) In the figure, $M$, $N$, $X$, $Y$, and $Z$ are coplanar, $X$ is the midpoint of $\overline{MN}$, $\angle M \cong \angle N$, and $\angle MXY \cong \angle NXZ$. Prove that $\angle Y \cong \angle Z$.

(b) Is it necessary that $M$, $N$, $X$, $Y$, and $Z$ be coplanar, for this conclusion to follow? Explain.

## 5-10 QUADRILATERALS, MEDIANS, AND BISECTORS

A quadrilateral is a four-sided figure.  Examples are:

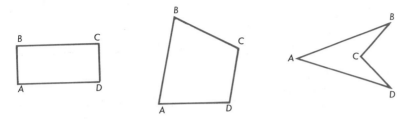

A figure like the one on the left below is *not* a quadrilateral.

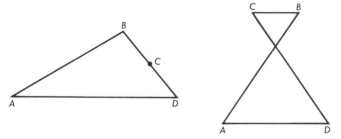

Also, the sides of quadrilateral are not allowed to cross each other.
The figure on the right above is *not* a quadrilateral.

The following definitions are stated so as to include the cases we want
to include and rule out the cases that we want to rule out.

### Definitions

Let *A*, *B*, *C*, and *D* be four coplanar points.  If no three of these points
are collinear, and the segments $\overline{AB}$, $\overline{BC}$, $\overline{CD}$, and $\overline{DA}$ intersect only at
their end points, then the union of the four segments is called a *quadri-
lateral*.  The four segments are called its *sides*,
and the points *A*, *B*, *C*, and *D* are called its
*vertices*.  The angles $\angle DAB$, $\angle ABC$, $\angle BCD$,
and $\angle CDA$ are called its *angles*, and may be
denoted briefly as $\angle A$, $\angle B$, $\angle C$, and $\angle D$.
$\overline{AC}$ and $\overline{BD}$ are called its *diagonals*.  The *perimeter* of a quadrilateral is the sum of the
lengths of its sides.

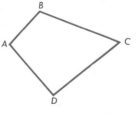

If all four angles of a quadrilateral are
right angles, then the quadrilateral is a
*rectangle*.

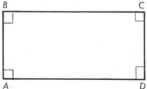

---

points *M*, *X*, *N*, and *Y* must be
coplanar.  Similarly points *M*,
*X*, *N*, and *Z* must be coplanar.
However, there is no necessity
for all five points *M*, *X*, *N*, *Y*, and
*Z* to be coplanar.

### 5-10 QUADRILATERALS, MEDIANS, AND BISECTORS

**Classroom Notes**

As you know, congruent triangles
frequently arise in our work with
quadrilaterals; our purpose in introducing these definitions of quadrilaterals at this time is simply to
give the student some practice with
congruent triangles which occur in
the context of quadrilaterals.  We
make, however, no further use of
quadrilaterals until Chapter 9,
where they are studied for their
own sake.  Learning these definitions can be easily postponed until
that time.

**Note of Interest**

Squares and rectangles are defined
in this section.  At this state, however, since the Parallel Postulate
has not been introduced, our postulates are not adequate to prove
that such figures exist.  In hyperbolic geometry, a branch of non-
euclidean geometry, no such
figures exist.  Note, however, that
there is nothing logically wrong
about using squares and rectangles
in the problems in this section.  If
the *hypothesis* of a theorem says
that □*ABCD* is a rectangle, then
*conclusions* can be drawn by the
methods of this chapter, and thus
we get true theorems.  The Parallel
Postulate is needed only when we
want to *conclude* that a certain
quadrilateral must be a rectangle.

## Explanation for Problems

This section also includes the important definitions of a *median* of a triangle and an *angle bisector* of a triangle. You should assign Problems 3, 4, 8, 9, 12, and 13 of Problem Set 5–10. Problems 3 and 4 of Problem Set 5–10 and Problem 3 of Problem Set 6–4 are very important and should be compared.

### Quiz

**1.** $\square ABCD$ is a square with $Q$ the midpoint of $\overline{AD}$. Prove $\triangle QBC$ is isosceles.
  Proof: $\overline{AB} \cong \overline{CD}$ because sides of squares are congruent. $\angle A \cong \angle D$ since angles of squares are congruent. Since $Q$ is the midpoint of $AD$, $AQ = QD$ and $\triangle ABQ \cong \triangle DCQ$ by SAS. Thus $BQ = QC$ and $\triangle BQC$ is isosceles by definition of isosceles triangle.
**2.** Prove the median $\overline{AD}$ of isosceles $\triangle ABC$ is perpendicular to the base $\overline{BC}$.
  Proof: $AB = AC$ and $\angle B \cong \angle C$ since $\triangle ABC$ is isosceles. $BD = DC$ by definition of median. $\triangle ABD \cong \triangle ACD$ by SAS and $\angle ADB \cong \angle ADC$. If two angles are congruent and supplementary, they are right angles. Thus $\overline{AD} \perp \overline{BC}$.

### Answers to Problems

**2.** A bisector of an angle is a ray; an angle bisector of a triangle is a segment.
**3.** Since $\overline{AD} \perp \overline{BC}$, $\angle ADB$ and $\angle ADC$ are each right angles and consequently $\angle ADB \cong \angle ADC$. Since $\overline{AD}$ is a median of $\triangle ABC$, $D$ is the midpoint of $\overline{BC}$: $BD = DC$. Therefore, $\triangle ADB \cong \triangle ADC$ (SAS) and consequently (1) $\angle BAD \cong \angle CAD$ so that $\overrightarrow{AD}$ bisects $\angle BAC$, and (2) $AB = AC$ so that $\triangle ABC$ is isosceles.
**4.** Use the figure and notation of Problem 3. Given: $AB = AC$ and $\overline{AD}$ is the median to $\overline{BC}$. Prove: (1) $\overline{AD} \perp \overline{BC}$, and (2) $\overrightarrow{AD}$ bisects $\angle BAC$. Proof: $\triangle ADB \cong \triangle ADC$ by SSS and consequently (1) $\angle ADB \cong \angle ADC$, which means that $\overline{AD} \perp \overline{BC}$, and (2) $\angle BAD \cong \angle CAD$, which means that $\overrightarrow{AD}$ bisects $\angle BAC$.
**5.** $\overline{OM} \cong \overline{PQ}$ and $\angle M \cong \angle Q$ since, by definition, the sides of a square are all congruent, and the angles are all congruent. Since it is given that $R$ is the

If all four of the angles are right angles, and all four sides are congruent, then the quadrilateral is a *square*.

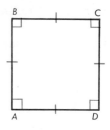

The quadrilateral itself is denoted by $\square ABCD$.

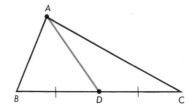

In this figure, the marks tell us that $\overline{AD}$ is a *median* of $\triangle ABC$. This can be formally stated as follows.

### Definition

A *median* of a triangle is a segment whose end points are a vertex of the triangle and the midpoint of the opposite side.

Every triangle has three medians—one for each vertex.

The marks on this figure indicate that $\overline{AE}$ is an *angle bisector of* $\triangle ABC$.

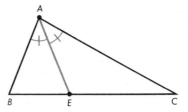

### Definition

A segment is an *angle bisector of a triangle* if (1) it lies in the ray which bisects an angle of the triangle, and (2) its end points are the vertex of this angle and a point of the opposite side.

[*Query:* How many angle bisectors does a triangle have?]

### Problem Set 5–10

**1.** Construct a large scalene triangle. Using a ruler, construct its three medians. Using a protractor, construct its three angle bisectors.

**2.** What is the distinction between *a bisector of an angle* and *an angle bisector of a triangle*?

**3.** Given: $\triangle ABC$ with median $\overline{AD}$ perpendicular to side $\overline{BC}$.

  Prove: $\overrightarrow{AD}$ bisects $\angle BAC$ and $\triangle ABC$ is isosceles.

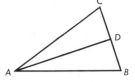

4. Prove: The median to the base of an isosceles triangle is perpendicular to the base and bisects the angle opposite the base.

5. Given that ☐$MOPQ$ is a square, with $R$ the midpoint of $\overline{MQ}$. Prove that $\triangle ROP$ is isosceles.

6. In ☐$GKHM$, $\angle G$ and $\angle H$ are right angles, $GK = MH$, and $GH = MK$. $G$ and $H$ are on opposite sides of $\overleftrightarrow{MK}$. Prove that ☐$GKHM$ is a rectangle.

7. In ☐$ABCD$, $\overline{AC} \perp \overline{BD}$ at $F$, $AC = BD$, and $FD = FC$. Prove that $\triangle ACD \cong \triangle BDC$.

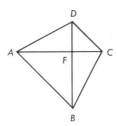

8. Prove: The medians to the congruent sides of an isosceles triangle are congruent. *Form necessary congruent △'s by SAS using base angles as included angles.*

9. Prove: In an isosceles triangle, the bisectors of the base angles are congruent. *Form necessary congruent △'s by ASA using base as included side.*

10. ☐$ABCD$ is a square and $P$, $Q$, $R$, and $S$ are the midpoints of $\overline{AB}$, $\overline{BC}$, $\overline{CD}$, and $\overline{DA}$, respectively. Prove that $\angle PQR \cong \angle PSR$.

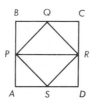

11. ☐$ABFH$ is a square. $X$ is a point on $\overrightarrow{AH}$, and $Y$ is a point on $\overrightarrow{BF}$ such that $AX = BY$. Prove that $AY = BX$. *△ABY ≅ △BAX (SAS) and therefore AY = BX. (CPCTC)*

12. $\overrightarrow{AP}$ bisects $\angle BAC$. $D$ is a point on $\overrightarrow{AB}$, and $E$ is a point on $\overrightarrow{AC}$ such that $AD = AE$. Prove that $PD = PE$. *△PAD ≅ △PAE (SAS) and therefore PD = PE. (CPCTC)*

13. Given the figure with $\overrightarrow{KM}$ bisecting both $\angle HKG$ and $\angle HSG$. Prove that $\overrightarrow{KM} \perp \overline{HG}$.

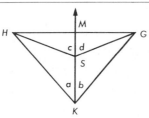

14. In the figure, $XU = XV$ and
$$\angle 1 \cong \angle 2 \cong \angle 3 \cong \angle 4.$$

Prove that
$$\angle 5 \cong \angle 6 \quad \text{and} \quad \angle 7 \cong \angle 8.$$

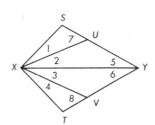

midpoint of $\overline{MQ}$, we can conclude that $\triangle OMR \cong \triangle PQR$, and consequently that $\overline{OR} \cong \overline{RP}$. Thus, $\triangle ORP$ is isosceles.

6. (1) Since $GK \cong MH$, $GH = MK$, and $HK = HK$, $\triangle GHK \cong \triangle MKH$ by SSS. (2) Therefore $\angle K \cong \angle H$, so $\angle K$ is a right angle. (3) Similarly, $\angle M$ is a right angle. (4) By definition, ☐$GKHM$ is a rectangle.

7. (1) Since $AC = BD$ and $FC = FD$, we can conclude, by subtraction, that $AF = FB$. (2) The vertical angles, $\angle AFD$ and $\angle BFC$ are congruent. (3) It is given that $FD = FC$. Therefore, $\triangle AFD \cong \triangle BFC$ (SAS), and consequently $AD = BC$. We can now conclude that $\triangle ACD \cong \triangle BDC$ by the SSS Postulate.

10. (1) Since ☐$ABCD$ is a square, all sides and angles are congruent. $P$, $Q$, $R$, $S$ are midpoints, so it follows that $AP = PB = QC = CR = RD = DS = SA = AP$. (2) Then $\triangle APS \cong \triangle BQP \cong \triangle CRQ \cong \triangle DSR$, making $PS = QP = RQ = SR$. (3) Then $\triangle PQR \cong \triangle PSR$ by SSS and $\angle PQR \cong \angle PSR$.

13. $\angle HSK \cong \angle GSK$ by Theorem 4-7. Therefore $\triangle HSK \cong \triangle GSK$ by ASA, giving $HK = GK$. Then $\triangle HMK \cong \triangle GMK$ by SAS, and $\overrightarrow{KM} \perp \overline{HG}$ by the definitions of right angle and of perpendicular.

14. $\triangle XUY \cong \triangle XVY$ by SAS, so that $\angle 5 \cong \angle 6$. Then $\triangle XSY \cong \triangle XTY$ by ASA so $XS = XT$. Finally, $\triangle XSU \cong \triangle XTV$ by SAS from which $\angle 7 \cong \angle 8$.

**3.** Since $m\angle ACE = m\angle ACD + m\angle DCE$ and $m\angle BCD = m\angle BCE + m\angle ECD$ by the AAP, and since $m\angle ACD = m\angle BCD$ is given, it follows that $\angle ACE \cong \angle BCD$. Since $\overline{CD} \cong \overline{CE}$ and $\overline{CB} \cong \overline{CA}$ by corresponding parts, $\triangle ACE \cong \triangle BCD$ by the SAS Postulate.

**4.** $\triangle MEG \cong \triangle MHG$ by SSS and thus $\angle EMG \cong \angle HMG$. Since these angles form a linear pair, each is a right angle by Theorem 4-5, and so $\overline{HE} \perp \overline{GK}$ (definition of perpendicular).

**6.** $\triangle AEB \cong \triangle CED$ by ASA and thus $AE = CE$. $AB = CB$ is given. Then $\triangle AEB \cong \triangle CEB$ by SSS.

**7.** $RQ = SQ$ by the definition of midpoint and $\angle RQP \cong \angle SQP$, since both are right angles. Thus $\triangle RQP \cong \triangle SQP$ by SAS and $RP = SP$ by corresponding parts. Therefore $\triangle PRS$ is isosceles. Also $\angle RPQ \cong \angle SPQ$ by corresponding parts; therefore $2m\angle RPQ = m\angle RPQ + m\angle SPQ = m\angle RPS$ by AAP and $m\angle RPS = 90$, since $\overline{PR} \perp \overline{PS}$ so $m\angle RPQ = 45$.

**10.** $CE = GE$ and $DE = FE$ by the definition of bisector and $\angle CED \cong \angle GEF$ by the Vertical Angle Theorem. Therefore $\triangle CED \cong \triangle GEF$ by SAS, and so $DC = FG$ and $\angle ECD \cong \angle EGF$. Then $\angle ACB \cong \angle ECD \cong \angle EGF \cong \angle HGI$ and $DB = FH$ is given, so $BC = DB - BC = FH - FG = HG$. Since $\angle B \cong \angle H$ is given, it follows that $\triangle ABC \cong \triangle IHG$ by ASA. Therefore $\angle A \cong \angle I$.

**11.** Prove $\triangle BCK \cong \triangle DCK$ by SSS, and conclude that $\angle BCK \cong \angle DCK$. Then prove $\triangle BCA \cong \triangle DCA$ by SAS, and conclude that $AB = AD$.

---

## Supplementary Problems

**1.** Given: $AC = BC$, $\angle A \cong \angle B$, $AD = BE$.
Prove: $DC = EC$. $\triangle ACD \cong \triangle BCE$ (SAS)

**2.** Given: $\triangle ACD \cong \triangle BCE$.
Prove: $\angle CDE \cong \angle CED$. Observe CD=CE and use Thm 5-4

**3.** Given: $\triangle ACD \cong \triangle BCE$.
Prove: $\triangle ACE \cong \triangle BCD$.

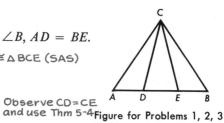

Figure for Problems 1, 2, 3

**4.** In the figure, $\overline{HE}$ and $\overline{GK}$ bisect each other at $M$, and $EG = GH = HK$. Prove that $\overline{HE}$ and $\overline{GK}$ are perpendicular at $M$.

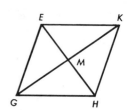

**5.** Given that $\triangle MPS \cong \triangle LTR$ and that $\triangle TLR \cong \triangle KQV$, what conclusion follows? What theorem supports your answer? $\triangle MPS \cong \triangle QKV$; Thm 5-1

**6.** In the figure, $AB = DC = BC$, $\angle DCE \cong \angle BCE \cong \angle BAE$, and $\angle CDE \cong \angle ABE$. Prove that $\triangle ABE \cong \triangle CBE$.

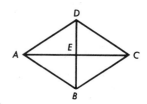

**7.** Given $\triangle PRS$ such that $\overline{PR} \perp \overline{PS}$. $Q$ is the midpoint of $\overline{RS}$ and $\overline{PQ} \perp \overline{RS}$. Prove that $\triangle PRS$ is isosceles and that $m\angle RPQ = 45$.

**8.** In the figure, $\angle A \cong \angle I$, $AB = HI$, and $\angle B \cong \angle H$. Prove that $AC = GI$. Use ASA

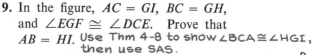

**9.** In the figure, $AC = GI$, $BC = GH$, and $\angle EGF \cong \angle DCE$. Prove that $AB = HI$. Use Thm 4-8 to show $\angle BCA \cong \angle HGI$, then use SAS.

**10.** In the figure, $\overline{DF}$ and $\overline{CG}$ bisect each other at $E$, $DB = FH$, and $\angle B \cong \angle H$. Prove that $\angle A \cong \angle I$.

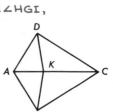

**11.** Given: $DC = BC$ and
$DK = BK$.
Prove: $AD = AB$.

**12.** Given two congruent triangles, the median to a side of one triangle is congruent to the median to the corresponding side of the other triangle. Use SAS with angles opposite medians as included angles.

**13.** Prove that the angle bisector of each angle of an equilateral triangle is a median of the triangle. Use SAS to show bisector meets at midpoint of opposite side.

14. In the figure, $MQ = PQ = PR = NR$.
Prove that $\triangle MNP$ is isosceles.

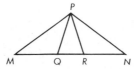

15. Given $\triangle RST$ with $S$-$X$-$T$ such that $SX = SR$. $Q$ is a point such that $R$-$Q$-$T$ and $\overrightarrow{SQ}$ bisects $\angle RST$. Draw $\overline{QX}$. Which angle is congruent to $\angle R$? Prove the congruence. △ SXQ ≅ △ SRQ by SAS

∠SXQ

16. In the figure, $XW = ZY$, $AX = BY$, and $AZ = BW$. Which angle is congruent to $\angle A$?∠B Prove the congruence.

Since AZ = BW, AZ+ZW = BW+ZW,
which means AW = BZ.
△ AWX ≅ △ BZY by SSS.

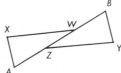

17. Given the figure on the left below, in which $\overline{QS}$ and $\overline{RT}$ bisect each other at $P$, prove that $AP = BP$. △ RPQ ≅ △ TPS (SAS) then
△ RPA ≅ △ TPB (ASA)

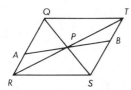

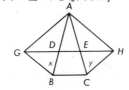

18. If, in the figure on the right above, $AB = AC$, $AD = AE$, and $\angle x \cong \angle y$, prove that $AG = AH$. △ BGD ≅ △ CHE (ASA), then
△ AGB ≅ △ AHC by SAS.

19. (a) In the figure on the left below $AD = BC$, $AB = DC$, and $\overline{MN}$ bisects $\overline{AC}$ at $K$. Does $\overline{AC}$ bisect $\overline{MN}$? Prove your answer.
Yes
(b) Must all points of the figure be coplanar? Yes, AKC and MKN
determine plane of figure.

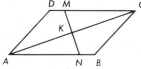

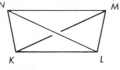

20. (a) In the figure on the right above, $NK = ML$ and $MK = NL$. Prove that $\angle MNK \cong \angle NML$. △ MNK ≅ △ NML (SSS) and
∠MNK ≅ ∠NML (CPCTC)
(b) Must $KM$ and $NL$ intersect? No

21. Given: The figure with $AB = AC$ and

$$\angle RCB \cong \angle TBC.$$

Prove: $RC = BT$.

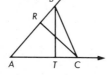

22. Prove that, given two congruent triangles, the angle bisector of an angle of one triangle is congruent to the angle bisector of the corresponding angle of the other triangle. Use ASA with sides opposite angle
bisectors as included sides.

14. Since $PQ = PR$, $\angle PQR \cong \angle PRQ$ by the Isosceles Triangle Theorem. Then by the Supplement Postulate and the theorem that supplements of congruent angles are congruent, we can conclude that $\angle MQP \cong \angle NRP$. Finally, $\triangle MQP \cong \triangle NRP$ by SAS, and consequently $MP = NP$, so $\triangle MNP$ is isosceles.

19. (a) Yes. $\triangle BAC \cong \triangle DCA$ by SSS, and consequently $\angle BAC \cong \angle DCA$. Also $AK = KC$, and $\angle AKN \cong \angle CKM$ since vertical angles are congruent. Therefore $\triangle AKN \cong \triangle CKN$, and consequently $MK = KN$, which means that $\overline{AC}$ bisects $\overline{MN}$.

21. $AB = AC$, and since the base angles of an isosceles triangle are congruent, $m\angle ACB = m\angle ABC$. But it is given that $m\angle RCB = m\angle TBC$, and so by subtraction $m\angle ACR = m\angle ABT$. Therefore $\triangle ACR \cong \triangle ABT$ by ASA, and consequently $RC = BT$.

**23.** (a) $\triangle CPR \cong \triangle CPS$ by SSS, and consequently $\angle CPR \cong \angle CPS$. But $\angle CPR$ and $\angle CPS$ also form a linear pair, and consequently are supplementary. Therefore, by Theorem 4-4, $\angle CPR$ and $\angle CPS$ are each right angles; this means that $\overline{CP} \perp \overline{RS}$.

(b) Observe that since $\overline{AP} \perp \overline{RS}$, $\triangle APR \cong \triangle APS$ by SAS, and that consequently $AR = AS$. This enables us to conclude that $\triangle ACR \cong \triangle ACS$ by SSS, and that consequently $\angle ACR \cong \angle ACS$.

**24.** Draw $\overline{AB}$. Prove $\triangle ABN \cong \triangle PCN$ by SAS. Prove $\triangle ABK \cong \triangle CQK$ by SAS. Then $PC = AB = CQ$.

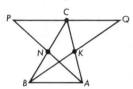

**25.** $\triangle DBA \cong \triangle EBC$ by SSS and $\angle DBA \cong \angle EBC$. Therefore $m\angle EBC + m\angle ABC = m\angle DBA + m\angle ABC$, and by the AAP $m\angle ABE = m\angle DBC$. Hence $\triangle ABE \cong \triangle DBC$ by SAS.

**27.** $\overleftrightarrow{XY}$ is perpendicular to the plane containing $A$, $B$, $C$, $X$. The triangles are congruent by SAS.

**28.** Prove $\triangle KPV \cong \triangle LPV$ by SSS making $\angle KPV \cong \angle LPV$. $\triangle KPM \cong \triangle LPM$ by SAS making $\angle KMP \cong \angle LMP$. $\angle SVM \cong \angle LVP \cong \angle KVP \cong \angle RVM$. Hence $\triangle MSV \cong \triangle MRV$ by ASA, making $MS = MR$. Then $\triangle MST \cong \triangle MRT$ by SAS, so that $ST = RT$.

**30.** $\triangle ABT$ is not necessarily congruent to $\triangle ACR$ since SSA is not a valid technique for proving two triangles congruent. Each of these figures satisfies the given conditions of the problem, but in the figure on the right surely $AR \neq AT$.

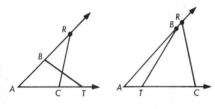

---

**23.** In the figure, $A$, $P$, and $C$ lie in the plane $E$, and $R$ and $S$ are on opposite sides of $E$. $\overline{AP} \perp \overline{RS}$, $RP = SP$, and $RC = SC$. Prove that

(a) $\overline{CP} \perp \overline{RS}$.

(b) $\angle ACR \cong \angle ACS$.

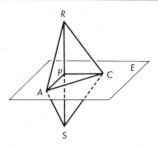

**24.** Let $\overline{AP}$ and $\overline{BC}$ bisect each other at $N$, and $\overline{AC}$ and $\overline{BQ}$ bisect each other at $K$. Show that $QC = PC$.

**25.** Given $\triangle ABC$ with $AB = BC$. Let $D$ be a point on the side of $\overleftrightarrow{AB}$ opposite to $C$ such that $\triangle ABD$ is equilateral. Let $E$ be a point on the side of $\overleftrightarrow{BC}$ opposite to $A$ such that $\triangle BCE$ is equilateral. Prove that $AE = CD$.

**26.** In the figure, $G$ and $B$ trisect $\overline{MR}$, and $G$ and $P$ trisect $\overline{AC}$. $AG \doteq BG$. Show that $\angle R \cong \angle C$. [*Note: Trisect* means to separate into three congruent parts.]

Since $AG = \frac{1}{3} AC$, $BG = \frac{1}{3} MR$ and $AG = BG$, $AC = MR$. $\triangle ABG \cong \triangle MGP$ by SAS so $\angle A \cong \angle M$ and $AB = MP$. $\triangle MPR \cong \triangle ABC$ by SAS. Thus, $\angle R \cong \angle C$.

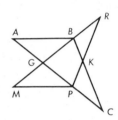

---

**27.** Prove that if $\overleftrightarrow{XY}$ is perpendicular to each of three different rays $\overrightarrow{XA}$, $\overrightarrow{XB}$, $\overrightarrow{XC}$, and $XA = XB = XC$, then $AY = BY = CY$.

**28.** Given: $\triangle KVL$ is isosceles with $KV = LV$, and $\overleftrightarrow{MP}$ contains the median $\overline{VP}$ of $\triangle KVL$.

Prove: $ST = RT$.

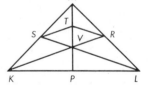

**29.** Let $\overline{AB}$ and $\overline{CD}$ bisect each other at $K$. Prove that $AC = BD$ and $AD = BC$. $\triangle AKC \cong \triangle BKD$ and $\triangle AKD \cong \triangle BKC$ by SAS

**30.** Given $\angle BAC$ such that $AB = AC$; $R$ is on $\overrightarrow{AB}$ and $T$ is on $\overrightarrow{AC}$ such that $RC = TB$. On the basis of this information, can you prove that $AR = AT$? If so, do so. If not, explain why not. NO

**31.** Let $\triangle PAB$ and $\triangle QAB$ lie in different planes but have a common side $\overline{AB}$. If $\triangle PAB \cong \triangle QAB$ and if $X$ is any point in $\overline{AB}$, then $\angle XPQ \cong \angle XQP$.

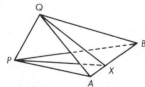

**32.** Complete Euclid's proof of the theorem that the base angles of an isosceles triangle are congruent.

Given: $\angle BAC$ with $AB = AC$.

Prove: $\angle ACB \cong \angle ABC$.

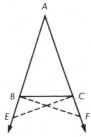

[*Hint:* First take a point $E$ such that $A$-$B$-$E$ and a point $F$ such that $A$-$C$-$F$ so that $AE = AF$. Draw $\overline{BF}$ and $\overline{CE}$.]

## CHAPTER REVIEW

1. Indicate whether each statement is true or false.

   (a) If in the correspondence $ABC \leftrightarrow KLM$, $\overline{AC} \cong \overline{KM}$, $\overline{AB} \cong \overline{KL}$, and $\angle A \cong \angle K$, then the correspondence is a congruence. T

   (b) If $\overline{AC} = \overline{BD}$, we can conclude that either $A = B$ and $C = D$ or that $A = D$ and $B = C$. T

   (c) Two triangles are congruent if the three angles of one triangle are congruent to the three angles of the other triangle. F

   (d) If in $\triangle DEF$, $m\angle D = m\angle E = m\angle F$, then $\triangle DEF$ is equilateral. T

   (e) A median of a triangle bisects an angle of the triangle. F

   (f) If $\triangle XYZ \cong \triangle BAC$, the $\angle X \cong \angle A$. F

   (g) In $\triangle ABC$, if $\angle A \cong \angle C$, then $AB = AC$. F

   (h) If $\triangle XYZ \cong \triangle ZXY$, then $\triangle XYZ$ is equilateral. T

   (i) Two triangles are congruent if two sides and an angle of one are congruent to two sides and an angle of the other. F

   (j) There is no $\triangle ABC$ in which $\angle A = \angle B$. T

2. Define *congruent segments*. See page 129

3. Define *bisector of an angle*. See page 152

4. Define *angle bisector of a triangle*. See page 168

5. Complete: If an angle bisector of a triangle is also perpendicular to the side opposite the angle, then the triangle is isosceles

6. Complete: A quadrilateral which has four right angles is called a _____. rectangle

7. Complete: In $\triangle PRQ$, $\angle Q$ is included by $\overline{QP}$ and $\overline{QR}$, and $\angle P$ and $\angle R$ include $\overline{PR}$.

8. $\square ABCD$ is a rectangle, with $\angle 1 \cong \angle 4$, $\angle 2 \cong \angle 3$, and $AB = CD$. Prove that $\triangle ABE \cong \triangle CDF$ and $\triangle EBD \cong \triangle FDB$.

**9.** No. We cannot conclude that the triangles are congruent unless we know that the given angle is, in each triangle, included between the given sides.

**13.** Given: The figure with $m\angle D = m\angle C = 90$. $DE = CE$. Prove: $\angle A \cong \angle B$.

**16.** If $\overline{AM}$ is the median to the side $\overline{BC}$ in $\triangle ABC$, then $BM = CM$ by the definition of median and $AB = AC$ since $\triangle ABC$ is isosceles, so $\triangle ABM \cong \triangle ACM$ by SSS and $\angle ABM \cong \angle ACM$ by corresponding parts.

**17.** If $\overline{AM} \perp \overline{BC}$, then $\angle AMB \cong \angle AMC$ and if $\angle MAB \cong \angle MAC$ then $\triangle AMB \cong \triangle AMC$ by ASA, so $AB = AC$ by corresponding parts.

**18.** (a) $\triangle BAR \cong \triangle CAR$ by SSS, and consequently, $RB = RC$.

(b) By Part (a), $\angle ARB \cong \angle ARC$. Let $S$ be a point on $\overrightarrow{AR}$ such that A-R-S. Then $\angle ARB$ and $\angle BRS$ form a linear pair, and are supplementary. Similarly, $\angle ARC$ and $\angle CRS$ are supplementary. But since supplements of congruent angles are congruent, we can conclude that $\angle BRS \cong \angle CRS$; hence by the definition of the bisector of an angle, $\overrightarrow{RS}$ bisects $\angle BRC$. And since $S$ is a point on $\overrightarrow{AR}$ such that A-R-S, this means that $\overrightarrow{AR}$ contains the bisector of $\angle BRC$.

**19.** Since $\triangle ABC$ is equilateral, $\overline{AB} \cong \overline{CA}$, $\overline{AC} \cong \overline{CB}$ and $\overline{BC} \cong \overline{AB}$ by definition. Hence, $\triangle ABC \cong \triangle CAB$ by SSS. Secondly, since $\angle A \cong \angle A$, and since $\overline{AB} \cong \overline{AC}$ by the definition of equilateral, we can conclude that $\triangle ABC \cong \triangle ACB$ by SAS. Finally, since congruence of triangles is a transitive relation we can conclude that all three triangles are congruent.

**20.** $\triangle ACK \cong \triangle BCK$ by SSS, $\angle ACK = \angle BCK$ by corresponding parts, $\triangle ACD \cong \triangle BCD$ by SAS, $AD = BD$ by corresponding parts, $\triangle AKD \cong \triangle BKD$ by SSS. There are no conclusions involving the points $G$ and $H$.

**21.** $AC = BC$ by the Isosceles Triangle Theorem, then $\triangle DAC \cong \triangle DBC$ by SAS, and $\overline{DC} \perp \overline{AB}$ since the congruent angles $\angle ADC$ and $\angle BDC$ form a linear pair.

---

**9.** $\triangle ABC$ and $\triangle PQR$ each have two sides whose lengths are 7 and an angle whose measure is 40. Are the triangles congruent? Why or why not? *No*

**10.** Name the three properties of an equivalence relation. *Reflexitivity, Symmetry, Transitivity*

**11.** Name four different ways of proving that a correspondence between two triangles is a congruence. (SAS is one.) *SAS, ASA, SSS, and the definition of congruent triangles.*

**12.** Write the theorem suggested by the figure on the left below.

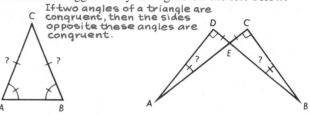
*If two angles of a triangle are congruent, then the sides opposite these angles are congruent.*

**13.** Write out a hypothesis and a conclusion for the figure on the right above.

**14.** State the converse of the Isosceles Triangle Theorem. *See page 156.*

**15.** In this three-dimensional figure, the points $Q$, $R$, and $S$ are in the plane $E$. $PR = PS$ and $\angle RPQ \cong \angle SPQ$. Prove that $\angle PQR \cong \angle PQS$. *Use SAS to prove $\triangle PQR \cong \triangle PQS$*

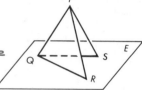

**16.** Prove: The median to the base of an isosceles triangle bisects the vertex angle.

**17.** Prove: If a segment perpendicular to one side of a triangle also bisects the angle opposite that side, the triangle is isosceles.

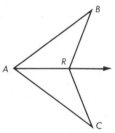

**18.** In the figure, $AB = AC$ and $\overrightarrow{AR}$ bisects $\angle BAC$. Prove that

(a) $RB = RC$,

(b) $\overrightarrow{AR}$ contains the bisector of $\angle BRC$.

---

**19.** Prove: If $\triangle ABC$ is equilateral, then $\triangle ABC \cong \triangle CAB \cong \triangle ACB$.

**20.** In the plane figure on the right, $AC = BC$ and $AK = BK$. Make a list of all the conclusions that follow. (You should be able to prove each one.) *Corresponding marks can be proved congruent, etc.*

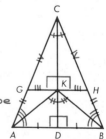

**21.** In this figure $A\text{-}D\text{-}B$, $AD = DB$ and $\angle A \cong \angle B$. Make a list of all the conclusions that follow. (You should be able to prove each one.)

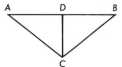

**22.** Given the figure on the left below with $\angle TPM \cong \angle TQN$, $\angle PTM \cong \angle QTN$, and the points $M$, $N$, $T$ are midpoints of segments $\overline{ST}$, $\overline{RT}$, and $\overline{PQ}$ respectively. Prove that $\angle RST \cong \angle SRT$.

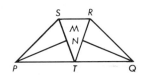 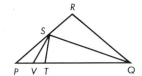

**23.** In an isosceles triangle, $\triangle PQR$ on the right above, the bisector of a base angle $\angle Q$ intersects the opposite side at $S$. $T$ is a point of base $\overline{PQ}$ such that $ST = P$ ˙, $\overleftrightarrow{SV}$ bisects $\angle PST$. Prove that $\angle TSV \cong \angle RQS$.

**24.** State all the converses of the following:

If a median of a triangle is perpendicular to the side it bisects, then it bisects the angle opposite that side and the triangle is isosceles.

---

**25.** In the figure, $A$, $B$, $C$, and $D$ are noncoplanar and $AB = AC = AD = BC = BD = CD$. $Q$ and $R$ are midpoints of $\overline{AC}$ and $\overline{AD}$, respectively, and $P$ is any point of $\overline{AB}$. Prove that $\triangle PQR$ is isosceles.

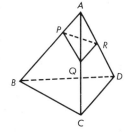

**26.** Let $L$ be the edge of two half-planes, $H_1$ and $H_2$. $A$ and $B$ are two points of $L$, $M$ is a point in $H_1$, and $R$ is a point in $H_2$ such that $\angle MAB \cong \angle RAB$, $AM = AR$, and $B$ is not between $M$ and $R$.

(a) Prove that $\triangle MRB$ is isosceles.

(b) Must $\overline{MR}$ intersect $L$? No, only if $H_1$ and $H_2$ are coplanar. $\overline{MR}$ intersects L by Postulate 9 in this case.

(c) Does the answer to (a) require that $H_1$ and $H_2$ be coplanar? No

**27.** In the figure, $\triangle CFG$ is isosceles, and $CD = CE$; $D$ and $E$ are the midpoints of $\overline{AC}$ and $\overline{BC}$ respectively.

Prove: (a) $DK = EK$,
(b) $\triangle AMB$ is isosceles.

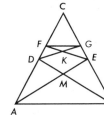

**22.** $PT = QT$ by the definition of bisector. Therefore $\triangle PTM \cong \triangle QTN$ by the ASA Postulate, and $MT = NT$ and $ST = 2MT = 2NT = RT$ by the definition of midpoint. Therefore $\angle RST = \angle SRT$ by the Isosceles Triangle Theorem.

**23.** Since $PR = QR$, $m\angle RQP = m\angle RPQ$. Since $ST = PT$, $m\angle SPT = m\angle PST$. $\angle RPQ \cong \angle SPT$. Therefore, $m\angle RQP = m\angle PST$. Since $\overrightarrow{QS}$ bisects $\angle RQP$, $m\angle RQS = \frac{1}{2}m\angle RQP$; and since $\overrightarrow{SV}$ bisects $\angle PST$, $m\angle TSV = \frac{1}{2}m\angle PST$. Consequently $m\angle TSV = m\angle RQS$.

**24.** Let (1) stand for "a median $\overline{AM}$ of a triangle is perpendicular to a side $\overline{BC}$," (2) stand for "the segment $\overline{AM}$ bisects $\angle BAC$," (3) stand for "$AB = AC$." Then the theorem takes the form "If (1), then (2) and (3)," and its converses are "If (2), then (1) and (3)" and "If (3), then (1) and (2)."

**25.** (1) Since $AC = AD$, and $Q$ and $R$ are the midpoints of $\overline{AC}$ and $\overline{AD}$ respectively, we can conclude that $AQ = AR$. (2) Since $\triangle BAC \cong \triangle BAD$, by SSS, we can conclude that $\angle BAC \cong \angle BAD$. (3) $PA = PA$. Therefore $\triangle PAQ \cong \triangle PAR$ by SAS, and consequently $PQ = PR$, which means that $\triangle PQR$ is isosceles.

**26.** (a) Since $AM = AR$ and $\angle MAB \cong \angle RAB$ we can conclude that $\triangle MAB \cong \triangle RAB$, and consequently that $MB = RB$ so that $\triangle MRB$ is isosceles.

**27.** (a) Introduce $\overline{DE}$. Then $\triangle CDG \cong \triangle CEF$ by SAS so $\angle CDG \cong \angle CEF$ (CPCTC). $\angle CDE \cong \angle CED$ by the Isosceles Triangle Theorem, $\angle GDE \cong \angle FED$ by AAP, and $\angle KDE \cong \angle KED$ and $DK = EK$ by Theorem 5-4.

(b) $CA = 2CD = 2CE = CB$ by the definition of midpoint, so that $\angle CAB \cong \angle CBA$ by the Isosceles Triangle Theorem. $\triangle CEA \cong \triangle CDB$ by SAS, so $\angle CAE \cong \angle CBD$ by corresponding parts, and $\angle EAB \cong \angle DBA$ by the AAP. Then $\angle MAB \cong \angle MBA$, and so $AM = BM$ by Theorem 5-4.

Chapter 6 introduces the student to a variety of important but rather difficult aspects of proof: the idea of a deductive system, indirect proof, existence and uniqueness theorems, characterization theorems, the technique of introducing auxiliary sets, and some fundamental theorems on betweenness and separation. These topics are difficult and will gradually become more meaningful to the student as he reencounters them in subsequent chapters of this text. For some classes, many of the topics in this chapter should be postponed or omitted. However, it is important for the student to acquire some facility with indirect proof, the Perpendicular Bisector Theorem, and the technique of introducing auxiliary sets.

Indirect proof is a practical technique for proving mathematical statements. Let us briefly clarify the relationship between the technique of indirect proof and the associated tautologies of deductive logic. Two observations suffice:

(1) The fundamental logical principle implicit in indirect proof is: *"If a statement A implies a false statement, then statement A is itself false."*

(2) The relation of the technique of indirect proof to the concept of the contrapositive of a statement: In an explanation of the logical foundations of indirect proof it is often stated that the technique of indirect proof is based on the fact that an implication and its contrapositive are equivalent, that is, the assertion "If $p$, then $q$" is equivalent to the assertion "If $\sim q$, then $\sim p$." This identification misses an essential point. In an indirect proof, we show that the supposition that the conclusion is false implies a false

# A Closer Look at Proof

## Objectives...

- Learn how to write an indirect proof.
- Prove and use the Perpendicular Bisector Theorem.
- Make a distinction between *existence* and *uniqueness*.
- Learn to introduce auxiliary sets to facilitate problem solving.

## 6–1 HOW A DEDUCTIVE SYSTEM WORKS

In Chapter 1 we tried to explain in general terms how our study of geometry was going to work. After the experience you have gained since then, you ought to be in a much better position to understand the explanation.

The idea of a set, the methods of algebra, and the process of logical reasoning are things that we have been working *with*. The geometry itself is what we have been working *on*. We started with *point, line,* and *plane* as undefined terms; and so far, we have used seventeen postulates. Sometimes, new terms have been defined by an appeal to postulates. (For example, the distance $PQ$ was defined to be the positive number given by the Distance Postulate.) Sometimes definitions have been based only on the undefined terms. (For example, a set of points is *collinear* if all points of the set lie on the same *line*.) But at every point we have built our definitions with terms that were, in some way, previously known. By now we have piled definitions on top of one another so often that the list is very long; and, in fact, the length of the list is one of the main reasons we had to be careful, at the outset, to keep the record straight.

Similarly, all the statements we make about geometry are ultimately based on the postulates. So far we have sometimes proved theorems directly from postulates, and sometimes we have based our proofs on theorems that were already proved. But in every case, the chain of reasoning can be traced back to the postulates.

You might find it a good idea, at this point, to reread Chapter 1. It will seem much clearer to you now than it did the first time. It is much easier to look back, and understand what you have done, than to understand an explanation of what you are about to do.

statement, and that statement is ordinarily false, not because it contradicts the given hypotheses, but because it contradicts some previous postulate or theorem.

The point is that in an indirect proof we simply show that our supposition implies a false statement; any false statement will do, and so we take the one that comes first and most naturally. We seldom go to the trouble to show that our supposition actually implies the negation of the hypothesis.

Hence we say that the concept of indirect proof is grounded in the principle that "If a statement $A$ implies a false statement, then statement $A$ is itself false," rather than in the fact that an implication and its contrapositive are logically equivalent.

It may clarify matters, here and elsewhere, to use the logical symbol $\Rightarrow$ for the relation *implies*. In these terms, we can say:

If $P \Rightarrow Q$, and $Q$ is false, then $P$ is false.

### Planning the Chapter

Three days on Sections 6–1, 6–2, and 6–3 is sufficient for an average class. Sections 6–4 and 6–5 together should take three or four days. Section 6–6 should be alluded to briefly, or simply omitted. An above-average class will usually take two days on the first three sections and spend two days each on the last three sections.

## 6-2 INDIRECT PROOFS

### Classroom Notes

Examples 1 and 2 of Section 6–2 and Problems 3 and 4 of Problem Set 6–2 are good illustrations of indirect reasoning in everyday life. If you first discuss these preliminary examples of indirect reasoning, you should find that it is easy to train students in the use of indirect proof in geometry. This is an important first step in gaining insight into indirect reasoning and to an awareness of its natural role in proving theorems.

Note that in Examples 1 and 2 the statements which are proved are *negative* statements. This is not an accident. The whole idea, in an indirect proof, is to show that a certain statement is *false,* by showing that it leads to a contradiction. It is therefore to be expected that the elementary examples of the use of the indirect method will take a negative form.

We recommend that you use Theorem 3–2 as a model in your discussion of indirect proof (see Section 6–3). First prove the theorem in class, then go back and examine the proof and abstract the following essential steps of an indirect proof.

(1) *Suppose that the statement which you want to establish is false.*

(2) *Construct a chain of reasoning leading to a statement which must be false, because it contradicts something that was given.*

(3) *Observe that by a correct line of reasoning, we arrived at a false conclusion. Therefore we must have begun with a false supposition. Our supposition was that the theorem is false. Therefore the theorem is true.*

## 6-2 INDIRECT PROOFS

We remarked in Chapter 1 that the best way to learn about logical reasoning is to do some of it. In general, this is true. But there is one kind of proof that calls for special discussion. For Theorem 3–1 (p. 54), we use what is called an *indirect proof.* The theorem and its proof are as follows.

### Theorem 3–1

*If two different lines intersect, their intersection contains only one point.*

**Proof.** Suppose two different lines intersected at two different points $P$ and $Q$. Then there would be two lines containing $P$ and $Q$. This would contradict the Line Postulate. Therefore the theorem holds.

The idea here is that if two statements contradict one another, then the statements cannot both be true. Therefore any statement which contradicts a known fact must be false. This sort of reasoning is used in ordinary conversation.

*Example 1*

"It must not be raining outside.

If it were raining, then those people coming in the door would be wet, but they aren't."

*Example 2*

"Today must not be the right day for the football game.

If the game were being played today, then by now the stadium would be full of people, but you and I are the only ones here."

In each case, the speaker wants to show that a certain statement is true. He starts his proof by *supposing* that the statement he wants to prove is false; he then observes that this leads to a conclusion which *contradicts* a known fact. In the first case, the speaker starts by supposing that it is raining; this leads to the conclusion that the people coming in the door would be wet; and this contradicts the known fact that the people are dry. Similarly, in the second case the speaker begins by supposing that the football game is to be played today; and this leads to a contradiction of the fact that the stadium contains only two people.

In the proof of Theorem 3–1, we start by supposing that some two different lines intersect in two different points. This contradicts the Line Postulate. Therefore the supposition is wrong, and this means that the theorem is right.

## Problem Set 6–2

1. For the sake of argument accept each of the following hypotheses and then give a logical completion for each conclusion.

(a) *Hypothesis:* All boys like to play football. My brother is fourteen years old.

*Conclusion:* My brother <u>likes to play football</u>.

(b) *Hypothesis:* Only careless people make mistakes. I am never careless.

*Conclusion:* I <u>never make mistakes</u>.

(c) *Hypothesis:* Jack always laughs when he tells a joke. Jack is telling a joke.

*Conclusion:* Jack <u>is laughing</u>.

(d) *Hypothesis:* In any isosceles triangle, the base angles are congruent. In $\triangle ABC$, $AC = BC$.

*Conclusion:* <u>In $\triangle ABC$, $\angle A \cong \angle B$</u>.

2. The time must be later than 4 P.M. If the time were not later than 4 P.M., I would hear the noise of the construction men at work. I do not hear any noise.

In this example of indirect proof, identify

(a) the statement to be proved  The time must be later than 4 P.M.

(b) the supposition made  If the time were not later than 4 P.M.

(c) the conclusion resulting from the supposition  I would hear the noise of construction men at work.

(d) the known fact contradictory to (c)
    I do not hear any noise.

3. Mrs. Adams purchased a set of kitchen utensils advertised as a stainless-steel product. After using the set a few weeks, she discovered that some of the utensils were beginning to rust. She thereupon decided that the set was not stainless steel and returned it for a refund.
Follow the directions of Problem 2.

## Explanation for Problems

Problems 2–4 are important because they allow the student to see how the proof of an everyday problem can be logically outlined. This will provide a basis for the outline of the more difficult geometric proofs to follow.

### Answers to Problems.

3. (a) The kitchen utensils are not stainless steel.
   (b) The kitchen utensils are stainless steel.
   (c) The kitchen utensils should not rust.
   (d) The kitchen utensils are beginning to rust.

**6.** Given scalene $\triangle ABF$. To prove that the bisector of any angle, $\angle F$, is not perpendicular to $\overline{AB}$.

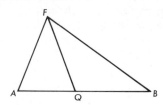

If we assume that the bisector of $\angle F$ is perpendicular to $\overline{AB}$, then $\triangle AFQ \cong \triangle BFQ$ (ASA) and $AF = BF$. The assumption that $\overline{FQ}$ is perpendicular to $\overline{AB}$ leads to the false conclusion that the scalene $\triangle ABF$ is isosceles.

**7.** Suppose two angles of a scalene triangle are congruent. Then by Theorem 5-5, the sides opposite those angles would be congruent and the triangle would be isosceles, contradicting the hypothesis that the triangle is scalene.

**8.** If $AB \neq AC$ in $\triangle ABC$, then the angle bisector $\overline{AQ}$ of $\angle A$ cannot be perpendicular to $\overline{BC}$. Otherwise $\angle AQB$ and $\angle AQC$ would be right angles, $AQ = AQ$, and $\angle BAQ \cong \angle CAQ$ by hypothesis, so $\triangle BAQ \cong \triangle CAQ$ by ASA. Therefore $AB = AC$, contradicting the hypothesis that $AB \neq AC$. Similarly assume $BC \neq BA$ and $CA \neq CB$ to arrive at each contradiction.

**9.** Let $p$ be ''someone is a member of the kite-flying club.''
Let $q$ be ''someone can play the piccolo.''
Let $r$ be ''someone is a turtle.''
Let $s$ be ''someone wears hip boots to the club.''

---

**4.** Follow the directions of Problem 2.

(a) The outside temperature must be below 0°C. (a) If it were not below 0°C, (c) the window panes would not be frosted. (d) But they are frosted. Therefore the outside temperature is below 0°C. (b)

(b) It must be time (a) to eat lunch. If it were not time for lunch, (c) I would not be hungry. (d) But I am very hungry. Therefore it must be time for lunch. (b)

(c) The concert must be finished. (a) If it were not finished, (c) the musicians would not be leaving the concert hall. (d) But the musicians are leaving the concert hall. Therefore the concert is finished. (b)

**5.** In $\triangle ABC$, $AC = BC$, and $AB \neq AC$. $\overline{AD}$ is a median. Prove that $\overline{AD}$ cannot be perpendicular to $\overline{BC}$.

If $\overline{AD} \perp \overline{BC}$, then $\angle ADB$ and $\angle ADC$ would be right angles, $BC = DC$ and $AD = AD$. So $\triangle ADB \cong ADC$ (SAS) and $AB = AC$ (CPCTC), which contradicts hypothesis $AB \neq AC$.

**6.** Prove that the bisector of any angle of a scalene triangle cannot be perpendicular to the opposite side.

**7.** Prove that no two angles of a scalene triangle are congruent.

---

**8.** Give an indirect proof of the following. If each of the three angle bisectors of a triangle is perpendicular to a side of the triangle, then the triangle is equilateral.

---

**9.** What conclusion follows from the following data? I am not a turtle.

(a) Nobody is allowed to join the kite-flying club unless he or she can play the piccolo. If p is true, then q is true.

(b) No turtle can play the piccolo. If q is true, then r is not true.

(c) Nobody is allowed to wear hip boots to the club unless he or she is a member of the club. If s is true, then p is true.

(d) I always wear hip boots to the club. s is true.

[*Hint*: Convert each statement to an *if . . . then* form and diagram the argument. For example, let $p$ be "someone is a member of the kite-flying club," etc.] See margin for meaning of symbols.

**10.** What conclusion follows from the following hypothesis?

      Tame lions have sharp teeth.

      Lions that eat people never get sick.

      Lions that never eat people have dull teeth.

      My pet lion has pneumonia. *My pet lion is not tame.*

Did you use indirect reasoning? *Yes* Explain. *Indirect reasoning was used at each step.*

**11.** What conclusion follows from the following hypothesis?

      Anyone who studies geometry is well educated.

      No monkey can read.

      Anyone who cannot read is not well educated.

      I study geometry. *I am not a monkey.*

Did you use indirect reasoning? Explain. *Used in last two steps. Yes*

## 6–3   THEOREMS ON LINES AND PLANES

It is now rather easy to prove the other theorems of Chapter 3. For convenience, we first restate the postulates on which the proofs are based.

**POSTULATE 4.**   The Line Postulate

*For every two points there is exactly one line that contains both points.*

**POSTULATE 5**

(a) *Every plane contains at least three noncollinear points.*

(b) *Space contains at least four noncoplanar points.*

**POSTULATE 6**

*If two points of a line lie in a plane, then the line lies in the same plane.*

**POSTULATE 7.**   The Plane Postulate

*Any three points lie in at least one plane, and any three noncollinear points lie in exactly one plane.*

---

**Quiz**

Prove by indirect reasoning:
If a line $P$ intersects a plane $E$ not containing it, then the intersection contains exactly one point.
Proof: Assume that $L$ intersects $E$ at two points $P$ and $Q$. Then by Postulate 6 $L$ lies in $E$. This conclusion is false: therefore $L$ intersects $E$ at exactly one point.

### 6–3 THEOREMS ON LINES AND PLANES

**Classroom Notes**

The postulates and theorems in this section are called incidence postulates and incidence theorems; incidence theorems deal, in general, with the question of whether two sets intersect (and if so, what the intersection looks like) or with the question of whether one set is contained in the other.

    The ideas of incidence are easy, but a formal treatment of them is not, and many students may feel that the latter is unworthy of the amount of effort that it requires. If this attitude appears, and it often will, it is best to insist only on the ideas that are really essential: direct versus indirect proof, existence versus uniqueness, and so on. Needless to say, the theorems themselves are all to be regarded as essential.

The distinction between an existence theorem and a uniqueness theorem is important. The development in the text is complete, but there is one point that needs to be emphasized: existence and uniqueness are consistent, but independent, concepts. We can often prove existence but not uniqueness, and, on the other hand we can often prove uniqueness but not existence. Even when we can prove both existence and uniqueness, we can usually prove them in either order. We customarily prove existence first and then uniqueness.

Intentional association of the phrase *at least one* with existence and *at most one* with uniqueness should help to clarify the mathematical meaning of these terms.

We shall now prove the following theorem.

### Theorem 3–2

*If a line intersects a plane not containing it, then the intersection contains only one point.*

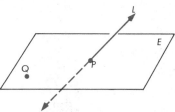

**Proof.** We are given a line $L$ and a plane $E$. By hypothesis, we have

(1) $L$ intersects $E$ in at least one point $P$, and

(2) $E$ does not contain $L$.

We shall give an indirect proof, and we therefore start by supposing that

(3) $L$ intersects $E$ in some other point $Q$.

We need to show that (3) leads to a contradiction of a known fact—and it does: If $P$ and $Q$ lie in $E$, then it follows by Postulate 6 that $L$ lies in $E$. This contradicts (2). Therefore (3) is false. Therefore Theorem 3–2 is true.

Of course, the figure for this proof looks rather peculiar. We have indicated a point $Q$, merely to remind ourselves of the notation of the proof. The proof itself shows that no such point can possibly exist. In fact, the figures for indirect proofs will always look ridiculous, for the excellent reason that they describe impossible situations. If we had drawn a figure for Theorem 3–1, it might have looked even worse:

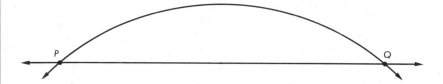

This figure suggests an impossible situation in which two lines intersect in two different points.

## Theorem 3–3

*Given a line and a point not on the line, there is exactly one plane containing both of them.*

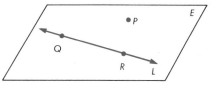

Let $L$ be the given line, and let $P$ be the given point. To prove the theorem, we need to show two things:

(1) there is a plane $E$, containing $P$ and $L$;

(2) there is only one plane $E$, containing $P$ and $L$.

Statements (1) and (2), taken together, tell us that there is *exactly* one plane containing $P$ and $L$.

**Proof of (1).** Let $Q$ and $R$ be any two points of $L$. By Postulate 7 there is a plane $E$, containing $P$, $Q$, and $R$. By Postulate 6, $E$ contains $L$. Thus $E$ contains $P$ and $L$.

**Proof of (2).** This proof will be indirect. *Suppose* that there is another plane $E'$ which contains $P$ and $L$. Then $E'$ contains $P$, $Q$, and $R$.

But $P$, $Q$, and $R$ are noncollinear. The reason is that $L$ is the only line that contains $Q$ and $R$ (why?), and $L$ does not contain $P$.

Thus we have two different planes, $E$ and $E'$, containing the noncollinear points $P$, $Q$, and $R$. This contradicts Postulate 7.

Note that this theorem and its proof split up naturally into two parts. This illustrates the distinction between *existence* and *uniqueness*. The first half of the proof shows the *existence* of a plane $E$ containing $P$ and $L$. The second half shows the *uniqueness* of the plane containing $P$ and $L$. When we prove existence, we show that there is *at least one* object of a certain kind. When we prove uniqueness, we show that there is *at most one*. If it happens that we can prove both, then we know that there is *exactly one*.

However, existence and uniqueness do not always go together, by any means; in many cases, we may have one without the other, and often we have neither. For example, for the fleas on a stray dog, we can usually prove existence but not uniqueness. (It is a lucky dog indeed that has only one flea.) Similarly, if $x$ is rational, then there *exist* integers $p$ and $q$ such that

$$x = \frac{p}{q}.$$

But these integers are not unique, because we also have

$$x = \frac{2p}{2q} = \frac{3p}{3q},$$

and so on. For the points common to two different segments, we don't necessarily have either existence or uniqueness; the intersection may contain a whole segment, or exactly one point, or no points at all:

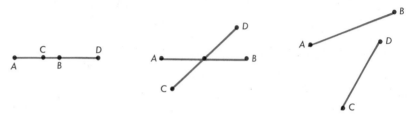

The phrase *one and only one* is often used instead of *exactly one*, to emphasize the double value of the statement.

Our next theorem splits into two parts, in the same way as the preceding one.

**Theorem 3–4**

> **Given two intersecting lines, there is exactly one plane containing them.**

We are given the lines $L_1$ and $L_2$ intersecting in the point $P$. We need to show two things:

(1) *Existence.* There is a plane $E$ containing $L_1$ and $L_2$.
(2) *Uniqueness.* There is only one plane $E$ which contains $L_1$ and $L_2$.
We give the proofs in double-column form.

### Proof of (1)

| STATEMENTS | REASONS |
|---|---|
| 1. $L_1$ contains a point $Q$ different from $P$. | 1. By the Ruler Postulate, every line contains infinitely many points. |
| 2. $Q$ is not on $L_2$. | 2. By Theorem 3–1, $L_1$ intersects $L_2$ only at $P$. |
| 3. There is a plane $E$ containing $Q$ and $L_2$. | 3. Theorem 3–3 |
| 4. $E$ contains $L_1$. | 4. By Postulate 6, since $E$ contains $P$ and $Q$ |

## Proof of (2)

| STATEMENTS | REASONS |
|---|---|
| 5. *Suppose* that another plane, $E'$, contains $L_1$ and $L_2$. | 5. Beginning of indirect proof |
| 6. $E'$ contains $Q$. | 6. $Q$ is on $L_1$. |
| 7. Both $E$ and $E'$ contain $Q$ and $L_2$. | 7. Steps 3, 5, and 6 |
| 8. $E$ is the only plane containing $L_1$ and $L_2$. | 8. Step 7 contradicts Theorem 3–3. |

Note that the proof of (2) supplies you with a pattern for writing up indirect proofs in the double-column form. Strictly speaking, of course, the phrase "Beginning of indirect proof" is not a "reason"; it is merely an explanation of what we had in mind when we wrote down step 5.

**Problem Set 6–3**

1. Which theorem may be restated as "Two intersecting lines determine a plane"? **Theorem 3-4**

2. Complete: To show uniqueness, we must show there is __*at most*__ one. To show existence, we must show there is __*at least*__ one.

3. Explain how the phrase "the King of Mexico" illustrates uniqueness without existence. **There can be at most one "King of Mexico".**

4. How do Sundays in March illustrate existence without uniqueness? **There is at least one Sunday in March, but not at most one.**

5. Which postulate or theorem stated in Section 6–3 asserts uniqueness of a point for which existence cannot be asserted? **Theorem 3-2**

6. If the three lines in the figure on the left below are not all coplanar, how many planes do they determine? List each plane by naming the lines which determine it. **Three (1) $\overleftrightarrow{AB}$ and $\overleftrightarrow{CD}$ (2) $\overleftrightarrow{AB}$ and $\overleftrightarrow{EF}$, (3) $\overleftrightarrow{CD}$ and $\overleftrightarrow{EF}$**

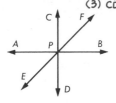
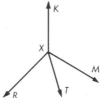

7. In the figure on the right above, no three of the rays are coplanar. How many planes do they determine? Name each plane by the points which determine it. **Six. KXR, KXT, KXM, RXT, RXM, and TXM.**

8.

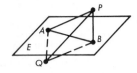

**Answers to Preparation Problems**

**8.** The points of a plane not on a given line in the plane form two sets such that (1) each set is convex and (2) if $P$ is in one set and $Q$ is in the other, then the segment $\overline{PQ}$ intersects the line.

**8.** As indicated in the figure, points $A$ and $B$ lie in the plane $E$, and point $P$ lies above $E$. Which postulate or theorem asserts that $\overleftrightarrow{AB}$ Postulate 6 is contained in $E$? There is a second plane implicit in the figure. ABP $\overleftrightarrow{AB}$ Name it. What is its intersection with $E$? If a fourth point, $Q$ lies below $E$ but is not collinear with $P$ and $A$ or $P$ and $B$, name the planes thereby determined. Draw the figure. ABP, ABQ, APQ, BPQ, and E

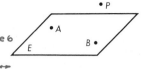

**9.** Complete: In the phrase *one and only one*, the *only one* indicates ___uniqueness___ and the *one* indicates ___existence___.

**10.** Suppose you wish to prove that in a plane, at a given point of a given line, there is at most one line perpendicular to the given line. Would you be proving existence or ⟨uniqueness⟩? If your proof is indirect, what supposition would you make to begin your reasoning? Suppose there exist two lines in the given plane ⊥ to given line at given point on line.

**11.** Suppose you wish to prove that in a plane, given a line and a point not on the line, there is at least one line through the point that is perpendicular to the given line. Would you be proving ⟨existence⟩ or uniqueness?

**Preparation for Section 6–4**

Before studying the next section you should answer these questions or review each topic mentioned.

**1.** Does the Angle Construction Postulate (p. 90) assert the existence of $\overrightarrow{AP}$, the uniqueness of $\overrightarrow{AP}$, or ⟨both⟩? Explain. Exactly one means one and only one.

**2.** Does the Angle Construction Postulate discuss ⟨rays⟩ lines or both?

**3.** Complete: On page 63 we said that a reference to "the two lines $L_1$ and $L_2$" would mean that the lines were ___different___. However, if we simply refer to "the lines $L_1$ and $L_2$," we allow the possibility that $L_1$ and $L_2$ are actually the ___same___ line.

**4.** What is the distinction between $\overline{AB}$ and $AB$? The first is a symbol for a segment, the other for distance between point A and B.

**5.** A common term for the reflexive property of congruence is ___identity___.

**6.** Which theorem of Chapter 2 guarantees that on every ray there is one and only one point at a given distance from the end point of the ray? Theorem 2-2. The Point-Plotting Theorem.

**7.** Complete: According to Theorem 4–5, two angles are right angles if they are both congruent and supplementary.

**8.** What two things does the Plane Separation Postulate tell us about the way a line separates a plane?

## 6-4 PERPENDICULARS

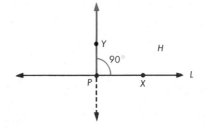

Using a ruler and a protractor, it is easy to draw the perpendicular to a given line at a given point of the line. We simply lay off a 90° angle, as in the figure, with vertex at the given point $P$, one side $\overrightarrow{PX}$ on the given line $L$, and the other side in one of the half-planes determined by $L$. The perpendicular ought to be unique because there is only one 90° mark on the protractor.

We shall now describe this situation in a theorem, and prove it on the basis of our postulates.

### Theorem 6-1

*In a given plane, through a given point of a given line, there is one and only one line perpendicular to the given line.*

**Restatement.** Let $E$ be a plane, let $L$ be a line in $E$, and let $P$ be a point of $L$. Then

(1) there is a line $M$ in $E$ such that $M$ contains $P$ and $M \perp L$; and

(2) there is only one such line $M$.

**Proof of (1).** Let $H$ be one of the two half-planes in $E$, determined by $L$, and let $X$ be any point of $L$, other than $P$. (See the figure above.) The Angle Construction Postulate asserts that there exists a ray $\overrightarrow{PY}$, with $Y$ in $H$, such that $m\angle YPX = 90$. Let $M = \overleftrightarrow{PY}$. Then $M \perp L$ at $P$.

**Proof of (2).** Suppose now that both $M_1$ and $M_2$ are perpendicular to $L$ at $P$. We shall show that $M_1 = M_2$.

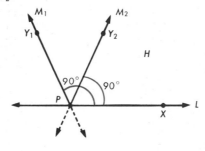

Now $M_1$ and $M_2$ contain rays $\overrightarrow{PY_1}$ and $\overrightarrow{PY_2}$ with $Y_1$ and $Y_2$ in $H$. By the definition of "perpendicular" and Theorem 4-9, both of the angles $\angle Y_1PX$ and $\angle Y_2PX$ are right angles, as indicated in the figure. The Angle Construction Postulate asserts that there is only one ray $\overrightarrow{PY}$, with $Y$ in $H$, such that $m\angle YPX = 90$. Therefore, $\overrightarrow{PY_1}$ and $\overrightarrow{PY_2}$ are the same ray. Since $M_1$ and $M_2$ have more than one point in common, they cannot be different lines. Therefore $M_1 = M_2$.

### Classroom Notes

Observe that this section deals with two topics: the basic theorem on perpendicular lines in a plane, and the Perpendicular Bisector Theorem.

The basic theorem on perpendicular lines breaks quite naturally into two cases. Theorem 6-1 deals with case 1; and Theorems 6-3 and 6-4 deal with case 2. Students tend to feel that these useful theorems are intuitively obvious; they scarcely seem to require proof. The proofs themselves are difficult on several accounts:

(1) These are existence and uniqueness theorems, and you cannot assume that the students have assimilated the discussion of existence and uniqueness theorems in Section 6-3.

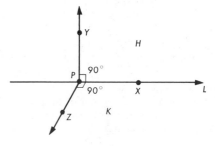

(2) The uniqueness proof in Theorem 6-1 seems unnecessary. Students often feel that the Angle Construction Postulate guarantees that there is a unique *line M* in the plane $B$ perpendicular to $L$ at $P$. This is not quite correct. The Angle Construction Postulate asserts that there is a unique *ray* $\overrightarrow{PY}$ with $Y$ in the half-plane $H$ such that $m\angle XPY = 90$. Then the *line* $\overleftrightarrow{PY} \perp L$. Suppose then that we apply the same process to the half-plane $K$ opposite to $H$.

The Angle Construction Postulate now asserts that there is a unique ray $\overrightarrow{PZ}$ with $Z$ in the half-plane $K$

such that $m \angle XPZ = 90$. Then $\overleftrightarrow{PZ} \perp L$. No one of our postulates or theorems tells us that the lines $\overleftrightarrow{PY}$ and $\overleftrightarrow{PZ}$ are identical. The uniqueness part of Theorem 6–1 takes care of this.

(3) The techniques used to prove existence in Theorem 6–3 and uniqueness in Theorem 6–4 are, admittedly, highly imaginative and scarcely the sort of thing the student would think of by himself.

We consequently recommend that with good students you treat these theorems somewhat informally and that with average students you take the theorems without proof.

The Perpendicular Bisector Theorem is a characterization theorem. To characterize a set means to state a condition which is satisfied by every point in that set and by no other points. Characterizations are discussed in detail in the comments on Section 15–1.

Note the importance of the restriction in Theorem 6–2 that all points considered lie in a plane. If this restriction is removed, we get a corresponding result in space: The perpendicular bisecting *plane* of a segment is the set of all points that are equidistant from the end points of the segment. This is Theorem 8–6 of Chapter 8.

Corollary 6–2.1 could also be called the Perpendicular Bisector Criterion. It gives us an easy way to show that a line $L$ is the perpendicular bisector of a segment $\overline{AB}$. See Problem 15 of Problem Set 6–4.

Note that to prove the uniqueness of the perpendiculars to $L$ at $P$, we had to restrict ourselves to a given plane. In space, every line has infinitely many perpendiculars at each of its points. For example, on a wagon, all spokes of a wheel are perpendicular to the axle.

The markings on the following figure indicate that $L$ is the *perpendicular bisector* of $\overline{AB}$.

### Definition

In a given plane, the *perpendicular bisector* of a segment is the line which is perpendicular to the segment at its midpoint.

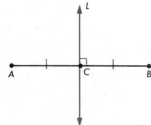

Every segment $\overline{AB}$ has one and only one midpoint $C$; and through $C$ there is one and only one line perpendicular to $\overleftrightarrow{AB}$. Therefore the perpendicular bisector exists and is unique.

The following theorem gives another description of the perpendicular bisector.

**Theorem 6–2.** The Perpendicular Bisector Theorem

**The perpendicular bisector of a segment, in a plane, is the set of all points of the plane that are equidistant from the end points of the segment.**

**Restatement.** Let $L$ be the perpendicular bisector of $\overline{AB}$ in the plane $E$. Then
(1) If $P$ is on $L$, then $PA = PB$, and (2) if $PA = PB$, then $P$ is on $L$.

This is an example of what is called a *characterization* theorem. To *characterize* a set of points, we state a condition which (1) is satisfied by the points of the given set, and (2) is not satisfied by any other points. In this case, the set of points is the perpendicular bisector of $\overline{AB}$, and the condition is $PA = PB$. Therefore the restatement of the theorem naturally splits into two parts, and so does the proof.

**Proof of (1).** Let $C$ be the midpoint of $\overline{AB}$, and let $P$ be any point of $L$. If $P = C$, then obviously $PA = PB$. Suppose, then, that $P$ is different from $C$, so that $P$ is not on $\overleftrightarrow{AB}$. We have $PC = PC$ by identity; $\angle PCA \cong \angle PCB$ because both are right angles; and $CA = CB$ because $C$ is the midpoint. By SAS, we have $\triangle PCA \cong \triangle PCB$. Therefore $PA = PB$.

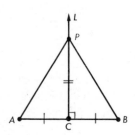

**Proof of (2).** Given $P$ is in the plane $E$, and $PA = PB$. If $P$ is on $\overleftrightarrow{AB}$, then $P = C$, because $\overline{AB}$ has only one midpoint. If $P$ is not on $\overleftrightarrow{AB}$, let $L'$ be the line $\overleftrightarrow{PC}$. Then $PC = PC$, $CA = CB$ and $PA = PB$. (Why?) By SSS, we have $\triangle PCA \cong \triangle PCB$, as before. Therefore, by definition, $\angle PCB$ is a right angle, and so $L' \perp \overline{AB}$ at $C$. By Theorem 6–1, perpendiculars are unique. Therefore $L' = L$. Therefore $P$ is on $L$, which was to be proved.

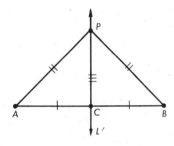

**Corollary 6–2.1**

> *Given a segment $\overline{AB}$ and a line $L$ in the same plane. If two points of $L$ are each equidistant from $A$ and $B$, then $L$ is the perpendicular bisector of $\overline{AB}$.*

**Proof.** By Theorem 6–2, $L$ contains two points of the perpendicular bisector of $\overline{AB}$. Since two points determine a line, this means that $L$ *is* the perpendicular bisector of $\overline{AB}$. We have found that there was really no problem in constructing the perpendicular to a line through a point *on* the line: we merely lay off a 90° angle. If the point is *not* on the line, the construction requires an idea.

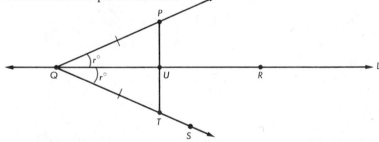

Given a line $L$, and a point $P$, not on $L$. We wish to construct a line through $P$, perpendicular to $L$. (We are working, of course, in a plane $E$ containing $L$ and $P$.)

Let $Q$ and $R$ be any two points of $L$. To get the perpendicular, we first draw the ray $\overrightarrow{QP}$ and measure $\angle PQR$. We then draw a ray $\overrightarrow{QS}$, with $S$ on the opposite side of $L$ from $P$, as indicated in the figure, such that $\angle SQR \cong \angle PQR$. (What postulate allows this?) We then plot a point $T$ on $\overrightarrow{QS}$ such that $TQ = PQ$. Then $\overline{TP}$ intersects $L$ in a point $U$. (Why?) Now $QU = QU$, $\angle PQU \cong \angle TQU$, and $TQ = PQ$. Therefore, by SAS, $\triangle PQU \cong \triangle TQU$, and $\angle PUQ$ and $\angle TUQ$ are right angles. Therefore $\overleftrightarrow{TP} \perp L$, and we have drawn the perpendicular to $L$ through $P$.

On the basis of this discussion, you ought to be able to complete the proof of the following theorem in double-column form.

### Theorem 6–3

*Through a given external point there is at least one line perpendicular to a given line.*

**Restatement.** Let $L$ be a line, and let $P$ be a point not on $L$. Then there is a line which is perpendicular to $L$ and contains $P$.

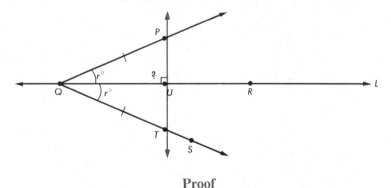

### Proof

| STATEMENTS | REASONS |
|---|---|
| 1. $L$ contains two points $Q$ and $R$. | 1. The Ruler Postulate |
| 2. There is a ray $\overrightarrow{QS}$, with $S$ on the opposite side of $L$ from $P$, such that $\angle SQR \cong \angle PQR$. | 2. ? Angle construction postulate |
| 3. There is a point $T$ of $\overrightarrow{QS}$ such that $TQ = PQ$. | 3. ? Point-Plotting Theorem |
| 4. $T$ and $P$ are on opposite sides of $L$. | 4. $P$ and $S$ are on opposite sides of $L$, and $S$ and $T$ are on the same side of $L$. |
| 5. $\overline{TP}$ intersects $L$ in a point $U$. | 5. ? Plane Separation Postulate |
| 6. $\triangle PQU \cong \triangle TQU$. | 6. ? SAS Postulate |
| 7. $UP = UT$. | 7. ? Theorem 4-5 |
| 8. $\overleftrightarrow{PU} \perp L$. | 8. Corollary 6–2.1 <br> Definition of perpendicular |

This proof, as we have written it, does not allow for the possibility $Q = U$. When we pick the point $Q$ at random, on $L$, it conceivably may happen that $\overleftrightarrow{PQ} \perp L$. But of course if this happens there is nothing to prove, because we already have our perpendicular, namely, the line $\overleftrightarrow{PQ}$.

Thus the perpendicular to a line, through an external point, *exists*. We show next that the perpendicular is *unique*.

## Theorem 6–4

> ***Through a given external point there is at most one line perpendicular to a given line.***

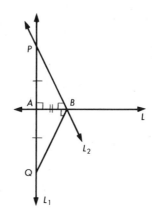

**Proof.** The proof is indirect, like most uniqueness proofs. Suppose that $L_1$ and $L_2$ are two different lines through $P$, each perpendicular to $L$. (It doesn't look that way in the figure, but remember that the figure is a picture of an impossible situation. Our job in the proof is to show that the situation pictured is impossible.)

Let $A$ and $B$ be the points where $L_1$ and $L_2$ intersect $L$. Let $Q$ be the point, on the ray opposite to $\overrightarrow{AP}$, for which $AQ = AP$ (by the Point-Plotting Theorem). By SAS, we have $\triangle PAB \cong \triangle QAB$.

Therefore $\angle PBA \cong \angle QBA$, because they are corresponding angles. Therefore $\overleftrightarrow{BQ} \perp L$ at $B$. Therefore there are two lines, $L_2$ and $\overleftrightarrow{BQ}$, which are perpendicular to $L$ at $B$. This contradicts Theorem 6–1, which says that there is only one line perpendicular to a given line through a point of the line, in a given plane. Hence our assumption, that there were two perpendiculars to $L$ through $P$, is false.

## Corollary 6–4.1

> ***No triangle has two right angles.***

**Proof.** In $\triangle ABC$, if both $\angle A$ and $\angle B$ were right angles, then there would be two perpendiculars to $\overleftrightarrow{AB}$ through $C$. By Theorem 6–4, this is impossible.

## Definitions

A *right triangle* is a triangle one of whose angles is a right angle. The side opposite the right angle is called the *hypotenuse*, and the other two sides are called the *legs*.

**5.** Since $E$ is equidistant from $G$ and $K$, and $M$ is equidistant from $G$ and $K$, $\overleftrightarrow{EM}$ is the perpendicular bisector of $\overline{GK}$ by Corollary 6-2.1. By Theorem 6-2, any point on the perpendicular bisector of a segment is equidistant from the end points of that segment: $GH = KH$.

## Problem Set 6–4

**1.** Let $M$ be a plane, let $L$ be a line lying in $M$, and let $A$ be a point of $L$. If $\overrightarrow{AT} \perp L$ and $\overrightarrow{AQ} \perp L$, what conclusion can you draw regarding $\overrightarrow{AQ}$ and $\overrightarrow{AT}$? Why? $\overleftrightarrow{AQ} = \overleftrightarrow{AT}$, Theorem 6-1 (Answer assumes Q, T and L are coplanar)

**2.** In the figure, $L$ is the perpendicular bisector of $\overline{AB}$. If the lengths of segments are as indicated, find $x$, $y$, and $z$.
$\begin{cases} x=9 \\ y=7 \\ z=8 \end{cases}$

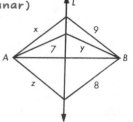

**3.** What theorem tells us that the vertex opposite the base of an isosceles triangle lies on the perpendicular bisector of the base? Theorem 6-2

**4.** If $D$ is the midpoint of $\overline{BC}$ and $\overrightarrow{AD} \perp \overline{BC}$, prove that $\triangle ABC$ is isosceles. Do *not* use congruent triangles in your proof.
$\overleftrightarrow{AD}$ is the perpendicular bisector of $\overline{BC}$ by definition, so AB = AC by Theorem 6-2.

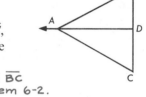

**5.** In a plane, $GE = KE$, $GM = KM$, and $H$ lies on $\overleftrightarrow{EM}$. Prove that $GH = KH$, *without* using congruent triangles.

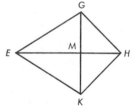

**6.** (a) In $\triangle PQR$, if $\angle R$ is a right angle, then $\overline{PQ}$ is called the hypotenuse, and $\overline{RQ}$ and $\overline{RP}$ are called the legs.

(b) In $\triangle ABC$, if $\angle C$ is a right angle, the hypotenuse is AB, and the legs are AC and CB.

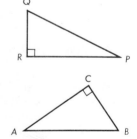

**7.** (a) In a plane, how many perpendiculars are there to a given line at a point of the line? One

(b) In space, how many perpendiculars are there to a given line at a point of the line? Infinitely many.

**10.**

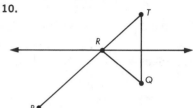

8. Copy the figure. Using ruler and protractor construct perpendiculars through $A$ and $C$ to $\overleftrightarrow{DB}$. Construct the perpendicular through $B$ to $\overleftrightarrow{DC}$ and the perpendicular through $A$ to $\overleftrightarrow{BC}$.

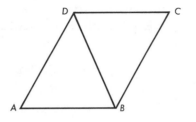

9. Copy the figure for Problem 8 again. Construct the perpendicular through $B$ to $\overleftrightarrow{AD}$ and the perpendicular through $C$ to $\overleftrightarrow{AB}$.

10. In a plane, line $L$ is the perpendicular bisector of $\overline{QT}$. $P$ is a point on the same side of $L$ as $Q$. $\overline{PT}$ intersects $L$ at $R$. Prove that $PT = PR + RQ$.

1. $PT = PR + RT$. (Definition of betweenness)
2. $RT = RQ$. (Theorem 6–2)
3. $PT = PR + RQ$. (Addition and Transitive Properties of Equality)

11. Which theorem allows us to say,

"*the* perpendicular to a line through a given external point"?
Theorem 6-4

12. Prove that if the median to the hypotenuse of a right triangle is perpendicular to the hypotenuse, then the right triangle is isosceles.

12. Since the median bisects the hypotenuse (by the definition of median), the median lies in the perpendicular bisector of the hypotenuse. Hence the triangle is isosceles by Theorem 6–2.

13. If, in the figure, $AB = BC$ and $AE = EC$, explain why $\overline{BD} \perp \overline{AC}$.

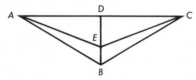

13. By Corollary 6–2.1, since $B$ and $E$ are equidistant from $A$ and $C$, the line containing $B$ and $E$ (and the segment $\overline{BD}$) must be perpendicular to $\overline{AC}$.

14. $A$, $B$, and $C$ lie in the plane $E$. $P$ and $Q$ are on opposite sides of $E$, with $P$-$A$-$Q$. Given that $\overleftrightarrow{AC}$ and $\overleftrightarrow{AB}$ are perpendicular bisectors of $\overline{PQ}$, prove that $\angle BPC \cong \angle BQC$.

14. 1. $\overleftrightarrow{AC}$ and $\overleftrightarrow{AB}$ are perpendicular bisectors of $\overline{PQ}$. (Given)
2. $PC = QC$, $PB = QB$. (Theorem 6–2)
3. $BC = BC$. (Reflexive Property)
4. $\triangle PBC \cong \triangle QBC$. (SSS)
5. $\angle BPC \cong \angle BQC$. (CPCTC)

15-17. See Solution Section for complete proofs.

15. Given $\triangle ABC$ with $AC = BC$. The bisectors of the base angles, $\angle A$ and $\angle B$, intersect each other at $F$. Prove that $\overleftrightarrow{CF}$ is perpendicular to $\overline{AB}$. (It is not necessary to use any congruent triangle in your proof.)

15. Prove $AF = BF$ by Theorem 4–6, and then show that $\overleftrightarrow{CF}$ is perpendicular to $\overline{AB}$.

16. One diagonal of a quadrilateral bisects two angles of the quadrilateral. Prove that it bisects the other diagonal.

16. Prove the diagonal divides the quadrilateral into two congruent triangles.

17. $A$, $B$, and $C$ lie in the plane $E$. $P$ and $Q$ are on opposite sides of $E$. Given that $PB = QB$, $A$ is the midpoint of $\overline{PQ}$, and $\angle PBC \cong \angle QBC$, prove that $\overline{PQ} \perp \overline{AC}$.

17. Prove that $\triangle PBC \cong \triangle QBC$.

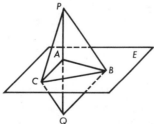

## 6-5 INTRODUCING AUXILIARY SETS INTO PROOFS. THE USE OF THE WORD "LET"

### Classroom Notes

The technique of introducing auxiliary sets into proofs developed in this section is different from the treatment of this topic in conventional texts. Four observations suffice to clarify our approach.

**I. The idea of introducing auxiliary sets.** In a typical geometry problem we are given (1) a set of points $A$, $B$, $C$ . . . , (2) a collection of rudimentary sets (segments, rays, lines, angles, and so on) determined by these points, and (3) a set of hypotheses applying to this collection of rudimentary sets. In writing a geometry problem an author has, of course, a particular figure in mind. If he takes extraordinary care, especially in regard to the use of betweenness and separation concepts, he can state a set of hypotheses which is adequate to characterize the configuration in mind. However, it is usually more practical to convey part of the given information by a figure, and this is, in practice, what we usually do.

It is often impossible to prove the assertion in a problem by an argument which employs only those rudimentary sets which are given in the problem. If, however, we introduce some auxiliary sets, we can often prove the assertion by an argument using this enlarged collection of rudimentary sets. To "introduce" an auxiliary set merely means to "add" it (in the set-theoretic sense of the word) to the collection of sets already given in the problem. Just as it is not necessary to use a figure to convey the restrictions given in the problem, it is not necessary to "draw" the auxiliary set. As soon as we have

## 6-5    INTRODUCING AUXILIARY SETS INTO PROOFS. THE USE OF THE WORD "LET"

You have probably noted that in some of our proofs, we have introduced points and lines that were not given in the statement of the theorem. Recall, for example, the place in Section 6-4 where we wanted to show that there is always a perpendicular to a given line, through a given external point.

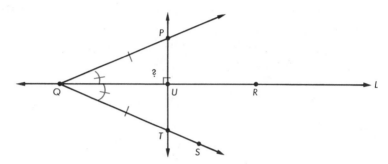

Only the line $L$ and the point $P$ were given, but to get the perpendicular $\overrightarrow{TP}$, we had to introduce the points $Q$ and $R$, the rays $\overrightarrow{QP}$ and $\overrightarrow{QS}$, and the point $T$.

In each step of the double-column proof of this theorem (Theorem 6-3), the statements assert that there really are points and rays of the sort that we want to talk about. And if you filled in the reasons correctly, then at each step you referred to a postulate (or perhaps a theorem) which justified the statement.

Most of the time, however, the reasons in such cases are very simple; and in writing paragraph proofs, we often use more informal language. In the discussion preceding Theorem 6-3, you have seen an example of this. We said:

> "*Let* $Q$ and $R$ be any two points of $L$. To get the perpendicular, we first *draw* the ray $\overrightarrow{QP}$ . . . ."

But if you are not keeping careful track of what is going on, this sort of language may easily lead to misunderstandings. Sometimes it may seem that mathematicians simply "let" things be whatever way they want them to be. This, of course, is not what they are doing. When we say, "let $Q$ and $R$ be any two points of $L$," we are claiming that $L$ contains two points, and we are claiming to know why. Once we have proved Theorems 6-3 and 6-4, we know that perpendiculars exist and are unique. We therefore have the right to say, "let $L'$ be the perpendicular to $L$ through $P$." This is an abbreviated way of referring to both these theorems at once.

In formal double-column proofs, when we introduce auxiliary sets, we need to refer to postulates and theorems as reasons. A list of the postulates and theorems that we shall refer to for this purpose follows. These are the statements that tell us that some point, line, or plane exists, or is unique, or both.

**POSTULATE 4.** The Line Postulate

*For every two points there is exactly one line that contains both points.*

**POSTULATE 5**

(*a*) *Every plane contains at least three noncollinear points.*

(*b*) *Space contains at least four noncoplanar points.*

**Theorem 2–2.** The Point-Plotting Theorem

*Let $\overrightarrow{AB}$ be a ray, and let x be a positive number. Then there is exactly one point P of $\overrightarrow{AB}$ such that $AP = x$.*

**Theorem 2–3**

*Every segment has exactly one midpoint.*

**Theorem 3–1**

*If two different lines intersect, their intersection contains only one point.*

**Theorem 3–2**

*If a line intersects a plane not containing it, then the intersection contains only one point.*

**POSTULATE 7.** The Plane Postulate

*Any three points lie in at least one plane, and any three noncollinear points lie in exactly one plane.*

**Theorem 3–3**

*Given a line and a point not on the line, there is exactly one plane containing both.*

**Theorem 3–4**

*Given two intersecting lines, there is exactly one plane containing both.*

shown the existence of the particular auxiliary set, we have the logical right to reason about it and to derive the properties of it in our geometry.

**II. The fundamental auxiliary sets.** We are not limited to introducing just segments; we may also introduce: (1) points, (2) lines (and segments), (3) rays, (4) complex configurations of points, segments, rays, and lines, and (5) planes. Hence we speak of introducing auxiliary "sets." Many different postulates and theorems are used to justify our choice. For example: (1) the introduction of a point is often based on the Point-Plotting Theorem; (2) the introduction of a line (or segment) is often based on the Line Postulate or (in Chapter 9 *et seq.*) the Parallel Postulate; (3) the introduction of a ray is often based on the Angle Construction Postulate; (4) complex figures are usually constructed by introducing, sequentially, certain rudimentary sets; (5) in Chapters 8 and 10 we often introduce planes and base these introductions on the Plane Postulate, or Theorem 3–3, or Theorem 3–4.

**III. The role of mathematical creativity in the introduction of useful auxiliary sets.** We can introduce an auxiliary set in a problem, provided we know that the set actually exists. There is, however, another important point: in addition to being plausible and legitimate, the introduction must also be *useful*. In Problem 11 of Problem Set 6–5, for example, it is legitimate to introduce either $\overline{QS}$ or $\overline{RT}$; but only the introduction of $\overline{RT}$ is effective. We make a specific introduction in the hope of obtaining an opportunity to apply some postulate or theorem. In the problems in Problem Set 6–5, the postulate or theorem to be applied is usually obvious, and the introduction which will make possible the application of that postulate or theorem is rather rudimentary. In Chapters 7 and 8, matters are more complex: (1) Although it is possible to reason as to which theorems *might* be useful, the actual choice is often neither obvious nor unique. (2) Even when we feel we know what theorem we would like to use, the introduction which will make the application of this theorem possible may require a great deal of ingenuity.

**IV. The existence of the introduced set.** Finally, when introducing an auxiliary set, you must be certain that there actually *exists* a set satisfying all the restrictions you impose upon it. For example, let us say that △ABC is given. A typical error then is to introduce $\overrightarrow{BD}$ which bisects both ∠B and $\overline{AC}$. Except in the special case where △ABC is isosceles with AB = BC, there does not exist a ray satisfying these restrictions. Uninitiated students frequently commit this sort of error because in a roughly drawn figure it may look as though it is possible to introduce an auxiliary set satisfying several restrictions.

We recommend that the teacher consider, in class, the separate problems of introducing in scalene triangle △ABC: (1) the bisector of ∠B, (2) the median $\overline{BM}$ to $\overline{AC}$, and (3) the altitude $\overline{BF}$ on $\overline{AC}$. This discussion will bear fruit in three ways: (1) the student learns three fundamental introductions, (2) he learns that in a scalene triangle, △ABC, the bisector of ∠B and the median on $\overline{AC}$ are two different segments, and that it is consequently illegal to "introduce" the ray which bisects ∠B *and* bisects $\overline{AC}$, and (3) he learns to distinguish among angle bisectors, medians, and altitudes.

Note that a more subtle difficulty arises when the restrictions im-

**POSTULATE 12.** The Angle Construction Postulate

*Let $\overrightarrow{AB}$ be a ray on the edge of the half-plane H. For every number r between 0 and 180 there is exactly one ray $\overrightarrow{AP}$, with P in H, such that $m\angle PAB = r$.*

**Theorem 5–2.** The Angle Bisector Theorem

*Every angle has exactly one bisector.*

**Theorem 6–1**

*In a given plane, through a given point of a given line, there is one and only one line perpendicular to the given line.*

**Theorem 6–3**

*Through a given external point there is at least one line perpendicular to a given line.*

**Theorem 6–4**

*Through a given external point there is at most one line perpendicular to a given line.*

There are no fixed rules for devising proofs; we learn by practice. Let us look at an example.

*Example*

> *Given:* The plane figure with
>
> $AD = AE$ and $CD = CE$.
>
> *To prove:* $\angle D \cong \angle E$.

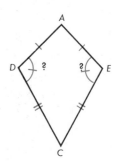

Since all our postulates and theorems concerning congruence have dealt with triangles, it seems reasonable that our figure should show some triangles. We can accomplish this easily by introducing either $\overline{AC}$ or $\overline{DE}$.

Suppose we introduce $\overline{DE}$ so that our figure looks like the one on the right. This allows us to complete the proof, since $m\angle ADE = m\angle AED$ and $m\angle CDE = m\angle CED$ give us $m\angle ADC = m\angle AEC$ by the Angle Addition Postulate.

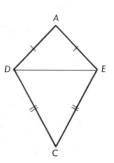

*A word of warning:* Before you "introduce" something, make sure that it exists. Nothing is easier than to describe imaginary objects by laying words hastily end to end. Consider, for example, the following "theorem" and its "proof."

### "Theorem"

**In any triangle $\triangle ABC$, we have $\angle B \cong \angle C$.**

**"Proof."** Let $D$ be a point between $B$ and $C$, such that $BD = DC$ and $\overline{AD} \perp \overline{BC}$. Then $\angle ADB \cong \angle ADC$, because both are right angles. Therefore $ADB \leftrightarrow ADC$ is an SAS correspondence. Therefore $\triangle ADB \cong \triangle ADC$, and $\angle B \cong \angle C$.

This "theorem" is ridiculous, and so its proof must be wrong. And it is not hard to see that the proof goes astray at its very start, with a light-hearted use of the word "let." Unless it happens that $\angle B \cong \angle C$, the midpoint of $\overline{BC}$ and the foot of the perpendicular from $A$ are two different points. Therefore, in most cases, the point $D$ that we were "letting" exist does not really exist at all. Note that this would have been quite obvious if the author of the wrong proof had been willing to use a scalene triangle in his figure. Good figures are no guarantee against errors, but they are a help.

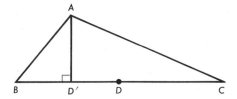

Among the theorems and postulates that we have presented so far, these are the ones that we shall use when we introduce auxiliary sets. But these surely aren't going to do us any good in proving new theorems for ourselves, unless we can think of a set that is *useful* to introduce. In fact, thinking of *useful* sets to introduce is both the difficult and the most interesting part of our job; the theorem citations are merely a way of making sure that our work is orderly.

posed upon the auxiliary set *are* consistent with the given information, but the consistency itself requires proof. For example: Given $\triangle ABC$ with $AB = BC$, introduce $\overrightarrow{BD}$ which bisects $\angle B$ and is perpendicular to $\overline{AC}$. It is obviously legitimate to introduce $\overrightarrow{BD}$, the bisector of $\angle B$, but to assert in the introduction itself that $\overrightarrow{BD} \perp \overline{AC}$ makes tacit use of the theorem that the bisector of the vertex angle of an isosceles triangle is perpendicular to the base. Introductions of this sort are dubious, not because there does not exist a set satisfying the restrictions imposed (there does), but because it is necessary to *prove* that there exists such a set. Unfortunately, many students fail to see the necessity of such a proof and, naturally, fail to supply it. Remind them that a smaller set of restrictions will suffice to determine the set they have in mind; introduce the auxiliary set using this smaller set of restrictions, and then *prove* that the introduced set has the additional properties they wanted to attribute to it.

**Answers to Problems**

**2.** 1. Introduce $\overline{QN}$. (Two points determine a line.)
2. $QN = QN$. (Identity)
3. $QM = NP$; $MN = PQ$. (Given)
4. $\triangle QMN \cong \triangle NPQ$. (SSS)
5. $\angle M \cong \angle P$. (Definition of congruent triangles)

**3.** 1. Introduce $\overline{MH}$. (Two points determine a line.)
2. $MH = MH$. (Identity)
3. $MK = MG$, $HK = HG$. (Given)
4. $\triangle MHG \cong \triangle MHK$. (SSS)
5. $\angle G \cong \angle K$. (Corresponding parts)

**4.** 1. Introduce $\overline{ST}$. (Two points determine a line.)
2. $ST = TS$. (Identity)
3. $RS = QT$, $RT = SQ$. (Given)
4. $\triangle RST \cong \triangle QTS$. (SSS)
5. $\angle R \cong \angle Q$. (Corresponding parts)

**5.** 1. Introduce $DA$ and $DB$. (Two points determine a line.)
2. $AE = BC$, $DE = DC$, $\angle E \cong \angle C$. (Given)
3. $\triangle DEA \cong \triangle DCB$. (SAS)
4. $DA = DB$. (Corresponding parts)
5. $D$ lies on the perpendicular bisector of $\overline{AB}$. (Theorem 6-2)

**6.** Introduce $\overline{DF}$, the perpendicular bisector of $\overline{AB}$. Show that $\triangle DAE \cong \triangle DBC$, $\angle EAB \cong \angle CBA$ and finally $\triangle EAB \cong \triangle CBA$.

**7.** 1. Introduce $\overline{AC}$. (Two points determine a line.)
2. $AC = AC$. (Reflexive Property)
3. $AD = CB$; $AB = CD$. (Given)
4. $\triangle BAC \cong \triangle DCA$. (SSS)
5. $\angle BAC \cong \angle DCA$. (Corresponding parts)
6. In $\triangle AKC$, $AK = KC$. (Theorem 5-5)

**8.** $\overleftrightarrow{AB}$ and $\overleftrightarrow{PQ}$ determine a plane, by Theorem 3-4. In this plane, $B$ is equidistant from $P$ and $Q$ by Theorem 6-2.

Note that the hypothesis of Theorem 6-2 guarantees only that the theorem holds in a plane, and so it is necessary to use Theorem 3-4.

---

**Problem Set 6–5**

**1.** Prove the theorem stated in the Example on p. 196 by introducing $\overline{AC}$.
Introducing $\overline{AC}$ gives us $\triangle ADC \cong \triangle AEC$ by SSS and $\angle D \cong \angle E$ by CPCTC.

**2.** Given the figure as marked. Prove that $\angle M \cong \angle P$.

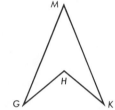

**3.** Given the figure with $MK = MG$, $HK = HG$.

Prove that $\angle G \cong \angle K$.

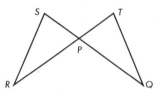

**4.** Given the figure with $RS = QT$ and $RT = SQ$. Prove that $\angle R \cong \angle Q$.

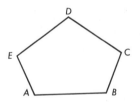

**5.** In the figure $AE = BC$, $DE = DC$, $\angle E \cong \angle C$. Prove that $D$ lies on the perpendicular bisector of $\overline{AB}$.

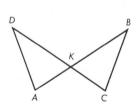

**6.** In the figure $AE = BC$ and $DE = DC$. If $D$ lies on the perpendicular bisector of $\overline{AB}$, prove that $AC = BE$.
See Solution Section for complete proof.

**7.** Given the figure with
$$AD = CB \quad \text{and} \quad AB = CD.$$
Prove that $AK = CK$.

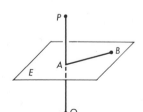

**8.** Given points $A$ and $B$ in the plane $E$, and points $P$ and $Q$ on opposite sides of $E$ such that $PA = QA$ and $\overleftrightarrow{AB} \perp \overleftrightarrow{PQ}$. Prove that $B$ is equidistant from $P$ and $Q$. How does Theorem 3-4 enter your proof?

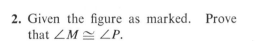

9. Find the error in the following "proof." In $\triangle PQR$, let $\overrightarrow{RS}$ bisect $\angle PRQ$ and be perpendicular to $\overline{PQ}$ at $S$. Then $\angle PRS \cong \angle QRS$, $RS = RS$ by identity, and $\angle PSR \cong \angle QSR$ since all right angles are congruent. Therefore $\triangle PRS \cong \triangle QRS$ by $ASA$, making $PR = QR$. This "proves" that all triangles are isosceles. **The angle bisector is not necessarily perpendicular to the third side.**

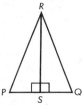

10. Find the error in the following "proof." On the sides of $\angle A$, points $B$ and $C$ are taken so that $AB = AC$. $D$ is any point in the interior of $\angle A$. Introduce the ray which bisects $\angle A$ and contains $D$. Introduce $\overline{DC}$ and $\overline{DB}$. By the definition of angle bisector, $\angle DAC \cong \angle DAB$. $AD = AD$ by identity. Therefore $\triangle ADC \cong \triangle ADB$ by $SAS$, and $DB = DC$. Thus $D$ is equidistant from $B$ and $C$. **The ray which bisects $\angle A$ does not contain every point $D$ in the interior of $\angle A$.**

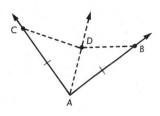

11. Given: $Q$, $R$, $S$, and $T$ are coplanar. $QR = QT$. $m\angle R = m\angle T$.

Prove: $SR = ST$. **See Solution Section.**

Does your proof hold if $Q$, $R$, $S$, and $T$ are not coplanar? **No, the AAP is used and thus the proof depends on the fact that these points are coplanar. [Hint: Introduce $\overline{RT}$. Show $\triangle QRT$ and $\triangle RTS$ are isosceles.]**

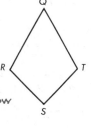

12. Given: $AB = PQ$ and $BP = AQ$.

Prove: (a) $\angle A \cong \angle P$.
(b) $\triangle ABM \cong \triangle PQM$.

**See Solution Section for complete proof.**

13. Given: $AH = RD$, $\angle A \cong \angle R$, and $H$, $A$, $R$, and $D$ are coplanar.

Prove: $\angle H \cong \angle D$. **See Solution Section.**

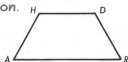

---

**Answers to Problems**

12. (a) Introduce $\overline{BQ}$ and show that $\triangle BAQ \cong \triangle QPB$.
(b) Use Part (a) and the Subtraction Property of Equality to show $\angle ADP \cong \angle PQA$.

13. Introduce $\overline{AD}$ and $\overline{RH}$ by Postulate 4. Then $\triangle HAR \cong \triangle DRA$ by SAS. This gives $HR = DA$, so $\triangle AHD \cong \triangle RDH$ by SSS. Therefore $\angle H \cong \angle D$.

**Quiz**

1. Given: $\square ABCD$, $AB = AD$, $\angle B \cong \angle D$
Prove: $BC = CD$

Proof: Introduce $\overline{BD}$. $\angle ABD \cong \angle ADB$ by Theorem 5–4, and by the Angle Addition Postulate $m\angle ABD + m\angle CBD = m\angle B$, $m\angle ADB + m\angle CBD = m\angle D$. $\angle CBD \cong \angle CDB$ by Subtraction Property. $CB = CD$ by Theorem 5–5.

2.

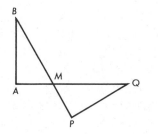

Given: $AB = CD$, $AC = BD$
Prove: $\angle BAM \cong \angle CDM$
Proof: Introduce $\overline{AD}$. Then $\triangle ABD \cong \triangle DCA$ by SSS, $\angle BAD \cong \angle CDA$, and $\angle CAD \cong \angle BDA$. By the Angle Addition Postulate and Subtraction Property of Equality $\angle BAM \cong \angle CDM$.

**14.** Introduce $M$, the midpoint of $\overline{AR}$ and then introduce $\overline{HM}$ and $\overline{DM}$. Then $\triangle HAM \cong \triangle DRM$ by SAS. This gives $m\angle AHM = m\angle RDM$ and $HM = DM$. By the Isosceles Triangle Theorem, $m\angle MHD = m\angle MDH$. By AAP and substitution, $m\angle H = m\angle D$.

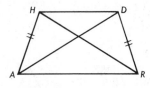

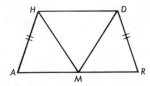

**16.**

| Postulate 4 | E U |
|---|---|
| Postulate 5 | E |
| Theorem 2–5 | E U |
| Theorem 2–6 | E U |
| Theorem 3–1 | U |
| Theorem 3–2 | U |
| Postulate 7 | E U |
| Theorem 3–3 | E U |
| Theorem 3–4 | E U |
| Postulate 12 | E U |
| Theorem 5–2 | E U |
| Theorem 6–1 | E U |
| Theorem 6–3 | E |
| Theorem 6–4 | U |

**17.** Introduce $\overline{CF}$ and show that $\triangle ACF \cong \triangle ECF$ and finally that $\triangle AFB \cong \triangle EFD$.

**18.** Introduce $\overleftrightarrow{CF}$. Show that $\triangle ACF \cong \triangle ECF$. Using AAP and the Subtraction Property show $\angle EFD \cong \angle AFB$. Finally show that $\triangle AFB \cong \triangle EFD$.

**20.** 1. $M$ is on the perpendicular bisector of $AB$ and $B$ is on the perpendicular bisector of $MK$. (Given)
2. $AM = MB$ and $MB = BK$. (Theorem 6–2)
3. $AM = BK$. (Transitivity)
The assumption that $\overleftrightarrow{AB}$ and $\overleftrightarrow{MK}$ intersect is not necessary in the proof.

---

**14.** Outline a second solution to Problem 13 by introducing auxiliary segments different from the ones you used before.

**15.** In the figure, the planes $R$ and $T$ intersect in $\overleftrightarrow{MN}$. $E$ is in $T$, $S$ is in $R$, and $\overleftrightarrow{MN}$ contains $A$ and $Y$. If $EY = EA$ and $SY = SA$, prove that $\angle EAS \cong \angle EYS$.
See Solution Section.

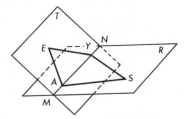

**16.** For each of the postulates and theorems listed on pages 195 and 196, tell whether it asserts existence, uniqueness, or both.

**17.** In the figure, $AF = EF$, $AC = EC$, and $\angle AFB \cong \angle EFD$. Prove that $\triangle BDF$ is isosceles.
See Solution Section for complete proof.

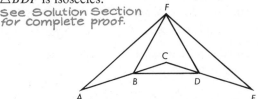

Figure for Problems 17 and 18

**18.** In the figure, $AF = EF$, $AC = EC$, and $\angle AFD \cong \angle EFB$. Prove that $\overleftrightarrow{CF} \perp \overline{BD}$. See Solution Section for complete proof.

**19.** Devise two proofs for the following and state which proof does not depend on the requirement that the points $A$, $B$, $C$, and $D$ be coplanar. See Solution Section.
Given: $AB = AC$ and $BD = CD$ in the figure.
Prove: $\angle ABD \cong \angle ACD$.

**20.** $\overleftrightarrow{AB}$ and $\overleftrightarrow{MK}$ intersect at $P$. $\overleftrightarrow{MD}$ is the perpendicular bisector of $\overline{AB}$, and $\overleftrightarrow{BC}$ is the perpendicular bisector of $\overline{MK}$. Prove that $AM = BK$. What part of the hypothesis is not necessary to your proof?

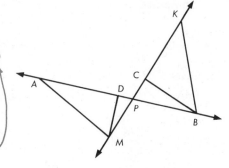

## 6–6  MAKING THEOREMS OF THE ASA AND SSS POSTULATES

In the preceding chapter, we based our study of triangle congruences on the three postulates SAS, ASA, and SSS. In fact, the only one of these that we really needed to accept as a postulate was SAS; if we assume only SAS, the other two can be proved. Let us first consider the case of ASA.

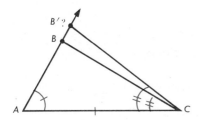 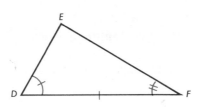

Given an ASA correspondence

$$ABC \leftrightarrow DEF,$$

as indicated in the figure.    We need to show that $\triangle ABC \cong \triangle DEF$.

**Proof**

| STATEMENTS | REASONS |
|---|---|
| 1. $\angle A \cong \angle D$ <br> $AC = DF$ <br> $\angle C \cong \angle F$. | 1. ASA correspondence |
| 2. $\overrightarrow{AB}$ contains a point $B'$ such that $AB' = DE$. | 2. The Point-Plotting Theorem |
| 3. $AB'C \leftrightarrow DEF$ is an $SAS$ correspondence. | 3. Steps 1 and 2 |
| 4. $\triangle AB'C \cong \triangle DEF$. | 4. SAS |
| 5. $\angle ACB' \cong \angle DFE$. | 5. Corresponding angles |
| 6. $\angle ACB' \cong \angle ACB$. | 6. Transitive Property |
| 7. $\overrightarrow{CB'} = \overrightarrow{CB}$. | 7. The Angle Construction Postulate |
| 8. $B' = B$. | 8. Two different lines intersect in at most one point. |
| 9. $\triangle ABC \cong \triangle DEF$. | 9. Steps 4 and 8 |

## 6–6 MAKING THEOREMS OF THE ASA AND SSS POSTULATES

**Background Material**

Although it is possible to prove the ASA and the SSS Postulates on the basis of the previous postulates and theorems, it is *not* possible to go one step further and prove the SAS Postulate on the basis of the postulates and theorems that precede it. See Section 6–4, "The Independence of the SAS Postulate," in *EGAS*.

**Classroom Notes**

By now the students should be sophisticated enough in producing their own proofs so that these proofs of the two postulates will be fairly easy for them to follow. For extra class discussion, you may wish to have the students prove the second and third cases of the SSS postulate as mentioned on page 203.

The material on betweenness and separation is difficult and is only of interest to potential mathematics majors. You may wish to discuss this part of the section thoroughly with honors classes. For a complete discussion of betweenness and separation, see Chapter 4 of *EGAS*.

We believe that many logically incomplete discussions are fully justifiable on pedagogical (and common-sense) grounds. But logical incompleteness should be avoided whenever a simple, satisfactory alternative is available. See, for example, the proof of the Isosceles Triangle Theorem, page 154, and the proof of the Basic Proportionality Theorem, page 373.

We shall now show that SSS can also be proved as a theorem.

First we recall that in proving the
Isosceles Triangle Theorem, all that
we used was SAS.   Since $ABC \leftrightarrow$
$ACB$ is an SAS correspondence, we
know that $\triangle ABC \cong \triangle ACB$, and so

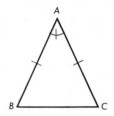

$$\angle B \cong \angle C.$$

We can therefore use the Isosceles Triangle Theorem in proving SSS,
without committing the error of reasoning in a circle.

Now suppose we have given an SSS correspondence

$$ABC \leftrightarrow DEF.$$

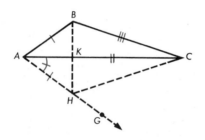

**Proof**

| STATEMENTS | REASONS |
|---|---|
| 1. $AB = DE$,   $AC = DF$, $BC = EF$. | 1. Given |
| 2. There is a point $G$ on the opposite side of $\overleftrightarrow{AC}$ from $B$ such that $\angle CAG \cong \angle D$. | 2. The Angle Construction Postulate |
| 3. There is a point $H$ of $\overrightarrow{AG}$ such that $AH = DE$. | 3. The Point-Plotting Theorem |
| 4. $\triangle AHC \cong \triangle DEF$. | 4. SAS |

Thus we have a congruent copy of $\triangle DEF$, on the under side of
$\triangle ABC$.  This finishes the first half of the proof.  In the second half,
we are going to show that $\triangle ABC \cong \triangle AHC$.  The following proof
applies to the case shown in the figure, in which $\overline{BH}$ intersects $\overleftrightarrow{AC}$ in a
point between $A$ and $C$.

**Proof** (*cont.*)

| STATEMENTS | REASONS |
|---|---|
| 5. $\angle ABH \cong \angle AHB$. | 5. Isosceles Triangle Theorem |
| 6. $\angle HBC \cong \angle CHB$. | 6. Isosceles Triangle Theorem |
| 7. $\angle ABC \cong \angle AHC$. | 7. Angle Addition Postulate |
| 8. $ABC \leftrightarrow AHC$ is an SAS correspondence. | 8. Steps 1, 5, and 8 |
| 9. $\triangle ABC \cong \triangle AHC$. | 9. SAS |
| 10. $\triangle ABC \cong \triangle DEF$. | 10. Steps 5 and 10; Transitive Property |

Of course, there are two other cases to consider:

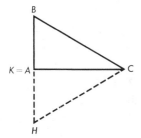 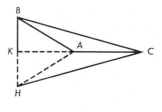

The proofs in these cases are left to you.

If you were watching very carefully, you may have noticed places where two of our proofs were not complete. In the proof of Theorem 5–3, we really needed to know that the midpoint $D$ of $\overline{BC}$ was in the interior of $\angle BAC$. We needed this information in order to know that $\overrightarrow{AD}$ satisfied the definition of an angle bisector. To use angle addition in step 7, we needed to know that the point $K$ was in the interior of $\angle AHC$.

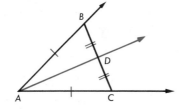

Strictly speaking, these statements call for proofs. But the proofs are omitted in nearly all books, including Euclid and most textbooks. This is not necessarily bad. Geometry is quite rightly guided by common sense; it is common sense that tells us that our postulates were reasonable in the first place. And the study of geometry was over two thousand years old before people managed to write postulates that were really adequate for the proofs of geometric theorems.

Once we have the postulates, however, and once we have learned to use them, we may as well get our work into better order by stating and proving the theorems that we need.

### Theorem 6–5

*If M is between A and C on a line L, then M and A are on the same side of any other line that contains C.*

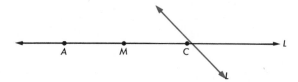

**Proof.** Let $L'$ be another line, containing $C$, and suppose that $A$ and $M$ are on opposite sides of $L'$. Then $\overline{AM}$ contains a point $D$ of $L'$. But $\overline{AM}$ lies on $L$, and $L$ intersects $L'$ only at $C$. Therefore $C = D$. Therefore, by definition of a segment, $C$ is between $A$ and $M$. This is impossible, because $M$ is between $A$ and $C$. [See Theorem 2–1.]

This easily leads to the theorem that we needed in the proofs of Theorem 5–3 and SSS:

### Theorem 6–6

*If M is between B and C, and A is any point not on $\overleftrightarrow{BC}$, then M is in the interior of $\angle BAC$.*

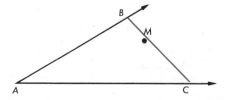

**Proof.** By the preceding theorem we know that (1) $M$ and $B$ are on the same side of $\overleftrightarrow{AC}$. By another application of the preceding theorem we know that (2) $M$ and $C$ are on the same side of $\overleftrightarrow{AB}$. By definition of the interior of an angle, this means that $M$ is in the interior of $\angle BAC$.

In the following problem set you will be asked to use some of the ideas given in this section. Even though it may be easier to solve the problem by reading information from the figure, it is essential that you use the knowledge you have learned.

## Problem Set 6–6

1. Draw a figure for the following statement and justify its validity: In any triangle, each point of a side of the triangle other than the end points lies in the interior of the angle opposite the side.
   *The statement is an immediate consequence of Theorem 6-6.*

2. Given $\overleftrightarrow{AC}$, with a point $R$ such that $R\text{-}A\text{-}C$, a point $B$ not on $\overleftrightarrow{AC}$, and points $P$ and $Q$ on $\overline{BC}$ and $\overline{BA}$ such that $B\text{-}P\text{-}C$ and $B\text{-}Q\text{-}A$. Complete each of the following statements and be prepared to justify your answers.

   (a) $P$ lies in the interior of $\angle$ __BAC__ .

   (b) $Q$ and $B$ lie on the __same__ side of $\overleftrightarrow{AC}$.

   (c) $P$ and $B$ lie on __same side__ of $\overleftrightarrow{AC}$.

   (d) $Q$ and $P$ lie on __same side__ of $\overleftrightarrow{AC}$.

   (e) $R$ and $P$ lie on __opposite sides__ of $\overleftrightarrow{AB}$.

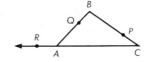

3. Prove: If $M$ is between $A$ and $C$ on a line $L$, then $A$ and $C$ are on opposite sides of any other line that contains $M$.

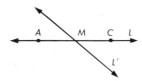

4. Given the coplanar points $A$, $B$, $C$, $D$, $E$, and $H$ such that $A$, $B$, and $C$ are noncollinear, $B\text{-}C\text{-}D$, $A\text{-}E\text{-}C$, and $B\text{-}E\text{-}H$, prove that $A$ and $H$ are on the same side of $\overrightarrow{BD}$.

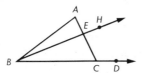

*See Solution Section.*

5. Prove: In a plane, if a line intersects a side of a triangle at a point not a vertex, then it must intersect at least one other side of the triangle.

   [*Hint:* Let $H_1$ and $H_2$ be the half-planes with edge $L$, with $C$ in $H_1$. There are three cases to consider: $B$ is on $L$, $B$ is in $H_1$, and $B$ is in $H_2$.]

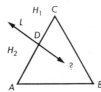

---

### Answers to Problems

2. Reasons:
   (a) Since $B\text{-}P\text{-}C$, Theorem 6-6 applies.
   (b) Since $B\text{-}Q\text{-}A$, Theorem 6-5 applies.
   (c) Since $B\text{-}P\text{-}C$, Theorem 6-5 applies.
   (d) This follows from Parts (b) and (c).
   (e) Since $B\text{-}P\text{-}C$, $P$, and $C$ are on the same side of $\overleftrightarrow{AB}$ by Theorem 6-5. Since $R\text{-}A\text{-}C$, $R$, and $C$ are on opposite sides of $\overleftrightarrow{AB}$. Therefore $P$ and $R$ are on opposite sides of $\overleftrightarrow{AB}$.

3. Proof by indirect reasoning: There are two possibilities: (1) Points $A$ and $C$ lie on the same side of $L'$. (2) Points $A$ and $C$ lie on opposite sides of $L'$. [Note: Points $A$ and $C$ cannot lie on line $L'$ itself. Lines $L$ and $L'$ intersect at point $M$. Line $L$ contains $A$. If $L'$, in addition, contained point $A$ then $L = L'$ by Postulate 4.] Suppose $A$ and $C$ lie on the same side of $L'$. Then by the Plane Separation Postulate, $\overline{AC}$ would not intersect $L'$. But, by hypothesis, $\overline{AC}$ intersects $L'$ at $M$. Hence, by contradiction, points $A$ and $C$ lie on opposite sides of $L'$.

4. (1) Since $C$ is on $\overleftrightarrow{BD}$ and $A\text{-}E\text{-}C$, $E$ is on the same side of $\overleftrightarrow{BD}$ as $A$ by Theorem 6-5. (2) Since $B$ is on $\overleftrightarrow{BD}$ and $B\text{-}E\text{-}H$, $E$ is on the same side of $\overleftrightarrow{BD}$ as $H$, again by Theorem 6-5. (3) Since $A$ and $H$ are each on the same side of $\overleftrightarrow{BD}$ as $E$, $A$ and $H$ are on the same side of $\overleftrightarrow{BD}$.

**6.** 1. By Problem 4, *A* and *H* are on the same side of $\overleftrightarrow{CD}$.

2. Since *B* and *H* are on opposite sides of $\overleftrightarrow{AC}$, and *B* and *D* are on opposite sides of $\overleftrightarrow{AC}$, *D* and *H* are on the same side of $\overleftrightarrow{AC}$.

3. Hence, *H* is, by definition, in the interior of ∠*ABC*.

**7.** (a) Since *D* is on the ray opposite to $\overrightarrow{BA}$, we know, by the definition of opposite rays that *A-B-D*. Then by Problem 3 of Problem Set 6-6 we can conclude that *A* and *D* are on opposite sides of $\overleftrightarrow{BC}$; and since *A* is in $H_1$, this means that *D* is in $H_2$.

(b) Since *K* is in the interior of ∠*ABC*, *K* is on the same side of $\overleftrightarrow{BC}$ as *A*, that is, *K* is in $H_1$.

(d) Each point of $\overrightarrow{BK}$ with the exception of *B*, lies in $H_1$. Each point of $\overline{DC}$, with the exception of *C*, lies in $H_2$. Points *B* and *C* lie on line $\overleftrightarrow{BC}$ separating $H_1$ and $H_2$, but they are distinct points.

(e) *K* and *C* are on the same side of $\overleftrightarrow{AB}$ since *K* is in the interior of ∠*ABC*. By Theorem 6-5, each point of $\overline{DC}$ other than *D* lies on the same side of $\overleftrightarrow{AB}$ as *C*. Also, each point of $\overrightarrow{BK}$ other than *B* lies on the same side of $\overleftrightarrow{AB}$ as *K*. Therefore, $\overline{DC}$ and $\overrightarrow{BK}$, except for the two points *D* and *B*, lie on the same side of $\overleftrightarrow{AB}$. But all points of the ray opposite to $\overrightarrow{BK}$ except for *B* are on the side of $\overleftrightarrow{AB}$ opposite to *K*. Therefore $\overline{DC}$ and the ray opposite to $\overrightarrow{BK}$, except for the distinct points *D* and *B*, are on opposite sides of $\overleftrightarrow{AB}$. Hence, $\overline{DC}$ does not intersect the ray opposite to $\overrightarrow{BK}$.

(g) By Problem 5 of this problem set, $\overleftrightarrow{BK}$ must intersect either $\overline{AC}$ or $\overline{DC}$ of △*ADC*. By part (f) $\overleftrightarrow{BK}$ does not intersect $\overline{DC}$. Therefore $\overleftrightarrow{BK}$ intersects $\overline{AC}$.

(h) Each point of $\overline{AC}$, other than *A*, lies on the same side of $\overleftrightarrow{AB}$ as *C* by Theorem 6-5, but each point of the ray opposite to $\overrightarrow{BK}$, with the exception of *B*, lies on the opposite side of $\overleftrightarrow{AB}$ from *K* and

---

**6.** Given the coplanar points *A*, *B*, *C*, *D*, *E*, and *H* such that *A*, *B*, and *C* are noncollinear, *B-C-D*, *A-E-C*, and *B-E-H*, prove that *H* is in the interior of ∠*ACD*. [*Hint:* By the definition of interior of an angle, you must show that *A* and *H* are on the same side of $\overleftrightarrow{CD}$ (see Problem 4) and that *D* and *H* are on the same side of $\overleftrightarrow{AC}$.]

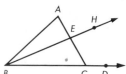

**7.** The following theorem, whose truth seems so obvious, is frequently accepted without proof.

> The Crossbar Theorem. If *K* is a point in the interior of ∠*ABC*, then $\overrightarrow{BK}$ intersects $\overline{AC}$.

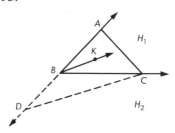

You should be able to supply a proof after answering the questions below. You may use other problems of this problem set to justify your reasoning.

(a) Let $H_1$ and $H_2$ be the half-planes having edge $\overleftrightarrow{BC}$, with *A* in $H_1$. Take any point *D* on the ray opposite to $\overrightarrow{BA}$. Draw $\overline{DC}$ forming △*DAC*. Why is *D* in $H_2$?

(b) Why is *K* in $H_1$? What theorem shows that each point of $\overrightarrow{BK}$ except *B* is in $H_1$? **Theorem 6-5**

(c) Why is each point of $\overline{DC}$ other than *C* in $H_2$? **Theorem 6-5**

(d) Why does $\overline{DC}$ not intersect $\overrightarrow{BK}$?

(e) Why does $\overline{DC}$ not intersect the ray opposite to $\overrightarrow{BK}$?

(f) Why does $\overline{DC}$ not intersect $\overleftrightarrow{BK}$? **This follows from (d) and (e).**

(g) Why must $\overleftrightarrow{BK}$ intersect $\overline{AC}$?

(h) Why does the ray opposite to $\overrightarrow{BK}$ not intersect *AC*?

(i) Why does $\overrightarrow{BK}$ intersect $\overline{AC}$?

**8.** Supply an indirect proof. **See Solution Section.**

> On $\overleftrightarrow{AB}$, *A-C-B* and $\overleftrightarrow{CD} \perp \overleftrightarrow{AB}$. *P* is in the interior of ∠*ACD* and *Q* is in the interior of ∠*BCD* such that ∠*PCA* ≅ ∠*QCB*. If *PC* ≠ *QC*, then $\overleftrightarrow{CD}$ is not perpendicular to $\overleftrightarrow{PQ}$. **Assume $\overleftrightarrow{CD} \perp \overleftrightarrow{PQ}$**

# HONORS PROBLEM

The following faulty argument which attempts to demonstrate that an obtuse angle is congruent to a right angle emphasizes the importance of knowing the side of a line on which a point lies. Suppose that $\square ABCD$ is a rectangle and that the side $\overline{BC}$ is swung outward so that $BC' = BC$ and $\angle ABC'$ is obtuse. Let the perpendicular bisector of $\overline{AB}$ intersect the perpendicular bisector of $\overline{DC'}$ at $X$. If $X$ is below $\overleftrightarrow{AB}$ as shown, we have

$$\triangle AXD \cong \triangle BXC'$$

by the SSS Theorem, and hence

$$m\angle DAX = m\angle C'BX.$$

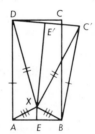

Also, $\triangle EAX \cong \triangle EBX$ by SSS, and so $m\angle EAX = m\angle EBX$. It follows by subtraction that $m\angle DAE = m\angle C'BE$. If $X$ lies above $\overleftrightarrow{AB}$, as in the second figure, we get, exactly as before, $m\angle DAX = m\angle C'BX$, $m\angle EAX = m\angle EBX$, and the desired equality, $m\angle DAE = m\angle C'BE$, follows by addition. What is wrong with the above argument?

[*Hint:* Try drawing an exact figure for the case in which $m\angle ABC$ is only a little less than 180. How much of the "proof" is valid in this case?] See Solution Section.

# CHAPTER REVIEW

1. Assume that you are going to try to prove each statement below by the indirect method. What is the supposition, for each statement, with which you would begin?

   (a) If a triangle has no two angles congruent, then it is not isosceles.

   (b) Given a line and a point not on the line, there is at most one line through the point and perpendicular to the given line.

   (c) If a point is equidistant from the ends of a segment, it lies on the perpendicular bisector of the segment.

   (d) If two coplanar lines are perpendicular to the same line, they are parallel.

   (e) In a plane, there is at most one line perpendicular to a given line at a given point of the line.

   (f) $\sqrt{2}$ is not a rational number.

   (g) Zero has no reciprocal.

2. Define *perpendicular bisector of a segment.* See page 188.

C. [See part (e).] *A* and *B* are distinct points.

(i) Since $\overleftrightarrow{BK}$ intersects $\overline{AC}$ and the ray opposite to $\overrightarrow{BK}$ does not intersect $\overline{AC}$, $\overrightarrow{BK}$ must intersect $\overline{AC}$.

**Answers to Chapter Review Problems**

1. (a) Suppose the triangle is isosceles.

   (b) Suppose there are two lines which contain the given point and are perpendicular to the given line.

   (c) Suppose a point *P* does not lie on the perpendicular bisector of a segment.

   (d) Suppose the two coplanar lines which are perpendicular to the same line intersect at a point.

   (e) Suppose, in the given plane, there are two lines perpendicular to the given line at the given point of that line.

   (f) Suppose $\sqrt{2}$ is a rational number.

   (g) Suppose zero has a reciprocal.

**7.** 1. $AD = AB$ and $CD = CB$. (Given)

2. $\overleftrightarrow{AC}$ is the perpendicular bisector of $\overline{DB}$. (Corollary 6-2.1)

3. Let $M$ be the intersection of $\overleftrightarrow{AC}$ and $\overline{DB}$. ($A$ and $C$ lie on opposite sides of the line $\overleftrightarrow{DB}$.)

4. $MD = MB$. ($M$· lies on $\overleftrightarrow{AC}$, the perpendicular bisector of $DB$.)

5. $\overleftrightarrow{AC}$ bisects $\overline{DB}$. (Definition of bisect for segments)

**8.** $\angle AMD \cong \angle DMC \cong \angle AMB \cong \angle CMB$, $\triangle ADC \cong \triangle ABC$, $\triangle ADM \cong \triangle ABM$, $\triangle CDM \cong \triangle CBM$, and all corresponding parts of these triangles are congruent.

**9.** The two vertices are each equidistant from the end points of the base, so the line they determine is perpendicular to the base by Corollary 6-2.1.

**10.** If $AB \neq AC$, then if the median $\overline{AM}$ were perpendicular to $\overline{BC}$, we would have $MB = CM, AM = AM$, and $\angle AMB \cong \angle AMC$. Therefore $\triangle AMB \cong \triangle AMC$ by SAS, so $AB = AC$, contradicting the hypothesis that $AB \neq AC$.

**11.** Introduce $\overline{AD}$ and $\overline{BD}$ by the Line Postulate. Then $\triangle EAD \cong \triangle CBD$ by SAS, making $AD = BD$. Since $G$ is the midpoint of $\overline{AB}$, $AG = BG$. Therefore $\overline{DG} \perp \overline{AB}$ by Corollary 6-2.1.

---

**3.** State the Perpendicular Bisector Theorem. **See page 188.**

**4.** Copy each triangle, making certain each is scalene. Construct the perpendicular bisector of each side of each triangle. Do any of the perpendicular bisectors bisect an angle of one of the triangles? **No**

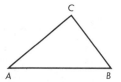

**5.** Indicate for each statement below whether it is true or false.

(a) In a plane there are at most two perpendiculars to a line at a point of the line. **F**

(b) Proving that "there is exactly one" means proving both existence and uniqueness. **T**

(c) The longest side of any triangle is called the hypotenuse. **F**

(d) In a right triangle, the side opposite the right angle is called the hypothesis. **F**

**6.** Which theorem states the uniqueness of the line perpendicular to a given line from a point not on the line? **Theorem 6-4**

**7.** In the plane figure, $AD = AB$ and $CD = CB$. Prove that $\overleftrightarrow{AC}$ bisects $\overline{BD}$. Do not use congruent triangles in your proof.

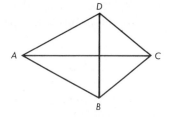

**8.** Using the hypothesis of Problem 7, list all the facts that follow from it. You should be able to prove each conclusion.

**9.** Two coplanar isosceles triangles have a common base. Prove that the line determined by the vertices of the two vertex angles is perpendicular to the common base. Do not use congruent triangles in your proof.

**10.** Prove that no median of a scalene triangle is perpendicular to a side of the triangle.

---

**11.** In the figure, $AE = BC$, $ED = CD$, $G$ is the midpoint of $\overline{AB}$ and $\angle E \cong \angle C$. Prove that

$$\overline{DG} \perp \overline{AB}.$$

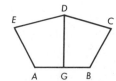

**12.** In the plane figure, line $L$ is a perpendicular bisector of both $\overline{PQ}$ and $\overline{SR}$. Prove that $PS = QR$. **See Solution Section.**

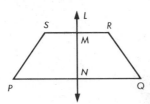

**13.** Line $L$ is the perpendicular bisector of $\overline{BC}$, with $A$ the midpoint of $\overline{BC}$. $K$ and $G$ are points on the same side of $\overleftrightarrow{BC}$. $K$ is on the same side of $L$ as $B$, and $G$ is on the same side of $L$ as $C$ such that $\angle BAK \cong \angle CAG$. The perpendicular to $\overline{BC}$ at $B$ intersects $\overrightarrow{AK}$ at $D$, and the perpendicular to $\overline{BC}$ at $C$ intersects $\overrightarrow{AG}$ at $E$. Prove that $\overline{BE}$ and $\overline{CD}$ intersect on $L$.

**14.** In the plane figure the points $A$, $B$, $M$ are collinear and the points $B$, $C$, $K$ are collinear. $AT = SC$, $MT = KS$, $\angle T \cong \angle S$, and $\angle M \cong \angle K$. Prove that $AB = BC$. **See Solution Section.**

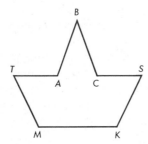

**15.** $\overline{AB}$ and $\overline{CD}$ are coplanar and congruent. The perpendicular bisector of $\overline{AD}$ and the perpendicular bisector of $\overline{BC}$ intersect at $X$. Prove that $\triangle ABX \cong \triangle DCX$. **See Solution Section.**

**16.** Using the Crossbar Theorem (Problem 7 of Problem Set 6–6), devise a different proof of the Isosceles Triangle Theorem. [*Hint:* Bisect an angle.]

---

### Answers to Chapter Review Problems

**13.** Let $H$ be $\overline{BE} \cap \overline{CD}$. To show that $H$ lies on $L$, it will suffice to show that $\overleftrightarrow{AH} = L$.

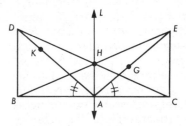

1. $BA = AC$, $\angle BAK \cong \angle CAG$. (Given)
2. $m\angle DBA = m\angle ECA$. (Given, definition of perpendicular, right angles, and congruent angles)
3. $\triangle DBA \cong \triangle ECA$. (ASA)
4. $BD = CE$. (Corresponding parts)
5. $BC = BC$. (Identity)
6. $\triangle DBC \cong \triangle ECB$. (SAS; Steps 2, 4, and 5)
7. $\angle DCB \cong \angle EBC$. (Corresponding parts; Step 6)
8. $BH = CH$. (Theorem 5–5)
9. $\overleftrightarrow{AH}$ is the $\perp$ bisector of $\overline{BC}$. (Corollary 6–2.1)
10. $L$ is $\perp$ bisector of $\overline{BC}$. (Given)
11. $\overleftrightarrow{AH} = L$. (Theorem 6–1) Therefore, $\overline{BE}$ and $\overline{CD}$ intersect on line $L$.

**16.**
1. $AB = AC$. (Given)
2. Let the bisector of $\angle A$ meet $\overline{BC}$ at $M$. (The Cross-Bar Theorem)
3. $AM = AM$. (Identity)
4. $\angle BAM \cong \angle CAM$. (Definition of bisector)
5. $\triangle BAM \cong \triangle CAM$. (SAS)
6. $\angle B \cong \angle C$. (Corresponding parts)

## Geometric Inequalities

The congruence problems for triangles (Chapter 5) and the theorems and problems on parallelograms (Chapter 9) are straightforward. To achieve success with these problems the student simply has to master systematic procedures for establishing congruence of triangles and for establishing that a quadrilateral is a parallelogram.

Geometric inequalities are of an essentially different nature. Here we find a vexatious absence of systematic procedures; each problem appears to be solved in a different way. It is often very hard to find a proof, and an ingenious idea which works for one problem is often of no use in the next. For these reasons, geometric inequalities present a greater challenge to the creative imagination than the preceding chapters do.

### Planning the Chapter

Section 7–3 (The Exterior Angle Theorem) is the most important section in this chapter and will thus require two days of study from both the average and above-average class. The rest of the sections of the chapter should only require one day on each section.

CHAPTER **7**

# Geometric Inequalities

## Objectives . . .

- Appreciate the role of conjectures in mathematics.
- Apply the properties of inequalities for numbers to geometric situations.
- Prove and use the Exterior Angle Theorem.
- Prove and use the SAA Theorem and the Hypotenuse-Leg Theorem for congruences between triangles.
- Prove and use theorems about geometric inequalities in single triangles and between two triangles.
- Learn about altitudes of triangles.

## 7–1  MAKING REASONABLE CONJECTURES

Up to now, in our study of the geometry of the triangle, we have been dealing only with conditions under which we can say that two segments are of equal length, or two angles are of equal measure. We will now proceed to study conditions under which we can say that one segment is longer than another (that is, has a greater length), or one angle is larger than another (that is, has a greater measure).

We shall not start, however, by proving theorems. Let us start, rather, by making some reasonable conjectures about the sort of statements that ought to be true.

Let us look at the following example: Given a triangle with two sides of unequal length, what can we say about the angles opposite these sides? Note that this problem is naturally suggested by Theorem 5–4, which says that if two sides of a triangle have the same length, then the angles opposite them have the same measure.

You can investigate this situation by sketching a triangle with two sides of obviously unequal lengths. Here *BC* is greater than *AB*, and $m\angle A$ is greater than $m\angle C$. After sketching a few more triangles, 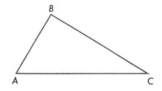 you will probably be convinced that the following statement ought to be true.

> *If two sides of a triangle are of unequal length,* then the angles opposite them are of unequal measure, and the larger angle is opposite the longer side.

Now try the same sort of procedure with the following problems.

**Classroom Notes**

Since geometric inequalities are inherently difficult, it is valuable to begin the chapter with a rough sketch of the subject. In Problem Set 7–1 we investigate specific examples, and infer the statements of the important inequality theorems. This preview is possible because in this course we are concerned with only a limited number of theorems on inequalities and they are all easily discovered by examining figures. The proofs, of course, are another matter entirely.

We suggest that you discuss the example in Section 7–1 at the end of the last lesson on Chapter 6, and then send the students home to do Problem Set 7–1 on their own. Instruct them to infer in each problem a general statement (analogous to the statement on page 211) which is independent of the notation used in the problem. You can then spend your first class day on Chapter 7 discussing their observations and reviewing the algebraic properties of inequalities.

It is reasonable to expect students to understand the proofs of Theorems 7–2, 7–5, 7–6, and 7–7. The triangle inequality is fundamental, but its proof and the problems related to it are all quite difficult. The proof of the Hinge Theorem is difficult, but the related problems are valuable because many of them are "two-step" inequality problems.

**1.** In $\triangle ABC$ and $\triangle DEF$, $AB = DE$, $BC = EF$ and $\angle B > \angle E$. What conjecture can be made about the triangles?
  (ans: $CA > FD$)

**2.** What conjecture can be made about $\angle DEG$ and $\angle EFD$? about $\angle DEG$ and $\angle EDF$?

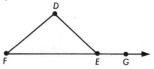

  (ans: $\angle DEG > \angle EFD$, $\angle DEG > \angle EDF$)

**Answers to Problems**

**2.** The sum of the lengths of any two sides of a triangle is greater than the length of the third side.

**3.** The examples suggest a reasonable conjecture, they do not prove it.

**7.**

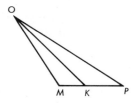

$MP > KP$, but $KO > MO$.

---

**Problem Set 7–1**

**1.** In each of these triangles, $m\angle A > m\angle B$. What conjecture can you make about the sides opposite $\angle A$ and $\angle B$? $BC > AC$

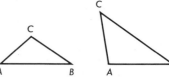

**2.** Consider any three triangles. Label each with $A$, $B$, and $C$. Does $AB + BC > AC$ seem to be true? Yes How does $BC + AC$ compare with $AB$? How about $BC$ and $AC + AB$? What general statement do your answers suggest? $BC + AC > AB$. $BC < AC + AB$

**3.** Consider several scalene triangles of various shapes. For each triangle list the longest side and the greatest angle. What conjecture ought to be true? Do your examples prove that it is true? The longest side lies opposite the greatest angle.

**4.** Draw $\triangle RST$ and $\triangle ABC$ such that $m\angle RST > m\angle ABC$, $RS = AB$, and $ST = BC$. Compare $RT$ and $AC$. $RT > AC$

**5.**

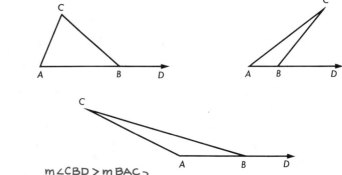

$m\angle CBD > m\, BAC$
What conjecture concerning $m\angle CBD$ and $m\angle BAC$ is suggested by the triangles shown here? In the third figure, if the vertex $C$ were moved very far to the left of $A$ and $B$, do you think your conjecture would still hold? Yes Can you think of a way to prove it?

**6.** Given a line $L$ and a point $P$ not on $L$. Let $Q$ be the foot of the perpendicular from $P$ to $L$, and let $A$ be any other point of $L$. What conjecture involving $PQ$ and $PA$ seems to be valid? $PA > PQ$

---

**7.** Draw any triangle, $\triangle MOP$. Let $K$ be a point between $M$ and the midpoint of $\overline{MP}$, and draw $\overline{KO}$. For the $\triangle MOP$ and $\triangle KOP$ we have $PO = PO$, $\angle P \cong \angle P$, and $MP > KP$. A hasty person might conjecture that $MO > KO$. Show that this does not always hold.

8. Does the following procedure describe a valid way of trisecting every angle? Make some drawings to help you decide.

No

> On the sides of any angle, ∠A, take points B and C so that AB = AC. Draw $\overline{BC}$ and trisect $\overline{BC}$ with points D and E so that BD = DE = EC. Draw $\overrightarrow{AD}$ and $\overrightarrow{AE}$. Then $\overrightarrow{AD}$ and $\overrightarrow{AE}$ are trisectors of ∠A.

9. $\overline{QC}$ and $\overline{QB}$ are noncollinear segments in a plane E. P is a point not in E such that ∠PQB and ∠PQC are right angles; QC < QB. Write a statement whose conclusion concerns PB and PC, and which you think is true.

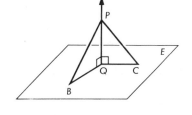

10. A is a point in a plane E, $\overrightarrow{AB}$ is a ray not lying in E, and $\overrightarrow{AC}$ is a ray lying in E. Considering different positions of $\overrightarrow{AC}$, describe as accurately as you can the position of $\overrightarrow{AC}$ which makes m∠BAC as large as possible; as small as possible. No proof is expected, but you are asked to guess the answer on the basis of your knowledge of space.

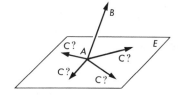

## .7–2   INEQUALITIES FOR NUMBERS, SEGMENTS, AND ANGLES

Inequalities between segments and angles are defined in terms of the numbers that measure the segments and angles.

### Definition

$\overline{AB} < \overline{CD}$   if   $AB < CD$.

In words: One segment is *less than* (or *shorter than*) another if its length is less. Similarly,

### Definition

∠A < ∠B   if   $m∠A < m∠B$.

## 7–2  INEQUALITIES FOR NUMBERS, SEGMENTS, AND ANGLES

**Classroom Notes**

This preliminary section presents the definitions of inequalities between segments and angles, the inequality properties of the real numbers, and a simple inequality theorem which has two very useful corollaries concerning geometric inequalities.

Observe that the metric approach to geometry makes it possible to give straightforward and mathematically satisfactory definitions of inequalities between segments and angles. Once having stated these definitions we can use, with complete justification, all the inequality properties of the real numbers.

It may be of interest to compare the above metric definitions with the purely synthetic definitions of the statements $\overline{AB} < \overline{CD}$ and ∠A < ∠B. The latter are rather tedious to state, and even more tedious to apply. See Section 8–3 of *EGAS*.

Theorem 7–1 has two very useful corollaries:

**Corollary 7–1.1.** If $D$ is a point on $\overline{AB}$ between $A$ and $B$, then $AB > AD$ and $AB > BD$.

*Proof.* Since $D$ is between $A$ and $B$, $AB = AD + DB$. But $AD$ and $DB$ are each positive, and so by Theorem 7–1, $AB > AD$ and $AB > BD$.

**Corollary 7–1.2.** If $D$ is a point in the interior of $\angle ABC$, then $\angle ABC > \angle ABD$ and $\angle ABC > \angle DBC$.

*Proof.* Since $D$ is in the interior of $\angle ABC$, $m\angle ABC = m\angle ABD + m\angle DBC$. But, $m\angle ABD$ and $m\angle DBC$ are each positive. Hence, by Theorem 7–1, $m\angle ABC > m\angle ABD$, which means that $\angle ABC > \angle ABD$. Similarly, $\angle ABC > \angle ABD$.

## Quiz

**1.** Identify the Properties illustrated below.
   (a) If $m > 6$ and $n = 7$ then $m + n > 13$.
   (ans: Addition Property)
   (b) If $AB \neq 12$, then $AB > 12$ or $AB < 12$.
   (ans: Trichotomy Property)
   (c) If $R$-$S$-$T$ and $G$-$H$-$K$ and $RS > GH$ and $ST > HK$, then $RT > GK$.
   (ans: Addition Property and betweenness definition)
   (d) If $6 < 7$ then $\frac{3}{7} < \frac{3}{6}$.
   (ans: Multiplication Property)
**2.** Given: $\triangle ABC$, $D$ in the interior such that $BD = CD$.
   Prove: $\angle ABC > \angle DBC$
   Proof: $m\angle ACB = m\angle ACD + m\angle DCB$ by AAP and $m\angle ACB > m\angle DCB$ by Theorem 7–1. In $\triangle DBC$, $m\angle DBC \cong m\angle DCB$ by Theorem 5–4 and $m\angle ACB > m\angle DBC$ by substitution.

Before proceeding to the study of inequalities between segments and angles, we should recall, from Section 2–2, some properties and a theorem that govern inequalities between numbers.

## Trichotomy Property

For every $x$ and $y$, one and only one of the following conditions holds: $x < y$, $x = y$, $x > y$.

## Transitive Property

If $x < y$ and $y < z$, then $x < z$.

## Addition Property

If $a < b$ and $x \leq y$, then $a + x < b + y$.

## Multiplication Property

If $x < y$ and $a > 0$, then $ax < ay$.

## Theorem 2–2

*If $a = b + c$ and $c > 0$, then $a > b$.*

Our first theorem about geometric inequalities is a direct consequence of Theorem 2–2. Its name refers to this statement often used to summarize its meaning: "The whole is greater than any one of its parts."

## Theorem 7–1.   The Parts Theorem

(1) If $D$ is a point on $\overline{AB}$ between $A$ and $B$, then $\overline{AB} > \overline{AD}$ and $\overline{AB} > \overline{DB}$.

(2) If $D$ is a point in the interior of $\angle ABC$, then $\angle ABC > \angle ABD$ and $\angle ABC > \angle DBC$.

**Proof.**   (1) Since $A$–$D$–$B$, $AB = AD + DB$. Since $AD$ and $DB$ are each positive numbers, then by Theorem 2–2, $AB > AD$ and $AB > DB$. By the definition of inequality between segments, this means that $\overline{AB} > \overline{AD}$ and $\overline{AB} > \overline{DB}$.

(2) Since $D$ is in the interior of $\angle ABC$, $m\angle ABC = m\angle ABD + m\angle DBC$. Since measures of angles are positive numbers, by Theorem 2–2 we have $m\angle ABC > m\angle ABD$ and $m\angle ABC > m\angle DBC$. By definition, this means that $\angle ABC > \angle ABD$ and $\angle ABC > \angle DBC$.

## Problem Set 7–2

1. For each of the following examples, identify the property that it illustrates.

   (a) If $m > 7$ and $n < 7$, then $n < m$. Transitive Property

   (b) If $4 < 6$, then $14 < 21$. Multiplication Property

   (c) If $AB < 13$, then $AB \neq 13$. Trichotomy Property

   (d) If $x - y = 7$ and $y < 3$, then $x < 10$. Addition Property

   (e) If $\angle A < \angle C$ and $\angle B > \angle C$, then $\angle A < \angle B$. Transitivity

   (f) If $RS < GH$ and $ST < HK$, then $RS + ST < GH + HK$.
       Addition Property

2. If $G$, $H$, $K$ are three points such that $G-K-H$, explain why $GH > GK$. GH > GK by theorem 7-1.

3. Complete each statement by filling the blank with either $<$ or $>$.

   (a) Since $15 = 11 + 4$, it follows that $15$ __>__ $11$.

   (b) Since $-3 = -7 + 4$, it follows that $-3$ __>__ $-7$.

   (c) If $-9 = x + 3$, it follows that $x$ __<__ $-9$.

   (d) If $y = -7 + 5$, it follows that $y$ __>__ $-7$.

4. In the figure the points are collinear and $AB < CD$. Prove that $AC < BD$.

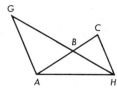

5. In the figure,

   $$AB < GB \quad \text{and} \quad BC < BH.$$

   Prove that $AC \neq GH$.

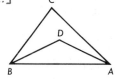

6. Given that $A$, $B$, and $C$ are collinear and that $G$, $H$, and $K$ are collinear. The points are spaced such that $AB < GH$ and $BC < HK$. Does it follow that $AC < GK$? No Why or why not? We must also assume A-B-C and G-H-K [or G-K-B-A-C-H, etc.]

7. Given: The figure with

   $\angle DAB < \angle DBA$ and $\angle DAC < \angle DBC$.

   Prove: $\angle CAB < \angle CBA$.

8. If $K$ is a point in the interior of $\angle GHJ$, explain why $\angle GHJ > \angle KHJ$. ∠GHJ > ∠KHJ by Theorem 7-1.

## Explanation for Problems

It is very desirable to assign Problem 11 on page 216; it is designed to prepare the student for the proof of the Exterior Angle Theorem in Section 7–3.

The Honors Problem should be given only to those students who have studied betweenness and separation in Chapter 6.

### Answers to Problems

**4.** $AB < CD$, so by the Addition Property, definition of betweenness, and transitivity, $AC = AB + BC < CD + BC = BC + CD = BD$.

**5.** Since $AB < GB$ and $BC < BH$, $AB + BC < GB + BH$, by the Addition Property. But, by definition of betweenness $AB + BC = AC$ and $GB + BH = GH$. Therefore, by substitution, $AC < GH$, and by the trichotomy property, $AC \neq GH$.

**7.** 1. $\angle DAB < \angle DBA$ and
       $\angle DAC < \angle DBC$. (Given)
    2. $m\angle DAB < m\angle DBA$.
       $m\angle DAC < m\angle DBC$. (Definition of $<$ for angles)
    3. $m\angle DAB + m\angle DAC < m\angle DBA + m\angle DBC$. (Addition Property)
    4. $m\angle DAB + m\angle DAC = m\angle CAB$.
       $m\angle DBA + m\angle DBC = m\angle CBA$. (Angle Addition Postulate)
    5. $m\angle CAB < m\angle CBA$. (Transitive Property)
    6. $\angle CAB < \angle CBA$. (Definition of $<$ for angles)

# Answers to Problems

**10.** By the interpretation of Theorem 7-1 in Problem 8, $m\angle ABC > m\angle DBC$. Since $BD = DC$, $m\angle DBC = m\angle DCB$. By substitution, $m\angle ABC > m\angle DCB$ or $\angle ABC > \angle DCB$.

**11.** $m\angle RQT > m\angle RQS$ by Theorem 7-1. But since $\triangle MQS \cong \triangle MRP$ by SAS, $m\angle RQS = m\angle R$. Hence by substitution $m\angle RQT > m\angle R$.

**12.** Let $x$ be a negative number and let $y$ be a positive number. By definition $x < 0$ and $0 < y$. By the Transitive Property of Inequality $x < y$.

**13.** Assume that for every $a$, $b$, and $x$, if $a < b$, then $a + x < b + x$. Since $x < y$, $b + x < b + y$. By transitivity, $a + x < b + y$.

**14.** 1. $AD = DB$. (Given)
    2. $\angle A \cong \angle ABD$. (Isosceles Triangle Theorem)
    3. $AC = DC$. (Given)
    4. $\angle A \cong \angle ADC$. (Isosceles Triangle Theorem)
    5. $B$ is in the interior of $\angle ADC$. (Given)
    6. $m\angle ADC = m\angle ADB + m\angle BDC$. (AAP)
    7. $m\angle ADC > m\angle ADB$. (Theorem 7-1)
    8. $m\angle ABD = m\angle A = m\angle ADC$. (Definition of congruence for angles)
    9. $m\angle ABD > m\angle ADB$. (Substitution)

## Answer to Honors Problem

Since $P$-$Q$-$T$, $P$, and $T$ are on opposite sides of $\overleftrightarrow{RQ}$ (Problem 3, Section 6-6). Since $P$ and $S$ are also on opposite sides of $\overleftrightarrow{RQ}$, $S$ and $T$ must be on the same side of $\overleftrightarrow{RQ}$. Secondly, $S$ and $R$ are on the same side of $\overleftrightarrow{QT}$ by hypothesis. Hence, by definition, $S$ is in the interior of $\angle RQT$.

**9.** In the figure why is it true that
$$m\angle ABC > m\angle ABD?$$
m∠ABC = m∠ABD + m∠DBC by AAP
Conclusion by Theorem 7-1.

**10.** In the figure, $BD = CD$. Prove that $\angle ABC > \angle DCB$.

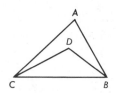

**11.** Given the figure with $M$ the midpoint of both $\overline{PS}$ and $\overline{RQ}$. Prove that $\angle RQT > \angle R$.

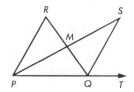

**12.** Use the Transitive Property to prove that any negative number is less than any positive number.

**13.** Suppose that the Addition Property had been stated simply as:

For every $a$, $b$, and $x$, if $a < b$, then $a + x < b + x$.

Show that the other part of this property would follow as a theorem:

For every $a$, $b$, $x$, and $y$, if $a < b$ and $x < y$, then $a + x < b + y$.

[*Hint:* Get $a + x < b + x$ and $x + b < y + b$, and use the Transitive Property.]

**14.** Given $\triangle ACD$ with $AC = DC$ and $AD = DB$. Prove that
$$\angle ABD > \angle ADB.$$

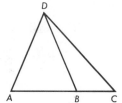

**15.** Given the real numbers $a$, $x$, and $y$ such that $0 < x < y$ and $a < 0$, prove that $ax > ay$ and that $1/y < 1/x$. See Solution Section.

## HONORS PROBLEM

Refer to the figure for Problem 11 but assume only the following hypothesis: $S$ and $P$ are on opposite sides of $\overleftrightarrow{RQ}$, $P$-$Q$-$T$, and $S$ and $R$ are on the same side of $\overleftrightarrow{PT}$. Prove that $S$ is in the interior of $\angle RQT$.

## 7-3   THE EXTERIOR ANGLE THEOREM

In the figures below, $\angle 1$ is called an *exterior angle* of $\triangle ABC$:

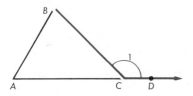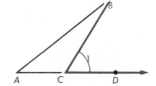

### Definition

If $C$ is between $A$ and $D$, then $\angle BCD$ is an *exterior* angle of $\triangle ABC$.

Every triangle has six exterior angles, as shown in the figure below.

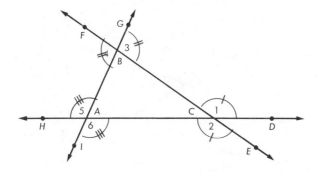

These form three pairs of vertical angles; and the angles in each vertical pair are congruent, as indicated in the figure.

Every exterior angle of a triangle forms a linear pair with one of the angles of the triangle itself. For example, in the figure, $\angle 1$ and $\angle C$ of $\triangle ABC$ form a linear pair. The other two angles of the triangle are called the *remote interior* angles.

### Definition

$\angle A$ and $\angle B$ of $\triangle ABC$ are called the *remote* interior angles of the exterior angles $\angle BCD$ and $\angle ACE$.

Similarly, $\angle A$ and $\angle C$ are the remote interior angles of $\angle ABF$ and $\angle CBG$.

The following theorem is the key to the study of geometric inequalities.

**Classroom Notes**

The Exterior Angle Theorem was anticipated in our preliminary discussion of geometric inequalities. The statement of the theorem was by no means obvious, especially since the concept of an exterior angle of a triangle had not been formulated, and the student cannot be expected to anticipate its crucial role in the study of geometric inequalities. It turns out, however, that the Exterior Angle Theorem is the best point of entry to the theory.

(Note that at no point in this chapter do we make any appeal to the Euclidean Parallel Postulate. In fact, all the theorems in Chapter 7 hold true also in hyperbolic geometry, and our proofs are valid in either geometry.)

The idea of an exterior angle of a triangle follows naturally upon the idea of an interior angle of a triangle, and the text states a very simple definition. It is possible to formulate a definition which does not mention the notation for the vertices: an *exterior angle* of a triangle is an angle which forms a linear pair with one of the angles of the triangle. The definition in the text, however, seems easier to apply.

Distinguish between an exterior angle and an angle vertical to an interior angle. Point out that an exterior angle is obviously supplementary to the adjacent interior angle (because they form a linear pair), and then introduce the question of the relation of an exterior angle to the remote interior angles. This question leads directly to a formulation of the Exterior Angle Theorem. The proof of this theorem depends on an ingenious introduction of auxiliary sets, and is very difficult to discover without assistance. Hence the teacher should supply the suggestion to introduce $E$, the midpoint of $\overline{BC}$, $\overrightarrow{AE}$, $F$ on $\overrightarrow{AE}$ with $A$-$E$-$F$ such that $EF = AE$, and finally, $\overline{CF}$. With this substantial hint the student should be able to complete the proof. The proof will seem more natural if you have previously assigned Problem 11 of Problem Set 7-2.

**Theorem 7-2.** The Exterior Angle Theorem

*An exterior angle of a triangle is greater than each of its remote interior angles.*

**Restatement.** Given $\triangle ABC$. If $C$ is between $A$ and $D$, then

$$\angle BCD > \angle B.$$

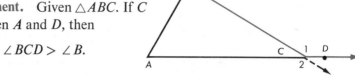

If we had chosen $D$ on the ray opposite $\overrightarrow{CB}$, then we would be trying to prove that $\angle 2 > \angle A$. Since $\angle 1 \cong \angle 2$, it would follow that $\angle 1 > \angle A$, also. Therefore the restatement is equivalent to the original statement, and conveys the whole content of the theorem.

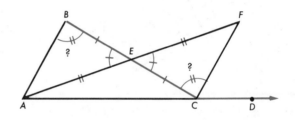

**Proof**

| STATEMENTS | REASONS |
|---|---|
| 1. Introduce $E$, the midpoint of $\overline{BC}$. | 1. Midpoint Theorem |
| 2. On the ray opposite to $\overrightarrow{EA}$ introduce the point $F$ such that $EF = EA$. | 2. Point-Plotting Theorem |
| 3. Introduce $\overline{FC}$. | 3. Line Postulate |
| 4. $\angle BEA \cong \angle CEF$. | 4. ? Vertical angles are congruent. |
| 5. $BE = EC$. | 5. ? Definition of midpoint |
| 6. $\triangle BEA \cong \triangle CEF$. | 6. ? SAS |
| 7. $\therefore \angle B \cong \angle ECF$. | 7. ? Definition of congruence |
| 8. $\angle BCD > \angle ECF$. | 8. Parts Theorem |
| 9. $\therefore \angle BCD > \angle B$. | 9. Transitive Property |

The Exterior Angle Theorem has an easy corollary.

## Corollary 7–2.1

*If a triangle has one right angle, then its other angles are acute.*

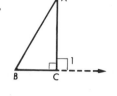

(If $\angle C$ is a right angle, then so is $\angle 1$. The Exterior Angle Theorem tells us that $\angle 1 > \angle B$ and $\angle 1 > \angle A$. Therefore $m\angle B < 90$ and $m\angle A < 90$.)

If we had known about the Exterior Angle Theorem, in the last chapter, we could have concluded more easily that the perpendicular to a line from an external point is unique. If there were two perpendiculars from $P$ to $L$, then $\angle 1$ would be congruent to $\angle PQR$, which is impossible: $\angle 1$ is an exterior angle of $\triangle PQR$, and $\angle PQR$ is one of its remote interior angles.

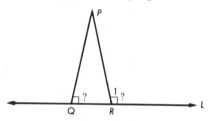

## Problem Set 7–3

1. (a) Name the remote interior angles of $\angle ABE$ in the figure. ∠ACB, ∠BAC
   (b) Which exterior angle has $\angle ABC$ and $\angle BAC$ as its remote interior angles? ∠BCF

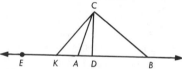

2. (a) In the figure, which angles are exterior angles of the triangle? ∠CAD, ∠BAE
   (b) What is the relation of $m\angle DAC$ to $m\angle B$? Why? m∠DAC > m∠B
   (c) What is the relationship of $m\angle DAC$ to $m\angle BAE$? Why? m∠DAC = m∠BAE
   (d) What is the relationship of $m\angle DAC$ to $m\angle BAC$? Why?
      m∠DAE + m∠BAC = 180

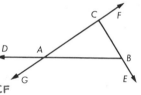

3. Use the figure only to explain notation, and complete each statement on the basis of theorems that you have seen proved.

   (a) If $x = 40$ and $y = 30$, then $w > \underline{\ 40\ }$.
   (b) If $x = 72$ and $y = 73$, then $w \underline{\ >73\ }$.
   (c) If $y = 54$ and $z = 68$, then $w \underline{\ =112\ }$.
   (d) If $w = 112$, then $x \underline{\ <112\ }$.
   (e) If $w = 150$, then $z \underline{\ =30\ }$.
   (f) If $x = 25$ and $z = 90$, then $w \underline{\ =90\ }$.
   (g) If $z = 90$ then $x \underline{\ <90\ }$ and $y \underline{\ <90\ }$.

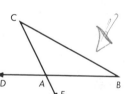

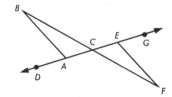
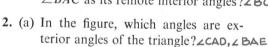

RQ and ST intersect at U.
en)

QTU > m∠S. (Theorem 7-2
△PST)

3. m∠UQV > m∠QTU. (Theorem
7-2 for △UTQ)

4. m∠RQV > m∠S. (Transitivity)

**9.** 1. Introduce AC. (Two points determine a line.)

2. m∠2 > m∠DAC, m∠2 >
m∠DCA, m∠1 > m∠CAB,
m∠1 > m∠BCA. (Theorem 7-2)

3. 2m∠2 > m∠DAC + m∠DCA,
2m∠1 > m∠CAB + m∠CBA.
(Addition Property of Inequalities)

4. m∠DAC + m∠CAB = m∠A,
m∠DCA + m∠BCA = m∠C.
(AAP)

5. 2(m∠1 + m∠2) > m∠A + m∠C.
(Addition Property)

6. m∠1 + m∠2 > ½(m∠A + m∠C).
(Multiplication Property)

**10.** (a) Since m∠SCM > m∠SVC, and
m∠SVC > m∠SPM, in each case
by the Exterior Angle Theorem,
m∠SCM > m∠SPM.

(b) Since m∠PRT = m∠SCM by the
Supplement Postulate, and
m∠SCM > m∠S by the Exterior
Angle Theorem, we can conclude that m∠PRT > m∠S.

**4.** Given the figure on the left below prove that ∠CAK > ∠G.
∠CAK >∠CBA >∠G . By Transitivity ∠CAK >∠G

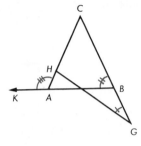
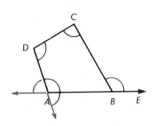

**5.** The figure on the right above is one illustration of this statement: An
exterior angle of a quadrilateral is greater than each remote interior angle.
Is this a true statement? No Explain. Consider exterior
angles at A.

**6.** Explain why the markings on the figure
indicate an impossible situation.
∠ADB is an exterior angle of △BDC
and consequently ∠ ADB > ∠ BCD

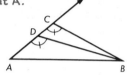

**7.** Given the figure, prove that

∠RQV > ∠S.

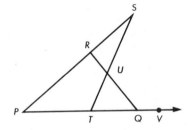

**8.** Given any two segments, $\overline{AB}$ and $\overline{DE}$. Can we make a statement relating
AB and DE that will always be true? What is it? Give a reason for
your answer. Either AB >CD, AB=CD, or AB <CD. Yes
Trichotomy Property.

**9.** Prove that

$$m∠1 + m∠2 > ½(m∠A + m∠C).$$

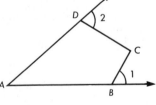

**10.** (a) In the figure, $\overrightarrow{PS}$ bisects ∠RPM.
Prove that ∠SCM > ∠SPM.

(b) Prove that if ∠SCV ≅ ∠PRV,
then ∠PRT > ∠S.

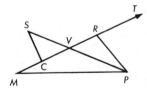

**11.** Prove the following theorem.

> The sum of the measures of any two angles of a triangle is less than 180.

**Restatement.** If the angles of a triangle have measures as indicated in the figure, then

$$a + b < 180,$$
$$b + c < 180,$$
$$a + c < 180.$$

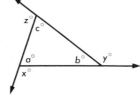

**12.** Prove the following theorem.

> The base angles of any isosceles triangle are acute.

[*Hint:* Use the theorem of Problem 11.]

**13.** Prove the following theorem.

> Each angle of an equilateral triangle is an acute angle.

## 7–4  CONGRUENCE THEOREMS BASED ON THE EXTERIOR ANGLE THEOREM

### Definition

Given a correspondence $ABC \leftrightarrow DEF$ between two triangles:

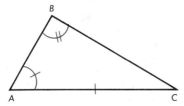 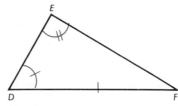

If a pair of corresponding sides are congruent, and two pairs of corresponding angles are congruent, then the correspondence is called an *SAA correspondence*. (Here, of course, SAA stands for Side Angle Angle.)

**Answers to Problems**

**11.** By the Supplement Postulate, $a + x = 180$. But $b < x$, by the Exterior Angle Theorem. Adding $a$ to each side of this inequality, we get $a + b < a + x$ which becomes $a + b < 180$, which was to be proved. Similarly, $b + c < 180$ and $a + c < 180$.

**12.** Given: $\triangle ABC$ with $\overline{AC} \cong \overline{BC}$.
Prove: $m\angle A < 90$. $m\angle B < 90$.
Proof: By the previous problem we have $m\angle A + m\angle B < 180$. But the base angles of an isosceles triangle are congruent, so $2(m\angle A) < 180$, and $m\angle A < 90$. Also, $m\angle B < 90$, since the measures of the base angles are equal.

**13.** Given: $\triangle ABC$ with $\overline{AC} \cong \overline{BC} \cong \overline{AB}$.
Prove: $m\angle A < 90$, $m\angle B < 90$, $m\angle C < 90$.
Proof: By the previous problem, $m\angle A < 90$ and $m\angle B < 90$. $m\angle A = m\angle C$, because an equilateral triangle is equiangular, and so $m < C < 90$.

**7–4 CONGRUENCE THEOREMS BASED ON THE EXTERIOR ANGLE THEOREM**

**Classroom Notes**

The SAA Theorem is usually established as a corollary to the Angle Sum Theorem (Theorem 9–13); the Hypotenuse-Leg Theorem is invariably proved as a consequence of the SAA Theorem. However, these congruence theorems are not dependent on the Parallel Postulate; we can prove them as soon as we have the Exterior Angle Theorem. There are, however, certain objections to proving the SAA and Hypotenuse-Leg Theorems at this time: each proof is difficult, and, to prove them now does interrupt the study of geometric inequalities. In addition, we make no important use of either theorem until the latter half of Chapter 9. You consequently should decide whether to prove these theorems at the present point, at the end of Chapter 7, or after Theorem 9–13.

**Theorem 7–3.**   The SAA Theorem

> *Every SAA correspondence is a congruence.*

If the congruent sides are included between the congruent angles, then we already know by ASA that the correspondence is a congruence. We may therefore assume, in the restatement, that we have the sort of correspondence suggested by the two figures on page 221.

**Restatement.**   Given $\triangle ABC$ and $\triangle DEF$. If $\angle A \cong \angle D$, $\angle B \cong \angle E$, and $\overline{AC} \cong \overline{DF}$, then $\triangle ABC \cong \triangle DEF$.

**Proof.**   There are three possibilities for $AB$ and $DE$:

$$(1)\ AB = DE,\ (2)\ AB < DE,\ (3)\ AB > DE.$$

If (1) holds, then the theorem follows, because in this case $ABC \leftrightarrow DEF$ is an SAS correspondence. We shall show that (2) and (3) are impossible.

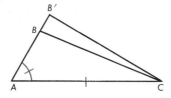 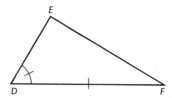

Suppose that (2) holds: $AB < DE$. Let $B'$ be the point of $\overrightarrow{AB}$ such that $AB' = DE$. Then $\triangle AB'C \cong \triangle DEF$, by SAS. Therefore $\angle AB'C \cong \angle DEF$. Therefore $\angle ABC \cong \angle AB'C$. (Why?) But this is impossible, because the Exterior Angle Theorem tells us that $\angle ABC > \angle AB'C$.

In a very similar way, we can show that (3) $AB > DE$ is impossible. You should be able to supply the details.

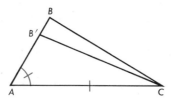 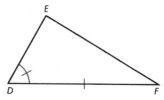

Since (2) and (3) are impossible, (1) must hold, and $\triangle ABC \cong \triangle DEF$ by SAS. This completes the proof.

We found, in Chapter 5 (p. 138), that there is no such thing as an SSA Postulate. That is, an SSA correspondence is not necessarily a congruence. For the case of *right* triangles, however, we can prove a theorem of this kind, as follows.

**Theorem 7–4.** The Hypotenuse-Leg Theorem

> *Given a correspondence between two right angles. If the hypotenuse and one leg of one of the triangles are congruent to the corresponding parts of the second triangle, then the correspondence is a congruence.*

**Restatement.** Given $\triangle ABC$ and $\triangle DEF$, such that $m\angle A = m\angle D = 90$, $AB = DE$, $BC = EF$. Then $\triangle ABC \cong \triangle DEF$.

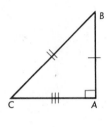

**Proof**

| STATEMENTS | REASONS |
|---|---|
| 1. On the ray opposite to $\overrightarrow{DF}$ take $G$ such that $DG = AC$. Draw $\overline{EG}$. | 1. Point-Plotting Theorem and Line Postulate |
| 2. $\angle GDE$ is supplementary to $\angle FDE$. | 2. ? Supp. Postulate |
| 3. $m\angle A = m\angle FDE = 90 = m\angle GDE$. | 3. ? Given, definition of supplementary |
| 4. $AB = DE$. | 4. ? Given |
| 5. $\therefore \triangle DEG \cong \triangle ABC$. | 5. ? SAS |
| 6. $BC = EF$. | 6. ? Given |
| 7. $EG = BC$. | 7. ? Definition of congruence |
| 8. $EG = EF$. | 8. ? Transitivity |
| 9. $\angle F \cong \angle G$. | 9. ? Isosceles triangle theorem |
| 10. $\therefore \triangle DEF \cong \triangle DEG$. | 10. SAA Theorem |
| 11. $\therefore \triangle ABC \cong \triangle DEF$. | 11. Theorem 5–2 |

**Problem Set 7–4**

1. Summarize all the methods that you know for proving that triangles are congruent.

2. Given: $\overline{PT} \perp \overline{RT}$    $\overline{SV} \perp \overline{QV}$
   $RT = QV$    $PQ = SR$.

   Prove: $PT = SV$.

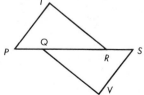

Note that in the proof of the Hypotenuse-Leg Theorem, we introduce $G$ on the ray opposite to $\overrightarrow{DF}$ so that $DG = AC$, and then prove that $DG = DF$.

**Quiz**

1. Given: $\overline{AC}$ intersects $\overline{BD}$ at $E$, $\angle BAC \cong \angle CDB$, $BE = CE$.
   Prove: $AB = CD$
   Proof: $\angle AEB \cong \angle DEC$ by the Vertical Angle Theorem and since $\angle BAC \cong \angle CDB$, and $BE = CE$, $\triangle BAE \cong \triangle CDE$ by SAA. Thus, $AB = CD$.

2. If the diagonals of rectangle $\square ABCD$ are congruent, prove that $AD = BC$.
   Proof: Since $\square ABCD$ is a rectangle, all angles are right angles and $\angle BAD \cong \angle CDA$. Since $AC = BD$ (given) and $AD = AD$, $\triangle ACD \cong \triangle DBA$ by HL. Consequently $AB = CD$.

**Answers to Problems**

2. Since $RT = QV$ and $PR = SQ$, $\triangle PTR \cong \triangle SVQ$ by HL. Therefore $PT = SV$.

**5.**

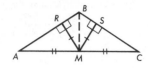

Given: △ABC, M the midpoint of $\overline{AC}$, $\overline{MR} \perp \overline{AB}$, $\overline{MS} \perp \overline{BC}$, $MR = MS$.

Prove: AB = BC.

Proof: △MRA ≅ △MSC (HL) and therefore ∠A ≅ ∠C. Consequently AB = BC, by the converse of the Isosceles Triangle Theorem.

**6.** From the given information, △AED ≅ △BEC by SAA. Therefore, ED = EC (CPCTC), and ∠EDC ≅ ∠ECD by the Isosceles Triangle Theorem.

**7.** 1. E is the midpoint of $\overline{AB}$. (Given)
2. AE = EB. (Definition of midpoint)
3. $\overline{AD} \perp \overline{AB}, \overline{BC} \perp \overline{AB}$. (Given)
4. △ADE and △BCE are right triangles. (Definition of right triangle)
5. DE = CE. (Given)
6. △ADE ≅ △BCE. (HL)
7. AD = BC. (CPCTC)

**8.**

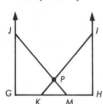

Given: (1) G-K-M-H with GK = KM = MH.
(2) $\overline{JG} \perp \overline{GH}, \overline{IH} \perp \overline{GH}$.
(3) JM = IK.
(4) $\overline{JM} \cap \overline{IK} = \{P\}$.

Prove: △PKM is isosceles.

Proof: △JMG ≅ △IKH by HL and consequently, ∠JMG ≅ ∠IKH. Now consider △PKM; since two angles of △PKM are congruent, the sides opposite these angles are congruent, that is, PK = PM.

**3.** In the figure, $\overline{CD}$ bisects $\overline{AB}$ and ∠C ≅ ∠D.   Prove that $\overline{AB}$ bisects $\overline{CD}$.

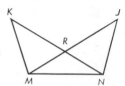

Since AE=EB, ∠C≅∠D, ∠AEC≅∠BED (vertical angles), △AEC≅△BED (SAA) and CE=ED.

**4.** Given: ∠K ≅ ∠J and MR = NR.

Prove: MK = NJ.

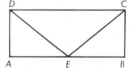

Since MR=NR, ∠K≅∠J, ∠KRM≅∠JRN (vertical angles), △KRM≅△JRN (SAA) and consequently MK=NJ.

**5.** From the midpoint of one side of a triangle, segments are drawn perpendicular to the other two sides. Prove that if the segments are congruent, the triangle is isosceles.

**6.** Given: E is the midpoint of $\overline{AB}$, $\overline{AD} \perp \overline{AB}$, $\overline{BC} \perp \overline{AB}$, and ∠ADE ≅ ∠BCE.

Prove: ∠EDC ≅ ∠ECD.

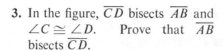

**7.** Given: E is the midpoint of $\overline{AB}$, $\overline{AD} \perp \overline{AB}$, $\overline{BC} \perp \overline{AB}$, and DE = CE.

Prove: AD = BC.

**8.** The points K and M trisect $\overline{GH}$, with G-K-M. The points J and I, on the same side of $\overleftrightarrow{GH}$, are on the perpendiculars to $\overline{GH}$ at G and H, respectively, such that JM = IK. $\overline{JM}$ and $\overline{IK}$ intersect at P. Prove that △PKM is isosceles.

**9.** Given the figure on the left below with right angles ∠D and ∠C and △APR ≅ △BQT. Prove that △ADF ≅ △BCE.

See solution section.

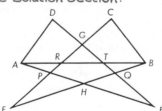

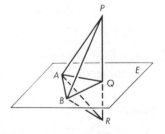

**10.** In the figure on the right above, A, B, and Q are in the plane E, $\overline{AQ} \perp \overline{PR}$, $\overline{BQ} \perp \overline{PR}$, and ∠PAB ≅ ∠PBA. Prove that ∠PAR ≅ ∠PBR.

See solution section.

## 7–5  INEQUALITIES IN A SINGLE TRIANGLE

We shall now proceed to prove some of the theorems that we conjectured at the beginning of the chapter.

### Theorem 7–5

*If two sides of a triangle are not congruent, then the angles opposite them are not congruent, and the larger angle is opposite the longer side.*

**Restatement.**  In any triangle $\triangle ABC$, if $AB > AC$, then $\angle C > \angle B$.

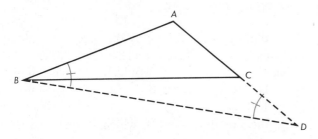

**Proof.**  Let $D$ be a point of $\overrightarrow{AC}$, such that $AD = AB$.  Then $\angle ABD \cong \angle D$, because the base angles of an isosceles triangle are congruent.  Since $AD = AB$ and $AB > AC$, $AD > AC$ and so, $C$ must be between $A$ and $D$.  Therefore, by the Angle Addition Postulate,

$$m\angle ABD = m\angle ABC + m\angle CBD.$$

Therefore

$$m\angle ABC < m\angle ABD.$$

(Why?)  We are now through using measures of angles, and so we rewrite the above simply as

$$\angle ABC < \angle ABD.$$

Since $\angle ABD \cong \angle D$, it follows that

$$\angle ABC < \angle D.$$

But we know by the Exterior Angle Theorem that

$$\angle D < \angle ACB.$$

Therefore,

$$\angle ABC < \angle ACB.$$

Therefore, in $\triangle ABC$ we have $\angle B < \angle C$, which is what we wanted.

**Classroom Notes**

If you review the conjectures made at the outset of this chapter, you may select Theorems 7–5 and 7–6 as the most basic observations and, consequently, the ones to prove first.  It is obvious that if we can prove one of them, then the other will follow by an indirect proof.  In proving Theorem 7–5 you have really two choices.  You can present the proof as is, and note that it works, that is, that it proves the theorem.  This approach is rapid and efficient (in the sense that it gets the theorem covered), but it is uninstructive; the student acquires no insight into, or first-hand experience with, inequality proofs.  On the other hand you can conduct a rewarding preliminary analysis and discover the theorems and techniques that will enable us to devise a proof.

By analyzing the assertion of Theorem 7–5 we can set up an arsenal of potentially effective geometric weapons:

(1) This theorem is obviously the inequality analog of the Isosceles Triangle Theorem.  This suggests that we may be able to use the Isosceles Triangle Theorem in its proof.

(2) However, the given figure does not contain an isosceles triangle.  This difficulty is easily overcome by introducing auxiliary sets.  There are several ways of introducing isosceles triangles into the given figure, and the teacher should know ahead of time which will work.  Following the text we will discuss the proof which uses the figure obtained by introducing $D$ on $\overrightarrow{AC}$ such that $AD = AB$.

(3) We can now apply the Exterior Angle Theorem to the augmented figure: $\angle ACB$ is an exterior angle of

△BCD, and consequently ∠C > ∠D.

(4) Recall Corollary 7–2.1; since we are trying to establish an inequality (∠B < ∠C) in which it is ∠ABC that is less than another angle, we shall use it to establish that ∠ABC < ∠ABD.

(5) We then introduce two auxiliary angles, ∠X and ∠Y, and show that $m\angle B < m\angle X = m\angle Y < m\angle C$. By the transitive property of < (for real numbers) we conclude that $m\angle B < m\angle C$.

If the figure is sketched on the board, and the above considerations have been elicited from your class, some student is likely to "discover" the proof. You can then have them write the proof formally as homework.

In retrospect you can make the following observations:

(1) Note that we deliberately introduce D on $\overrightarrow{AC}$ with AD = AB so that we could use the Isosceles Triangle Theorem. Logically there are two other possibilities for the location of D on $\overrightarrow{AC}$: (a) AC < AD < AB and (b) AD > AB. [*Query:* if we introduce D in either of these ways, can we still complete the proof?]

(2) Note that in using the Angle Addition Postulate we tacitly assumed that C is in the interior of ∠ABD. This follows from Theorem 6–6 of Section 6–8.

Theorem 7–6 is an excellent example of an indirect proof. We think you will find it valuable to have your class write out a detailed proof.

**Explanation for Problems**

Note that all the problems in this set (with the exception of Problem 1) involve the application of Theorem 7–6 rather than Theorem 7–5. Problems 10, 11, 12, and 16 should not all be assigned at the same time since they are more difficult than they appear to be;

**Theorem 7–6**

*If two angles of a triangle are not congruent, then the sides opposite them are not congruent, and the longer side is opposite the larger angle.*

**Restatement.** In any triangle △ABC, if ∠C > ∠B, then AB > AC.

**Proof.** There are three possibilities for the numbers AB and AC:

(1)     AB < AC

(2)     AB = AC

(3)     AB > AC.

If (1) were true, then it would follow by the preceding theorem that ∠C < ∠B, and this is false. Therefore (1) is impossible.

If (2) were true, then ∠B and ∠C would be the base angles of an isosceles triangle. This would give ∠B ≅ ∠C, which is false. Therefore (2) is impossible.

The only remaining possibility is (3), which is what we wanted to prove.

The above is merely a convenient way of writing an indirect proof. We might have said the same thing more formally as follows:

"Suppose that the theorem is false. Then either AB = AC or AB < AC. AB = AC is impossible, because .... AB < AC is impossible, because .... Therefore the theorem is not false. Therefore the theorem is true."

But the scheme that we used the first time is probably easier to follow, and we shall be using it again. The idea is to list all of the "possibilities" in a given situation, and then to show that only one of them is really possible.

**Problem Set 7–5**

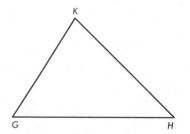

1. In the figure, GH > KH and KH > GK. Prove that ∠H is the smallest angle of the triangle.

2. In the figure, ∠K > ∠G and ∠G > ∠H. Prove that $\overline{GH}$ is the longest side of the triangle.

**3.** In $\triangle ABC$, $AB = 12$, $BC = 7$, $AC = 9$.  Name the largest angle; the smallest angle.  ∠C , ∠A

**4.** In $\triangle PQR$, $m\angle P = 72$, $m\angle Q = 37$, $m\angle R = 71$.  Name the longest side; the shortest side.  $\overline{QR}$ , $\overline{PR}$

**5.** In $\triangle ABC$, $\overline{CD} \perp \overline{AB}$.  Prove: $CD < AC$, and $CD < BC$.

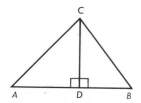 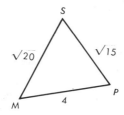

**6.** For $\triangle MPS$ as marked, name the angles in order of increasing size.
∠M , ∠S , ∠P

**7.** Name the sides of the figure on the right in order of increasing length.  $\overline{ST}, \overline{RT}, \overline{RS}$

Note: $m\angle T + m\angle R + m\angle S \neq 180$.
We have not proven this theorem yet, since the Parallel Postulate has not been introduced.  Here the sum = 177°.

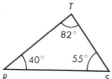

**8.** In the figure on the left below as marked, all of the angles are acute except for the two right angles.  Arrange the angles $\angle GKH$, $\angle GKM$, $\angle G$, and $\angle H$ in order of increasing size.  ∠GKM , ∠G , ∠GKH , ∠H

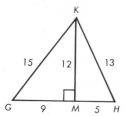 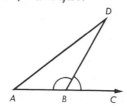

**9.** In the figure on the right above, $\angle ABD > \angle DBC$.  Prove that $AD > BD$.

**10.** Given the figure on the left below with angle measures as marked.  Prove that $\overline{PR}$ is the longest segment.

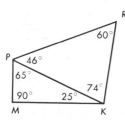 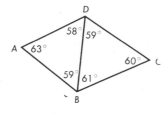

**11.** In the figure on the right above, if the angles have the indicated measures, which segment is longest?  $\overline{DC}$

**1.** Given: $\overline{PQ} \perp L$, R a〰 ⌣ther point of
L and Q a point on L.
Prove: $PQ < PR$.
Proof: $m\angle Q = 90$ and by Corollary
7–2.1, $\angle R$ is acute, so $m\angle R < m\angle Q$.
Thus $PR > PQ$ by Theorem 7–6.

**2.** In a plane $\triangle ABC$ and $\triangle BCD$ have a common side.  A and D are on opposite sides of $\overleftrightarrow{BC}$.  If $m\angle A = 110$, $m\angle D = 40$, $m\angle ACB = 20$, $m\angle ABC = 50$, $m\angle DCB = 80$, and $m\angle CBD = 60$, which segment is the longest?
(ans: $\overline{BD}$)

**Answers to Problems**

**1.** 1. $GH > KH$. (Given)
2. $\angle K > \angle G$. (Theorem 7–5)
3. $KH > GK$. (Given)
4. $\angle G > \angle H$. (Theorem 7–5)
5. $\angle K > \angle H$. (Transitive Property)

**2.** 1. $\angle G > \angle H$. (Given)
2. $KH > GK$. (Theorem 7–6)
3. $\angle K > \angle G$. (Given)
4. $GH > KH$. (Theorem 7–5)
5. $GH > GK$. (Transitive Property)

**5.** 1. $\overline{CD} \perp \overline{AB}$. (Given)
2. $\triangle ADC$ and $\triangle BDC$ are right triangles. (Definition of right triangle)
3. $\angle A$ and $\angle B$ are acute. (Corollary 7–2.1)
4. $AC > CD$ and $BC > CD$. (Theorem 7–6)

**9.** $\angle ABD > \angle DBC$, $\angle DBC > \angle DAB$ (Exterior Angle Theorem).  Therefore $\angle ABD > \angle DAB$ (Transitivity) and $AD > BD$ (Theorem 7–6).

**10.** In $\triangle PMK$, $\overline{PK}$ is the longest segment.  But in $\triangle RPK$, $\overline{PK}$ lies opposite the 60° angle, whereas $PR$ lies opposite the 74° angle.  Therefore $\overline{PR}$ is the longest segment in $\triangle RPK$, and in the figure.

e ∠C > ∠A, AE > CE. Since ∠B, EB > ED. Therefore, AE + > CE + ED, which means that AB > CD since in the figure E is between A and B and E is between C and D.

**14.** 1. Introduce $\overline{RP}$. (Two points determine a line.)
2. SR < SP, RQ < PQ. (Given)
3. ∠SRP > ∠SPR, ∠PRQ > ∠RPQ. (Theorem 7-5)
4. P is in the interior of ∠SRQ and R is in the interior of ∠SPQ. (Given—the quadrilateral is convex.)
5. m∠R = m∠SRP + m∠PRQ, m∠P = m∠SPR + m∠RPQ. (AAP)
6. m∠SRP > m∠SPR, m∠PRQ > m∠RPQ. (Definition of > for angles)
7. m∠R = m∠SRP + m∠PRQ > m∠SPR + m∠RPQ = m∠P. (Addition and Transitive Properties)

**15.** Since ∠KGH is an exterior angle of △KPG, we can conclude that ∠KPG < ∠KGH. Since △KGH is isosceles, ∠KGH ≅ ∠KHG. Therefore, in △KPH, ∠KPH < ∠KHP, and consequently KH < KP by Theorem 7-6.

**16.** From △MDE, ME > DE = MD, from △ABM, AB > AM > MB, from △CMB, CB > MB = MC, and from △MCD, MC = MD > CD. So $\overline{CD}$ is the shortest segment.

**17.** 1. m∠MDK > m∠G. (Theorem 7-2 applied to △MDG)
2. m∠G = m∠K. (Isosceles Triangle Theorem)
3. m∠MDK > m∠K. (Transitivity)
4. MK > MD. (Theorem 7-6)
5. MK = MG. (Given)
6. MG > MD. (Steps 4 and 5)

**18.** 1. Let B′ be the point on $\overrightarrow{DC}$ such that DB′ = BD. (Theorem 2-2)
2. BD < DC. (Given)
3. DB′ < DC. (Steps 1 and 2)
4. D-B′-C. (Theorem 2-1)
5. Introduce $\overline{AB'}$. (Two points determine a line.)
6. ∠AB′D > ∠C. (Theorem 7-2)
7. ∠B ≅ ∠AB′D. (Isosceles Triangle Theorem)
8. ∠B > ∠C. (Steps 6 and 7)
9. AC > AB. (Theorem 7-6)

---

**228**

**12.** If the angles have the indicated measures, which segment is shortest? $\overline{QR}$

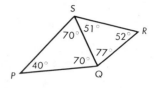

**13.** $\overline{AB}$ and $\overline{CD}$ intersect at E, ∠C > ∠A and ∠D > ∠B. Prove that AB > CD.

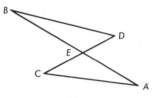

**14.** As in the figure, $\overline{PQ}$ is the longest side and $\overline{SR}$ is the shortest side of ▱PQRS. Prove that m∠R > m∠P.

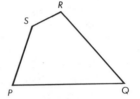

**15.** In △KGH, KG = KH; P is any point of $\overleftrightarrow{GH}$ not in $\overline{GH}$. Prove that PK is always greater than either KG or KH.

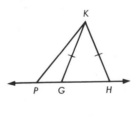

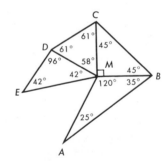

**16.** If the angles in the figure on the right above have the indicated measures, which segment is shortest? $\overline{CD}$

---

**17.** Let △GKM be an isosceles triangle having base $\overline{GK}$. Let D be any point such that G-D-K. Prove that $\overline{MD}$ is always shorter than either of the congruent sides.

18. *B*, *D*, and *C* are points of line *L*
such that *B-D-C* and *BD < DC*.
If $\overline{AD} \perp L$, prove that *AB < AC*.

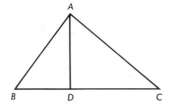

## 7–6  THE DISTANCE BETWEEN A LINE AND A POINT. THE TRIANGLE INEQUALITY

**Theorem 7–7.**   The First Minimum Theorem

> ### The shortest segment joining a point to a line is the perpendicular segment.

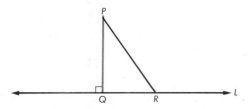

**Restatement.**   Given a line *L* and an external point *P*.  If $\overline{PQ} \perp L$ at *Q*, and *R* is any other point of *L*, then *PQ < PR*.

**Proof.**   By hypothesis, $m\angle Q = 90$.  By Corollary 7–2.1, $\angle R$ is acute. Thus $m\angle R < m\angle Q$.  By Theorem 7–6, *PR > PQ*.

The distance between a point *P* and a line *L* ought to be the *minimum* distance between *P* and the points of *L*.  In light of the preceding theorem, we know that there is such a minimum distance, and we know where it occurs.  We can therefore write our definition as follows.

### Definition

The *distance* between a line and an external point is the length of the perpendicular segment from the point to the line.  The distance between a line and a point on the line is defined to be zero.

The following theorem tells us, not surprisingly, that no detour is a shortcut.

**Classroom Notes**

The First Minimum Theorem is easy and can be left to the student. Be prepared, however, to correct statements to the effect that "The shortest *distance* from an external point to a line *is* the perpendicular *segment* from the point to the line." Problems 1 and 2 of Problem Set 7–7 involve the use of the First Minimum Theorem.

The Triangle Inequality is a mathematical statement of a familiar fact: "The shortest distance between two points is a straight line." This vernacular statement does not observe our distinction between distances, segments, and lines. The statement, "No detour is a shortcut," is a satisfactory paraphrase.

The proof of the Triangle Inequality depends on the ingenious introduction of auxiliary sets.  The student's response to the proof is usually: "Great, but how do you expect me to think of that?"   A preliminary analysis of the problem will show that the techniques used in the proof are plausible and easily anticipated.

In Chapter 5, while explaining how to think of a proof of an assertion, we suggested that the student ask (1) what use he can make of the hypothesis, and (2) what tools he might use to obtain the desired conclusion.  We draw a blank when we try to exploit the hypothesis; there is only the statement: "Given $\triangle ABC$."  Turning our attention to the conclusion we note that it is an inequality concerning the length of segments: "*AB + BC > AC*."  Do we have any theorems in this chapter concerning inequalities between the lengths of segments?  Yes, and the most important one is Theorem 7–6.

The inequality which we want to establish is $AB + BC > AC$. To obtain this inequality from Theorem 7–6 we would have to have a triangle in which one side has length $AC$ and the other side has length $AB + BC$. [Remember that $AB + BC$ is a positive real number.] In the given figure, we have a segment of length $AC$, namely $\overline{AC}$. What we need, then, is a triangle which has $\overline{AC}$ as one side and which has a side whose length is the real number $AB + BC$. Since the length of $\overline{BC}$ is $BC$, we can easily·obtain such a side by using the Point-Plotting Theorem to introduce a point $D$ on $\overrightarrow{CB}$ beyond $B$ such that $BD = BA$. Then $DC = DB + BC = AB + BC$. And we can easily obtain the desired triangle by introducing $\overline{AD}$.

We now have a triangle from which we can obtain the desired conclusion *provided* we can show that the hypothesis of Theorem 7–6 is satisfied, that is, that $m\angle DAC > m\angle D$. You can ask the student to verify this and then write up a statement-and-reason proof. [Note: The fact that $B$ is in the interior of $\angle DAC$ follows from Theorem 6–6 of Section 6–6.]

The theorem can also be proved by introducing $E$ on $\overrightarrow{AB}$ beyond $B$ such that $BE = BC$.

## Explanation for Problems

Problem Set 7–6 is rather difficult. Problems 1 through 8 are work enough for the first assignment. Problem 6 requires the use of the additive property of inequality. Problem 5 requires the introduction of an auxiliary segment and the use of the Additive Property of Inequality. Problems 7 and 9 obviously go together. They can be explained in common-sense terms. The proofs are accomplished by use of the Triangle Inequality.

Problem 10 (the Mirror Problem) is more interesting as an exercise

**Theorem 7–8**   The Triangle Inequality

*The sum of the lengths of any two sides of a triangle is greater than the length of the third side.*

**Restatement.**   In any triangle $\triangle ABC$, we have

$$AB + BC > AC.$$

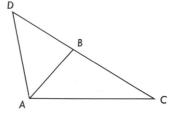

**Proof.**   Let $D$ be a point of the ray opposite to $\overrightarrow{BC}$, such that $DB = AB$, as indicated in the figure. Then

$$DC = DB + BC$$

because $B$ is between $D$ and $C$. Replacing $DB$ by $AB$, we get

$$(1) \qquad DC = AB + BC.$$

Now, since $B$ is in the interior of $\angle DAC$,

$$m\angle DAC = m\angle DAB + m\angle BAC,$$

by the Angle Addition Postulate. By Theorem 7–1,

$$m\angle DAC > m\angle DAB.$$

But

$$m\angle D = m\angle DAB,$$

by the Isosceles Triangle Theorem. Therefore

$$(2) \qquad m\angle DAC > m\angle D.$$

Applying Theorem 7–6 to these two angles of $\triangle ADC$, we get

$$(3) \qquad DC > AC.$$

Combining (1) and (3), we get $AB + BC > AC$, which was to be proved.

## Problem Set 7–6

1. For the figure on the right, we can assert that $CD < \underline{CA}$ and $CD < \underline{CB}$, and that $BE < \underline{BA}$ and $BE < \underline{BC}$. State the theorem involved. Theorem 7-7

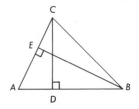

2. Using the angle measures shown in the figure, place $PS$, $PR$, and $PQ$ in the correct order. __PR__ < __PQ__ < __PS__. Quote theorems to support your conclusion.
   Theorem 7-7, Theorem 7-6

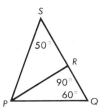

3. Can the distance between a point and a line ever be zero?  Explain.  Yes
   If the point is on the line, the distance is defined as zero.

4. Given a line and a point not on it, can there ever be two distances between the point and the line under our definition?  Explain.  NO

5. Given the figure, prove that $EP + PM + MK > EK$.
   Introduce $\overline{EM}$. In $\triangle EPM$, $EP+PM > EM$.(Theorem 7-8)
   In $\triangle EMK$, $EM+MK > EK$.
   (Theorem 7-8)
   Therefore $EP+PM+MK +$
   $EM > EK+EM$ or
   $EP+PM+MK > EK$.

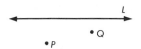

6. Prove that the sum of the lengths of the diagonals of a quadrilateral is less than the perimeter of the quadrilateral.

7. You can answer this problem by experimenting or, perhaps, by reasoning. Suppose that you are to draw a triangle having two sides of length 3 cm and 7 cm.  The third side must have a length less than __10__, and greater than __4__.

8. Which of the following sets of numbers could be the lengths of the sides of a triangle?
   (a) {3, 8, 12}
   (b) {4, 7, 9}
   (c) {6, 15, 7}
   (d) {3, 5, 1}

9. Two sides of a triangle have lengths $j$ and $k$.  If $j < k$, what are the possible values of $x$, the length of the third side? $k-j < x < k+j$

10. Given a line $L$ and two points, $P$ and $Q$, on the same side of $L$.  Find the point $R$ on $L$ for which $PR + RQ$ is as small as possible.  [*Hint:* This should be easy if you did Problem 10 of Problem Set 6–4.]

in class if you do not give Problem 10 of Problem Set 6–4 as a hint. The student must then discover the "ideal" location for $R$; you will be fascinated by their conjectures. You can use the law of reflection to suggest the location of $R$ for which $PR + RQ$ is as small as possible.

Problem 11 is also more interesting as a class exercise if you introduce it as a question: "For what location of $X$ is $XA + XB + XC + XD$ as small as possible?"

Problems 12 and 13 are very hard, and are meant for your best honors students.

**Answers to Problems**

4. There is a unique perpendicular from the point to the line and the distance is the length of this segment.

6. Given quadrilateral $\square ABCD$ with diagonals $\overline{AC}$ and $\overline{BD}$.
In $\triangle ACD$,
$$AC < AD + DC.$$
In $\triangle ACB$,
$$AC < AB + BC.$$
In $\triangle ABD$,
$$BD < AB + AD.$$
In $\triangle BCD$,
$$BD < BC + CD.$$
$2(AC + BD) < 2(AB + BC + CD + DA)$
or  $AC + BD <$ perimeter of $\square ABCD$.

10.

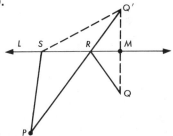

Consider the reflection $Q'$ of $Q$ with respect to $L$.  Then $L$ is the perpendicular bisector of $\overline{QQ'}$ and intersects $\overline{QQ'}$ at a point $M$.  The point $R$ on $L$ which makes $PR + RQ$ a minimum is the intersection of $\overline{PQ'}$ and $L$.

Proof: Let $S$ be any point of $L$ other than $R$.  By the Perpendicular Bisector Theorem, $SQ = SQ'$, so that $PS + SQ = PS + SQ'$.  In $\triangle PSQ'$, $PS + SQ' > PQ'$.  But $PQ' = PR + RQ' = PR + RQ$.  Therefore $PS + SQ > PR + RQ$.

**11.** $XA + XC > PA + PC$ except when $X$ is on $\overline{AC}$, in which case the equality sign holds. Similarly, $XB + XD > PB + PD$ except when $X$ is on $\overline{BD}$, in which case equality holds. Therefore, $XA + XB + XC + XD > PA + PB + PC + PD$ except when $X$ is on $\overline{AC}$ and also on $\overline{BD}$, and this can happen only if $X = P$, which is excluded by hypothesis.

## Quiz

**1.** Let $A$, $B$, $C$, and $D$ be four points, no three of which are collinear. Show that $AB + BC + CD > AD$.

    Proof: In $\triangle ABC$, $AB + BC > AC$ by Theorem 7–8. Therefore $AB + BC + CD > AC + CD$. In $\triangle ACD$, $AC + CD > AD$ by Theorem 7–8. Thus $AB + BC + CD > AD$ by the Transitivity of Inequalities.

**2.** Prove the length of either diagonal of a quadrilateral is less than one-half the perimeter of the quadrilateral.

    Proof: Let $\square ABCD$ be any quadrilateral and $\overline{AC}$ be the specific diagonal. By Theorem 7–8 $AC < AB + BC$ and $AC < CD + DA$ or $2AC < AB + BC + CD + DA = p$ by the Addition Property of Inequalities. Thus $2AC < p$ and $AC < (\tfrac{1}{2})p$.

## 7–7 THE HINGE THEOREM AND ITS CONVERSE

### Classroom Notes

The Hinge Theorem expresses a plausible idea but its proof is difficult. Problem Set 7–7 contains some interesting problems which can be solved by use of the Hinge Theorem and its converse, but we must admit that we make no further use of either theorem. Consequently omission of this section will not lead to trouble later.

    In the proof in the text we reconstructed $\triangle AKC \cong \triangle DEF$ in such a way that $K$ was on the same side of $\overleftrightarrow{AC}$ as $B$. The figure in the text assumes that $K$ falls on the same side of $\overleftrightarrow{BC}$ as $A$. There are actually three possibilities: (1) $K$ falls on the same side of $\overleftrightarrow{BC}$ as $A$, (2) $K$

**11.** Given two segments, $\overline{AC}$ and $\overline{BD}$, intersecting at $P$. Prove that if $X$ is any point of the plane of $\overline{AC}$ and $\overline{BD}$ other than $P$, then

$$XA + XB + XC + XD > PA + PB + PC + PD.$$

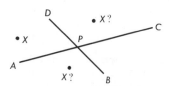

Will this result hold if $X$ is not in the plane of $\overline{AC}$ and $\overline{BD}$? Yes

**12.** Let $A$, $B$, and $C$ be points, not necessarily different. Prove that $AB + BC \geq AC$. (There are several cases to consider.)
See Solution Section.

**13.** Prove that the shortest polygonal path from one point to another is the segment joining them. See Solution Section.
(use problem 12.)

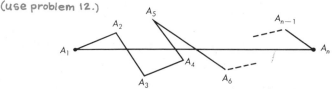

**Restatement:** Given $n$ points $A_1, A_2, \ldots, A_n$, prove that

$$A_1 A_2 + A_2 A_3 + \cdots + A_{n-1} A_n \geq A_1 A_n.$$

## 7–7    THE HINGE THEOREM AND ITS CONVERSE

Consider two sticks, connected by a hinge at $A$, with the other ends $B$ and $C$ joined by a rubber band. As the hinge is opened wider, the rubber band ought to be stretched longer.

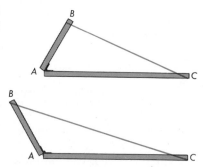

Putting this in geometric language, we get the following theorem. (You may find that the restatement is easier to read than the theorem itself.)

**Theorem 7–9.**   The Hinge Theorem

> *If two sides of one triangle are congruent, respectively, to two sides of a second triangle, and the included angle of the first triangle is larger than the included angle of the second, then the third side of the first triangle is longer than the third side of the second.*

**Restatement.**   Given $\triangle ABC$ and $\triangle DEF$, with $AB = DE$ and $AC = DF$. If $\angle A > \angle D$, then $BC > EF$.

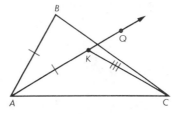

**Proof.**   *Step 1.*   First we construct $\triangle AKC$, with $K$ in the interior of $\angle BAC$, such that $\triangle AKC \cong \triangle DEF$. To do this, we first take $\overrightarrow{AQ}$, with $Q$ on the same side of $\overleftrightarrow{AC}$ as $B$, such that $\angle QAC \cong \angle D$ (by the Angle Construction Postulate).   Then we take a point $K$ of $\overrightarrow{AQ}$ such that $AK = DE$ (by the Point-Plotting Theorem). By SAS, we have $\triangle AKC \cong \triangle DEF$, which is what we wanted.

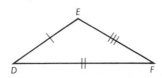

*Step. 2.*   Now we bisect $\angle BAK$, and let $M$ be the point where the bisector crosses $\overline{BC}$.

We are now almost done.   By SAS, we have

$$\triangle AMB \cong \triangle AMK.$$

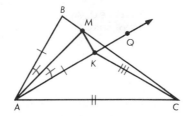

Therefore $MB = MK$.   Applying the Triangle Inequality (Theorem 7–8) to $\triangle CKM$, we get

$$CK < CM + MK.$$

Therefore

$$CK < CM + MB$$

because $MB = MK$.   Since

$$CK = EF \text{ and } CM + MB = BC,$$

we have $EF < BC$, which is what we wanted.
The converse of the Hinge Theorem is also true.

falls on $\overleftrightarrow{BC}$, and (3) $K$ falls on the side of $\overleftrightarrow{BC}$ opposite $A$. The proof given for case (1) applies word for word to case (3). In case (2) we merely need to give a different reason for the inequality $CK < CM + MK$.

**Background Material**

The Hinge Theorem and its converse are very reminiscent of the two basic theorems on inequalities in a single triangle. This analogy suggests that Theorem 7–6 (rather than the Triangle Inequality) could be used in the proof of the Hinge Theorem. It is possible to prove the Hinge Theorem by use of Theorem 7–6, but this proof leans heavily on the betweenness and separation theorems of Section 6–6.

*Given:* $\triangle ABC$ and $\triangle DEF$ with
$$AB = DE,$$
$$\angle A > \angle D,$$
$$AC = DF.$$

*Prove:* $BC > EF$.

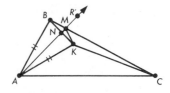

*Proof.*
(1) Construct $\triangle AKC$, with $K$ on the same side of $\overleftrightarrow{AC}$ as $B$, such that $\triangle AKC \cong \triangle DEF$. Introduce $\overline{BK}$. If we can show that $m\angle CBK < m\angle BKC$, we can conclude by Theorem 7–6 that $CK < BC$ and hence that $EF < BC$.

(2) Introduce $\overrightarrow{AR}$, the bisector of $\angle BAK$, let $M$ be the point at which $\overrightarrow{AR}$ intersects $\overline{BC}$, and let $N$ be the point at which $\overrightarrow{AR}$ intersects $\overline{BK}$. Introduce $\overline{MK}$. Since $\overrightarrow{AR}$ is the perpendicular bisector of $\overline{BK}$ and $M$ is on $\overrightarrow{AR}$, $M$ is equidistant from $B$ and $K$.   Therefore $MB = MK$ and hence, by the Isosceles Triangle Theorem, $m\angle MBK = m\angle MKB$.

(3) Since $M$ is between $B$ and $C$, $M$ is in the interior of $\angle BKC$ by Theorem 6–6; therefore $m\angle MKB < m\angle BKC$. Hence $m\angle MBK < m\angle BKC$, and this implies that $CK < BC$.

Note that the Hinge Theorem actually has three converses, only one of which is true. We have deliberately stated the hypotheses $AB = DE$ and $AC = DF$ as part of the given information and isolated the implication "If $\angle A > \angle D$, then $BC > EF$," so that there will be no doubt as to what we mean by the Converse Hinge Theorem.

### Explanation for Problems

Problems 1–8 are solved by direct application of the Hinge Theorem or the Converse Hinge Theorem.

Problems 11–15 are "two-step" problems involving a sequence of two theorems, one of Theorems 7–5 and 7–6 and one of Theorems 7–9 and 7–10.

**Theorem 7–10.**   The Converse Hinge Theorem

*If two sides of one triangle are congruent respectively to two sides of a second triangle, and the third side of the first triangle is longer than the third side of the second, then the included angle of the first triangle is larger than the included angle of the second.*

**Restatement.**  Given  $\triangle ABC$  and  $\triangle DEF$, with  $AB = DE$ and $AC = DF$. If $BC > EF$, then $\angle A > \angle D$.

To derive this theorem from the Hinge Theorem, we use the same method that we used to derive Theorem 7–6 from Theorem 7–5. That is, we show that $\angle A < \angle D$ and $\angle A \cong \angle D$ are impossible, so that the only remaining possibility is $\angle A > \angle D$. For the first half of the proof we need the Hinge Theorem; and for the second half we need SAS. You should fill in the details for yourself.

### Problem Set 7–7

1. Given the figure as marked, with $AB = AC$. Prove that $BD > CD$. What theorem supports this conclusion?

   Since AB=AC, AD=AD and ∠DAB >∠CAD, it follows that BD >CD by the Hinge Theorem.

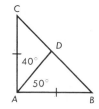

2. In the figure as marked, what conclusion follows regarding $\angle ESA$ and $\angle ESY$? regarding $\angle A$ and $\angle Y$? What theorem supports each conclusion?
   ∠ESA <∠ESY (Theorem 7-10)
   ∠A >∠Y (Theorem 7-5)

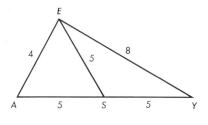

3. In the figure as marked, what can you conclude about $YD$? about $m\angle ARH$? What theorem supports each conclusion? YD >8 (Theorem 7-9)
   m∠ARH >55 (Theorem 7-10)

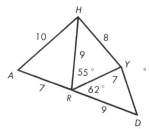

**4.** In the figure,

$$AD = CD \text{ and } \angle ADB > \angle CDB.$$

Prove that $AB > BC$.
Follows from Hinge Theorem.

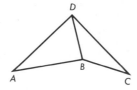

**5.** In isosceles triangle $\triangle PQR$, $S$ is a point of the base other than the midpoint. Prove that $\overline{PS}$ does not bisect $\angle RPQ$. Use Converse Hinge Theorem.

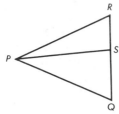

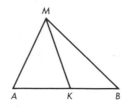

**6.** Given: $\triangle ABM$ with median $\overline{MK}$ and $\angle MKB > \angle MKA$.

Prove: $AM < MB$. Use Hinge Theorem.

**7.** $\triangle ABC$ and $\triangle ABD$ have a common side $\overline{AB}$, and $AC = AD$. If $C$ is in the interior of $\angle DAB$, prove that $BD > BC$.

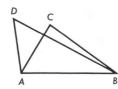

**8.** In $\triangle RST$, $RT > ST$ and $M$ is the midpoint of $\overline{RS}$. Is $\angle TMR$ acute or obtuse? Explain. $\angle TMR$ is obtuse.

**9.** Given $\square ABCD$ with $AD = BC$, $DE > AE$, and $BE > EC$. Prove that $\angle DAB > \angle ABC$.
DB = DE + EB > AE + EC = AC
so $\angle DAB > \angle ABC$ by Theorem 7-10.

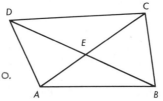

**10.** $\triangle RSP$ and $\triangle RPK$ have a common side $\overline{RP}$. $K$ and $S$ are on opposite sides of $\overleftrightarrow{RP}$ such that $PK = RS$ and $RK > SP$. Prove that $\angle RPK > \angle PRS$. PK = RS, PR = RP, RK > SP so $\angle RPK > \angle PRS$ by Theorem 7-10.

**11.** Given the figure as marked. Prove that

$$\angle W > \angle U.$$

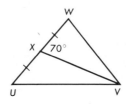

**Quiz**

**1.** Given: $\square ABCD$ with $AB = BC = CD = BD$ and $\angle ABD > \angle BCD$.
Prove: $AD > BC$.
Proof: In $\triangle ABD$ and $\triangle DBC$, $AB = BD$ and $BD = BC$, $\angle ABD > \angle BDC$ so that $AD > CD$ by Theorem 7–9. Since $BD = CD$ (given) $AD > BC$.

**2.** Given: $\triangle ABC$ and $\overline{AD}$ the median to side $\overline{BC}$, $m\angle CDA = 65$.
Prove: $\angle C > \angle B$.
Proof: In $\triangle ADC$ and $\triangle ADB$, $CD = DB$, $AD = AD$, $m\angle ADC = 65$ and $m\angle BDA = 115$ by supplementary angles, so $AB > AC$ by Theorem 7–9. Thus in $\triangle ABC$, $\angle C > \angle B$ by Theorem 7–5.

**Answers to Problems**

**7.** By AAP, $m\angle DAB = m\angle DAC + m\angle CAB$. By Theorem 7–1, $m\angle DAB > m\angle CAB$. Therefore $BD > BC$ by the Hinge Theorem.

**8.** By the Hinge Theorem, $m\angle TMR > m\angle TMS$. By the Supplement Postulate, $m\angle TMR + m\angle TMS = 180$. Therefore $m\angle TMR > 90$.

**11.** Applying the Supplement Postulate, we get $m\angle UXV = 110$, so that $\angle UXV > \angle WXV$. Applying the Hinge Theorem to $\triangle WXV$ and $\triangle UXV$ we conclude that $UV > WV$. Then applying Theorem 7–5 to $\triangle UVW$ we conclude that $\angle W > \angle U$.

**12.** Compare △ADC and △BCD: DA = CB (Given), DC = CD (Reflexive Property) and ∠ADC > ∠BCD (Exterior Angle Theorem). Hence by the Hinge Theorem (7–9), AC > DB.

**13.** (1) *TP* > *ST* by Theorem 7–9, so *TP* > *ST* > *RS*. (2) ∠*SQT* > ∠*RQS* by Theorem 7–10, so ∠*TQP* > ∠*SQT* > ∠*RQS*.

**14.** (1) Applying the Converse Hinge Theorem to △*AFH* and △*FAQ*, we conclude that ∠*AFH* > ∠*FAQ*. (2) Then applying Theorem 7–6 to △*AFB* we conclude that *AB* > *FB*.

**15.** In △*ABC*, since *AB* > *AC*, ∠*ACB* > ∠*ABC* (Theorem 7–5). In △*BCD* and △*FBC*, *BC* = *BC*, *FC* = *DB*, and ∠*ACB* > ∠*ABC*. Hence by the Hinge Theorem *FB* > *CD*.

**12.** Given the figure with $AD = BC$, prove that $AC > DB$.

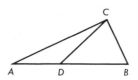

**13.** In this three-dimensional figure, $RQ = QT$, $QS = QP$, $ST > RS$, and $\angle TQP > \angle SQT$.

Prove: (a) $TP > RS$.

       (b) $\angle TQP > \angle RQS$.

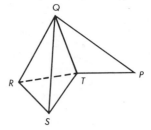

**14.** In this figure, $FH = AQ$ and $AH > FQ$. Prove that $AB > FB$.

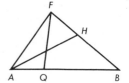

**15.** In $\triangle ABC$, $A$-$F$-$C$ and $A$-$D$-$B$ such that $FC = DB$. If $AB > AC$, prove that $FB > CD$.

## 7–8 ALTITUDES OF TRIANGLES

In each of the figures below, the segment $\overline{BD}$ is an *altitude* of $\triangle ABC$:

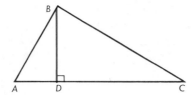 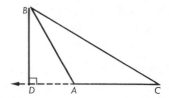

In each case, $\overline{BD}$ is the perpendicular from $B$ to $\overleftrightarrow{AC}$, and is called the *altitude* from $B$ to $\overleftrightarrow{AC}$. Note that the foot of this perpendicular does not necessarily lie on the segment $\overline{AC}$. But all cases are allowed for in the following definition.

## Definition

An *altitude* of a triangle is a perpendicular segment from a vertex of the triangle to the line containing the opposite side.

[*Query:* Is it possible for an altitude of a triangle to be a *side* of the triangle? If so, under what conditions does this happen?]

Of course, every triangle has three altitudes, one from each vertex, as shown in this figure. Here $\overline{BD}$ is the altitude from $B$, $\overline{AF}$ is the altitude from $A$, and $\overline{CE}$ is the altitude from $C$. Note that in this particular case, although no two of the segments $\overline{BD}$, $\overline{AF}$, and $\overline{CE}$ have a point in common, the lines containing them all seem to intersect in a point $G$.

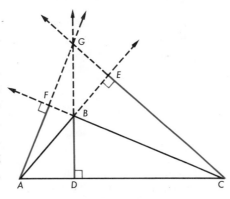

Unfortunately, the same word "altitude" is used in two other ways.

(1) Sometimes the *length* of an altitude is also called an altitude. Thus, if the distance $BD$ is 6, we may say that the altitude from $B$ is 6.

(2) A *line containing* an altitude is also called an altitude. Thus, in the figure above, the lines $\overleftrightarrow{BD}$, $\overleftrightarrow{AF}$, and $\overleftrightarrow{CE}$ may be referred to as altitudes. This is the way we shall be using the word, in Chapter 15, when we show that the three "altitudes" of a triangle always intersect at one point. If an altitude had to be a segment, this theorem would of course be false, as the above figure shows.

This triple use of a single word might easily lead to trouble, but it usually doesn't, because in most cases we can tell from the context what meaning is intended.

## Problem Set 7–8

1. Copy $\triangle ABC$. Note that it is scalene. Draw the angle bisector of $\angle C$. Next put in the median from $C$ to $\overline{AB}$. Finally, draw the altitude from $C$ to $\overline{AB}$. If you have worked carefully, you should see that these segments are distinct. In what kind of triangle would the angle bisector, median, and altitude be the same segment? **An Isosceles Triangle (AC=BC)**

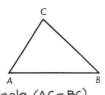

**Background Material**

A *median of a triangle* and an *angle bisector of an angle of a triangle* are defined in Section 5–8. The teacher may talk about an altitude of a triangle at that time, but the term cannot be defined until we have Theorems 6–3 and 6–4. The definition has been postponed until Chapter 7, because we cannot prove any important assertions involving altitudes until we have the SAA Theorem and the Hypotenuse-Leg Theorem.

**Quiz**

Prove that the perimeter of $\triangle ABC$ is greater than the sum of its altitudes.

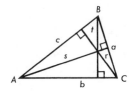

(ans: See the proof for Problem 10 of Problem Set 7–8.)

**5.** If $AB = AC$ and $\overline{AM}$ is the altitude to the base $\overline{BC}$, then $\triangle ABM$ and $\triangle ACM$ are right triangles and $AM = AM$. Therefore $\triangle ABM \cong \triangle ACM$ by HL, so $BM = CM$ by CPCTC.

**6.** (1) If $m\angle C < 90$, or if $m\angle C > 90$: Since $CA = CB$, $\angle CBA \cong \angle CAB$. Then $\triangle GAB \cong \triangle HBA$ by SAA, and consequently $AH = BG$. (2) If $m\angle C = 90$: Then $\overline{AH} = \overline{AC}$ and $\overline{BG} = \overline{BC}$. Since $\overline{AC} \cong \overline{BC}$ by hypothesis we can immediately conclude that the altitudes are congruent.

**8.** $\triangle ABG \cong \triangle BAH$ by the Hypotenuse-Leg Theorem, and consequently $\angle CAB \cong \angle CBA$. In $\triangle ACB$, since $\angle CAB \cong \angle CBA$, $CA = CB$.

**9.** $\triangle BCG \cong \triangle EFH$ by HL, and consequently $\angle ABC \cong \angle DEF$. Therefore $\triangle ABC \cong \triangle DEF$ by SAS.

**10.**

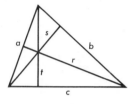

Let $r$, $s$, $t$ designate the "altitudes" on the sides whose lengths are designated $a$, $b$, $c$. If the triangle is acute $a > t$, $b > r$, $c > s$ by Theorem 7–6, and consequently $a + b + c > r + s + t$. If the triangle is obtuse the proof still holds. If the triangle is a right triangle, simply replace two of the $>$ symbols by $\geq$ symbols.

**2.** Copy the obtuse triangle, $\triangle PQR$, and draw its three altitudes.

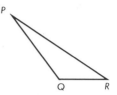

**3.** Carefully sketch a right triangle. Draw its three altitudes.

**4.** What theorem proves the following statement?

Any altitude of a triangle is less than or equal to the lengths of at least two sides of the triangle. (Which of the uses of *altitude* is intended in the previous statement?) *Theorem 7–7, altitude stands for "length of an altitude".*

**5.** Prove that the altitude to the base of an isosceles triangle is also a median.

**6.** Prove the following theorem.

The altitudes to the congruent sides of an isosceles triangle are congruent.

(The figure shows the case for $m\angle C < 90$. Consider also $m\angle C = 90$ and $m\angle C > 90$.)

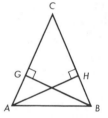

**7.** Prove: The altitudes of an equilateral triangle are congruent. *Apply Problem 6 twice.*

**8.** Prove the converse of the theorem of Problem 6:

If two altitudes of a triangle are congruent, the triangle is isosceles.

**9.** Prove the following theorem in the case described by the figure and the restatement.

Given a correspondence $ABC \leftrightarrow DEF$. If $AB = DE$, $BC = EF$, and the altitude from $C$ is congruent to the altitude from $F$, then the correspondence is a congruence.

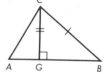

**Restatement**

Given: $AB = DE$ and $BC = EF$. $\overline{CG}$ and $\overline{FH}$ are altitudes, with $A$-$G$-$B$ and $D$-$H$-$E$. $CG = FH$.

Prove: $\triangle ABC \cong \triangle DEF$.

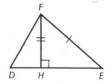

**10.** Prove that the perimeter of a triangle is greater than the sum of the three altitudes.

**11.** Prove that the altitude from a given vertex of a triangle is unique.
The perpendicular segment from a point to a line not containing the point is unique.

---

**12.** In $\triangle ABC$, the altitude, angle bisector, and median from the vertex $C$ all intersect side $\overline{AB}$, at points $D$, $E$, and $M$, respectively, with $D$-$E$-$M$. Prove that the altitude is the shortest and the median is the longest of these three segments. See Solution Section.

**13.** In Problem 9 above, you proved the theorem for the case in which $A$-$G$-$B$ and $D$-$H$-$E$. Draw figures and prove the theorem for the other cases. See Solution Section.

## CHAPTER REVIEW

**1.** For each example, identify the law that it illustrates.

(a) If $r > 6$ and $6 > t$, then $t < r$. Transitive Property of Inequality

(b) If $MP = 3$ and $RS = 7$, then $MP + RS = 10$. Add. Prop. of Eq.

(c) If $DK \geq 11$ and $DK \leq 11$, then $DK = 11$. Trichotomy Law

**2.** If $D$ is a point in the interior of $\angle ABC$, explain why $\angle ABC > \angle DBC$. Which theorem is essential to your explanation?

**3.** Prove: If a median of a triangle is not perpendicular to the side it bisects, then at least two sides of the triangle are not congruent.

**4.** In an equilateral triangle a median, an angle bisector, and an altitude are drawn at different vertices. How do their lengths compare? Equal

**5.** Given the figure, prove that $\angle ADB > \angle C$.
$\angle ADB > \angle BED$ (Exterior Angle Theorem)
$\angle BED > \angle C$ (Exterior Angle Theorem)
$\angle ADB > \angle C$ (Transitivity)

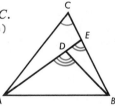

**6.** With measures of angles as indicated, which segment is the shortest? Give your reasoning. $\overline{SP}$

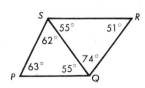

**Answers to Chapter Review Problems**

**2.** Since $D$ is in the interior of $\angle ABC$, $m\angle ABC = m\angle ABD + m\angle DBC$, by the AAP. Since the measure of an angle is a real number and since $m\angle ABD > 0$, we can conclude by Theorem 7–1 that $m\angle ABC > m\angle DBC$, or, by definition, $\angle ABC > \angle DBC$.

**3.** If the median $\overline{MA}$ is not perpendicular to the side $\overline{KL}$ then $\angle MAK$ and $\angle MAL$ are unequal. But $MA = MA$ and $AK = AL$ since $\overline{MA}$ is a median. Therefore $MK$ and $ML$ are unequal by the Hinge Theorem applied to $\triangle MAK$ and $\triangle MAL$.

**6.** In $\triangle QRS$, $\angle R$ has the smallest measure, and therefore $\overline{SQ}$ is the shortest segment in $\triangle QRS$. But in $\triangle PQS$, $m\angle PQS < m\angle SPQ$. Hence $SP < SQ$. Therefore $\overline{SP}$ is the shortest segment in $\triangle SPQ$ and also the shortest in the figure.

**7.** Since $AC > AB$, $m\angle B > m\angle C$. $\angle ADC$ is an exterior angle of $\triangle ABD$ and so $m\angle ADC > m\angle B$. Therefore $m\angle ADC > m\angle C$. Hence, $AC > AD$.

**9.** Yes, if the trunk is perpendicular to the ground. There are three congruent triangles by the HL Theorem.

**11.**

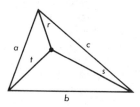

Let $a$, $b$, and $c$ be the lengths of the sides as shown.

$t + r > a.$
$t + s > b.$
$r + s > c.$
$2(t + r + s) > a + b + c.$
$t + r + s > \frac{1}{2}(a + b + c).$

**12.**

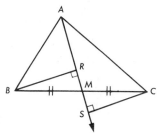

**13.** $\angle RTQ > \angle P$ by the Exterior Angle Theorem. Since $TR = RQ$, $\angle RTQ \cong \angle Q$, so $\angle Q > \angle P$. Therefore, in $\triangle PRQ$, $PR > RQ$ by Theorem 7-9.

**14.**

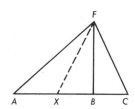

Given: $\overline{FB} \perp \overline{AC}$.
　　　　$AB > BC$.
Prove: $AF > FC$.
Proof: Locate $X$ on $\overleftrightarrow{AC}$ so that $BX = BC$. $\angle FXB > \angle A$ by the Exterior Angle Theorem. $\angle C \cong \angle FXB > \angle A$. Therefore, $AF > CF$.

---

**7.** In $\triangle ABC$, $AC > AB$. Prove that if $D$ is any point between $B$ and $C$, then $AD < AC$.

**8.** Prove the following theorem.

> Any point on the bisector of an angle is equidistant from the sides of the angle.

Given: $\overrightarrow{AP}$ bisects $\angle BAC$,
　　　　$\overline{PE} \perp \overrightarrow{AB}$,
　　　　$\overline{PF} \perp \overrightarrow{AC}$.

Prove: $PE = PF$.

$\triangle APE \cong \triangle APF$ by SAA
$PE = PF$ by CPCTC

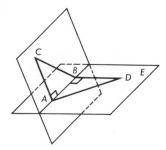

**9.** Three guy wires of equal length support a newly planted tree on level ground. If they are all fastened to the tree at the same height, will they be pegged to the ground at equal distances from the foot of the tree? Why?

**10.** Planes $E$ and $F$ intersect in $\overleftrightarrow{AB}$. $C$ is in $F$; $D$ is in $E$. $CB = AD$. $\overline{CA} \perp \overline{AB}$ and $\overline{DB} \perp \overline{AB}$. Prove that $CA = DB$.

$\triangle CAB \cong \triangle DBA$ by HL
$CA = DB$ by CPCTC

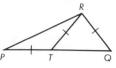

---

**11.** Segments drawn from a point in the interior of a triangle to the three vertices have lengths $r$, $s$, $t$. Prove that $r + s + t$ is greater than one-half the perimeter of the triangle.

**12.** Prove: If $\overline{AM}$ is a median of $\triangle ABC$, then segments from $B$ and $C$ perpendicular to $\overleftrightarrow{AM}$ are congruent. $\triangle BRM \cong \triangle CSM$ (SAA) and $BR = CS$ (CPCTC)

**13.** In the figure, $PT = TR = RQ$. Prove that

$$PR > RQ.$$

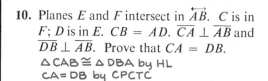

**14.** Prove the following theorem.

> If two oblique (nonperpendicular) segments are drawn to a line from any point on a perpendicular to the line, the segment whose end point in the line is more remote from the foot of the perpendicular is the longer segment.

15. Given that $AC = BC$, $AB < AC$, and $A$-$C$-$D$.
Prove that $\triangle ABD$ is scalene.

16. The sum of the measures of the angles of a triangle is less than 270.

17. On the basis of the postulates we have stated and the theorems we have proved so far in this book it is impossible to prove that the sum of the measures of the three angles of a triangle is 180 (a fact with which you have been familiar for some time). However, we can easily construct a special triangle and prove that the sum of the measures of its angles is less than 181. Let $\angle BAC$ have measure 1 (Angle Construction Postulate). On $\overrightarrow{AB}$ and $\overrightarrow{AC}$ take points $K$ and $M$ such that $AK = AM$. The sum of the measures of the angles of $\triangle AKM$ is less than 181. Why? If we made $m\angle A = \frac{1}{2}$, what could we say of the angle sum?

Sum $\angle 180\frac{1}{2}$

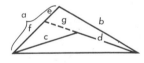

18. Prove: The sum of the distances from a point in the interior of a triangle to the ends of one side is less than the sum of the lengths of the other two sides; that is, prove that $a + b > c + d$.

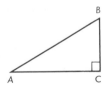

19. In $\triangle ABC$, $\angle C$ is a right angle. If $m\angle B = 2m\angle A$, then prove that $AB = 2BC$. [*Hint:* Introduce the bisector of $\angle B$.]

20. (a) Given $\triangle ABC$ with $BC = a$, $AC = b$, and $AB = c$. Prove that

$$|a - b| < c.$$

(b) State in words the generalization of part (a) as a theorem.
The absolute value of the difference of the lengths of any two sides of a triangle is less than the length of the third side.

## HONORS PROBLEM

Let $\overleftrightarrow{BD}$ intersect $\overleftrightarrow{AC}$ at $B$, between $A$ and $C$. Perpendiculars from $A$ and $C$ to $\overleftrightarrow{BD}$ meet $\overleftrightarrow{BD}$ at $P$ and $Q$, respectively. Prove that $P$ and $Q$ are not on the same side of $\overleftrightarrow{AC}$. See Solution Section.

---

### Answers to Chapter Review Problems

**15.** In $\triangle ABC$, $m < a$, since $AB < AC$. And $y < m$ by the Exterior Angle Theorem. Therefore, $y < a$. Also, $a < a + x$, which means that $\angle A < \angle ABD$. We now have $\angle D < \angle A < \angle ABD$, and by applying Theorem 7–6, we conclude that $AB < BD < AD$, and that $\triangle ABD$ is scalene.

**16.**

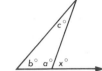

The conclusion is obvious if each angle is acute, so we suppose we have a figure as shown, so $a > 90$. Then $x < 90$ and $a + b + c < (a + x) + x < 180 + 90 = 270$.

**17.** Since $m\angle AKM < m\angle KMC$ by Theorem 7–1, $m\angle A + m\angle AMK + m\angle AKM < 1 + m\angle AMK + m\angle KMC = 1 + 180 = 181$.

**18.** 1. $b + e > d + g$.
   $g + f > c$. (Triangle Inequality)
2. $b + e + g + f > d + g + c$. (Addition)
3. $b + (e + f) > d + c$. (Subtraction)
4. $b + a > d + c$. ($a = e + f$.)

**19.**

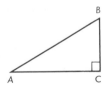

Introduce $\overline{BX}$, the angle bisector of $\angle B$, and introduce $\overline{XY} \perp \overline{AB}$, as shown in the figure. Then $m\angle XBY = m\angle A$, since by hypothesis $m\angle B = 2m\angle A$. Therefore $\triangle AXY \cong \triangle BXY$ by SAA, and consequently $AY = BY$. Secondly, $\triangle XBC \cong \triangle XBY$ by SAA, and consequently $BC = BY$. Therefore $AB = AY + BY = 2BY = 2BC$.

**20.** (a) By the Triangle Inequality, $a < b + c$, and hence $a - b < c$. Also by the Triangle Inequality, $b < a + c$, and hence $b - a < c$, which means that $-(a - b) < c$. Since $a - b < c$, and $-(a - b) < c$ we can conclude that $|a - b| < c$.

## Perpendicular Lines and Planes in Space

Chapters 8 and 10 establish the fundamental facts about lines and planes in space. The key theorem is the Basic Theorem on Perpendiculars, and the technique which is most fruitful is that of introducing auxiliary lines and planes in space. Note that the development of three-dimensional geometry in this chapter does not require any additional postulates; all the theorems are proved on the basis of the postulates which have already been stated. We have already provided, in Postulates 5 and 8, the basis for a logical extension of plane geometry into three dimensions. Please remember that this is the only course in geometry that a student is likely to take, and it is here that he will learn all that he is going to learn about lines and planes in space. We have deliberately introduced the elements of space geometry into our development of geometry at the outset. Early in this development we established the basic incidence properties of lines and planes in space. Throughout the text we have included many problems which, while solvable by planar methods, nevertheless involve nonplanar figures. And here in Chapters 8 and 10 we devote ourselves to the study of perpendicularity and parallelism of lines and planes in space.

The teacher is faced with the responsibility of covering the text during the school year; and just as it is necessary to be selective in the choice of problems, it is also necessary to be selective in the choice of sections and in the choice of chapters. The geometry of lines and planes in space is a topic on which the subsequent chapters (with the exception of Chapter 19) are not

CHAPTER **8**

# Perpendicular Lines and Planes in Space

## Objectives . . .

- Understand the Basic Theorem on Perpendiculars.
- Get a feel for perpendicular planes in space.
- Find and describe the plane that bisects a given line segment.

substantially dependent. We would
like to have the student prove the
theorems in Chapters 8 and 10, but
we must admit that there may not
be time enough to cover these chapters thoroughly. In this case we
recommend that you give at least an
intuitive presentation of lines and
planes in space and concentrate on
the results rather than the proofs.

**Planning the Chapter**

Both average and above-average
classes will require approximately
the same amount of study time for
this chapter: two days on Section
8–1 and one day each on the rest of
the sections should be sufficient.
However, a weaker class may omit
this chapter, or at least approach it
with lesser thoroughness.

## 8–1   THE DEFINITION OF PERPENDICULARITY FOR LINES AND PLANES

In this chapter, we shall be concerned with figures that do not lie in
a single plane.   Therefore, before you start reading this chapter, it
would be worthwhile to review Chapter 3, in which the basic ideas of
space geometry were introduced.

Perpendicularity between lines and planes is defined as follows.

### 8–1 THE DEFINITION OF PERPENDICULARITY FOR LINES AND PLANES

**Classroom Notes**

The concept of a line and a plane
perpendicular to each other is
the basic concept of this chapter.
The definition and the basic perpendicularity criterion should be
presented carefully.   Teach the
definition first: consider a line
which is perpendicular to a plane
(a blackboard pointer and a desk
top are effective) and observe that
the line is perpendicular to every
line in the plane which passes
through the point of intersection.
Then, on the basis of this observation, formulate the basic definition.
Then note that this definition as it
stands is hard to use, since it requires us to know that $L$ is perpendicular to *every* line in $E$ passing
through $P$.   This suggests the question of what minimal set of conditions will guarantee that a line is
perpendicular to a plane.

### Definition

A line and a plane are *perpendicular* if they intersect and if every line
lying in the plane and passing through the point of intersection is
perpendicular to the given line.

If the line $L$ and the plane $E$ are
perpendicular, then we write
$L \perp E$ or $E \perp L$.   If $P$ is their
point of intersection, then we
say that $L \perp E$ at $P$.

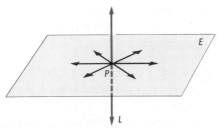

In the figure, we have shown three lines in $E$, passing through $P$.
According to our definition, all three are supposed to be perpendicular
to $L$ at $P$, although they may not look that way.   (In a perspective
drawing, perpendicular lines don't necessarily look perpendicular.)
Note that if we had required merely that *one* line in $E$ be perpendicular
to $L$, this wouldn't have meant a thing: you can easily convince yourself that *every* plane through $P$ contains such a line.   On the other
hand, it will turn out that if $E$ contains *two* lines which are perpendicular
to $L$ at $P$, then $L \perp E$ at $P$.   We shall pursue this idea in the next section.

The mere fact that a line is perpendicular to *one* line in the plane is obviously not enough to guarantee that the line is perpendicular to the plane; *every* line which intersects the plane is perpendicular to at least one line in the plane. If, however, the line is perpendicular to two lines in the plane passing through the point of intersection, it appears that the line is perpendicular to the plane. Formulate this observation into the basic perpendicularity criterion, that is, Theorem 8–2.

*Warning:* It is important to distinguish and contrast the *definition* and the basic perpendicularity *criterion*. Students, even good students, are slow to understand the difference. The trouble is caused partly by the fact that mathematically we had a choice; we could equally well have stated the following definition and theorem.

> DEFINITION. A line *L* and a plane *E* are perpendicular if they intersect, and *E* contains two lines which are perpendicular to *L* at the point of intersection.

> **Theorem.** If $L \perp E$ at *P*, then *L* is perpendicular to every line which lies in *E* and contains *P*.

This amounts to the same thing in the end.

## Problem Set 8–1

1. The figure at the right represents plane *E*.
   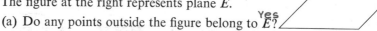
   (a) Do any points outside the figure belong to *E*? Yes
   (b) Is plane *E* intended to include every point outside the figure? No

2. (a) Sketch a plane perpendicular to a vertical line.
   (b) Sketch a plane perpendicular to a horizontal line.
   (c) In each plane in parts (a) and (b) sketch three lines which pass through the point of intersection with the original line. State for each case, the relationship of each of the three lines to the original line. They are all perpendicular to the given line.

3. Reread the definition of perpendicularity of a line and a plane and decide whether the following is true on the basis of that definition:

   > If a line is perpendicular to a plane, then it is perpendicular to every line in the plane passing through the point of intersection.
   > The statement is true.

4. How many right angles are shown in the figure on the left below? Assume that $\overline{KC} \perp E$, $\square ABCD$ is a square, and $\overline{AC} \perp \overline{BD}$. Eleven

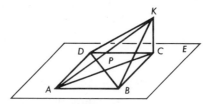
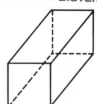

5. How many pairs of perpendicular segments are shown in the figure on the right above? 24 Assume that every two intersecting segments are perpendicular.

6. If $\angle KPM$ is a right angle and $\overleftrightarrow{PM}$ is in *E*, can you conclude that *E* is perpendicular to $\overleftrightarrow{PK}$? No Why or why not?
   Must know that $\overleftrightarrow{PK}$ is perpendicular to at least two lines in E through P.

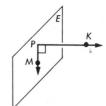

7. Given that *G*, *H*, *J*, and *P* are in plane *E* and $\overleftrightarrow{AB} \perp E$ at *P*. Which of the following must be right angles?

   $\widehat{\angle APJ}$   $\angle HPJ$   $\angle GPH$
   $\widehat{\angle GPB}$   $\widehat{\angle HPB}$   $\widehat{\angle HPA}$

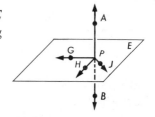

**Answers to Problems**

**12.** If a line is perpendicular to each of two lines at their point of intersection, then it is perpendicular to the plane containing the lines.

**13.** (1) $\triangle ABQ \cong \triangle ABP$ (SSS) and therefore $\angle ABQ \cong \angle ABP$.

   (2) From (1) and the facts that $QB = PB$ and $XB = XB$ we conclude that $\triangle QBX \cong \triangle PBX$ (SAS) and hence $QX = PX$.

The proof is still valid if $P$ and $Q$ are on opposite sides of $E$, or if $P$ and $Q$ are in $E$.

**Quiz**

Points $A$, $B$, and $C$ lie in plane $E$ and $\overrightarrow{BP} \perp E$. $BA = BC$.
Prove: $PA = PC$.
Proof: Since $\overrightarrow{BP} \perp E$, $\overline{BP} \perp \overline{BA}$ and $\overline{BP} \perp \overline{BC}$. $\triangle PBA \cong \triangle PBC$ by SAS and so $PA = PC$.

**8.** In the figure, $H$, $K$, and $R$ are in plane $E$ and $F$ is not in $E$.

(a) Name the planes determined by the points of the figure. E, FHK , FHR ,FKR

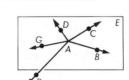

(b) If $\overrightarrow{HR}$ is perpendicular to plane $HKF$, which angles in the figure must be right angles? ∠RHF and ∠RHK

**9.** Points $A$, $B$, $C$, $D$, and $G$ lie in the vertical plane $E$ and $\overrightarrow{AP} \perp E$. Name all angles which must be right angles.

∠PAB,∠PAC,∠PAD,∠PAG

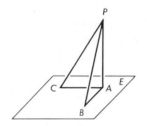

**10.** Given the figure with $A$, $B$, and $C$ in plane $E$. $\overline{PA} \perp E$ and $PC = PB$. Prove that $AC = AB$.

Since $\overline{PA} \perp E$, $\overline{PA} \perp \overline{AC}$ and $\overline{PA} \perp \overline{AB}$. $\triangle APB \cong \triangle APC$ by HL and $AB = AC$ by corresponding parts.

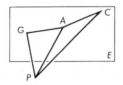

**11.** Points $A$, $G$, and $C$ lie in vertical plane $E$, and $P$ is a point "in front" of $E$. If $\overline{PA} \perp E$ and $AG = AC$, prove that $PG = PC$.

Since $\overline{PA} \perp E$, $\overline{PA} \perp \overline{AC}$ and $\overline{PA} \perp \overline{AG}$. $\triangle PAC \cong \triangle PAG$ (SAS) and $PG = PC$.

**12.** On a sheet of paper, draw two lines $L_1$ and $L_2$ intersecting at a point $A$. Try the following experiments.

(a) Place the tip of a pencil at $A$ so that the pencil appears to be perpendicular to $L_1$ but not to $L_2$.

(b) Place the tip of a pencil at $A$ so that the pencil appears to be perpendicular to $L_2$ but not to $L_1$.

(c) Place the tip of a pencil at $A$ so that the pencil appears to be perpendicular to both $L_1$ and $L_2$.

Now state the conjecture suggested by what you have observed.

**13.** $A$, $B$, and $X$ are collinear points in the plane $E$, and $P$ and $Q$ are points on the same side of $E$. If $PB = QB$ and $PA = QA$, prove that $PX = QX$. Will your proof hold if $P$ and $Q$ are on opposite sides of $E$? if $P$ and $Q$ are in $E$?

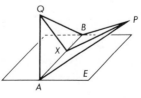

## Background Material

The classical proof of the basic Theorem on Perpendiculars is long, primarily because it makes use of some elementary considerations about congruent triangles. To free ourselves from these elementary considerations in the proof itself we first state a preliminary theorem and restate a previous corollary. This enables us to write a brief proof of the basic theorem on perpendiculars in which we can concentrate on the important ideas.

## Classroom Notes

Theorem 8–1 is the key to our simplification of the Basic Theorem on Perpendiculars. The proof of this theorem is easy; it is a two-step congruence proof. The only difficult aspect of this theorem is the visual problem of perceiving how the nonplanar figure looks in perspective. (See Problem 13 of Problem Set 8–1.) It is very important to discuss the theorem for the case in which $\triangle BPC$ and $\triangle BQC$ are noncoplanar, because (as the text says) this is precisely the case in which we are going to need the theorem.

We recommend that you have your students construct models out of straws, thin wooden dowels, or segments of wire for the figures of Theorems 8–1 and 8–2.

Be sure they understand Theorem 8–1 and Corollary 6–2.1 before you take up the Basic Theorem on Perpendiculars.

## 8–2 THE BASIC THEOREM ON PERPENDICULARS

At the end of the preceding section, we said that if $E$ contains two lines which are perpendicular to $L$ at $P$, then $E \perp L$ at $P$. The proof of this theorem is rather long. To make it seem a little easier, we shall first prove a preliminary theorem, to help us in the main proof.

### Theorem 8–1

*If B and C are equidistant from P and Q, then every point between B and C is equidistant from P and Q.*

The restatement is conveyed by the figure. Note that $P$, $B$, $X$, and $C$ must lie in a single plane, because $X$ lies on $\overleftrightarrow{BC}$ and some plane contains $\overleftrightarrow{BC}$ and $P$. But it can easily happen that $\triangle BPC$ and $\triangle BQC$ lie in different planes, and this is the case in which we shall need the theorem.

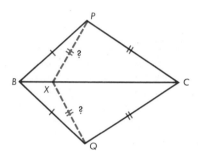

**Proof.** (1) We have given $BP = BQ$, and $CP = CQ$ as indicated in the figure. By SSS it follows that $\triangle BPC \cong \triangle BQC$.

(2) Therefore $\angle PBC \cong \angle QBC$.

(3) By SAS it follows that $\triangle PBX \cong \triangle QBX$.

(4) Therefore $PX = QX$, and $X$ is equidistant from $P$ and $Q$, which was to be proved.

We shall also need Corollary 6–2.1 from Chapter 6.

### Corollary 6–2.1

*Given a segment $\overline{AB}$ and a line L in the same plane. If two points of L are equidistant from A and B, then L is the perpendicular bisector of $\overline{AB}$.*

We shall need this corollary for the case in which one of the two points of $L$ is the intersection of $L$ and $\overline{AB}$.

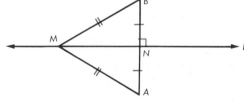

**Theorem 8–2.** The Basic Theorem on Perpendiculars

*If a line is perpendicular to each of two intersecting lines at their point of intersection, then it is perpendicular to the plane that contains them.*

**Restatement.** Let $L_1$ and $L_2$ be two lines in a plane $E$, intersecting at $A$. Let $L$ be a line which is perpendicular to both $L_1$ and $L_2$ at $A$. Then $L$ is perpendicular to every line $L_3$ which lies in $E$ and contains $A$.

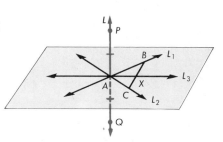

**Proof.** (1) Let $P$ and $Q$ be two points of $L$ which are equidistant from $A$. Then $L_1$ *and* $L_2$ *are perpendicular bisectors of* $\overline{PQ}$ (in two different planes, of course).

(2) Each of the lines $L_1$ and $L_2$ contains points on each side of $L_3$ in $E$. Let $B$ and $C$ be points of $L_1$ and $L_2$, lying on opposite sides of $L_3$ in $E$. Then line $L_3$ *contains a point X, lying between B and C.*

(3) By (1) and Theorem 6–2, *each of the points B and C is equidistant from P and Q.*

(4) By Theorem 8–1, $X$ *is equidistant from P and Q.*

(5) Thus $L_3$ contains the midpoint of $\overline{PQ}$, and contains another point $X$ which is equidistant from $P$ and $Q$. By Corollary 6–2.1, $L_3 \perp L$, which was to be proved.

## Problem Set 8–2

1. In this three-dimensional figure each quadrilateral is a rectangle.
   (a) Name two planes perpendicular to $\overline{AD}$. Explain why each is perpendicular. EDFC, AHGB, Theorem 8–2
   (b) Name three segments perpendicular to plane $ABCD$. $\overline{ED}, \overline{AH}, \overline{FC}, \overline{BG}$
   (c) Is $\angle EDF$ a right angle? No
   (d) Is $\angle DFG$ a right angle? Yes

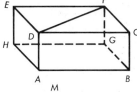

2. In the figure, $MY = MX$, $KY = KX$, and $\overline{MK} \perp \overline{KX}$. Prove that $\overline{MK} \perp E$.

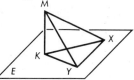

The Basic Theorem on Perpendiculars should be carefully presented in class.

**Explanation for Problems**

There is ample material in Problem Set 8–2 for two assignments. The first assignment can include the proof of Theorem 8–2 and Problems 1 through 8. Note that Problems 6 through 8 are similar in nature; it is advisable to discuss Problem 6 in class first before assigning the others. The second assignment can include the rest of the problems.

**Quiz**

1. Points $A$, $B$, $C$ lie in plane $E$ and $P$ does not lie in $E$. $\overline{PB} \perp \overline{BC}$, $\overline{AB} \perp \overline{BC}$ and $AB = PB$. What segment is perpendicular to which plane?
(ans: $\overline{CB} \perp$ plane $ABP$)
2. Prove $\triangle PBC \cong \triangle ABC$ in Problem 1. Proof: $\angle PBC \cong \angle ABC$ since both are right angles and together with given and $BC = BC$, $\triangle ABC \cong \triangle PBC$ by SAS.

**Answers to Problems**

2. Since $MY = MX$, $KY = KX$, and $MK = MK$ by the reflexive property, $\triangle MKX \cong \triangle MKY$ by SSS so $\angle MKY \cong \angle MKX$ by corresponding parts. But $\overline{MK} \perp \overline{KX}$, so $\angle MKX$ is a right angle; thus $\angle MKY$ is also a right angle (all right angles are congruent) and $\overline{MK} \perp \overline{KY}$. Therefore $\overline{MK} \perp E$ by Theorem 8–2.

**4.** Since $\overleftrightarrow{AP} \perp \overleftrightarrow{AG}$ and $\overleftrightarrow{AP} \perp \overleftrightarrow{AJ}$, $\overleftrightarrow{AP}$ is perpendicular to plane $E$ (Theorem 8–2). Since $\overleftrightarrow{AP} \perp E$, $\overleftrightarrow{AP}$ is, by definition, perpendicular to $\overleftrightarrow{AK}$ and $\overleftrightarrow{AM}$.

**5.** Since $AB = DB$, $m\angle ABC = m\angle DBC = 90$, and $BC = BC$, we can conclude that $\triangle ABC \cong \triangle DBC$ (SAS). $AB$ is not necessarily perpendicular to $E$. However, since $\overline{CB} \perp \overline{BA}$ and $\overline{CB} \perp \overline{BD}$, $\overline{CB} \perp$ plane $ABD$ (Theorem 8–2).

**6.** (a) The sides of the square all lie in one plane, $E$. $\overline{PA}$ and $\overline{AB}$ determine another plane; $\overline{PA}$ and $\overline{AD}$ determine a third plane.
   (b) Since $\overline{BA} \perp \overline{AP}$ and $\overline{BA} \perp \overline{AD}$, $\overline{BA} \perp$ plane $ADP$.

**8.** Since $A$ is equidistant from $D$ and $G$, and $K$ is equidistant from $D$ and $G$, we conclude by Corollary 6–2.1 that $\overline{AK} \perp \overline{DG}$. Since it is also given that $\overline{AK} \perp \overline{KP}$, we can conclude that $\overline{AK} \perp$ plane $PDG$.

**3.** Given points $A$, $B$, $C$, $D$ in the plane $E$. $PB = QB$, $PD = QD$, $PA = QA$, and $PC = QC$. Prove that

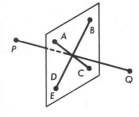

   (a) $\overleftrightarrow{PQ} \perp \overleftrightarrow{AC}$. by Corollary 6-2.1
   (b) $\overleftrightarrow{PQ} \perp \overleftrightarrow{BD}$. by Corollary 6-2.1
   (c) $\overleftrightarrow{PQ} \perp E$. by Theorem 8-2

**4.** In the figure on the left below, let $A$, $G$, $H$, $K$, $J$ and $M$ be points in the plane $E$. $\overleftrightarrow{AP} \perp \overleftrightarrow{AG}$, $\overleftrightarrow{AP} \perp \overleftrightarrow{AJ}$, and $A$, $G$, and $J$ are noncollinear. Prove that $\overleftrightarrow{AP}$ is perpendicular to $\overleftrightarrow{AK}$ and to $\overleftrightarrow{AM}$.

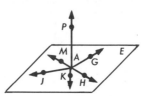

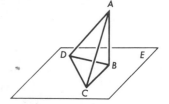

**5.** In the figure on the right above, $\overline{AB} \perp \overline{BC}$, $\overline{DB} \perp \overline{BC}$, and $AB = DB$. Prove that $\triangle ABC \cong \triangle DBC$. Is $\overline{AB} \perp E$? Why or why not?
   Not necessarily ↙

**6.** $\square ABCD$ is a square in the plane $E$. $P$ is a point not in $E$ such that $\overline{PA} \perp \overline{AB}$.

   (a) Name all the planes determined by pairs of segments. E, PAB, PAD

   (b) At least one of the segments is perpendicular to one of the planes asked for in part (a). Which segment? Which plane? How does Theorem 8–2 help you to give a correct answer?

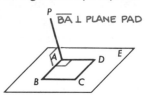

$\overline{BA} \perp$ PLANE PAD

**7.** In Problem 5, which segment is perpendicular to which plane? $\overline{CB} \perp$ plane ABD

**8.** Given that $K$ is the midpoint of $\overline{DG}$, $AD = AG$, and $\overleftrightarrow{KP} \perp \overline{AK}$, $P$ not in the plane $ADG$. If there is a segment perpendicular to a plane, name the segment and the plane. $\overline{AK} \perp$ plane PDG

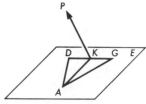

**9.** In the figure, $\overline{PQ} \perp \overline{MP}$, $\overline{PQ} \perp \overline{TQ}$, and $\overline{MP} \perp \overline{MT}$. Is any segment of the figure perpendicular to any plane of the figure? No Name all such pairs, if any.

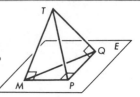

**10.** $\overline{AB}$ and $\overline{CD}$ are congruent segments which bisect each other at $M$. $L$ is a line perpendicular to each of $\overline{AB}$ and $\overline{CD}$ at $M$. $P$ is any point of $L$. Draw a figure and prove that $P$ is equidistant from $A$, $B$, $C$, and $D$.

**11.** If $A$, $B$, $C$, and $D$ are noncoplanar,

$$AD = DC, \qquad BC = BA,$$

and $\angle DBA$ is a right angle, then at least one of the segments in the figure is perpendicular to one of the planes. Which segment and which plane? Prove your answer. $\overline{DB} \perp$ plane $ABC$

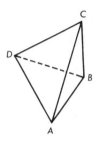

## 8-3 EXISTENCE AND UNIQUENESS

The hard part of this chapter was over with when we proved Theorem 8-2. The other things we need follow rather easily.

### Theorem 8-3

> *Through a given point of a given line there passes a plane perpendicular to the given line.*

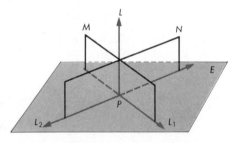

**Proof.** Let $L$ and $P$ be the given line and point.

(1) Let $M$ and $N$ be any two different planes containing $L$.

  [*Query:* How do we know that there *are* two different planes containing $L$? Remember Postulate 5 and Theorem 3-3.]

(2) There is a line $L_1$ in $M$, perpendicular to $L$ at $P$ (Theorem 6-1).
(3) There is a line $L_2$ in $N$, perpendicular to $L$ at $P$ (Theorem 6-1).
(4) There is a plane $E$, containing $L_1$ and $L_2$ (Theorem 3-4).
(5) $E \perp L$ at $P$ (by (2), (3), and Theorem 8-2).

**Answers to Problems**

**10.**

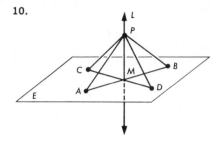

$\triangle PMA \cong \triangle PMB \cong \triangle PMC \cong \triangle PMD$ (SAS). Therefore $PA = PB = PC = PD$.

**11.** Since $\triangle ABD \cong \triangle CBD$ (SSS), $\angle ABD \cong \angle CBD$, and since, by hypothesis, $\angle ABD$ is a right angle, $\angle CBD$ is a right angle. Hence, by Theorem 8-2, $\overline{DB} \perp$ plane $ABC$.

## 8-3 EXISTENCE AND UNIQUENESS

### Background Material

The Basic Theorem on Perpendiculars is the most important theorem in this chapter. The proofs of the remaining theorems are interesting, and so are many of the problems. The teacher must, however (as we mentioned earlier), decide how much time he can allot to Chapters 8 and 10 and consequently how thoroughly he can afford to cover them.

### Classroom Notes

The key to success in proving statements about lines and planes in space is the technique of introducing auxiliary sets, especially auxiliary planes. Most of our theorems to date have dealt with geometry in a plane. In order to use these theorems we must have planes in which to apply them. We can use Postulate 7, Theorem 3-3, Theorem 3-4, and now Theorem 8-3 to introduce auxiliary planes. The teacher may wish to use the notation $E(A, B, C)$, $E(L, P)$, and $E(L_1, L_2)$ to denote, respectively, the plane determined

**249**

by the three noncollinear points $A$, $B$, and $C$, the plane determined by line $L$ and point $P$ not on line $L$, and the plane determined by the intersecting lines $L_1$ and $L_2$. If the student keeps the idea of introducing auxiliary planes in mind, he should find it easy to understand the proofs of Theorems 8–3, 8–4, 8–5, and 8–6, and to write proofs for Theorems 8–8 and 8–9.

**Alternative proof of Theorem 8–5.** Given a point $P$ on the line $L$: By Theorem 8–3 there exists at least one plane $E$ perpendicular to $L$ at $P$. Suppose that there exists another plane $F$ perpendicular to $L$ at $P$. Since $E$ and $F$ are distinct but intersect at $P$, their intersection is, by Postulate 8, a line $K$. Introduce a plane $G$ which contains $L$ but does not contain $K$, let $M$ be the intersection of $G$ and $E$, and let $N$ be the intersection of $G$ and $F$. Since $L \perp E$, it follows that $L \perp M$; and similarly, since $L \perp F$, $L \perp N$. This means that $M$ and $N$ are two distinct lines in G each perpendicular to $L$ (which is also in $G$) at $P$. This contradicts Theorem 6–1.

**The proof of the Perpendicular Bisecting Plane Theorem.** We give two proofs. The first proof makes use of congruent triangles and will appeal to the average student:
*Proof of (1).* If $P = C$, then we already know that $PA = PB$. If $P \neq C$, then $\overleftrightarrow{CP}$ lies in $E$ by Postulate 6, and $\overleftrightarrow{AB} \perp \overleftrightarrow{CP}$ by the definition of a line perpendicular to a plane. It follows that $\angle ACP \cong \angle BCP$, and, since $CA = CB$ and $CP = CP$, we have $\triangle ACP \cong \triangle BCP$ by SAS. Therefore, $PA = PB$ by corresponding parts.
*Proof of (2).* If $P = C$, then certainly $P$ is in $E$. If $P \neq C$, then $\triangle ACP \cong \triangle BCP$ by SSS. Thus $\angle ACP \cong \angle BCP$ and $\overleftrightarrow{CP} \perp \overleftrightarrow{AB}$. $E$ contains $\overleftrightarrow{CP}$ by Theorem 8–5, and $P$ lies in $E$.

The second proof makes use of the analogous theorem about the

## Theorem 8–4

*If a line and a plane are perpendicular, then the plane contains every line perpendicular to the given line at its point of intersection with the given plane.*

**Restatement.** If the line $L$ is perpendicular to the plane $E$ at the point $P$, and $L_1$ is a line perpendicular to $L$ at $P$, then $L_1$ lies in $E$.

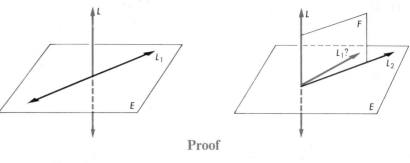

**Proof**

| STATEMENTS | REASONS |
|---|---|
| 1. $L$ and $L_1$ lie in a plane $F$. | 1. ? Theorem 3-4 |
| 2. The intersection of $F$ and $E$ is a line $L_2$. | 2. ? Postulate 8 |
| 3. $L_2 \perp L$ at $P$. | 3. Definition of $E \perp L$ |
| 4. $L_1 \perp L$ at $P$. | 4. Given |
| 5. $L_1$ and $L_2$ are the same line. | 5. By Theorem 6–1, there is only one line in $F$ which is perpendicular to $L$ at $P$. |
| 6. $L_1$ lies in $E$. | 6. By step 2, $L_2$ lies in $E$, and by step 5, $L_1 = L_2$. |

Theorem 8–4 enables us to show that the perpendicular plane given by Theorem 8–3 is unique.

## Theorem 8–5

*Through a given point of a given line there is only one plane perpendicular to the line.*

**Proof.** If there were two different perpendicular planes, then their intersection would be a single line. This is impossible because each of them contains *all* lines which are perpendicular to the given line at the given point.

We remember that the perpendicular bisector of a segment, in a given plane, was characterized as the set of all points of the plane that are equidistant from the end points of the segment. For the perpendicular bisecting plane of a segment, in space, we have a characterization theorem of exactly the same kind.

### Theorem 8–6   The Perpendicular Bisecting Plane Theorem

***The perpendicular bisecting plane of a segment is the set of all points equidistant from the end points of the segment.***

Restatement. Let $E$ be the perpendicular bisecting plane of $\overline{AB}$. Then

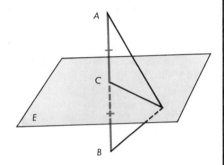

(1) if $P$ is in $E$, then $PA = PB$;
(2) if $PA = PB$, then $P$ is in $E$.

In the figure, $C$ is the midpoint of $\overline{AB}$. Note that the restatement is in two parts, as we expect for a characterization theorem.

To prove (1), you need to know the definition of perpendicularity between a line and a plane, and the characterization of perpendicular bisecting lines in a plane. To prove (2), you also need Theorem 8–5. The details of these two proofs are left to you.

### Problem Set 8–3

1. Which theorem of this section asserts uniqueness? Theorem 8-5.

2. How can one be sure that for any given segment there is only one perpendicular bisecting plane? Theorem 8-5

3. (a) How many lines are perpendicular to a line at a given point of the line? Infinitely many

   (b) How many planes are perpendicular to a line at a given point of the line? One

4. Given that $\overrightarrow{AP}$ is perpendicular to each of $\overrightarrow{AK}$, $\overrightarrow{AM}$, $\overrightarrow{AS}$, $\overrightarrow{AR}$, $\overrightarrow{AT}$. How many planes are determined by intersecting rays? Are there more than three points of the figure that are coplanar? If so, why? (Assume that no three of given points are collinear.) Six; yes; Theorem 8-4. PAT, PAR, PAS, PAM, PAK, TARSMK

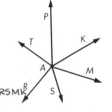

perpendicular bisecting *line* (Theorem 6–2) and Corollary 6–2.1 and should appeal to good students:
   *Alternative proof of* (1). Let C be the midpoint of $\overline{AB}$. If $P = C$, then certainly $PA = PB$. If $P \ne C$, then $\overleftrightarrow{CP}$ is the perpendicular bisector of $\overline{AB}$, in the plane containing A, B, and P, and therefore $PA = PB$ by Theorem 6–2.
   *Alternative proof of* (2). If $P = C$, then certainly P is in E. If $P \ne C$, then $\overleftrightarrow{CP}$ is the perpendicular bisector of $\overline{AB}$, in the plane containing A, B, and P. Since E contains $\overleftrightarrow{CP}$ by Theorem 8–4, P lies in E.

**Quiz**

If A, B, C, D and E are not all coplanar and $AC = CB$, $AD = DB$, $AE = EB$, what conclusion can be drawn?
   (ans: C, D and E lie on the perpendicular bisecting plane of $\overline{AB}$ by Theorem 8–6.)

**5.** $\overleftrightarrow{AB}$ is not perpendicular to $\overleftrightarrow{BC}$. By Theorem 8–4, all the perpendiculars to $\overleftrightarrow{AB}$ at $B$ lie in plane $E$. But $\overleftrightarrow{BC}$ lies in plane $F$, and not in plane $E$. Hence $\overleftrightarrow{BC}$ is not perpendicular to $\overleftrightarrow{AB}$.

**10.** See the figure in the text. $E$ is the perpendicular bisecting plane of $\overline{AB}$, and $C$ is the midpoint of $\overline{AB}$.
Part I. If $P$ is in $E$, then $PA = PB$.
Proof: Since $\overline{AB} \perp E$ and $P$ is in $E$, $\overline{AB} \perp \overline{PC}$. Hence $\overline{PC} \perp \overline{AB}$ and $\overline{PC}$ bisects $\overline{AB}$, that is, $\overleftrightarrow{PC}$ is the perpendicular bisector (in plane $PAB$) of $\overline{AB}$. But by Theorem 6–2, any point on the perpendicular bisector of a line segment is equidistant from the end points of the line segment. Hence $PA = PB$.
Part II. If $PA = PB$, then $P$ is in plane $E$. Proof: By Theorem 6–2, any point $P$ which is equidistant from the end points of a line segment lies on the perpendicular bisecting line (in plane $PAB$) of $\overline{AB}$. Therefore $\overleftrightarrow{CP} \perp \overline{AB}$ at $C$. But by hypothesis, $E \perp \overline{AB}$ at $C$. And by Theorem 8–4, if a line $(\overleftrightarrow{CP})$ and a plane $(E)$ are each perpendicular to a given line $(\overleftrightarrow{AB})$, at the same point $(C)$, then the line $(\overleftrightarrow{CP})$ lies in the plane $(E)$.

**11.** Through a given point of a given line there is exactly one plane perpendicular to the given line.

**12.** Let $E$ be the perpendicular bisecting plane of $\overline{AB}$. Point $P$ is in $E$ if and only if $PA = PB$.

**13.** Theorem 8–5 depends on Theorem 8–4, but not on Theorem 8–3. Theorem 8–4 does not depend on Theorem 8–3. Therefore, the order could have been Theorem 8–4, Theorem 8–5, Theorem 8–3.

**14.** Let $E$ and $F$ be planes perpendicular to a line $L$ at points $A$ and $B$ respectively. If $E$ and $F$ contained a common point $P$, then $\overline{AP}$ and $\overline{BP}$ would be distinct perpendiculars from $P$ to the line $L$, contradicting Theorem 6–4.

**15.** By Theorem 8–3 there exists a plane $F$ perpendicular to $L$ at $M$. Plane $F$ intersects plane $E$ in a line $L'$. Since $L \perp F$ at $M$ and $L'$ lies in $F$ and passes through $M$, $L \perp L'$. If $F = E$, then there are infinitely many lines $L'$ perpendicular to $L$ at $M$.

**16.** The "only if" statement is true but the "if" statement is false (see Solution Section).

---

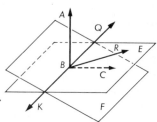

**5.** The planes $E$ and $F$ intersect in $\overleftrightarrow{KQ}$. $\overleftrightarrow{AB} \perp E$, with $B$ on $\overleftrightarrow{KQ}$. $R$ is in $E$ and $C$ is in $F$.

Is $\overleftrightarrow{AB} \perp \overleftrightarrow{BR}$? Why? **Yes, because $\overleftrightarrow{AB} \perp E$**
Is $\overleftrightarrow{AB} \perp \overleftrightarrow{KQ}$? Why? **Yes, because $\overleftrightarrow{AB} \perp E$**
Is $\overleftrightarrow{AB} \perp \overleftrightarrow{BC}$? Why? **No**

**6.** In the figure, $\overline{GH} \perp E$ at $M$, $MG = MH$, and $\overline{PQ} \perp \overline{GH}$ at $M$. Does $E$ contain $\overline{PQ}$? Why? With respect to $\overleftrightarrow{GH}$, what term applies to plane $E$?
**Plane $E$ contains $\overline{PQ}$ by Theorem 8–4.**
**$E$ is the perpendicular bisecting plane of $\overline{GH}$.**

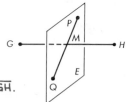

**7.** Two segments $\overline{AB}$ and $\overline{CD}$ are perpendicular and bisect each other at $K$. A plane $Z$ contains $\overline{AB}$, but does not contain $\overline{CD}$. Is $Z$ the perpendicular bisecting plane of $\overline{CD}$? Draw a figure to illustrate your conclusion.
**$Z$ is not necessarily the perpendicular bisecting plane of $\overline{CD}$.**

**8.** $E$ is the perpendicular bisecting plane of $\overline{PQ}$, as shown in the figure.

(a) $PR = $ ___**RQ**___.
$\quad TQ = $ ___**PT**___.
$\quad PS = $ ___**SQ**___.
$\quad \angle PTM \cong $ __**$\angle QTM$**__.
$\quad \triangle PTM \cong $ __**$\triangle QTM$**__.

(b) Does $MR = MS = MT$? Explain.
**If, and only if, $PR = PS = PT$.**

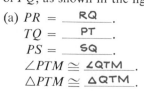

**9.** Given the figure with not all points coplanar. If $AW = BW$, $AX = BX$, $AY = BY$, and $AZ = BZ$, prove that $W$, $X$, $Y$, and $Z$ are coplanar. **Points $W, X, Y,$ and $Z$ all lie on the perpendicular bisecting plane of $\overline{AB}$ by Theorem 8–6.**

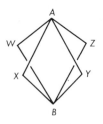

---

**10.** Prove Theorem 8–6, the Perpendicular Bisecting Plane Theorem.

**11.** Write Theorems 8–3 and 8–5 as one theorem, using *exactly one*.

**12.** Write Theorem 8–6, using *if and only if*.

**13.** Could Theorem 8–5 have been proved before Theorem 8–3? Explain. **Yes**

**14.** Prove: If two planes are perpendicular to the same line at different points of the line, the planes do not intersect.

**15.** Prove the following theorem.

> If $L$ is a line intersecting the plane $E$ at the point $M$, there is at least one line $L'$ in $E$ such that $L' \perp L$.

**16.** Is the following statement true? Prove your answer.

> Four points, each equidistant from two fixed points, are coplanar with the two fixed points if and only if the four points are collinear.

**17.** In the figure, $E$ is the perpendicular bisecting plane of $\overline{AB}$ at $C$. $H$ is on the same side of $E$ as $B$, and $K$ is on the same side of $E$ as $A$, such that $K\text{-}C\text{-}H$, $\overline{HB} \perp \overline{AB}$, and $\overline{KA} \perp \overline{AB}$. Prove that

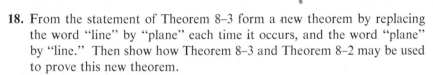

(a) $\overline{AK}$ and $\overline{BH}$ are coplanar, and

(b) $AH = BK$.

**18.** From the statement of Theorem 8–3 form a new theorem by replacing the word "line" by "plane" each time it occurs, and the word "plane" by "line." Then show how Theorem 8–3 and Theorem 8–2 may be used to prove this new theorem.

**19.** Prove that the line obtained in Problem 18 is unique.

## 8–4 PERPENDICULAR LINES AND PLANES: A SUMMARY

The following theorems are a summary of some of the basic facts about perpendicular lines and planes. Some of the proofs are easy, but some are rather long, and we shall not stop to do all of them here. We shall, however, give you a sample of the kind of reasoning that is involved, by giving lengthy hints for the proof of the following theorem.

### Theorem 8–7

> *Two lines perpendicular to the same plane are coplanar.*

To get an idea of how the proof ought to go, let us first consider what the situation is *if* the theorem is true; that is, supposing that the two lines really do lie in a plane, *which* plane do they lie in?

## Proof of Theorem 8–8

**Part I.** Through a given point on a given line there is at least one plane perpendicular to the line. This is Theorem 8–3, which is proved in the text.

**Part II.** Through a given point on a given line there is at most one plane perpendicular to the line. This is Theorem 8–5, which is proved in the text.

**Part III.** Through a given point not on a given line, there is at least one plane perpendicular to the given line.

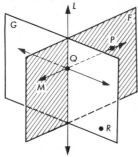

*Given:* Line $L$ and point $P$ not on $L$.

*Prove:* There is a plane $E$ through $P$ with $E$ perpendicular to $L$.

*Proof.* (1) There exists a line $M$ through $P$ perpendicular to $L$. Let $Q$ be the point at which $M$ intersects $L$, and let $F$ be the plane determined by $P$ and $L$.

(2) There exists a point $R$ not in $F$. Let $G$ be the plane determined by $L$ and $R$. In $G$ there exists a line $N$ perpendicular to $L$ at $Q$.

(3) By Postulate 8 there exists a plane $E$ containing $M$ and $N$. Then $E \perp L$ by the Basic Theorem on Perpendiculars.

*Part IV.* Through a given point not on a given line there is at most one plane perpendicular to the given line.

*Proof.* Suppose that there are two planes $E_1$ and $E_2$, each perpendicular to the line $L$ and each containing the point $P$. If $E_1$ and $E_2$ intersect $L$ in the same point $Q$, we have two planes perpendicular to $L$ at $Q$, and this contradicts Theorem 8–8, Part

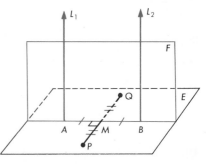

We have given that $L_1 \perp E$ at $A$ and $L_2 \perp E$ at $B$; and we are *supposing* that $L_1$ and $L_2$ lie in a plane $F$. In the figure, we show the midpoint $M$ of $\overline{AB}$, and we also show a segment $\overline{PQ}$ in $E$, such that $\overline{AB}$ and $\overline{PQ}$ bisect each other at right angles.

It surely looks as if $\overline{PQ} \perp F$ at $M$. If this is true, then $F$ is the *perpendicular bisecting plane of* $\overline{PQ}$.

So far, of course, we haven't proved anything, because we have been assuming that the theorem is true. But we now have a clue to the way the proof ought to go: first we should set up $\overline{PQ}$ in $E$, such that $\overline{PQ}$ and $\overline{AB}$ bisect each other at right angles; and then we should show that $L_1$ *and* $L_2$ *lie in the perpendicular bisecting plane of* $\overline{PQ}$.

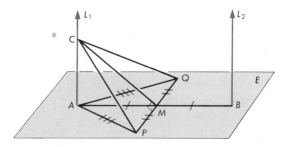

This idea works. The main steps in the proof are as follows:

(1)   $AP = AQ$ (as indicated in the figure).
(2)   $\triangle CAP \cong \triangle CAQ$.
(3)   $CP = CQ$.
(4)   $C$ lies in the perpendicular bisecting plane of $\overline{PQ}$. Let this plane be $F$.
(5)   $L_1$ lies in $F$.

In exactly the same way, we conclude that

(6)   $L_2$ lies in $F$.

Therefore the plane we were looking for is indeed the perpendicular bisecting plane of $\overline{PQ}$; this plane contains both $L_1$ and $L_2$; and therefore $L_1$ and $L_2$ are coplanar.

You may find that the discussion that led up to this proof will be worth more to you than the proof. A proof, once you get it, is logical, but the process by which you manage to think of it is very seldom logical. You have to find your way as best you can. And one of the best methods of doing this is the "method of wishful thinking" which we illustrated at the beginning of this section.

The theorems of this chapter, so far, give incomplete information about perpendicular lines and planes. The following theorems fill in the gaps.

### Theorem 8–8

*Through a given point there passes one and only one* **plane** *perpendicular to a given* **line.**

### Theorem 8–9

*Through a given point there passes one and only one* **line** *perpendicular to a given* **plane.**

These theorems convey quite a lot of information in very few words. Each of them has two cases, depending on whether the given point is on or off the given line or plane. In each of these four cases, the theorems tell us that we have both existence and uniqueness. This means that we need a total of eight proofs. Two of these have already been given in Theorems 8–3 and 8–5.

Theorem 8–9 assures us of the existence of a unique perpendicular to a given plane from an external point and allows us to prove the following theorem.

### Theorem 8–10.   The Second Minimum Theorem

*The shortest segment to a plane from an external point is the perpendicular segment.*

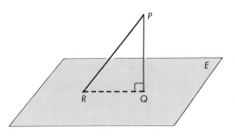

The proof is very similar to that of Theorem 7–7, the First Minimum Theorem. Given the perpendicular segment $\overline{PQ}$, and any other segment $\overline{PR}$ from $P$ to $E$, we start the proof by passing a plane through the lines $\overleftrightarrow{PR}$ and $\overleftrightarrow{PQ}$. The rest of the proof is left to you.

We are now justified in giving the following definition, analogous to the one following Theorem 7–7.

### Definition

The *distance* to a plane from an external point is the length of the perpendicular segment from the point to the plane.

II.   On the other hand, if $E_1$ and $E_2$ intersect $L$ in distinct points $A$ and $B$, then $\overleftrightarrow{PA}$ and $\overleftrightarrow{PB}$ are distinct lines through $P$ perpendicular to $L$, contradicting Theorem 6–3.

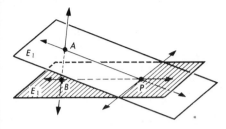

### Proof of Theorem 8–9

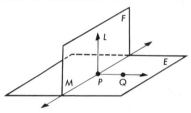

*Part I.* Through a given point in a given plane there is at least one line perpendicular to the plane.

*Proof.* Let $P$ be a point in the plane $E$. By Postulate 5(a) there is another point $Q$ in $E$. Introduce the plane $F$ perpendicular to $\overleftrightarrow{PQ}$ at $P$ (Theorem 8–8, Part I).

Since $F$ intersects $E$, their intersection is a line $M$, by Postulate 8. Introduce the line $L$ in $F$, perpendicular to $M$.

Since $F \perp \overleftrightarrow{PQ}$, and $L$ lies in $F$ and contains $P$, we have, from the definition of a line perpendicular to a plane, that $L \perp \overleftrightarrow{PQ}$. Also, from above, $L \perp M$. Hence $L \perp E$, by Theorem 8–3.

*Part II.* Through a given point in a given plane there is at most one line perpendicular to the given plane.

*Proof.* Suppose $L_1$ and $L_2$ are distinct lines, each perpendicular to the plane $E$ at the point $P$. $L_1$ and $L_2$ determine a plane $F$ (Theorem 3–4) which intersects $E$ in a line $L$. In $F$, we then have two perpendiculars to $L$ at the same point $P$, contradicting Theorem 6–1.

*Part III.* Through a given point not in a given plane there is at least one line perpendicular to the given plane.

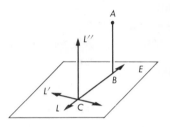

*Proof.* Let $P$ be a point not in the plane $E$. Let $A$ be any point of $E$, and $M$ a line through $A$ perpendicular to $E$ (Theorem 8–9, Part I).

If $M$ contains $P$, it is the desired perpendicular.

If $M$ does not contain $P$, let $F$ be the plane containing $M$ and $P$, and $N$ the line of intersection of $F$ and $E$. In $F$, let $B$ be the foot of a perpendicular from $P$ to $N$.

Let the line $L$ be perpendicular to $E$ at $B$ (Theorem 8–9, Part I). By Theorem 8–7, $L$ and $M$ are coplanar, and hence $L$ lies in $F$, since $M$ and $B$ determine $F$.

In $F$, $L \perp N$, since $L \perp E$ and $N$ lies in $E$. Since by Theorem 6–1 there is only one line in $F$ perpendicular to $N$ at $B$, $L$ and $\overleftrightarrow{BP}$ must coincide. That is, $L$ contains $P$ and so is the desired perpendicular.

*Part IV.* Through a given point not in a given plane there is at most one line perpendicular to the given plane.

The proof is word for word the same as that of Theorem 8–9, Part II, except for the replacement of "at the point $P$" by "from the point $P$" and of "Theorem 6–1" by "Theorem 6–4."

**Answers to Problems**

**1.** In the plane $F$ containing $\overleftrightarrow{PR}$ and $\overrightarrow{PQ}$, the perpendicular segment $\overline{PQ}$ is the shortest segment to the line $L$ containing $R$ and $K$ by the first minimum theorem.

**3.** Since $\overline{PQ}$ is the perpendicular bisector of $\overline{AB}$, $BP = BQ$. $\triangle DBP \cong \triangle DBQ$ as in Problem 2, so $DP = DQ$. Therefore $D$ lies in the perpendicular bisecting plane of $\overline{PQ}$ by Theorem 8–6.

256

**Problem Set 8–4**

**1.** Complete the proof of Theorem 8–10.

**2.** In the proof of Theorem 8–7, explain in detail why $\triangle CAP \cong \triangle CAQ$.
Since $\overline{CA} \perp \overleftrightarrow{AP}$, $\angle CAP \cong \angle CAQ$ and $CA = CA$, $AP = AQ$ so $\triangle CAP \cong \triangle CAQ$ (SAS)

**3.** Draw (or trace) the figure on page 254 for Theorem 8–7, but include only the plane $E$, the lines $L_1$ and $L_2$, $\overrightarrow{AB}$, and $\overline{PQ}$. Next pick any point $D$, except $B$, on $L_2$, and explain, step by step, why $D$ lies in the perpendicular bisecting plane of $\overline{PQ}$.

**4.** From a point $A$ not in a plane $E$, the shortest segment to plane $E$ is drawn, intersecting $E$ at $B$. $L$ and $L'$ are lines in $E$ such that $L$ contains $B$ and $L' \perp L$. If $L''$ is drawn so that $L'' \perp L$ and $L'' \perp L'$, show that $L''$ and $\overleftrightarrow{AB}$ are coplanar.

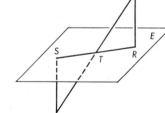

**5.** Prove the following special case of Theorem 8–9.

Through a point not in a given plane, there is at most one line perpendicular to the plane. See Part II of proof in margin.

**6.** Prove: If two lines are perpendicular to the same plane at different points of the plane, the lines do not intersect. If the lines intersected at P, there would be two distinct perpendicular segments from P to the plane, contradicting Theorem 8–9.

**7.** Given a plane $E$ and a point $P$ not in $E$. Citing appropriate theorems, explain in detail how to construct the shortest segment from $P$ to $E$. [*Hint:* Let $L$ be any line in $E$.]

**8.** $P$ and $Q$ are on opposite sides of the plane $E$ and are equidistant from $E$. The perpendiculars from $P$ and $Q$ to $E$ intersect $E$ at $R$ and $S$, respectively. Prove that

(a) $\overline{PQ}$ intersects $\overline{SR}$ at a point $T$, and

(b) $T$ is the midpoint of $\overline{SR}$.

**9.** Given: Plane $E$ contains $\triangle ABC$. Line $L \perp E$ at $T$. $T$ is equidistant from $A$, $B$, and $C$. $X$ is any point on $L$.
Prove: $X$ is equidistant from $A$, $B$, and $C$. Since $\triangle XTA \cong \triangle XTB \cong \triangle XTC$ (SAS), $XA = XB = XC$

## CHAPTER REVIEW

1. Use a figure, if necessary, to help you decide whether each statement is true or false.

   (a) If two planes intersect, their intersection is a line.  T

   (b) Three lines may intersect in a common point such that each line is perpendicular to the other two.  T

   (c) If a line is perpendicular to each of two coplanar lines, it is perpendicular to the plane containing the two lines.  F

   (d) The intersection of two planes may be a segment.  F

   (e) At a point in a plane there is exactly one line perpendicular to the plane.  T

   (f) For any four points, there is a plane containing them.  F

   (g) If a line intersects a plane in only one point, there are at least two lines in the plane which are perpendicular to the line.  F

   (h) Only one line can be drawn through a given point perpendicular to a given line.  F

   (i) If three lines intersect in pairs but no point belongs to all three lines, then the three lines are coplanar.  T

   (j) Three planes can separate space into eight regions.  T

2. Complete: The set of all points equidistant from the end points of a segment is the ___perp. bisecting plane___ of the segment.

3. Complete: The distance to a plane from a point not in the plane is _the length of the perpendicular segment from the point to the plane._

4. Complete: If a line is perpendicular to each of two _intersecting_ lines at _their point of intersection_, then it is perpendicular to the _plane_ that contains them.

5. In the figure, $\triangle ABC$ is an equilateral triangle in the plane $E$, and $\overline{CD}$ bisects $\angle BCA$. If $\overline{HD}$ is perpendicular to $\overline{CD}$, at least one segment of the figure is perpendicular to one of the planes. Which segment? Which plane?  $\overline{CD} \perp ABH$

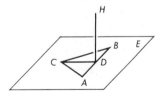

6. The plane $E$ contains points $A$ and $K$; $\overline{JA} \perp E$, $\overline{CK} \perp E$, but $A \neq K$. How many planes are determined by $A$, $K$, $C$, and $J$? Explain.  One, Theorem 8-7

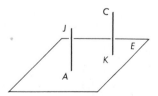

4. Since $\overline{AB}$ is the shortest segment from $A$ to plane $E$, $\overline{AB}$ is perpendicular to $E$ (Theorem 8-10). Since $L'' \perp L$ and $L'' \perp L'$ at the point of intersection of $L$ and $L'$, $L'' \perp E$ (Theorem 8-2). Since $\overline{AB} \perp E$ and $L'' \perp E$, $\overline{AB}$ and $L''$ are coplanar by Theorem 8-7.

7. Let $L_1$ be any line in the plane $E$ and construct the perpendicular segment $\overline{PQ}$ from $P$ to $L_1$ by Theorems 6-3 and 6-4. Construct the line $L_2$ in $E$ perpendicular to $L_1$ at $Q$, and construct the perpendicular segment $\overline{PM}$ by Theorem 8-10 from $P$ to $L_2$. Then $\overline{PM}$ will be the shortest segment from $P$ to $E$.

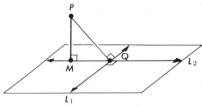

8. (a) 1. Since $\overline{PR} \perp E$ and $\overline{QS} \perp E$, $\overline{PR}$ and $\overline{QS}$ are coplanar. (Theorem 8-7). Let the plane containing points $P$, $Q$, $R$, and $S$ be described by $F$.

   2. Planes $E$ and $F$ intersect in $\overleftrightarrow{SR}$, and since $P$ and $Q$ are on opposite sides of plane $E$, they are on opposite sides of $\overleftrightarrow{SR}$.

   3. Since $P$ and $Q$ are on opposite sides of $\overleftrightarrow{SR}$ in $F$, we can conclude by the Plane Separation Postulate that $\overline{PQ}$ intersects $\overleftrightarrow{SR}$ at a point $T$ between $P$ and $Q$.

   4. Since $\overline{PQ}$ and line $\overleftrightarrow{SR}$ intersect at a point $T$ between $P$ and $Q$, and since the perpendiculars from $P$ and $Q$ to $\overleftrightarrow{SR}$ meet $\overleftrightarrow{SR}$ at points $R$ and $S$, we can conclude from Problem 17, Chapter Review for Chapter 7, that $S$-$T$-$R$.

   5. Since $\overline{PQ}$ intersects $\overleftrightarrow{SR}$ at a point $T$ such that $S$-$T$-$R$, $\overline{PQ}$ intersects $\overline{SR}$.

   (b) $\triangle PRT \cong \triangle QST$ by SAA, and therefore $ST = TR$.

**1.** Given seven points $A, B, C, D, E, F, G$ in space. If $AC = AF$, $BC = BF$, $BD = AB$, $CE = EF$, $AD = FG$ and $GF = CG$, which four points must be coplanar?

(ans: $A, B, E$ and $G$)

**2.** From $A$ not on $E$, the shortest segment is drawn to $E$ intersecting $E$ at $B$. $C$ and $D$ are any other points in plane $E$ such that $B$ lies on the perpendicular bisector of $\overline{CD}$. Prove that $\angle CAB \cong \angle DAB$.

(ans: Since $\overline{AB}$ is the shortest segment to $E$ from $A$, then $\overline{AB} \perp E$ by Theorem 8-10. $BC = BD$ by Theorem 6-2. Since $\angle ABD \cong \angle ABC$ because they are right angles and $AB = AB$, $\triangle ABC \cong \angle ABD$ by SAS and $\angle ABD \cong \angle ABC$ by CPCTC.)

### Answers to Chapter Review Problems

**10.** Since $\overline{KM} \perp E$, $\overline{KM} \perp \overline{MH}$ and $\overline{KM} \perp \overline{MT}$. Hence $\triangle KMH \cong \triangle KMT$. (SAS), and $KH = KT$. Therefore $\triangle KHT$ is isosceles, and $\angle KHT \cong \angle KTH$ by the Isosceles Triangle Theorem.

**11.** Since $\overleftrightarrow{BC} \perp G$, then $\overleftrightarrow{BC} \perp \overleftrightarrow{AB}$; and since $\overleftrightarrow{BD} \perp F$, $\overleftrightarrow{BD} \perp \overleftrightarrow{AB}$ by definition. Therefore $\overleftrightarrow{AB} \perp E$ by Theorem 8-2.

**12.** Since $\overline{PR} \perp E$, $\overline{PR} \perp \overline{RQ}$, and $\overline{PR} \perp \overline{RS}$, $PR = PR$ and $\angle PQR \cong \angle PSR$ (Given). Therefore $\triangle PQR \cong \triangle PSR$ (SAA) and therefore $PS = PQ$. Finally, the base angles of isosceles triangle $\triangle SPQ$ are congruent, that is, $\angle PSQ \cong \angle PQS$.

**13.** (1) Since $\overline{PR} \perp E$, $PQ > PR$ (Theorem 8-10). (2) $PR > RS$, by hypothesis. (3) Since $\overline{SQ} \perp \overline{RQ}$ and $\overline{SQ} \perp \overline{PQ}$, $\overline{SQ} \perp PQR$ (Theorem 8-2). Therefore $RS > QS$ (Theorem 8-10). (4) Since $PQ > PR$, $PR > RS$, and $RS > QS$, then $PQ > QS$.

---

**7.** If the goal posts at one end of a football field are perpendicular to the ground, then they are coplanar even without a brace between them. Which theorem supports this conclusion? If they are not perpendicular to the ground, can they still be coplanar? Will putting a brace between them guarantee that they will always be coplanar? Theorem 8-7, Yes, No

**8.** $\overrightarrow{AP}$ is perpendicular to the vertical plane $E$, and $A, B, C, D, G,$ and $H$ are points in $E$. What is

$$m\angle DAP + m\angle CAP? = 180$$

If $\angle CAB$ is a right angle, then at least one ray other than $\overrightarrow{AP}$, and one plane other than $E$, are perpendicular. Name all such pairs. $\overrightarrow{AB} \perp PAC$ and $\overrightarrow{AC} \perp PAB$

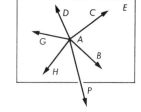

**9.** $\triangle ABC$ is in the plane $E$. $P$ is a point not in $E$ such that $\overline{PA} \perp \overline{AB}$, $\overline{PA} \perp \overline{AC}$, and $\overline{PD} \perp \overline{BC}$ with $D$ on $\overline{BC}$. Which is true: $PA > PD$, $PA = PD$, or ($PA < PD$?) Why? Since $\overline{PA} \perp AB, \overline{PA} \perp AC, \overline{PA} \perp E$ (Th. 8-2). By Th. 8-10, $PA < PD$.

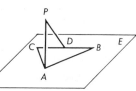

**10.** $\triangle HMT$ is in the plane $E$. $HM = TM$ and $\overline{KM} \perp E$. Which is true:

$$\angle KHT > \angle KTH$$
$$\boxed{\angle KHT \cong \angle KTH}$$
or
$$\angle KHT < \angle KTH?$$

Why?

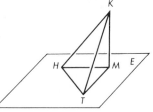

---

**11.** Given: $\overleftrightarrow{BC}$ and $\overleftrightarrow{BD}$ lie in the plane $E$; plane $F \perp \overleftrightarrow{BD}$ at $B$; plane $G \perp \overleftrightarrow{BC}$ at $B$; $G$ and $F$ intersect in $\overleftrightarrow{AB}$.

Prove: $\overleftrightarrow{AB} \perp E$.

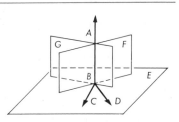

**12.** In the figure, $\triangle RSQ$ is in the plane $E$ and $\overline{PR} \perp E$. If $\angle PQR \cong \angle PSR$, then $\angle PQS \cong \angle PSQ$.

**13.** In the figure, if $\overline{PR} \perp E$, $PR > RS$, $\overline{SQ} \perp \overline{RQ}$, and $\overline{SQ} \perp \overline{PQ}$, prove that $PQ > QS$.

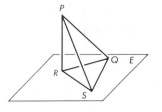

**14.** Prove that if $A$ and $B$ are each equidistant from $P$ and $Q$, then each point of $\overleftrightarrow{AB}$ is equidistant from $P$ and $Q$.

**15.** In the figure, the planes $E$ and $F$ intersect in $\overleftrightarrow{AB}$. $\overleftrightarrow{RQ}$ is in $F$ and $\overleftrightarrow{WX}$ is in $E$. $\overleftrightarrow{RQ} \perp \overleftrightarrow{AB}$ and $\overleftrightarrow{WX} \perp F$. Prove that $\overleftrightarrow{RQ} \perp E$.

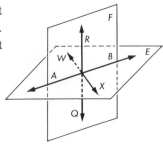

**16.** Given the cube shown here, with $BK = BM$. Prove that $H$ is equidistant from $K$ and $M$. You may use the following properties of a cube in your proof. (a) Each face of a cube lies in a plane. (b) The twelve edges of a cube are congruent. (c) Any two intersecting edges are perpendicular.

**17.** Given the cube shown in the figure for Problem 16, let $BK = BM$ and let $P$ be the midpoint of $\overline{KM}$. Prove that the plane $HDP$ is the perpendicular bisecting plane of $\overline{KM}$.

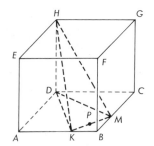

**18.** Prove that it is impossible for each of four rays $\overrightarrow{AB}$, $\overrightarrow{AC}$, $\overrightarrow{AD}$, and $\overrightarrow{AE}$ to be perpendicular to the other three.

## HONORS PROBLEM

Given: $\overline{AP} \perp \overline{PQ}$, $\overline{AP} \perp \overline{PC}$,
$\quad\quad\ \ \overline{PQ} \perp \overleftrightarrow{BC}$, $Q\text{-}B\text{-}C$.

Prove: $\overline{AQ} \perp \overleftrightarrow{BC}$.

[*Hint:* Take $R$ on $\overleftrightarrow{BC}$ so that $QR = QB$.]

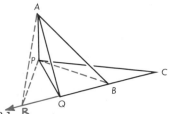

## Parallel Lines in a Plane

Chapter 9 contains important material; it is really two chapters in one: the first part deals with parallel lines, and the second part deals with quadrilaterals. Students enjoy this material; you should plan to spend an adequate period of time on it.

### Planning the Chapter

Again because the chapter is long and important a brief chart is shown below to facilitate teacher planning.

| Section | Average Class | Above-average Class |
|---|---|---|
| 9–1 | 1 | ⎫ 1 |
| 9–2 | 1 | ⎭ |
| 9–3 | 2 | 2 |
| 9–4 | 3 | 2 |
| 9–5 | 3 | 2 |
| 9–6 | 2 | 2 |
| 9–7 | 2 | 2 |
| 9–8 | 1 | 1 |
| 9–9/Review | 1 | 1 |
| Test | 1 | 1 |

The midyear examination is appropriate at this point for the average class. The above-average class will probably be able to finish Chapter 10 before taking the exam.

### 9–1 CONDITIONS WHICH GUARANTEE PARALLELISM

### Background Material

In Section 9–1 and 9–2 we state our definitions and establish four important conditions which guarantee parallelism.

By way of introduction, you may ask the students to tell what they mean by parallel lines. One very common answer is that parallel lines are lines that are everywhere

**CHAPTER**

# 9

# Parallel Lines in a Plane

## Objectives...

- Learn the definition of parallel lines and the facts about parallels that *are not* dependent on the Parallel Postulate.
- Learn the Parallel Postulate and the facts about parallels that *are* dependent on the Parallel Postulate.
- Learn the facts about special quadrilaterals.
- Learn some facts about 30–60–90 triangles and about medians of triangles.

## 9-1 CONDITIONS WHICH GUARANTEE PARALLELISM

There are three ways in which two lines can be situated in space:

(1) They may fail to intersect and fail to be coplanar, like the lines $L_1$ and $L_3$, in the figure. In this case, they are called *skew lines*.

(2) They may intersect in a point, like the lines $L_1$ and $L_2$. In this case, Theorem 3–4 tells us that they are coplanar.

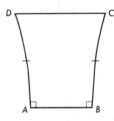

(3) They may be coplanar without intersecting each other, like the lines $L_2$ and $L_3$. In this case we say that the two lines are *parallel*.

### Definitions

Two lines are *skew lines* if they do not lie in the same plane. Two lines are *parallel* if (1) they are coplanar and (2) they do not intersect.

We shall write $L_1 \parallel L_2$ to mean that $L_1$ and $L_2$ are parallel. If two segments $\overline{AB}$ and $\overline{CD}$ lie on parallel lines, then we shall say for short that the segments are parallel, and we shall write $\overline{AB} \parallel \overline{CD}$.

We shall speak similarly of two rays, a ray and a segment, and so on.

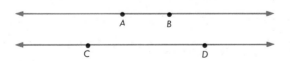

For example, if we are given that $\overleftrightarrow{AB} \parallel \overleftrightarrow{CD}$, we may also write $\overrightarrow{AB} \parallel \overrightarrow{CD}$, $\overline{AB} \parallel \overline{CD}, \overrightarrow{BA} \parallel \overleftrightarrow{CD}$, and so on, for twelve more similar cases.

**261**

equidistant. In Euclidean geometry, it is true that parallel lines are everywhere equidistant. But a much weaker property is adequate as a definition. We can then prove that parallel lines always have the stronger property. (Corollary 9–15.1, page 283.) This corollary depends essentially on the Parallel Postulate; in hyperbolic geometry no three points of any line are equidistant from any other line. This question should not be raised in class, because the answer is too long to be presented. It is based on the following theorem from page 319 of EGAS.

**Theorem.** In hyperbolic geometry, the upper base angles of a Saccheri quadrilateral are acute.

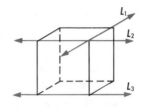

That is, if $\square ABCD$ has right angles at $A$ and $B$, and $AD = BC$, then $\angle C$ and $\angle D$ are acute.

This means that in hyperbolic geometry, the following configuration is impossible:

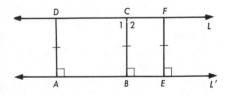

Here the points $D$, $C$, and $F$ of $L$ are supposed to be equidistant from $L'$. By the above theorem it would follow that $\angle 1$ and $\angle 2$ are both acute; and this is impossible, because they form a linear pair.

## Classroom Notes

The definition of parallel lines requires that the lines be coplanar, that is, that there exist *at least one* plane containing the two lines. Theorem 9–1 guarantees that there exists *at most one* plane containing the two lines. The definition and Theorem 9–1 may be combined in the useful statement, "Two parallel lines determine a plane." The proof of Theorem 9–1 is easy but somewhat sophisticated; if your students do not grasp it readily you should move on to Theorem 9–2.

The theorems in this chapter all deal with lines *in a plane,* and it is important to note how this restriction is imposed:

(1) The definition of parallel lines guarantees that parallel lines are coplanar.

(2) In Section 9–3, we talk about lines which are not by hypothesis parallel, and so it may seem that our lines may not be coplanar. For example, Theorem 9–9 states: "If two lines are cut by a transversal, and a pair of alternate interior angles are congruent, then the lines are parallel." Recall, however, that we have defined *transversal,* and, consequently, *alternate interior angles* and *corresponding angles* only for lines that are coplanar. Hence, when we talk about two lines cut by a transversal, we are implying that the lines are coplanar.

(3) Finally, in Section 9–5 *et seq.* we discuss quadrilaterals. The definition of quadrilateral requires that the four vertices, and consequently the quadrilateral itself, lie in a plane. There are such things as skew (that is, nonplanar) quadrilaterals, but they are not discussed in this chapter.

Theorem 9–2 gives us our first condition which guarantees parallelism. The proof of Theorem 9–2 is important for a reason beyond

The following theorem enables us to speak of *the* plane containing two parallel lines.

### Theorem 9–1

**Two parallel lines lie in exactly one plane.**

**Proof.** If $L_1$ and $L_2$ are parallel, then we know at once from the definition that they lie in a plane $E$. We need to show that they lie in only one plane.

Let $P$ be any point of $L_2$. By Theorem 3–3 there is only one plane containing $L_1$ and $P$. Therefore there is only one plane containing $L_1$ and $L_2$, because every plane that contains $L_2$ contains $P$.

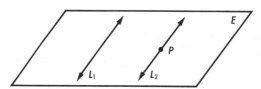

On the basis of the definition, it may not seem easy to tell whether two lines are parallel. Each of the lines stretches out infinitely far in two directions, and to tell whether they intersect, it may seem that we have to look at the entire line in both cases. In some cases, however, we can tell that two lines are parallel by looking at only a short segment of each, as the following theorems show.

### Theorem 9–2

**In a plane, if two lines are both perpendicular to the same line, then they are parallel.**

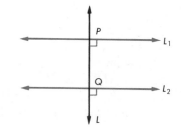

**Proof.** Given that $L_1 \perp L$ at $P$ and $L_2 \perp L$ at $Q$. It is given that $L_1$ and $L_2$ are coplanar. We need to show that they do not intersect.

Suppose that $L_1$ intersects $L_2$ at a point $R$. Then there are two perpendiculars from $R$ to $L$. By Theorem 6–4, this is impossible. Therefore $L_1 \parallel L_2$. [*Query:* What method of proof is being used here?] *Indirect*

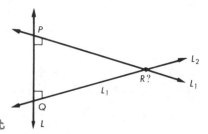

Theorem 9–2 enables us to show that parallels exist.

### Theorem 9–3.   Existence of Parallels

***Let L be a line and let P be a point not on L.   Then there is at least one line through P, parallel to L.***

**Proof.**   Let $L_1$ be the perpendicular from $P$ to $L$.  Let $L_2$ be the perpendicular to $L_1$ at $P$ (in the plane that contains $L$ and $P$.)   By Theorem 9–2, $L_2 \parallel L$.

It may seem natural to try to prove next that the parallel given by Theorem 9–3 is unique.   That is, we might try to prove the following.

*Through a given external point there is only one line parallel to a given line.*

It is a fact, however, that this statement cannot be proved as a theorem, on the basis of the postulates that we have so far.   It must be taken as a new postulate.   This postulate has a long and interesting history.   For well over two thousand years, the standard textbook of geometry was Euclid's *Elements*, written about 300 B.C.   In the *Elements*, Euclid used a postulate which says that parallels are unique.   Usually, mathematicians like to assume as little as they can get by with, and prove as much as they can manage to prove.   For this reason, many of them tried to turn Euclid's Parallel Postulate into a theorem.   All of them failed.   Finally, in the nineteenth century, it was discovered that the Parallel Postulate *cannot* be proved on the basis of the other postulates.

We shall return to this question later.   Meanwhile, let us investigate a little further the conditions under which we can say that two lines are parallel.

In the figure on the left, the line $T$ is a *transversal* of the coplanar lines $L_1$ and $L_2$.   In the figure on the right, $T$ is *not* a transversal.

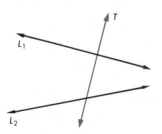 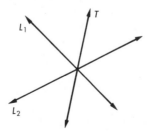

its obvious purpose; it is important because it helps to prepare the student for the proof of the basic theorem in this section, Theorem 9–5.

The concept of alternate interior angles is most readily taught by appealing to figures, and on page 264 of the text we have done just that.   You should note that the formal definition reconstructs the figures exactly.   This is a good example of a mathematical definition.   It often happens that a simple concept is hard to describe in words.

Theorem 9–4 is a theorem which simplifies the details involved in the proof of Theorem 9–5.

## Definition

A *transversal* of two coplanar lines is a line which intersects them in two different points.

In each of the following figures, $\angle 1$ and $\angle 2$ are *alternate interior angles*.

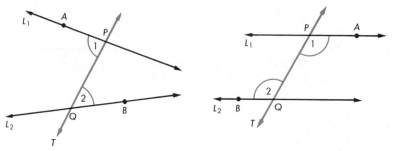

Note that the lines cut by the transversal may or may not be parallel. The labels in the figures suggest how we should describe alternate interior angles in a definition.

## Definition

Given two lines $L_1$ and $L_2$, cut by a transversal $T$ at points $P$ and $Q$. Let $A$ be a point of $L_1$ and let $B$ be a point of $L_2$, such that $A$ and $B$ lie on opposite sides of $T$. Then $\angle APQ$ and $\angle PQB$ are *alternate interior angles*.

### Theorem 9–4

*If two lines are cut by a transversal, and one pair of alternate interior angles are congruent, then the other pair of alternate interior angles are also congruent.*

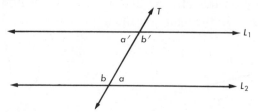

That is, if $\angle a \cong \angle a'$, then $\angle b \cong \angle b'$. And if $\angle b \cong \angle b'$, then $\angle a \cong \angle a'$. The proof is left to you.

The following theorem is a generalization of Theorem 9–2. That is, it includes Theorem 9–2 as a special case. Since it applies in more cases than Theorem 9–2, it is more useful.

**Theorem 9–5.**    The AIP Theorem

> *Given two lines cut by a transversal. If a pair of alternate interior angles are congruent, then the lines are parallel.*

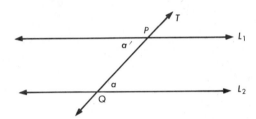

**Proof.**   Let $T$ be a transversal, intersecting $L_1$ and $L_2$ at $P$ and $Q$. We have given that a pair of alternate interior angles are congruent. By the preceding theorem, we have

(1)    *both* pairs of alternate interior angles are congruent.

Now suppose that $L_1$ intersects $L_2$ at a point $R$. We shall show that this leads to a contradiction of (1).

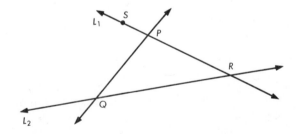

Let $S$ be a point of $L_1$, on the side of $T$ opposite to $R$. Then $\angle SPQ$ is an exterior angle of $\triangle PQR$, and $\angle PQR$ is one of its remote interior angles. By the Exterior Angle Theorem,

(2)    $\angle SPQ > \angle PQR.$

This contradicts (1), because these are alternate interior angles. Therefore $L_1$ does not intersect $L_2$, and $L_1 \parallel L_2$, which was to be proved.

The AIP Theorem gives us the second condition which guarantees parallelism. It is an important theorem because the first and third conditions which guarantee parallelism (Theorems 9–2 and 9–7) are direct corollaries of it. We have established Theorem 9–2 independently because it *can* be established independently, and because the proof of Theorem 9–2 serves as a preparation for the proof of Theorem 9–5. Note that the proof of Theorem 9–5 is an indirect proof and that we obtain our contradiction by use of the Exterior Angle Theorem. We recommend that you hold the students responsible for the proof of Theorem 9–5.

## Explanation for Problems

We have included a problem set immediately following the AIP Theorem so the student can obtain practice in proving that lines are parallel, by use of alternate interior angles, without having to decide first whether to use alternate interior angles or corresponding angles.

We suggest that you spread Problem Set 9–1 over two assignments: do some of the easy problems in conjunction with Theorem 9–5, and then take up some of the harder ones in conjunction with Section 9–2. Note that Problem Set 9–2 is very short.

The quadrilateral in Problem 11 is a Saccheri quadrilateral. A quadrilateral $\square ABCD$ is a Saccheri quadrilateral if $\angle A$ and $\angle B$ are right angles and $AD = BC$. (See the beginning of the commentary on Section 9–1.) It is impossible to prove, on the basis of the postulates we have so far and without the use of the Parallel Postulate, that the upper base angles, $\angle C$ and $\angle D$, are right angles, that is, to prove that a Saccheri quadrilateral is a rectangle. In fact, in hyperbolic geometry $\angle C$ and $\angle D$ are always acute, and *no* quadrilateral is a rectangle. Saccheri quadrilaterals are used to show, without the use of the Parallel Postulate, that in any triangle the sum of the measures of the angles is less than or equal to 180. See Chapter 10 of *EGAS*.

### Problem Set 9–1

1. Given the plane figure, name a pair of alternate interior angles for
   (a) $L_1$ and $L_2$. $\angle 4, \angle 6$ or $\angle 3, \angle 5$
   (b) $L_2$ and $L_3$. $\angle 7, \angle 9$ or $\angle 8, \angle 10$
   (c) $L_1$ and $L_3$. $\angle 4, \angle 10$ or $\angle 3, \angle 9$

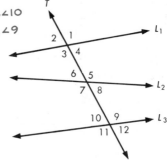

2. In this plane figure $L_2$, $L_4$, and $L_5$ intersect at a point. Name at least three pairs of alternate interior angles for $L_1$ and $L_3$.
   $(\angle d, \angle e), (\angle c, \angle f),$
   $(\angle b, \angle g), (\angle a, \angle h)$

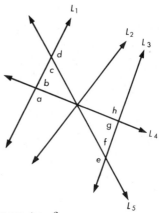

3. Which of the following statements are true?
   (a) If two lines do not lie in the same plane, they may be parallel. False, the lines must be skew.
   (b) The definition of parallel lines states that the lines must remain the same distance apart. False
   (c) If two lines are perpendicular to the same line at different points of the line, they are parallel. False, the lines may be skew.
   (d) If two lines in a plane are intersected by a transversal, the alternate interior angles are congruent. False

4. Construct a plane figure that satisfies the following description:

   $M$, $R$, $Q$, and $S$ are distinct and coplanar points. $R$ and $S$ are on opposite sides of $\overleftrightarrow{MQ}$ such that $\angle RMQ \cong \angle SQM$.

   What conclusion can you make concerning $\overleftrightarrow{RM}$ and $\overleftrightarrow{QS}$? They are parallel.

**5.** Is it possible to find two lines in space which are neither parallel nor intersecting? Yes, two skew lines

**6.** Given: $\overrightarrow{AD}$ bisects $\angle CAB$ and $CA = CD$.

Prove: $\overleftrightarrow{CD} \parallel \overleftrightarrow{AB}$.

Since CA=CD, ∠x ≅ ∠y.
Since AD bisects ∠CAB, ∠y ≅ ∠z.
Therefore, ∠x ≅ ∠z and CD ∥ AB by AIP.

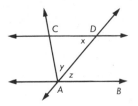

**7.** Would it follow that $L_1 \parallel L_2$ if

(a) $m\angle q = 100$ and    (b) $m\angle p = 80$ and
   $m\angle r = 100$? Yes        $m\angle r = 100$? Yes

(c) $m\angle s = 120$ and   (d) $m\angle r = 90$ and
   $m\angle p = 60$? Yes        $m\angle p = 90$? Yes

**8.** Given a line $L$ and a point $P$ not on $L$, show how a protractor and a ruler can be used to draw a line through $P$ parallel to $L$.

**9.** In this figure, which lines would be parallel if

(a) $m\angle a = 90$, $m\angle f = 68$,
   $m\angle c = 68$? L₃ and L₄

(b) $m\angle d = 90$, $m\angle b = 42$,
   $m\angle c = 48$? L₁ and L₂

(c) $m\angle f = 54$, $m\angle e = 46$,
   $m\angle b = 46$? L₁ and L₂

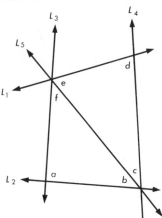

**10.** $\overline{AB}$ and $\overline{CD}$ bisect each other at $E$. Prove that

$$\overline{AD} \parallel \overline{CB}.$$

△AED ≅ △BEC by SAS and ∠A ≅ ∠B.
Therefore AD ∥ CB by AIP.

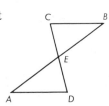

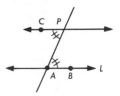

11. $\triangle ABD \cong \triangle BAC$ by SAS. Then $DB =$ CA. Therefore $\triangle DCB \cong \triangle CDA$ by SSS and $\angle BCD \cong \angle ADC$. (It is not possible to prove that $\angle BCD$ and $\angle ADC$ are right angles. Attempts to do so suggest the need for some further postulate.)

12. (1) Since $\overrightarrow{PK} \perp E$ and $\overrightarrow{RM} \perp E$, $\overrightarrow{PK}$ and $\overrightarrow{RM}$ are coplanar.
  (2) Since $\overrightarrow{PK} \perp E$, $\overrightarrow{PK} \perp \overrightarrow{PR}$ by definition. Similarly, $\overleftrightarrow{MR} \perp \overrightarrow{PR}$. But, by Theorem 9–2, if two lines in a plane are perpendicular to the same line, the lines are parallel. $\therefore \overleftrightarrow{PK} \parallel \overleftrightarrow{MR}$.

13. Since $A$ and $B$ are equidistant from $P$ and $Q$, $\overleftrightarrow{AB}$ is the perpendicular bisector of $\overline{PQ}$ (Corollary 6–2.1). Similarly, since $B$ and $C$ are equidistant from $X$ and $Y$, $\overleftrightarrow{BC}$ is the perpendicular bisector of $\overline{XY}$. By hypothesis, $A$, $B$, and $C$ are collinear; thus $\overline{PQ}$ and $\overline{XY}$ are each perpendicular to the same line, and so $\overline{PQ} \parallel \overline{XY}$ by Theorem 9–2.

14. (1) Since $\triangle DAH \cong \triangle CBH$ (SAS), $H$ is equidistant from $D$ and $C$. And since $G$ is also equidistant from $D$ and $C$, $\overleftrightarrow{GH} \perp \overline{DC}$ by Corollary 6–2.1.
  (2) Since $\triangle DAH \cong \triangle CBH$ (again, SAS), $m \angle AHD = m \angle BHC$. Since $\triangle DHG \cong \triangle CHG$ (SAS or SSS), $m \angle DHG = m \angle CHG$. Hence by the AAP, $m \angle AHG = m \angle BHG$, and thus $\overleftrightarrow{GH} \perp \overline{AB}$ by definition of perpendicular.
  (3) By Theorem 9–2 and (1) and (2) we have $\overline{AB} \parallel \overline{DC}$.

15. Proof: $\triangle APR \cong \triangle PBQ \cong \triangle RQC \cong \triangle QRP$ by SSS. By corresponding parts, $m \angle BPQ = m \angle A$, $m \angle APR = m \angle B$, and $m \angle RPQ = m \angle C$. Since the sum of the measures of $\angle BPQ$, $\angle APR$, and $\angle RPQ$ is 180 by Postulates 13 and 14, $m \angle A + m \angle B + m \angle C = 180$.

In this problem the hypothesis assumes the existence of a triangle in which the length of each segment joining the midpoints of two sides is one-half the length of the third side. This cannot be proved before assuming the Parallel Postulate. Moreover, if we assume that such a triangle exists, and if we can show that the sum of the measures of the angles is 180, then we can prove the Parallel Postulate.

---

11. Given the quadrilateral $\square ABCD$ with right angles $\angle A$ and $\angle B$ and $AD = BC$. Prove that $\angle D \cong \angle C$. [*Hint:* Draw $\overline{AC}$ and $\overline{BD}$.] Can you also prove that $\angle D$ and $\angle C$ are right angles? No

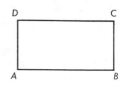

---

12. In the figure, $P$, $Q$, and $R$ are three noncollinear points in the plane $E$, $\overleftrightarrow{PK} \perp E$ and $\overleftrightarrow{RM} \perp E$. Prove that $\overleftrightarrow{PK} \parallel \overleftrightarrow{RM}$.

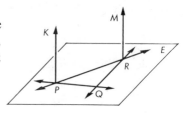

13. In the figure, $A$, $B$, and $C$ are collinear, $AP = AQ$, $BP = BQ$, $BX = BY$, and $CX = CY$. Prove that $\overline{PQ} \parallel \overline{XY}$.

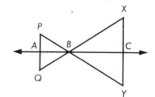

---

14. Given: $\square ABCD$ with $H$ the midpoint of $\overline{AB}$, $G$ the midpoint of $\overline{DC}$, $AD = BC$, and $\angle A \cong \angle B$.

Prove: $\overleftrightarrow{GH} \perp \overline{DC}$.
$\overleftrightarrow{GH} \perp \overline{AB}$.
$\overline{AB} \parallel \overline{DC}$.

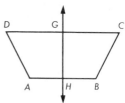

15. Given: $\triangle ABC$ in which
$$AP = PB = RQ,$$
$$BQ = QC = PR,$$
$$AR = RC = PQ.$$

Prove: $m \angle A + m \angle B + m \angle C = 180$.

Why does this *not* prove that the sum of the measures of the angles of any triangle is 180?

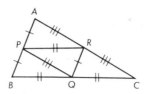

## HONORS PROBLEM

Suppose that the following two definitions are agreed upon.

A *vertical line* is a line containing the center of the earth.

A *horizontal line* is a line perpendicular to some vertical line.

(a) Could two horizontal lines be parallel? Yes

(b) Could two vertical lines be parallel? No

(c) Could two vertical lines be perpendicular? Yes

(d) Could two horizontal lines be perpendicular? Yes

(e) Would every vertical line be a horizontal line? Yes

(f) Would every horizontal line be a vertical line? No

(g) Could a horizontal line be parallel to a vertical line? Yes

(h) Would every line be horizontal? Yes

## 9–2  OTHER CONDITIONS THAT GUARANTEE PARALLELISM

Much of your work in Section 9–1 dealt with alternate interior angles for two lines cut by a transversal. All eight angles formed are important in the study of parallel lines, and so descriptive names are given to several pairs of these angles.

Alternate interior angles:   $\angle 3$ and $\angle 6$
$\angle 4$ and $\angle 5$

Corresponding angles:   $\angle 1$ and $\angle 5$
$\angle 2$ and $\angle 6$
$\angle 3$ and $\angle 7$
$\angle 4$ and $\angle 8$

Interior angles on the same side of the transversal:

$\angle 3$ and $\angle 5$
$\angle 4$ and $\angle 6$

### Definition

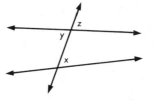

Given two lines cut by a transversal. If $\angle x$ and $\angle y$ are alternate interior angles, and $\angle y$ and $\angle z$ are vertical angles, then $\angle x$ and $\angle z$ are *corresponding angles.*

---

## 9–2 OTHER CONDITIONS THAT GUARANTEE PARALLELISM

### Background Material

In Section 9–2 we establish the third and fourth conditions which guarantee parallelism.

### Classroom Notes

Note that it is easy to define corresponding angles once we have defined alternate interior angles. It is possible to state a definition of corresponding angles which does not make use of the idea of alternate interior angles, but which does, like the preceding definition, make use of betweenness and separation concepts. Do not overlook the obvious meaning of the word "corresponding": two angles are *corresponding angles* if they occupy *corresponding positions* relative to the two lines and the transversal.

Theorem 9–6 is a theorem which enables us to obtain the third condition (Theorem 9–7) guaranteeing parallelism as a corollary to Theorem 9–5. The fact that Theorem 9–7 is a simple corollary to Theorem 9–5 does not mean that it is any less important or less useful than Theorem 9–5.

## Quiz

**1.** What value of x will make $L_1 \parallel L_2$?

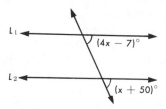

(ans: $x = 19$)

**2.** Given the figure below as marked, what conclusion can be drawn?

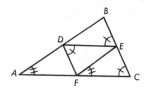

(ans: $\overline{AC} \parallel \overline{DE}$, $\overline{BC} \parallel \overline{DF}$ and $\overline{AB} \parallel \overline{EF}$)

## Definition

Given two lines cut by a transversal. If (1) $\angle x$ and $\angle y$ are alternate interior angles, (2) $\angle v$ and $\angle w$ are alternate interior angles, and (3) $\angle v$ and $\angle x$ form a linear pair, then $\angle x$ and $\angle w$ are *interior angles on the same side of the transversal.*

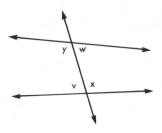

You should prove the following three theorems.

## Theorem 9–6

> *Given two lines cut by a transversal. If a pair of corresponding angles are congruent, then a pair of alternate interior angles are congruent.*

(Remember the Vertical Angle Theorem.)

## Theorem 9–7. The CAP Theorem

> *Given two lines cut by a transversal. If a pair of corresponding angles are congruent, then the lines are parallel.*

## Theorem 9–8

> *Given two lines cut by a transversal. If a pair of interior angles on the same side of the transversal are supplementary, the lines are parallel.*

It looks as if the converses of Theorems 9–5, 9–7, and 9–8 ought to be true. That is, if two parallel lines are cut by a transversal, then alternate interior angles ought to be congruent, corresponding angles ought to be congruent, and interior angles on the same side of the transversal ought to be supplementary. It is important to note, however, that the proof of these converses depends upon the uniqueness property stated in the Parallel Postulate. We shall state this postulate in the next section and use it to continue our discussion of parallels.

## Problem Set 9–2

1. Given the plane figure at the right. Name

   (a) three pairs of corresponding angles for lines $L_1$ and $L_2$ $(\angle1,\angle5),(\angle4,\angle8),$ $(\angle2,\angle6),(\angle3,\angle7)$

   (b) two pairs of corresponding angles for lines $L_1$ and $L_3$ $(\angle1,\angle9),(\angle2,\angle10),$ $(\angle4,\angle12),(\angle3,\angle11)$

   (c) two pairs of alternate interior angles for lines $L_2$ and $L_3$
   $(\angle8,\angle10)$ and $(\angle7,\angle9)$

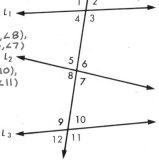

2. Prove Theorem 9–7.

3. In the figure, $AC = BC$ and $\angle DCE \cong \angle B$. Prove that $\overrightarrow{CE} \parallel \overrightarrow{AB}$.
   Since AC=BC, $\angle$A$\cong\angle$B (Theorem 5-4). Therefore $\angle$A$\cong\angle$DCE and $\overrightarrow{CE}\parallel\overrightarrow{AB}$ by Theorem 9-7.

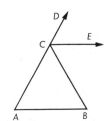

4. Given: $\triangle KMJ$ with $KJ = MJ$, $GJ = HJ$, and $\angle HGJ \cong \angle HMK$.
   Prove: $\overline{GH} \parallel \overline{KM}$.
   $\angle$HGJ$\cong\angle$GHJ and $\angle$HMK$\cong\angle$GKM (Theorem 5-4) By hypothesis $\angle$HMK$\cong\angle$HGJ, so $\angle$HGJ$\cong\angle$GKM or $\angle$GHJ$\cong\angle$HMK. Therefore $\overline{GH}\parallel\overline{KM}$ by Theorem 9-7.

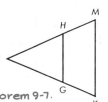

5. In the figure, $\angle B$ and $\angle D$ are right angles, and $DC = AB$. Prove that $\overline{AD} \parallel \overline{BC}$.
   $\triangle$ABC$\cong\triangle$CDA by HL and consequently $\angle$ACB$\cong\angle$CAD. Therefore $\overline{AD}\parallel\overline{BC}$ by the AIP Theorem.

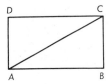

6. In the figure as marked, why is $\overline{PQ} \parallel \overline{AB}$? $\overline{AC} \parallel \overline{QR}$? $\overline{PS} \parallel \overline{BC}$?
   $\overline{PQ}\parallel\overline{AB}$ since $\angle$CQP$\cong\angle$B (Theorem 9-7) $\overline{AC}\parallel\overline{QR}$ since $\angle$A$\cong\angle$QRB(Theorem 9-7) $\overline{PS}\parallel\overline{BC}$ since $\angle$SPQ$\cong\angle$PQC (AIP)

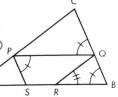

### Explanation for Problems

Problem 2 is an important problem in this set. Problems 3 and 4 give the student practice in the use of Theorem 9–7. In Problems 5 and 6 he has to decide whether he can use Theorem 9–5 or Theorem 9–7. Since Problem Set 9–2 is relatively short, you can also assign some of the harder problems from Problem Set 9–1.

### Answers to Problems

**2.** If a pair of corresponding angles are congruent then a pair of alternate interior angles are congruent by Theorem 9–6. Therefore the lines are parallel by Theorem 9–5.

**Answers to Problems**

8. (a) $\triangle ADB \cong \triangle BEC$ (HL) and $\angle BCE \cong \angle ABD$. $L_2 \parallel L_3$ by Theorem 9–7.
   (b) $\angle CBE \cong \angle FBA$ by the Vertical Angle Theorem. $\triangle FBA \cong \triangle EBC$ (SAS) and $\angle BAF \cong \angle BCE$ by corresponding parts. $L_1 \parallel L_3$ by AIP.

**Answers to Preparation Problems**

1. Converse of Theorem 9–2: If $L_1 \parallel L_2$, then $L_1$ and $L_2$ are perpendicular to the same line.
   Converse of Theorem 9–5: If two parallel lines are cut by a transversal, then alternate interior angles are congruent.
   Converse of Theorem 9–7: If $L_1 \parallel L_2$ and $L$ is a transversal, then any pair of corresponding angles are congruent.
   Converse of Theorem 9–8: If $L_1 \parallel L_2$ and $L$ is a transversal, then any pair of interior angles on the same side of the transversal are supplementary.

2. For any two angles $\angle A$ and $\angle B$, exactly one of the following is true: $m\angle A < m\angle B$, $m\angle A = m\angle B$, or $m\angle A > m\angle B$.

## 9–3 THE PARALLEL POSTULATE

### Background Material

The mathematical background of the Euclidean Parallel Postulate is developed in Chapter 9, "Three Geometries," Chapter 10, "Absolute Plane Geometry," and Chapter 11, "The Parallel Postulate and Parallel Projection," of *EGAS*.

7. For each plane figure below, find a value for $x$ that will make $L_1 \parallel L_2$.

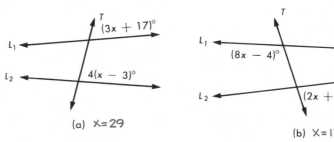

(a) $x = 29$

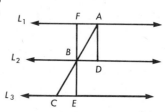

(b) $x = 13.6$

8. Given the plane figure with $\overline{AD} \perp L_2$, $\overline{FE} \perp L_3$, $AB = BC$, and $AD = BE = BF$. Prove that
   (a) $L_2 \parallel L_3$.
   (b) $L_1 \parallel L_3$.

### Preparation for Section 9–3

1. State the converses of Theorems 9–2, 9–5, 9–7, and 9–8, carefully noting each hypothesis and each conclusion. Do you see how each converse differs from its theorem?

2. Write a statement that applies the Trichotomy Property to $\angle A$ and $\angle B$.

3. Does the Angle Construction Postulate guarantee existence or uniqueness, or both?

## 9–3  THE PARALLEL POSTULATE

**POSTULATE 18.**  The Parallel Postulate

*Through a given external point there is only one parallel to a given line.*

Note that since we have proved that parallels *exist*, the postulate needs to say only that they are unique. It is the uniqueness of parallels that gives us the converses of the theorems in the preceding section. We start with the converse of Theorem 9–5.

**Classroom Notes**

**Theorem 9–9.** The PAI Theorem

*If two parallel lines are cut by a transversal, then alternate interior angles are congruent.*

**Proof.** We have given parallel lines $L_1$ and $L_2$, and a transversal $T$, intersecting them in $P$ and $Q$.

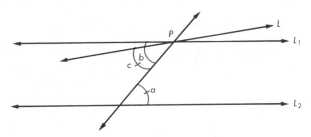

Suppose that $\angle a$ and $\angle b$ are *not* congruent. Let $L$ be the line through $P$ for which alternate interior angles *are* congruent. That is, in the figure below, $\angle a \cong \angle c$. By the Angle Construction Postulate, there is exactly one such line $L$; and this means also that $L \neq L_1$.

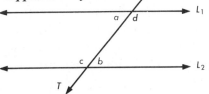

Then $L \parallel L_2$, by Theorem 9–5. Since $L \neq L_1$, it follows that there are two lines through $P$, parallel to $L_2$. This contradicts the Parallel Postulate. Therefore $\angle a \cong \angle b$, which was to be proved.

The proofs of the following two corollaries and three theorems follow easily from the formal definitions.

**Corollary 9–9.1.** The PCA Corollary

*If two parallel lines are cut by a transversal, each pair of corresponding angles are congruent.*

**Corollary 9–9.2**

*If two parallel lines are cut by a transversal, the interior angles on the same side of the transversal are supplementary.*

**Restatement.** Given $L_1 \parallel L_2$, with a transversal $T$. Then $\angle b$ and $\angle d$ are supplementary and $\angle a$ and $\angle c$ are supplementary.

Note that Theorem 9–9 and Corollaries 9–9.1 and 9–9.2 are, respectively, the converses of Theorems 9–5, 9–7, and 9–8. The Preparation Problems will remind average students of the difference between a statement and its converse, although they may not see the necessity for also proving the converse. You should therefore carefully distinguish these theorems from their converses, and then watch carefully the students' use of them; they may want to use Theorem 9–5 and 9–9 interchangeably.

The proof of the PAI Theorem is hard; it is an indirect proof and the contradiction is obtained by use of the Parallel Postulate. It should not, however, be skipped, and the students should be held responsible for it.

We suggest that before proving the PAI Theorem, you review the Angle Construction Postulate and, with the appropriate orientation, anticipate its use in this proof.

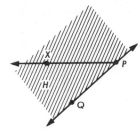

**The Angle Construction Postulate.** Given a ray $\overrightarrow{PQ}$ on the edge of a half-plane $H$ and a real number $r$, $0 < r < 180$ (in this case $r = m\angle a$), there exists exactly one ray $\overrightarrow{PX}$ (and hence exactly one line $\overleftrightarrow{PX} = L$), with $X$ in $H$, such that $m\angle XPQ = r$.

Corollaries 9–9.1 and 9–9.2 are an immediate consequence of Theorem 9–9. We recommend that you complete the discussion of Theorem 9–9 and its corollaries and the related problems before you take up the remaining consequences of the PAI Theorem.

The PAI Theorem has two more important consequences: Theorems 9–11 and 9–12. There are no proofs in the text; this means that you should assign the proofs as homework and then discuss them in class. Good students find the proofs easy; average students do not. Plan to spend a day on the proofs of these theorems.

**Proof of Theorem 9–10**

Suppose $L$ does not intersect $L_2$. Then $L_1$ and $L$ are both parallel to $L_2$, which contradicts the Parallel Postulate.

**Quiz**
Given the figure below with $\overline{AB} \parallel \overline{DE}$, $\overline{AC} \parallel \overline{EF}$, $\overline{DF} \parallel \overline{CB}$, and $DF = EB$. Prove $\triangle DEF \cong \triangle BFE$.

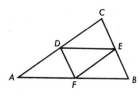

Proof: Since $\overline{BC} \parallel \overline{DF}$, $\angle DFE \cong \angle FEB$ by PAI. $EF = EF$ and $DF = EB$ (given) so that $\triangle DEF \cong \triangle BFE$ by SAS.

*Remark:* If you use an indirect proof for either of the preceding corollaries, you are working too hard. Remember the definition of corresponding angles and the Vertical Angle Theorem.

The next theorem, for which you should use an indirect proof, is necessary in proving the two theorems that follow it.

**Theorem 9–10**

*In a plane, if a line intersects one of two parallel lines in only one point, then it intersects the other.*

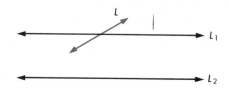

**Restatement.**  Given $L_1 \parallel L_2$ and $L$ intersecting $L_1$.  Then $L$ intersects $L_2$.

**Theorem 9–11**

*In a plane, if two lines are each parallel to a third line, then they are parallel to each other.*

The same theorem holds for the case in which the three lines are not coplanar.  (See Corollary 10–4.2.)  But the theorem cannot be proved in the general case by the methods of this chapter.

**Theorem 9–12**

*In a plane, if a line is perpendicular to one of two parallel lines it is perpendicular to the other.*

A quick proof of this theorem is suggested by the figure on the right.  (An angle is a right angle if and only if it is congruent to an angle with which it forms a linear pair.)

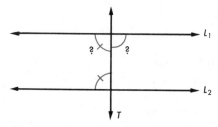

## Problem Set 9–3

1. Prove Corollary 9–9.2.

2. Prove Theorem 9–10.

3. Given the figure with $\angle CDE \cong \angle A$ and $L \perp \overleftrightarrow{AB}$. Prove that $L \perp \overleftrightarrow{DE}$.

   Since $\angle CDE \cong \angle A$, $\overleftrightarrow{DE} \parallel \overleftrightarrow{AB}$ by Theorem 9-7. Since $L \perp \overleftrightarrow{AB}$, one of two parallel lines, it is perpendicular to $\overleftrightarrow{DE}$ by Theorem 9-12.

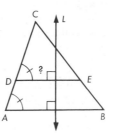

4. Given: Quadrilateral $\square EASY$ with right angles $\angle E$, $\angle A$, and $\angle S$.

   Prove: $\overline{EY} \perp \overline{SY}$.

   Since $\overline{AE} \perp \overline{AS}$ and $\overline{SY} \perp \overline{AS}$, $\overline{AE} \parallel \overline{SY}$. Since $\overline{EY} \perp \overline{AE}$, then $\overline{EY} \perp \overline{SY}$ by Theorem 9-12.

5. Prove that a line parallel to the base of an isosceles triangle and intersecting the other two sides of the triangle at different points forms another isosceles triangle.

6. If $\overleftrightarrow{AB} \parallel \overleftrightarrow{DC}$ and $m\angle BAD = 115$, what is $m\angle ADC$? If also $\overleftrightarrow{AD} \parallel \overleftrightarrow{BC}$, what is $m\angle BCD$?
   $m\angle ADC = 65$
   $m\angle BCD = 115$

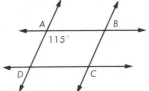

7. Given: In the figure, $RT = RS$, $\overleftrightarrow{PQ} \parallel \overleftrightarrow{RS}$.

   Prove: $PQ = PT$.

   Since $\overleftrightarrow{PQ} \parallel \overleftrightarrow{RS}$, $\angle PQT \cong \angle S$. Since $RT = RS$, $\angle S \cong \angle T$ (Theorem 5-4). Consequently, $\angle PQT \cong \angle T$ and $PQ = PT$ by Th. 5-5.

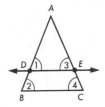

8. In the figure, $\angle x \cong \angle y$ and $\angle a \cong \angle b$. Prove that $L_1 \parallel L_3$.
   Use Theorems 9-5, 9-7 and 9-11.

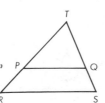

---

### Explanation for Problems

Note that Problems 9, 10, 11, 12, and 17 of Problem Set 9–3 can be solved using Theorem 9–9. Problem 17 is an extension of Problem 11. Problem 12 anticipates the proof of Theorem 9–13.

Problems 7, 14, and 15(a) of Problem Set 9–3 are exercises in the use of Corollary 9–9.1.

Problems 1, 2, 3, 4, 6, 8, and 15(b) of Problem Set 9–3 are related to Corollary 9–9.2 and Theorems 9–10, 9–11, and 9–12.

### Answers to Problems

1. By PAI, $\angle a \cong \angle b$ so $m\angle a = m\angle b$, and $m\angle a + m\angle d = 180$ since $\angle a$ and $\angle d$ form a linear pair. Then $m\angle b + m\angle d = 180$ so $\angle b$ and $\angle d$ are supplementary. Similarly $\angle a$ and $\angle c$ are supplementary.

2. If $L$ intersects $L_1$ at $P$ and $L$ does not intersect $L_2$, then $L \parallel L_2$ and these would be two lines through $P$ parallel to $L_2$. This contradicts the Parallel Postulate.

5. Given: $\triangle ABC$ with $AB = AC$. Line $L \parallel \overline{BC}$, intersecting $\overline{AB}$ at $D$ and $\overline{AC}$ at $E$. Prove: $\triangle ADE$ is isosceles.

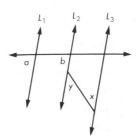

Proof: By the Isosceles Triangle Theorem, $\angle 2 \cong \angle 3$. Since $\overleftrightarrow{DE} \parallel \overline{BC}$, $\angle 1 \cong \angle 2$ and $\angle 3 \cong \angle 4$ by the PAI Theorem. $\therefore \angle 1 \cong \angle 4$, and $\triangle ADE$ is isosceles by the converse of the Isosceles Triangle Theorem.

10. $\angle A \cong \angle C$ and $\angle D \cong \angle B$ by PAI, $\triangle ADE \cong \triangle CBE$ (ASA), and therefore $AE = CE$ and $DE = BE$.

11. Since $\overline{QR} \parallel \overline{MN}$, $\angle QXM \cong \angle XMN$ (Theorem 9-9). Since $\overrightarrow{MX}$ bisects $\angle M$, $\angle XMN \cong \angle QMX$. $\therefore \angle QXM \cong \angle QMX$ and $QM = QX$ (Theorem 5-5). Similarly, $RN = RX$, and $\triangle QMX$ and $\triangle RXN$ are isosceles.

14. (1) Since $\overleftrightarrow{AB} \parallel \overleftrightarrow{CD}$, $\angle REB \cong \angle EFD$. (Theorem 9-9)
    (2) Since $\overrightarrow{EG}$ bisects $\angle REB$ and $\overrightarrow{FH}$ bisects $\angle EFD$, $\angle REG \cong \angle EFH$, and $\overrightarrow{EG} \parallel \overrightarrow{FH}$ by Theorem 9-7.

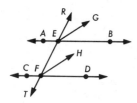

15. [Note: Figures in text are annotated to correspond to proofs below.]

(a) Two angles in a plane which have their sides respectively parallel and extending both in the same (or both in opposite) directions are congruent.
Given: $\overrightarrow{BA} \parallel \overrightarrow{YX}$, $\overrightarrow{BC} \parallel \overrightarrow{YZ}$.
Prove: $\angle ABC \cong \angle XYZ$.
Proof: $\angle Y \cong \angle BQY$ and $\angle B \cong \angle BQY$ by Theorem 9-9. Therefore, $\angle B \cong \angle Y$.

(b) Two angles in a plane which have their sides respectively parallel but have one and only one pair extending in the same direction are supplementary.
Given: $\overrightarrow{BA} \parallel \overrightarrow{YX}$, $\overrightarrow{BC} \parallel \overrightarrow{YZ}$.
Prove: $m\angle ABC + m\angle XYZ = 180$.
Proof: Consider $\overleftrightarrow{YX}$ forming $\angle PYZ$ with sides extending in the same direction as those of $\angle ABC$. Then, from part (a), $m\angle PYZ = m\angle ABC$. But $m\angle PYZ + m\angle XYZ = 180$, and therefore $m\angle ABC + m\angle XYZ = 180$.

16. Since any point on the perpendicular bisector of a line segment is equidistant from the end points of that segment, $GA = GD$ (Theorem 6-2) and consequently, $\angle 1 \cong \angle 2$. Since $\overrightarrow{AD}$ bisects $\angle CAB$, $\angle 2 \cong \angle 3$. $\therefore \angle 1 \cong \angle 3$, and $\overline{GD} \parallel \overline{AB}$ by Theorem 9-5. (See sketch at top of page 277.)

---

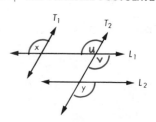

9. Given the figure with $L_1 \parallel L_2$ and $T_1 \parallel T_2$. Prove that $\angle x \cong \angle y$.
Since $T_1 \parallel T_2$, $\angle x \cong \angle u$.
$\angle u \cong \angle v$ (vertical angles) and since $L_1 \parallel L_2$, $\angle v \cong \angle y$.
$\angle x \cong \angle y$ by Transitivity.

10. Given that $\overline{AC}$ and $\overline{DB}$ intersect at $E$, with $A$-$E$-$C$ and $D$-$E$-$B$, such that $AD = BC$ and $\overline{AD} \parallel \overline{BC}$. Prove that $\overline{AC}$ and $\overline{DB}$ bisect each other at $E$.

---

11. Given $\triangle PMN$, $\overrightarrow{MX}$ bisects $\angle M$, $\overrightarrow{NX}$ bisects $\angle N$, and $\overline{QR}$, through $X$, is parallel to $\overline{MN}$. Prove that $\triangle QMX$ and $\triangle RXN$ are isosceles.

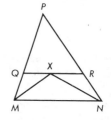

12. Given $\triangle ABC$. Prove that if $A$ lies on a line parallel to $\overline{BC}$, then $m\angle A + m\angle B + m\angle C = 180$. **See proof of Theorem 9-13.**

13. Given the same hypothesis as that of Problem 11. If $PM = 10$, $MN = 15$, and $PN = 17$, what is the perimeter of $\triangle PQR$? **27**

14. Prove: If two parallel lines are cut by a transversal, then the bisectors of any two corresponding angles are parallel.

15. Prove: In a plane, if the sides of an angle are parallel to the sides of another angle, the two angles are either (a) congruent or (b) supplementary.

(*Note:* The figure shows only two cases, but similar, easy proofs may be given for all other cases. For a hint, see Problem 9 of this problem set.)

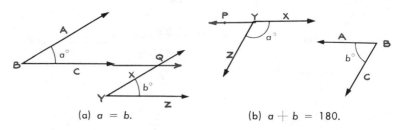

(a) $a = b$.     (b) $a + b = 180$.

---

16. In $\triangle ABC$ the bisector of $\angle A$ intersects $\overline{BC}$ at $D$. The perpendicular bisector of $\overline{AD}$ intersects $\overline{AC}$ at $G$. Prove that $\overleftrightarrow{GD} \parallel \overleftrightarrow{AB}$.

17. In $\triangle FGH$ the bisector of $\angle F$ and the bisector of $\angle G$ intersect at $C$. The line through $C$ and parallel to $\overline{FG}$ intersects $\overline{FH}$ at $A$ and $\overline{GH}$ at $B$. Prove that the perimeter of $\triangle ABH$ equals the sum of $FH$ and $GH$.

18. If Theorem 9–9 is taken as a postulate instead of the Parallel Postulate, then the Parallel Postulate can be proved as a theorem.

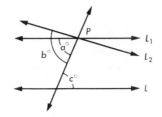

> Given a line $L$ and a point $P$ not on $L$. Then there is at most one line $L_1$, containing $P$ and parallel to $L$.

[*Hint:* Does $a = c = b$?]

19. Show that if Theorem 9–12 is taken as a postulate, the Parallel Postulate follows as a theorem.

## 9–4   TRIANGLES

### Theorem 9–13

*For every triangle, the sum of the measures of the angles is 180.*

**Proof.** Given $\triangle ABC$, let $L$ be the line through $B$, parallel to $\overline{AC}$. Let $\angle x$, $\angle x'$, $\angle y$, $\angle y'$, and $\angle z$ be as shown in the figure.

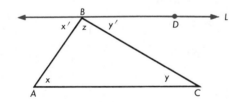

| STATEMENTS | REASONS |
|---|---|
| 1. $m\angle x = m\angle x'$. | 1. The **PAI** Theorem |
| 2. $m\angle y = m\angle y'$. | 2. The **PAI** Theorem |
| 3. $m\angle ABD = m\angle z + m\angle y'$. | 3. Angle Addition Postulate |
| 4. $m\angle x' + m\angle ABD =$ $m\angle x' + m\angle z + m\angle y'$. | 4. Addition Property of Equality |
| 5. $m\angle x' + m\angle ABD = 180$. | 5. Supplement Postulate |
| 6. $m\angle x' + m\angle z + m\angle y' = 180$. | 6. Transitive Property |
| 7. $m\angle x + m\angle z + m\angle y = 180$. | 7. Steps 1, 2, and 6 |

From this theorem we get some very important corollaries.

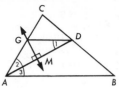

**17.** Since $\overrightarrow{FC}$ bisects $\angle F$, $\angle 1 \cong \angle 2$. Since $\overline{AB} \parallel \overline{FG}$, $\angle 2 \cong \angle 3$. Consequently, $\angle 1 \cong \angle 3$, and $AC = AF$ (Theorem 5–5). Similarly, $BC = BG$. Therefore $HA + AC = HA + AF = HF$, and $HB + BC = HB + BG = HG$. $(HA + AC) + (HB + BC) = HF + HG$.

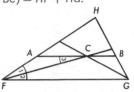

**18.** Draw a transversal $\overrightarrow{PQ}$ of $L_1$ and $L$ and also of $L_2$ and $L$, forming angles of $a°$, $b°$ and $c°$ as shown. If $L_2 \parallel L$, then $b = c$; and since $L_1 \parallel L$, $a = c$ by Theorem 9–9. Therefore, $a = b$. But then $L_1 = L_2$ by the Angle Construction Postulate, so there cannot be a second parallel to $L$ through $P$.

**19.** Consider a line $T$ perpendicular to $L$ from $P$. By Theorem 9–12, $T \perp L_1$. Assume $L_2$ parallel to $L$. Then $T \perp L_2$. Since $L_1$ and $L_2$ cannot both be perpendicular to $T$ at $P$ (Theorem 6–1), $L_2$ cannot be parallel to $L$ as was assumed.

## 9–4 TRIANGLES

### Background Material

Theorem 9–13 is one of the fundamental theorems in Euclidean plane geometry: it is a direct consequence of the Euclidean Parallel Postulate and *cannot*, in fact, be proved without using this postulate. (In hyperbolic geometry, the theorem is actually false: in any triangle $\triangle ABC$, we have $m\angle A + m\angle B + m\angle C < 180$.) You may wish to refer to Problems 18 and 19, page 94, which relate to Theorem 9–13.

## Classroom Notes

In Chapter 7 we proved the Exterior Angle Inequality Theorem: the measure of an exterior angle of a triangle is greater than the measure of each of its remote interior angles. We can now prove a stronger assertion:

### Corollary 9–13.3. The Exterior Angle Equality Theorem

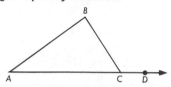

Given: $\triangle ABC$ with exterior angle $\angle BCD$.

Prove: $m \angle BCD = m \angle A + m \angle B$.

Proof. By the Supplement Postulate, $m \angle BCD = 180 - m \angle BCA$. From Theorem 9–13 it follows that $m \angle A + m \angle B = 180 - m \angle BCA$. Therefore $m \angle BCD = m \angle A + m \angle B$.

Note that we could prove the Exterior Angle Inequality Theorem as a corollary to the Exterior Angle Equality Theorem by making use of Theorem 7–1. To do so, however, would make the Exterior Angle Inequality Theorem seem to depend on the Parallel Postulate, which, of course, it does not.

### Explanation for Problems

Problems 1 through 5 are simple applications of Theorem 9–13. Problems 9, 10, 16, and 17 use Corollary 9–13.2. Problems 6, 7, 8, 12, 13, 14, and 18 involve the use of the Exterior Angle Inequality Theorem (Corollary 9–13.3).

Problem Set 9–4 marks the end of Part 1 (Parallel Lines) of Chapter 9. We strongly recommend that you test the students on this material before going on to Part 2 (Quadrilaterals in a Plane).

### Corollary 9–13.1

*Given a correspondence between two triangles. If two pairs of corresponding angles are congruent, then the third pair of corresponding angles are also congruent.*

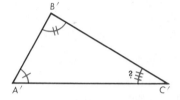

### Corollary 9–13.2

*The acute angles of a right triangle are complementary.*

### Corollary 9–13.3

*For any triangle, the measure of an exterior angle is the sum of the measures of the two remote interior angles.*

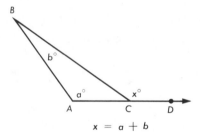

$$x = a + b$$

Obviously, we used the Parallel Postulate to prove Theorem 9–13. This was not just a matter of convenience; in fact, the theorem *cannot* be proved without using the Parallel Postulate. It was discovered in the nineteenth century that there is a kind of geometry (now called *hyperbolic* geometry) in which Euclid's Parallel Postulate fails to hold. Hyperbolic geometry is not only a respectable branch of mathematics but a useful one in physics. In hyperbolic geometry, Theorem 9–13 is not only unprovable but actually *false*. And many other peculiar things happen. For example, in hyperbolic geometry, scale models are impossible, because no two figures ever have exactly the same shape unless they have exactly the same size.

Euclidean geometry is, however, an excellent approximation of physical space; and it is, of course, the kind of geometry that everybody should study first.

## Problem Set 9–4

1. If two angles of a triangle have the following measures, what is the measure of the third angle?

   (a) 64 and 59  **57**     (b) 26 and 134  **20**     (c) $k$ and $2k$  **180–3k**
                                                      **0<k<60**

   (d) $u$ and $v$  **180–(u+v)**   (e) 90 and $n$  **90–n**     (f) $60 + a$ and $60 - a$
     **0<u+v<180**                  **0<n<90**                            **60**

2. The measures of the angles of a triangle are in the ratio of $1 : 2 : 3$. Find the measure of each angle. **30–60–90**

3. The measure of one angle of a triangle is 25 more than that of a second angle, and the measure of the third angle is 9 less than twice the measure of the second angle. Find each measure. **66–41–73**

4. In the figure shown, determine the measure of each angle.

5. Given that $\angle A \cong \angle D$ and $\angle B \cong \angle E$, explain why you can or cannot conclude that

   (a) $\angle C \cong \angle F$. **Yes, by Corollary 9-13.1**

   (b) $\overline{AB} \cong \overline{DE}$. **No, insufficient hypothesis to prove triangles congruent.**

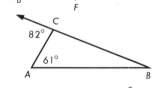

6. For the figure as marked, what is $m\angle B$? $m\angle ACB$? **m∠B = 21**
                                         **m∠ACB =98**

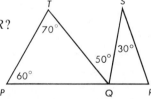

7. For the figure as marked, what is $m\angle R$? **m∠R =70**

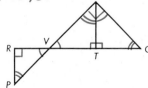

8. The measure of one angle of a triangle is five times that of a second angle, and the measure of an exterior angle at the third vertex is 120. Find the measure of each angle of the triangle. **20, 100, 60**

9. In the figure, $\overline{PR} \perp \overline{RQ}$, $\overline{ST} \perp \overline{RQ}$, and $\overline{SQ} \perp \overline{PS}$. Prove that $\angle P \cong \angle Q$.

## Quiz

1. Given two isosceles triangles $\triangle ABC$ and $\triangle DEF$. The measure of the vertex angle of $\triangle ABC$ is twice that of the vertex angle of $\triangle DEF$ and one-half that of a base angle of $\triangle DEF$. Find the measure of each base angle of $\triangle ABC$.

   (ans: The base angles of $\triangle ABC$ are each 70°.)

2. Prove that the measure of an exterior angle of a triangle is the sum of the measures of the two remote interior angles.

   (ans: Let $x$ be the measure of the exterior angle, $y$ the measure of the interior angle forming a linear pair, and $a$ and $b$ the measures of the re-mote interior angles. Now $x + y = 180$ and by Theorem 9–13, $a + b + y = 180$. Thus $x = a + b$ by the Subtraction and Transitive Properties of Equality.)

### Answers to Problems

9. $\angle P$ is complementary to $\angle RVP$; $\angle RVP \cong \angle SVQ$; $\angle SVQ$ is complementary to $\angle Q$. $\therefore \angle P \cong \angle Q$ by Theorem 4–7.

11. The Parallel Postulate assures us that $L$ is the only parallel to $\overleftrightarrow{AC}$ through $B$. It is also used to prove that alternate interior angles are congruent when parallels are cut by a transversal, and this theorem in turn is used in the proof of Theorem 9–13.

12. (See annotated markings on the figure in the text.) By Corollary 9–13.3, $a = m\angle 1 + m\angle 3$ and $b = m\angle 2 + m\angle 4$. $\therefore a + b = (m\angle 1 + m\angle 2) + (m\angle 3 + m\angle 4) = m\angle M + m\angle H = x + y$.

13. Given: $\overrightarrow{CE}$ bisects $\angle DCB$. $\overrightarrow{CE} \parallel \overline{AB}$.
Prove: $CA = CB$.

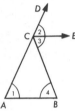

Proof: Since $\overrightarrow{CE} \parallel \overline{AB}$, $\angle 1 \cong \angle 2$. Since $\overrightarrow{CE}$ bisects $\angle DCB$, $\angle 2 \cong \angle 3$. Since $\overrightarrow{CE} \parallel \overline{AB}$, $\angle 3 \cong \angle 4$. $\therefore \angle 1 \cong \angle 4$, and $CA = CB$.

14. Given: $CA = CB$. F-C-E. $\overleftrightarrow{FE} \parallel \overline{AB}$.
Prove: $\overrightarrow{CE}$ bisects $\angle DCB$. $\overrightarrow{CF}$ bisects $\angle GCA$.

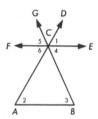

Proof: Since $\overleftrightarrow{CE} \parallel \overline{AB}$, $\angle 1 \cong \angle 2$. Since $CA = CB$, $\angle 2 \cong \angle 3$. Since $\overleftrightarrow{CE} \parallel \overline{AB}$, $\angle 3 \cong \angle 4$. Therefore, $\angle 1 \cong \angle 4$ and, $\overrightarrow{CE}$ bisects $\angle DCB$. Similarly, $\overrightarrow{CF}$ bisects $\angle GCA$. Note that the rays $\overrightarrow{CE}$ and $\overrightarrow{CF}$ which bisect the exterior angles at $C$ are opposite rays.

15. The problem asks the student to discover the statement of Theorem 9–22.

17. In $\triangle PQR$, $m\angle Q = 90 - a$.

In $\triangle PVS$, $m\angle PVS = \dfrac{180 - a}{2}$.

In $\triangle QVT$,

$m\angle QVT = \dfrac{180 - (90 - a)}{2} = \dfrac{90 + a}{2}$.

$\therefore m\angle SVT$
$= 180 - (m\angle PVS + m\angle QVT)$
$= 180 - \left( \dfrac{180 - a}{2} + \dfrac{90 + a}{2} \right)$
$= 180 - 135 = 45$.

---

10. In $\triangle ABC$, $\angle ACB$ is a right angle and $\overline{CD} \perp \overline{AB}$. Prove that $\angle A \cong \angle BCD$.
$\angle A$ is the complement of $\angle ACD$.
$\angle ACD$ is the complement of $\angle BCD$.
$\angle A \cong \angle BCD$ by Theorem 4-7.

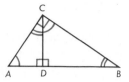

11. Why is the Parallel Postulate essential to the proof of Theorem 9–13?

12. Given: The figure
Prove: $a + b = x + y$.
[Hint: Draw $\overline{MH}$.]

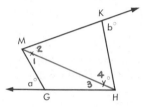

13. Prove: If the bisector of an exterior angle of a triangle is parallel to a side of the triangle, the triangle is isosceles.

14. Prove: If a line containing a vertex of an isosceles triangle is parallel to the base of the triangle, it bisects each exterior angle at the vertex.

15.

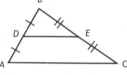 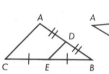 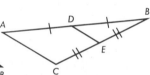

Consider the three triangles shown here. What seems to be true for $\overline{DE}$ and $\overline{AC}$ in each case? How does $DE$ compare with $AC$ in each case? What are $D$ and $E$? Do your answers so far suggest an important property of triangles? Write a conjecture concerning $\overline{DE}$ and $\overline{AC}$ and $DE$ and $AC$. Can you find an example to prove the conjecture false? Can you prove that it is true? **yes** $\overline{DE} \parallel \overline{AC}$; $DE = \frac{1}{2} AC$, **No** midpoints of the sides of the triangles

16. In $\triangle ABC$, $\angle C$ is a right angle, and $M$ is a point of the hypotenuse such that $AM = CM$. Prove that $M$ is equidistant from $A$, $B$, and $C$.
Student anticipates proof of Theorem 9-26

17. Given: In $\triangle PQR$, $\angle R$ is a right angle,

$QT = QV$, and $PS = PV$.

Prove: $x = 45$.

[Hint: Let $m\angle P = a$. Write formulas for other angle measures.]

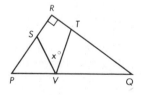

18. In $\triangle ABC$, $AC = BC$. $D$ is a point of $\overleftrightarrow{BC}$ with C-B-D, and $E$ is a point of $\overline{AB}$ with A-E-B such that $BD = BE$. $\overleftrightarrow{DE}$ intersects $\overleftrightarrow{AC}$ at $F$. Prove that $m\angle CFE = 3(m\angle D)$.

## 9-5   QUADRILATERALS IN A PLANE

From Section 5–10 we recall some definitions about quadrilaterals.

### Part A

### Definitions

Let $A$, $B$, $C$, and $D$ be four points of the same plane. If no three of these points are collinear, and the segments $\overline{AB}$, $\overline{BC}$, $\overline{CD}$, and $\overline{DA}$ intersect only at their end points, then the union of these four segments is called a *quadrilateral*. The four segments are called its *sides*, and the points $A$, $B$, $C$, and $D$ are called its *vertices*. The angles $\angle DAB$, $\angle ABC$, $\angle BCD$, and $\angle CDA$ are called its *angles*.

Both figures below satisfy this definition of quadrilateral.

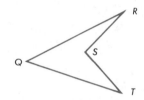

$\square ABCD$ is called *convex* but $\square QRST$ is not. To see how the difference between these quadrilaterals can be described, draw each line that contains a side and notice where the other two vertices lie.

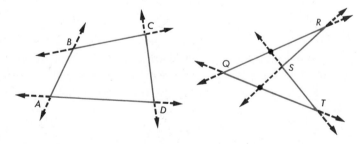

### Definition

A quadrilateral is *convex* if no two of its vertices lie on opposite sides of a line containing a side of the quadrilateral.

Thus $\square QRST$ is not a convex quadrilateral, because $Q$ and $R$ lie on opposite sides of $\overleftrightarrow{ST}$.

---

**Answers to Problems**

18. $m\angle 1 = m\angle 2 + m\angle 3$
$\qquad$ (Corollary 9–13.3)
$\quad = m\angle 6 + m\angle 3$
$\qquad$ (Theorem 5–2)
$\quad = (m\angle 4 + m\angle 5) + m\angle 3$
$\qquad$ (Corollary 9–13.3)
$\quad = (m\angle 5 + m\angle 5) + m\angle 3$
$\qquad$ (Theorem 5–2)
$\quad = (m\angle 5 + m\angle 5) + m\angle 5$
$\quad = 3m\angle 5 \qquad$ (Theorem 4–7)

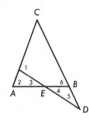

### 9-5 QUADRILATERALS IN A PLANE

**Background Material**

Section 9–5 is really three sections in one: The first part deals with the properties of parallelograms, the second deals with the conditions that suffice to prove that a quadrilateral is a parallelogram, and the third deals with Theorem 9–22, the Midline Theorem. You may need a full day on each of these parts, assigning each night the appropriate problems from Problem Set 9–5. The proofs of the theorems in the first two parts of Section 9–5 are omitted in the text because they are no harder to write than they are to read. This is the ideal time to give the average student, and the good student, the opportunity to prove important theorems on his own.

## Classroom Notes

The order of the letters in the notation for the quadrilaterals is important. Successive letters always denote a side of the quadrilateral. You should call this to the attention of the students.

**Properties of a parallelogram.** Note that Theorems 9–15 and 9–16 are immediate consequences of Theorem 9–14; hence all three theorems can be established in one proof. Also note that in the definition of *the distance between two parallel lines* the distance from any point of one to the other is defined to be the perpendicular distance. Theorem 9–17 is an immediate consequence of Corollary 9–9.2.

### Explanation for Problems

You should assign and discuss Problems 1 through 10 and 20 of Problem Set 9–5 before taking up the second part of Section 9–5. (See also Part 1 of Problem 9 of Problem Set 9–6 and Problem 5 of Chapter Review—Set B, page 303.)

**Conditions which suffice to prove that a quadrilateral is a parallelogram.** It is necessary to distinguish the problem of establishing the properties of a parallelogram and the converse problem. The theorems in Section 9–5, Part A establish *properties* of a parallelogram. Phrased in "if-then" form, each theorem begins: "If a quadrilateral is a parallelogram, then . . ." The *hypothesis* in each theorem is that the quadrilateral *is* a parallelogram. In the converse problem we ask what conditions will suffice to enable us to *conclude* that a quadrilateral is a parallelogram. "If certain conditions hold, *then* the quadrilateral is a parallelogram." The average student does not distinguish between these two problems; you have to drive the distinction home.

---

## Definitions

Two sides of a quadrilateral are *opposite* if they do not intersect. Two of its angles are *opposite* if they do not have a side of the quadrilateral in common. Two sides are *consecutive* if they have a common end point. Two angles are *consecutive* if they have a side of the quadrilateral in common. A *diagonal* of a quadrilateral is a segment joining two nonconsecutive vertices.

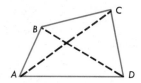  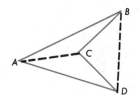

Thus, in $\square ABCD$, the following pairs of sides and angles are opposite: $\overline{AB}$ and $\overline{CD}$, $\overline{BC}$ and $\overline{AD}$, $\angle A$ and $\angle C$, $\angle B$ and $\angle D$. A few of the consecutive pairs are: $\overline{AB}$ and $\overline{BC}$, $\overline{BC}$ and $\overline{CD}$, $\angle D$ and $\angle A$, $\angle A$ and $\angle B$. The diagonals of $\boxdot ABCD$ are $\overline{AC}$ and $\overline{BD}$.

## Definition

A *parallelogram* is a quadrilateral in which both pairs of opposite sides are parallel.

## Definition

A *trapezoid* is a quadrilateral in which one and only one pair of opposite sides are parallel. The parallel sides are called the *bases* of the trapezoid. The segment joining the midpoints of the nonparallel sides is called the *median*.

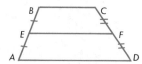

Note that under these definitions, no parallelogram is a trapezoid. The proofs of the following theorems are straightforward.

## Theorem 9–14

*Each diagonal separates a parallelogram into two congruent triangles.*

That is, if $\square ABCD$ is a parallelogram, then $\triangle ABC \cong \triangle CDA$.

## Theorem 9–15

*In a parallelogram, any two opposite sides are congruent.*

## Corollary 9–15.1

*If two lines are parallel, then all points of each line are equidistant from the other line.*

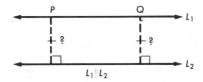

We recall, from Section 7–6, that the distance between a line and an external point is defined to be the length of the perpendicular segment from the point to the line. We sometimes refer to Corollary 9–15.1 by saying that "parallel lines are everywhere equidistant."

## Definition

The *distance between two parallel lines* is the distance from any point of one to the other.

## Theorem 9–16

*In a parallelogram, any two opposite angles are congruent.*

## Theorem 9–17

*In a parallelogram, any two consecutive angles are supplementary.*

## Theorem 9–18

*The diagonals of a parallelogram bisect each other.*

Before proving Theorems 9–19, 9–20, and 9–21, we have only one way to show that a quadrilateral is a parallelogram: by definition. It is valuable to conduct a preliminary survey, and get the students to conjecture additional ways to prove that a quadrilateral is a parallelogram. Theorems 9–19 and 9–21 are easily obtained by considering the converses of Theorems 9–15 and 9–18. Theorem 9–20 can be obtained by the following considerations: we have two conditions which are sufficient to prove that a quadrilateral is a parallelogram, but these conditions require knowing something about *both* pairs of opposite sides of the quadrilateral. In many cases we can get information about *only one* pair of opposite sides. What conditions on a single pair of opposite sides are enough to prove that the quadrilateral is a parallelogram? The fact that a pair of opposite sides are parallel will suffice only to prove that the quadrilateral is a trapezoid; the fact that a pair of opposite sides are congruent will not enable us to prove anything at all. If, however, a pair of opposite sides are *both* parallel and congruent, then the quadrilateral will be a parallelogram.

Having conjectured Theorems 9–19, 9–20, and 9–21, the student still has to prove them. Emphasize that in proving Theorem 9–19 he has only one technique at his disposal, the definition. In proving Theorem 9–20, he has two techniques at his disposal, the definition and Theorem 9–19. Similarly, when he comes to Theorem 9–21 he has three techniques available.

## Explanation for Problems

Problems 11, 18, and 19 of Problem Set 9-5 and Problems 3 and 4 of the Chapter Review—Set B are exercises in the use of Theorems 9-19, 9-20, and 9-21. We recommend that you assign them before taking up "The Midline Theorem" in Section 9-5.

## Classroom Notes

DEFINITION. A *midline* of a triangle is a segment between the midpoints of two sides of the triangle.

Theorem 9-22 is important; the proof is involved and should be taught with care.

## Explanation for Problems

In connection with Theorem 9-22, assign and discuss Problems 12, 13, 21, and 22 of Problem Set 9-5. Also note Problem 15 of the Chapter Review—Set B and Problems 6 and 7 of Problem Set 9-8.

## Quiz

If any of the following statements are true, prove each true statement.
**1.** The diagonals of a rectangle bisect the angles of the rectangle.
(ans: False)
**2.** If the diagonals of a quadrilateral are perpendicular, the quadrilateral is a parallelogram.
(ans: False)
**3.** If the diagonals of a quadrilateral bisect each other, the quadrilateral is a parallelogram.
(ans: Let $\square ABCD$ be a quadrilateral such that $\overline{AC}$ and $\overline{BD}$ bisect each other at $M$. Then $AM = MC$ and $BM = MD$ by the definition of bisect. $\angle AMB \cong \angle DMP$ by the Vertical Angle Theorem and $\triangle AMB \cong \triangle CMD$ by SAS. Thus $AB = CD$ and $\angle ABM \cong \angle MDC$ which in turn leads to $\overline{AB} \parallel \overline{CD}$ by PAI so that $\square ABCD$ is a parallelogram by Theorem 9-20.)

**Part B**

Given that $\square ABCD$ is a parallelogram, the preceding theorems enable us to draw various conclusions about its properties. We now consider the *converse* problem: what do we need to know about $\square ABCD$ to conclude that it is a parallelogram?

### Theorem 9-19

*Given a quadrilateral in which both pairs of opposite sides are congruent. Then the quadrilateral is a parallelogram.*

### Theorem 9-20

*If two sides of a quadrilateral are parallel and congruent, then the quadrilateral is a parallelogram.*

### Theorem 9-21

*If the diagonals of a quadrilateral bisect each other, then the quadrilateral is a parallelogram.*

The following theorem is not obvious, and neither is its proof. We shall give the proof in full.

**Part C**

### Theorem 9-22. The Midline Theorem

*The segment between the midpoints of two sides of a triangle is parallel to the third side and half as long.*

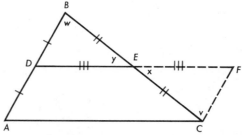

**Restatement.** Given $\triangle ABC$. If $D$ and $E$ are the midpoints of $\overline{AB}$ and $\overline{BC}$, then $\overline{DE} \parallel \overline{AC}$ and $DE = \frac{1}{2}AC$.

**Proof.** Let $F$ be the point, on the ray opposite to $\overrightarrow{ED}$, such that $EF = DE$. We now have the situation described by the marks in the figure. The notation below is that of the figure.

| Statements | Reasons |
|---|---|
| 1. $EF = DE$. | 1. Point-plotting Theorem |
| 2. $EB = EC$. | 2. Definition of midpoint |
| 3. $\angle x \cong \angle y$. | 3. Vertical Angle Theorem |
| 4. $\triangle EFC \cong \triangle EDB$. | 4. SAS |
| 5. $\angle v \cong \angle w$. | 5. Definition of congruent triangles |
| 6. $\overleftrightarrow{AB} \parallel \overleftrightarrow{CF}$. | 6. The AIP Theorem |
| 7. $AD = DB$. | 7. Definition of midpoint |
| 8. $DB = FC$. | 8. Definition of congruent triangles |
| 9. $AD = FC$. | 9. Transitive Property |
| 10. $\square ADFC$ is a parallelogram. | 10. Theorem 9–20 |
| 11. $\overline{DE} \parallel \overline{AC}$. | 11. Definition of a parallelogram |
| 12. $DF = DE + EF = 2DE$. | 12. Definition of between, Step 1, and Addition Property of Equality |
| 13. $AC = 2DE$. | 13. Theorem 9–15 and Transitive Property |
| 14. $DE = \frac{1}{2}AC$. | 14. Multiplication Property of Equality |

## Problem Set 9–5

**1.** Which of the following pairs name the same quadrilateral?

(a) $\square ABCD,\ \square CDAB$ ⟵

(b) $\square ADBC,\ \square CADB$

(c) $\square ABCD,\ \square CADB$

(d) $\square BCDA,\ \square ADCB$ ⟵

(e) $\square BCDA,\ \square BADC$ ⟵

(f) $\square DACB,\ \square CABD$

**2.** The measure of one angle of a parallelogram is 45. What are the measures of the other angles? **135, 45, 135**

**3.** Given a parallelogram $\square ABCD$ with $m\angle B = 4x + 15$ and $m\angle D = 6x - 27$. Find the measures of the four angles. Which theorem did you use?
$m\angle A = m\angle C = 81,\ m\angle B = m\angle D = 99$
Theorem 9–16

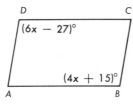

**4.** Two consecutive angles of a parallelogram have measures $(x + 30)$ and $(2x - 60)$, respectively. Determine the measure of each angle of the parallelogram. **100, 80, 100, 80**

**Answers to Problems**

**6.** (See annotated figure in text.) Since $\square AKMJ$ is a parallelogram, $\angle 1 \cong \angle 2$. Since $KJ = KM$, $\angle 2 \cong \angle 3$. Since $\square BMJK$ is a parallelogram, $\angle 3 \cong \angle 4$. $\therefore \angle 1 \cong \angle 4$ and $AC = CB$.

**7.** Introduce the diagonal $\overline{AC}$. Since $\square ABCD$ is a parallelogram, $\angle BAC \cong \angle DCA$ and $\angle BCA \cong \angle DAC$ by Theorem 9–2. Also $AC = AC$ by the Reflexive Property, so $\triangle BAC \cong \triangle DCA$ by ASA.

**8.** Let $\overline{PS}$ be the perpendicular segment from $P$ to $L_2$ and let $\overline{QR}$ be the perpendicular segment from $Q$ to $L_2$. Then $\overline{PS} \parallel \overline{QR}$ by Theorem 9–2 and $\overline{PQ} \parallel \overline{RS}$ since $L_1 \parallel L_2$ by hypothesis. Thus $\square PQRS$ is a parallelogram and $PS = QR$ by Theorem 9–15.

**9.** Any two consecutive angles of a parallelogram are interior angles on the same side of a transversal to two parallel lines, so they are supplementary by Corollary 9–9.2.

**10.** (1) First observe that $\overline{DG} \parallel \overline{BH}$ by Theorem 9–2.
(2) The opposite sides of parallelogram $\square ABCD$ are congruent by Theorem 9–15: $AD = BC$. By definition the opposite sides of parallelogram $\square ABCD$ are parallel: $\overline{AD} \parallel \overline{BC}$, so by Theorem 9–8 $\angle DAG \cong \angle BCH$. Since $\overline{DG} \perp \overline{AC}$ and $\overline{BH} \perp \overline{AC}$, $\angle AGD \cong \angle CHB$. Consequently, $\triangle ADG \cong \triangle CBH$ (SAA), so $DG = BH$.

**11.** (1) The opposite sides of parallelogram $\square PQRS$ are congruent: $PS = RQ$, and by hypothesis $PW = PS$ and $RU = RQ$, so $PW = RU$. By Theorem 9–14, $\triangle SPR \cong \triangle QRP$, so $\angle SPW \cong \angle QRU$.
$\therefore \triangle SPW \cong \triangle QRU$ (SAS) and so $SW = QU$.
(2) $\triangle PQW \cong \triangle RSU$ (SAS) and so $QW = SU$.
(3) Hence by Theorem 9–19, $\square SWQU$ is a parallelogram.

**16.** Introduce the diagonal $\overline{AC}$ in $\square ABCD$. By Theorem 9–13, $m\angle CAB + m\angle B + m\angle BCA = 180 = m\angle CAD + m\angle D + m\angle DCA$. Since $C$ lies in the interior of $\angle BAD$ and $A$ lies in the interior of $\angle BCD$, $m\angle CAB + m\angle DAC = m\angle A$ and $m\angle BCA + m\angle ACD = \angle C$ by the AAP. Therefore $m\angle A + m\angle B + m\angle C + m\angle D = 360$.

**17.**

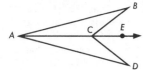

Introduce the interior diagonal $\overrightarrow{AC}$ and let $E$ be a point such that $A$-$C$-$E$. Then $m\angle BCE = m\angle B + m\angle BAC$ and $m\angle ECD = m\angle D + m\angle CAD$ by Corollary 9–13.3. Also since $E$ is in the interior of $\angle BCD$ and $C$ is in the interior of $\angle BAD$, $m\angle BCD = m\angle BCE + m\angle ECD$ and $m\angle BAD = m\angle BAC + m\angle CAD$ by the AAP. Therefore $m\angle BCD = m\angle BCE + m\angle ECD = m\angle B + m\angle BAC + m\angle CAD + m\angle D = m\angle B + m\angle A + m\angle D$.

**18.** Given: In the figure $\overline{RS} \cong \overline{RT}$, $\overline{PX} \parallel \overline{RT}$, $\overline{PY} \parallel \overline{RX}$.
Prove: (1) $\square PXRY$ is a parallelogram.
(2) $PX + XR + RY + YP = RS + RT$.

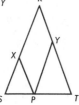

Proof: (1) $\square PXRY$ is a parallelogram by the definition of parallelogram. (2) $PX = RY$, $RX = PY$ (Theorem 9–15), $\angle XPS \cong \angle T$ (Corollary 9–9.2), and $\angle S \cong \angle T$ by Theorem 5–4, so $\angle XPS \cong \angle S$. $PX = SX$ (Theorem 5–5) and similarly $PY = TY$. By the Addition Property of Equality $PX + XR + RY + YP = SX + XR + RY + YT = RS + RT$.

**20.** Since $\square ABCD$ is a parallelogram, $BM = DM$ (Theorem 9–18) and $\overline{AD} \parallel \overline{BC}$ (Definition). Consequently $\angle MBY \cong \angle MDX$ and $\angle MYB \cong \angle MXD$ (PAI Theorem). $\therefore \triangle MBY \cong \triangle MDX$ (SAA) and so $MX = MY$.

**21.** Theorem: The quadrilateral formed by joining the midpoints of the consecutive sides of a quadrilateral is a parallelogram.
Proof: Introduce diagonal $\overline{AC}$ in $\square ABCD$. Then in $\triangle ADC$, $\overline{SR}$ connects the midpoints of two sides of the triangle, and consequently, $\overline{SR} \parallel \overline{AC}$ and $SR = \frac{1}{2}AC$. Similarly, $\overline{PQ} \parallel \overline{AC}$ and $PQ = \frac{1}{2}AC$. Therefore $\overline{SR} \parallel \overline{PQ}$ and $SR = PQ$ so $\square SPQR$ is a parallelogram by Theorem 9–20.

---

**5.** In the figure, $\square ABCD$ and $\square AKRS$ are parallelograms. What is the relationship of $\angle D$ to $\angle R$? of $\angle R$ to $\angle C$? Prove your answer.

∠D and ∠R are supplementary, ∠C ≅ ∠R.
Proof: ∠R ≅ ∠A, ∠A and ∠D are supplementary
∠C ≅ ∠A
∠A ≅ ∠R
∴ ∠C ≅ ∠R

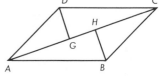

**6.** In the figure $\square AKMJ$ and $\square BMJK$ are parallelograms. If $KJ = KM$, then $\triangle ABC$ is isosceles.

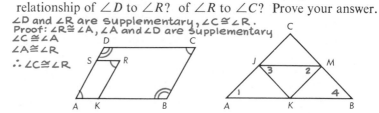

**7.** Prove Theorem 9–14.

**8.** Prove Corollary 9–15.1.

**9.** Prove Theorem 9–17.

**10.** Given a parallelogram and one diagonal. Prove that if segments from opposite vertices are perpendicular to the diagonal, the segments are parallel and congruent.

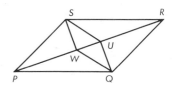

**11.** $\square PQRS$ is a parallelogram.

$PW = PS$    and    $RU = RQ$.

Prove that $\square SWQU$ is a parallelogram.

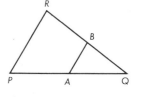

**12.** In $\triangle PQR$, $A$ and $B$ are midpoints of $\overline{PQ}$ and $\overline{RQ}$, respectively. If $RP = 16$, $m\angle P = 58$, and $m\angle Q = 38$, what are $AB$ and $m\angle ABR$? AB=8, m∠ABR=96

**13.** Given any triangle, $\triangle ABC$, with the midpoints of the sides, $P$, $Q$, and $R$. Prove that the perimeter of $\triangle PQR$ is one-half the perimeter of $\triangle ABC$. Use Theorem 9-22 three times.

**14.** In $\triangle GHK$, $S$, $T$, and $V$ are midpoints of sides. If the perimeter of $\triangle STV$ is $28\frac{1}{2}$, what is the perimeter of $\triangle GHK$? 57

**15.** (a) Do the diagonals of a quadrilateral always intersect each other?
(b) Sketch a quadrilateral $\square ABCD$ in which $B$ and $D$ are on the same side of diagonal $\overline{AC}$.
No, only a convex quadrilateral.

**16.** Prove: In a convex quadrilateral the sum of the measures of the angles is 360.

17. Prove: In a non-convex quadrilateral the measure of the angle whose interior does not intersect the interior of the quadrilateral equals the sum of the measures of the other three angles of the quadrilateral.

18. Given an isosceles triangle and a point $P$, of the base, other than its end points. If through $P$ a parallel to each congruent side is drawn, then (1) a parallelogram is formed, and (2) the perimeter of the parallelogram equals the sum of the lengths of the triangle's congruent sides.

19. In the plane figure, $\square ABCD$ and $\square BEFC$ are parallelograms. Prove that $\square AEFD$ is a parallelogram.
  $\overline{AD} \parallel \overline{BC}$, AD=BC and $\overline{BC} \parallel \overline{EF}$, BC=EF.
  (Def. and Th. 9-15)
  $\overline{AD} \parallel \overline{EF}$ (Th. 9-11) and AD=EF.
  □ AEFD is a parallelogram (Th. 9-20)

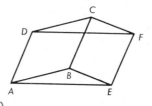

20. The diagonals $\overline{AC}$ and $\overline{BD}$ of the parallelogram $\square ABCD$ intersect at $M$. Prove that if $X$ and $Y$ are points on opposite sides of the parallelogram such that $\overline{XY}$ contains $M$, then $M$ bisects $\overline{XY}$.

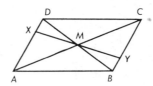

21. State and prove a theorem suggested by the figures given, where $P$, $Q$, $R$, and $S$ are midpoints. [*Hint:* Introduce a diagonal of $\square ABCD$.]

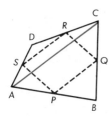
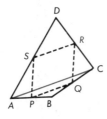
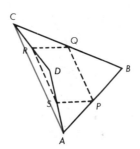

22. Prove: The segments joining the midpoints of opposite sides of any quadrilateral bisect each other. [*Hint:* See Problem 21.]
  Use Theorem above and Theorem 9-18.

23. A trapezoid is *isosceles* if its non-parallel sides are congruent. Show that the base angles of an isosceles trapezoid are congruent. [*Hint:* See Corollary 9–15.1.]

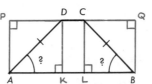

24. Prove that the diagonals of an isosceles trapezoid are congruent. Is the converse true? Yes

Answers to Problems

23. Let $\overline{DK}$ and $\overline{CL}$ be the perpendicular segments from $\overleftrightarrow{DC}$ to $\overleftrightarrow{AB}$. Since $\overleftrightarrow{DC} \parallel \overleftrightarrow{AB}$, $DK = CL$ by Corollary 9–15.1. Also $AD = BC$ by hypothesis, so the right triangles $\triangle ADK$ and $\triangle BCL$ are congruent by the Hypotenuse-Leg Theorem; therefore $\angle A \cong \angle B$.

24. Since $DA = CB$, $AB = BA$, and $\angle A \cong \angle B$ by Problem 23, $\triangle DAB \cong \triangle CBA$ by SAS, so $DB = CA$.

  The converse is also true: If the diagonals $\overline{DB}$ and $\overline{CA}$ of a trapezoid are congruent, then the trapezoid is isosceles. Proof: (See annotated figure for Problem 23.) Let $\overline{AP}$ and $\overline{BQ}$ be perpendicular segments from $\overleftrightarrow{AB}$ to $\overleftrightarrow{CD}$. Then $AP = BQ$, and $DB = CA$, so the right triangles $\triangle APC$ and $\triangle BQD$ are congruent by the Hypotenuse-Leg Theorem, so $\angle ACP \cong \angle BDQ$. Therefore $\angle ACD \cong \angle BDC$, $AC = BD$ by hypothesis and $CD = DC$ by identity, so $\triangle ACD \cong \triangle BDC$ by SAS and $AD = BC$.

25. Given $\square ABCD$ with the following properties: (1) $\square ABCD$ is a trapezoid, (2) $\angle A \cong \angle B$, (3) $\angle A$ and $\angle B$ are not supplementary. Note that we can conclude from (3) that $\overline{AD} \parallel \overline{BC}$, and therefore from (1) that $\overline{AB} \parallel \overline{CD}$. Note also that (3) now implies that $AB \neq CD$. Therefore, let us assume that $AB > CD$.

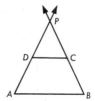

Proof: $\overrightarrow{AD}$ and $\overrightarrow{BC}$ intersect at a point $P$. Since $\angle A \cong \angle B$, $AP = BP$ by Theorem 5–5. Since $\overline{DC} \parallel \overline{AB}$, $\angle PDC \cong \angle A$, and $\angle PCD \cong \angle B$, then $\angle PDC \cong \angle PCD$. Hence by Theorem 5–5 again $DP = CP$. Finally, by subtraction, $AD = BC$.

26. (1) $A$ and $D$ are on the same side of $\overleftrightarrow{BC}$ because $\overrightarrow{AD} \parallel \overrightarrow{BC}$.
  (2) Similarly, $C$ and $D$ are on the same side of $\overleftrightarrow{AB}$.
  (3) $D$ is in the interior of $\angle A$ by the definition of the interior of an angle.

**27.** (1) In parallelogram $\square ABCD$, $D$ is in the interior of $\angle ABC$ by the preceding problem.

    (2) $\overrightarrow{BD}$ intersects $\overline{AC}$ by Problem 7 of Problem Set 6–6.

    (3) Similarly $\overrightarrow{DB}$ intersects $\overline{AC}$.

    (4) Recall that the intersection of $\overrightarrow{BD}$ and $\overrightarrow{DB}$ is $\overline{BD}$. Therefore, $\overline{BD}$ intersects $\overline{AC}$.

## 9–6 RHOMBUS, RECTANGLE, AND SQUARE

### Classroom Notes

Our discussion of the rhombus, rectangle, and square is brief. Theorems 9–24 and 9–25 are converses: If a parallelogram is a rhombus, then the diagonals of the parallelogram are perpendicular. If the diagonals of a parallelogram are perpendicular, then the parallelogram is a rhombus. Theorem 9–23 merely amends the definition of a rectangle. A square is, by definition, a rectangle all of whose sides are congruent. The student should be able to prove that if one of the angles of a rhombus is a right angle, then the rhombus is a square.

It is possible to conduct a thorough investigation of rhombuses, rectangles, and squares. Such an investigation would, however, be elementary, repetitious, and time consuming. It requires good judgment to know when to proceed formally and when to proceed informally: the student already has a firm grasp on the facts concerning parallelograms and this is, consequently, one time when we feel that we can proceed informally.

### Quiz

**1.** Which of the following conditions are sufficient to prove that a quadrilateral is a rectangle?

    (a) Its diagonals are congruent. (ans: No)

    (b) Two pairs of opposite sides are congruent. (ans: No)

---

**25.** Prove: If two consecutive angles of a trapezoid are congruent, but not supplementary, the trapezoid is isosceles.

**26.** Prove that if $\square ABCD$ is a parallelogram, then $D$ is in the interior of $\angle ABC$.

**27.** Prove that the diagonals of a parallelogram intersect each other. [*Hint:* Use Problem 26 above and the Crossbar Theorem, Problem 7, p. 206.]

## 9–6   RHOMBUS, RECTANGLE, AND SQUARE

### Definitions

A *rhombus* is a parallelogram all of whose sides are congruent.
A *rectangle* is a parallelogram all of whose angles are right angles.
A *square* is a rectangle all of whose sides are congruent.

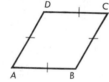 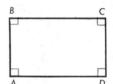 

As before, we leave the proofs of the following theorems to you.

### Theorem 9–23

*If a parallelogram has one right angle, then it has four right angles, and the parallelogram is a rectangle.*

### Theorem 9–24

*In a rhombus, the diagonals are perpendicular to one another.*

[*Hint:* See Corollary 6–2.1.]

### Theorem 9–25

*If the diagonals of a quadrilateral bisect each other and are perpendicular, then the quadrilateral is a rhombus.*

## Problem Set 9–6

1. Prove Theorem 9–23. By Th. 9-17, two consecutive angles are supplementary, if ∠A is a right angle, then so are ∠B, ∠C, and ∠D.

2. Explain how Corollary 6–2.1 is used to prove Theorem 9–24.
   AB = AD, CB = CD ⟹ $\overline{AC}$ is the perpendicular bisector of $\overline{BD}$ by corollary 6-2.1

3. Prove: The diagonals of a rectangle are congruent.

4. □*ABCD* is a rectangle and *P, Q, R, S* are the midpoints of its sides. If the diagonal $\overline{AC}$ has length 15, what is the perimeter of □*PQRS*? 30

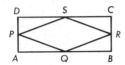

5. For each of the statements below, indicate whether it is true or false.

   (a) Every rectangle is a trapezoid. F

   (b) Every rhombus is a square. F

   (c) Every square is a rectangle. T

   (d) Every square is a parallelogram. T

   (e) Every rectangle is a square. F

   (f) Every square is a rhombus. T

   (g) The diagonals of a rhombus bisect each other. T

   (h) The diagonals of a rectangle are perpendicular to each other. F

   (i) The diagonals of a square are perpendicular and bisect each other. T

   (j) If the diagonals of a quadrilateral are perpendicular, the quadrilateral is a rhombus. F

   In rhombus □ ABCD introduce AC, △ADC ≅ △ABC (SSS) and
6. Prove: The diagonals of a rhombus bisect the angles of the rhombus.
   ∠DAC ≅ ∠BAC. m∠DAC + m∠BAC = 2m∠BAC = m∠A. $\overline{AC}$ is bisector of ∠A.

7. Given: △*ABC* with *AC = BC; P, Q,* and *R* are midpoints.

   Prove: □*PQCR* is a rhombus.

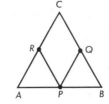

8. Given: □*MPQS* is a rhombus. *G, H, I,* and *K* are midpoints.

   Prove: □*GHIK* is a rectangle.

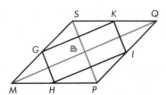

(c) It has three right angles.
   (ans: Yes)
(d) Its diagonals bisect each other.
   (ans: No)
2. Prove: the diagonals of a rhombus are perpendicular.
   (ans: Given rhombus □*ABCD* with diagonals $\overline{BD}$ and $\overline{AC}$. Since □*ABCD* is also a parallelogram, the diagonals bisect each other at *M* by Theorem 9–18. In △*BCM* and △*DCM*, *MB = DM* (definition of bisect), *BC = CD* (definition of rhombus) and *CM = CM* so △*BCM* ≅ △*DCM* by SSS. Thus ∠*BMC* ≅ ∠*DMC*. Since these angles are congruent and supplementary (they form a linear pair), they are right angles. Hence $\overline{BD} \perp \overline{CA}$.)

### Explanation for Problems

Problem 9 of this Problem Set investigates the *properties* of each of these quadrilaterals; Problem 10 investigates the question of what conditions are sufficient to prove that a quadrilateral is a rhombus, and so on. Problems 9 and 10 include a large number of facts about quadrilaterals, and the teacher should explain how to handle them. It is convenient to organize the answers in table form. We recommend that you do not assign all of Problem 9 and Problem 10 at the same time.

   Problem Set 9–6 includes, in addition, a few representative "originals": Problem 15 is an exercise in proving that a figure is a parallelogram; Problem 13, a rhombus; Problem 8, a rectangle; and Problem 11, a square.

### Answers to Problems

   **3.** In rectangle □*ABCD*, introduce diagonals $\overline{AC}$ and $\overline{BD}$. Since *AD = BC* (Theorem 9–15), *AB = AB*, and ∠*A* ≅ ∠*B* (from definition), △*ABD* ≅ △*BAC* (SAS) and *AC = BD*.

   **7.** Since the segment between the midpoints of two sides of a triangle is parallel to the third side, □*PQCR* is, by definition, a parallelogram. Since the segment between the midpoints of two sides of a triangle is half as long as the third side and since it is given that $AC = BC$, $PQ = QC = CR = RP$. ∴ Parallelogram $\square PQCR$ is, by definition, a rhombus.

8. Introduce diagonals $\overline{MQ}$ and $\overline{SP}$. Designate the points of intersection $B$. (See annotated figure in text.) (1) By the Theorem in Problem 21, Section 9–5, the quadrilateral formed by joining the midpoints of the consecutive sides of *any* quadrilateral is a parallelogram; ∴ $\square GHIK$ is a parallelogram. (2) By Theorem 9–22, $\overline{GH} \parallel \overline{SP}$ and by Theorem 9–24 $\overline{MQ} \perp \overline{SP}$. Therefore $\overline{MQ} \perp \overline{GH}$ by Theorem 9–12. But $\overline{GK} \parallel \overline{MQ}$ by Theorem 9–22, so that $\overline{GH} \perp \overline{GK}$ by Theorem 9–12, and $\angle HGK$ is a right angle. (3) Therefore, by Theorem 9–23, $\square GHIK$ is a rectangle.

11. (1) By SAS, the four triangles are congruent, and consequently $\overline{JK} \cong \overline{KL} \cong \overline{LM} \cong \overline{MJ}$. (2) Since the *opposite* sides of $\square JKLM$ are congruent, $\square JKLM$ is a parallelogram (Theorem 9–19). (3) Since the right triangles $\triangle KLP$ and $\triangle LMQ$ are congruent, $\angle KLP$ and $\angle MLQ$ are complementary. (4) Therefore the third angle at $L$, $\angle KLM$ is a right angle. (5) Since parallelogram $\square JKLM$ has one right angle, it has, by Theorem 9–23 four right angles and is therefore a rectangle. (6) But by step 1, all four sides of $\square JKLM$ are congruent, so $\square JKLM$ is, by definition, a square.

12. Given: $\square AQBP$ with diagonals $\overline{PQ} \perp \overline{AB}$ at $M$, $AM = MB$, $PM \neq MQ$
Prove:
(1) $PA = PB$,
    $QA = QB$.
(2) $AP \neq BQ$
    and $AQ \neq BP$.

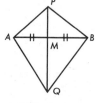

Proof: Part (1). Since $\overline{PQ}$ is the perpendicular bisector of $\overline{AB}$, $P$ is equidistant from $A$ and $B$ and $Q$ is equidistant from $A$ and $B$ (Theorem 6–2). Part (2). Indirect proof. Suppose the opposite sides of kite $\square AQBP$ are congruent: $AP = BQ$ and $AQ = BP$. By Theorem 9–19, if the opposite sides of a quadrilateral are congruent, the quadrilateral is a parallelogram. And, by Theorem 9–18, the diagonals of a parallelogram bisect each other: $AM = MB$ and $PM = MQ$. This contradicts the hypothesis that $PM \neq MQ$.

9. For which of the four quadrilaterals—parallelogram, rectangle, rhombus, square—can each of the following properties be proved?

(a) The diagonals bisect each other. P, R, Rh, S

(b) The diagonals are congruent. R, S

(c) Consecutive angles are congruent. R, S

(d) The diagonals bisect the angles of the quadrilateral. Rh, S

(e) The diagonals are perpendicular. Rh, S

(f) Opposite angles are congruent. P, R, Rh, S

(g) The diagonals are congruent and perpendicular. S

10. Would the following conditions for a quadrilateral be sufficient to prove that it is a parallelogram? a rectangle? a rhombus? a square? Consider each item separately.

(a) It has two pairs of parallel sides. P

(b) Three of its angles are right angles. R, and consequently P

(c) It is equilateral. Rh, and consequently P

(d) Its diagonals are congruent and perpendicular. None

(e) Each pair of consecutive angles is supplementary. P

(f) Two sides are parallel. None [A trapezoid, but a trapezoid is not listed in this problem.]

(g) Its diagonals bisect each other. P

(h) Its diagonals are congruent, are perpendicular, and bisect each other. S, and consequently R, Rh, and P

11. Given: $\square PQRS$ is a square. $J, K, L, M$ separate the sides into segments, as in the figure, of lengths $a$ and $b$.

Prove: $\square JKLM$ is a square.

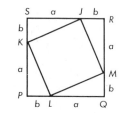

12. A quadrilateral in which exactly one diagonal is the perpendicular bisector of the other diagonal is called a *kite*. Prove that a kite has two pairs of congruent sides, but that its opposite sides are not congruent.

13. Given a parallelogram $\square ABCD$, with $AD > AB$. The bisector of $\angle A$ intersects $\overline{BC}$ at $G$, and the bisector of $\angle B$ intersects $\overline{AD}$ at $H$. Prove that $\square ABGH$ is a rhombus.

14. In the convex quadrilateral $\square ABCD$, $\overline{AD}$ is the shortest side and $\overline{BC}$ is the longest side. Prove that $\angle D > \angle B$. [*Hint:* Draw a diagonal.] Is this theorem true if $\square ABCD$ is not required to be convex?

**15.** Prove: If in $\square ABCD$, $\angle A \cong \angle C$ and $\angle B \cong \angle D$, then $\square ABCD$ is a parallelogram. [*Hint:* Introduce a diagonal and use variables for angle measures. Apply Theorem 9–13.]

## 9–7  SOME THEOREMS ON RIGHT TRIANGLES

Our knowledge of quadrilaterals gives us some information about right triangles.

### Theorem 9–26

***The median to the hypotenuse of a right triangle is half as long as the hypotenuse.***

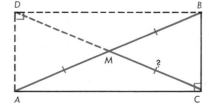

**Proof.** Given $\triangle ABC$, with $\angle C$ a right angle and $M$ the midpoint of $\overline{AB}$. Take a point $D$ on $\overrightarrow{CM}$ such that $\square ADBC$ is a parallelogram. (How do you find such a point?) Then $\square ADBC$ is a rectangle. (Why?) Then $CD = AB$. (Why?) Therefore $CM = \frac{1}{2}AB$, which is what we wanted.

The theorem below tells us something about the shapes of certain special triangles.

### Theorem 9–27  The 30–60–90 Triangle Theorem

***If an acute angle of a right triangle has measure 30, then the opposite side is half as long as the hypotenuse.***

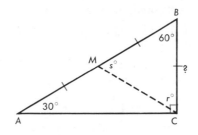

**Proof.** Given $\triangle ABC$, with a right angle at $C$ and with $m\angle A = 30$. Let $M$ be the midpoint of the hypotenuse $\overline{AB}$. Then by Theorem 9–26 we know that $AM = MB = MC$, as indicated in the figure.

Now $m\angle B = 60$. (Why?) Therefore $r = 60$, by the Isosceles Triangle Theorem.

But $r + s + 60 = 180$. Therefore $s = 60$, and $\triangle MBC$ is equiangular. Therefore $\triangle MBC$ is equilateral. Therefore $BC = MC = \frac{1}{2}AB$, which was to be proved.

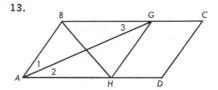
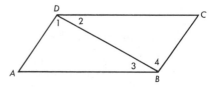

△ABD to conclude that $m\angle A + m\angle 1 + m\angle 3 = 180$, and to △BCD to conclude that $m\angle C + m\angle 2 + m\angle 4 = 180$. Hence by the AAP and the Addition Property of Equality, $m\angle A + m\angle B + m\angle C + m\angle D = 360$. But by hypothesis, $m\angle A = m\angle C$ and $m\angle B = m\angle D$; $\therefore 2m\angle A + 2m\angle B = 360$, or $m\angle A + m\angle B = 180$. $\overline{AD} \parallel \overline{BC}$ by Theorem 9–8. It can be shown similarly that $\overline{AB} \parallel \overline{CD}$. Hence $\square ABCD$ is a parallelogram by definition.

## 9–7 SOME THEOREMS ON RIGHT TRIANGLES

### Classroom Notes

We cannot prove that in a 30-60-90 triangle the longer leg is $\sqrt{3}/2$ times as long as the hypotenuse (Theorem 11–12) until we have the Pythagorean Theorem (Theorem 11–9).

### Quiz

**1.** In △ABC, $m\angle B = 90$ and $AC = 16\sqrt{2}$. If $D$ is the midpoint of $\overline{AC}$, what is $BD$?
(ans: $8\sqrt{2}$)
**2.** In △KEM, $m\angle M = 90$, $KE = 12\sqrt{3}$, $KM = 6\sqrt{3}$. What is $m\angle K$?
(ans: 60)

### Explanation for Problems

Problems 1, 2, 5, 10 and 14 involve the use of Theorem 9–26; Problems 11 and 13, the use of the theorem in Problem 9; Problems 6, 7, 8 and 12, the use of Theorem 9–27; and Problems 3 and 4, the use of Theorem 9–28.

We sometimes refer to this theorem by saying that "in a 30-60-90 triangle, the hypotenuse is twice as long as the shorter leg."

The converse of this theorem is also true.

### Theorem 9–28

*If one leg of a right triangle is half as long as the hypotenuse, then the opposite angle has measure 30.*

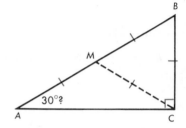

**Proof.** Given △ABC, with a right angle at $C$, and $BC = \frac{1}{2}AB$. Let $M$ be the midpoint of $\overline{AB}$. Then $AM = MB = BC$. By Theorem 9–26, $MC = MB$. (We have now justified all the marks in the figure.)

Since △MBC is equilateral, it is equiangular. Therefore $m\angle B = 60$. By Corollary 9–13.2, $m\angle A = 30$, which was to be proved.

### Problem Set 9–7

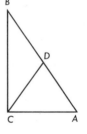

**1.** In △ABC, $\angle C$ is a right angle, $AB = 16$, and $\overline{CD}$ is a median. What is the length of $\overline{CD}$?  CD=8

**2.** In △ABC, $\angle C$ is a right angle, $AC = 6$, and the length of median $\overline{CD}$ is 5. What is $AB$?  AB=10

**3.** In △GHK, $\angle H$ is a right angle and $GH = \frac{1}{2}GK$. What is $m\angle K$? What theorem did you use?  m∠k=30, Theorem 9-28

**4.** In the figure, $RQ = 2RP$. What is the measure of $\angle R$?  m∠R=60

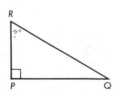

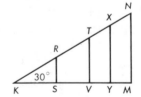

RS=3, TV=5, XY=6½, MN=8, Theorem 9-27.
**5.** In △KMN, $\angle M$ is a right angle and $m\angle K = 30$. $\overline{RS}$, $\overline{TV}$, and $\overline{XY}$ are each perpendicular to $\overline{KM}$. If $KR = 6$, $KT = 10$, $KX = 13$, and $KN = 16$, what are $RS$, $TV$, $XY$, and $MN$? What theorem did you use?

**6.** In the figure, $\overline{AC} \perp \overline{AB}$ and $\overline{AD} \perp \overline{BC}$. If $BC = 12$, what is $AB$? What is $DB$?
AB=6, DB=3

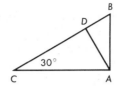

**7.** In an equilateral triangle $\triangle GHK$, the altitude $\overline{GM}$ has length 9. Through $M$, perpendiculars are drawn to the other two sides. Prove that these perpendicular segments are congruent, and find their length.

**8.** In the figure, $\overline{AD}$ is a median, $BC = CE$, and $m\angle GCE = 30$. If $AD = 6$, what is $KM$? KM=1½

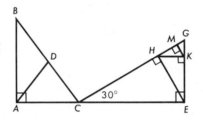

---

**9.** Prove the converse of Theorem 9–26:

In a triangle, if a median is half as long as the side which it bisects, then the triangle is a right triangle and the side is its hypotenuse.

Given: $\triangle ABC$, median $\overline{AD}$, $AD = \frac{1}{2}BC$.

Prove: $\triangle ABC$ is a right triangle, and $\overline{BC}$ is its hypotenuse.

[*Hint:* Prove $x + y = 90$.]

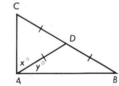

**10.** In the figure, $F$ is the midpoint of $\overline{AE}$, and $\angle ABE$, $\angle ACE$, and $\angle ADE$ are right angles. Prove that $F$ is equidistant from $A$, $B$, $C$, $D$, and $E$.

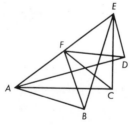

---

Apply theorem of Problem 9 to △XPY and △XQY to conclude $\overline{XQ} \perp \overline{YQ}$ and $\overline{XP} \perp \overline{YP}$.

**11.** $\triangle PQR$ is isosceles, with $PR = QR = a$. $L$ is any line through $R$, but not containing $P$ or $Q$. $X$ and $Y$ are two points of $L$ at distance $a$ from $R$. Prove that $\overline{XP} \perp \overline{YP}$ and $\overline{XQ} \perp \overline{YQ}$.

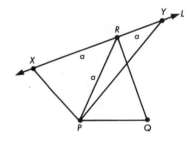

**12.** In any right triangle, the altitude to the hypotenuse separates the hypotenuse into two segments. Prove that in a 30-60-90 triangle, the lengths of these segments are in the ratio 1 : 3.
Use Th. 9-27 twice.

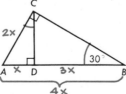

## Answers to Problems

**13.** (1) Since $P$ and $Q$ are the midpoints of $\overline{AC}$ and $\overline{AB}$ respectively, $PQ = \frac{1}{2}CB$ by Theorem 9–22. (2) Since $\overline{AD} \perp E$, $\overline{AD} \perp \overline{DB}$ by definition, and thus $\triangle ADB$ is a right triangle. Applying Theorem 9–26 to $\triangle ADB$ we conclude $DQ = \frac{1}{2}AB$. (3) Similarly $DP = \frac{1}{2}AC$. (4) But since $\triangle ABC$ is equilateral, $AB = AC = CB$. $\therefore PQ = DQ = DP$ and $\triangle PDQ$ is equilateral.

## 9–8 TRANSVERSALS TO MANY PARALLEL LINES

**Classroom Notes**

Theorem 9–29 is a preliminary lemma which simplifies the proof of Theorem 9–30. Note that two special cases can arise in the proof of Theorem 9–30: $T_2$ contains $A$ and $T_2$ contains $B$, the proof of each of these special cases is obvious once a figure is drawn.

**13.** In the figure, $\triangle ABC$ is equilateral, $\overline{AD} \perp E$ at $D$, and $P$ and $Q$ are the midpoints of $\overline{AC}$ and $\overline{AB}$, respectively. Prove that $\triangle PDQ$ is equilateral.

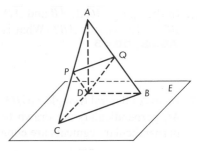

## 9–8  TRANSVERSALS TO MANY PARALLEL LINES

**Definitions**

If a transversal intersects two lines $L_1$, $L_2$ in points $A$ and $B$, then we say that $L_1$ and $L_2$ *intercept* the segment $\overline{AB}$ on the transversal.

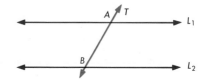

Suppose that we have given three lines $L_1$, $L_2$, $L_3$ and a transversal intersecting them in points $A$, $B$, and $C$. If $AB = BC$, then we say that the three lines *intercept congruent segments* on the transversal.

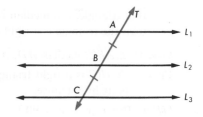

We shall show that if three parallel lines intercept congruent segments on one transversal, then they intercept congruent segments on any other transversal. Our first step is to prove the following theorem.

**Theorem 9–29**

*If three parallel lines intercept congruent segments on one transversal T, then they intercept congruent segments on every transversal T′ which is parallel to T.*

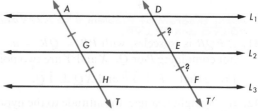

**Proof.** First we observe that $\square AGED$ and $\square GHFE$ are parallelograms. (Why?) We have given $AG = GH$. By Theorem 9–15, $AG = DE$ and $GH = EF$. Therefore $DE = EF$.

We can now prove the theorem in the general case. You should be able to fill in the details in the proof.

**Theorem 9–30**

*If three parallel lines intercept congruent segments on one transversal, then they intercept congruent segments on any other transversal.*

**Restatement.** Given $L_1 \parallel L_2 \parallel L_3$ and transversals $T_1$ and $T_2$, with $AB = BC$. We must prove that $DE = EF$.

**Proof.** By Theorem 9–29, we already know that $DE = EF$ if $T_2 \parallel T_1$. Therefore we consider the case that $T_2$ and $T_1$ are not parallel.

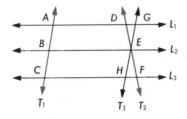

(1) First introduce transversal $T_3$ through $E$ and parallel to $T_1$. $T_3$ intersects $L_1$ at $G$ and $L_3$ at $H$.

(2) We now know that $GE = EF$. (Why?)

(3) Also, $\angle GDE \cong \angle EFH$ and $\angle DGE \cong \angle EHF$. (Why?)

(4) Therefore, $\triangle GDE \cong \triangle HFE$ (Why?) and $DE = EF$, which is what we had to prove.

Theorem 9–30 extends to any number of parallel lines as Corollary 9–30.1 shows.

**Corollary 9–30.1**

*If three or more parallel lines intercept congruent segments on one transversal, then they intercept congruent segments on any other transversal.*

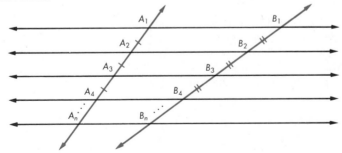

That is, given that $A_1A_2 = A_2A_3 = A_3A_4 = \cdots$, it follows that $B_1B_2 = B_2B_3 = B_3B_4 = \cdots$, and so on. This follows by repeated applications of the theorem that we have just proved.

## Answers to Problems

**2.** Given: $D$ is the midpoint of $\overline{AC}$.
   $L$ contains $D$ and $L \parallel \overleftrightarrow{AB}$.
   $L$ intersects $\overline{CB}$ at a point $E$.
Prove: $E$ is the midpoint of $\overline{BC}$.

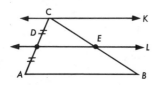

Proof: Let $K$ be the line through $C$ and parallel to $\overleftrightarrow{AB}$. Then $K \parallel L \parallel \overleftrightarrow{AB}$ by Theorem 9–11. Now apply Theorem 9–30: Since the three parallel lines $K$, $L$, and $\overleftrightarrow{AB}$ intercept congruent segments on $\overleftrightarrow{AC}$, they intercept congruent segments on $\overleftrightarrow{BC}$: $BE = EC$.

**3.** By the theorem in Problem 2 of this set, since $\overleftrightarrow{DE}$ bisects $\overline{AC}$ and $\overleftrightarrow{DE} \parallel \overleftrightarrow{AB}$, $\overleftrightarrow{DE}$ bisects $\overline{CB}$: $CE = EB$. Since $\overleftrightarrow{DE} \parallel \overleftrightarrow{AB}$, the corresponding angles, $\angle CED$ and $\angle EBF$ are congruent by Corollary 9–9.1. Similarly, since $\overleftrightarrow{EF} \parallel \overleftrightarrow{AC}$, the corresponding angles, $\angle DCE$ and $\angle FEB$, are congruent. Therefore $\triangle CDE \cong \triangle EFB$ (ASA).

**4.** Let $M$ be the midpoint of the diagonal $\overline{DB}$, and let $E$ and $F$ be the midpoints of the sides $\overline{DA}$ and $\overline{CB}$ respectively. Then $\overleftrightarrow{EM} \parallel \overleftrightarrow{AB}$ and $\overleftrightarrow{MF} \parallel \overleftrightarrow{DC}$ by Theorem 9–22 and $\overleftrightarrow{DC} \parallel \overleftrightarrow{AB}$ by hypothesis, so $\overleftrightarrow{MF} \parallel \overleftrightarrow{AB}$ by Theorem 9–11. Thus $\overleftrightarrow{EM}$ and $\overleftrightarrow{MF}$ are both lines through $M$ parallel to $\overleftrightarrow{AB}$, so $E$, $M$, and $F$ are collinear and $M$ lies on the median $\overline{EF}$ of the trapezoid.

---

### Problem Set 9–8

**1.** Given: $AB = BC$,
   $\overline{AP} \parallel \overline{BQ} \parallel \overline{CR}$,
   $\overline{PX} \parallel \overline{QY} \parallel \overline{RZ}$.

Prove: $XY = YZ$. *Apply Theorem 9–30 twice*
Must $\overleftrightarrow{AC}$ and $\overleftrightarrow{XZ}$ be coplanar for the proof to hold? *No*

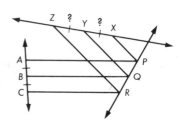

**2.** Prove the following theorem.

If a line bisects one side of a triangle and is parallel to a second side, then it bisects the third side.

**3.** In the figure,

$$\overleftrightarrow{DE} \parallel \overleftrightarrow{AB}, \quad \overleftrightarrow{EF} \parallel \overleftrightarrow{AC},$$

and $D$ is the midpoint of $\overline{AC}$. Prove that

$$\triangle CDE \cong \triangle EFB.$$

[*Hint:* Use the theorem of Problem 2.]

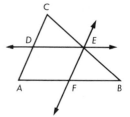

**4.** Show that the median of a trapezoid is parallel to the bases. [*Hint:* Let $L$ be the line parallel to the bases, through the midpoint of one of the sloping sides. Show that $L$ contains the median.]

**5.** Prove that the median of a trapezoid bisects each diagonal of the trapezoid. [*Hint:* Use the result of Problem 4.]

**6.** Prove the following theorem.

The median of a trapezoid is one-half the sum of the bases.
*From 4, $EM = \frac{1}{2}AB$ and $MF = \frac{1}{2}DC$ (Th. 9–22).*
**Restatement.** Given a trapezoid $\square ABCD$ with median $\overline{EF}$, as in the figure. Then

$$EF = \tfrac{1}{2}(AB + CD).$$
*So $EF = EM + MF = \frac{1}{2}(AB + DC)$*

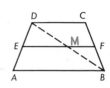

**7.** $\square ABCD$ is a trapezoid with $\overline{AB} \parallel \overline{DC}$. $\overline{EF}$ is the median.
   (a) If $AB = 12$ and $DC = 7$, then $EF = $ ? *9.5*
   (b) If $AB = 14$ and $DC = 14$, then $EF = $ ? *14*
   (c) If $DC = 6$ and $EF = 14$, then $AB = $ ? *22*
   (d) If $AB = 27$ and $EF = 18$, then $DC = $ ? *9*

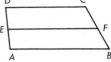

## 9-9 THE MEDIAN CONCURRENCE THEOREM

### Definition

Two or more lines are *concurrent* if there is a single point which lies on all of them. The common point is called the *point of concurrency*.

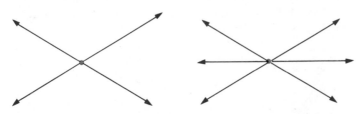

Of course, it is easy for *two* lines in the same plane to be concurrent. This is what we expect, when we draw two lines at random: if two lines happen to be parallel, and we rotate one of them even a little bit, they become concurrent.

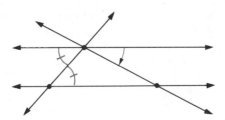

But for *three* lines to be concurrent is another matter. We normally expect three lines in a plane to contain a triangle.

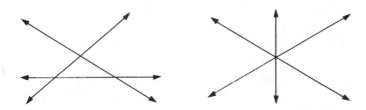

If they happen to be concurrent, and we move one of them even a little bit, the chances are that the lines will not be concurrent any more.

Under certain conditions, however, we can show that three lines must be concurrent. The following theorem shows that this is true for the three medians of a triangle.

**Answers to Problems**

5.
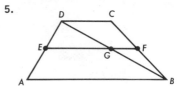

[Note: The median of a trapezoid has the following properties: (1) It is parallel to the parallel sides, (2) Its end points are the midpoints of the non-parallel sides of the trapezoid.]

Designate the intersection of median $\overline{EF}$ and diagonal $\overline{DB}$ by G. Now apply the Theorem in Problem 2 of this set to $\triangle DAB$: Since $\overleftrightarrow{EF}$ bisects $\overline{AD}$ and $\overleftrightarrow{EF} \parallel \overleftrightarrow{AB}$, $\overleftrightarrow{EF}$ bisects $\overline{DB}$, that is, $DG = GB$. It can be similarly shown that median $\overline{EF}$ bisects the other diagonal $\overline{AC}$.

**Theorem 9-31.**   The Median Concurrence Theorem

*The medians of every triangle are concurrent. Their point of concurrency is two-thirds of the way along each median, from the vertex to the opposite side.*

**Restatement.**   In $\triangle ABC$, let $D$, $E$, and $F$ be the midpoints of $\overline{BC}$, $\overline{AB}$, and $\overline{AC}$ respectively. Then the medians $\overline{AD}$, $\overline{BF}$, and $\overline{CE}$ intersect in a point $P$ such that $AP = \frac{2}{3}AD$, $BP = \frac{2}{3}BF$, and $CP = \frac{2}{3}CE$.

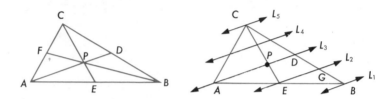

**Proof.**   (1) As shown in the figure on the right above, let $L_1$, $L_2$, $L_3$, $L_4$, and $L_5$ be parallel lines, dividing $\overline{BC}$ into four congruent segments, with $L_3 = \overleftrightarrow{AD}$. Let $P$ be the point where the medians $\overline{AD}$ and $\overline{CE}$ intersect.

(2) Since $L_1$, $L_2$, $L_3$, $L_4$, and $L_5$ divide $\overline{BC}$ into four congruent segments, it follows that $L_1$, $L_2$, and $L_3$ divide $\overline{BD}$ into two congruent segments. By Theorem 9-30, $L_1$, $L_2$, and $L_3$ divide $\overline{AB}$ into two congruent segments. Therefore $L_2$ *intersects* $\overline{AB}$ at $E$.

(3) Now $L_2$, $L_3$, $L_4$, and $L_5$ divide $\overline{GC}$ into three congruent segments. (Why?) By Theorem 9-30, $L_2$, $L_3$, $L_4$, and $L_5$ divide $\overline{CE}$ into three congruent segments. Therefore $CP = \frac{2}{3}CE$. Thus what we know so far is:

(4) *The medians $\overline{CE}$ and $\overline{AD}$ intersect at a point $P$ such that $CP = \frac{2}{3}CE$.*
By exactly the same reasoning, using lines parallel to $\overline{BF}$, we get:

(5) The medians $\overline{CE}$ and $\overline{BF}$ intersect at a point $P'$, such that $CP' = \frac{2}{3}CE$.

But by the Point-Plotting Theorem, this means that $P = P'$. Therefore *all three medians intersect in the same point $P$, and $CP = \frac{2}{3}CE$.*

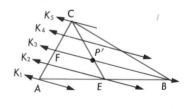

Finally, we need to show that $AP = \frac{2}{3}AD$ and $BP = \frac{2}{3}BF$. This is clear from an inspection of the following figure.

The parallel lines divide $\overline{AC}$, $\overline{BC}$, and $\overline{CE}$ into six congruent segments, so that $P$ lies on $M_3$. Therefore the lines divide $\overline{AD}$ and $\overline{BF}$ into three congruent segments, with $P$ two-thirds of the way up on each median.

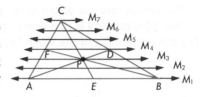

The point of intersection of the medians has an important application: it is the center of gravity of the triangle. This means that, for example, a piece of a board cut in a triangular shape would balance on the point of a pin placed precisely at the point of intersection of the three medians. This point is called the *centroid* of the triangle.

## Problem Set 9–9

1. In the figure on the right $\overline{AD}$ and $\overline{CE}$ are medians. If $AD = 15$ and $CE = 12$, what are $AP$ and $CP$? AP = 10, CP = 8

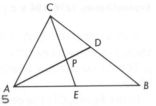

2. $\overline{AD}$ and $\overline{CE}$ are medians. If $PE = 2$ and $PD = 3.5$, what are $CP$ and $AP$? What are $CE$ and $AD$? CP = 4, AP = 7, CE = 6, AD = 10.5

3. In $\triangle MNK$ on the left below $\overline{MS}$ and $\overline{NR}$ are medians. If $MS = 15$, $NR = 18$, and $MN = 21$, what is the perimeter of $\triangle PRS$? 21.5

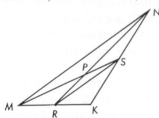

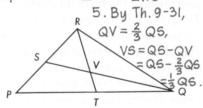

5. By Th. 9-31,
$QV = \frac{2}{3} QS$,
$VS = QS - QV$
$= QS - \frac{2}{3}QS$
$= \frac{1}{3}QS$.

4. $\triangle RSV$ on the right above is equilateral and $S$ and $T$ are midpoints of sides $\overline{PR}$ and $\overline{PQ}$, respectively. If the perimeter of $\triangle RSV$ is 12, what are $RT$ and $QS$? RT = 6, QS = 12

5. Prove that the length of the segment whose end points are (1) the centroid of a triangle and (2) the midpoint of a side of the triangle is one-third the length of the median to that side.
    Use $\triangle PQR$ above.

6. Given the figure with midpoints $E$, $F$, $G$, $H$, and $K$. $AF = AG$ and $CE = CH$. Prove that $\triangle EPF \cong \triangle HQG$.

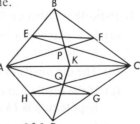

$PF = \frac{1}{3}AF$ and $QG = \frac{1}{3}AG$. (See Prob. 5.)
Since $AF = AG$, $PF = QG$. Also $PE = \frac{1}{3}CE$
and $QH = \frac{1}{3}CH$, So $PE = QH$. By Th. 9-22,
$EF = \frac{1}{2}AC$ and $HG = \frac{1}{2}AC$. So $\triangle EPF \cong \triangle HQG$ by SSS.□

Nearly all of the significant applications of elementary mathematics are commonly taught, and can best be taught, in science courses, because their main intellectual substance is in natural science, and their scientific background cannot be explained in a mathematics course without prohibitively long digressions.

This historical note represents one of the rare and happy exceptions to the general rule.

The circumference of the earth at the equator is about 40 065 metres. In the third century B.C. a Greek mathematician, Eratosthenes, measured the circumference of the earth in the following way.

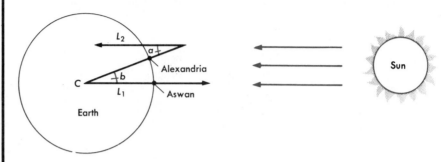

**Eratosthenes (276-194 B.C.)**

It was observed that at Aswan on the Nile, at noon on the summer solstice, the sun was exactly overhead. That is, at noon on this day, a vertical pole cast no shadow at all, and the bottom of a deep well was completely lit up.

In the figure, $C$ is the center of the earth. At noon on the summer solstice, in Alexandria, Eratosthenes measured the angle marked $\angle a$ on the figure, that is, the angle between a vertical pole and the ray from the top of the pole through the tip of its shadow. He found that this was an angle of about 7 degrees 12 minutes, or about 1/50 of a complete circumference.

Assuming that the sun's rays are parallel, it follows that $\angle a \cong \angle b$. Therefore the distance from Aswan to Alexandria must be about 1/50 of the circumference of the earth.

The distance from Aswan to Alexandria was known to be about 5000 Greek stadia. Eratosthenes concluded that the circumference of the earth must be about 250 000 stadia, which is equivalent to about 39 682 km. Thus Eratosthenes' error was well under two percent.

## CHAPTER REVIEW

### SET A

1. Indicate whether each statement is true or false.

   (a) In a plane, if a line is parallel to one of two parallels, it is parallel to the other.  T

   (b) The diagonals of a rhombus bisect the angles of the rhombus.  T

   (c) If the median to the hypotenuse of a right triangle is 7 cm long, the hypotenuse is 14 cm long.  T

   (d) Every parallelogram is a trapezoid.  F

(e) If two lines are cut by a transversal, the corresponding angles are congruent. **F**

(f) Either diagonal of a parallelogram forms, with the sides, two congruent triangles. **T**

(g) The diagonals of a rhombus are congruent. **F**

(h) If one leg of a 30-60-90 triangle is 8 cm long, the hypotenuse is 16 cm long. **F**

(i) Two lines are either parallel or intersecting. **F**

(j) In a plane, if a line intersects one of two parallel lines in only one point, then it intersects the other. **T**

2. Complete each statement.

(a) If two parallel lines are cut by a transversal, the interior angles on the same side of the transversal are _supplementary_ .

(b) If two angles of a triangle are congruent to two angles of another triangle, then _the third angles are congruent_

(c) The acute angles of a right triangle are _complementary_ .

(d) The hypotenuse of a 30-60-90 triangle is of length 13. The leg opposite the _30°_ angle is congruent to the _median_ to the hypotenuse, and the length of each is _6.5_ .

(e) If three or more parallels intercept _congruent_ segments on one transversal, then _they intercept congruent segments on any other transversal._

(f) The Parallel Postulate establishes the _uniqueness_ of a line which contains a point and which is _parallel_ to a line which does not contain the point.

3. For each example, select the one choice which makes the statement true.

(a) If the diagonals of a quadrilateral bisect each other, the quadrilateral is a _____ .

 (i) rhombus  (ii) square  (iii) parallelogram  (iv) rectangle

(b) The figure formed by joining the consecutive midpoints of the sides of any quadrilateral is _____ .

 (i) a rectangle  (ii) a parallelogram

 (iii) a rhombus  (iv) none of these

(c) The bisectors of the opposite angles of a nonrhombic parallelogram are _____ .

 (i) parallel  (ii) collinear  (iii) perpendicular  (iv) skew

(d) The bisectors of the interior angles on the same side of a transversal to two parallel lines are _____ .

 (i) parallel  (ii) perpendicular

 (iii) intersecting, but not perpendicular  (iv) skew

---

**Answers to Chapter Review Problems**

**3.** Since the opposite sides of parallelogram $\square GHKM$ are congruent, $MK = GH$. But, by hypothesis, $MQ = HP$; hence by subtraction $QK = GP$. Since the opposite sides of parallelogram $\square GHKM$ are parallel, $\angle QKR \cong \angle RGP$ and $\angle KQR \cong \angle GPR$ by PAI. $\therefore \triangle KQR \cong \triangle GPR$ (ASA) and thus $GR = KR$ and $PR = QR$.

**4.** Since $\square DEBF$ is a parallelogram, its diagonals bisect each other: $BG = GD$ and $EG = GF$ (Theorem 9–18). By hypothesis, $AE = FC$, so by addition: $AE + EG = GF + FC$, and since $A$-$E$-$G$ and $G$-$F$-$C$, $AG = GC$. Now since the diagonals of $\square ABCD$ bisect each other, $\square ABCD$ is a parallelogram by Theorem 9–21, the converse of Theorem 9–18.

**5.** Given: □ABCD is a parallelogram.
$\overrightarrow{AE}$ bisects $\angle A$; $\overrightarrow{BF}$ bisects $\angle B$.
$\overrightarrow{AE}$ and $\overrightarrow{BF}$
intersect at $P$.
Prove: $\overrightarrow{AP} \perp \overrightarrow{BP}$.

Proof: By Theorem 9-17, $m\angle ABD + m\angle BAC = 180$; hence $\frac{1}{2}m\angle ABD + \frac{1}{2}m\angle BAC = 90$. Since $\overrightarrow{AP}$ bisects $\angle A$, $m\angle ABP = \frac{1}{2}m\angle ABD$, and similarly, $m\angle BAP = \frac{1}{2}m\angle BAC$. $\therefore m\angle ABP + m\angle BAP = 90$. But since the sum of the measures of the angles of a triangle is 180 (Theorem 9-13) this implies that $\angle APB = 90$. $\therefore \overrightarrow{AP} \perp \overrightarrow{BP}$.

**7.** Alternative Answer: The proof of Theorem 9-11 depends on acceptance of the Parallel Postulate. But the hypothesis of the problem contains information contradictory to the Parallel Postulate, namely, two lines through one point, $P$, both parallel to the same line, $L$. Therefore, under the Parallel Postulate, the conclusion must be false.

**9.** Given: $L_1$ and $L_2$ intersect at $P$.
$L \perp L_1$.
Prove: $L$ is not perpendicular to $L_2$.

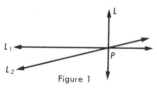

Figure 1

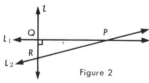

Figure 2

There are two cases to consider: (1) $L$ contains $P$, (2) $L$ does not contain $P$, but the proofs are essentially the same.
Proof by contradiction: Suppose $L \perp L_2$. Then we have two lines $L_1$ and $L_2$ each perpendicular to $L$. In case (1) $L_1$ and $L_2$ are two different perpendiculars to $L$ at a point $P$ of the line $L$, contradicting Theorem 6-1. In case (2), $L_1$ and $L_2$ are two different perpendiculars to $L$ through a given external point, contradicting Theorem 6-4. Therefore $L$ cannot be perpendicular to $L_2$.

---

**4.** Would the following conditions about a quadrilateral be sufficient to prove it a trapezoid? a parallelogram? a rectangle? a rhombus? a square? Consider each item separately.
    Rh, and consequently P

(a) All four sides are congruent.   (b) Only two sides are parallel. None

(c) Two sides are congruent. None   (d) Its diagonals bisect each other. P

(e) Its diagonals are congruent and bisect each other. R

(f) It is equiangular. R

(g) Its diagonals are congruent and perpendicular. None

(h) It is equilateral and equiangular. S

(i) Every two opposite angles are congruent. P

(j) Each diagonal bisects two of its angles. Rh

**5.** Indicate, using the letter A, S, or N, whether each statement is true in ALL cases, true in SOME CASES and false in others, or NOT true in any case.

(a) Line segments in the same plane which do not intersect are parallel. S

(b) If two lines are cut by a transversal, the rays bisecting a pair of alternate interior angles are parallel. S

(c) The diagonals of a rhombus bisect each other. A

(d) The diagonals of a quadrilateral are parallel. N

(e) The opposite angles of a parallelogram are supplementary. S

(f) A square is a rectangle. A

(g) If a diagonal of a quadrilateral forms with the sides two congruent triangles, the quadrilateral is a parallelogram. S

(h) If a median of a triangle is half as long as the side it bisects, the triangle is a right triangle. A

(i) If two opposite sides of a quadrilateral are parallel and the other two sides are congruent, the quadrilateral is a parallelogram. S

(j) If two opposite angles of a quadrilateral are right angles, the quadrilateral is a rectangle. S

## SET B

**1.** Given the figure with $D$ and $E$ the midpoints of $\overline{AB}$ and $\overline{AC}$.

(a) If $m\angle A = 33$ and $m\angle C = 45$, what are $m\angle CBF$ and $m\angle CED$?
   78, 135

(b) If $BC = 6$, then what is $DE$? =3

(c) □DBCE is a ___trapezoid___.

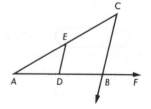

**2.** If in $\triangle ABC$, $AB = 12$, $BC = 9$, $AC = 13$, and $P$, $Q$, and $R$ are the midpoints of the sides, what is the perimeter of $\triangle PQR$? p△PQR=17

**3.** Given: $\square GHKM$ is a parallelogram and

$$MQ = HP.$$

Prove: $\overline{GK}$ and $\overline{PQ}$ bisect each other.

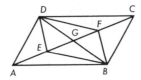

**4.** In the figure, $\square DEBF$ is a parallelogram and $AE = CF$. Prove that $\square ABCD$ is a parallelogram.

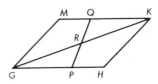

**5.** Prove: If the bisectors of two consecutive angles of a parallelogram intersect, they are perpendicular.

**6.** Given $\overleftrightarrow{AC} \parallel \overleftrightarrow{BD}$. The bisectors of $\angle CAB$ and $\angle DBA$ intersect at $P$, and
△ABP is 30-60-90 (Problem 5, Th.9-28)

$$AB = 2PB.$$

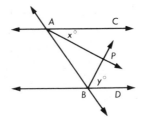

Find $x$ and $y$.
Since $\overrightarrow{AP}$ and $\overrightarrow{BP}$ are bisectors,
X= m∠CAP=m∠PAB=30,
y= m∠PBD=m∠ABP=60

**7.** Why is the following reasoning invalid?
Incorrect application of Th. 9-11, must have two **different** lines.
By Theorem 9–11 we know that in a plane, two lines parallel to the same line are parallel to each other. Therefore, if $\overleftrightarrow{AP} \parallel L$ and $\overleftrightarrow{BP} \parallel L$ and $\overleftrightarrow{AP}$, $\overleftrightarrow{BP}$, and $L$ are coplanar, then $\overleftrightarrow{AP} \parallel \overleftrightarrow{BP}$. This proves that two intersecting lines may, in fact, be parallel!
Hypothesis of Th. 9-11 not satisfied.

**8.** Determine the measure of each angle in the figure given here.

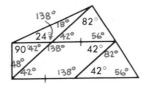

**9.** Prove: In a plane, if a line is perpendicular to one of two intersecting lines, it is not perpendicular to the other line.

**10.** Given: $\angle a \cong \angle b$

$$\angle p \cong \angle q.$$

Prove: $\angle x$ is a right angle.

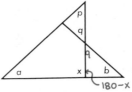
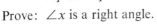

---

**Answers to Chapter Review Problems**

**10.** Let the letters of the angles (in this instance) stand for the measures of the angles. Then $a + p + x = 180$ and $q + b + (180 - x) = 180$. Since $a = b$ and $p = q$, $180 - x = x$ and $x = 90$.

**12.** Given: Trapezoid $\square ABCD$ with $\overline{BC} \parallel \overline{AD}$, $AB = BC = CD$.

Prove: $\overline{AC}$ bisects $\angle A$.
$\overline{DB}$ bisects $\angle D$.

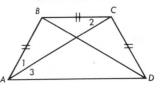

Proof: Since $AB = BC$, $\angle 1 \cong \angle 2$. Since $\overline{BC} \parallel \overline{AD}$, $\angle 2 \cong \angle 3$. Hence $\angle 1 \cong \angle 3$ and $\overrightarrow{AC}$ bisects $\angle A$. Similarly, we can show that $\overrightarrow{DB}$ bisects $\angle D$.

**15.** Introduce $\overline{PQ}$ and $\overline{EB}$, and $\overline{PD}$ and $\overline{QR}$. (1) Since $\overline{ED} \parallel \overline{BC}$ and $ED = BC$, $\square BCDE$ is a parallelogram by Theorem 9-20, and consequently, $\overline{BE} \parallel \overline{CD}$ and $BE = CD$ by Theorem 9-15. (2) Since $P$ and $Q$ are the midpoints of two sides of $\triangle BAE$, $\overline{PQ} \parallel \overline{BE}$ and $PQ = \frac{1}{2}BE$ by Theorem 9-22. Trivially $DR = \frac{1}{2}CD$. Consequently, $\overline{PQ} \parallel \overline{DR}$ by Theorem 9-11, and $PQ = DR$. (3) Hence, since a pair of opposite sides of $\square PQRD$ are parallel and congruent, $\square PQRD$ is a parallelogram by Theorem 9-20. And since the diagonals of a parallelogram bisect each other, $\overline{QD}$ bisects $\overline{PR}$ (Theorem 9-18).

**17.** Given: $\square ABCD$ in which $AC = BD$. $AP = PC$ and $BP = PD$.

Prove: $\square ABCD$ is a rectangle.

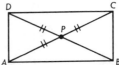

Proof: (1) Since the diagonals of $\square ABCD$ bisect each other, $\square ABCD$ is a parallelogram by Theorem 9-21. (2) Now consider $\triangle DAB$. Since the median $\overline{AP}$ is half as long as the side $\overline{DB}$ which it bisects, the triangle is a right triangle by the Theorem in Problem 5 of Set 9-7. Specifically, $\overline{DB}$ is the hypotenuse and $\angle DAB$ is the right angle. (3) But this is all we need to show, for if a parallelogram has one right angle, it has four right angles, and the parallelogram is a rectangle (Theorem 9-23).

**Answers to Chapter Review Problems**

**19.** Given: $\square ABCD$; $\overline{AC}$ bisects $\angle A$ and $\angle C$. $\overline{BD}$ bisects $\angle B$ and $\angle D$.
Prove: $\square ABCD$ is a rhombus.

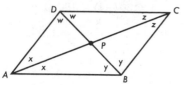

Proof: (1) Since the sum of the measures of the angles of a triangle is 180, we can conclude from $\triangle ABD$ that $2x + y + w = 180$ and from $\triangle CBD$ that $2z + y + w = 180$, and consequently,

$$2x - 2z = 0.$$

Therefore, $x = z$, and similarly $y = w$. Thus, $m\angle A = m\angle C$ and $m\angle B = m\angle D$. (2) Hence by Problem 15 of Problem Set 9-6, $\square ABCD$ is a parallelogram. (3) Since $w = y$, $AB = AD$ by the Converse of the Isosceles Triangle Theorem. Since the opposite sides of a parallelogram are congruent, $AB = BC = CD = DA$. Therefore, $\square ABCD$ is, by definition, a rhombus.

**21.** Let the parallel to $\overline{AC}$ through $P$ intersect $\overline{BT}$ at $Q$. (Theorem 9–3 and the Parallel Postulate.) $\square PQTR$ is a parallelogram and $PR = QT$. Since $\angle QPB \cong \angle A$ (Corollary 9-9.1) and $\angle SBP \cong \angle A$ (Theorem 5–4), $\angle QPB \cong \angle SBP$. $\overline{BQ} \perp \overline{PQ}$ (Theorem 9–12) and $\angle PQB \cong \angle BSP$ since both are right angles. Since $PB = PB$, $\triangle PQB \cong BSP$ (SAA) and $PS = BQ$, so $PR + PS = BQ + QT = BT$.

**22.**

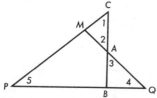

Since $\overline{CB} \perp \overline{PQ}$, $\triangle CBP$ is a right triangle and thus $\angle 1$ and $\angle 5$ are complementary; also $\triangle ABQ$ is a right triangle and so $\angle 2$ (which is congruent to $\angle 3$ by vertical angles) and $\angle 4$ are complementary (Corollary 9-13.2). Since the base angles of an isosceles triangle are congruent, $\angle 5 = \angle 4$. Finally, since complements of congruent angles are congruent (Theorem 4–6), $\angle 1 \cong \angle 2$, and thus $MC = MA$, by Theorem 5–5.

**11.** In $\triangle MPK$, $\angle K$ is a right angle and $m\angle P = 30$. If $\overline{KH} \perp \overline{MP}$, $\overline{HR} \perp \overline{MK}$, $\overline{RQ} \perp \overline{MP}$, and $MP = 80$, find $MQ$. $MQ = 5$

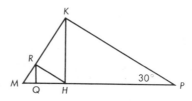

**12.** Prove: If a trapezoid has two nonparallel sides each congruent to one of the parallel sides, then the diagonals bisect the angles at the other parallel side.

**13.** When a beam of light is reflected from a smooth surface, the angle formed by the incoming beam with the surface is congruent to the angle formed by the reflected beam and the surface. In the figure, $m\angle ABC = 90$, $m\angle BCD = 75$, and the beam of light makes an angle of $35°$ with $\overrightarrow{RA}$. Copy the figure and complete the path of the light beam as it reflects from $\overline{AB}$, from $\overline{BC}$, from $\overline{DC}$, and from $\overline{AB}$ again. At what angle does the beam reflect from $\overline{AB}$ the second time?

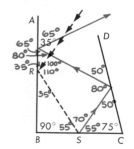

**14.** Prove either the truth or falsity of the following statement.

> If a quadrilateral has one pair of parallel sides and one pair of congruent sides, the quadrilateral is a parallelogram.
> False, a trapezoid fits the description.

**15.** In the figure, $\overline{ED} \parallel \overline{BC}$, $ED = BC$, and $P$, $Q$, and $R$ are midpoints. Prove that $\overline{QD}$ bisects $\overline{PR}$. [*Hint:* Introduce $\overline{PQ}$ and $\overline{EB}$.]

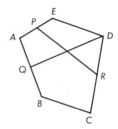

**16.** Prove either the truth or falsity of this statement.

> If the diagonals of a quadrilateral are congruent and perpendicular, the quadrilateral is a square.
> False, a rhombus fits the description.

**17.** Prove either the truth or falsity of the following statement.

> If the diagonals of a quadrilateral are congruent and bisect each other, the quadrilateral is a rectangle.

23.

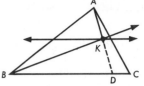

18. In the figure, $\overrightarrow{AC} \perp \overrightarrow{AE}$, and the bisectors of $\angle DCB$ and $\angle EBC$ intersect at $P$. Find $m\angle P$ and show your reasoning.

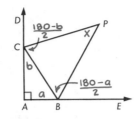

$$\frac{180-b}{2} + \frac{180-a}{2} + x = 180$$
$$180 - \frac{a+b}{2} + x = 180$$
$$x = \frac{a+b}{2} \text{ and } a+b = 90 \text{ (Cor. 9-13.2)}$$
$$\text{so } x = 45$$

19. Prove: If each diagonal of a quadrilateral bisects two angles of the quadrilateral, the quadrilateral is a rhombus.

Apply Th. 9-26 four times.

20. The diagonals of $\square ABCD$ are perpendicular at $M$, and $P, Q, R, S$ are midpoints of the sides. Prove that twice the sum $MP + MQ + MR + MS$ equals the perimeter of $\square ABCD$. $MP + MQ + MR + MS = \frac{1}{2}\,p\square\,ABCD$
$$2(MP + MR + MQ + MS) = p\square ABCD$$

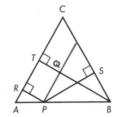

21. Prove: The sum of the lengths of the perpendiculars from any point in the base of an isosceles triangle to the congruent sides equals the altitude to either congruent side. [*Hint:* Let a parallel to $\overline{AC}$ through $P$ meet $\overline{BT}$ at $Q$. Show $RP + PS = BT$.]

22. Let $\triangle MPQ$ be isosceles, with $MP = MQ$. Through any point $A$ between $M$ and $Q$ draw a perpendicular to $\overline{PQ}$, meeting $\overline{PQ}$ at $B$ and meeting $\overrightarrow{PM}$ at $C$. Prove that $\triangle MCA$ is isosceles.

23. In any triangle $\triangle ABC$, a line through $A$ is perpendicular to the bisector of $\angle B$ at $K$. Another line through $K$ is parallel to $\overline{BC}$ and intersects $\overline{AB}$ at $M$. Prove that $M$ is the midpoint of $\overline{AB}$. Can you also prove that $\overleftrightarrow{MK}$ bisects $AC$?

24. $\triangle ABC$ is a triangle with $G$ and $H$ the midpoints of $\overline{AC}$ and $\overline{BC}$. On the ray opposite to $\overrightarrow{HA}$ take $R$ such that $HR = HA$. Similarly, on the ray opposite to $\overrightarrow{GB}$ take $S$ such that $GS = GB$. Prove that $R, C,$ and $S$ are collinear and that $CR = CS$.

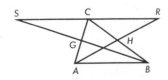

Let $\overrightarrow{AK}$ intersect $\overline{BC}$ at a point $D$. Then, since $\overrightarrow{BK}$ bisects $\angle B$ and $\overrightarrow{BK} \perp \overline{AD}$, $\triangle BKA \cong \triangle BKD$ (ASA), and thus $AK = KD$. Since $\overleftrightarrow{MK}$ bisects one side of $\triangle ABD$ and is parallel to a second, $\overleftrightarrow{MK}$ bisects the third side: $AM = MB$ (Theorem of Problem 2 in Problem Set 9–8 or Theorem 9–30). Similarly, $\overleftrightarrow{MK}$ bisects $AC$.

24.

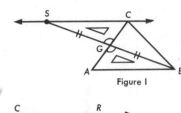

Figure I

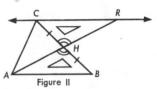

Figure II

Since $G$ is the midpoint of $\overline{AC}$ and $GS = GB$, $\triangle SCG \cong \triangle BAG$ (SAS), and thus $\angle SCG \cong \angle BAG$. By the AIP Theorem we conclude that $\overleftrightarrow{SC}$ is a line through $C$ parallel to $\overleftrightarrow{AB}$. In the same manner, we can prove that $\overleftrightarrow{CR}$ is a line through $C$ parallel to $\overleftrightarrow{AB}$. But by the Parallel Postulate, through a given external point, there is only one line parallel to a given line. Hence $\overleftrightarrow{SC} = \overleftrightarrow{CR}$, or points $S, C,$ and $R$ are collinear. Trivially, since the corresponding parts of congruent triangles are congruent, $SC = AB$ (Figure 1) and $AB = CR$ (Figure 2), so $SC = CR$.

## Parallel Lines and Planes

This chapter develops the basic properties of parallelism and perpendicularity of lines and planes in space, and applies these properties to the study of projections of figures into a plane. The treatment is conventional. A minimum program would cover Section 10–1, studying the essential properties of parallelism of lines and planes and the related properties of perpendicularity. Section 10–2, which probably is more difficult, is devoted to dihedral angles and, in particular, to their application to the concept of perpendicular planes. Sections 10–1 and 10–2 cover the basic subject matter. Section 10–3 takes up the problem of projecting figures into a plane; it can, however, be considered a supplementary or honors topic since it is not essential to the rest of the course.

In this chapter you will see an analogy between the material on parallel lines in a plane, as described in Chapter 9, and the discussion of parallel planes in space. For example, Theorem 10–2, on a line perpendicular to one of two parallel planes, is analogous to Theorem 9–12; and Theorem 10–3, two planes perpendicular to the same line are parallel, is analogous to Theorem 9–2, expressed in the form: In a plane, two lines perpendicular to the same line are parallel. In proving a statement about lines and planes in space you will often find that the key method is to introduce an auxiliary plane, and then make use of an analogous statement about parallel or perpendicular lines in a plane.

It is important for the student to acquire an understanding of the basic facts about parallelism and perpendicularity of lines and planes in space. But if time is short, the

CHAPTER **10**

# Parallel Lines and Planes

Objectives...

- Study relationships of lines and planes in space.
- Learn how to measure dihedral angles.
- Develop the vocabulary and concepts of projections.

## 10–1 BASIC FACTS ABOUT PARALLEL PLANES

### Definition

Two planes, or a plane and a line, are *parallel* if they do not intersect.

If the planes $E_1$ and $E_2$ are parallel, we write $E_1 \parallel E_2$. If the line $L$ and the plane $E$ are parallel, we write $L \parallel E$ or $E \parallel L$.

As we shall see, parallels in space behave in much the same way as parallel lines in a plane. There are, however, important differences. For one thing, there is no such thing as a pair of skew planes: every two planes in space either intersect or are parallel. Furthermore, if two lines lie in parallel planes, it does not follow that the lines are parallel. (See the figure on the left below.) Also, if two lines are parallel, we can always find two planes containing them which are not parallel. (See the figure on the right below.)

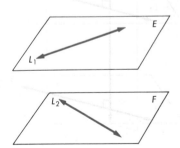
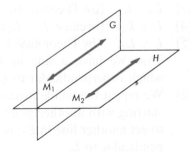

The following theorem describes a common situation in which parallel planes and parallel lines occur in the same figure.

student can acquire a reasonably adequate understanding by covering this chapter informally. It is possible to discuss the theorems on an intuitive level and to select those problems which fit in with an informal treatment.

### Planning the Chapter

Chapter 10 can be considered an optional chapter. An average class may spend one day on each section for information only with no test scheduled. For an above-average class, you may wish to spend two days each on the first two sections and one day on the last. A midyear examination may be scheduled following this chapter for the above-average class.

### 10–1 BASIC FACTS ABOUT PARALLEL PLANES

#### Classroom Notes

The proof of Theorem 10–2 is in one way trickier than it looks. We let $A$ be any point which lies in $E_2$ but not on $L$, and we let $E$ be the plane which contains $L$ and $A$. Step 2 of the proof is then obvious. But if we had taken $A$ as a point of $E_1$, not on $L$, and let $E$ be the plane through $L$ and $A$, as before, then we would have the problem of proving that $E$ intersects $E_2$. Thus a very harmless-looking variation on the proof in the text leads to real trouble.

**Theorem 10–1**

*If a plane intersects two parallel planes, then it intersects them in two parallel lines.*

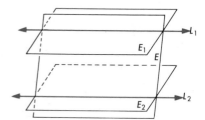

**Proof.** Given a plane $E$, intersecting two parallel planes $E_1$ and $E_2$. By Postulate 8 we have

(1)  $E$ intersects $E_1$ in a line $L_1$, and
(2)  $E$ intersects $E_2$ in a line $L_2$.
 Obviously
(3)  $L_1$ and $L_2$ are coplanar
 (because both of them lie in $E$).  And
(4)  $L_1$ and $L_2$ have no point in common (because $E_1$ and $E_2$ have no point in common).  Statements (3) and (4) tell us that
(5)  $L_1 \parallel L_2$.

**Theorem 10–2**

*If a line is perpendicular to one of two parallel planes it is perpendicular to the other.*

**Proof.** We have given $E_2 \parallel E_1$ and $L \perp E_1$.  Let $A$ be any point which lies in $E_2$ but not on $L$.  Then

(1)  $L$ and $A$ lie in a plane $E$.  (Why?)
(2)  $E$ intersects $E_1$ and $E_2$ in lines $L_1$ and $L_2$.  (Why?)
(3)  $L_1 \parallel L_2$  (by Theorem 10–1).
(4)  $L \perp L_1$  (because $L \perp E_1$).
(5)  $L \perp L_2$  (by Theorem 9–12). Thus we have a line in $E_2$ which is perpendicular to $L$.
(6)  We repeat the whole process, starting with another point $B$ to get another line in $E_2$, perpendicular to $L$.
(7)  We now have $L \perp E_2$, by Theorem 8–2.

The following theorem is analogous to Theorem 9–2.

## Theorem 10–3

*Two planes perpendicular to the same line are parallel.*

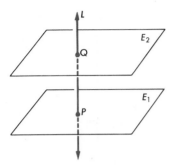 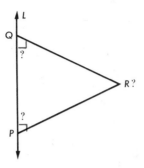

**Proof.** We have given $E_1 \perp L$ at $P$ and $E_2 \perp L$ at $Q$. We want to show that $E_1 \parallel E_2$. If this is not true, then $E_1$ intersects $E_2$ in at least one point, $R$.

Now $\overleftrightarrow{RP} \perp L$ and $\overleftrightarrow{RQ} \perp L$, because $L$ is perpendicular to every line in $E_1$ through $P$ and also to every line in $E_2$ through $Q$. This gives us two perpendiculars from $R$ to $L$, which is impossible. (See Theorem 6–4.) Therefore $E_1$ and $E_2$ are parallel.

## Corollary 10–3.1

*If each of two planes is parallel to a third plane, they are parallel to each other.*

(You should be able to follow the proof without a figure. Try it!)

**Proof.** Given $E_1 \parallel E_3$, $E_2 \parallel E_3$. Let $L$ be a line perpendicular to $E_3$. Then

(1) $L \perp E_1$ (by Theorem 10–2).
(2) $L \perp E_2$ (by Theorem 10–2).
(3) $E_1 \parallel E_2$ (by Theorem 10–3).

## Theorem 10–4

*Two lines perpendicular to the same plane are parallel.*

**Proof.** Given $L_1 \perp E$ at $A$ and $L_2 \perp E$ at $B$. By Theorem 8–7, $L_1$ and $L_2$ are coplanar. Since $L_1 \perp E$, $L_1 \perp \overleftrightarrow{AB}$. Since $L_2 \perp E$, $L_2 \perp \overleftrightarrow{AB}$. By Theorem 9–2, $L_1 \parallel L_2$.

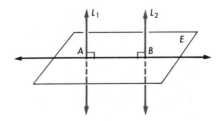

## Explanation for Problems

In Problem Set 10-1, Problem 4 is instructive. Problem 15 is hard and should be assigned only to honors students, but the theorem stated in this problem should be known to all students. No solution to Problem 15 should use perpendicular planes, since they are not defined until page 315.

### Answers to Problems

**1.** Since $\overline{AC} \perp F$ and $\overline{BD} \perp F$, $\overline{AC} \parallel \overline{BD}$ by Theorem 10-4. Since $\overline{AC} \parallel \overline{BD}$, $A$, $B$, $C$, and $D$ lie in exactly one plane, so $\overleftrightarrow{AB} \parallel \overleftrightarrow{CD}$ by Theorem 10-1. Therefore by definition, $\square ABDC$ is a parallelogram, and its diagonals $\overline{AD}$ and $\overline{BC}$ bisect each other, by Theorem 9-18.

**5.** (a) Since $\square ADEK$ is a parallelogram, $\overline{EK} \parallel \overline{AD}$. Since $\square ABCD$ is a parallelogram, $\overline{AD} \parallel \overline{BC}$. By Corollary 10-4.2, if two lines are each parallel to a third line, they are parallel to each other. Thus $\overline{EK} \parallel \overline{AD} \parallel \overline{BC}$.

(b) By Theorem 9-15, the opposite sides of parallelogram $\square ADEK$ are congruent: $\overline{AK} \cong \overline{DE}$. Similarly, $\overline{AB} \cong \overline{DC}$ and $\overline{BK} \cong \overline{CE}$. Hence $\triangle KAB \cong \triangle EDC$ (SSS), and thus $\angle KAB \cong \angle EDC$.

**6.** Since $M \parallel K$, planes $M$ and $K$ are everywhere equidistant by Theorem 10-5. Thus, $AD = BC$. (Recall that the distance from a point $P$ to a plane $E$ is the length of the perpendicular segment from $P$ to $E$.) By Theorem 10-2, $\overline{AD} \perp M$. Introduce $\overline{AC}$ and note that $AC = AC$. Therefore $\triangle ABC \cong \triangle CDA$ (SAS), and $AB = CD$.

**7.** Given: $L_1 \parallel L_2$,

$E \parallel F$.

Prove:

$AB = CD$.

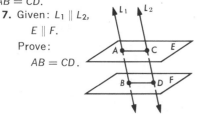

Proof: (1) Since $L_1 \parallel L_2$, $\overline{AB} \parallel \overline{CD}$. (2) Since $L_1 \parallel L_2$, $L_1$ and $L_2$ are, by definition, coplanar. Hence, by Theorem 10-1, the plane containing $A$, $B$, $C$, and $D$ which intersects the parallel planes $E$ and $F$, intersects them in parallel lines:

---

### Corollary 10-4.1

*A plane perpendicular to one of two parallel lines is perpendicular to the other.*

**Proof.** Given $L_1 \parallel L_2$ and $L_1 \perp E$. Let $L_3$ be a line through any point $A$ of $L_2$, perpendicular to $E$. $L_3$ exists by Theorem 8-9. Then by Theorem 10-4, $L_1 \parallel L_3$. By the Parallel Postulate, $L_3 = L_2$. That is, $L_3$ and $L_2$ must be the same line. Since $L_3 \perp E$, we have $L_2 \perp E$.

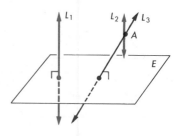

### Corollary 10-4.2

*If each of two lines is parallel to a third line, then they are parallel to each other.*

**Proof.** Given that $L_1 \parallel L_3$ and $L_2 \parallel L_3$. We want to show that $L_1 \parallel L_2$.

Let $E$ be a plane perpendicular to $L_3$. By the preceding corollary, $L_1 \perp E$ and $L_2 \perp E$. By Theorem 10-4, $L_1 \parallel L_2$.

### Theorem 10-5

*Parallel planes are everywhere equidistant.*

**Restatement.** If $E_1 \parallel E_2$, then all points of $E_1$ are equidistant from $E_2$.

We recall that the distance between a point $P$ and a plane $E$ is the length of the perpendicular segment from $P$ to $E$.

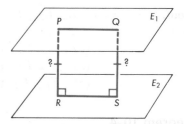

**Proof.** Let $P$ and $Q$ be any two points of $E_1$, and let $\overline{PR}$ and $\overline{QS}$ be the perpendicular segments from $P$ and $Q$ to $E_2$. Then
(1) $\overleftrightarrow{PR} \parallel \overleftrightarrow{QS}$ (by Theorem 10-4).
(2) $P$, $Q$, $R$, and $S$ are coplanar, because these points lie on two parallel lines.
(3) $\overleftrightarrow{PQ} \parallel \overleftrightarrow{RS}$ (by Theorem 10-1).
(4) $\square PQSR$ is a parallelogram, by (1), (2), and (3).
(5) $PR = QS$, because opposite sides of a parallelogram are congruent.

We know by Theorem 10–2 that the segments from $E_1$, perpendicular to $E_2$, are precisely the segments from $E_2$, perpendicular to $E_1$. We therefore know more than our restatement actually says; that is, we know the following: *If two planes are parallel, then all perpendicular segments from one of the planes to the other have the same length.* Hereafter, we shall interpret Theorem 10–5 to mean this.

Note that $\square PQSR$ is, in fact, a rectangle. But this fact is not needed in the proof.

## Problem Set 10–1

**1.** Given: $E$ and $F$ are parallel planes, $E$ contains $\overleftrightarrow{AB}$, $F$ contains $\overleftrightarrow{CD}$, $\overline{AC} \perp F$, and $\overline{BD} \perp F$.

Prove: $\overline{AD}$ and $\overline{BC}$ bisect each other.

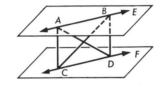

**2.** If $K$ and $M$ are planes, $K \perp L$ at $P$, and plane $M \perp L$ at $T$, what can you conclude about $K$ and $M$? Why?

    K ∥ M Theorem 10–3

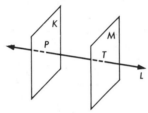

**3.** Prove the following statement true or false.

    False, see page 307 for counter examples.
If $E$ and $F$ are parallel planes and $E$ contains line $L_1$ and $F$ contains line $L_2$, then $L_1 \parallel L_2$.

**4.** Plane $G$ contains points $A$, $B$, $C$, and plane $H$ contains points $D$, $E$, $F$ such that $\overline{AD} \perp G$, $\overline{AD} \perp H$, and $AB = DF$. Which of the following statements must be true?

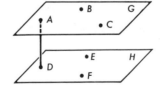

   (a) $AF = BD.$      (b) $\overline{BC} \parallel \overline{EF}.$      (c) $\triangle ABC \cong \triangle DFE.$

   (d) $G \parallel H.$      (e) $\overline{AC} \perp \overline{AD}.$      (f) $\angle AFD \cong \angle DBA.$

   (g) $\overline{AF}$ and $\overline{BD}$ bisect each other.      (h) $\overline{AC} \parallel \overline{DF}.$

**5.** In the figure, $\square ABCD$, $\square ADEK$, and $\square BCEK$ are parallelograms. Prove that

(a) $\overline{EK} \parallel \overline{AD} \parallel \overline{BC}$, and

(b) $\angle KAB \cong \angle EDC$.

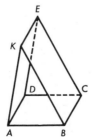

$\overline{AC} \parallel \overline{BD}$. (3) $\therefore \square ABDC$ is, by definition, a parallelogram, and by Theorem 9–16 $AB = CD$.

**8.** (1) By Theorem 10–1, the plane containing $\triangle ACR$ intersects parallel planes $F$ and $G$ in two parallel lines, $\overleftrightarrow{BK}$ and $\overleftrightarrow{CR}$. In the plane of $\triangle ACR$, since $\overleftrightarrow{BK}$ bisects one side of $\triangle ACR$ and is parallel to a second side, it bisects the third side so that $AK = KR$. (2) Similarly, in the plane of $\triangle ARP$, since $\overleftrightarrow{KQ}$ bisects $\overline{AR}$ and is parallel to $\overline{AP}$, it bisects $\overline{PR}$, and so $PQ = QR$.

**10.** Introduce $\overline{CG}$ and $\overline{DH}$. (1) Since $E \parallel F$ and $\overline{AD}$ and $\overline{BC}$ lie in $M$, $\overline{AD} \parallel \overline{BC}$ by Theorem 10–1. Then since the opposite sides $\overline{AD}$ and $\overline{BC}$ of $\square ABCD$ are also, by hypothesis, congruent, we can conclude that $\square ABCD$ is a parallelogram by Theorem 9–20. (2) Similarly $\square ABGH$ is a parallelogram. (3) Since the opposite sides of a parallelogram are congruent, $GH = BA$ and $BA = CD$, and thus, $GH = CD$. Since the opposite sides of a parallelogram are parallel, $\overline{GH} \parallel \overline{AB}$ and $\overline{BA} \parallel \overline{CD}$, and thus, by Corollary 10–4.2, $\overline{GH} \parallel \overline{CD}$. (4) Now, since the opposite sides $\overline{GH}$ and $\overline{CD}$ of $\square GHDC$ are both congruent and parallel, $\square GHDC$ is a parallelogram by Theorem 9–20, and thus $GC = HD$. (5) Finally, $\triangle DAH \cong \triangle CBG$ (SSS), and thus $\angle DAH \cong \angle CBG$.

**12.** Let $L_1$ and $L_2$ be two skew lines. Take a point $P$ on $L_2$, and let $L_3$ be the line through $P$ which is parallel to $L_1$ (Theorem 9–3 and the Parallel Postulate). The two intersecting lines $L_2$ and $L_3$ determine a plane $E$, by Theorem 3–3. $E$ obviously contains one of the two skew lines, say $L_2$. Let us show that $L_1$ and $E$ are parallel. The parallel lines $L_1$ and $L_3$ determine a plane $F$ and the intersection of $E$ and $F$ is precisely $L_3$. Since $L_1$ lies in $F$, if $L_1$ intersects $E$ it must intersect $E$ at a point on $L_3$. But this would contradict the fact that $L_1 \parallel L_3$. Consequently, $L_1 \parallel E$.

**13.** Introduce $\overline{PR}$ so that $\overline{PR} \parallel \overline{KM} \parallel \overline{QS}$. (This can be done by Theorem 9–3, The Parallel Postulate, and Corollary 10–4.2). (1) Parallels $\overline{KM}$ and $\overline{PR}$ are coplanar by definition, and in that plane we can conclude that since $\overline{PM}$ is perpendicular to one of these two parallel lines, it is perpendicular to the other: $\overline{PR} \perp \overline{PM}$. (2) In the same way, $\overline{QS} \perp \overline{PS}$. (3) Hence, by Theorem 8–2, $\overline{PR} \perp E$. (4) Finally, by Corollary 10–4.1, since $E$ is perpendicular to one ($\overline{PR}$) of two parallels ($\overline{PR}$ and $\overline{KM}$), $E$ is perpendicular to the other: $\overline{KM} \perp E$. Similarly, $\overline{QS} \perp E$.

**14.** (1) Since $E \parallel F$ and $\overline{PA} \perp F$, $\overline{PA} \perp E$ by Theorem 10–2, and hence, by definition, $\overline{PA} \perp \overline{AB}$. (2) By Theorem 9–22, the segment $\overline{TR}$ between the midpoints of two sides of $\triangle PAB$ is parallel to the third side: $\overline{TR} \parallel \overline{AB}$. (3) But, in the plane of $\triangle PAB$, since $\overline{PA}$ is perpendicular to one ($\overline{AB}$) of two parallel lines ($\overline{TR}$ and $\overline{AB}$), it is perpendicular to the other: $\overline{PA} \perp \overline{TR}$. (4) In the same way we can show that $\overline{PA} \perp \overline{TV}$. (5) But, by Theorem 8–2, if a line is perpendicular to each of two intersecting lines at their point of intersection, it is perpendicular to the plane of those lines: $\overline{PA} \perp$ plane $RTV$. (6) Finally, since plane $RTV$ and plane $F$ are each perpendicular to $\overline{PA}$, planes $RTV$ and $F$ are parallel by Theorem 10–3.

**15.**

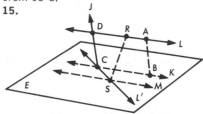

Part I. Existence.
1. Introduce the plane $E$ which contains $L'$ and is parallel to $L$. (Problem 12 of Problem Set 10–1.)
2. From a point, $A$, on $L$ introduce a segment perpendicular to $E$; let $B$ be the foot of the perpendicular.
3. Introduce the plane $F$ determined by $L$ and $B$. Let $K$ be the line of intersection of $E$ and $F$. If $K$ and $L'$ were parallel, then $L'$ and $L$ would be parallel, which is false.

**6.** Given plane $M$ parallel to plane $K$. $A$ and $C$ are points in $M$, and $B$ and $D$ are points in $K$ such that $\overline{AD} \perp K$ and $\overline{BC} \perp M$. Prove that $AB = CD$.

**7.** Prove the following.

> If two parallel lines are intersected by two parallel planes, then the planes intercept congruent segments on the two lines.

**8.** In the figure, $L_1$ and $L_2$ are skew lines intersecting the parallel planes $E, F, G$; and $\overline{AR}$ intersects $F$ at $K$. If $AB = BC$, prove that $PQ = QR$.

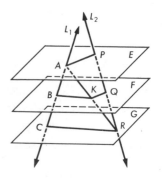

**9.** In Problem 8, prove also that

$$BQ < \tfrac{1}{2}(AP + CR).$$

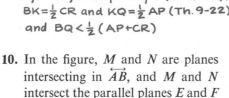

By triangle inequality $BQ < BK + KQ$.
$BK = \tfrac{1}{2}CR$ and $KQ = \tfrac{1}{2}AP$ (Th. 9-22)
and $BQ < \tfrac{1}{2}(AP + CR)$

**10.** In the figure, $M$ and $N$ are planes intersecting in $\overleftrightarrow{AB}$, and $M$ and $N$ intersect the parallel planes $E$ and $F$ in $\overleftrightarrow{AD}, \overleftrightarrow{BC}, \overleftrightarrow{AH}$, and $\overleftrightarrow{BG}$. If $AD = BC$ and $AH = BG$, prove that

$$\angle DAH \cong \angle CBG.$$

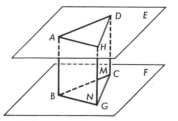

**11.** Indicate whether each statement is true or false. Draw a small sketch to illustrate each statement if it is true, or provide a sketch of a counter-example if it is false.

(a) If a line lies in a plane, a line parallel to the line is parallel to the plane. **F**

(b) If a line and a plane are parallel, every line in the plane is parallel to the given line. **F**

(c) Two lines parallel to the same plane may be perpendicular to each other. **T**

(d) If two lines are parallel, every plane containing only one of the lines is parallel to the other line. **T**

(e) If a plane intersects two parallel planes, the lines of intersection are parallel. **T**

(f) If a plane intersects two intersecting planes, the lines of intersection may be parallel. **T**

**12.** Show how to determine a plane which contains one of two given skew lines and is parallel to the other line. Prove your construction.

**13.** Given: $\overline{PM}$ and $\overline{PS}$ lie in plane $E$. $P$, $M$, and $S$ are noncollinear. $\overline{KM} \perp \overline{PM}$, $\overline{QS} \perp \overline{PS}$, and $\overline{KM} \parallel \overline{QS}$.

Prove: $\overline{KM} \perp E$ and $\overline{QS} \perp E$.

[*Hint:* Introduce another parallel.]

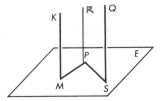

**14.** $F$ and $E$ are parallel planes. $A$, $B$, $C$ are in $E$, $P$ is in $F$, and $\overline{PA} \perp F$. $R$, $T$, $V$ are midpoints of $\overline{PB}$, $\overline{PA}$, and $\overline{PC}$, respectively. Prove that the plane $RTV$ is parallel to $F$.

**15.** Prove the following theorem.

> There is one, and only one, line which is perpendicular to each of two given skew lines.

[*Hint:* The figure indicates how to obtain the common perpendicular. Dashed lines and segments indicate auxiliary sets.]

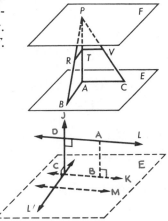

## 10–2 DIHEDRAL ANGLES. PERPENDICULAR PLANES

We know that when two lines in a plane intersect, they form four angles:

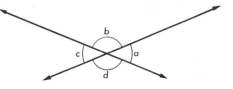

Consider now two planes in space, intersecting in a line as in the figure on the left below.

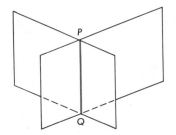

They form four figures, each of which looks like the figure on the right above. Such a figure is called a *dihedral angle*, and the line $\overleftrightarrow{PQ}$ shown in the figure is called its *edge*.

---

Therefore $K$ intersects $L'$, in a point $C$.

4. Introduce the line $J$ perpendicular to $E$ at $C$. Observe that $J$ intersects $L$ at a point $D$.
5. Observe that $\overleftrightarrow{CD}$ is perpendicular to $L$ and $L'$.

Part II. Uniqueness.

1. Suppose there exists another line $\overleftrightarrow{RS}$, with $R$ on $L$ and $S$ on $L'$, which is also perpendicular to $L$ and $L'$.
2. Introduce line $M$, in plane $E$, containing $S$ and parallel to $K$.
3. $\overleftrightarrow{RS} \perp L'$ by assumption. Since $M \parallel K$, and $K \parallel L$, $M$ is parallel to $L$. Since $\overleftrightarrow{RS} \perp L$, $\overleftrightarrow{RS} \perp M$. Hence, by the fundamental perpendicular criterion, $\overleftrightarrow{RS} \perp E$.
4. But, by Part I, $\overleftrightarrow{CD} \perp E$.
5. Hence, by Theorem 8–7, $\overleftrightarrow{CD}$ and $\overleftrightarrow{RS}$ are coplanar. Since $L$ contains $D$ and $R$, and $L'$ contains $C$ and $S$, this means that $L$ and $L'$ are coplanar. This contradicts the assumption that $L$ and $L'$ are skew.

## 10–2 DIHEDRAL ANGLES. PERPENDICULAR PLANES

### Background Material

We remember that while a ray contains its end point, a half-plane does not contain its edge. Therefore a dihedral angle is not the union of two half-planes, but the union of two half-planes together with their common edge. Similarly, each side of a dihedral angle is the union of a half-plane and its edge.

We might have introduced the term *closed half-plane* and defined it to mean the union of a half-plane and its edge. But it appeared that the term would not be used often enough to justify defining it.

**The definition of the interior and exterior of a dihedral angle, and the definition of vertical dihedral angles.**

DEFINITION. The *interior* of dihedral angle ∠*A-PQ-B* is the set of all points which are on the same side of the plane *APQ* as *B* and are on the same side of the plane *BPQ* as *A*. The *exterior* of a dihedral angle is the set of all points which are not in the interior of the angle and are not in the angle itself.

DEFINITION. Two dihedral angles, ∠*A-PQ-B* and ∠*A'-PQ-B'*, are *vertical* if *A* and *A'* are on opposite sides of $\overleftrightarrow{PQ}$, and *B* and *B'* are on opposite sides of $\overleftrightarrow{PQ}$.

**Classroom Notes**

While it is possible to give a postulational development for the measure of a dihedral angle, such a development would be repetitious; we can *define* the measure of a dihedral angle in terms of the measure of an associated plane angle. You can motivate this definition by the following approach:

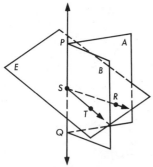

Let *E* be any plane which intersects the edge $\overleftrightarrow{PQ}$ of the dihedral angle ∠*A-PQ-B* in exactly one point *S*. Let $\overleftrightarrow{SR}$ be the ray in which *E* intersects half-plane *H*($\overleftrightarrow{PQ}$, *A*) and let $\overleftrightarrow{ST}$ be the ray in which *E* intersects the half-plane *H*($\overleftrightarrow{PQ}$, *B*). Thus

**Definitions**

If two half-planes have the same edge, but do not lie in the same plane, then the union of the two half-planes and their common edge is a *dihedral angle*. The line which is their common edge is called the *edge* of the dihedral angle. The union of the edge and either of the two half-planes is called a *side*, or a *face*, of the dihedral angle.

To describe a particular dihedral angle, we need to say what line is its edge, and what its sides are. We usually do this by naming two points *P* and *Q* of the edge, and two points *A* and *B* lying in the two sides. (See the figure above.) We then denote the dihedral angle by ∠*A-PQ-B*.

We may speak of the *interior* and *exterior* of a dihedral angle; and we may also speak of *vertical* dihedral angles. The ideas here are very similar to familiar ideas about angles in a plane, and you ought to be able to furnish your own definitions for them.

It would be nice to be able to say that vertical dihedral angles are congruent. But first we need to explain what is meant by the *measure* of a dihedral angle. We do this in the following way.

**Definition**

Given a dihedral angle, and a plane perpendicular to its edge. The intersection of the perpendicular plane with the dihedral angle is called a *plane angle* of the dihedral angle.

In the figure, the marks indicate that ∠*PYC* and ∠*PYD* are right angles. This means that the plane containing ∠*CYD* is perpendicular to $\overleftrightarrow{PQ}$ at *Y*. Under the definition that we have just given, this means that ∠*CYD* really is a plane angle of ∠*A-PQ-B*.

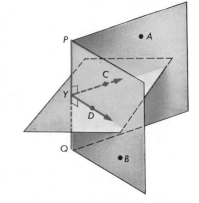

It seems natural to define the measure of ∠*A-PQ-B* as the measure of ∠*CYD*. But this would hardly make sense if different plane angles of the same dihedral angle had different measures. We therefore need to prove the following theorem.

## Theorem 10–6

***All plane angles of the same dihedral angle are congruent.***

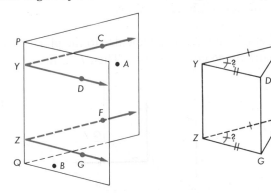

**Proof.** Given two plane angles of $\angle A\text{-}PQ\text{-}B$, with vertices at $Y$ and $Z$. We take points $C$, $D$, $F$, and $G$, on the sides of the angles, so that $YC = ZF$ and $YD = ZG$, as indicated in the figure on the right. We now have

(1)  $\square YCFZ$ is a parallelogram. ($\overline{YC}$ and $\overline{FZ}$ are congruent. And they are parallel, because they lie in the same plane and are perpendicular to the same line. See Theorem 9–20.)

In exactly the same way, we obtain

(2)  $\square YDGZ$ is a parallelogram.

Therefore

(3)  $\overline{DG} \parallel \overline{CF}$. (They are both parallel to $\overline{YZ}$.)

(4)  $DG = CF$ (because $DG = YZ = CF$).

(5)  $\square DGFC$ is a parallelogram (because $\overline{DG}$ and $\overline{CF}$ are congruent and parallel).

(6)  $DC = GF$. (Why?)

(7)  $\triangle CYD \cong \triangle FZG$  (by SSS).

(8)  $\angle CYD \cong \angle FZG$.

Of course, (8) is what we wanted.

We can now make the following definitions.

### Definitions

The *measure* of a dihedral angle is the real number which is the measure of each of its plane angles. A *right* dihedral angle is one whose plane angles are right angles. Two planes are *perpendicular* if they contain a right dihedral angle.

The following theorems are easy to prove, on the basis of the definitions.

we obtain a plane angle $\angle RST$ associated with the dihedral angle $\angle A\text{-}PQ\text{-}B$. Now consider the measure of $\angle RST$: If we were to imagine the plane $E$ pivoting about the point $S$, we could observe that $m \angle RST$ depends on the position of $E$ relative to the edge and sides of the dihedral angle $\angle A\text{-}PQ\text{-}B$. *Queries:* Is there a position of $E$ for which $m \angle RST$ is a minimum? a maximum?     Most students are amazed to discover that $m \angle RST$ ranges from 0 to 180 no matter how "wide-open" the sides of the dihedral angle are.

This idea is mentioned in the text on page 316. It is probably best to let the students decide the best way to define the measure of the dihedral angle.

Although there are infinitely many positions for the plane $E$, there is only one which is in any way distinguished from the others: the position in which $E$ is perpendicular to $\overleftrightarrow{PQ}$ at $S$. Hence we use a plane perpendicular to the edge of the dihedral angle to define a plane angle of the dihedral angle.

Theorem 10–6 is, of course, essential. However, the proof is elementary, and you can simply ask the student to study the proof in the text.

We could have given a definition of right dihedral angle very similar to that for right angle. First, by analogy with the idea of a linear pair of angles, we can define a "planar pair" of dihedral angles as follows: the dihedral angles $\angle A\text{-}PQ\text{-}B$ and $\angle A'\text{-}PQ\text{-}B$ form a *planar pair* if $A$ and $A'$ are on opposite sides of $\overleftrightarrow{PQ}$. Then, if the dihedral angles of a planar pair have the same measure, each is said to be a *right dihedral angle*.

Note that we do not define perpendicular planes until we have defined a dihedral angle, the measure of a dihedral angle, and a right dihedral angle.

# Theorem 10–7

*Given:* (1) $\overleftrightarrow{AC} \perp E$ at $A$.
       (2) $F$ contains $\overleftrightarrow{AC}$.
*Prove:* $F \perp E$.

*Proof.* Let $\overleftrightarrow{PQ}$ be the line in which $F$ intersects $E$. Since $\overleftrightarrow{AC} \perp E$, $\overleftrightarrow{AC} \perp \overleftrightarrow{PQ}$. Introduce $\overleftrightarrow{AB}$ in $E$ such that $\overleftrightarrow{AB} \perp \overleftrightarrow{PQ}$. By the Basic Theorem on Perpendiculars, it follows that the plane containing $\overleftrightarrow{AB}$ and $\overleftrightarrow{AC}$ is perpendicular to $\overleftrightarrow{PQ}$. This means that $\angle BAC$ is a plane angle of the dihedral angle $\angle B\text{-}PQ\text{-}C$. Since $\overleftrightarrow{AC}$ is perpendicular to $E$, we know that $\overleftrightarrow{AC}$ is perpendicular to $\overleftrightarrow{AB}$. This means that $\angle CAB$ is a right angle. Therefore the dihedral angle $\angle C\text{-}PQ\text{-}B$ is a right dihedral angle, and $F$ and $E$ are perpendicular.

# Theorem 10–8

*Given:* (1) The planes $E$ and $F$ are perpendicular; $\overleftrightarrow{PQ}$ is the line of intersection. (2) $\overleftrightarrow{AC}$ lies in $F$, and $\overleftrightarrow{AC} \perp \overleftrightarrow{PQ}$ at $A$.
*Prove:* $\overleftrightarrow{AC} \perp E$.

*Proof.* Introduce $\overleftrightarrow{AB}$ in $E$, perpendicular to $\overleftrightarrow{PQ}$ at $A$. Since $\overleftrightarrow{AB} \perp \overleftrightarrow{PQ}$ and $\overleftrightarrow{AC} \perp \overleftrightarrow{PQ}$, the plane containing $\overleftrightarrow{AB}$ and $\overleftrightarrow{AC}$ is perpendicular to $\overleftrightarrow{PQ}$ at $A$, and hence $\angle BAC$ is a plane angle of the dihedral angle $\angle B\text{-}PQ\text{-}C$. Since $E$ and $F$ are perpendicular, $\angle BAC$ is a right angle. Therefore $\overleftrightarrow{AC} \perp \overleftrightarrow{PQ}$ and $\overleftrightarrow{AC} \perp \overleftrightarrow{AB}$, and hence, by the Basic Theorem on Perpendiculars, $\overleftrightarrow{AC} \perp E$.

## Quiz

**1.** Three different planes intersect in a common line. What is the minimum number of dihedral angles determined? (ans: 6)

**2.** Each of $\overline{AQ}$, $\overline{BQ}$, and $\overline{CQ}$ is perpendicular to the other two and $AC = BC$. Prove that $m \angle QAB = 45$.
Proof: Since $AC = BC$, $\overline{AQ} \perp \overline{CQ}$ and $\overline{BQ} \perp \overline{CQ}$, and $CQ = CQ$, $\triangle ACQ \cong \triangle BCQ$ by HL. Thus $BQ = AQ$. Since $\overline{AQ} \perp \overline{BQ}$, $\triangle AQB$ is an isosceles right triangle and $m \angle QAB = 45$.)

---

## Theorem 10–7

***If a line is perpendicular to a plane, then every plane containing the line is perpendicular to the given plane.***

**Restatement.** Let $L$ be a line, perpendicular to the plane $E$ at the point $A$, and let $F$ be any plane containing $L$. Then $F \perp E$.

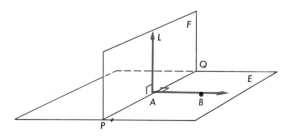

[*Hint for the proof:* Let $\overleftrightarrow{PQ}$ be the line in which $F$ intersects $E$. Take $\overleftrightarrow{AB} \perp \overleftrightarrow{PQ}$ in $E$. Now remember the definitions of the statements $L \perp E$ and $F \perp E$, and show that $F$ and $E$ really are perpendicular.]

## Theorem 10–8

***If two planes are perpendicular, then any line in one of them, perpendicular to their line of intersection, is perpendicular to the other plane.***

You can use the same figure as for the preceding theorem. Let $L$ be the given line, perpendicular to $\overleftrightarrow{PQ}$ at $A$, and take $\overleftrightarrow{AB} \perp \overleftrightarrow{PQ}$ as before. This time $E \perp F$ is given, and we want to prove that $L \perp E$.

It is a curious fact that every dihedral angle can be sliced by planes to give ordinary angles whose measures are as close to 0, or as close to 180, as we please. For example, planes intersect the dihedral angle shown at the right at the point $Y$ to form $\angle CYD$, which has measure near 0, and $\angle CYF$, which has measure near 180.

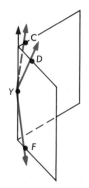

In our definition of a *plane angle* of a dihedral angle, we ruled out these possibilities by requiring that the dihedral angle be sliced by a plane perpendicular to its edge. Without this requirement, Theorem 10–6 would not be true.

## Problem Set 10–2

**1.** Name all the dihedral angles in the figure on the left below.

∠A-PQ-B
∠A-PQ-C
∠B-PQ-C

∠Q-MK-T
∠T-MK-R
∠R-MK-P
∠Q-MK-R
∠T-MK-P

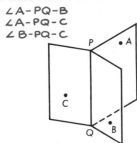

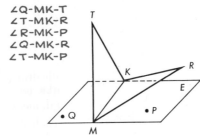

**2.** Name all the dihedral angles in the figure on the right above. (There are more than three. Note that *E* is a plane, not a point.)

**3.** Name the six dihedral angles in this tetrahedron.

∠C-AB-D     ∠B-AD-C
∠A-BC-D     ∠B-AC-D
∠A-CD-B     ∠A-BD-C

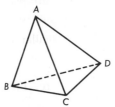

**4.** Prove the following theorem.

Vertical dihedral angles are congruent.

**5.** Prove the following theorem.

If two parallel planes are intersected by a third plane, the alternate interior dihedral angles are congruent.

[*Hint:* Introduce another plane.]

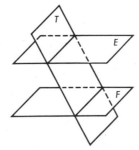

**6.** In the figure, $\overrightarrow{AM} \parallel \overrightarrow{BK}$ and $\overrightarrow{BK} \perp E$. *D* is the midpoint of $\overline{BC}$ and

$$AC = AD.$$

Find the measure of each angle of the figure.

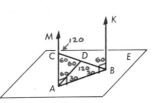

**7.** In the figure for Problem 2, if *T* and *R* are in the perpendicular bisecting plane of $\overline{MK}$, *S* is the midpoint of $\overline{MK}$, and $m\angle RST = 110$, what is $m\angle T\text{-}MK\text{-}R$? What is $m\angle T\text{-}MK\text{-}Q + m\angle R\text{-}MK\text{-}P$? 70
110

**8.** (1) Since $AC = BC$, $\triangle APC \cong \triangle BPC$ by HL, and thus $AP = BP$. Therefore $\triangle APB$ is an isosceles right triangle, and $m \angle PAB = 45$.

(2) The second half of the proof consists of showing that $\triangle EDF$ is also an isosceles right triangle. $\overline{ED} \parallel \overline{AP}$ and $\overline{FD} \parallel \overline{PB}$ by Theorem 9–22, and so $\overline{ED} \perp \overline{PC}$ and $\overline{FD} \perp \overline{PC}$, so $\angle EDF$ is a plane angle of $\angle A\text{-}\overleftrightarrow{PC}\text{-}B$. By Theorem 10–6, $\angle EDF \cong \angle APB$; therefore $\angle EDF$ is a right angle. By Theorem 9–22, $ED = \frac{1}{2}AP$ and $FD = \frac{1}{2}BP$. Since $AP = BP$, $ED = FD$. Hence, $\triangle EDF$ is an isosceles right triangle and $m \angle DEF = 45$. Since $m \angle PAB = 45 = m \angle DEF$, $\angle PAB \cong \angle DEF$.

**12.** The segment $\overline{PS}$ between the midpoints of two sides of $\triangle ADC$ is parallel to the third side and half as long as the third side: $\overline{PS} \parallel \overline{AC}$, $PS = \frac{1}{2}AC$. Similarly, $\overline{RQ} \parallel \overline{AC}$, and $RQ = \frac{1}{2}AC$. Therefore $PS = RQ$ and $\overline{PS} \parallel \overline{RQ}$ by Corollary 10–4.2 (the transitive property of parallelism). By the definition of parallel lines, $P$, $Q$, $R$, and $S$ are coplanar. Since $\square PQRS$ has a pair of sides which are both congruent and parallel, $\square PQRS$ is a parallelogram.

**13.** Given: Planes $F$ and $G$ intersect in $\overleftrightarrow{AB}$.
$F \perp E$, $F \cap E = \overleftrightarrow{RS}$.
$G \perp E$, $G \cap E = \overleftrightarrow{MK}$.
(Assume $A$ is in $E$.)
Prove: $\overleftrightarrow{AB} \perp E$.
Analysis: The most useful technique for showing that a line is perpendicular to a plane is Theorem 8–2: we show that $\overleftrightarrow{AB}$ is perpendicular to each of two lines in $E$ which intersect at point $A$. Towards this end, we introduce a line $\overleftrightarrow{AP}$ in $E$ such that $\overleftrightarrow{AP} \perp \overleftrightarrow{MK}$, and a line $\overleftrightarrow{AQ}$ in $E$ such that $\overleftrightarrow{AQ} \perp \overleftrightarrow{RS}$, and we shall show that $\overleftrightarrow{AB} \perp \overleftrightarrow{AP}$ and $\overleftrightarrow{AB} \perp \overleftrightarrow{AQ}$.
Proof: (1) Since $E$ and $F$ are perpendicular, and $\overleftrightarrow{AQ}$ is a line in $E$ perpendicular to their line of intersection, $\overleftrightarrow{RS}$, we can conclude by Theorem 10–8 that $\overleftrightarrow{AQ}$ is perpendicular to $F$. (1) Since $\overleftrightarrow{AQ} \perp F$, $\overleftrightarrow{AQ}$ is, by definition, perpendicular to any line in $F$ through point $A$, specifically, $\overleftrightarrow{AQ} \perp \overleftrightarrow{AB}$, that is, $\overleftrightarrow{AB}$ is perpendicular to $\overleftrightarrow{AQ}$. (3) In the same way, we can

---

**8.** Each of $\overline{AP}$, $\overline{BP}$, and $\overline{CP}$ is perpendicular to the other two. $AC = BC$ and $D$, $E$, $F$ are midpoints. Prove that

$$\angle DEF \cong \angle PAB$$

and find their measure.

m∠ DEF = m∠ PAB = 45

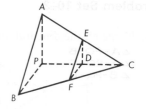

---

**9.** Define the interior of a dihedral angle.
See Teachers Comments page 314.

**10.** Indicate whether each statement is true or false. You should draw a small sketch to illustrate each statement if it is true, or sketch a counterexample if it is false.

(a) Each side of a dihedral angle contains the common edge. T

(b) Two dihedral angles are congruent if a plane angle of one is congruent to a plane angle of the other. T

(c) If a plane and a line are perpendicular, every plane which contains the line is perpendicular to the plane. T

(d) Two planes perpendicular to the same plane are parallel to each other. F

**11.** Given the cube shown here. Find

$$m \angle DHE = 90 \quad m \angle DEH = 45$$
$$m \angle HGD = 45 \quad m \angle EGD = 60$$

[You may use the following properties of a cube: (1) the twelve edges are congruent; (2) any two intersecting edges are perpendicular.]

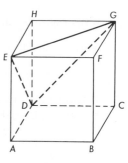

**12.** If $A$, $B$, $C$, and $D$ are four noncoplanar points, no three of which are collinear, the union of $\overline{AB}$, $\overline{BC}$, $\overline{CD}$, and $\overline{DA}$ is called a *skew quadrilateral*. Prove that the figure formed by joining consecutively the midpoints of the sides of a skew quadrilateral is a parallelogram.

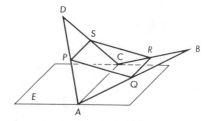

**13.** Prove the following.

If two intersecting planes are each perpendicular to a third plane, their intersection is perpendicular to the third plane.

[*Hint:* In plane $E$, draw $\overleftrightarrow{PA} \perp \overleftrightarrow{MK}$ and $\overleftrightarrow{QA} \perp \overleftrightarrow{RS}$. Use Theorems 10–8 and 8–2.]

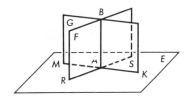

**14.** Prove the following.

If three planes $E_1$, $E_2$, and $E_3$ intersect in the three lines $L_{12}$, $L_{23}$, $L_{13}$, then either the three lines intersect in a common point or each line is parallel to the other two lines.

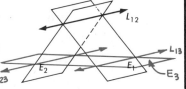

[*Hint:* The figure shows $E_1$ and $E_2$ intersecting in $L_{12}$. Consider the two possibilities for $E_3$: (1) $E_3 \parallel L_{12}$; (2) $E_3$ intersects $L_{12}$.]

## HONORS PROBLEM

### Desargues' Theorem

Given two triangles lying in nonparallel planes such that the lines joining their corresponding vertices intersect in a common point. If the lines containing corresponding sides of the triangles intersect, the points of intersection are collinear.

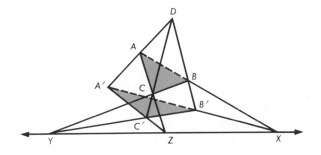

**Restatement.** Given $\triangle ABC$ and $\triangle A'B'C'$ in nonparallel planes such that $\overleftrightarrow{AA'}$, $\overleftrightarrow{BB'}$, and $\overleftrightarrow{CC'}$ intersect at $D$. If $\overleftrightarrow{AB}$ and $\overleftrightarrow{A'B'}$ intersect at $X$, $\overleftrightarrow{BC}$ and $\overleftrightarrow{B'C'}$ intersect at $Y$, and $\overleftrightarrow{AC}$ and $\overleftrightarrow{A'C'}$ intersect at $Z$, then $X$, $Y$, and $Z$ are collinear.

show that $\overleftrightarrow{AB} \perp \overleftrightarrow{AP}$. Since $\overleftrightarrow{AB}$ is perpendicular to two intersecting lines in $E$ at their point of intersection, we conclude, by Theorem 8–2, that $\overleftrightarrow{AB} \perp E$.

**14.** If $E_3 \parallel L_{12}$, then $E_3$ and $L_{12}$ do not meet. Then $L_{12}$ and $L_{13}$ do not meet; and since they both lie in $E_1$, they are parallel. Similarly, $L_{12}$ and $L_{23}$ are parallel. By Corollary 10–4.2, $L_{13} \parallel L_{23}$.

If $E_3$ intersects $L_{12}$ at point $P$, $P$ lies on each of $E_1$, $E_2$, and $E_3$, and hence in $L_{12}$, $L_{13}$, and $L_{23}$. Hence all three lines would have $P$ as a common point.

**Answer to Honors Problem**

Point $X$ lies in plane $ABC$ and also in plane $A'B'C'$, and hence on their intersection. Similarly, $Y$ and $Z$ lie on the intersection of these two planes, or the points $X, Y, Z$ lie on a line, which was to be proved.

*Remark 1.* The two nonparallel planes always intersect, but it might happen that $\overleftrightarrow{B'C'}$ and $\overleftrightarrow{BC}$ are parallel lines, so there would be no point $Y$. This would happen if and only if $\overleftrightarrow{BC}$ and $\overleftrightarrow{B'C'}$ are both parallel to $\overleftrightarrow{XZ}$. This could not happen for two pairs of side-lines, because we could not have two lines through a vertex parallel to $\overleftrightarrow{XZ}$.

*Remark 2.* The theorem is also valid if plane $ABC$ = plane $A'B'C'$, but we have not proved it.

Desargues' Theorem is an interesting and important incidence theorem relating concurrence of lines with collinearity of points. The theorem is also valid when the two triangles are coplanar, but is much harder to prove. In this case the student can get an intuitive appreciation of its correctness by imagining the figure to collapse into a plane.

**Classroom Notes**

Section 10-3 is an introduction to the idea of a projection; the section is interesting, but since we make no further use of it in this course, it can be regarded as optional.

## 10-3 PROJECTIONS

### Definition

The *projection* of a point into a plane is the foot of the perpendicular from the point to the plane.

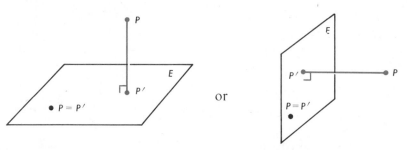

By Theorem 8–9, there is one and only one such perpendicular. In each of the figures, $P'$ is the projection of $P$ into $E$. We allow the possibility that $P$ lies in $E$. In this case, the projection of $P$ is $P$ itself.

### Definition

The *projection* of a line into a plane is the set of all points of the plane which are projections of points of the line.

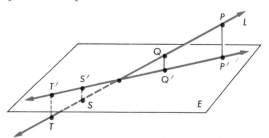

In the figure, $P'$ is the projection of $P$, $Q'$ is the projection of $Q$, $S'$ is the projection of $S$, and so on. The figure suggests that the projection of a line is always a line; and, in fact, this is what always happens, except when the line and the plane are perpendicular, as in the figure on the right. Here $A$ is the projection of *every* point $P$ of the line, and therefore $A$ is the projection of the whole line. To get a true theorem, we need to rule out this possibility.

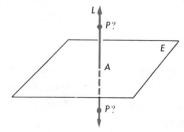

### Theorem 10–9

*If a line and a plane are not perpendicular, then the projection of the line into the plane is a line.*

**Proof.** Given that the line $L$ is not perpendicular to the plane $E$.

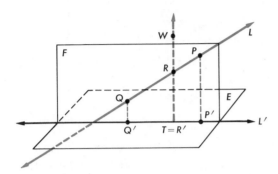

Let $P$ and $Q$ be any two points of $L$, and let $P'$ and $Q'$ be their projections. Then $P' \neq Q'$. (Why?) And $\overleftrightarrow{PP'}$ and $\overleftrightarrow{QQ'}$ are coplanar, because they are both perpendicular to the same plane (Theorem 8–7). Let $F$ be the plane which contains $\overleftrightarrow{PP'}$ and $\overleftrightarrow{QQ'}$; and let $L'$ be the line in which $F$ intersects $E$. Now $L$ lies in $F$, because $F$ contains two points of $L$. We are going to prove that $L'$ is the projection of $L$ into $E$. Since $L'$ is a line, this will complete the proof of the theorem.

Now $F \perp E$. This is true for two reasons: every plane containing $\overleftrightarrow{PP'}$ is perpendicular to $E$, and so also is every plane containing $\overleftrightarrow{QQ'}$ (Theorem 10–7).

We shall prove two things:

(1)   If $R$ is a point of $L$, then the projection $R'$ lies in $L'$.
(2)   If $T$ is a point of $L'$, then $T$ is the projection of some point of $L$.

**Proof of (1).** Let $T$ be the foot of the perpendicular from $R$ to $L'$ in the plane $F$. By Theorem 10–8, $\overline{RT} \perp E$. Therefore $T = R'$, because perpendiculars are unique. Therefore $R'$ lies in $L'$.

**Proof of (2).** Given a point $T$ of $L'$, let $\overleftrightarrow{TW}$ be the perpendicular to $L'$ at $T$, in the plane $F$. By Theorem 10–8, $\overleftrightarrow{TW} \perp E$. Therefore $\overleftrightarrow{TW}$ and $L$ are not parallel. (Why?) Let $R$ be the point at which $\overleftrightarrow{TW}$ intersects $L$. Then $T = R'$.

We have shown that every point of the projection is in $L'$, and every point of $L'$ is in the projection. Therefore $L'$ and the projection are exactly the same set of points. Therefore the projection is a line, which was to be proved.

## Quiz

In the figure below the plane *F* is perpendicular to the plane *E*, and □*ABCD* lies in the plane *F* with the point *A* in *E*. What is the projection in *E* of each of the following?

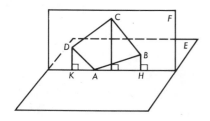

(a) $\overline{DC}$
  (ans: $\overline{KG}$)
(b) $\overline{AC}$
  (ans: $\overline{AG}$)
(c) ∠*KAD*
  (ans: $\overrightarrow{AK}$)
(d) □*ABCD*
  (ans: $\overline{KH}$)
(e) ∠*BCG*
  (ans: $\overrightarrow{GH}$)

The idea of a projection can be defined more generally, for *any* set of points.

### Definition

If *A* is any set of points in space, and *E* is a plane, then the *projection of A into E* is the set of all points which are projections of points of *A* into *E*.

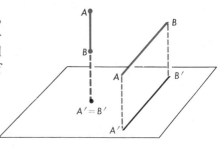

For example, the projection of a segment is usually a segment, although in some cases it may be a point. Similarly, the projection of a triangle is usually a triangle, although it may turn out to be a segment.

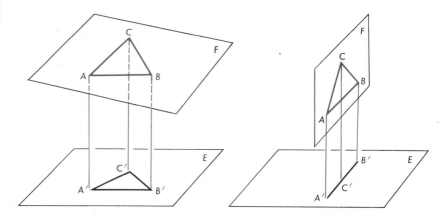

The second possibility arises whenever the plane of the triangle is perpendicular to *E*, as in the figure on the right.

### Problem Set 10–3

1. In the figure, planes *E* and *F* are perpendicular at $\overleftrightarrow{AB}$, *C* is in *F*, and $\overline{CD} \perp \overline{AB}$. What is the projection of $\overline{AC}$? of $\overline{BC}$? of △*ABC*?
   AD
   DB
   AB

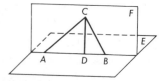

2. If one diagonal of a rhombus is perpendicular to a plane at an end point, what sort of figure is the projection of the rhombus into the plane?
   The projection is a segment.

**Answers to Problems**

**6.** In general, the projection of a square is a parallelogram. However, if the square is appropriately oriented, relative to the edge of the dihedral angle, we can be more precise: (1) If a side of the square is parallel to the edge of the dihedral angle, the projection is a rectangle. (2) If a diagonal of the square is parallel to the edge of the dihedral angle, the projection is a rhombus. [Note that it is possible to prove a more general theorem: the projection of a parallelogram, which lies in one face of an acute dihedral angle, into the other face, is a parallelogram.]

**3.** In the figure, $E$ and $F$ are planes intersecting in $\overleftrightarrow{PQ}$. $\overline{AB}$, in $F$, is twice as long as its projection, $\overline{BC}$. $\overleftrightarrow{PQ} \perp$ plane $ABC$. Find $m\angle A\text{-}PQ\text{-}C$.

$m\angle A\text{-}PQ\text{-}C = 60$

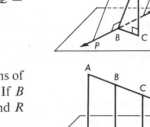

**4.** $P$, $Q$, $R$, and $S$ are the projections of $A$, $B$, $C$, and $D$ into plane $E$. If $B$ and $C$ trisect $\overline{AD}$, why do $Q$ and $R$ trisect $\overline{PS}$? **Corollary 9-30.1**

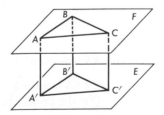

**7.** Since $A'$ is the projection of $A$ into $E$ and $B'$ is the projection of $B$ into $E$, $\overleftrightarrow{AA'} \perp E$ and $\overleftrightarrow{BB'} \perp E$, by definition. Hence by Theorem 10–4, $\overleftrightarrow{AA'} \parallel \overleftrightarrow{BB'}$. $\overleftrightarrow{AA'}$ and $\overleftrightarrow{BB'}$ are coplanar (Theorem 8–7), and so the lines of intersection of the plane containing them with the parallel planes $E$ and $F$ are, by Theorem 10–1, parallel: $\overleftrightarrow{AB} \parallel \overleftrightarrow{A'B'}$. Therefore $\square ABB'A'$ is a parallelogram, and since the opposite sides of a parallelogram are congruent $AB = A'B'$. (Theorem 9–15) Similarly, $BC = B'C'$ and $CA = C'A'$. Consequently $\triangle ABC \cong \triangle A'B'C'$. The projection of $\triangle ABC$ into $E$ is a triangle congruent to $\triangle ABC$.

**5.** (a) Is the projection of a point always a point? **Yes**

(b) Is the projection of a segment always a segment? **No**

(c) Can the projection of an angle be a ray? a line? a segment? **No** **Yes** **Yes**

(d) Can the projection of an acute angle be an obtuse angle? **Yes**

(e) Is the projection of a right angle ever a right angle? **Yes**

(f) Can the projection of a segment be longer than the segment? shorter? **No** **Yes**

(g) Can the projection of two intersecting lines be two parallel lines? **No**

(h) Can the projection of two skew lines ever be two parallel lines? **Yes**

(i) Can the projection of two skew lines ever be two intersecting lines? **Yes**

(j) Is the projection of two parallel lines always two parallel lines? **No**

**6.** One face of an acute dihedral angle contains a square. What sort of figure is the projection of the square into the other face?

**7.** Given two parallel planes, $E$ and $F$. $\triangle ABC$ is in $F$. Prove that the projection of $\triangle ABC$ into $E$ is a triangle congruent to $\triangle ABC$.

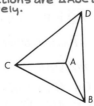

**8.** The figure on the left is a tetrahedron. The figure on the right is the projection of the tetrahedron into the plane $BCD$. Sketch the projections into the planes $ABC$ and $ACD$. **The projections are $\triangle ABC$ and $\triangle ACD$ respectively.**

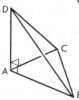

**9.** If a diagonal of a cube is perpendicular to a plane, then the projection of the edges of the cube into that plane is a regular hexagon, together with the segments from the center of the hexagon, (that is, the foot of the perpendicular diagonal) to each vertex.

**10.** Since *D* is on the perpendicular bisector, in *E*, of $\overline{AB}$, *D* is equidistant from *A* and *B*: $AD = DB$. Since *D* is the projection of *C* into *E*, $\overline{CD}$ is perpendicular to *E* by definition, and so $\overline{CD} \perp \overline{DA}$ and $\overline{CD} \perp \overline{DB}$. Therefore $\triangle ADC \cong \triangle BDC$ (SAS), and thus $AC = BC$, so $\triangle ABC$ is isosceles.

**12.** Introduce $\overrightarrow{RT} \perp E$. Since *Q* is the projection of *P*, $\overline{PQ} \perp E$. Therefore $\overline{PQ} \parallel \overline{RT}$ (Theorem 10–4), so *P*, *Q*, *R*, and *T* lie in a plane *F*. By Theorem 9–1, plane *F* is unique, and it contains $\overrightarrow{RP}$, $\overrightarrow{RQ}$, and $\overrightarrow{RT}$ by Postulate 6. Now $\overrightarrow{RS} \perp \overrightarrow{RP}$ by hypothesis, and $\overrightarrow{RS} \perp \overrightarrow{RT}$ by the definition of $\overrightarrow{RT} \perp E$, so $\overrightarrow{RS} \perp F$ by the Basic Theorem on Perpendiculars (Theorem 8–2). Therefore $\overrightarrow{RS} \perp \overrightarrow{RQ}$, by the definition of $\overrightarrow{RS} \perp F$. This means that $\angle QRS$ is a right angle.

**13.** (1) Since *R'* is the projection of *R* into *E*, $\overline{RR'} \perp E$, and so $\overline{RR'} \perp \overline{R'K}$. Therefore $\triangle RR'K$ is a right triangle, and $RK > RR'$. · (2) Now compare $\triangle RAK$ and $\triangle RAR'$. Since two sides of one triangle are congruent respectively to two sides of the second triangle, and the third side of the first triangle is longer than the third side of the second $(RK > RR')$, we can conclude by Theorem 7–10 that $m\angle RAK > m\angle RAR'$. Thus $m\angle QAR < m\angle PAR$.

---

**9.** If a diagonal of a cube is perpendicular to a plane, sketch the projection into the plane of all the edges of the cube.

**10.** In plane *E*, *M* is the midpoint of $\overline{AB}$. *C* is a point not in *E*, but its projection, *D*, is on the perpendicular bisector of $\overline{AB}$. Prove that $\triangle ABC$ is isosceles.

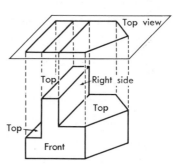

**11.** In mechanical drawing, the top view, or "plan," of a solid may be considered to be the projection of the various segments of the solid into a horizontal plane above the solid, as illustrated below on the left. The top view as it would actually be drawn is shown on the right. (No attempt is made here to obtain true scale.)

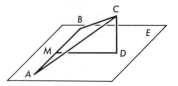

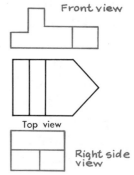

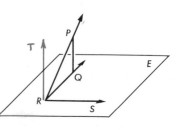

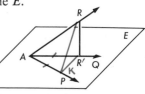

(a) Sketch a front view of the solid; that is, sketch the projection of the segments of the solid into a plane parallel to the front face.

(b) Sketch the right side view of the solid.

---

**12.** Given: $\overrightarrow{RS}$ is in plane *E*.

$\angle PRS$ is a right angle.
*Q* is the projection of *P*.

Prove: $\angle QRS$ is a right angle.

[*Hint:* Introduce $\overrightarrow{RT}$, the perpendicular to *E* at *R*.]

**13.** Given: $\overrightarrow{AQ}$ is the projection of $\overrightarrow{AR}$ into plane *E*.

$\overrightarrow{AP}$ is any other ray from *A* in *E*.

Prove: $m\angle QAR < m\angle PAR$.

[*Hint:* On $\overrightarrow{AP}$, introduce point *K* such that $AK = AR'$. Draw $\overline{KR'}$ and $\overline{KR}$.]

**Answers to Chapter Review Problems**

**2.** Since $E$ and $F$ are each perpendicular to $\overline{AC}$, $E \parallel F$ by Theorem 10-3. Since $\overline{BD}$ is perpendicular to one of the two parallel planes, $F$, it follows that $\overline{BD}$ is perpendicular to the other, and so $\overline{BD} \perp E$ (Theorem 10-2). Since $\overline{AC}$ and $\overline{BD}$ are each perpendicular to $F$, $\overline{AC} \parallel \overline{BD}$ (Theorem 10-4).

# CHAPTER REVIEW

1. Name the dihedral angles in this figure, assuming that no two of the indicated triangles are coplanar.

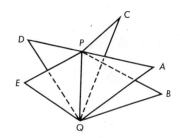

∠A-PQ-B, ∠A-PQ-C, ∠A-PQ-D,
∠A-PQ-E, ∠B-PQ-C, ∠B-PQ-D,
∠B-PQ-E, ∠C-PQ-D, ∠C-PQ-E,
∠D-PQ-E

2. Given: $E \perp \overline{AC}, F \perp \overline{AC}, F \perp \overline{BD}$.
   Prove: $E \perp \overline{BD}$ and $\overline{AC} \parallel \overline{BD}$.

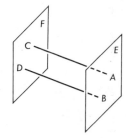
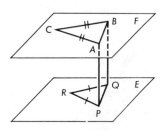

3. Given the figure (on the right above) as marked. $\triangle ABC$ is in plane $F$; $\triangle PQR$ is in plane $E$; $\square ABQP$ is a rectangle and $\overline{AP} \perp E$. Which of the following statements are true?

   (a) $\overline{BQ} \perp E$. T  (b) $AQ = BP$. T  (c) $F \parallel E$. F
   (d) $\overline{PQ}$ is the projection of $\overline{AB}$ into $E$. T  (e) $\triangle ABC \cong \triangle PQR$. F
   (f) $PC = QC$. T  (g) $\overline{BC} \parallel \overline{RQ}$. F  (h) $\triangle PAC \cong \triangle RBC$. F

4. Indicate, by A, S, or N, whether each statement is true in ALL cases, true in SOME cases and false in others, or true in NO cases.

   (a) Two lines parallel to the same plane are perpendicular to each other. S

   (b) If a plane intersects each of two parallel planes, the lines of intersection are skew. N

   (c) If two planes are parallel to the same line, they are parallel to each other. S

   (d) The intersection of a plane with the faces of a dihedral angle is a plane angle of the dihedral angle. S

   (e) If two lines are perpendicular to the same plane, the lines are parallel. A

   (f) If two lines are parallel to the same plane, the lines are parallel. S

   (g) If a line is perpendicular to a plane, every plane containing the line is perpendicular to the plane. A

   (h) Two lines are parallel if each is perpendicular to the same line. S

   (i) If each of two intersecting planes is perpendicular to a third plane, their line of intersection is perpendicular to the third plane. A

**8.** The plane of $\triangle AQB$ intersects parallel planes $E$ and $F$ in two parallel lines $\overleftrightarrow{AB}$ and $\overleftrightarrow{KM}$ (Theorem 10–1). Since $\overleftrightarrow{KM}$ bisects one side of $\triangle AQB$ and is parallel to a second side, it bisects the third side: $BM = MQ$ (Problem 2, Section 9–8). Since $\overline{KM}$ joins the midpoints of two sides of $\triangle AQB$, $KM = \frac{1}{2}AB$ by Theorem 9–22. Similarly, $MP = \frac{1}{2}BC$ and $PK = \frac{1}{2}CA$. ∴Perimeter of $\triangle ABC =$ 2 (Perimeter of $\triangle KMP$).

**9.** Let $Q$ be the projection of $P$ into $E$. If $\overline{PQ}$ is, as it seems to be, the median of trapezoid $\square AKMC$ and of trapezoid $\square BLDN$, we can conclude that $PQ = \frac{1}{2}(AK + CM)$ and $PQ = \frac{1}{2}(BL + DN)$ by the theorem in Problem 6, Problem Set 9–8, and consequently, that $AK + CM = BL + DN$. We must verify, however, that $\square AKMS$ and $\square BLDN$ are trapezoids and that $\overline{PQ}$ is the median of each.

Since $K$, $M$, and $Q$ are the projections of $A$, $C$, and $P$ respectively, it follows that $\overline{AK} \perp E$, $\overline{CM} \perp E$, and $\overline{PQ} \perp E$. Hence by Theorem 10–4 and Corollary 10–4.2, $\overline{AK} \parallel \overline{CM} \parallel \overline{PQ}$. By definition, $\square AKMC$ is a trapezoid. Since $\square ABCD$ is a parallelogram by hypothesis, its diagonals bisect each other, so $P$ is the midpoint of $\overline{AC}$. Therefore, by the definition of median of a trapezoid $\overline{PQ}$ is the median. Similarly, $\overline{PQ}$ is the median of trapezoid $\square BLND$.

[Note: The following easily proved theorem may have occurred to you. The projection of a parallelogram, which lies in one face of an acute dihedral angle, into the other face, is a parallelogram.]

---

**5.** $\overleftrightarrow{AB}$ is the edge of $\angle S\text{-}AB\text{-}T$ and $P$ is on $\overline{AB}$. If $m\angle SPT = 90$, is $\angle S\text{-}AB\text{-}T$ a right dihedral angle? Explain.

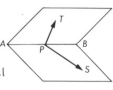

∠S-AB-T will be a rt. dihedral ∠, if ∠SPT is the plane angle of the dihedral angle, $\overrightarrow{PS} \perp \overleftrightarrow{AB}$ and $\overrightarrow{PT} \perp \overleftrightarrow{AB}$

---

**6.** $E$ and $F$ are planes intersecting in $\overleftrightarrow{KM}$; $\overrightarrow{AB}$ and $\overrightarrow{PQ}$ are in $E$; $\overrightarrow{AC}$ and $\overrightarrow{PR}$ are in $F$. If $m\angle MAB = 90$ and $m\angle KAC = 90$, is $\angle BAC$ a plane angle of $\angle B\text{-}KM\text{-}C$? Yes If $m\angle RPQ = 90$, is $\overrightarrow{PQ} \parallel \overrightarrow{AB}$?

Not necessarily

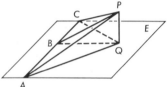

**7.** In the figure, $PQ = \frac{1}{2}PC = \frac{1}{2}PA$, $AB = BC$, and $\overline{PQ} \perp E$. Which of the following is true?

$$m\angle P\text{-}AC\text{-}Q < 30$$
$$m\angle P\text{-}AC\text{-}Q = 30$$
$$\boxed{m\angle P\text{-}AC\text{-}Q > 30.}$$

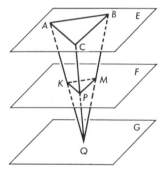

**8.** Given: Parallel planes $E$, $F$, and $G$, with $Q$ in $G$, $\triangle KMP$ in $F$, and $\triangle ABC$ in $E$. $AK = KQ$.

Prove: The perimeter of $\triangle ABC$ is twice the perimeter of $\triangle KMP$.

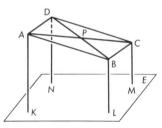

**9.** In the figure, parallelogram $\square ABCD$ is not parallel to plane $E$. $K$, $L$, $M$, $N$ are the projections into $E$ of the vertices $A$, $B$, $C$, $D$, respectively. Prove that

$$AK + CM = BL + DN.$$

[*Hint:* Let $Q$ be the projection of $P$ into $E$. Draw $\overline{PQ}$.]

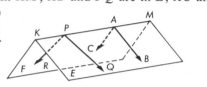

**10.** Sketch a figure showing the intersection of a plane with all six faces of a cube. Then imagine the intersection projected into a plane parallel to the first plane but not intersecting the cube and draw the result.

**Answers to Chapter Review Problems**

**10.** In the figure shown, $A$, $B$, $C$, $D$, $E$, and $F$ are midpoints of the respective edges. The projection of figure $ABCDEF$ into a plane parallel to it will be, of course, a hexagon congruent to figure $ABCDEF$. In this case the hexagon will be regular. (For a discussion of regular polygons see Chapter 16.)

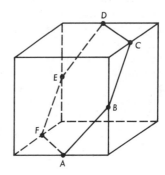

**Nikolai Ivanovitch Lobachevsky (1793–1856)**

Early in the nineteenth century, non-Euclidean geometry was discovered by three men, working independently in three different countries. These men were Karl Friedrich Gauss in Germany, János Bolyai in Hungary, and Nikolai Ivanovitch Lobachevsky in Russia.

Until then, everybody had believed that the uniqueness of parallels was simply a fact, both of geometry and of physics. These three men tried assuming the contrary: they assumed that through a given external point there is *more than one* parallel to a given line. This led to a new kind of geometry, which was mathematically just as good as the familiar geometry of Euclid. And this new geometry turned out to be useful in physics—after the discovery of relativity theory by Albert Einstein.

Lobachevsky is usually given most of the credit for non-Euclidean geometry. He carried the theory further than Bolyai did. And unlike Gauss, he had the courage to publish his work. Gauss seems to have been afraid of looking foolish. He was considered to be the greatest mathematician of his time, and so he would have had a long way to fall.

## CHAPTER 11

## Polygonal Regions and Their Areas

This chapter deals with the areas of triangles, parallelograms, trapezoids, and so on. Although the treatment is essentially conventional, two points may seem novel: first the introduction of the term "polygonal region," and second the study of area by postulating its properties rather than by deriving them from a definition based on a measurement process. Actually both of these ideas are implicit in the conventional treatment—we have only brought them to the surface and clarified them. Once the basis has been laid, our methods of proof are simple and conventional.

In this chapter we are not trying to develop a general theory of area, applicable to figures with curvilinear boundaries; this is a different theory, and is far more difficult, because it makes use of limiting processes. We restrict ourselves to the simple case of a region whose boundary is a union of segments.

### Planning the Chapter

For an average class allow four days for Sections 11-1 and 11-2, three days each for Sections 11-3 and 11-4. An above-average class should complete Sections 11-1 and 11-2 in three days, spend three days on Section 11-3 and three days on Section 11-4 and the chapter review.

CHAPTER

# 11

# Polygonal Regions and Their Areas

## Objectives...

- Learn the postulates for areas of polygonal regions.
- Learn formulas for the areas of rectangles, triangles, parallelograms, and rhombuses.
- Prove, and use, the Pythagorean Theorem for right triangles.
- Learn special formulas for 30–60–90 triangles and 45–45–90 triangles.

## 11-1 POLYGONAL REGIONS

### Definition

A *triangular region* is the union of a triangle and its interior.

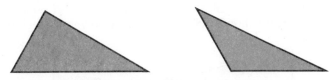

A *polygonal region* is a plane figure formed by fitting together a finite number of triangular regions:

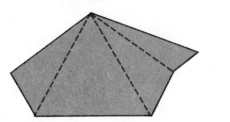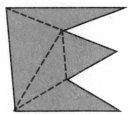

Hereafter we shall not use shading in pictures of regions in cases where it is plain what region is being described.

### Definition

A *polygonal region* is the union of a finite number of triangular regions, in a plane, such that if two of these intersect, their intersection is either a point or a segment.

The dashed lines in the figures above show how each of the two polygonal regions can be expressed as such a union. Some more

**Background Material**

It is usual, in introductory books, to speak not of the area of a polygonal region, but of the "area of a polygon," where *polygon* means *simple closed polygon*. This terminology is open to a number of objections of various degrees of seriousness:

(1) The language is loose: what we really mean is the area of the figure consisting of the polygon together with its interior. This in itself is not very bad, because the student understands from the context that we are using an abbreviation. Thus the student ordinarily supplies for himself the explanation given at the bottom of page 332. (Also, unfortunately, he infers that authors cannot be relied upon to mean what they say.)

(2) The idea of the "area of a polygon" is not adequate, even for the purposes of an introductory course. One of the commonplaces of "shop mathematics" is the problem of finding the area of a square region with a square hole in it. See also Problem 20 on page 336. These are simple regions, but they are not the sort of regions that the conventional theory claims to deal with. One of the hazards in teaching is a tendency on the part of the student to regard the theory merely as a gesture. This hazard becomes more serious in situations where the theory is plainly inadequate to justify the student's problem work; and this is especially unfortunate in cases where the gap between theory and practice is gratuitous.

(3) It is easy to show that every *convex* polygon (page 536) has an interior; the interior of the polygon is the intersection of the interiors of its angles. The same is true of polygons in general: every polygon, convex or not, separates the plane

into exactly two parts, and the bounded part is called its interior. But the proof in the general case is startlingly long and hard; and the whole question is foreign to the purposes of Chapter 11. In elementary geometry we don't need to worry about the *existence* of the region with a given polygon as boundary: in every case that we need to deal with, the region is simply given, in the same sense in which the polygon is given. There are times, as in Chapters 16 and 19, when we cannot give exact definitions and work with them, because the essential logic of the topic is too complicated to present in full. But Chapter 11 presents no such problem: if the ideas are presented in the forms in which we need them, then the questions that we cannot adequately answer are questions that simply do not arise.

(4) Some have objected that it is pedantic to distinguish between a triangle and the corresponding triangular region, or between a polygon and the corresponding polygonal region. These objections are evidence of the force of custom: on the merits, the distinction between a region and its boundary is just as gross as the distinction between a man and his skin. Ellipsis and abbreviation are fair enough, as a matter of convenience, but first there should be an adequate language, so that we will know what it is that we are abbreviating, and so that we can, when we want to, say exactly what we mean. Moreover, our terms ought to be chosen so as to focus attention on the main ideas; and in this chapter the main idea is that of a polygonal region rather than a polygon.

examples are shown below.

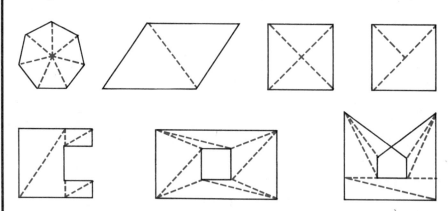

In the last two examples, the regions have "holes" in them. This is allowed by the definition, and these last two figures are perfectly good polygonal regions.

The shaded region shown below is in fact a polygonal region.

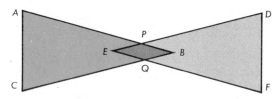

Note, however, that you can't prove this by mentioning the triangular regions determined by △*ABC* and △*DEF*. The trouble is that the intersection of these two triangular regions is not a point or a segment, as the definition says it should be. The intersection is the little diamond-shaped region in the middle of the figure.

On the other hand, it is easy to cut up this region differently, so as to show that it is a polygonal region.

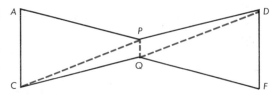

If a figure can be cut up into triangular regions at all, then this can be done in many ways. For example, a parallelogram plus its interior can be cut up in at least the three ways shown below.

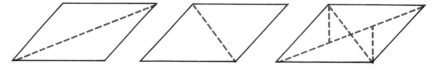

And it is easy to see that there are infinitely many other ways of cutting up such a figure.

In this chapter, we shall study the areas of polygonal regions, and learn to compute them. For this purpose, we shall use four new postulates.

## POSTULATE 19.   The Area Postulate

*To every polygonal region there corresponds a unique positive real number.*

## Definition

The *area* of a polygonal region is the number assigned to it by Postulate 19. The area of the region $R$ is denoted by $aR$. This is pronounced *area of R*.

Hereafter in this chapter, when we speak of a *region* we shall always mean a polygonal region.

Surely the area of a region ought to depend only on the size and shape of the region; it ought not to depend on the place where the region happens to be located in space. We state this fact as a postulate, for the case of triangular regions.

## POSTULATE 20.   The Congruence Postulate

*If two triangles are congruent, then the triangular regions determined by them have the same area.*

If we cut a region into two pieces, then the area of the region ought to be the sum of the areas of the two pieces.

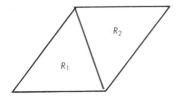
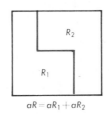
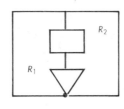

$$aR = aR_1 + aR_2$$

In each of these figures, the total region $R$ is the union of two regions $R_1$ and $R_2$ and in each case, $aR = aR_1 + aR_2$. We say this in the next postulate.

---

### Classroom Notes

Note the analogy between the Distance Postulate, the Angle Measurement Postulate, and Postulate 19, the Area Postulate. The Area Postulate might also be called the Polygonal Region Measurement Postulate.

The Area Addition Postulate can be restated using the idea of a partition:

> DEFINITION. A *partition* of a region $R$ is a decomposition of $R$ into two subregions $R_1$ and $R_2$ such that:
> (1) the union of these two subregions, $R_1$ and $R_2$, is the region $R$.
> (2) the intersection of these two subregions is contained in the union of a finite number of points or line segments.
> (We can define a partition of $R$ into more than two subregions in an obvious way.)

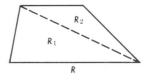

The Area Addition Postulate now says: If a region $R$ is partitioned into subregions $R_1$, and $R_2$, then $aR = aR_1 + aR_2$.

Note that the Area Addition Postulate can also be used to justify the subtraction of areas. Consider, for example, the trapezoidal region $R$. The diagonal separates $R$ into two subregions $R_1$ and $R_2$. By the Area Addition Postulate, $aR = aR_1 + aR_2$, and so $aR_1 = aR - aR_2$.

## Postulate 22. The Unit Postulate.

We wish to establish the familiar formulas for the area of a triangle, square, rectangle, parallelogram, trapezoid, and rhombus. If we postulate one of these formulas, we can then derive the others. It is interesting to ask the students which formula they would expect to postulate. The usual answer is the formula for the area of a triangle. Their expectation is well grounded: we defined a polygonal region in terms of triangular regions, and in using the Area Addition Postulate we usually partition the given region into triangular subregions. The students thus get the impression that the triangular region is the fundamental region, and they expect to begin by postulating that the area of a triangular region is given by $\frac{1}{2}bh$. This postulate is, however, too "strong." The other area formulas are immediate consequences of it; use Theorem 9–14 to get the area formula for a parallelogram and you are done. The formula for the area of a square is, on the other hand, a very "weak" postulate; note the ingenuity required to derive the area formula for a rectangle. To postulate the formula for the area of a square makes sense to the student since he already knows that we measure area in "square units." Remember also that he learned in elementary school to compute the area of a rectangle, for example, by counting the number of unit squares that it contains.

## POSTULATE 21.   The Area Addition Postulate

*If two polygonal regions intersect only in edges and vertices (or do not intersect at all), then the area of their union is the sum of their areas.*

Thus, if $R = R_1 \cup R_2$, then $aR = aR_1 + aR_2$, providing the intersection of the regions $R_1$ and $R_2$ is contained in a finite number of segments. If $R_1$ and $R_2$ are triangular regions as in the figure below, and $R$ is their

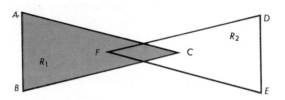

union, then $aR < aR_1 + aR_2$. (When we add, the area of the diamond-shaped region is counted twice.) In this case, however, we can determine the correct value of $aR$ by cutting the region up into non-overlapping triangles, and counting each triangular region only once.

We remember from Chapter 2 that the unit of distance could be chosen at will. The same is true of the unit of area. But we ought to be consistent in choosing our units: if we are measuring distance in centimetres, then we ought to measure area in square centimetres; if we use metres, then we should use square metres; and so on. This is the idea behind the following postulate.

## POSTULATE 22.   The Unit Postulate

*The area of a square region is the square of the length of its edge.*

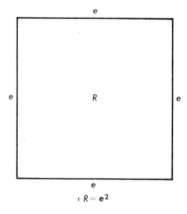

For short, we may speak of *the area of a square* or *the area of a triangle*. By this we shall mean the area of the corresponding region. The short terms conform to ordinary usage. Strictly speaking, of course, triangles and squares have area 0, because they are made up of three or four segments, and a segment has area 0. But the areas of the corresponding regions are always positive, as stated in Postulate 19.

In a similar manner, we shall speak of the base and altitude of a rectangle, meaning the length of the base and the length of the altitude. This is convenient, and, in each case, you ought to be able to tell from the context whether we are talking about a segment or about the number which measures its length.

By a simple trick, we shall now find the area of a rectangle.

### Theorem 11–1

***The area of a rectangle is the product of its base and its altitude.***

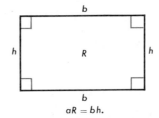

$aR = bh.$

**Proof.** Consider the figure on the right.

Here $A$ denotes the unknown area of our rectangle. The areas of our two squares are $b^2$ and $h^2$, by Postulate 22; and the area of the total figure is $(b + h)^2$. Therefore, by repeated applications of the Area Addition Postulate,

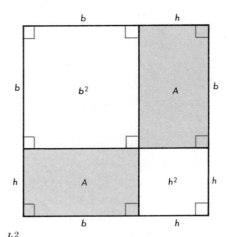

$$b^2 + 2A + h^2 = (b + h)^2$$
$$= b^2 + 2bh + h^2,$$

and

$$A = bh,$$

which is what we wanted.

If you wonder how we knew from our postulates that the two rectangles in the figure have the same area, you should examine the figure on the right. All four triangles are congruent, and so have the same area; and the area of each rectangle is twice the area of each triangle.

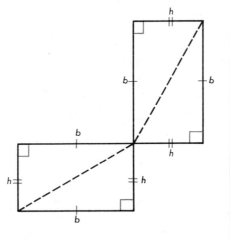

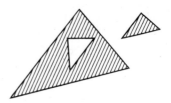

**3.** $AC = CR$ and $CR = RP$ by the definition of midpoint, and so $AC = PR$. Also $BC = CH = HR = RQ$. By the Isosceles Triangle Theorem, $\angle HCR \cong \angle HRC$, and by the Vertical Angle Theorem, $\angle ACB \cong \angle HCR$ and $\angle PRQ \cong \angle HRC$. Thus $\angle ACB \cong \angle PRQ$, so $\triangle ACB \cong \triangle PRQ$ by SAS. Thus $a\triangle ABC = a\triangle PQR$ by Postulate 20.

**Problem Set 11–1**

**1.** Trace each figure below. Show that each region is polygonal by triangulating each one according to the definition of polygonal region. Try to find the smallest number of triangular regions in each case.

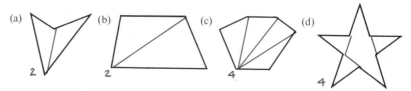

(a) 2    (b) 2    (c) 4    (d) 4

**2.** What is the area of a rectangular region 16 m long by 10.2 m wide?
163.2 m²

**3.** In the figure $\overline{AR}$ and $\overline{BH}$ bisect each other, and $\overline{PC}$ and $\overline{HQ}$ bisect each other. Also $HC = HR$. Prove that $a\triangle ABC = a\triangle PQR$.

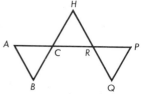

**4.** In the figure the length of the larger rectangle is three times that of the smaller rectangle. The altitude of the larger one is twice that of the smaller. How do their areas compare?
The larger is 6 times the smaller.

**5.** (a) If the altitude of a rectangle is doubled while the base stays the same, how is the area changed? Doubled

(b) If the base of a rectangle is doubled while the altitude stays the same, how is the area changed? Doubled

(c) If both the base and the altitude of a rectangle are doubled, how is the area changed? Quadrupled

**6.** How is the area of a square changed if the length of each side is doubled? tripled? halved? Multiplied by a factor of 4, 9, ¼

**7.** If, in the figure on the left below, $aR_1 = 50$, $aR_2 = 25$, and $R$ is the union of $R_1$ and $R_2$, what is $aR$? Quote a postulate or theorem to support your conclusion. aR = 75, The Area Addition Postulate

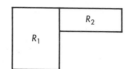

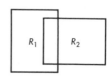

**8.** If, in the figure on the right above, $aR_1 = 30$, $aR_2 = 30$, and $R$ is the union of $R_1$ and $R_2$, is $aR = 60$? Quote a postulate or theorem to support your conclusion. No, Postulate 21.

9. How many square regions 2.5 cm on a side are needed to completely cover a square region 1 dm on a side? **16**

10. How many square regions 1 dm on a side are needed to completely cover a square region 50 cm on a side? **25**

11. How many tiles, each 10 cm square (i.e., 10 cm on a side) are needed to cover a rectangular wall 4.6 m by 2.2 m? **46 × 22 = 1012**

12. In the figure on the left below, $\square ABCE$ is a rectangle and $\square ACDE$ is a parallelogram. Prove that $a\triangle ABC = a\triangle ECD$.

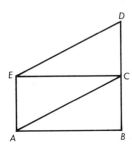 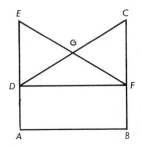

13. In the figure on the right above, $\square ABFD$ is a rectangle and $\overline{EF}$ and $\overline{DC}$ bisect each other. Prove that $a\square ABFE = a\square ABCD$.

14. A square and a rectangle have equal areas. If the rectangle is 25 cm by 16 cm, what is a side of the square? **20 cm**

15. Indicate whether each statement is true or false. Support your answers with reasons.

   (a) A square is a polygonal region. **F**

   (b) To every positive number there corresponds a unique polygonal region. **F**

   (c) If two triangles are congruent, then the triangular regions have equal areas. **T**

   (d) A triangular region does not include the triangle. **F**

   (e) The area of the union of two polygonal regions is the sum of their areas. **F**

   (f) A triangular region is a polygonal region. **T**

   (g) There exists a square region with area $\sqrt{17}$. **T**

   (h) There exists a rectangular region with area $4\sqrt{5}$ whose base is a rational number. **T**

16. Compute the area of a rectangle having base $b$ and altitude $h$, given that

   (a) $b = 17$ and $h = 12$ **204**     (b) $b = 1\frac{1}{3}$ and $h = 5\frac{3}{4}$ **7⅔**

   (c) $b = 3$ and $h = \sqrt{5}$ **3√5**     (d) $b = \sqrt{10}$ and $h = \sqrt{15}$ **5√6**

17. Compute the area of a square having side $s$, given that

   (a) $s = 24$ **576**  (b) $s = 3\frac{3}{5}$ **12$\frac{24}{25}$**  (c) $s = \sqrt{7}$ **7**  (d) $s = 4\sqrt{6}$ **96**

For Problem 21 the actual outside surface area is 336 m². Although 2.6 liters of paint will cover this surface, 3 liters must be purchased (since it is impossible to purchase 2.6 liters in a paint store). Any student who wishes to paint the inside as well will have an answer of 6 liters.

**Answers to Problems**

**22.** (c) The change produces three additional faces, four additional edges, and one additional vertex. Hence for the new figure

$$f' - e' + v'$$
$$= (f + 3) - (e + 4) + (v + 1)$$
$$= f - e + v = 2.$$

(d) The change produces one additional face, two additional edges and one additional vertex. Hence for the new figure

$$f' - e' + v'$$
$$= (f + 1) - (e + 2) + (v + 1)$$
$$= f - e + v = 2.$$

---

**18.** Prove: If two rectangles have the same base, $b$, then the ratio of their areas equals the ratio of their altitudes.

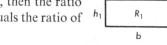

$$\frac{aR_1}{aR_2} = \frac{bh_1}{bh_2} = \frac{h_1}{h_2}$$

Prove: $\dfrac{aR_1}{aR_2} = \dfrac{h_1}{h_2}$.

**19.** A rectangular plot of land is to be planted with grass seed. The dimensions of the plot are 22 m by 28 m. If one 1-kg bag of grass seed is needed for each 84 m² of land, how many bags must be provided? **8 bags of seed**

**20.** The figure is the face of a certain machine part. To compute the cost of painting a number of these parts, one must know the area of a face. The shaded regions are not to be painted. Find the area of the region to be painted. What postulates and theorems do you use in computing the area? $aR = $ **229 cm²** **Postulates 21 and 22 and Theorem 11-1.**

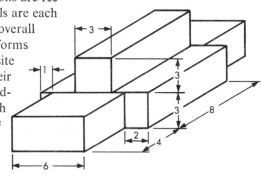

---

**21.** A wooden covering for a large unit of machinery is constructed as in the figure. All surface regions are rectangular. The two levels are each 3 m high making an overall height of 6 m. The forms which project on opposite ends are identical in their dimensions. If the building is to be painted with paint that covers 130 m² per litre, how many litres of paint will be required? **3 liters**

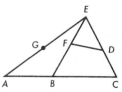

**22.** In the figure below, $A$, $B$, $C$, $D$, $E$, $F$, and $G$ are called *vertices*, $\overline{AB}$, $\overline{BC}$, $\overline{CD}$, $\overline{DE}$, $\overline{EG}$, $\overline{GA}$, $\overline{EF}$, $\overline{FD}$, and $\overline{FB}$ are called *edges*, and the polygonal regions $ABE$, $FED$, and $BCDF$ are called *faces*. The exterior of the figure is also considered a face. Let the number of faces be $f$, the number of vertices be $v$, and the number of edges be $e$. A theorem originated by a famous mathematician, Euler, relates $f$, $v$, and $e$ in the formula $f - e + v$. It refers to a large class of figures of which the above is one possibility. Let us compute $f - e + v$ for the figure above: $f = 4$, $e = 9$, and $v = 7$; hence, $4 - 9 + 7 = 2$.

(a) Compute $f - e + v$ for each of the two figures below. Note that the edges are not necessarily segments. The figure on the right could be a section of a map showing counties.

$7-12+7=2$

$7-17+12=2$

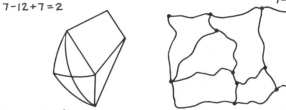

$f-e+v=2$ for any planar network.

(b) What pattern do you observe in the results of the three computations?

(c) In the figure on the left take a point in the interior of the quadrilateral and draw segments from each of its vertices to the point. How does this affect the computation of $f - e + v$? Can you explain why?

(d) Take a point in the exterior of either figure and join it to the nearest two vertices. How does this affect the computation?

(e) If you are interested in this problem and would like to pursue it further, you will find it discussed in *The Enjoyment of Mathematics* by Rademacher and Toeplitz and in *Fundamental Concepts of Geometry* by Meserve.

## 11–2   AREAS OF TRIANGLES AND QUADRILATERALS

Let us now get some more area formulas, on the basis of our postulates.

### Theorem 11–2

**The area of a right triangle is half the product of its legs.**

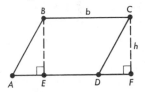

$A = \frac{1}{2}ab$

**Proof.** Given a right triangle with legs $a$ and $b$. Let its area be $A$. We form a rectangle $\square UVWX$ (as on the right) having the legs of our right triangle as two of its sides. Then

(1)   $\triangle VUX \cong \triangle XWV$
(2)   $a\triangle XWV = A$
(3)   $A + A = ab$
(4)   $A = \frac{1}{2}ab$.

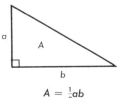

$aR = ab = 2A.$

Reasons? (You may need more than one reason for some of the steps.)

**Classroom Notes**

The proofs of the area formulas are easy and readable; you should assign the proofs in the text and concentrate on the problems, many of which are not easy.

Note that we have derived the area formulas in the following order: rectangle, right triangle, triangle, trapezoid, and finally parallelogram. This is not the order of derivations that we most often see; most texts get the area formula for parallelograms first and then derive the general area formula for triangles. In such a development the proof of the area formula for parallelograms looks like this:

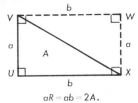

(1) $a\square ABCD = a\triangle ABE + a\square BCDE$, by the Area Addition Postulate.
(2) $a\triangle ABE = a\triangle DCF$, because $\triangle ABE \cong \triangle DCF$.
(3) $a\square ABCD = a\square BCDE + a\triangle DCF$.
(4) $a\square BCDE + a\triangle DCF = a\square BCFE$, by the Area Addition Postulate.
(5) $a\square BCFE = bh$, because $\square BCFE$ is a rectangle.

This "proof" works only in the cases described by the figures that are drawn to illustrate it. Consider the following case. If the parallelogram looks like the figure below,

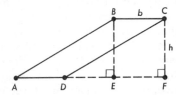

then the above discussion becomes nonsense in the very first step, because there is no such thing as "the quadrilateral $\square BCDE$," and even if we allowed quadrilaterals to cross themselves, the equation a☐ABCD = a△ABE + a☐BCDE would not hold for the areas of the corresponding polygonal regions.

## Explanation for Problems

Students find Problem Set 11–2 harder than you might expect. They did area problems in junior high school, but those problems were for the most part straightforward applications of formulas. The problems of this problem set, in contrast, require ingenuity, the use of many theorems, and the use of a variety of techniques. Before assigning the problems you should discuss with your class the following techniques for solving area problems.

(1) *The idea of introducing altitudes.* Each of the area formulas involves both a base (or bases) and the altitude upon that base. The base is always a segment in the given figure. The altitude, on the other hand, is not necessarily a segment in the given figure. Since each of the area formulas involves the use of an altitude it is often valuable to introduce one or more altitudes into the given figure. See, for example, Problems 3, 4, 5, 7, 9, 13, 14, etc., of Problem Set 11–2.

(2) *The idea of using the uniqueness clause in the Area Postulate.* The area of a triangle can, by Theorem 11–3, be computed in three different ways by using any one of the three bases and the altitude upon that base: $\frac{1}{2}b_1h_1$, $\frac{1}{2}b_2h_2$, $\frac{1}{2}b_3h_3$. The area of any polygonal region is, by the Area Postulate, a *unique* positive real number; this means that the three numbers $\frac{1}{2}b_1h_1$, $\frac{1}{2}b_2h_2$, and $\frac{1}{2}b_3h_3$ are equal. Hence, if we are given any three of the numbers $b_1$, $h_1$, $b_2$, $h_2$, we can find the fourth by using the fact that $\frac{1}{2}b_1h_1 = \frac{1}{2}b_2h_2$. This idea is used in Problems 7 and 8, and a

From this theorem we can get a formula for the area of any triangle. As soon as we have done this, we shall have no further need for Theorem 11–2, because our general theorem will include it as a special case.

### Theorem 11–3

*The area of a triangle is half the product of any base and the corresponding altitude.*

**Proof.** Let the given base and altitude be $b$ and $h$, and let the area be $A$. There are three cases to consider.

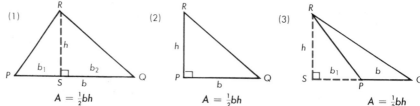

(1) If the foot of the altitude is between the end points of the base, then the altitude cuts our triangle into two triangles with bases $b_1$ and $b_2$, and $b_1 + b_2 = b$. By the preceding theorem, the areas of these triangles are $\frac{1}{2}b_1h$ and $\frac{1}{2}b_2h$. By the Area Addition Postulate,

$$A = \tfrac{1}{2}b_1h + \tfrac{1}{2}b_2h.$$

Therefore

$$A = \tfrac{1}{2}(b_1 + b_2)h = \tfrac{1}{2}bh,$$

which is what we wanted.

(2) If the foot of the altitude is an end point of the base, then our triangle is a right triangle, and $A = \frac{1}{2}bh$, by the preceding theorem.

(3) If the foot of the altitude misses the base, as in the third figure, we have

$$\tfrac{1}{2}b_1h + A = \tfrac{1}{2}(b_1 + b)h$$
$$= \tfrac{1}{2}b_1h + \tfrac{1}{2}bh$$

and

$$A = \tfrac{1}{2}bh,$$

as before. (Reasons?)

Note that Theorem 11–3 can be applied to any triangle in three

ways: we can choose any of the
three sides as base, multiply by the
corresponding altitude, and divide
by 2.  Note that

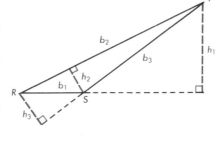

$$\tfrac{1}{2}b_1h_1, \quad \tfrac{1}{2}b_2h_2, \quad \text{and} \quad \tfrac{1}{2}b_3h_3$$

must be the same number, because
each of them is the right answer to
the same problem.

Now that we know how to find areas of triangles, the rest is simple:
to find the area of a polygonal region, we cut it up into triangles and
add.  This procedure is especially easy for trapezoids.

First, recall from Section 9–5 that the distance between two parallel
lines is the length of a perpendicular from any point of one to the other.
We use this to define the altitude of a trapezoid.

### Definition

The *altitude* of a trapezoid is the distance between the lines containing
its parallel sides.

### Theorem 11–4

*The area of a trapezoid is half the product of its altitude and the sum
of its bases.*

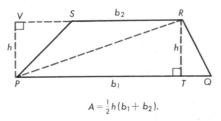

$$A = \tfrac{1}{2}h(b_1 + b_2).$$

**Proof.**  Let $A$ be the area of the trapezoid.  Either diagonal divides the
trapezoid into two triangles, with bases $b_1$ and $b_2$ and the same altitude
$h$.  (Why is $PV = TR$?)  By the Area Addition Postulate,

$$A = \tfrac{1}{2}b_1h + \tfrac{1}{2}b_2h$$
$$= \tfrac{1}{2}h(b_1 + b_2),$$

which is what we wanted.

similar observation about the area
of a parallelogram is used in
Problem 10.

(3) *How to compare the areas of
different regions.*  Theorems 11–6
and 11–7 are the basis for problems
involving the comparison of the
areas of different regions.  Theorem 11–6 states:

> If two triangles have the same
> base and the same altitude,
> then they have the same area.

An immediate consequence is the
fact that a median of a triangle
separates the triangle into two triangular regions which have the
same area.  Theorem 11–7 states:

> If two triangles have the same
> altitudes, then the ratio of
> their areas is equal to the
> ratio of their bases.

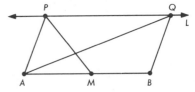

For example, in the figure above,
$M$ is the midpoint of $\overline{AB}$ and $L$ is
parallel to $\overline{AB}$; therefore $a\triangle APM =
\tfrac{1}{2}a\triangle AQB$.

The above example illustrates
another important point: a good
way to show that two triangles
have equal altitudes is to make use
of Corollary 9–15.1: parallel lines
are everywhere equidistant.

You can mention two further facts
and allow the students to use them:

(a) If two triangles have the same
base, then the ratio of their
areas is equal to the ratio of
their altitudes.

(b) More generally: Given two
triangles, if a base of the first
triangle is $k$ times a base of
the second triangle, and the
altitude upon that base in the
first triangle is $j$ times the
corresponding altitude in the

second triangle, then the area of the first triangle is *kj* times the area of the second triangle.

(4) *The idea of using the Area Addition Postulate.* We can frequently obtain information about the area of a triangle by making use of the Area Addition Postulate:

If △*ABC* is partitioned into two triangles, △*ABP* and △*PBC*, then

$$a\triangle ABC = a\triangle ABP + a\triangle PBC.$$

And we may be able to obtain information about $a\triangle ABP$ and $a\triangle PBC$. Consider, for example, Problem 24 of Problem Set 11-2, letting *P* be the point of intersection of $\overline{AC}$ and $\overline{BD}$.

By the Area Addition Postulate,

$$a\triangle ABC = a\triangle ABP + a\triangle PBC$$

and

$$a\triangle ADC = a\triangle ADP + a\triangle PDC.$$

But by Theorem 11-6,

$$a\triangle ABP = a\triangle ADP$$

and

$$a\triangle PBC = a\triangle PDC.$$

Therefore,

$$a\triangle ABC = a\triangle ADC.$$

We can also use the Area Addition Postulate to justify subtracting areas (see Problem 26 of Problem Set 11-2).

By exactly the same method, we get an area formula for parallelograms.

### Theorem 11-5

***The area of a parallelogram is the product of any base and the corresponding altitude.***

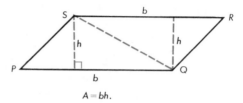

$A = bh.$

**Proof.** Let *A* be the area of the parallelogram. Either diagonal divides the parallelogram into two triangles, with the same base *b* and the same altitude *h*. By the Area Addition Postulate,

$$A = \tfrac{1}{2}bh + \tfrac{1}{2}bh = bh.$$

The area formula for triangles has two easy but useful consequences.

### Theorem 11-6

***If two triangles have the same base b and the same altitude h, then they have the same area.***

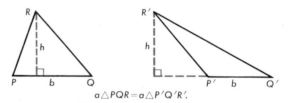

$a\triangle PQR = a\triangle P'Q'R'.$

This is obvious, because the area of each of them is $\tfrac{1}{2}bh$.

### Theorem 11-7

***If two triangles have the same altitude h, then the ratio of their areas is equal to the ratio of their bases.***

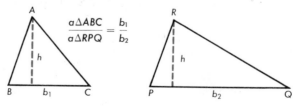

$$\frac{a\triangle ABC}{a\triangle RPQ} = \frac{b_1}{b_2}$$

**Proof.** Let the bases be $b_1$ and $b_2$.

Then
$$\frac{a\triangle ABC}{a\triangle PQR} = \frac{\frac{1}{2}b_1 h}{\frac{1}{2}b_2 h} = \frac{b_1}{b_2}.$$

## Problem Set 11-2

**1.** In $\triangle ABC$ below, $AC = 8$, and the altitude to $\overline{AC}$ is 3. In $\triangle DEF$, $EF = 6$. If $a\triangle ABC = a\triangle DEF$, find the altitude to $\overline{EF}$. 4

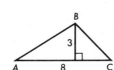

**2.** In $\triangle PQR, \angle P$ is a right angle, $PR = 16$, $PQ = 12$, and $RQ = 20$.

(a) Find the area of $\triangle PQR$. 96 (b) Find the altitude to the hypotenuse. 192/20 = 9.6

**3.** In the figure, $B$ is the midpoint of $\overline{AC}$ and $\overline{ED} \parallel \overline{AC}$. Prove that $a\triangle ABE = a\triangle BCD$.
Use corollary 9-15.1 and Theorem 11-6.

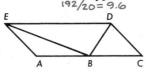

**4.** $\square KMPR$ is a parallelogram. Given that $m\angle K = 30$, $KM = 11$, and $KR = 8$, find $a\square KMPR$. a□ KMPR =44

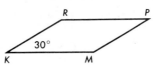

**5.** A rhombus has a side of 12 and the measure of one angle is 150. Find the area of the rhombus. 72

**6.** One right triangle has legs 18 cm and 14 cm. Another right triangle has legs 14 cm and 24 cm. What is the ratio of the areas of the two triangles? 3/4 or 4/3

**7.** Two sides of a triangle are 15 cm and 20 cm long, and the altitude to the 15-cm side is 8 cm. How long is the altitude to the 20-cm side? 6 cm

**8.** In $\triangle ABC, \overleftrightarrow{CD}$ is the altitude to $\overleftrightarrow{AB}$, and $\overline{AE}$ is the altitude to $\overleftrightarrow{BC}$.

(a) If $AB = 8$, $CD = 9$, $AE = 6$, find $BC$. = 12
(b) If $AB = 11$, $AE = 5$, $BC = 15$, find $CD$. = 75/11
(c) If $CD = h$, $AB = c$, $BC = a$, find $AE$. = ch/a
(d) If $AB = 15$, $CD = 14$, $BC = 21$, find $AE$. =10

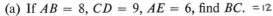

**9.** The hypotenuse of a right triangle is 50 cm long, one leg is 14 cm long, and the area of the triangle is 336 cm². How long is the altitude to the hypotenuse? How long is the altitude to the given leg? 13.44 cm, 48cm

**Quiz**

**1.** Given a parallelogram $\square ABCD$ with $AB = 12$, $BC = 8$, and the altitude to $\overline{BC}$ equal to 9. How long is the altitude to $\overline{AB}$?
(ans: 6)
**2.** In $\triangle RST$, $RS = 18$, $ST = 14$, and $m\angle S = 30$. What is $a\triangle RST$? Must $\triangle RST$ be a right triangle?
(ans: 63, no)
**3.** Complete the following so that the resulting statement is true. If two triangular regions have the same bases, then the ratio of their area equals the ratio of their _____.
(ans: altitudes)

**10.** A triangle and a parallelogram have equal areas and equal bases. How do their altitudes compare?
*The altitude of the triangle is twice that of the parallelogram.*

**11.** $\square ABCD$ is a parallelogram, $\overleftrightarrow{EH} \perp \overleftrightarrow{DC}$, $\overleftrightarrow{CF} \perp \overleftrightarrow{AB}$, and $\overleftrightarrow{BG} \perp \overleftrightarrow{DA}$.

(a) If $AB = 18$, $EH = 10$, and $BG = 15$, what is $AD? =12$

(b) If $AD = 22$, $BG = 7$, and $EH = 14$, what is $DC? =11$

(c) If $CF = 12$, $BG = 16$, $BC = 17$, then $AB = $ ? $22\frac{2}{3}$

(d) If $BG = 24$, $AD = 28$, $AB = 32$, then $EH = $ ? $21$

(e) If $AB = \sqrt{50}$, $CF = 6$, $GB = \sqrt{18}$, then $BC = $ ? $10$

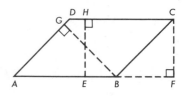

**12.** In the figure, $\square ABCD$ is a square, and the segments forming the boundary of the star are congruent. Find the area of the star in terms of $s$ and $b$. $s^2 - 2bs$

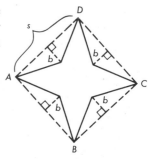

**13.** Prove: The two regions into which a median of a triangle separates the triangular region have equal areas. (See figure on the left below.)
*Use Theorem 11-6*

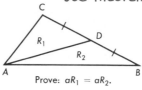

Prove: $aR_1 = aR_2$.

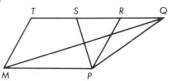

**14.** In the figure on the right above, $\square MPRT$ is a parallelogram and $TS = SR = RQ$. What is the ratio of

(a) $a\triangle PRS$ and $a\triangle PRQ$? $1:1$     (b) $a\triangle PMQ$ and $a\square MPRT$? $1:2$

(c) $a\triangle PMQ$ and $a\triangle PQS$? $1:1$     (d) $a\triangle PQR$ and $a\square MPST$? $1:3$

**15.** $\square ABCD$ is a trapezoid with parallel sides $\overline{AB}$ and $\overline{CD}$.

(a) If $AB = 18$, $DC = 12$, $h = 9$, then $a\square ABCD = $ ? $135$

(b) If $a\square ABCD = 84$, $AB = 17$, $CD = 11$, then $h = $ ? $6$

(c) If $a\square ABCD = 375$, $h = 15$, $AB = 38$, then $CD = $ ? $12$

(d) If $AB = 15$, $DC = 8$, $BC = 10$, and $m\angle B = 30$, then $a\square ABCD = $ ? $57.5$

(e) If $AB = 13$, $h = 5$, $a\square ABCD = 65$, then $CD = $ ? $13$

16. What is the area of a trapezoid if its altitude is 6 and its median is 12?
Median = ½ sum of bases; area = altitude × median = 72

17. A surveyor was to determine the area of the plot of land $ABCDE$ diagramed here. He located the north-south line through $E$ and the east-west lines through $A$, $B$, $C$, and $D$. He found that $AO = 37$ m, $BR = 47$ m, $CQ = 42$ m, $DP = 28$ m, $PQ = 13$ m, $QE = 7$ m, $ER = 19$ m, and $RO = 18$ m. He then computed the required area. Find the required area. 1404 m²

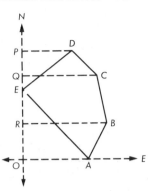

18. Prove the following theorem.

If the diagonals of a convex quadrilateral are perpendicular to each other, then the area of the quadrilateral equals one-half the product of the lengths of the diagonals.

Use Theorem 11-2 in
Δ ABC and Δ ADC
and the Area
Addition Postulate.

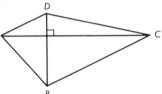

Prove: $a \square ABCD = \frac{1}{2}(AC)(BD)$.

Would this theorem be true if the quadrilateral were not required to be convex? Yes

19. $\square PQRS$ is convex, and $\overline{PR} \perp \overline{QS}$.

(a) If $PR = 12$ and $QS = 16$, what is $a\square PQRS$? 96

(b) If $a\square PQRS = 153$ and $PR = 17$, what is $QS$? 18

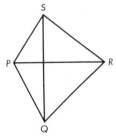

20. The diagonals of a rhombus are 15 and 20. What is its area? 150 If an altitude of the rhombus is 12, what is a side? [*Hint:* Does Problem 18 apply?] S = $\frac{150}{12}$ = 12.5

21. Prove: If the diagonals of a rhombus are $d$ and $d'$, then the area of the rhombus is $dd'/2$. This statement is a corollary to the theorem of Problem 18.

22. The area of a rhombus is 348 and one diagonal is 24. Find the other diagonal. 29

## Answers to Problems

**29.** Let $H$ be the intersection of $\overleftrightarrow{RQ}$ and $\overleftrightarrow{SM}$. First, observe that $a\square PQRS = a\square PKHS$ since they have the same base, $\overline{PS}$, and equal altitudes. Then observe that a $\square PKHS = a\square PKML$ since they have the same base, $\overline{PK}$, and equal altitudes. Therefore $a\square PQRS = a\square PKML$.

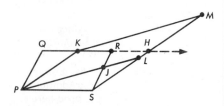

**30.** Since $\square ABQP$ and $\square CDPQ$ are trapezoids, $a\square ABQP = \frac{1}{2}h(m + r)$ and $a\square CDPQ = \frac{1}{2}h(n + s)$, where $h$ is the distance from $\overleftrightarrow{AD}$ to $\overleftrightarrow{BC}$. By hypothesis, $a\square ABQP = a\square CDPQ$, so that $m + r = n + s$. But since the opposite sides of parallelogram $\square ABCD$ are congruent, $m + n = r + s$. Hence, by subtraction $r - n = n - r$, so that $n = r$, and $m = s$. Finally, let $M$ be the point at which diagonal $\overline{AC}$ intersects $\overline{PQ}$. Then $\triangle AMP \cong \triangle CMQ$ (ASA) and so $AM = MC$. Hence $M$ is the point of intersection of the diagonals of the parallelogram $\square ABCD$. Therefore $L$ does contain the point of intersection of the diagonals of the parallelogram.

**23.** In $\square ABCD$ on the left below, $\overleftrightarrow{AC} \perp \overleftrightarrow{BD}$. If $AC = 13$ and $BD = 8$, can you find $a\square ABCD$? **a$\square$ ABCD = a$\triangle$BCD + a $\triangle$BAD =52**

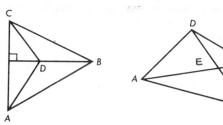

**24.** In $\square ABCD$ on the right above, $\overline{AC}$ bisects $\overline{BD}$. Prove that $a\triangle ABC = a\triangle ADC$. **△CDE△CEB have same altitude and base. a△CDE =a△ CEB (Th. 11-6). Similarly, a△ADE =a△ AEB. a△ADC =a△ABC by Area Addition Postulate.**

**25.** Given $\square ABCD$ is a parallelogram and $P$, $Q$, $R$, and $S$ are the midpoints of the sides. Prove that $a\square PQRS = \frac{1}{2}a\square ABCD$.

**26.** Given any triangle, $\triangle MQR$, with two medians, $\overline{RS}$ and $\overline{MT}$, intersecting at $P$. Prove that $a\triangle PMS = a\triangle PRT$.

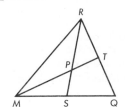

**27.** $\square ABCD$ is a trapezoid with $\overline{DC} \parallel \overline{AB}$, $E$ is the midpoint of $\overline{AB}$, $F$ is the midpoint of $\overline{DE}$, and $G$ is the midpoint of $\overline{CE}$. Prove that $a\triangle AFD = a\triangle BGC$.

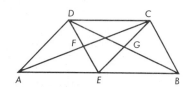

**28.** Let $\overline{AB}$ be given in a plane $E$. For each positive number $k$, there is at least one point $P$ such that $a\triangle ABP = k$. Is there more than one such point? How many? Describe the set of all points $P$ in $E$ such that $a\triangle ABP \overset{\text{Yes}}{=} k$. Describe the set of all points $P$ in space such that $a\triangle ABP = k$.

**29.** $\square PQRS$ is a parallelogram. $J$ is a point of $\overline{RS}$ such that $RJ < \frac{1}{2}RS$. $K$ is a point of $\overline{RQ}$ such that $RK < \frac{1}{2}RQ$. A line through $S$ and parallel to $\overline{PK}$ intersects a line through $K$ and parallel to $\overline{PJ}$ at $M$. $\overleftrightarrow{PJ}$ intersects $\overline{SM}$ at $L$. Prove that $a\square PQRS = a\square PKML$. [*Hint:* Does $\overleftrightarrow{RQ}$ intersect $\overline{SM}$?]

**30.** Prove: If a line $L$ separates a parallelogram region into two regions of equal areas, then $L$ contains the point of intersection of the diagonals of the parallelogram.

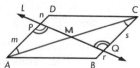

## 11–3  THE PYTHAGOREAN THEOREM

Now that we know about areas, the Pythagorean Theorem is rather easily proved.

**Theorem 11–8.**  The Pythagorean Theorem

> ***In a right triangle, the square of the hypotenuse is equal to the sum of the squares of the legs.***

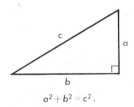

$$a^2 + b^2 = c^2.$$

**Proof.**  First we take a square with edges of length $a + b$.  In the square we draw four right triangles with legs $a$ and $b$.

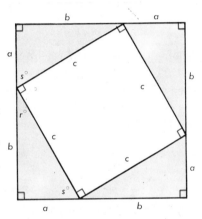

(1) By SAS, each of these four triangles is congruent to our given one. Therefore they all have hypotenuses equal to $c$, as shown in the figure.

(2) The quadrilateral formed by the four hypotenuses is a square.  In the notation of the figure, we have

$$r + s = 90$$

because the acute angles of a right triangle are complementary.  Since

$$r + s + t = 180,$$

it follows that $t = 90$.  Similarly for the other angles of the quadrilateral.

(3) By the Area Addition Postulate, the area of the large square is equal to the area of the small square, plus the sum of the areas of the four congruent triangles.  This gives

$$(a + b)^2 = c^2 + 4 \cdot \tfrac{1}{2}ab.$$

Therefore

$$a^2 + 2ab + b^2 = c^2 + 2ab, \quad \text{and} \quad a^2 + b^2 = c^2,$$

which was to be proved.

---

**Classroom Notes**

The text contains five different proofs of the Pythagorean Theorem:

(1) The proof following Theorem 11–8, page 345.

(2) Garfield's proof (Problem 23 of Problem Set 11–3, page 349)

(3) Euclid's proof (Problem 30 of Problem Set 11–3, page 350)

(4) The proof using Theorem 12–9, Part (2) (Problem 9 of Problem Set 12–5, page 393)

(5) The proof using Theorem 12–10 (Problem 23 of Problem Set 12–6, page 398)

**Quiz**

**1.** In the proof of Theorem 11–8, the Pythagorean Theorem, what postulates and/or theorems are reasons that support the statement

$$(a + b)^2 = c^2 + 4 \cdot \tfrac{1}{2}ab?$$

(ans: Area Addition Postulate)

**2.** The legs of a right triangle are 8 and 15.  Find the altitude to the hypotenuse.

(ans: 120/17)

**3.** A rectangular solid has edges of length 6, 8, and 15.  Find the lengths of the diagonals of each face and the length of a diagonal of the solid.

(ans: 10, 17, $3\sqrt{29}$, $5\sqrt{13}$)

**Explanation for Problems**

Problems 1, 5, 6, and 9 are straightforward applications of the Pythagorean Theorem or its converse. Problems 10 through 17 use the Pythagorean Theorem or its converse, but also make use of the area techniques discussed in the comments for Section 11–2.

**Special Notes on Problems 23 and 29.**  Problem 23, Garfield's proof of the Pythagorean Theorem is *very* closely related to the proof given in the text.  If the figure in the text is "sliced in half" along the diagonal of the inner square, then either of the pieces can be used for Problem 23.

The proof in Problem 29 is quite different in spirit, and in an important way, more elegant than the one that we have seen already. One way of expressing it is that while the proof following Theorem 11-8 depends on calculations, Euclid's reasoning is more geometric and more conceptual. The figure that goes with it is more than a reminder of the hypothesis and the notation; it is, in a sense, a picture of the Pythagorean phenomenon, so that if you understand the figure, you understand why the theorem is true.

In a way, the presentation of Euclid's proof in Problem 29 is misleading. It suggests that the Pythagorean theorem meant the same thing to Euclid, in the *Elements*, that it means to us in Chapter 11 of the text; and this is far from being true. Theorem 11-8 states that under certain conditions, the numbers a, b, and c must satisfy the equation $a^2 + b^2 = c^2$; and the theorem appears in a presentation of geometry in which the real numbers are given, independently of geometric concepts, and are used in the geometry to measure things. We use the number $AB$ as the measure of the length of the segment $\overline{AB}$; we use the number $a\triangle ABC$ as the measure of the area of the triangle $\triangle ABC$; and so on. In Euclid's *Elements*, however, there are no numbers independent of geometric concepts, except, of course, for the positive integers, which are used to count things. To recast his theory, in a form meeting modern standards of explicitness and exactitude, is a rather formidable task. See Chapter 8, "The Euclidean Program: Congruence without Distance," of *EGAS*.

The converse of the Pythagorean Theorem is also true.

## Theorem 11–9

*If the square of one side of a triangle is equal to the sum of the squares of the other two sides, then the triangle is a right triangle, with its right angle opposite the longest side.*

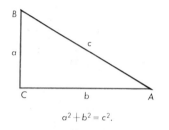

$a^2 + b^2 = c^2.$

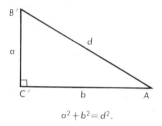

$a^2 + b^2 = d^2.$

**Proof.** Given $\triangle ABC$, with $a^2 + b^2 = c^2$, as in the figure. Let $\triangle A'B'C'$ be a *right* triangle with legs $a$ and $b$, and hypotenuse $d$. Then $c = d$, because $d^2 = a^2 + b^2 = c^2$. By SSS, $\triangle ABC \cong \angle A'B'C'$. Therefore $\angle C \cong \angle C'$. Since $\angle C'$ is a right angle, so also is $\angle C$.

### Pythagoras

Pythagoras is generally regarded as the first of the great Greek mathematicians, but very little is known about him as a person. He was born in about 582 B.C., and lived first on the island of Samos, in the Aegean Sea, and later in the south of Italy.

Pythagoras and his students devoted themselves to mathematics, astronomy, and philosophy. They are credited with having developed geometry into a science; they proved the Pythagorean Theorem, and they discovered the existence of irrational numbers. In astronomy they were equally good: they knew, in the sixth century B.C., that the earth is round and moves around the sun. They did not leave any written record of their work, and so nobody knows how they achieved these things, or which of their discoveries were due to Pythagoras personally.

## Problem Set 11–3

**1.** In the right triangle $\triangle ABC$, $c$ is the length of the hypotenuse, and $a$ and $b$ are the lengths of the legs.

(a) If $a = 12$ and $b = 16$, then $c =$ ?  **20**

(b) If $a = 24$ and $c = 25$, then $b =$ ?  **7**

(c) If $a = 1$ and $b = 2$, then $c =$ ?  **$\sqrt{5}$**

(d) If $b = 18$ and $c = 20$, then $a =$ ?  **$2\sqrt{19}$**

(e) If $a = 7$ and $b = 7$, then $c =$ ?  **$7\sqrt{2}$**

(f) If $a = 6$ and $c = 12$, then $b =$ ?  **$6\sqrt{3}$**

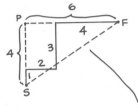

**2.** A man travels 7 km due north, then goes 3 km due east, and then 3 km due south. How far is he from his starting point?  **5 km**

**3.** A man travels 1 km north, 2 km east, 3 km north, and 4 km east. How far is he from his starting point?  **$\sqrt{52} = 2\sqrt{13}$ km = 7.21 km** ←

**4.** In the rectangular solid, every two intersecting edges are perpendicular. If $AE = 3$, $AB = 4$, and $BC = 12$, find the length of the diagonal $\overline{BE}$; of the diagonal $\overline{BH}$.  **BE = 5**  **BH = 13**

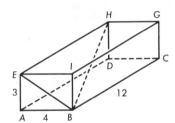

**5.** The hypotenuse of a right triangle is 17 and one leg is 15. Find the area of the triangle. What theorem did you use?  **60**

**6.** The sides of a triangle are 6 cm, 9 cm, and 11 cm. Is it a right triangle? If it is, which side is the hypotenuse?  **No  None**

**7.** (a) Prove: If $m$ and $n$ are positive integers with $m > n$, then $m^2 + n^2$ will be the length of the hypotenuse of a right triangle whose legs will have lengths $m^2 - n^2$ and $2mn$. What theorem did you use?  **Converse of Pythagorean Theorem**

(b) Make a table with the following column headings:

$$| \; m \; | \; n \; | \; m^2 - n^2 \; | \; 2mn \; | \; m^2 + n^2 \; |$$

Use the method of part (a) to list in the table the integral lengths of the sides of right triangles having hypotenuse less than or equal to 25. There are six such "Pythagorean triples." [*Hint:* The first row in the table will be 2, 1, 3, 4, 5.]

**8.** If $p$ and $q$ are lengths of the legs of a right triangle and $r$ is the length of the hypotenuse, show that for any positive number $k$, the numbers $kp$, $kq$, and $kr$ are also the lengths of the sides of a right triangle.

---

**Answers to Problems**

**3.** We have tacitly assumed in Problems 2 and 3 that the travelling is done on a plane and that we can therefore use the Pythagorean Theorem. If, in Problem 3, the man starts from the South Pole of the earth, which is, of course, a sphere, every direction is north and his journey will appear as in the sketch below. He will end up four kilometers from his starting point.

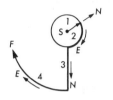

**7.** (a) Prove: $(m^2 - n^2)^2 + (2mn)^2$
$= (m^2 + n^2)^2$
Proof: $(m^2 + n^2)^2$
$= m^4 + 2m^2n^2 + n^4$
$= m^4 + 2m^2n^2 + n^2 - 4m^2n^2$
$\qquad\qquad\qquad\qquad + 4m^2n^2$
$= m^4 - 2m^2n^2 + n^2 + 4m^2n^2$
$= (m^2 - n^2)^2 + (2mn)^2$

(b)

| $m$ | $n$ | $m^2 - n^2$ | $2mn$ | $m^2 + n^2$ |
|---|---|---|---|---|
| 2 | 1 | 3 | 4 | 5 |
| 3 | 1 | 8 | 6 | 10 |
| 3 | 2 | 5 | 12 | 13 |
| 4 | 1 | 15 | 8 | 17 |
| 4 | 2 | 12 | 16 | 20 |
| 4 | 3 | 7 | 24 | 25 |

[Note that there are two other right triangles with hypotenuse less than or equal to 25: (9, 12, 15) and (15, 20, 25) but they cannot be obtained by this method.]

**8.** By the Pythagorean Theorem, the numbers $p$, $q$, and $r$ satisfy the equation $p^2 + q^2 = r^2$. If we can show that $(kp)^2 + (kq)^2 = (kr)^2$ we can conclude, by the converse of the Pythagorean Theorem, that a triangle with sides of lengths $kp$, $kq$, and $kr$ is a right triangle. But this is easy: $(kp)^2 + (kq)^2 = k^2p^2 + k^2q^2 = k^2(p^2 + q^2) = kr^2$.

**17.** By the Pythagorean Theorem, the hypotenuse is $\sqrt{a^2 + b^2}$. By the Area Postulate (19), $\frac{1}{2}h\sqrt{a^2 + b^2} = \frac{1}{2}ab$, so

$$h = \frac{ab}{\sqrt{a^2 + b^2}}.$$

**9.** Which of the following sets of numbers could be the lengths of the sides of a right triangle?

(a) 30, 40, 60     (b) 16, 30, 34     (c) 10, 24, 26

(d) $\frac{3}{4}$, 1, $1\frac{1}{4}$     (e) 1.4, 4.8, 5.0     (f) $1\frac{2}{3}$, $2\frac{2}{3}$, $3\frac{1}{3}$

**10.** In $\triangle ABC$, $\angle C$ is a right angle, $AC = 20$, and $BC = 15$. Find

(a) $a\triangle ABC = 150$

(b) $AB = 25$

(c) the altitude to the hypotenuse
    $CD = 12$

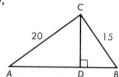

**11.** The hypotenuse of a triangle is 51 and another side is 24. Find the area of the triangle. **540**

**12.** In the figure, $QR = 5$, $RP = 12$, $RT = h$, and $\overline{QR} \perp \overline{RP}$, $\overline{RT} \perp \overline{PQ}$. Find $h$.
By Pythagorean Theorem QP = 13.
By Area Postulate 13·h = 12·5,
so that h = 4 8/13.

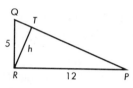

**13.** In a rhombus, each side is 5 cm long, and one diagonal is 8 cm long. What is the length of the other diagonal? **6 cm**

**14.** $\square ABCD$ is a parallelogram. $AD = 15$, $AB = 21$. The altitude $\overline{DE}$ meets $\overline{AB}$ at a point between $A$ and $\cdot B$, and $AE = 9$. What is $a\square ABCD$? **252**

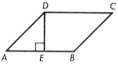

**15.** $\square PQRS$ is a trapezoid with $\overline{SP} \perp \overline{PQ}$. $PQ = 25$, $SR = 13$, and $RQ = 13$. Find $a\square PQRS$. a□ PQRS = 95

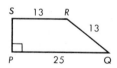

**16.** In $\triangle ABC$, $AC = 20$, $BC = 13$, and the altitude $\overline{CD}$ has length 12. If $A$-$D$-$B$, what is $a\triangle ABC$? If $A$-$B$-$D$, what is $a\triangle ABC$? 126, 66

**17.** If the lengths of the legs of a right triangle are $a$ and $b$, find the length, $h$, of the altitude to the hypotenuse in terms of $a$ and $b$.

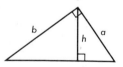

**18.** The legs of a right triangle are 24 and 32. Find the altitude to the hypotenuse. 19.2 (See Problem 17)

**19.** In a rhombus, each side is 10 cm long, and one diagonal is 12 cm long. The other diagonal is 16 cm. Find the area of the rhombus. Find its altitude to any side. 9.6 cm
96 cm²

**20.** One angle of a rhombus has measure 60 and a side has length 5. Find the length of each diagonal. 5 and 5√3

**21.** $\square ABCD$ is a trapezoid with $\overline{AB} \parallel \overline{DC}$. If segments have lengths as marked in the figure, find the area of the trapezoid.

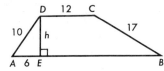

**22.** (a) With right angles and lengths as marked in the figure, find $PB$, $PC$, and $PD$. √2, √3, √4=2

(b) If you continue the pattern of the figure, making $m\angle PDE = 90$ and $DE = 1$, what will $PE$ be? What would be the length of the next segment from $P$? You should discover an interesting pattern. PE = √5, PF = √6

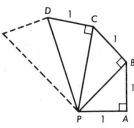

**23.** A proof of the Pythagorean Theorem making use of the figure on the right was discovered by General James A. Garfield several years before he became President of the United States. It appeared in about 1875 in the *New England Journal of Education*. Prove that $a^2 + b^2 = c^2$ by stating algebraically that the area of the trapezoid equals the sum of the areas of the three triangles. You must include a proof that $\angle EBA$ is a right angle.

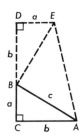

**24.** In $\triangle PQR$, $\overline{RV}$ is an altitude, and $\overline{RS}$ is a median. If $PR = 15$, $RQ = 20$, and $RV = 12$, what is $a\triangle RVS$? VP=9 and QV=16. a△RVS=a△RSP−a△RVP=75−54=21 or SV=3½ by subtraction and a△RVS= ½(3½)(12)=21

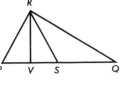

**25.** In $\triangle ABC$ on the left below, $AC = 13$, $AB = 14$, $BC = 15$.

(a) Find the altitude $h_c$. 12      (b) Find the altitude, $h_b$, to the side $\overline{AC}$. 12 12/13

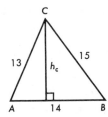

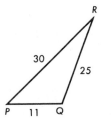

**26.** In $\triangle PQR$ on the right above, $\angle Q$ is obtuse, $PQ = 11$, $QR = 25$, $PR = 30$. Find the altitude to $\overleftrightarrow{PQ}$; find $a\triangle PQR$. 132

---

**Answers to Problems**

**21.** Let $F$ be the point at which the perpendicular from $C$ meets $\overline{AB}$. Observe that $DE = 8$, $EF = 12$, $CF = 8$, $FB = 15$ and $AB = 33$. Therefore $a\square ABCD = \frac{1}{2}h(AB + CD) = \frac{1}{2} \cdot 8 \cdot (33 + 12) = 180$.

**22.** (b) The terms in the sequence are the positive square roots of the consecutive integers 1, 2, 3 . . .

**23.** Since $\triangle ABC \cong \triangle BED$, $m\angle BAC = m\angle EBD$. But $\angle BAC$ is complementary to $\angle ABC$, so $\angle EBD$ is complementary to $\angle ABC$. Since $m\angle EBD + m\angle EBA + m\angle ABC = 180$, it follows that $m\angle EBA = 90$. Now $a\square CAED = a\triangle ABC + a\triangle AEB + a\triangle BED$.

$$\frac{1}{2}(a + b)(a + b) = \frac{1}{2}ab + \frac{1}{2}c^2 + \frac{1}{2}ab.$$
$$a^2 + 2ab + b^2 = 2ab + c^2.$$
$$a^2 + b^2 = c^2.$$

**25.** (a) Let $D$ be the foot of the altitude to $\overline{AB}$, and let $AD = x$ and $DB = 14 - x$. Then in $\triangle ADC$, $h_c^2 = 13^2 - x^2 = 169 - x^2$. And in $\triangle BDC$, $h_c^2 = 15^2 - (14 - x)^2 = 225 - 196 + 28x - x^2$. Hence, by eliminating $h_c^2$: $160 - x^2 = 29 + 28x - x^2$; $28x = 140$; $x = 5$ and $h_c = 12$.

(b) By the Area Postulate, $a\triangle ABC$ is a *unique* positive real number; hence, we will get the same answer for the area regardless of the side and corresponding altitude which we use in our calculations. Therefore,

$$h_b \cdot AC = h_c \cdot AB,$$
$$h_b \cdot 13 = 12 \cdot 14,$$
$$h_b = \frac{168}{13} = 12\frac{12}{13}.$$

**26.** Let $S$ be the projection of $R$ on $\overleftrightarrow{PQ}$, and let $QS = x$ and $RS = h$. Then in $\triangle RPS$, $h^2 = 30^2 - (11 + x)^2$, and in $\triangle RQS$, $h^2 = 25^2 - x^2$. Hence, $900 - 121 - 22x - x^2 = 625 - x^2$. Therefore $22x = 154$, so that $x = 7$ and $h = 24$. Finally, $a\triangle PQR = \frac{1}{2}(PQ)(h) = \frac{1}{2} \cdot 11 \cdot 24 = 132$.

**27.** By the Pythagorean Theorem, $MP = \sqrt{2}$. Therefore $PQ = \sqrt{2}$ and $OQ = 1 + \sqrt{2}$. Hence, by the Pythagorean Theorem again, $(MQ)^2 = (MO)^2 + (OQ)^2 = 1^2 + (1 + \sqrt{2})^2 = 4 + 2\sqrt{2}$, so $MQ = \sqrt{4 + 2\sqrt{2}}$.

Now $m\angle MPO = 45$, and thus $m\angle Q + m\angle QMP = 45$ by the Exterior Angle Corollary. But since $MP = PQ$, $m\angle Q = m\angle QMP$, so $m\angle Q = 22\frac{1}{2}$. Finally, $m\angle QMO = 67\frac{1}{2}$.

**28.** (a) Introduce $\overline{SC}$ and $\overline{SD}$. Since $\overline{SC}$ is the median on the base of isosceles triangle $\triangle ACB$, $\overline{SC} \perp \overline{AB}$. Similarly, $\overline{SD} \perp \overline{AB}$. Hence by the fundamental perpendicularity criterion (Theorem 8–2), $\overline{AB} \perp$ plane $SCD$. Since $\overline{RS}$ is a segment in the plane $SCD$, $\overline{AB} \perp \overline{RS}$. Secondly, since $\overline{SC}$ and $\overline{SD}$ are corresponding medians of congruent equilateral triangles, $SC = SD$. But, by hypothesis, $RC = RD$. Hence, by Corollary, 6–2.1, $\overline{RS} \perp \overline{DC}$.

(b) In $\triangle CSB$, $(SC)^2 + 1^2 = 2^2$, so that $SC = \sqrt{3}$. In $\triangle CSR$, $(RS)^2 + (RC)^2 = (SC)^2$. Thus, $(RS)^2 + 1^2 = (\sqrt{3})^2$ and $RS = \sqrt{2}$.

**29.** (a) Definition of a square. All right angles are congruent. Every angle is congruent to itself. Definition of the congruent angles. The Angle Addition Postulate. Substitution.

(e) If a triangle and a rectangle have equal bases and equal altitudes, then the area of the rectangle is twice the area of the triangle.

(i) $a\square AMKB = a\square AMQP + a\square PQKB$, by the Area Addition Postulate. Hence, by Steps (g), (h), and (i) we conclude that $a\square AMKB = a\square ACSR + a\square BHGC$.

---

**27.** In $\triangle MOQ$, $\overline{MO} \perp \overline{OQ}$,

$$MO = OP = 1, \text{ and } MP = PQ.$$

Find $MQ$. Find $m\angle Q$ and $m\angle QMO$.
$MQ = \sqrt{4+2\sqrt{2}}$, $m\angle Q = 22\frac{1}{2}$
$m\angle QMO = 67\frac{1}{2}$

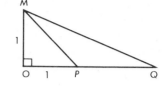

**28.** Figure $ABCD$ is a tetrahedron with all of its edges congruent and each of length 2. $R$ and $S$ are midpoints of $\overline{DC}$ and $\overline{AB}$, respectively.

(a) Prove that $\overline{RS}$ is a common perpendicular to $\overline{AB}$ and $\overline{DC}$.

(b) Find $RS$. $RS = \sqrt{2}$

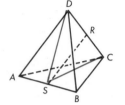

**29.** The Pythagorean Theorem was known to the ancient Greeks in the following form.

> The area of the square upon the hypotenuse of a right triangle is equal to the sum of the areas of the squares upon its legs.

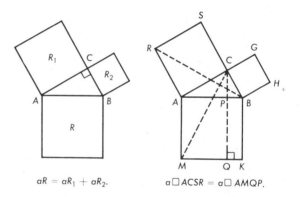

$aR = aR_1 + aR_2.$      $a\square ACSR = a\square AMQP.$

The figure on the left illustrates the theorem; the figure on the right is used in the proof. The following questions, together with your answers, suggest the method of proof.

(a) Why is $\angle RAB \cong \angle CAM$?

(b) Why is $\triangle RAB \cong \triangle CAM$? SAS ($RA = CA$, $\angle RAB \cong \angle CAM$, $AB = AM$)

(c) Why is $a\triangle RAB = a\triangle CAM$? Postulate 20

(d) Is one altitude of $\triangle RAB$ equal to $AC$? Yes, altitude upon $\overleftrightarrow{RA}$

(e) Why is $a\square ACSR = 2a\triangle RAB$?

(f) Is $a\square AMQP = 2a\triangle CAM$? Yes, same as step (e)

(g) Why is $a\square ACSR = a\square AMQP$? Substitution, steps (e) and (f)

(h) Is $a\square BHGC = a\square PQKB$? Yes, similar to steps (a)–(g)

(i) Is $a\square AMKB = a\square AMQP + a\square PQKB$? Why? Yes

## HONORS PROBLEM

$\square ABCD$ is a square, $H$, $I$, $J$, and $K$ are the midpoints of its sides, as shown, and $\square PQRS$ is a square. Find the ratio:

$$\frac{a\square PQRS}{a\square ABCD}.$$

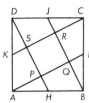

## 11–4   SPECIAL TRIANGLES

The Pythagorean Theorem gives us information about some special triangles.

**Theorem 11–10.**   The Isosceles Right Triangle Theorem

*In an isosceles right triangle, the hypotenuse is $\sqrt{2}$ times as long as each of the legs.*

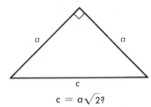

$$c = a\sqrt{2}?$$

You should supply a proof.
The converse is also true.

**Theorem 11–11**

*If the base of an isosceles triangle is $\sqrt{2}$ times as long as each of the two congruent sides, then the angle opposite the base is a right angle.*

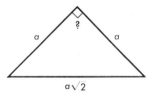

The proof begins with the observation that $a^2 + a^2 = (a\sqrt{2})^2$.

We learned in Section 9–7 that in a 30-60-90 triangle, the side opposite the 30 degree angle is half as long as the hypotenuse, and we also know the converse:

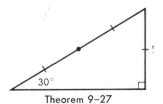

Theorem 9–27

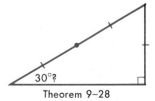

Theorem 9–28

The Pythagorean Theorem now tells us the relation between the hypotenuse and the *longer* of the two legs, for 30-60-90 triangles.

---

**Answer to Honors Problem**

There are many different solutions to this problem. By moving the four small triangular regions as shown in the figure we conclude that $\dfrac{a\square PQRS}{a\square ABCD} = \dfrac{1}{5}$.

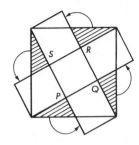

**11–4 SPECIAL TRIANGLES**

**Classroom Notes**

Section 11–4 completes the study of 30-60-90 and 45-90 triangles begun in Section 9–7.

**Theorem 11–12**

*In a 30-60-90 triangle, the longer leg is $\frac{1}{2}\sqrt{3}$ times as long as the hypotenuse.*

**Proof.** Let $c$ be the length of the hypotenuse, and let $b$ be the length of the longer leg. Then the length of the shorter leg is $\frac{1}{2}c$. (Why?) By the Pythagorean Theorem,

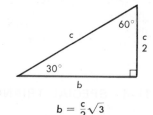

$$b = \frac{c}{2}\sqrt{3}$$

$$\left(\frac{c}{2}\right)^2 + b^2 = c^2.$$

So that

$$b^2 = c^2 - \frac{c^2}{4} = \frac{3}{4}c^2 = \frac{\sqrt{3}}{2}c = \frac{c}{2}\sqrt{3}.$$

**Problem Set 11–4**

**1.** In $\triangle ABC$, $\angle A$ is a right angle and $m\angle B = 45$. How long is $\overline{BC}$ if $AB = 3$? if $AC = 5$? if $AB = 6$? if $AB + AC = 8$?   $3\sqrt{2}$, $5\sqrt{2}$, $6\sqrt{2}$, $4\sqrt{2}$

**2.** In $\triangle DEF$, $\angle D$ is a right angle and $m\angle F = 30$.

  (a) How long is $DE$ if $FE = 6$? if $FE = 10$? if $FE = 15$? if $FE = 25$?   $3,5,7\frac{1}{2},12\frac{1}{2}$

  (b) How long is $DF$ if $DE = 2$? if $DE = 5$? if $DE = 8$? if $FE + DE = 12$?
    $2\sqrt{3}$, $5\sqrt{3}$, $8\sqrt{3}$, $4\sqrt{3}$

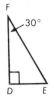

**3.** In $\triangle PQR$, $m\angle P = 45$, $m\angle Q = 30$, and $\overline{RS} \perp \overline{PQ}$. If $RS = 4$, what are the following?

  (a) $PR = 4\sqrt{2}$

  (b) $RQ = 8$

  (c) $SQ = 4\sqrt{3}$

  (d) The perimeter of $\triangle PQR = $   $12 + 4\sqrt{2} + 4\sqrt{3}$

  (e) $a\triangle PQR = 8 + 8\sqrt{3}$

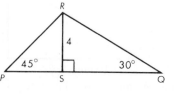

**4.** In $\triangle ABC$, $AB = 5$, $BC = 5\sqrt{3}$, and $AC = 10$. Find the measure of each angle of the triangle. **m∠B=90, m∠C=30, m∠A=60**

**5.** How long is the diagonal of a square if its side is 6? 9? 78? $\sqrt{2}$? $\sqrt{6}$? **6√2, 9√2, 78√2, 2, 2√3**

**6.** Find the longer leg of a 30-60-90 triangle if its hypotenuse is 4; 18; 98; $2\sqrt{3}$; 13. **2√3, 9√3, 49√3, 3, $\frac{13}{2}$√3**

**7.** $\triangle ABC$ is equilateral. If each side is 8 cm long, how long is the altitude to $\overline{AB}$? What is the area of $\triangle ABC$? **h= 4√3 cm, a△ABC= 16√3 cm²**

**8.** The acute angles of a right triangle are congruent and one of the congruent sides has length 15. How long is the third side? **15√2**

**9.** In $\triangle PQR$, $m\angle P = 30$, $PR = 8$, $PQ = 11$. Find the altitude to $\overline{PQ}$ and the area of $\triangle PQR$. **h=4, a△PQR=22**

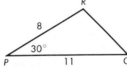

**10.** The measure of each base angle of an isosceles triangle is 30, and each of the two congruent sides has length 14. How long is the base? What is the area of the triangle? **Base= 14√3, area= 49√3**

**11.** A parallelogram has two sides of lengths 18 and 8, and the measure of one angle is 30. Find the area of the parallelogram. **72**

**12.** What is the area of an isosceles triangle whose congruent sides each have length 20 and whose base angles have measures of 30? 45? 60? **100√3, 200, 100√3**

**13.** In $\triangle ABC$, $\angle A$ is a right angle and $m\angle B = m\angle C = 45$. Given that $BC = 6$, find $AB$. **AB = 3√2**

**14.** Prove: If the hypotenuse of an isosceles right triangle has length $m$, then each of the two congruent sides has length $\frac{1}{2}m\sqrt{2}$.
**$s^2+s^2=m^2$, $2s^2=m^2$, $s^2 = \frac{m^2}{2}$**
**$s= \frac{m\sqrt{2}}{2}$  (by Pythagorean Theorem)**

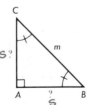

**15.** What is the area of the isosceles triangle whose congruent sides are each 12 cm long if the base angles have the following measures?

(a) 45 **72 cm²**          (b) 30 **36√3 cm²**          (c) 60 **36√3 cm²**

**16.** What is the area of an isosceles triangle whose base is 12 if the base angles have the following measures?

(a) 45 **36**          (b) 30 **12√3**          (c) 60 **36√3**

**Answers to Problems**

**23.** (1) Since $\overline{PA} \perp E$, $m\angle PAB = 90$, and since $m\angle BPA = 30$, $m\angle PBA = 60$. Hence, in 30-60-90 triangle $\triangle PBA$, $AB = 4$ and $PA = 4\sqrt{3}$.

(2) Since $\overline{PA} \perp E$, $\overline{PA} \perp \overline{CA}$ and $m\angle PAC = 90$. By the Pythagorean Theorem, $AC^2 = PC^2 - PA^2 = (4\sqrt{6})^2 - (4\sqrt{3})^2 = 48$, so $AC = 4\sqrt{3}$. Therefore $\triangle PAC$ is an isosceles right triangle in which $m\angle ACP = 45$ and $m\angle APC = 45$.

(3) Consider $\triangle ABC$. Since $AB = 4$, $BC = 8$, and $AC = 4\sqrt{3}$, we can conclude by the converse of the Pythagorean Theorem that $m\angle BAC = 90$ and then that $m\angle ABC = 60$ and $m\angle ACB = 30$.

(4) $\triangle PBC$ is isosceles, but it is not possible to determine the measure of its angles without using formulas from trigonometry.

(5) $a\triangle PBC = 15$. The area of $\triangle PBC$ can be computed as follows: Since $\triangle PBC$ is isosceles, the altitude $\overline{BH}$ to base $\overline{CP}$ bisects the base, so $CH = 2\sqrt{6}$. By the Pythagorean Theorem, $BH^2 = BC^2 - CH^2 = 8^2 - (2\sqrt{6})^2 = 40$, so $BH = 2\sqrt{10}$. Hence $a\triangle PBC = \frac{1}{2}(4\sqrt{6})(2\sqrt{10}) = 8\sqrt{15}$.

**24.** Since $\overline{AC}$ is the hypotenuse of isosceles right triangle $\triangle ABC$, $AC = 6\sqrt{2}$ by Theorem 11-10. Therefore the area of rectangle $\square ACGE = 36\sqrt{2}$. Since $\overline{AC}$, $\overline{CF}$, and $\overline{FA}$ are each $6\sqrt{2}$, $\triangle ACF$ is equilateral and

$$a\triangle ACF = \frac{S^2\sqrt{3}}{4} = \frac{(6\sqrt{2})^2\sqrt{3}}{4} = 18\sqrt{3}.$$

## Answers to Problems

**25.** Let $\overline{CD}$ be the altitude to $\overline{AB}$. In 30-60-90 $\triangle ACD$, $CD = 2$ and $AD = 2\sqrt{3}$. Therefore $DB = AB - AD = 3\sqrt{3} - 2\sqrt{3} = \sqrt{3}$. Hence, in right triangle $\triangle BDC$, $BC = \sqrt{7}$ by the Pythagorean Theorem. Is $\angle C$ a right angle? Check to see whether $AC^2 + BC^2 = AB^2$. $(4)^2 + (\sqrt{7})^2 \neq (3\sqrt{3})^2$. $\therefore \angle C$ is not a right angle.

**26.** Let $\overline{RS}$ be the perpendicular from $R$ to $\overleftrightarrow{PQ}$. In isosceles right triangle $\triangle RPS$, $RS = 5\sqrt{2}$ and $PS = 5\sqrt{2}$ so $QS = 5\sqrt{2} - 3$. Then in $\triangle RQS$, we have by the Pythagorean Theorem, $RQ^2 = RS^2 + QS^2 = (5\sqrt{2})^2(5\sqrt{2}-3)^2 = 109 - 30\sqrt{2}$, so $RQ = \sqrt{109 - 30\sqrt{2}} \doteq 8.2$.

Also, $a\triangle PQR = \frac{1}{2}(PQ)(RS) = \frac{1}{2}(3)(5\sqrt{2}) = \frac{15}{2}\sqrt{2}$.

**28.** (1) If a square lies in one face of an acute dihedral angle and has a side parallel to the edge of the dihedral angle, then its projection into the other face of the dihedral angle is a rectangle: $\square EFGH$ is a rectangle.

(2) In the plane of trapezoid $\square BFGC$, let $\overline{BJ}$ be the perpendicular segment from $B$ to $\overleftrightarrow{GC}$. Since $m\angle K - PQ - M = 60$, $m\angle CBJ = 60$, so $BJ = \frac{1}{2}\sqrt{26}$ by Theorem 9–27. Since $\square BFGJ$ is a rectangle, $FG = \frac{1}{2}\sqrt{26}$.

(3) If a line $\overleftrightarrow{AB}$, not contained in a plane, is parallel to a line $\overrightarrow{PQ}$, in that plane, then $\overleftrightarrow{AB}$ is parallel to the plane. If a segment $\overline{AB}$ is parallel to a given plane, then its projection into that plane is a segment congruent to $\overline{AB}$. $\therefore EF = \sqrt{26}$.

(4) Therefore, $a\square EFGH = (EF) \times (FG) = (\sqrt{26})(\frac{1}{2}\sqrt{26}) = 13$.

---

**354**

**17.** In the trapezoid $\square ABCD$, the measures of the base angles are 45 and 30, as shown; $BC = 16$, $DC = 5$. Find

$$a\square ABCD. = 72 + 32\sqrt{3}$$

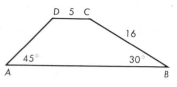

**18.** The altitude of an equilateral triangle is 12. Find the length of a side and the area of the triangle. $s = 8\sqrt{3}$, $area = 48\sqrt{3}$

**19.** Prove: The area of an equilateral triangle whose side is of length $s$ is given by $\dfrac{s^2}{4}\sqrt{3}$.

$$\text{Area} = \frac{1}{2}bh = \frac{1}{2}(s)\left(\frac{s\sqrt{3}}{2}\right) = \frac{s^2\sqrt{3}}{4}$$

**20.** The side of one equilateral triangle equals the altitude of a second. What is the ratio of their areas? $\frac{3}{4}$ or $\frac{4}{3}$

**21.** The area of an equilateral triangle is $25\sqrt{3}$. Determine the lengths of its sides and altitudes. $s = 10$, $h = 5\sqrt{3}$

**22.** A square whose area is 81 has its perimeter equal to the perimeter of an equilateral triangle. What is the area of the triangle? $36\sqrt{3}$

**23.** In the figure, $\triangle ABC$ lies in the plane $E$ and $\overline{PA} \perp E$.

$$PB = BC = 8$$
$$PC = 4\sqrt{6}$$
$$m\angle BPA = 30.$$

Determine the measures of as many other angles and segments as possible. Also, find $a\triangle PBC$.

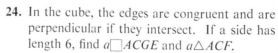

**24.** In the cube, the edges are congruent and are perpendicular if they intersect. If a side has length 6, find $a\square ACGE$ and $a\triangle ACF$.

$$a\square\ ACGE = 36\sqrt{2}$$
$$a\triangle ACF = 18\sqrt{3}$$

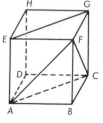

**25.** In $\triangle ABC$, $m\angle A = 30$, $AC = 4$, $AB = 3\sqrt{3}$. Find $BC$. Is $\angle C$ a right angle? How do you know?

     ∠C is not a right angle

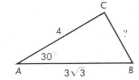

**26.** In $\triangle PQR$, $\angle Q$ is obtuse,

$$m\angle P = 45, \quad PR = 10, \quad PQ = 3.$$

Find $RQ$ and $a\triangle PQR$.

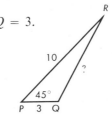

**27.** A farmer wishes to fence and plant a triangular plot of ground. One side of the plot makes a 45° angle with an east-west line, and is 500 m long. A second side runs parallel to the east-west line, and the third side makes a 30° angle with the east-west line. Show that the perimeter of the plot is $250(2 + \sqrt{2} + \sqrt{6})$ yd. What is its area? **91 600 m²**

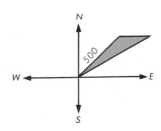

**28.** In the figure to the right, $m\angle K\text{-}PQ\text{-}M = 60$. $\square ABCD$ is a square in one face, with $\overline{AB} \parallel \overrightarrow{PQ}$, and is projected into the other face, resulting in $\square EFGH$. If $AB = \sqrt{26}$, find $a\square EFGH$. **13**

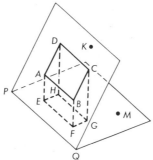

**29.** In the figure on the right, $m\angle K\text{-}PQ\text{-}M = 45$. $\square ABCD$ is a square in one face, with $\overrightarrow{BD} \perp \overrightarrow{PQ}$, and is projected into the other face, resulting in $\square EFGH$. If $AB = 8$, find $a\square EFGH$. **32√2**

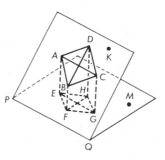

**Answers to Problems**

**29.** (1) If a square lies in one face of an acute dihedral angle and has a diagonal which lies in a line perpendicular to the edge of the dihedral angle, then its projection into the other face of the dihedral angle is a rhombus.

(2) Since the area of a rhombus is equal to one-half the product of its diagonals, our problem is reduced to that of finding the lengths of the diagonals $\overline{EG}$ and $\overline{FH}$ of rhombus $\square EFGH$.

(3) $AC = 8\sqrt{2}$, and the projection into a plane of a segment parallel to the plane is a segment congruent to the original segment. $\therefore EG = 8\sqrt{2}$.

(4) In the plane of trapezoid $\square BFHD$, let $\overline{BJ}$ be the perpendicular segment from $B$ to $\overline{HD}$. Since $m\angle K - PQ - M = 45$, $m\angle DBJ = 45$. Then since $BD = 8\sqrt{2}$, $BJ = 8$, and thus $FH = 8$.

(5) Finally, the area of $\square EFGH = \frac{1}{2}(EG)(FH) = \frac{1}{2}(8\sqrt{2})(8) = 32\sqrt{2}$.

## CHAPTER REVIEW

**1.** For each formula in the column on the left, choose the corresponding identification in the column on the right.

(a) $\frac{1}{2}bh$   C

(b) $s^2$   F

(c) $\frac{s}{2}\sqrt{3}$   M,N

(d) $a^2 + b^2 = c^2$   H

(e) $s\sqrt{2}$   K,I

(f) $\frac{1}{2}h(b_1 + b_2)$   B

(g) $bh$   A,D,E,F

(h) $\frac{s^2}{4}\sqrt{3}$   G

(i) $\frac{s}{2}$   L

(A) area of a parallelogram

(B) area of a trapezoid

(C) area of a triangle

(D) area of a rhombus

(E) area of a rectangle

(F) area of a square

(G) area of an equilateral triangle

(H) Pythagorean relation

(I) hypotenuse of an isosceles right triangle

(J) leg of an isosceles right triangle

(K) diagonal of a square

(L) shorter leg of a 30-60-90 triangle

(M) longer leg of a 30-60-90 triangle

(N) altitude of an equilateral triangle

**2.** Complete: A polygonal region is the __union__ of a __finite__ number of __triangular region__ in a plane, such that if two of these __intersect__, their __intersection__ is either a __point__ _____ or a __segment__.

**3.** Which of the following sets of numbers can be the lengths of sides of a right triangle?

(a) 5, 13, 12

(c) 1, $\sqrt{2}$, 3

(e) 25, 24, 7

(g) 4, 7.5, 8.5

(b) 1, $\sqrt{3}$, 2

(d) $\frac{3}{4}$, 1, $1\frac{1}{4}$

(f) $\sqrt{3}$, $\sqrt{4}$, $\sqrt{5}$

(h) $\sqrt{12}$, $\sqrt{3}$, 3

**4.** Which theorem is applied in answering Problem 3? Theorem 11-9

**5.** The diagonals of the parallelogram $\square ABCD$ intersect at $E$. Prove that $a\triangle AED = a\triangle BEC$. By Th. 9-18, AE=CE, DE=BE. Since ∠DEA ≅ ∠BEC by Th. 4-8, △AED ≅ △BEC (SAS) So a△AED=a△BEC by Postulate 20.

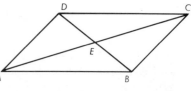

**6.** Both dimensions of a rectangular region are doubled. How is the area changed? Multiplied by 4

**7.** If one side of a square is three times as long as a side of a second square, the area of the first square is how many times the area of the second square? 9 (Try to answer this one without using any area formulas at all.)

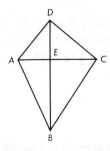

8. In the figure, $\overline{AC} \perp \overline{DB}$. If $DE = 8$ and $BE = 12$, what is the ratio of $a\triangle ACD$ to $a\triangle ABC$? $\dfrac{a\triangle ACD}{a\triangle ABC} = \dfrac{2}{3}$

9. If the diagonal of a square is 18 cm long, how long is each side? What is the area of the square? $9\sqrt{2}$ cm, $162$ cm²

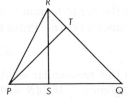

10. In $\triangle PQR$, $\overline{PT}$ and $\overline{RS}$ are altitudes. Given that $PR = 13$, $PS = 5$, and $m\angle Q = 45$, find $PT$. $PT = \dfrac{17\sqrt{2}}{2}$

11. A triangle has sides measuring 25, 25, and 48. Find its area. 168

12. An equilateral triangle has a median 15 cm long. What is its area? $75\sqrt{3}$ cm²

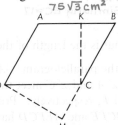

13. $\square ABCD$ is a parallelogram. $\overline{CK} \perp \overline{AB}$ and $\angle M$ is a right angle.
   (a) If $BC = 12$, $DM = 15$, and $KC = 9$, find $DC$ and $CM$. $20, 5\sqrt{7}$
   (b) If $KC = \sqrt{24}$, $AK = \sqrt{18}$, and $KB = \sqrt{8}$, find $AD$ and $DM$. $4\sqrt{2}, \dfrac{5}{2}\sqrt{6}$

14. The side of a rhombus is 13 and one of its diagonals is 24. Find the area of the rhombus. 120

15. A kite is made from two isosceles triangles having a common base, as in the figure. If the lengths of the sides are as marked, what is the area of the kite? 168

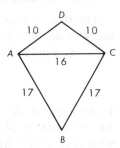

16. In $\triangle ABC$, $AB = 14$, the length of the median $\overline{CD}$ is 8, and $m\angle ADC = 60$. What is $a\triangle ABC$? $28\sqrt{3}$

17. In Problem 16, what is $AC$? $\sqrt{57}$ $BC$? 13 Is $\triangle ABC$ a right triangle? No

**20.** Introduce $\overline{AC}$. Then observe that since $\triangle AKC$ and $\triangle KBC$ have equal bases and equal altitudes, $a\triangle AKC = \frac{1}{2}a\triangle ABC$. Similarly, $a\triangle AMC = \frac{1}{2}a\triangle ADC$. Hence, by the Area Addition Postulate, $a\square AKCM = \frac{1}{2}a\square ABCD$.

**23.** Note first that $\triangle ABD \cong \triangle CDB$ (by Theorem 9–14) and $\triangle ADE \cong \triangle CBF$ by ASA, and recall that if two triangles are congruent, they have equal areas. Then observe that

$a(ABCFE)$

$$= a\triangle ABD - a\triangle ADE + a\triangle CBF$$
$$= a\triangle ABD$$

and that

$a(AEFCD)$

$$= a\triangle CBD - a\triangle CBF + a\triangle ADE$$
$$= a\triangle CBD.$$

Therefore

$$a(ABCFE) = a(AEFCD).$$

**27.** Consider the diagram:

**29.** Since $\overline{AB} \perp \overline{BC}$ and $\overline{EB} \perp \overline{FB}$, $\angle ABE$ and $\angle CBF$ are each complementary to $\angle EBC$. Therefore $\angle ABE \cong \angle CBF$. Hence $\triangle ABE \cong \triangle CBF$ by ASA, and $EB = BF$. Since $a\triangle EBF = 200$, $FB = 20$. Since $a\square ABCD = 256$, $BC = 16$. Hence $CF = 12$.

**30.** Let $h$ be the length of the altitude. Then $h^2 = a^2 - c^2$ and $h^2 = b^2 - d^2$.

$$\therefore a^2 - c^2 = b^2 - d^2,$$
$$a^2 - b^2 = c^2 - d^2,$$
$$(a+b)(a-b) = (c+d)(c-d).$$

**31.** The existence of $M$ is not essential to the solution of this problem. Consider the first proof given below. A second proof, using $M$, is also given.

*First Proof.* Introduce a line through $C$ parallel to $\overline{AD}$ and let $Q$ be its intersection with $\overline{AB}$. Observe first that $AQ = CD$, and second that since $K$ is the midpoint $\overline{BC}$ and $\overline{KP} \parallel \overline{CQ}$, it follows that $P$ is the midpoint of $\overline{QB}$: $QB = 2PB$. Finally, let $h$ be the distance between $\overleftrightarrow{AB}$ and $\overleftrightarrow{CD}$. Then,

**18.** Derive a formula for the area of this figure in terms of $a$, $b$, and $c$.

$$bc + \frac{1}{2}(a-c)^2$$

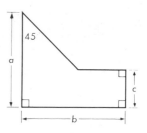

**19.** A trapezoid has parallel sides 13 cm and 21 cm long. The longer of the two nonparallel sides is 17, and the shorter is perpendicular to a parallel side. What is the area of the trapezoid? **225 cm²**

**20.** In the parallelogram $\square ABCD$, $M$ is the midpoint of $\overline{AD}$ and $K$ is the midpoint of $\overline{AB}$. Prove that

$$a\square AKCM = \frac{1}{2}a\square ABCD.$$

**21.** In this rectangular solid, $\overline{AG}$ and $\overline{EC}$ are diagonals. If $AB = 9$, $BF = 12$, and $AD = 8$, find $AG$ and $EC$. **17, 17**

In $\triangle AFG$, $AF = 15$ so that
$(AG)^2 = 15^2 + 8^2 = 289$
$AG = 17$
Similarly $EC = 17$

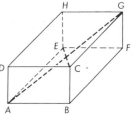

**22.** What is the length of the diagonal of a cube whose edge is 6? **$6\sqrt{3}$**

**23.** In the parallelogram $\square ABCD$, the bisectors of $\angle A$ and $\angle C$ meet the diagonal $\overline{DB}$ at $E$ and $F$, respectively. Prove that the regions $ABCFE$ and $AEFCD$ have the same area.

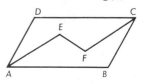

**24.** The area of an equilateral triangle is $100\sqrt{3}$. How long are its sides and altitudes? **$s = 20$, $h = 10\sqrt{3}$**

**25.** $\square ABCD$ is a trapezoid with $\overline{AB} \parallel \overline{CD}$. $m\angle A = m\angle B = 60$, $AB = 12$, and $BC = 8$. Find $a\square ABCD$. **$= 32\sqrt{3}$**

**26.** In the figure, if $AC = BC = 52$, $AB = 40$, $BK = 32$, $AK = 24$, $DK = 4$, and $EK = 6$, what is $a\triangle CDE$? **420**

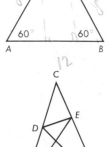

27. A given segment is a side of a square and also the hypotenuse of an isosceles right triangle. Prove that the area of the square is four times the area of the triangle. (Try to do this without using any area formulas at all.)

28. Give two different proofs of the Pythagorean Theorem. **Refer to Thm. 11-8, or Problems 25 and 29 of Problem Set 11-3.**

29. $\square ABCD$ is a square. $E$ is on $\overleftrightarrow{AD}$ and $F$ is on $\overleftrightarrow{DC}$ so that $\overline{EB} \perp \overline{FB}$. If $a\square ABCD = 256$ and $a\triangle EBF = 200$, find $CF$.

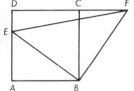

30. In a triangle two sides have lengths $a$ and $b$. The altitude to the third side separates that side into segments of lengths $c$ and $d$ respectively. Prove that
$$(a + b)(a - b) = (c + d)(c - d).$$

31. Given: $\square ABCD$ is a trapezoid with $\overline{AB} \parallel \overline{CD}$. $M$ and $K$ are the midpoints of $\overline{AD}$ and $\overline{BC}$, respectively. $\overline{PK} \parallel \overline{AD}$.

Prove: $a\triangle APD = a\square PBCD$
$$= \tfrac{1}{2}a\square ABCD.$$

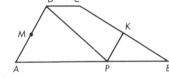

32. Given any two parallelograms in a plane. Explain how a single line can be drawn which will separate each parallelogram region into two regions of equal area.

## HONORS PROBLEM

The figure at the right consists of four right triangles, four rectangles, and a square "hole" one unit on a side.

(a) Find the sum of the areas of the eight regions. (Don't count the hole!) **104**

(b) Find the base, $DE$, and the altitude from $A$ to $\overline{DE}$. Find one-half the product of these two numbers. **DE=16, h=13** $\frac{1}{2}h(DE)=104$

(c) Can you explain why the results of parts (a) and (b) are the same, in spite of the hole?

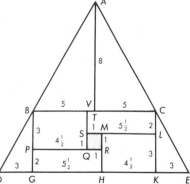

---

$a\square ABCD = \tfrac{1}{2}h[AB + CD]$
$\qquad = \tfrac{1}{2}h[(AQ + QB) + CD]$
$\qquad = \tfrac{1}{2}h[2PB + 2CD]$
(since $QB = 2PQ$ and $AQ = CD$)
$\qquad = 2 \cdot \tfrac{1}{2}h[PB + CD]$
$\qquad = 2a\square PBCD.$

Therefore, $a\square PBCD = \tfrac{1}{2}a\square ABCD$, and by the Area Addition Postulate, $a\triangle APD = \tfrac{1}{2}a\square ABCD$.

*Second Proof.*

(1) Introduce $\overline{MK}$. Then $\square APKM$ is a parallelogram. $MK = \tfrac{1}{2}(AB + CD)$ by Problem 6 of Problem Set 9-8. Also, since $\overline{MK} \parallel \overline{AB} \parallel \overline{DC}$ and $M$ and $K$ are midpoints, $\overline{MK}$ bisects the altitude from $D$ to $\overline{AB}$. Hence, if the altitude of $\square ABCD$ is $h$, the altitude of $\square APKM$ is $\tfrac{1}{2}h$. Therefore
$a\square APKM = \tfrac{1}{2}h \cdot \tfrac{1}{2}(AB + CD)$
$\qquad = \tfrac{1}{2}[\tfrac{1}{2}h(AB + CD)]$;
that is,
$\qquad \tfrac{1}{2}a\square ABCD.$

(2) Let $\overline{MK}$ intersect $\overline{DP}$ at $F$. Then $\triangle DMF \cong \triangle PKF$ by ASA, so $a\triangle DMF = a\triangle PKF$.

(3) Now $a\triangle APD = a\square APFM + a\triangle DMF = a\square APFM + a\triangle PKF = a\square APKM = \tfrac{1}{2}a\square ABCD$.

(4) Finally, since $a\square ABCD = a\triangle APD + a\square PBCD$, $a\square PBCD = \tfrac{1}{2}\square ABCD$.

**32.** The line $L$ which contains the points of intersection of the diagonals of each of the parallelograms separates each parallelogram into two regions of equal areas. See Problem 30, Problem Set 11-2.

**Answer to Honors Problem**

(c) The calculations in Part (a) are correct. In Part (b) we compute that $a\triangle ADE = \tfrac{1}{2}bh = \tfrac{1}{2}(16)(13) = 104$. This computation is not valid because the figure is not a triangle. Note that $\triangle DGB$ and $\triangle BVA$ are not similar, ($\tfrac{5}{3} \neq \tfrac{8}{5}$), and that consequently points $D$, $B$, and $A$ are not collinear. This means that polygon $DBACE$ is a pentagon rather than a triangle. The formula $K = \tfrac{1}{2}bh$ is the formula for the area of a triangle, not the formula for the area of a pentagon.

The material in this chapter is conventional in content and presentation, with two important exceptions: (1) we define a similarity as a type of correspondence, just as we defined a congruence as a type of correspondence, and (2) we use area theory to prove the Basic Proportionality Theorem.

**Planning the Chapter**

Both average and above-average classes will require approximately the same amount of time to study this chapter. Three days may be spent on the first two sections, two days each on Sections 12–3 and 12–4, and three days on the last two sections.

CHAPTER **12**

# Similarity

## Objectives . . .

- Become familiar with the algebraic properties of ratios and proportionalities, including the geometric mean.
- Learn the definition of similarity for triangles.
- Apply the Basic Proportionality Theorem and its converse.
- Develop and apply the basic theorems for similar triangles.
- Apply similarity theorems to right triangles.
- Study areas of similar triangles.

## 12–1 THE IDEA OF A SIMILARITY. PROPORTIONALITY

Roughly speaking, two geometric figures are similar if they have exactly the same shape, but not necessarily the same size. For example, any two circles are similar; any two squares are similar; any two equilateral triangles are similar; and any two segments are similar.

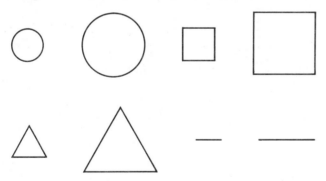

Another way of expressing this is to say that two figures are similar if one of them is an exact scale model of the other.

The marks in the figure below indicate that the two triangles ought to be similar.

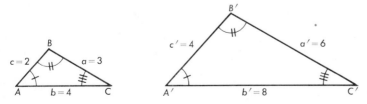

It ought to be possible to "stretch" the first triangle, doubling its size without changing its shape, so as to get the second triangle. The

### 12–1 THE IDEA OF A SIMILARITY. PROPORTIONALITY

**Classroom Notes**

Section 12–1 develops the idea of similarity on an intuitive level. To define similarity, we need the idea of a proportionality between sequences of numbers. Since the latter idea is new to the student, we first explain it and establish its basic algebraic properties.

Note that we define proportionality only for sequences of *positive* real numbers. There are two reasons for this restriction: (1) we shall be writing proportionalities involving the lengths of segments, and the length of a segment is, by the Distance Postulate, a *positive* real number; (2) in defining the geometric mean of two numbers, $a$ and $b$, we must know that the product, $ab$, whose square root we take, is never negative.

In discussing proportionalities we have avoided the conventional notation, terminology, and laws of proportions. We have done so deliberately; the conventional presentation of proportions gave the impression that proportions and their properties are a new algebraic system, governed by its own laws, which have to be learned from the beginning. This impression is incorrect: once we have written a proportion in the form

$$\frac{a}{b} = \frac{c}{d},$$

we simply have an equation between fractions, and all of the algebra we know can be applied to it. Thus the statement that "the product of the extremes is equal to the product of the means" is merely an obscure way of describing cross multiplication:

if $\quad \dfrac{a}{b} = \dfrac{c}{d}, \quad$ then $\quad ad = bc.$

The old language of proportions is merely a linguistic remnant of an earlier and pre-algebraic theory. It is surely unprofitable to learn algebra twice, and to learn to talk about it in two languages, one of which is archaic.

"stretching" scheme can be described by the correspondence

$$ABC \leftrightarrow A'B'C'.$$

Of course, this correspondence is not a congruence, because each side of the second triangle is twice as long as the corresponding side of the first. Correspondences of this kind are called *similarities*. An exact definition of a similarity will be given later in this chapter.

Similarities may shrink things instead of stretching them. For example, the correspondence $A'B'C' \leftrightarrow ABC$ shrinks the second triangle onto the first.

Note that the lengths of the sides of our two triangles form two sequences of positive numbers, $a$, $b$, $c$ and $a'$, $b'$, $c'$. These sequences stand in a special relation: each number in the second sequence is exactly twice the corresponding number in the first sequence. Thus

$$a' = 2a, \qquad b' = 2b, \qquad c' = 2c.$$

Or, putting it the other way around, we can say that each number in the first sequence is exactly half of the corresponding number in the second:

$$a = \tfrac{1}{2}a', \qquad b = \tfrac{1}{2}b', \qquad c = \tfrac{1}{2}c'.$$

Thus

$$\frac{a'}{a} = \frac{b'}{b} = \frac{c'}{c}$$

because each of these fractions is equal to 2; and

$$\frac{a}{a'} = \frac{b}{b'} = \frac{c}{c'}$$

because each of these fractions is equal to $\tfrac{1}{2}$. Sequences which are related in this way are called *proportional*.

## Definition

Given two sequences $a$, $b$, $c$, ... and $p$, $q$, $r$, ... of positive numbers. If

$$\frac{a}{p} = \frac{b}{q} = \frac{c}{r} = \cdots,$$

then the sequences $a$, $b$, $c$, ... and $p$, $q$, $r$, ... are called *proportional*, and we write

$$a, b, c, \ldots \sim p, q, r, \ldots.$$

The symbol $\sim$, when used between sequences, is pronounced "is proportional to."

The notation $a, b, c, \ldots \sim p, q, r, \ldots$ is often convenient because it is easy to read off from a figure.  In the preceding figure, reading off corresponding sides in their proper order, we get $a, b, c \sim a', b', c'$; numerically this means that $3, 4, 2 \sim 6, 8, 4$.  This is correct, because

$$\frac{3}{6} = \frac{4}{8} = \frac{2}{4}.$$

## Theorem 12–1

*Proportionality between sequences is an equivalence relation.*

**Proof.**  We have three things to check.
  (1) (Reflexive Property)  For every sequence $a, b, c, \ldots$,

$$a, b, c, \ldots \sim a, b, c, \ldots.$$

  (2) (Symmetric Property)
      If $a, b, c, \ldots \sim p, q, r, \ldots$, then $p, q, r, \ldots \sim a, b, c, \ldots.$
  (3) (Transitive Property)
      If $a, b, c, \ldots \sim p, q, r, \ldots$ and $p, q, r, \ldots \sim x, y, z, \ldots$,
      then $a, b, c, \ldots \sim x, y, z, \ldots.$

All three of these are easy.  The Reflexive Property holds because

$$\frac{a}{a} = \frac{b}{b} = \frac{c}{c} = \cdots = 1.$$

We have already observed that the Symmetric Property holds: if

$$\frac{a}{p} = \frac{b}{q} = \frac{c}{r},$$

then

$$\frac{p}{a} = \frac{q}{b} = \frac{r}{c}.$$

We check the Transitive Property as follows.  If

$$\frac{a}{p} = \frac{b}{q} = \frac{c}{r} \quad \text{and} \quad \frac{p}{x} = \frac{q}{y} = \frac{r}{z},$$

then multiplying term by term we get

$$\frac{a}{x} = \frac{b}{y} = \frac{c}{z},$$

and so $a, b, c, \ldots \sim x, y, z, \ldots.$

We deal with proportionalities by the usual methods of algebra. The easiest proportionalities to work with are those which involve only four numbers. We often refer to such a proportionality as a *proportion*. Below are some examples of what you can conclude, given that $a$, $b$ and $p$, $q$ are proportional. Given:

$$(1) \qquad \frac{a}{p} = \frac{b}{q},$$

by definition of proportionality. Multiplying on both sides by $pq$, we obtain

$$(2) \qquad aq = bp.$$

Dividing on both sides by $bq$, we get

$$(3) \qquad \frac{a}{b} = \frac{p}{q}.$$

There is no danger of dividing by 0 here, because all the numbers in a proportionality must be positive. Next, adding 1 to both sides and simplifying, we get

$$(4) \qquad \frac{a + b}{b} = \frac{p + q}{q}.$$

Subtracting 1 from both sides of equation (3), we obtain

$$(5) \qquad \frac{a - b}{b} = \frac{p - q}{q}.$$

These are merely the most useful of the equations that can be derived from (1); there are many others. These equations need not be memorized. If you try to learn things like this by rote, then half the time you will misremember them when you need them. What you need to remember is the algebraic method that we use in obtaining one equation from another.

**Definition**   If $a$, $b$, $c$ are positive numbers, and

$$\frac{a}{b} = \frac{b}{c},$$

then $b$ is called the *geometric mean* between $a$ and $c$.

It is easy to calculate that $b = \sqrt{ac}$.

## Problem Set 12–1

**1.** Supply the missing numbers which will make each statement a proportionality.

(a) $\dfrac{3}{4} = \dfrac{?\,9}{12} = \dfrac{?\,15}{20} = \dfrac{?\,63}{84}.$

(b) $\dfrac{?\,5}{6} = \dfrac{15}{18} = \dfrac{35}{?\,42} = \dfrac{?\,85}{102}.$

(c) $\dfrac{2}{?\,11} = \dfrac{?\,10}{55} = \dfrac{12}{66} = \dfrac{22}{?\,121}.$

(d) $\dfrac{2310}{9240} = \dfrac{?\,231}{924} = \dfrac{77}{?\,308} = \dfrac{?\,7}{28}.$

**2.** Supply the numbers which will make each statement a proportionality.

(a) $\dfrac{2}{3} = \dfrac{?\,4}{6} = \dfrac{?\,10}{15} = \dfrac{2x}{?\,3x} = \dfrac{?\,1}{1.5}.$

(b) $\dfrac{792}{3960} = \dfrac{198}{?\,990} = \dfrac{?\,99}{495} = \dfrac{9}{?\,45} = \dfrac{1}{?\,5}.$

(c) $\dfrac{?\,4}{3} = \dfrac{6x}{?\,4.5x} = \dfrac{24}{18} = \dfrac{?\,8\sqrt{3}}{6\sqrt{3}}.$

(d) $\dfrac{5}{4} = \dfrac{10}{?\,8} = \dfrac{?\,35}{28} = \dfrac{5\sqrt{2}}{?\,4\sqrt{2}} = \dfrac{?\,0.05}{0.04}.$

**3.** Write each of the following as a simple ratio of nonzero numbers or
variables.

(a) $\dfrac{1}{2} + \dfrac{1}{3} = \dfrac{5}{6}$

(b) $\dfrac{7}{15} + \dfrac{6}{35} = \dfrac{67}{105}$

(c) $\dfrac{1}{x} + \dfrac{1}{y} = \dfrac{x+y}{xy}$

(d) $\dfrac{2}{3x} + \dfrac{5}{6x} = \dfrac{9}{6x}$

**4.** Express each of the following numbers by a fraction in lowest terms.

(a) $\dfrac{26}{65} = \dfrac{2}{5}$

(b) $\dfrac{3\cdot7\cdot8\cdot23}{23\cdot24\cdot25} = \dfrac{7}{25}$

(c) $\dfrac{364}{1001} = \dfrac{4}{11}$

(d) $\dfrac{15(14 + 63)}{11(45 + 60)} = 1$

(e) $\dfrac{62(101 + 10)}{(37 + 259)(31 + 62)} = \dfrac{1}{4}$

(f) $\dfrac{(\sqrt{7} + \sqrt{5})(\sqrt{7} - \sqrt{5})}{(\sqrt{44} + \sqrt{12})(\sqrt{11} - \sqrt{3})} = \dfrac{1}{8}$

**5.** Complete each statement.

(a) If $\dfrac{2}{3} = \dfrac{6}{9}$, then $3 \cdot 6 = 2 \cdot \underline{?\,9}.$

(b) If $\dfrac{a}{b} = \dfrac{3}{7}$, then $7a = \underline{?\,3b}.$

(c) If $\dfrac{x}{12} = \dfrac{5}{8}$, then $8x = \underline{?\,60}.$

**6.** In each proportionality, solve for $x$.

(a) $\dfrac{x}{2} = \dfrac{3}{4}.$      (b) $\dfrac{5}{x} = \dfrac{4}{7}.$          (c) $\dfrac{5}{4} = \dfrac{2x}{13}.$      (d) $\dfrac{2}{3} = \dfrac{11}{x + 3}.$

$x = 3/2$          $x = 35/4$          $x = 65/8$          $x = 27/2$

**7.** Complete each statement.

(a) If $\dfrac{x}{3} = \dfrac{5}{7}$, then $x = \dfrac{3\,?}{} \cdot \dfrac{5}{7}.$     (b) If $\dfrac{5}{9} = \dfrac{10}{18}$, then $\dfrac{5}{10} = \dfrac{?\,9}{18}.$

(c) If $\dfrac{3}{4} = \dfrac{12}{16}$, then $\dfrac{16}{4} = \dfrac{12}{?\,3}.$      (d) If $\dfrac{a}{b} = \dfrac{c}{d}$, then $\dfrac{a}{c} = \underline{\,?\,} \cdot \dfrac{b}{d}.$

Complete the following so the resulting sentence is a true statement.

**1.** If $x, y \ldots \sim 5, 9 \ldots$, then $9x = $ _____.

(ans: 5y)

**2.** If $7x = 12y$, then $x/y = $ _____.

(ans: $\frac{12}{7}$)

**3.** If $a/4 = \frac{7}{11}$, then $(a + 4)/4 = $ _____/11.

(ans: 18)

**4.** The geometric mean of 44 and 121 is _____.

(ans: $22\sqrt{11}$)

**5.** If $x, y, z, \ldots \sim 3, 4, 5, \ldots$, and $x, y, z, \ldots \sim 6, 8, 10, \ldots$, then $3, 4, 5, \ldots \sim 6, 8, 10, \ldots$, by the _____ of an equivalence relation.

(ans: Symmetric and Transitive Properties)

**8.** Find the geometric mean between 4 and 9; between 7 and 14; between 15 and 60; between 72 and 242. $\sqrt{4 \cdot 9} = 6$ ; $\sqrt{7 \cdot 14} = 7\sqrt{2}$ ; $\sqrt{15 \cdot 60} = 30$ ; $\sqrt{72 \cdot 242} = 132$

**9.** Complete each statement.

(a) If $3a = 2b$, then $\dfrac{a}{b} = \underline{2/3}$ and $\dfrac{a}{2} = \underline{b/3}$.

(b) If $4m = 15$, then $\dfrac{m}{5} = \underline{3/4}$ and $\dfrac{m}{3} = \underline{5/4}$.

(c) If $6x = 5 \cdot 9$, then $\dfrac{x}{5} = \underline{3/2}$ and $\dfrac{5}{x} = \underline{2/3}$.

(d) If $\dfrac{2a}{3b} = \dfrac{7c}{5d}$, then $\dfrac{a}{b} = \underline{21c/10d}$ and $\dfrac{b}{a} = \underline{10d/21c}$.

**10.** Complete each statement.

(a) If $4x = 7y$, then $\dfrac{x}{y} = \underline{7/4}$ and $\dfrac{y}{4} = \underline{x/7}$.

(b) If $6a = 35$, then $\dfrac{a}{5} = \underline{7/6}$ and $\dfrac{a}{7} = \underline{5/6}$.

(c) If $12m = 21$, then $4m = \underline{7}$, and $\dfrac{m}{7} = \underline{1/4}$.

(d) If $\dfrac{15x}{28y} = \dfrac{5a}{4b}$, then $bx = \underline{7ay/3}$ and $\dfrac{x}{a} = \underline{7y/3b}$.

**11.** Write a proof of this theorem:

If $\dfrac{a}{b} = \dfrac{c}{d}$, then $\dfrac{a + b}{b} = \dfrac{c + d}{d}$. $\dfrac{a}{b} + 1 = \dfrac{c}{d} + 1$, so $\dfrac{a+b}{b} = \dfrac{c+d}{d}$

**12.** Complete each statement.

(a) If $\dfrac{5}{12} = \dfrac{15}{36}$, then $\dfrac{5 + 12}{12} = \dfrac{15 + ?}{36}$. 36

(b) If $\dfrac{7}{9} = \dfrac{28}{36}$, then $\dfrac{7}{2} = \dfrac{28}{36 - ?}$. 28

(c) If $\dfrac{a}{b} = \dfrac{6}{5}$, then $\dfrac{a + b}{b} = \underline{11/5}$ and $\dfrac{a - b}{b} = \underline{1/5}$.

(d) If $\dfrac{a + c}{c} = \dfrac{11}{7}$, then $\dfrac{a}{c} = \underline{4/7}$ and $\dfrac{c}{a} = \underline{7/4}$.

**13.** For any two positive numbers $a$ and $c$, the geometric mean is $b = \sqrt{ac}$, and the arithmetic mean is $d = \frac{1}{2}(a + c)$. Make a table of the geometric mean and arithmetic mean for the following pairs. What conjecture can you make on the relation between the geometric mean and the arithmetic mean of two positive numbers? $b < d$

(a) 2 and 8  4, 5

(b) 3 and 12  6, 7½

(c) 5 and 45  15, 25

(d) 4 and 9  6, 6½

(e) 9 and 16  12, 12½

(f) 12 and 15  $6\sqrt{5}$, 13½

**Answers to Problems**

21. $0 < (a - b)^2$.

$0 < a^2 - 2ab + b^2$.

$4ab < a^2 + 2ab + b^2$.

$ab < \dfrac{(a + b)^2}{4}$.

$\sqrt{ab} < \dfrac{a + b}{2}$.

14. Consider these three sequences. How many pairs of sequences are proportional?

(a) 3, 8, 12, 17        (b) 9, 24, 36, 51        (c) $\frac{7}{2}$, $\frac{28}{3}$, 15, $\frac{119}{6}$

It is easy to see that sequences (a) and (b) are proportional, since each number in (b) is three times the corresponding number in (a). But comparing (a) and (c) or (b) and (c) is not a simple matter. One efficient way is to change each sequence to a proportional sequence beginning with 1, as in the following.

(a) 1, $\frac{8}{3}$, 4, $\frac{17}{3}$

(b) 1, $\frac{24}{9}$, 4, $\frac{51}{9}$; or 1, $\frac{8}{3}$, ——, ——        4    17/3

(c) 1, $\frac{8}{3}$, ——, ——        30/7  17/3

Now answer the question.

---

15. Which pairs of the following sequences are proportional? You may want to use the method of Problem 14 to help you decide.

(a) 5, 7, 9        (b) 1, 2, 3        (c) $2\frac{1}{2}$, $3\frac{1}{2}$, $4\frac{1}{2}$        (d) 8, 15, 17

(e) 15, 30, 45        (f) 16, 30, 34        (g) $\frac{1}{3}$, $\frac{2}{3}$, 1        (h) 1.25, 1.75, 2.25

(a),(c) and (h); (b),(e) and (g); (d) and (f)

16. Given $x/40 = y/50 = 30/20$. Solve for $x$ and $y$.  X= 60, y = 75

17. Given $3/p = 5/q = r/26 = q/20$. Solve for $p$, $q$, and $r$. P=6, q=10, r=13

$q^2 = 100 \Rightarrow q = 10$

18. Given $\dfrac{5}{a} = \dfrac{b}{27} = \dfrac{12\sqrt{3}}{c} = \dfrac{9}{b}$. Solve for $a$, $b$, and $c$. a= 5√3, b=9√3,

$b^2 = 27 \cdot 9 \Rightarrow b = 9\sqrt{3}$        C= 36

19. Let $h, m, k, 10 \sim 24, 3, h + 4, m + 7$. Solve for $h$, $m$, and $k$.

h=24, m=3, K=28

20. Which of the following are true for all values of the variables used, except, of course, those values which would make any term of a sequence zero or negative?

(a) $5x, 5 \sim 6x, 6$.        (b) $a, b \sim 8b, 8a$.

(c) $r, s, t \sim r^2, rs, tr$.        (d) $a + b, 1 \sim a^2 - b^2, a - b$.

(e) $a + b, a^2 + b^2 \sim 1, a + b$.        (f) $2, x - y \sim x + y, xy$.

21. Prove the following theorem.

The geometric mean of two positive numbers is always less than their arithmetic mean (i.e., average).

[*Hint:* Take $a > b > 0$. Show $\sqrt{ab} < \frac{1}{2}(a + b)$. Try assuming that the proposed inequality holds and derive from it an inequality that you *know* is true. This will show you where to begin the proof.]

## 12-2 SIMILARITIES BETWEEN TRIANGLES

### Classroom Notes

Section 12–2 presents the definition of a similarity. A similarity is a type of *correspondence;* hence we use the standard notation for correspondences. The statement $\triangle ABC \sim \triangle A'B'C'$ means not merely that the triangles are similar, but also that they are similar under the particular correspondence $ABC \leftrightarrow A'B'C'$.

The definition of a similarity states that the corresponding sides of the two triangles are proportional. This means that the ratios of (the lengths of) the corresponding sides are equal.

The correspondence referred to in this definition is a correspondence between the vertices of two triangles: $ABC \leftrightarrow A'B'C'$. Under this correspondence $\overline{AB}$ in $\triangle ABC$ corresponds to $\overline{A'B'}$ in $\triangle A'B'C'$, and so on. Hence, to represent the fact that the corresponding sides are proportional we write

$$\frac{AB}{A'B'} = \frac{BC}{B'C'}.$$

From this we can easily get

$$\frac{AB}{BC} = \frac{A'B'}{B'C'};$$

but it is the first of these equations that occurs in the definition of a similarity.

Note that we have defined similarity for triangles only. The definition does not carry over to polygons (which moreover, are not defined until Chapter 16).

---

22. (a) Consider the proportionality $\frac{2}{3} = \frac{4}{6} = \frac{6}{9} = \frac{8}{12} = \frac{18}{27}$. Verify that

$$\frac{2 + 4 + 6 + 8 + 18}{3 + 6 + 9 + 12 + 27} = \frac{2}{3}. \quad \frac{38}{57} = \frac{2}{3}$$

Does the same procedure work for any other proportionality? Try one!

(b) Prove: If

$$\frac{a}{b} = \frac{c}{d} = \frac{e}{f} = \frac{g}{h},$$

then

$$\frac{a + c + e + g}{b + d + f + h} = \frac{a}{b}.$$

Since $a = kb, c = kd, e = kf,$ $q = kh$, we have $a + c + e + q = k(b + d + f + h)$ and $\dfrac{a + c + e + q}{b + d + f + h} = k$

[*Hint:* Let $a/b = k$. Then $a = kb$. Also, $c = kd, e = kf, g = kh$. Does

$$\frac{a + c + e + g}{b + d + f + h} = k?]$$

### 12–2  SIMILARITIES BETWEEN TRIANGLES

We now state the definition of a similarity between two triangles. Suppose we have given a correspondence $ABC \leftrightarrow A'B'C'$ between $\triangle ABC$ and $\triangle A'B'C'$. As usual, $a$ is the length of the side opposite $A$, $b$ is the length of the side opposite $B$, and so on. If corresponding angles are congruent and

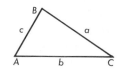

$$\frac{a}{a'} = \frac{b}{b'} = \frac{c}{c'},$$

then we say that the correspondence $ABC \leftrightarrow A'B'C'$ is a *similarity,* and we write

$$\triangle ABC \sim \triangle A'B'C'.$$

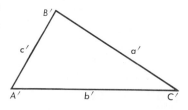

### Definition

Given a correspondence between two triangles. If corresponding angles are congruent, and corresponding sides are proportional, then the correspondence is called a *similarity,* and the triangles are said to be *similar.*

The situation here is like that for congruence: $\triangle ABC \sim \triangle A'B'C'$ means not merely that the triangles are similar, but also that the particular correspondence $ABC \leftrightarrow A'B'C'$ is a similarity. Thus, given

$\triangle ABC \sim \triangle A'B'C'$, we can immediately write the proportionality

$$\frac{a}{a'} = \frac{b}{b'} = \frac{c}{c'}$$

without referring to a figure. If the lengths of the sides are not labeled, these equations take the form

$$\frac{BC}{B'C'} = \frac{AC}{A'C'} = \frac{AB}{A'B'}.$$

The definition of a similarity requires two things: (1) corresponding angles must be congruent, and (2) corresponding sides must be proportional. For triangles, it will turn out that if one of these conditions holds, then so does the other. That is, if corresponding angles are congruent, then corresponding sides are proportional, and conversely. These facts are given in the AAA Similarity Theorem and the SSS Similarity Theorem, which will be proved later in this chapter.

In requiring both (1) and (2), we were playing it safe; and this was a good plan, because triangles are the only figures for which similarity is a simple idea. Consider, for example, a square and a rectangle:

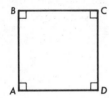
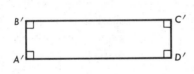

Under the correspondence $ABCD \leftrightarrow A'B'C'D'$, corresponding angles are congruent, because all the angles are right angles. But corresponding sides are not proportional, and surely neither of the two figures is a scale model of the other.

For other quadrilaterals, exactly the opposite trouble can come up. Consider a square and a rhombus:

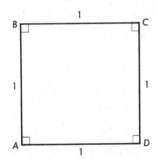
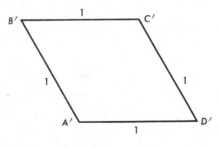

Under the correspondence $ABCD \leftrightarrow A'B'C'D'$, corresponding sides are proportional, but the figures have quite different shapes.

A piece of plywood is cut, as in the figure below, with the inner and outer boundaries similar quadrilaterals. If the outer boundary has a perimeter of 72 and other edges are as marked, what are a, b, x, and y?

(ans: $\frac{45}{4}$, $\frac{81}{4}$, 9, 10)

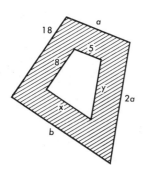

## Problem Set 12–2

**1.** Given $\triangle ABC \sim \triangle KLM$. $\angle B$ and $\angle L$ are right angles and lengths of sides are as marked. Find $y$ in terms of $x$. $y = \frac{7x}{3}$

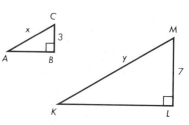

**2.** Given $\triangle PQR \sim \triangle GHI$. If $PQ = 8$, $QR = 6$, $PR = 11$, and $HI = 24$, what is the perimeter of $\triangle GHI$? **100**

**3.** Given $\triangle ABC \sim \triangle DEF$ and lengths of sides as marked. Find $x$ and $y$.

$x = \frac{21}{4}$     $y = \frac{15}{2}$

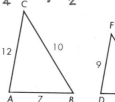

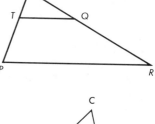

**4.** A piece of cardboard is cut, as in the figure on the right above, with the inner and outer boundaries similar quadrilaterals. If the lengths of sides are as marked, what are $r$, $s$, and $t$? $r = \frac{28}{3}$, $s = \frac{49}{4}$, $t = \frac{35}{6}$

**5.** In the figure, $\triangle STQ \sim \triangle SPR$. If $ST = 3$, $TQ = 7$, and $SP = 10$, what is $PR$? $\frac{70}{3}$

**6.** In the figure, $\triangle STQ \sim \triangle SPR$.

(a) If $ST = 4$, $TP = 6$, and $TQ = 8$, what is $PR$? **20**

(b) If $TQ = 5$, $PR = 15$, and $SQ = 4$, what is $QR$? **8**

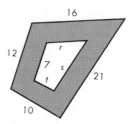

**7.** In the figure, $\triangle ABC \sim \triangle ADE$. If

$AD = 5$,     $AE = 6$,     $BC = 12$,

and

$$AB = 15,$$

what are $AC$ and $DE$? $AC = 18$, $DE = 4$

**8.** If $\triangle ABC \cong \triangle A'B'C'$, does it follow that $\triangle ABC \sim \triangle A'B'C'$? **Yes** Why?
Angles are congruent and the ratios of sides equal one.

**9.** Two photographic prints of a negative are made, one a contact print and one an enlarged print. In the contact print an object has a width of 2 cm and a height of 2.3 cm. In the enlargement the same object has a width of 7.5 cm. What is its height in the enlargement? **8.6cm**

**Answers to Problems**

10. By Theorem 9–22, the segment between the midpoints of two sides of a triangle is parallel to the third side and half as long as the third side. Hence the sides of △CDE and △CAB are proportional. Secondly, if two parallel lines are cut by a transversal, each pair of corresponding angles are congruent. Hence, the angles of △CDE are congruent to the corresponding angles of △CAB. Therefore △CDE ∼ △CAB by definition.

10. Prove: If $D$ and $E$ are the midpoints of $\overline{AC}$ and $\overline{BC}$, respectively, in $\triangle ABC$, then $\triangle CDE \sim \triangle CAB$.

11. Which of the following statements are true?

   (a) Every two equilateral triangles are similar.

   (b) Every two rectangles are similar.

   (c) Every two equilateral quadrilaterals are similar.

   (d) Every two squares are similar.

   (e) Every two isosceles triangles are similar.

12. Given $\triangle ABC$ and points $R$ and $T$ such that $A$-$R$-$C$ and $B$-$T$-$C$. If $\triangle ABC \sim \triangle RTC$, prove that $\overline{RT} \parallel \overline{AB}$. ∠RTC ≅ ∠ABC since △ABC ∼ △RTC so RT ‖ AB by Theorem 9–7 (CAP)

---

13. In the figure, $\triangle ADE \sim \triangle ABC$, and lengths of segments are as marked. Write the formula for $AC$; for $AB$. Write a proportion and solve for $x$.
AC = x + 5, AB = x + 13
$\dfrac{x}{x+5} = \dfrac{6}{x+13}$ , x = 3

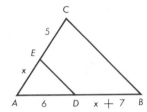

14. John can get a good approximation of the height of a tall tree by the following procedure. First he stands next to the tree and notes where a point on the tree about 1.5 m from the ground would be. Then he walks 40 paces (or 30 m) from the tree. Turning toward the tree he holds a small ruler, 15 cm long, vertically in front of his eyes, until the ruler just obscures the tree above the 1.5-m mark. Using a string tied through a hole in one end of the ruler, he measures in centimetres the distance from his eye to the ruler. He then easily computes the height of the tree by the formula

$$h = 30 \cdot \frac{15}{AB} + 1.5$$

$\dfrac{C'B'}{AB'} = \dfrac{CB}{AB}$ so C'B' = AB' · $\dfrac{CB}{AB}$ =

$30 \cdot \dfrac{15}{AB}$

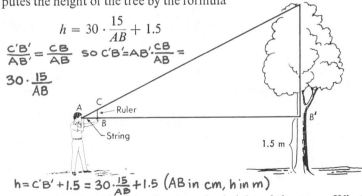

$h = C'B' + 1.5 = 30 \cdot \dfrac{15}{AB} + 1.5$ (AB in cm, h in m)

   (a) Explain why this formula gives the height of the tree. What is the unit of measure?

   (b) If the string measures 20 cm, how tall is the tree? 24 m

**15.** Theorem 9–22, Corollary 9–9.1, and the definition of similar triangles.

**16.** Since $\triangle PMK \sim \triangle KLR$, $\angle KPM \cong \angle RKL$, so $\overline{PQ} \parallel \overline{KL}$. Similarly $\angle PKM \cong \angle KRL$ so $\overline{KM} \parallel \overline{RQ}$. Therefore $\square KLQM$ is a parallelogram, by definition. By Theorem 9–16, any two opposite angles of a parallelogram are congruent. Hence $\angle Q \cong \angle MKL$.

**18.** It is given that $\triangle CDE \sim \triangle ABE$. Therefore, $DE/BE = CE/AE$, or $DE/CE = BE/AE$. Since it is given that $\triangle AED \sim \triangle BEC$, we know that $DE/CE = AE/BE$. Therefore, $BE/AE = AE/BE$, $(AE)^2 = (BE)^2$ and $AE = BE$ since both $AE$ and $BE$ are positive. $\angle EAD \cong \angle EBC$ and $\angle DEA \cong \angle CEB$ by the definition of similar triangles, so $\triangle AED \cong \triangle BEC$ by ASA. Therefore $AD = BC$.

**20.** (a) $AD/AB = AB/BC$, so $AB = \sqrt{BC \cdot AD}$.

(b) Since $\triangle ABC \sim \triangle DAB$, we have $DA$, $DB$, $AB \sim AB$, $AC$, $BC$. Therefore, $DA$, $DB$, $AB \sim AH$, $AB$, $BH$ by the transitivity of proportionality, and so $\triangle DAB \sim \triangle AHB$.

---

**15.** Prove: The triangle whose vertices are the midpoints of the sides of a given triangle is similar to the given triangle.

**16.** Given the figure with $\triangle PMK \sim \triangle KLR$. Prove that $\angle Q \cong \angle MKL$.

**17.** Given the figure with $\triangle PMK \sim \triangle KLR$. If $KR = 8, KP = 4, RL = 15,$ and the altitude from $K$ to $RL$ is 6, what is $a\square KMQR$? **90**

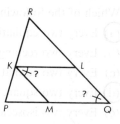

---

**18.** Given the trapezoid $\square ABCD$ with $\overline{AB} \parallel \overline{CD}$, $\triangle AED \sim \triangle BEC$, and $\triangle AEB \sim \triangle CED$.

Prove: $AD = BC$.

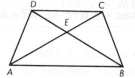

**19.** In the figure on the left below, $\triangle RST \sim \triangle RQP$. If $RT = 12, TQ = 3,$ and $RP$ is 8 more than $RS$, what is $RS$? **10**

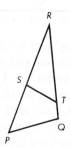
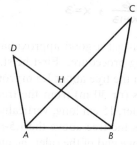

**20.** In the figure on the right above, $\triangle ABC \sim \triangle DAB$.

(a) Prove that $AB$ is the geometric mean between $AD$ and $BC$.

(b) If $AB, AC, BC \sim AH, AB, BH$, prove that $\triangle AHB \sim \triangle DAB$.

## Preparation for Section 12-3

**1.** Copy the figure at the right and introduce the altitude for $\triangle ADC$ from vertex $C$.

**2.** For the figure explain why

(a) $\dfrac{a\triangle ADC}{a\triangle BDC} = \dfrac{AD}{BD}$ Theorem 11-7

(b) $\dfrac{a\triangle ADC}{a\triangle ABC} = \dfrac{AD}{AB}$ Theorem 11-7

(c) $\dfrac{a\triangle DBC}{a\triangle ABC} = \dfrac{DB}{AB}$ Theorem 11-7

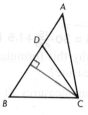

**3.** Given that $\square BCED$ is a trapezoid with $\overline{DE} \parallel \overline{BC}$. Prove that

$$a\triangle DEB = a\triangle DEC.$$

The altitude of $\triangle$ DEB = the
distance between $\overleftrightarrow{DE}$ and $\overleftrightarrow{BC}$
= the altitude of $\triangle$ DEC.
Since DE is the base of
both triangles,
$a\triangle$ DEB = $a\triangle$ DEC by
Theorem 11-6.

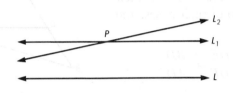

**4.** In a plane, let $L_1 \parallel L$. If a line $L_2$ is parallel to $L$ and $L_1 \cap L_2 = \{P\}$, what conclusion can you draw? Why? $L_1 = L_2$. By Parallel Postulate there is exactly one line through P parallel to L.

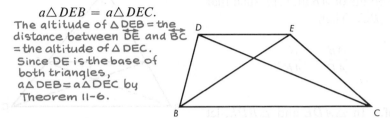

## 12–3 THE BASIC PROPORTIONALITY THEOREM AND ITS CONVERSE

Consider a triangle $\triangle ABC$, with a cross bar $\overline{DE}$, parallel to the base $\overline{BC}$. It looks as though the correspondence $ABC \leftrightarrow ADE$ ought to be a similarity. In fact, it is rather easy to prove that corresponding angles are congruent. (Proof?) To show that corresponding sides are proportional is a little more difficult. We begin with the following theorem, which says that the *sloping* sides in the figure below are proportional.

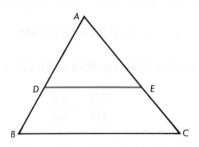

**Theorem 12–2**    The Basic Proportionality Theorem

*If a line parallel to one side of a triangle intersects the other two sides in distinct points, then it cuts off segments which are proportional to these sides.*

## 12–3 THE BASIC PROPORTIONALITY THEOREM AND ITS CONVERSE

**Classroom Notes**

The proof of the Basic Proportionality Theorem uses areas of triangles. This is the proof given in Euclid's *Elements* (Book VI, Proposition 1).

Note that the conclusion of the theorem (equation 5) states that

$$\frac{AB}{AD} = \frac{AC}{AE},$$

that is, "one entire side is to its top segment as the other entire side is to its top segment." In the course of obtaining this result we established (equation 4) that

$$\frac{BD}{AD} = \frac{CE}{AE},$$

that is, "the bottom segment is to the top segment as the bottom segment is to the top segment." We can also obtain

$$\frac{AB}{BD} = \frac{AC}{CE},$$

and we could rewrite each of these proportionalities by inversion. We recommend that you allow students to use the conclusion of the Basic Proportionality Theorem in whatever form is convenient.

A rather widely used proof of the Basic Proportionality Theorem runs as follows. Suppose that there are positive integers $m$, $n$, $k$, with $m + n = k$, such that $AD = m(AB/k)$ and $DB = n(AB/k)$. We then introduce a set of lines, each parallel to $\overline{BC}$, dividing $\overline{AB}$ into $k$ congruent segments. It follows, by Corollary 9–30.1, that the lines also divide $AC$ into $k$ congruent segments. We then have

$$\frac{AB}{AD} = \frac{k}{m} = \frac{AC}{AE}.$$

The form of this last equation reminds us of the limitation of the proof: it shows that

$$\frac{AB}{AD} = \frac{AC}{AE}$$

only for the case in which both are rational, that is, the "commensurable case." This proof can be extended to cover the general case, but the extended proof is much too hard for an introductory course. See *EGAS*, Section 11–4. It appears that the area proof of Theorem 12–2 is the only complete proof that is simple enough to be teachable.

The converse of the Basic Proportionality Theorem is easy and its proof can be left to the student. There is, however, one technical point: In the proof we tacitly assume that $E$ is between $A'$ and $C'$. It is obvious from a figure that parallel projection preserves betweenness, but we should prove this.

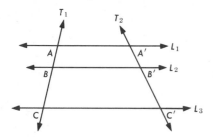

**The Parallel Projection Theorem.** Given two transversals $T_1$ and $T_2$ intersecting three parallel lines $L_1, L_2, L_3$ in points $A$, $B$, and $C$ and $A'$, $B'$, and $C'$, respectively. If $B$ is between $A$ and $C$, then $B'$ is between $A'$ and $C'$.

*Proof.* Since $L_1 \parallel L_2$, the segment $\overline{AA'}$ cannot intersect $L_2$, and hence $A$ and $A'$ are on the same side of $L_2$. Likewise, since $L_3 \parallel L_2$, the segment $\overline{CC'}$ cannot intersect $L_2$, and $C$ and $C'$ are on the same side of $L_2$. Since $B$ is between $A$ and $C$ by hypothesis, $\overline{AC}$ intersects $L_2$ at $B$; hence, $A$ and $C$ are on opposite sides of $L_2$. Since

**Restatement.** In $\triangle ABC$ let $D$ and $E$ be points of $\overline{AB}$ and $\overline{AC}$ such that $\overline{DE} \parallel \overline{BC}$. Then

$$\frac{AB}{AD} = \frac{AC}{AE}.$$

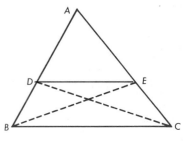

**Proof.** In $\triangle ADE$ and $\triangle BDE$, let us regard $\overline{AD}$ and $\overline{BD}$ as the bases. Then these triangles have the same altitude. (Why?) Therefore, by Theorem 11–7, the ratio of their areas is the ratio of their bases, and we have

(1)   $$\frac{a\triangle BDE}{a\triangle ADE} = \frac{BD}{AD}.$$

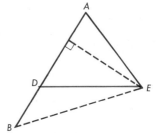

Similarly, in $\triangle ADE$ and $\triangle CDE$ let us consider $\overline{AE}$ and $\overline{CE}$ as the bases. Since these triangles have the same altitude, we conclude as before that

(2)   $$\frac{a\triangle CDE}{a\triangle ADE} = \frac{CE}{AE}.$$

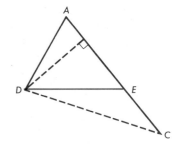

Now $\triangle BDE$ and $\triangle CDE$ have the same base $\overline{DE}$. (See the figure to the right of the restatement.) And they have the same altitude, because $\overleftrightarrow{DE}$ and $\overleftrightarrow{BC}$ are parallel. Therefore, by Theorem 11–6,

(3)   $$a\triangle BDE = a\triangle CDE.$$

Fitting together the three equations (1), (2), and (3), we get

(4)   $$\frac{BD}{AD} = \frac{CE}{AE}.$$

Adding 1 to both sides of equation (4), we get

(5)   $$\frac{BD + AD}{AD} = \frac{CE + AE}{AE}, \quad \text{or} \quad \frac{AB}{AD} = \frac{AC}{AE},$$

which is what we wanted.

The converse of the Basic Proportionality Theorem is much easier to prove.

### Theorem 12-3

*If a line intersects two sides of a triangle, and cuts off segments proportional to these two sides, then it is parallel to the third side.*

**Restatement.** Given $\triangle ABC$. Let $D$ be a point between $A$ and $B$, and let $E$ be a point between $A$ and $C$. If

$$\frac{AB}{AD} = \frac{AC}{AE},$$

then $\overleftrightarrow{DE} \parallel \overleftrightarrow{BC}$.

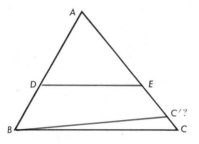

**Proof.** Let $\overleftrightarrow{BC'}$ be the line through $B$, parallel to $\overleftrightarrow{DE}$, intersecting $\overleftrightarrow{AC}$ at $C'$. By the preceding theorem,

$$\frac{AB}{AD} = \frac{AC'}{AE}.$$

Since, by hypothesis,

$$\frac{AB}{AD} = \frac{AC}{AE},$$

we have

$$\frac{AC'}{AE} = \frac{AC}{AE},$$

and $AC' = AC$. Therefore $C = C'$, and $\overleftrightarrow{DE} \parallel \overleftrightarrow{BC}$.

$A'$ and $A$ are in the same half-plane determined by $L_2$, and $C'$ and $C$ are in the same half-plane, and $A$ and $C$ are in opposite half-planes, it follows that $A'$ and $C'$ are in opposite half-planes determined by $L_2$. Hence $\overline{A'C'}$ meets $L_2$ in a point, which must be $B'$, since $B'$ is the intersection of $\overleftrightarrow{A'C'}$ and $L_2$. Therefore $B'$ is between $A'$ and $C'$. We have assumed that $A \neq A'$ and $C \neq C'$. The argument above is easily modified to apply to the cases where $A = A'$ or $C = C'$.

Note that the application of this principle to Theorem 12-3 involves the case $A = A'$.

### Explanation for Problems

Note that Problems 1 through 4 involve the use of the Basic Proportionality Theorem and that Problems 5 through 8 involve the use of the converse of the Basic Proportionality Theorem. Be sure to assign the theorem in Problem 11 (and the associated numerical exercise in Problem 12) and the theorem in Problem 15 (and its generalization in Problem 19.)

### Problem Set 12-3

1. In $\triangle ABC$, $\overline{DE} \parallel \overline{AB}$.

  (a) Given that $AC = 12$, $CD = 4$, and $BC = 24$, find $CE$. $= 8$

  (b) Given $AC = 15$, $AD = 3$, and $BC = 25$. Find $BE$. $= 5$

  (c) Given $AD = 6$, $CD = 4$, and $CE = 7$. Find $BC$. $= \frac{35}{2}$

  (d) Given $CD = 8$, $AC = 18$, and $BE = 6$. Find $CE$. $= 4.8$

  (e) Given $AD = CE$, $CD = 4$, $EB = 9$. Find $AC$. $= 10$

**1.** In $\triangle ABC$, $D$ and $E$ are points on $\overline{AC}$ and $\overline{BC}$ respectively such that $\overline{DE} \parallel \overline{AB}$. If $AC = 11$, $DC = 6$, and $BC = 15$, what is the length of $\overline{BE}$?

(ans: $\frac{75}{11}$)

**2.** The sides of a triangle are 16, 20, and 28. How long are the segments into which the bisector of the largest angle separates the opposite side?

(ans: $\frac{112}{9}$, $\frac{140}{9}$)

**2.** Given $\triangle PQR$ with $\overline{ST} \parallel \overline{PQ}$ and lengths of segments as marked. Which of the following proportions are correct?

(a) $\dfrac{b}{a} = \dfrac{d}{c}$

(b) $\dfrac{a+b}{a} = \dfrac{c+d}{d}$

(c) $\dfrac{c}{d+c} = \dfrac{a}{b+a}$

(d) $\dfrac{a}{c} = \dfrac{b}{d}$

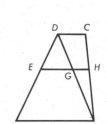

**3.** In the figure, $\overline{EH} \parallel \overline{DC} \parallel \overline{AB}$.

(a) Given $DE = 3$, $EA = 4$, and $DG = 5$. Find $GB$. $= \frac{20}{3}$

(b) Given $BH = 6$, $CB = 16$, and $DB = 20$. Find $DG$. $= \frac{25}{2}$

(c) Given $DA = 36$, $EA = 22$, and $DG = 15$. Find $DB$. $= \frac{270}{7}$

(d) Given $DE = 20$, $EA = 25$, and $HB = 22$. Find $CH$. $= \frac{88}{5}$

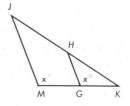

**4.** In $\triangle JMK$, $m\angle M = m\angle HGK = x$.

(a) Given $JH = 7$, $JK = 21$, and $GK = 10$. Find $MG$. $= 5$

(b) Given $HK = MG$, $MK = 6$, and $JH = 8$. Find $GK$. $= 2$

(c) Given $GK = 7$, $HK = 2MG$, and $JH = 14$. Find $JK$. $= 28$

(d) Given $KJ = 24$, $HK = MK$, and $KG = 4$. Find $MK$. $= 4\sqrt{6}$

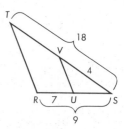

**5.** If the segments in the figure on the right have the lengths indicated, is $\overline{UV} \parallel \overline{RT}$? Justify your answer. Yes $\frac{4}{18} = \frac{2}{9}$

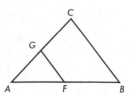

**6.** Which of the following sets of lengths will make $\overline{FG} \parallel \overline{BC}$?

(a) $AB = 14$, $AF = 6$, $AC = 7$, $AG = 3$.

(b) $AB = 12$, $FB = 3$, $AC = 8$, $AG = 6$.

(c) $AF = 6$, $FB = 5$, $AG = 9$, $GC = 8$.

(d) $AC = 21$, $GC = 9$, $AB = 14$, $AF = 5$.

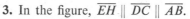

**7.** If the segments in the figure on the left below have the lengths indicated, is $\overline{PQ} \parallel \overline{AB}$? Justify your answer. **No $\frac{16}{20} \neq \frac{25}{30}$**

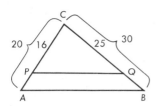
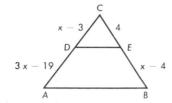

**8.** Given the figure as marked, find all values of $x$ which will make $\overline{DE} \parallel \overline{AB}$.
**$x = 8$ or $x = 11$**

**9.** Given the figure as marked with $\overline{ST} \parallel \overline{PQ}$, find all values of $RP$. **= 24**

$$\frac{x+3}{2x} = \frac{3x-6}{2x+7}$$

$$x = 7$$

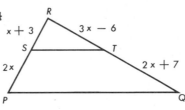

**10.** In $\triangle GHK$, $\overline{MP} \parallel \overline{GK}$. If $KP = 12$, $MG = 16$, and $MH = 9$, what is

$$\frac{a\triangle MPH}{a\triangle MPK}? \quad \frac{9}{16}$$

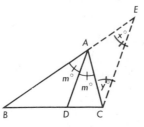

**11.** Prove the following theorem.

The bisector of an angle of a triangle separates the opposite side into segments whose lengths are proportional to the lengths of the adjacent sides.

**Restatement.** In $\triangle ABC$, if $\overrightarrow{AD}$ bisects $\angle A$ and $D$ is on $\overline{BC}$, then

$$\frac{BD}{CD} = \frac{BA}{CA}.$$

[*Hint:* Introduce $\overleftrightarrow{CE}$ parallel to $\overleftrightarrow{AD}$. Show that $AC = AE$.]

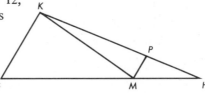

**12.** Use the theorem of Problem 11 in answering the following.

(a) The sides of a triangle are 15, 20, and 28. How long are the segments into which the bisector of the largest angle separates the opposite side? of the smallest angle? **12 and 16, $6\frac{1}{4}$ and $8\frac{3}{4}$**

(b) The sides of a triangle are 12, 18, and 24. Find the lengths of the segments into which the bisector of each angle separates its opposite side. **24: $9\frac{3}{5}$ and $14\frac{2}{5}$, 18: 6 and 12, 12: $5\frac{1}{7}$ and $6\frac{6}{7}$**

**14.** Since $\overline{PS} \parallel \overline{AD}$, $EP/EA = ES/ED$. Since $\overline{SR} = \overline{DC}$, $ES/ED = ER/EC$. Since $\overline{RQ} \parallel \overline{DC}$, $ER/EC = EQ/EB$. Hence, by the Transitive Property of Equality $EP/EA = EQ/EB$, and by Theorem 12-3, $\overline{PQ} \parallel \overline{AB}$.

**15.** Introduce $\overline{AF}$ and let G be the intersection of $\overline{AF}$ and $\overline{BE}$. Now apply the Basic Proportionality Theorem twice, once to $\triangle ACF$ and once to $\triangle DFA$.

**17.** Given a trapezoid $\square ABCD$ in which $\overline{AB} \parallel \overline{CD}$ and diagonals $\overline{AC}$ and $\overline{BD}$ intersect at P. Since $\overline{AB} \parallel \overline{CD}$, $\triangle APB \sim \triangle CPD$ by the AA Corollary and therefore $AP/PC = BP/PD$ by the definition of similar triangles.

**13.** In each of the following triangles a segment is drawn parallel to a base, and the lengths of certain segments are marked. In each case, solve for $x$ in terms of the other letters.

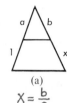 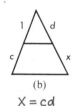 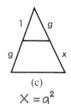 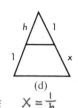

(a)      (b)      (c)      (d)

$X = \dfrac{b}{a}$      $X = cd$      $X = g^2$      $X = \dfrac{1}{h}$

**14.** In the figure, $\overline{PS} \parallel \overline{AD}$, $\overline{SR} \parallel \overline{DC}$, and $\overline{RQ} \parallel \overline{BC}$. Prove that $\overline{PQ} \parallel \overline{AB}$.

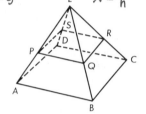

**15.** Prove the following theorem.

> If three or more parallels are each cut by two transversals, the intercepted segments on the two transversals are proportional.

**Restatement:** If transversals $T_1$ and $T_2$ cut parallels $L_1$, $L_2$, and $L_3$ in $A$, $B$, $C$ and $D$, $E$, $F$, respectively, then

$$\frac{AB}{BC} = \frac{DE}{EF}.$$

[*Hint:* Introduce $\overline{DC}$ or $\overline{AF}$.]

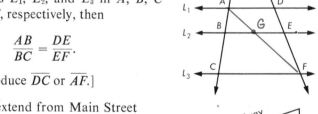

**16.** Three lots extend from Main Street to Broadway, as shown in the sketch. The side boundaries are perpendicular to Main Street. If the total frontage on Broadway is 135 m, find the frontage of each lot on Broadway.

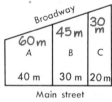

**17.** Prove: The diagonals of a trapezoid intersect each other at a point which makes the lengths of the segments of one diagonal proportional to the lengths of the segments of the other diagonal.

**18.** A printer wants to make a card 6 cm long and of a width such that when folded in half, as shown, it will have the same shape as when it is unfolded. What should be the width? $\dfrac{6}{w} = \dfrac{w}{3}$, $w^2 = 18$, $w = 3\sqrt{2}$ cm

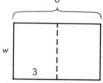

**19.** Given: Parallel planes $E$, $F$, and $G$ are intersected by transversals $T_1$ and $T_2$, as in the figure.

Prove: $\dfrac{AB}{BC} = \dfrac{PQ}{QR}$.

[*Hint:* Introduce $\overline{AR}$.]

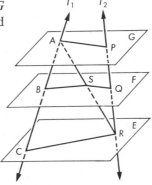

**20.** In $\triangle ABC$, $\overline{DE} \parallel \overline{AB}$, and $\triangle CMN$ is isosceles.    If $CD = 12$, $DA = 9$, $CE = 10$,   and   $EB = CF = CG$, what is $CM$?  $= \dfrac{105}{8}$

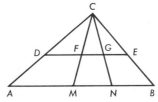

**21.** Prove the following theorem.

   Given any triangle, $\triangle ABC$.  If the bisectors of the interior and exterior angles at $A$ intersect $\overleftrightarrow{BC}$ at points $D$ and $D'$, respectively, then

   $$\dfrac{BD}{BD'} = \dfrac{CD}{CD'}.$$

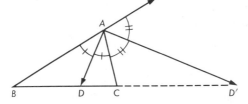

   [*Hint:* Introduce $\overleftrightarrow{CE}$ parallel to $\overline{AD'}$, use Theorem 12–2 and Problem 11 of this problem set.]

**22.** (a) In Problem 21, if $AC = 9$, $AB = 15$, and $BC = 16$, what are $BD$, $DC$, and $CD'$?  BD=10, DC=6, CD'= 24

   (b) In Problem 21, if $m\angle BAC = 90$, $AC = 6$, and $AB = 8$, what are $BD$, $DC$, and $CD'$?  BD=5⅗, DC=4²⁄₇ , CD'= 30

**23.** Does the theorem of Problem 21 hold if $AB < AC$?  Illustrate and explain.  How does the theorem change if $AB = AC$?

**24.** A triangle has sides of 6, 12, and 16.  The bisectors of the largest interior angle and the smallest exterior angle intersect the line containing the opposite side at points $X$ and $Y$, respectively.  Determine the distances of $X$ and $Y$ from the vertex of the smallest angle of the triangle. $\dfrac{32}{3}$, 32

**Answers to Problems**

**19.** Introduce $\overline{AR}$.   Let $\overline{AR}$ intersect $F$ at $S$: Observe that $\triangle ARC$ and $\triangle ARP$ determine two distinct planes.    (1) Since the plane of $\triangle ARC$ intersects the two parallel planes $E$ and $F$, it intersects them in two parallel lines: $\overleftrightarrow{BS} \parallel \overleftrightarrow{CR}$. Therefore by the Basic Proportionality Theorem $AB/BC = AS/SR$.    (2) Since $F \parallel G$, the lines formed by the intersection of the plane $\triangle ARP$ with planes $F$ and $G$ are parallel: $\overleftrightarrow{SQ} \parallel \overleftrightarrow{AP}$.  Therefore, by the BPT, $AS/SR = PQ/QR$.   Hence, $AB/BC = PQ/QR$.

**21.** From Problem 11 we know $BD/CD = BA/CA$.  If we introduce $\overleftrightarrow{CE} \parallel \overline{AD'}$, with $E$ on $\overline{AB}$, we can conclude by a proof similar to the one in Problem 11 that $BD'/CD' = BA/CA$.   $\therefore BD/CD = BD'/CD'$, and $BD/BD' = CD/CD'$.

**23.** The theorem still holds if $AB < AC$. Observe that as in the figure for Problem 21 there are two exterior angles at vertex $A$, and only one of these exterior angles has the property that its bisector (a ray) intersects $\overleftrightarrow{BC}$.

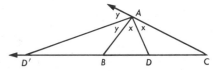

If $AB = AC$, the triangle is isosceles, and the bisector of each exterior angle at $A$ is parallel to the base $\overline{BC}$. Consequently the point $D'$, defined in the hypothesis of the theorem as the intersection of $\overleftrightarrow{BC}$ and the bisector of the exterior angle at $A$, does not exist.  Since, in this case, the hypothesis of the theorem is not satisfied, we can draw no conclusion.

**24.** Since $\dfrac{AX}{XC} = \dfrac{AB}{BC}$, $\dfrac{x}{16-x} = \dfrac{12}{6}$ so that $AX = \dfrac{32}{3}$ and $XC = \dfrac{16}{3}$.   Since $\dfrac{AX}{AY} = \dfrac{CX}{CY}$, we have $\dfrac{\frac{32}{3}}{z + 16} = \dfrac{\frac{16}{3}}{z}$, so that $z = 16$.    Therefore $AY = AC + CY = 16 + 16 = 32$.

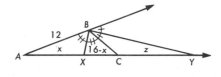

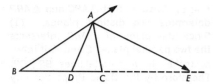

It is easy to show that $\overline{AD} \perp \overline{AE}$; therefore $\triangle ADE$ is a right triangle and $DE = \sqrt{(AD)^2 + (AE)^2}$. Hence, what we must show is that $DE/CD - DE/BD = 2$.

By Problem 21 of Problem Set 12–3, $BD/BE = CD/CE$. Observe that the terms $BD$ and $CD$ in the numerators of this equation are in the denominators of the equation above; we rewrite this equation $BE/BD = CE/CD$.

Observe that $BE = BD + DE$. Therefore, $BE/BD = CE/CD$; $(BD + DE)/BD = CE/CD$; $1 = CE/CD = DE/BD$.

Now, adding 1 to both members of the equation, $2 = 1 + CE/CD - DE/BD = (CD/CD + CE/CD) - DE/BD = DE/CD - DE/BD$, which is what we needed to show.

25. $\triangle ABC$ has a right angle at $C$. The bisector of an exterior angle at $B$ intersects $\overleftrightarrow{AC}$ at $D$. If $AB = 13$ and $BC = 5$, what is the length of $\overline{BD}$?

$\dfrac{5}{2}\sqrt{13}$

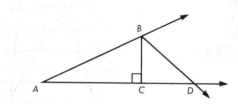

## HONORS PROBLEM

Given $\triangle ABC$ with $AB > AC$. The bisectors of the interior and exterior angles at $A$ intersect $\overleftrightarrow{BC}$ at points $D$ and $E$, respectively. Prove that

$$\frac{\sqrt{AD^2 + AE^2}}{CD} - \frac{\sqrt{AD^2 + AE^2}}{BD} = 2.$$

## 12–4   THE BASIC SIMILARITY THEOREMS

**Theorem 12–4.**   The AAA Similarity Theorem

*Given a correspondence between two triangles. If corresponding angles are congruent, then the correspondence is a similarity.*

**Restatement.**   Given a correspondence $ABC \leftrightarrow DEF$ between two triangles. If $\angle A \cong \angle D$, $\angle B \cong \angle E$, and $\angle C \cong \angle F$, then $\triangle ABC \sim \triangle DEF$.

**Proof.**   Since we know by hypothesis that corresponding angles are congruent, what we need to prove is that corresponding sides are proportional. That is, we need to show that

$$\frac{AB}{DE} = \frac{AC}{DF} = \frac{BC}{EF}.$$

We shall show that the *first* of these equations holds. By exactly the same proof, with merely a change of notation, it will follow that the second equation also holds.

We proceed to the proof that

$$\frac{AB}{DE} = \frac{AC}{DF}.$$

Let $E'$ and $F'$ be points of $\overrightarrow{AB}$ and $\overrightarrow{AC}$, such that $AE' = DE$ and $AF' = DF$. By SAS we have

*Note use of Point-Plotting Theorem.*

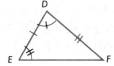

$$\triangle AE'F' \cong \triangle DEF.$$

Therefore $\angle AE'F' \cong \angle E$. Since $\angle E \cong \angle B$, it follows that

$$\angle AE'F' \cong \angle B.$$

We consider two cases:

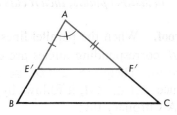

(1) If $E' = B$, then $\triangle AE'F'$ and $\triangle ABC$ are the same triangle. In this case $\triangle ABC \cong \triangle DEF$, and

$$\frac{AB}{DE} = \frac{AC}{DF}$$

because each of these fractions is equal to 1. (Why?)

(2) If $E'$ is different from $B$, then $\overleftrightarrow{E'F'}$ and $\overleftrightarrow{BC}$ are parallel. (Why?) By the Basic Proportionality Theorem, we have

$$\frac{AB}{AE'} = \frac{AC}{AF'}.$$

Since $AE' = DE$ and $AF' = DF$, it follows that

$$\frac{AB}{DE} = \frac{AC}{DF},$$

which was to be proved.

We recall, from Corollary 9–13.1, that if *two* pairs of corresponding angles are congruent, then the third pair must also be congruent. (The reason, of course, is that in any triangle, the sum of the measures of the angles is 180.) This gives us the following corollary:

**Corollary 12–4.1.**   The AA Corollary

*Given a correspondence between two triangles. If two pairs of corresponding angles are congruent, then the correspondence is a similarity.*

## 12–4 THE BASIC SIMILARITY THEOREMS

**Classroom Notes**

Section 12–4 establishes in rapid succession the three similarity theorems. Note the logical interdependence of these theorems.

Problem Set 12–4A is intended to give the student practice with the AAA Similarity Theorem before taking up the SAS and SSS Similarity Theorems. Note that the AAA Similarity Theorem is used only to prove the AA Corollary; it is the AA Corollary that is used thereafter.

**Quiz**

**1.** The proof of Corollary 12–4.1, the AA Corollary, depends on an important theorem from Chapter 12 and an important corollary from Chapter 9. What theorem and what corollary?

(ans: The AAA Similarity Theorem. Corollary 9–13.1: If two pairs of corresponding angles are congruent, then the third pair must also be congruent.)

**2.** Given a trapezoid $\square ABCD$ with bases $\overline{AB}$ and $\overline{DC}$. Diagonals $\overline{AC}$ and $\overline{BD}$ intersect at $K$. Prove that $AK \cdot DK = BK \cdot CK$.

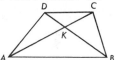

Proof: Since $DC \parallel AB$, $\angle CDK \cong \angle KBA$ and $\angle DCK \cong \angle KAB$ (The PAI Theorem). $\angle AKB \cong \angle DKC$ (Vertical angles). Thus, $\triangle AKB \sim \triangle CKD$ (The AAA Similarity Theorem). This shows that $AK/CK = BK/DK$, and therefore $AK \cdot DK = CK \cdot BK$.

**3.** A triangle has sides 3, 4, and 5, and a second triangle has a perimeter of 20. If the two triangles are similar, what is the length of the longest side of the second triangle?

(ans: $\frac{25}{3}$)

**4.** Illustrate the SAS Theorem by stating a specific example.

(ans: For example, if $m\angle B = m\angle E = 60$, $AB = 3$, $BC = 4$, $DE = 6$, and $EF = 8$, then $\triangle ABC \sim \triangle DEF$.)

**1.** Since $\overline{AC} \parallel \overline{BD}$, $\triangle ACE \sim \triangle BDE$ by the AA Corollary, and consequently $AE/EB = CE/ED$ and $AE \cdot ED = CE \cdot EB$.

**3.** $\triangle ABC \sim \triangle BAD$, $\triangle ADC \sim \triangle BCD$, $\triangle AED \sim \triangle BEC$, $\triangle ABE \sim \triangle CDE$.

**4.** Since the base angles of an isosceles triangle are congruent, $\angle G \cong \angle H$, and consequently $\triangle GRP \sim \triangle HQP$ by the AA Corollary. Hence, $GR/HQ = PR/PQ$, so $GR \cdot PQ = PR \cdot HQ$.

**6.** [Note: This theorem is useful in the proof of Theorem 12–8.] The AA Corollary and the definition of similar triangles.

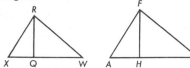

Since $\triangle ABF \sim \triangle XWR$ then $\angle X \cong \angle A$ and $XR/AF = XW/AB = WR/BF$. $m\angle AHF = m\angle XQR$ and so $\triangle XQR \sim \triangle AHF$ by the AA Corollary. Therefore $RQ/FH = XR/AF$. A similar proof can be used for each of the other altitudes.

---

We can now prove a stronger version of the Basic Proportionality Theorem, justifying the remarks made at the beginning of the preceding section, on p. 373.

### Corollary 12–4.2

*If a line parallel to one side of a triangle intersects the other two sides in distinct points, then it cuts off a triangle similar to the given triangle.*

**Proof.** When the parallel lines $\overleftrightarrow{DE}$ and $\overleftrightarrow{BC}$ are cut by the transversal $\overleftrightarrow{AB}$, corresponding angles are congruent. Therefore $\angle ADE \cong \angle B$. Since $\angle A \cong \angle A$, it follows by the AA Corollary that

$$\triangle ADE \sim \triangle ABC.$$

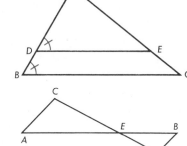

### Problem Set 12–4A

**1.** Given: The figure with $\overline{AC} \parallel \overline{BD}$.

    Prove: (1) $\triangle ACE \sim \triangle BDE$.

              (2) $AE \cdot ED = CE \cdot EB$.

**2.** In $\square PQRS$, $\overline{SR} \parallel \overline{PQ}$, $\overline{SQ}$ is a diagonal, and $U$ and $V$ are midpoints.

    Prove: $US \cdot MQ = VQ \cdot MS$.

    $\triangle SMU \sim \triangle QMV$ (AA corollary)

    $\dfrac{US}{VQ} = \dfrac{MS}{MQ}$ and $US \cdot MQ = VQ \cdot MS$

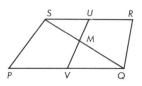

**3.** Let $\square ABCD$ be an isosceles trapezoid with bases $\overline{AB}$ and $\overline{DC}$, and let the diagonals intersect at $E$. Name four pairs of similar triangles.

**4.** In $\triangle GHK$, $GK = HK$, $\overline{PR} \perp \overline{GK}$, and $\overline{PQ} \perp \overline{HK}$. Prove that

$$GR \cdot PQ = PR \cdot HQ.$$

$$\frac{AC}{14} = \frac{15}{12}$$

$$\frac{AE}{AE+4} = \frac{12}{15}$$

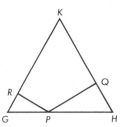

**5.** Given the figure, with $AD = 14$, $ED = 12$, $BC = 15$, and $EB = 4$. Find $AC$, $AE$, and $AB$. $AC = 17.5$, $AE = 16$, $AB = 20$

**6.** Prove: Any two corresponding altitudes of similar triangles have the same ratio as the corresponding sides.

7. In the figure, $\angle ABC$ is a right angle, $\overline{ED} \perp \overline{BC}$, $\overline{EF} \perp \overline{AB}$, and $\overline{EG} \parallel \overline{DF}$. List all sets of similar triangles.

$\triangle CDE \sim \triangle CBA \sim \triangle EFA$

$\triangle DBF \sim \triangle FED \sim \triangle EFG$

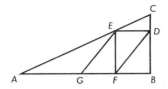

8. In $\triangle ABC$, $\angle C$ is a right angle and $\overline{CD}$ is the altitude to the hypotenuse.

(a) Name at least one angle congruent to $\angle ACB$. $\angle ADC, \angle BDC$

(b) Name an angle congruent to $\angle z$. $\angle y$

(c) Name a triangle similar to $\triangle ABC$. Write the similarity between the two. $\triangle ABC \sim \triangle ACD$
$\triangle ABC \sim \triangle CBD$

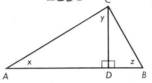

9. Two angles of $\triangle PQR$ have measures of 15 and 45. Two angles of $\triangle STV$ have measures of 45 and 120. Are the triangles similar? **Yes**

10. Two isosceles triangles each have an angle of 40 degrees. Does it follow that the triangles are similar? **No, one may be 40-40-100 and the other 40-70-70.** L

11. In the figure, if $a = 8$, $b = 4$, and $c = 12$, find the value of $x$. **= 6**

12. In the figure, if $a = 7$, $b = 2\sqrt{3}$, and $c = 5\sqrt{3}$, find the value of $x$. **= 5**

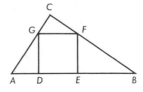

13. Given the figure, express $x$ in terms of $a$, $b$, and $c$. $x = \dfrac{ac}{b+c}$

14. In the figure, $\overline{RQ} \perp \overline{PQ}$, $\overline{PQ} \perp \overline{PT}$, and $\overline{ST} \perp \overline{PR}$. Prove that

$$ST \cdot RQ = PS \cdot PQ.$$

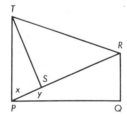

15. Prove: Any two corresponding angle bisectors of similar triangles have the same ratio as the corresponding sides. **Use AA Corollary and definition of similarity. (See Problem 6.)**

16. In the figure, $\square DEFG$ is a square and $\angle C$ is a right angle.

Prove: (1) $\triangle ADG \sim \triangle GCF$.

(2) $\triangle ADG \sim \triangle FEB$.

(3) $AD \cdot EB = DG \cdot FE$.

(4) $DE = \sqrt{AD \cdot EB}$.

17. In the figure for Problem 16, if $AD = 8$ and $EB = 18$, find $a\square ABFG$. **300**

**14.** Since $\overline{PT} \perp \overline{PQ}$, $\angle TPS$ and $\angle RPQ$ are complementary. Also the acute angles $\angle RPQ$ and $\angle PRQ$ of right $\triangle RPQ$ are complementary. Therefore $\angle TPS \cong \angle PRQ$ since complements of congruent angles are congruent. Thus $\triangle TPS \sim \triangle PRQ$ by the AA Corollary, and consequently $ST/PQ = PS/RQ$, or, $ST \cdot RQ = PS \cdot PQ$.

**16.** (1) Since $\angle C \cong \angle ADG$ and $\angle CGF \cong \angle A$, $\triangle ADG \sim \triangle GCF$ by the AA Corollary.

(2) First observe that $\triangle ADG \sim \triangle FEB$ by the AA Corollary: In right $\triangle ABC$, the acute angles, $\angle A$ and $\angle B$, are complementary. In right $\triangle EFB$, the acute angles, $\angle B$ and $\angle EFB$, are complementary. Therefore, since complements of congruent angles are congruent, $\angle A \cong \angle EFB$.

(3) Since $\triangle ADG \sim \triangle FEB$, $AD/FE = DG/EB$ or $AD \cdot EB = DG \cdot FE$.

(4) But, since $\square DEFG$ is a square, $DG = DE$ and $FE = DE$, so $(DE)^2 = AD \cdot EB$. Therefore, $DE = \sqrt{AD \cdot EB}$.

**18.** (1) $\triangle ABK \sim \triangle PQK$ (AA), and so $AB/PQ = AK/KP$.

(2) $\triangle ACK \sim \triangle PRK$ (AA), so that $AC/PR = AK/KP$, and therefore $AB/PQ = AC/PR$.

(3) $\triangle BCK \sim \triangle QRK$ (AA), and so, ultimately, $AB/PQ = AC/PR = BC/RQ$.

**19.** (d) $\dfrac{z}{x} + \dfrac{z}{y} = \dfrac{m+n}{m+n} = 1$, by the Addition Property of Equality, and thus, $\dfrac{1}{x} + \dfrac{1}{y} = \dfrac{1}{z}$.

**20.** In $\triangle ABC$, let $\overline{AM}$ and $\overline{BN}$ be the altitudes to $\overline{BC}$ and $\overline{AC}$ respectively. Then $a\triangle ABC = \frac{1}{2}AM \cdot BC = \frac{1}{2}BN \cdot AC$, so $BC/AC = BN/AM$.

**21.** (a) Since $\overline{AC} \perp \overline{CB}$, $\angle BCF$ and $\angle FCA$ are complementary. Since $\overline{FC} \perp \overline{CD}$, $\angle FCA$ and $\angle ACD$ are complementary. Therefore $\angle BCF \cong \angle ACD$, since complements of congruent angles are congruent. $\therefore \triangle BFC \sim \triangle ADC$ by the AA Corollary.

(c) $BE = BF + FE$, so $BE/AB = BF/AB + FE/AB$. But by Part (b) $BF/AB = AD/AC \cdot BC/AB$. And $FE/AB = CD/AB = CD/AC \cdot AC/AB$. Therefore, $BE/AB = CD/AC \cdot AC/AB + AD/AC \cdot BC/AB$. [Note that this says that $\sin(x+y) = \sin x \cos y + \cos x \sin y$.]

**23.** The altitude of $\triangle EGD$ equals the distance between $\overleftrightarrow{EF}$ and $\overleftrightarrow{DC}$, which also equals the altitude of $\triangle GCF$. Since $\overline{EF} \parallel \overline{AB}$, $\angle DEG \cong \angle DAB$, $\angle DGE \cong \angle DBA$ and $\triangle EDG \sim \triangle ADB$ (AA). Similarly $\triangle GCF \sim \triangle ACB$, $EG/AB = DE/DA$, and $GF/AB = CG/CA$. $DE/DA = CG/CA$, by Problem 15 of Problem Set 12–3, so that $EG/AB = GF/AB$ and $EG = GF$. Since the bases and altitudes of the triangles are congruent, $a\triangle EGD = a\triangle GCF$.

---

**18.** Given the figure with $L_1 \parallel L_2$ and $\overline{AP}$, $\overline{BQ}$, $\overline{CR}$ intersecting at $K$.

(a) Name three pairs of similar triangles and write the three similarities.

(b) Prove that

$$\frac{AB}{PQ} = \frac{AC}{PR} = \frac{BC}{RQ}.$$

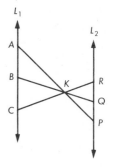

**19.** In the figure, $\overline{PA}$, $\overline{QB}$, and $\overline{RC}$ are each perpendicular to $\overline{AC}$.

(a) Complete: $\triangle PAC \sim \triangle \underline{QBC}$ and $\triangle ABQ \sim \triangle \underline{ACR}$.

(b) Which is correct:

$$\frac{z}{x} = \frac{n}{m} \quad \text{or} \quad \boxed{\frac{z}{x} = \frac{n}{m+n}}?$$

(c) Which is correct:

$$\frac{z}{y} = \frac{m}{n} \quad \text{or} \quad \boxed{\frac{z}{y} = \frac{m}{m+n}}?$$

(d) Show that

$$\frac{1}{x} + \frac{1}{y} = \frac{1}{z}.$$

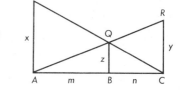

**20.** Prove that in any triangle, the ratio of any two sides is the reciprocal of the ratio of the corresponding altitudes.

---

**21.** Given the figure with perpendiculars as marked.

(a) Prove that $\triangle BFC \sim \triangle ADC$.

(b) Prove that from (a) $\dfrac{BF}{AD} = \dfrac{BC}{AC}$

$$\therefore \quad BF = \frac{AD \cdot BC}{AC}.$$

(c) Prove that

$$\frac{BE}{AB} = \frac{CD}{AC} \cdot \frac{AC}{AB} + \frac{AD}{AC} \cdot \frac{BC}{AB}.$$

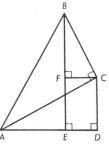

**22.** In the figure for Problem 21, if $AB = 8$, $AD = 6$, and $BC = 4$, evaluate $\dfrac{BE}{AB}$ and find $m\angle DAB$.   $\dfrac{BE}{AB} = \dfrac{\sqrt{3}}{2}$,   $m\angle DAB = 60$

**23.** $\square ABCD$ is a trapezoid as shown in the figure. If $\overline{EF} \parallel \overline{AB}$, show that $a\triangle EGD = a\triangle GCF$.

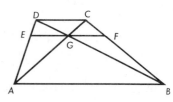

**24.** Given a parallelogram, $\square ABCD$, with its diagonals. A line through $B$ intersects $\overline{AC}$ at $E$, $\overline{DC}$ at $G$, and $\overleftrightarrow{AD}$ at $F$. Prove that

(1) $\triangle AEF \sim \triangle CEB$ and

(2) $EB$ is the geometric mean of $EG$ and $EF$.

**25.** One man can complete a job in 6 h, and another man can complete the same job in 3 h. If they work together, how long will it take to complete the job? This problem can be answered by solving the equation

$$\frac{1}{6} + \frac{1}{3} = \frac{1}{n}.$$

Solve the equation *geometrically*. [*Hint:* See Problem 19.]

The following theorem will be convenient, and is easily proved.

**Theorem 12–5**

*Similarity between triangles is an equivalence relation.*

**Proof.** As usual, we have three things to check.

(1) (Reflexive Property) $\triangle ABC \sim \triangle ABC$, for every $\triangle ABC$.

(2) (Symmetric Property) If $\triangle ABC \sim \triangle DEF$, then $\triangle DEF \sim \triangle ABC$.

(3) (Transitive Property) If $\triangle ABC \sim \triangle DEF$ and $\triangle DEF \sim \triangle GHI$, then $\triangle ABC \sim \triangle GHI$.

Each of these follows from the corresponding property of congruence between angles and proportionality between sequences. For example, the Reflexive Property holds because every angle is congruent to itself and every sequence is proportional to itself.

**Corollary 12–5.1**

*If $\triangle ABC \sim \triangle DEF$, and $\triangle DEF \cong \triangle GHI$, then $\triangle ABC \sim \triangle GHI$.*

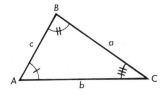 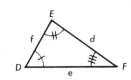 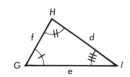

This follows from Theorem 12–5, because $\triangle DEF \sim \triangle GHI$, and similarity is transitive.

**Answers to Problems**

**24.** First observe that $\triangle AEF \sim \triangle CEB$ by the AA Corollary, and that consequently $EB/EF = CE/AE$. Secondly, observe that $\triangle CEG \sim \triangle AEB$ by the AA Corollary, and that consequently $CE/AE = EG/EB$. Therefore $EB/EF = EG/EB$, that is, $EB$ is the geometric mean of $EG$ and $EF$.

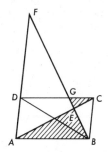

**25.** Construct perpendiculars 6 and 3 units long at opposite ends (but on the same side) of any segment $\overline{BD}$. Join the ends of these perpendiculars to the opposite ends of the segment, and where these lines intersect, draw a perpendicular to $\overline{BD}$. Measure this perpendicular. It should be 2 units long. Therefore the task would require 2 hours.

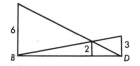

The proof of the SAS Similarity Theorem is essentially the same as the proof of the AAA Similarity Theorem, and so the proof can be made a reading assignment. Note that Problems 3, 5, 8, and 9 of Problem Set 12–4B use the SAS Similarity Theorem.

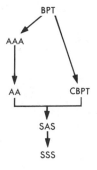

**Theorem 12–6**   The SAS Similarity Theorem

> *Given a correspondence between two triangles.  If two pairs of corresponding sides are proportional, and the included angles are congruent, then the correspondence is a similarity.*

**Restatement.**   Given $\triangle ABC$, $\triangle DEF$ and the correspondence

$$ABC \leftrightarrow DEF.$$

If

$$\frac{AB}{DE} = \frac{AC}{DF}$$

and

$$\angle A \cong \angle D,$$

then

$$\triangle ABC \sim \triangle DEF.$$

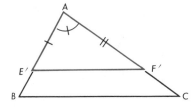
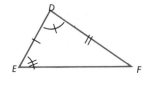

**Proof.**   (1) Let $E'$ and $F'$ be points of $\overrightarrow{AB}$ and $\overrightarrow{AC}$ such that $AE' = DE$ and $AF' = DF$.  By SAS we have

$$\triangle AE'F' \cong \triangle DEF.$$

Therefore

$$\frac{AB}{AE'} = \frac{AC}{AF'}.$$

(2) By Theorem 12–3 (the converse of the Basic Proportionality Theorem), we have $\overleftrightarrow{E'F'} \parallel \overleftrightarrow{BC}$.

(3) Therefore $\angle B \cong \angle AE'F'$.  (Why?)

(4) Since $\angle A \cong \angle A$, it follows by the AA Corollary that

$$\triangle ABC \sim \triangle AE'F'.$$

(5) But $\triangle AE'F' \cong \triangle DEF$.  Therefore, by Corollary 12–5.1, we have

$$\triangle ABC \sim \triangle DEF,$$

which was to be proved.

Finally, we get a sort of converse of the AAA Similarity Theorem.

**Theorem 12–7**   The SSS Similarity Theorem

*Given a correspondence between two triangles. If corresponding sides are proportional, then the correspondence is a similarity.*

**Restatement.**   Given $\triangle ABC$, $\triangle DEF$ and the correspondence

$$ABC \leftrightarrow DEF.$$

If

$$\frac{AB}{DE} = \frac{AC}{DF} = \frac{BC}{EF},$$

then

$$\triangle ABC \sim \triangle DEF.$$

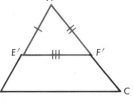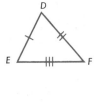

**Proof.**   As usual in this chapter, let $E'$ and $F'$ be points of $\overrightarrow{AB}$ and $\overrightarrow{AC}$ such that $AE' = DE$ and $AF' = DF$. Introduce $\overline{E'F'}$.

| STATEMENTS | REASONS |
|---|---|
| 1. $\dfrac{AB}{DE} = \dfrac{AC}{DF} = \dfrac{BC}{EF}$. | 1. Given |
| 2. $AE' = DE$; $AF' = DF$. | 2. Given |
| 3. $\dfrac{AB}{AE'} = \dfrac{AC}{AF'}$. | 3. Substitution |
| 4. $\angle A \cong \angle A$. | 4. Reflexive Property |
| 5. $\triangle ABC \sim \triangle AE'F'$. | 5. The SAS Similarity Theorem |
| 6. $\dfrac{E'F'}{BC} = \dfrac{AE'}{AB}$. | 6. Definition of similarity |
| 7. $E'F' = BC\,\dfrac{AE'}{AB} = BC\,\dfrac{DE}{AB}$. | 7. Multiplication Property of Equality |
| 8. $EF = BC\,\dfrac{DE}{AB}$. | 8. Multiplication Property of Equality in Statement 1 |
| 9. $E'F' = EF$. | 9. Transitive Property |
| 10. $\triangle AE'F' \cong \triangle DEF$. | 10. SSS |
| 11. $\triangle ABC \sim \triangle DEF$. | 11. Statements 5 and 10 and Corollary 12–5.1 |

The proof of the SSS Similarity Theorem is hard, and the techniques used in the proof are rather special. Furthermore, when trying to prove that two triangles are similar, we can almost always find at least one, and often two pairs of congruent angles, and thus prove the triangles similar by either SAS or AA. We have included the SSS Similarity Theorem mainly because to a thoughtful student its absence would seem unnatural: if corresponding sides are proportional, then surely corresponding angles ought to be congruent.

## Problem Set 12–4B

1. For each pair of triangles indicate whether the two triangles are similar and, if they are similar, according to which theorem or definition.

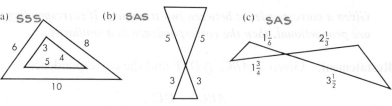

(a) SSS   (b) SAS   (c) SAS

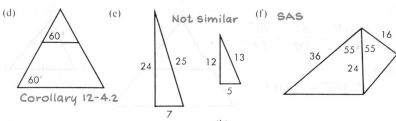

(d)   (e) Not similar   (f) SAS

Corollary 12-4.2

(g) AAA   (h) Not similar

2. Which of these similarity theorems do not have comparable congruence theorems: SAS, SSS, AAA, AA?  AAA and AA

3. Given the figure with

$$\frac{AE}{EC} = \frac{BE}{ED}.$$

Use SAS Similarity Theorem

Prove: (1) $\triangle AEB \sim \triangle CED$.

(2) $\overline{AB} \parallel \overline{DC}$.  Use AIP Theorem

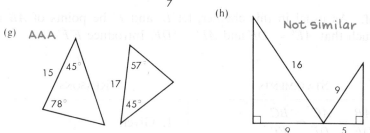

4. Is it possible for two triangles to be similar if

(a) two angles of one have measures 60 and 70, whereas two angles of the other have measures 50 and 80?  No

(b) two angles of one have measures 45 and 75, whereas two angles of the other have measures 45 and 60?  Yes

(c) one has an angle of measure 40 and two sides each of which is 5, whereas the other has an angle of measure 70 and two sides each of which is 8?  Yes

(d) one has sides which are 5, 6, and 9, whereas the other has a perimeter of 8 420 000?  Yes

5. Prove: If two isosceles triangles have congruent vertex angles, the triangles are similar. **Use SAS Similarity Theorem**

6. Given the figure on the left below, prove that $\overline{PQ} \parallel \overline{AB}$.

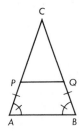
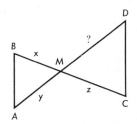

7. In the figure, $x$, $y$, and $z$ are lengths of $\overline{MB}$, $\overline{MA}$, and $\overline{MC}$. **MD = $\frac{y^2}{x}$**
   (a) What must be the length of $\overline{MD}$ for the triangles to be similar?
   (b) If $z = 2x$, must $m\angle D = 2m\angle A$? **No**

8. Prove: Any two corresponding medians of similar triangles have the same ratio as the corresponding sides.

9. In the figure, $\triangle ADC \sim \triangle PSR$, and $\overline{CD}$ and $\overline{RS}$ are medians. Prove that $\triangle ABC \sim \triangle PQR$.

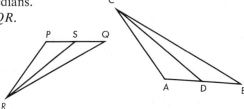

10. If the following statement is true, prove it; if it is false, provide a counterexample. **False**

   Given a correspondence between two triangles such that the lengths of two sides of one triangle are proportional to the lengths of the corresponding sides of the other triangle, and the angle opposite one of the sides is congruent to the corresponding angle, then the triangles are similar.

11. In the figure, $PQ = PR$ and $\overline{PQ} \parallel \overline{AC}$. Which of these statements are true?

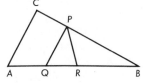

   (a) $\dfrac{BP}{BC} = \dfrac{PQ}{AC}$. **T**  (b) $\dfrac{BP}{BC} = \dfrac{PR}{AC}$. **T**

   (c) $\dfrac{BP}{BC} = \dfrac{PQ}{AC}$, $\angle PBQ \cong \angle CBA$, and $\triangle PBQ \sim \triangle CBA$. **T**

   (d) $\dfrac{BP}{BC} = \dfrac{PR}{AC}$, $\angle PBQ \cong \angle CBA$, and $\triangle PBR \sim \triangle CBA$. **F**

**Answers to Problems**

**6.** Since $\angle A \cong \angle B$, $CA = CB$. Since it is given that $AP = BQ$ we have by subtraction that $CP = CQ$. Therefore $CP/CA = CQ/CB$, and so by Theorem 12–3, $\overline{PQ} \parallel \overline{AB}$.

**8.**

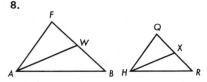

Since $\triangle ABF \sim \triangle HRQ$, we know $\angle F \cong \angle Q$ and $AF/HQ = AB/HR = BF/RQ$. Also $\dfrac{FB}{QR} = \dfrac{FB/2}{QR/2} = \dfrac{FW}{QX} = \dfrac{AF}{QH}$. Then $\triangle AWF \sim \triangle HXQ$ by the SAS Similarity Theorem, and then $AW/HX = AF/HQ = FB/QR = AB/HR$. We can continue in the same way for the other medians.

**9.** Since $\triangle ADC \sim \triangle PSR$, $CD/RS = AD/PS$ and thus $CD/RS = 2AD/2PS = AB/PQ$. Secondly, since $\triangle ADC \sim \triangle PSR$, $\angle CAD \cong \angle RPQ$. Therefore $\triangle ABC \sim \triangle PQR$ by the SAS Similarity Theorem.

**10.**

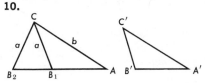

Let $\triangle AB_1C$ and $\triangle AB_2C$ be such that $AC = AC$, $\angle A \cong \angle A$, and $CB_1 = CB_2$, as in the diagram, but the triangles are not congruent. Construct $\triangle A'B'C' \sim \triangle AB_1C$. The triangles $A'B'C'$ and $AB_2C$ satisfy the statements in the hypothesis, but these triangles are not similar.

**11.** This problem provides another counterexample to show that the statement in Problem 10 is false. There is no SSA Similarity Theorem just as there is no SSA Congruence Theorem.

**12.** The two intersecting lines $\overleftrightarrow{MS}$ and $\overleftrightarrow{RK}$ determine a plane G. The intersection of E and G is $\overleftrightarrow{RS}$ and the intersection of F and G is $\overleftrightarrow{MK}$. Since $E \parallel F$, $\overleftrightarrow{MK} \parallel \overleftrightarrow{RS}$, and hence by the PAI Theorem we have, in plane G, that $\angle M \cong \angle S$ and $\angle K \cong \angle R$. Therefore $\triangle MPK \sim \triangle SPR$ by the AA Similarity Theorem. Hence, $MK/RS = MP/PS = \frac{6}{15} = \frac{2}{5}$. In the same way, $MH/ST = MP/PS = \frac{2}{5}$. And, in the same way, $HK/TR = KP/RP = \frac{4}{10} = \frac{2}{5}$. Therefore $MK/RS = MH/ST = HK/TR$, and hence $\triangle HMK \sim \triangle TSR$, by the SSS Similarity Theorem.

### Answer to Honors Problem

(b) By the Point-Plotting Theorem, there is a point E on the ray opposite to $\overrightarrow{AB}$ such that $AE = v$. Then $\triangle AEC$ is equilateral, and $EC = v$. Since $AD \parallel \overline{EC}$, $\triangle ECB \sim \triangle ADB$ and so
$$\frac{EC}{AD} = \frac{EB}{AB}, \quad \text{or} \quad \frac{v}{t} = \frac{v+r}{r}.$$
Thus, $\dfrac{v}{t} = \dfrac{v}{r} + 1$, and $\dfrac{1}{t} = \dfrac{1}{r} + \dfrac{1}{v}$.

Another Honors Problem you may wish to give your more advanced students is the following:

### Honors Problem

In $\triangle ABC$, D is the midpoint of $\overline{AB}$ and E is a point of $\overline{AC}$ such that $AE > EC$. $\overleftrightarrow{DE}$ and $\overleftrightarrow{BC}$ intersect at F. Prove that $FB \cdot CE = FC \cdot EA$. [*Hint:* Let the line through C parallel to $\overline{AB}$ intersect $\overleftrightarrow{EF}$ at P.]

### Answer to Honors Problem

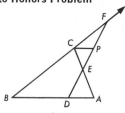

Since $\overline{PC} \parallel \overline{DB}$ we conclude by Corollary 12–4.2 that $\triangle FBD \sim \triangle FCP$, and consequently that $FB/FC = BD/CP$. Since $\overline{PC} \parallel \overline{AD}$, $\triangle EAD \sim \triangle ECP$ (AA) and so $EA/EC = AD/CP$. But since D is the midpoint of $\overline{AB}$, $AD = BD$ and therefore $FB/FC = EA/EC$, or $FB \cdot CE = FC \cdot EA$.

---

**12.** Three lines which have a common intersection at point P intersect the parallel planes E and F at R and K, S and M, and T and H, respectively. If $KP = 4$, $MP = 6$, $HP = 7$, $RP = 10$, $SP = 15$, and $TP = 17.5$, prove that $\triangle HMK \sim \triangle TSR$.

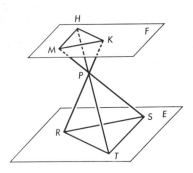

## HONORS PROBLEM

A common problem involving electrical circuits is the following. A circuit consists of two wires in parallel, with resistances $R_1$ and $R_2$. What is the resistance of the circuit?

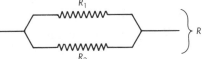

The resistance of the circuit, R, is given by the equation
$$\frac{1}{R} = \frac{1}{R_1} + \frac{1}{R_2}.$$

Solve this equation for R in terms of $R_1$ and $R_2$.
The following scheme has been used to find R when $R_1$ and $R_2$ are known. Numerical scales are marked on three rays, as shown below. A straightedge is placed so as to pass through $R_1$ and $R_2$ on the two outer scales, and R is read on the remaining scale. For example, if $R_1 = 12$ and $R_2 = 6$, then $R = 4$; if $R_1 = 10$ and $R_2 = 10$, then $R = 5$.

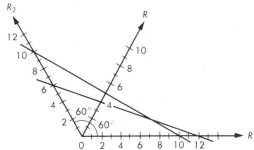

(a) Find R, given that
$R_1 = 4$ and $R_2 = 12$; **R=3**
$R_1 = 6$ and $R_2 = 3$; **R=2**
$R_1 = 7$ and $R_2 = 7$. **R=3.5**

(b) By using the figure to the right, explain why the scheme described above gives solutions to the equation.

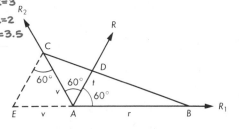

## 12–5    SIMILARITIES IN RIGHT TRIANGLES

### Theorem 12–8

*In any right triangle, the altitude to the hypotenuse separates the triangle into two triangles which are similar to each other and to the original triangle.*

**Restatement.**   Let $\triangle ABC$ be a right triangle with its right angle at $C$, and let $\overline{CD}$ be the altitude from $C$ to $\overline{AB}$. Then

$$\triangle ACD \sim \triangle ABC \sim \triangle CBD.$$

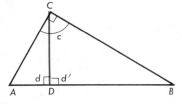

(Note that in this case the restatement tells us more than the theorem does, because it states which correspondences are similarities. Note also that it is easy to figure out (and to remember) what these correspondences are. In the correspondence between $\triangle ACD$ and $\triangle ABC$, we must have $A \leftrightarrow A$, because $\angle A$ is common to the two triangles. We must also have $D \leftrightarrow C$, because these are the vertices where the right angles are. Finally, we must have $C \leftrightarrow B$, because at this stage $C$ has nowhere else to go. This gives $ACD \leftrightarrow ABC$. Similarly for the second correspondence, $ABC \leftrightarrow CBD$.)

**Proof.**   Obviously $\angle d \cong \angle c$, because both are right angles; and $\angle A \cong \angle A$. Therefore, under the correspondence $ACD \leftrightarrow ABC$, two pairs of corresponding angles are congruent. By the AA Corollary, we have $\triangle ACD \sim \triangle ABC$.

The proof of the other half of the theorem is exactly the same: since $\angle d' \cong \angle c$ and $\angle B \cong \angle B$, the AA Corollary gives us

$$\triangle ABC \sim \triangle CBD.$$

### Theorem 12–9

*Given a right triangle and the altitude to the hypotenuse.*

*(1) The altitude is the geometric mean of the segments into which it separates the hypotenuse.*

*(2) Each leg is the geometric mean of the hypotenuse and the segment of the hypotenuse adjacent to the leg.*

**Classroom Notes**

Problems 6 and 8 of Problem Set 12–4A anticipate Theorem 12–8. In discussing these problems you can formulate Theorem 12–8 and then go on to establish the proportionalities in Theorem 12–9. In discussing these proportionalities you can probably elicit the statement of Theorem 12–9 from the students. One should be careful in writing the proportionalities in Theorem 12–9 correctly; they are rather tricky.

In the proof of Theorem 12–8 we assumed that the altitude $\overline{CD}$ is an interior altitude, that is, that $D$ is between $A$ and $B$. It is easy to show that the contrary is impossible.

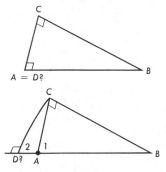

If $A = D$, then $\triangle ABC$ has two right angles, which is impossible. If $A$ is between $D$ and $B$, then it follows by the Exterior Angle Theorem that $\angle 1 > \angle 2$, and this is impossible, because $\angle 2$ is a right angle and $\angle 1$ is acute. Similarly, we cannot have $D = B$, and $B$ cannot be between $A$ and $D$. Therefore $D$ must be between $A$ and $B$, which was to be proved.

## Explanation for Problems

The problems in Problem Set 12–5 give the student practice in using Theorem 12–9. It is doubtful that you will want to assign all of Problems 3, 4, and 13 at the same time; note that many of the parts of these three problems involve radicals and that parts (c), (d), and (e) of Problem 13 involve the solution of quadratic equations.

**Restatement.** Let $\triangle ABC$ be a right triangle with its right angle at $C$, and let $\overline{CD}$ be the altitude to the hypotenuse $\overline{AB}$. Then

(1) $\dfrac{AD}{CD} = \dfrac{CD}{BD}$

(2a) $\dfrac{AD}{AC} = \dfrac{AC}{AB}$

(2b) $\dfrac{BD}{BC} = \dfrac{BC}{BA}$.

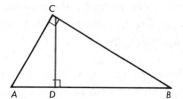

**Proof.** By Theorem 12–8, we have the similarities

(1)  $\triangle ACD \sim \triangle CBD$
(2a)  $\triangle ACD \sim \triangle ABC$
(2b)  $\triangle CBD \sim \triangle ABC$.

The equations given in the restatement describe proportionalities for pairs of corresponding sides.

### Problem Set 12–5

[*Note:* Express irrational numbers in simplified radical form.]

$\triangle ABC \sim \triangle ACD$
$\sim \triangle CBD$
$\sim \triangle ADF$
$\sim \triangle DCF$
$\sim \triangle DBE$
$\sim \triangle CDE$

**1.** In the figure, $\overline{CD} \perp \overline{AB}$ and $\square CFDE$ is a rectangle. Write out all the similarities for the triangles similar to $\triangle ABC$. Remember that you must establish the correct correspondences.

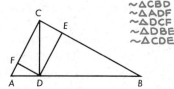

**2.** In the figure above, what is the geometric mean between

(a) $AD$ and $DB$? CD
(b) $AF$ and $FC$? FD
(c) $CE$ and $EB$? ED
(d) $CE$ and $CB$? CD
(e) $AD$ and $AB$? AC
(f) $AC$ and $FC$? CD

**3.** In the figure, $\overline{CD}$ is the altitude to the hypotenuse of $\triangle ABC$.

(a) Given $r = 4$, $s = 9$. Find $h$. $=6$
(b) Given $r = 7$, $s = 28$. Find $h$. $=14$
(c) Given $r = 9$, $s = 3$. Find $a$. $=6$
(d) Given $r = 7$, $s = 21$. Find $b$. $=14$
(e) Given $r = \sqrt{3}$, $s = \sqrt{12}$. Find $h$, $a$, and $b$.
  $h = \sqrt{6}, \ a = 3\sqrt{2}, \ b = 3$

4. In the figure, $\overline{RS}$ is the altitude to the hypotenuse $\overline{PQ}$ of $\triangle PQR$.

(a) Given $m = 27$ and $n = 3$. Find $a$, $p$, and $q$. **9, 3√10, 9√10**

(b) Given $m = 24$ and $n = 6$. Find $a$, $p$, and $q$. **12, 6√5, 12√5**

(c) Given $m = \sqrt{18}$ and $n = \sqrt{8}$. Find $a$, $p$, and $q$.

(d) Given $p = 15$ and $n = 9$. Find $m$ and $q$. **16, 20**

(e) Given $a = 8$ and $m = 16$. Find $n$, $p$, and $q$. **n=4, p=4√5, q=8√5**

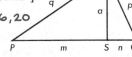

5. In the figure, $\overline{HM}$ is the altitude to the hypotenuse $\overline{GK}$ of right triangle $\triangle GHK$.

(a) Given $a = 18$ and $b = 8$. Find $c$. **12**

(b) Given $a = 10\frac{2}{3}$ and $c = 8$. Find $b$ and $d$. **6, 10**

(c) Given $a = 15$ and $b = 4\frac{4}{15}$. Find $f$ and $c$. **17, 8**

(d) Given $f = 20$ and $c = 12$. Find $a$ and $b$. **16, 9**

(e) Given $d = 12$ and $b = 4$. Find $a$ and $c$. **32, 8√2**

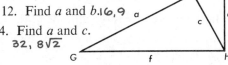

6. The altitude to the hypotenuse of a right triangle separates the hypotenuse into two segments whose lengths are $r$ and $s$. Prove that the area of the triangle is equal to the product of the geometric mean of $r$ and $s$ and the arithmetic mean of $r$ and $s$. **A=½bh=½(r+s)(√rs)=$\frac{r+s}{2}$·√rs**

7. Find the area of a right triangle, given that the altitude to the hypotenuse separates the hypotenuse into segments of lengths 9 and 16; of lengths 7 and 21. **150, 98√3**

8. Given the figure, in which $\square PRHQ$ is a rectangle and $\overline{HP} \perp \overline{GK}$. Prove that

$a\square PRHQ = \sqrt{GQ \cdot QH \cdot HR \cdot RK}.$

**By Th.12-9, QP=√GQ·QH and PR=√HR·RK. a□PRHQ=QP·PR = √GQ·QH · √HR·RK = √GQ·HQ·HR·RK**

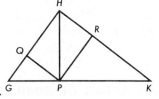

9. *The Pythagorean Theorem.* In Section 11–3 we proved the Pythagorean Theorem, using a proof based upon area formulas. Theorem 12–9 suggests another proof of this theorem.

**a²+b²=(√cs)²+(√cr)²= cs+cr=c(s+r)=c·c=c²**

In the figure, $\angle ACB$ is a right angle and $\overline{CD}$ is the altitude to the hypotenuse. By Theorem 12–9 we have $a = \sqrt{cs}$ and $b = \sqrt{cr}$. With this as a beginning, complete the proof that $a^2 + b^2 = c^2$.

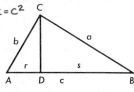

**Quiz**

**1.** In $\triangle PQR$, $\angle R$ is a right angle and $T$ is on $\overline{PQ}$ such that $\overline{RT} \perp \overline{PQ}$. If $PT = 7$ and $TQ = 21$, what is $RT$?
(ans: $7\sqrt{3}$)

**2.** In $\triangle ABC$, $\angle C$ is a right angle and $\overline{CD}$ is the altitude to the hypotenuse. If $AC = 6$ and $BD = 5$, what are $AD$ and $CD$?
(ans: 4, $2\sqrt{5}$)

**Answers to Problems**

**4.** (c) $a = 2\sqrt{3}$, $p = 2\sqrt{5}$, $q = \sqrt{30}$.

**10.** In $\triangle ACD$, $(CD)^2 = (AC)^2 - (AD)^2$. In $\triangle BCD$, $(CD)^2 = (BC)^2 - (BD)^2$. Therefore $(AC)^2 - (AD)^2 = (BC)^2 - (BD)^2$, or $(AC)^2 - (BC)^2 = (AD)^2 - (BD)^2$.

**13.** (a) $15 = \sqrt{5 \cdot f}$, so $f = 45$; $b = \sqrt{5 \cdot 50} = 5\sqrt{10}$; $c = \sqrt{50 \cdot 45} = 15\sqrt{10}$.

(b) $(f + 4)4 = (4\sqrt{3})^2$, so $f = 8$; $h = \sqrt{4 \cdot 8} = 4\sqrt{2}$; $c = \sqrt{12 \cdot 8} = 4\sqrt{6}$.

(c) $f(f + 4) = (6\sqrt{2})^2$, so $f^2 + 4f - 72 = 0$, and $f = -2 + 2\sqrt{19}$; $b^2 = (e+f)e$, so $b^2 = 4(2+2\sqrt{19})$, and $b = 2\sqrt{2 + 2\sqrt{19}}$; $h = \sqrt{e \cdot f} = \sqrt{4 \cdot (-2 + 2\sqrt{19})} = 2\sqrt{-2 + 2\sqrt{19}}$.

(d) $b^2 = e(e + f)$, $(3\sqrt{10})^2 = e(e + 13)$, $e^2 + 13e - 90 = 0$, $(e + 18)(e - 5) = 0$, $e = 5$. $h = \sqrt{e \cdot f} = \sqrt{5 \cdot 13} = \sqrt{65}$. $c = \sqrt{f(e + f)} = \sqrt{13 \cdot 18} = 3\sqrt{26}$.

(e) $e(e + f) = b^2$, $e(e + 8) = 8^2$, $e^2 + 8e - 64 = 0$, $e = -4 + 4\sqrt{5}$. $h = \sqrt{e \cdot f} = \sqrt{(-4 + 4\sqrt{5})(8)} = 4\sqrt{-2 + 2\sqrt{5}}$. $c^2 = f(e + f)$, $c^2 = 8(4 + 4\sqrt{5})$, $c = 4\sqrt{2 + 2\sqrt{5}}$.

**14.**

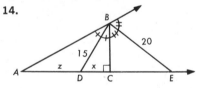

The bisectors of the interior and exterior angles at $B$ are perpendicular, and so $\triangle DBE$ is a right triangle. Therefore, $DE = 25$ by the Pythagorean Theorem. By Theorem 12-9, $BD$ is the geometric mean of $DE$ and $DC$: $25x = 15^2$, so $x = DC = 9$, and $CE = 16$. Trivially, in right $\triangle BDC$, $(BC)^2 = 15^2 - 9^2 = 144$ so that $BC = 12$. By the Theorem in Problem 21, Section 12-3, $AD/AE = CD/CE$.

$\dfrac{z}{z + 25} = \dfrac{9}{16}$, so $7z = 225$ and $z = 32\frac{1}{7}$.

Therefore, $AC = AD + DC = 32\frac{1}{7} + 9 = 41\frac{2}{7}$. Finally, by the Pythagorean Theorem, $(AB)^2 = (AC)^2 + (BC)^2$

$$= (41\tfrac{1}{7})^2 + (12)^2$$
$$= (\tfrac{288}{7})^2 + (\tfrac{84}{7})^2$$
$$= \dfrac{24^2 \cdot 12^2}{7} + \dfrac{7^2 \cdot 12^2}{7^2}$$

**10.** Given $\triangle ABC$ with $\overline{CD}$ the altitude to the hypotenuse $\overline{AB}$. Prove that

$$AC^2 - BC^2 = AD^2 - BD^2.$$

**11.** Given the figure with $\overline{AC} \perp \overline{BC}$, $\overline{CD} \perp \overline{AB}$, $\overline{GE} \parallel \overline{CD} \parallel \overline{HF}$, and $\square CHDG$ a rectangle. If $AE = 1$, $ED = 4$, $DF = 4$, and $FB = 16$, find

(a) $GE$ and $HF$. GE=2, HF=8

(b) $a\square CHDG$. =40

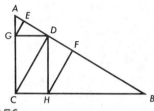

**12.** Given the figure and the relationships and lengths of segments as in Problem 11. Prove that $a\triangle BHF = 64\, a\triangle AEG$.

$a\triangle BHF = \frac{1}{2} \cdot 8 \cdot 16 = 64 = 64 \cdot \frac{1}{2} \cdot 2 \cdot 1 = 64\, a\triangle AEG$

**13.** In the figure, $\overline{AK}$ is the altitude to the hypotenuse of $\triangle ABC$.

(a) Given $e = 5$ and $h = 15$. Find $f$, $b$, and $c$.

(b) Given $b = 4\sqrt{3}$ and $e = 4$. Find $f$, $h$, and $c$.

(c) Given $c = 6\sqrt{2}$ and $e = 4$. Find $f$, $b$, and $h$.

(d) Given $b = 3\sqrt{10}$ and $f = 13$. Find $e$, $h$, and $c$.

(e) Given $b = f = 8$. Find $e$, $h$, and $c$.

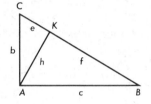

**14.** $\triangle ABC$ is a right triangle with its right angle at $C$. The bisector of $\angle B$ intersects $\overline{AC}$ at $D$, and the bisector of the exterior angle at $B$ intersects $\overleftrightarrow{AC}$ at $E$. If $BD = 15$ and $BE = 20$, what are the lengths of the sides of $\triangle ABC$? BC=12, AC=41$\frac{1}{7}$, AB=42$\frac{6}{7}$

## 12-6 AREAS OF SIMILAR TRIANGLES

Given a square of edge $a$ and a square of edge $2a$, it is easy to see that the area of the second square is four times the area of the first: $(2a)^2 = 4a^2$. (This is also easy to see geometrically, without using area formulas at all.) In general, if the second square has edge $ka$, then the ratio of the areas is $k^2$, because

$$\frac{(ka)^2}{a^2} = \frac{k^2 a^2}{a^2} = k^2.$$

An analogous result holds for similar triangles.

## Theorem 12–10

*If two triangles are similar, then the ratio of their areas is the square of the ratio of any two corresponding sides.*

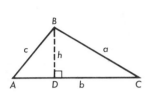 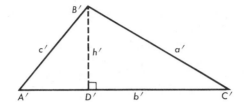

**Proof.** Given $\triangle ABC \sim \triangle A'B'C'$. Let their areas be $A_1$ and $A_2$. We have

$$\frac{a'}{a} = \frac{b'}{b} = \frac{c'}{c}.$$

Let $k$ be the common value of these three fractions. We want to show that

$$\frac{A_2}{A_1} = k^2.$$

Let $\overline{BD}$ and $\overline{B'D'}$ be the altitudes from $B$ and $B'$ in the two triangles; and let $h$ and $h'$ be their lengths. Now $\angle A \cong \angle A'$, because $\triangle ABC \sim \triangle A'B'C'$. And $\angle ADB \cong \angle A'D'B'$, because both are right angles. By the AA Corollary it follows that

$$\triangle ABD \sim \triangle A'B'D'.$$

Therefore

$$\frac{b'}{b} = \frac{h'}{h} = k,$$

because corresponding sides are proportional. This gives

$$b' = kb, \qquad h' = kh.$$

But

$$A_1 = \tfrac{1}{2}bh, \qquad A_2 = \tfrac{1}{2}b'h'.$$

Therefore

$$A_2 = \tfrac{1}{2}b'h' = \tfrac{1}{2}(kb)(kh) = \tfrac{1}{2}k^2bh,$$

and

$$\frac{A_2}{A_1} = k^2,$$

which was to be proved.

---

$$= \frac{(24^2 + 7^2)12^2}{7^2}$$

$$= \frac{25^2 \cdot 12^2}{7^2}.$$

Therefore $AB = \dfrac{25 \cdot 12}{7} = 42\tfrac{6}{7}$.

## 12–6 AREAS OF SIMILAR TRIANGLES

### Classroom Notes

The proof of Theorem 12–10 can be simplified by use of the Theorem in Problem 6 of Problem Set 12–4A: If two triangles are similar, then the ratio of a pair of corresponding altitudes is equal to the ratio of a pair of corresponding sides.

You should point out that Theorem 12–10 can also be stated in the following way: Given a similarity between two triangles, the ratio of any pair of corresponding sides is equal to the square root of the ratio of the areas of the triangles. This formulation is useful in Problems 7, 9, and 10 of Problem Set 12–6.

### Quiz

**1.** How long must a side of an equilateral triangle be in order for its area to be four times the area of an equilateral triangle whose side is 7?
(ans: 14)

**2.** The areas of two similar triangles are 17 and 153. What is the ratio of a pair of corresponding sides?
(ans: $\tfrac{1}{3}$)

# Answers to Problems

4. (b) $a\square DBCE = a\triangle ABC - a\triangle ADE = \frac{3}{5}a\triangle ABC$, so $\frac{2}{3}\square DBCE = \frac{2}{5}a\triangle ABC = a\triangle ADE$ from part (a).

5. (a) Introduce $\overline{KH}$. Then $a\triangle KGN = \frac{1}{2}a\triangle KGH$, since the triangles have the same altitude and $GN = \frac{1}{2}GH$. Similarly, $a\triangle KMI = \frac{1}{2}a\triangle KHI$. But $\triangle KGH \cong \triangle IHK$ by Theorem 9–14. Therefore $a\triangle KGH = a\triangle IHK$ and $a\triangle GKN = a\triangle KMI$.

(b) Therefore
$$a\triangle GKN = \frac{1}{2}(\frac{1}{2}a\triangle KGH + \frac{1}{2}a\triangle KHI)$$
$$= \frac{1}{4}a\square GHIK.$$

(c) Also
$a\triangle KMI = a\triangle KMH = a\triangle KHN$
and
$a\square NHMK = a\triangle KMH + a\triangle KHN$
by the Area Addition Postulate,
so $a\triangle KMI = \frac{1}{2}a\square NHMK.$

## Problem Set 12–6

1. What is the ratio of the areas of two similar triangles whose longest sides are 3 cm and 4 cm long, respectively?  **9 : 16**

2. In the figure, $\angle A \cong \angle A'$ and $\angle B \cong \angle B'$. What is the ratio of the areas of the triangles if $x = 5$ and $x' = 7$? if $y = 4$ and $y' = 3\sqrt{3}$? if $x = 6$, $y = 2\sqrt{5}$, and $y' = x$?  **25 : 49, 16 : 27, 9 : 5**

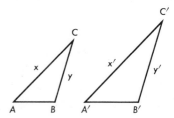

3. A side of one of two similar triangles is five times as long as the corresponding side of the other. If the area of the smaller triangle is 6 cm², what is the area of the larger one?  **150 cm²**

4. In the figure,
$$\frac{a\triangle ADE}{a\triangle ABC} = \frac{2}{5}.$$
Show that  **Multiply by $a\triangle ABC$**
(a) $a\triangle ADE = \frac{2}{5}a\triangle ABC.$
(b) $a\triangle ADE = \frac{2}{3}a\square DBCE.$

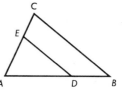

5. Given that $\square GHIK$ is a parallelogram and that $N$ and $M$ are the midpoints of $\overline{GH}$ and $\overline{HI}$, respectively. Show that

(a) $a\triangle GKN = a\triangle KMI.$

(b) $\dfrac{a\triangle GKN}{a\square GHIK} = \dfrac{1}{4}.$

(c) $a\triangle KMI = \frac{1}{2}a\square NHMK.$

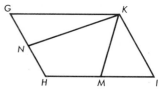

6. In $\triangle PQR$, $G$ is the midpoint of $\overline{PR}$ and $H$ is the midpoint of $\overline{QR}$. What is the ratio of $a\triangle GHR$ to $a\triangle PQR$? of $a\triangle GHR$ to $a\square PQHG$?  **1 : 4**    **1 : 3**

7. The areas of two similar triangles are 16 and 25. What is the ratio of a pair of corresponding sides?  **4 to 5**

8. The ratio of the areas of two similar triangles is $\frac{81}{121}$. What is the ratio of a pair of corresponding sides?  **$\frac{9}{11}$**

9. The area of the larger of two similar triangles is 9 times the area of the smaller. If a side of the smaller triangle is 5 cm long, how long is the corresponding side of the larger triangle?  **15 cm**

10. The areas of two similar triangles are 144 and 81. If the base of the larger triangle is 30, what is the corresponding base of the smaller triangle?  **22.5**

**11.** In $\triangle ABC$, $D$ is a point of $\overline{AC}$ such that $AD = 2CD$. $E$ is on $\overline{BC}$ such that $\overline{DE} \parallel \overline{AB}$. Compare the areas of $\triangle CDE$ and $\triangle ABC$. If $a\square ABED = 40$, what is $a\triangle ABC$?  $1:9$ , $a\triangle ABC = 45$

**12.** Prove that the ratio of the areas of two similar triangles equals the square of the ratio of any two corresponding altitudes. [*Hint:* See Problem 6 of Problem Set 12–4A.]

**13.** In the figure $\overline{AB} \cap \overline{CD} = \{E\}$, $\overline{CG} \perp \overline{AB}$, $\overline{DH} \perp \overline{AB}$, and $\dfrac{EA}{EC} = \dfrac{EB}{ED}$. If $CG = 6$, $DH = 8$, and $AB = 35$, find

(a) $\dfrac{a\triangle ACE}{a\triangle BDE}$.  $= \dfrac{9}{16}$

(b) $a\triangle BDE. = 80$

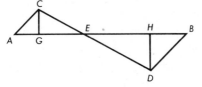

**14.** How long must the side of a square be in order that its area be five times the area of a square whose side is 6?  $6\sqrt{5}$

**15.** How long must a side of an equilateral triangle be in order that its area be twice the area of an equilateral triangle whose side is 10?  $10\sqrt{2}$

**16.** In the figure, $\overline{DE} \parallel \overline{AB}$ and $\overline{CH} \perp \overline{AB}$. If $a\triangle CDE = \frac{1}{6}a\triangle ABC$, what is the ratio of the altitude of $\triangle CDE$ to the corresponding altitude of $\triangle ABC$?  $1 : \sqrt{6}$

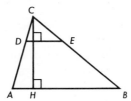

**17.** $\triangle ABC$ and $\triangle A'B'C'$ are equilateral triangles. An altitude of $\triangle A'B'C'$ has the same length as a side of $\triangle ABC$. Prove that

$$a\triangle A'B'C' = \tfrac{4}{3}a\triangle ABC.$$

**18.** Prove that the ratio of the areas of two similar triangles equals the square of the ratio of any two corresponding medians. Use Problem 8 of Problem set 12–4B and Problem 12 above.

**19.** In $\triangle ABC$, $\overline{CD}$ is the altitude to base $\overline{AB}$. We want to find a line $L$, parallel to $\overline{AB}$, which will cut off a triangle similar to $\triangle ABC$ but only one-half the area of $\triangle ABC$. If $L$ intersects $\overline{CD}$ at a point $M$, and $CD = 1$, how long is $\overline{CM}$?  $\left(\dfrac{CM}{CD}\right)^2 = \dfrac{1}{2}$, but $CD = 1$ so $CM = \dfrac{1}{2}\sqrt{2}$

**20.** Given the quadrilaterals as labeled.

$\angle x \cong \angle x'$, $\angle y \cong \angle y'$,

$\dfrac{a'}{a} = \dfrac{b'}{b} = \dfrac{c'}{c} = k.$

Prove:  $\dfrac{a\square P'Q'R'S'}{a\square PQRS} = k^2.$

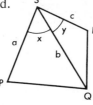

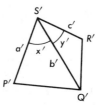

**24.** If the length of the wire is $d$, the side of the square is $\frac{1}{4}d$ and that of the triangles is $\frac{1}{3}d$. Then the area of the square is $d^2/16$ and that of the triangle is $(d^2/36)\sqrt{3}$. Then

$$\frac{\text{Area of the triangle}}{\text{Area of the square}} = \frac{\dfrac{d^2}{36}\sqrt{3}}{\dfrac{d^2}{16}} = \frac{4\sqrt{3}}{9}.$$

**25.** Since $\triangle DPR \sim \triangle DQA$, $DR/DA = DP/DQ$. Since $\triangle DRS \sim \triangle DAB$, $DR/DA = RS/AB$. $\triangle RST \sim \triangle ABC$, and therefore $a\triangle RST/a\triangle ABC = (RS/AB)^2 = (DP/DQ)^2$.

**21.** Prove that the ratio of the areas of two similar triangles equals the square of the ratio of the perimeters of the triangles. [*Hint:* See Problem 22 of Problem Set 12–1.] **Use Problem 12 above.**

**22.** The perimeters of two triangles are 15 and 25. The area of the smaller triangle is 36. If the triangles are similar, what is the area of the larger triangle? **100**

**23.** *The Pythagorean Theorem.* Theorem 12–10 provides another way of proving the Pythagorean Theorem. You should supply reasons for the statements in the proof.

In the figure, $\angle ACB$ is a right angle and $\overline{CD}$ is the altitude to the hypotenuse.

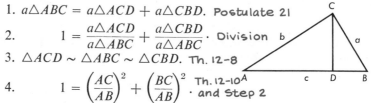

1. $a\triangle ABC = a\triangle ACD + a\triangle CBD.$ **Postulate 21**
2. $\quad 1 = \dfrac{a\triangle ACD}{a\triangle ABC} + \dfrac{a\triangle CBD}{a\triangle ABC}.$ **Division**
3. $\triangle ACD \sim \triangle ABC \sim \triangle CBD.$ **Th. 12-8**
4. $\quad 1 = \left(\dfrac{AC}{AB}\right)^2 + \left(\dfrac{BC}{AB}\right)^2.$ **Th. 12-10 and Step 2**
5. $\quad AB^2 = AC^2 + BC^2 \quad$ or $\quad c^2 = b^2 + a^2.$ **Multiplication**

**24.** Two pieces of wire of equal length are bent, one in the shape of a square and the other in the shape of an equilateral triangle. What is the ratio of the areas of the regions enclosed by each wire? **4√3 : 9**

**25.** Given the tetrahedron $ABCD$ with base $\triangle ABC$. A plane parallel to the base intersects the faces of the tetrahedron in $\triangle RST$. $\overline{DQ}$ is the perpendicular from $D$ to the plane of $\triangle ABC$, and $\overline{DQ}$ intersects the parallel plane at $P$.

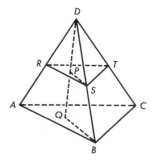

Prove: $\quad \dfrac{a\triangle RST}{a\triangle ABC} = \left(\dfrac{DP}{DQ}\right)^2.$

**26.** In $\triangle ABC$, $\angle C$ is a right angle and $m\angle B = 30$. $\overline{CD}, \overline{PE},$ and $\overline{QG}$ are each perpendicular to $\overline{AB}$, and $\overline{PD}, \overline{EQ},$ and $\overline{GR}$ are each perpendicular to $\overline{BC}$. Find $\dfrac{a\triangle GBR}{a\triangle ABC}$. **$\dfrac{729}{4096}$**

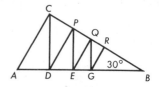

[*Hint:* Find $GB$ in terms of $AB$.]

## HONORS PROBLEM

A triangular lot has sides with lengths 100 m, 98 m, and 48 m, as indicated in the figure. The length of the perpendicular from a corner to the 48-m side is 96 m. A fence is to be erected perpendicular to the 48-m side so that the area of the lot is equally divided. How far from $A$ along $\overline{AB}$ should this perpendicular be drawn?

   **26m from A.**

## CHAPTER REVIEW

**1.** Complete each statement.

   (a) If $5x = 8y$, then $\dfrac{y}{x} = \dfrac{?\,\frac{5}{8}}{\ }$.   (b) If $\dfrac{3}{4} = \dfrac{21}{28}$, then $\dfrac{7}{4} = \dfrac{?\,49}{28}$.

   (c) If $\dfrac{a+b}{a} = \dfrac{15}{12}$, then $\dfrac{b}{a} = ?\,\frac{1}{4}$.   (d) If $48 = 16k$, then $\dfrac{k}{3} = ?\,1$.

**2.** The sequences 2, $a$, 6, 5, $b$ and 5, 10, $c$, $d$, 9 are proportional. Determine $a$, $b$, $c$, and $d$. $a=4, b=\frac{18}{5}, c=15, d=\frac{25}{2}$

**3.** Give the geometric mean and the arithmetic mean of each number pair listed below.

   (a) 6 and 24  12, 15   (b) 12 and 20  $4\sqrt{15}$, 16

   (c) $7\sqrt{3}$ and $21\sqrt{3}$  21, $14\sqrt{3}$   (d) $4\frac{1}{4}$ and $6\frac{3}{8}$  $\frac{17}{8}\sqrt{6}$, $\frac{85}{16}$

**4.** Sketch two figures whose corresponding sides are proportional, but which are not similar. Consider a square and a rhombus with proportional sides.

**5.** Sketch two figures whose corresponding angles are congruent, but which are not similar. Consider a square and a rectangle which always have congruent angles.

**6.** In $\triangle ABC$, $\overline{HK} \parallel \overline{AB}$.

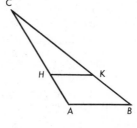

   (a) If $AH = 3$, $BK = 5$, $CK = 12$, then $CH = ?\ \frac{36}{5}$

   (b) If $AC = 14$, $AH = 6$, $CK = 12$, then $BC = ?\ 21$

   (c) If $CH = 9$, $AH = 4$, $HK = 3$, then $AB = ?\ \frac{13}{3}$

   (d) If $AH = 4$, $CH = BK$, $BC = 48$, then $CH = ?\ 12$

**7.** The sides of a triangle have lengths 5, 8, and 11. A similar triangle has a perimeter of 60. What are the lengths of its sides? 12.5, 20, 27.5.

**8.** $\overline{AC}$ and $\overline{BD}$ intersect at $E$ such that $\overline{AB} \parallel \overline{CD}$ and $AB = 3CD$. If $AC = 21$, what are $AE$ and $EC$? $AE = \frac{3}{4}(21)$, $EC = \frac{1}{4}(21)$

**11.** (1) Since $\overline{EF} \parallel \overline{AD}$, $\triangle EBF \sim \triangle ABC$.
(2) Since $\overline{DF} \parallel \overline{AB}$, $\triangle DCF \sim \triangle ACB$. (3)
From (1) we obtain $AE/BE = CF/BF$.
From (2) we obtain $CD/AD = CF/BF$.
Therefore, $AE/BE = CD/AD$; or

$$\frac{AE \cdot AD}{BE \cdot CD} = 1.$$

**13.** Since $AB/AC = BC/CD = AC/AD = k = \frac{2}{3}$, $\triangle ABC \sim \triangle ACD$ by SSS, and therefore $\angle BAC \cong \angle CAD$ so that $\overrightarrow{AC}$ bisects $\angle DAB$.

---

**9.** The sides of a triangle have lengths 7, 9, and 14. What is the perimeter of a similar triangle whose longest side is 21? **45**

**10.** In $\triangle PQR$, $\overline{AB} \parallel \overline{QR}$ and $\overline{BC} \parallel \overline{PR}$.
  (a) If $PA = 4$, $AR = 6$, and $PQ = 25$, then $BQ = $ ? **15**
  (b) If $RC = 3$, $CQ = 5$, and $PQ = 24$, then $PB = $ ? **9**
  (c) If $PA = 2$, $AR = 8$, and $RC = 3$, then $CQ = $ ? **12**
  (d) If $PB = 4$, $BQ = 5$, $PR = 15$, and $RQ = 18$, then $PA = $ ? and $CQ = $ ? **10** $\frac{20}{3}$

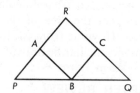

**11.** In the figure, $\square AEFD$ is a parallelogram. List all the similarities between triangles and show that

$$\frac{AE \cdot AD}{BE \cdot CD} = 1.$$

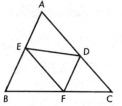

**12.** Given the figure on the left below with $\angle MGN \cong \angle HGK$, $GH = 8$, $GK = 12$, $GM = 10$, and $KN = 3$. Prove that $\angle HKG \cong \angle N$.
**$\triangle HGK \sim \triangle MGN$ (SAS) and $\angle HKG \cong \angle N$ by definition of similar triangles.**

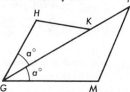
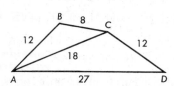

**13.** Given the figure on the right above with lengths of segments as marked. Prove that $\overrightarrow{AC}$ bisects $\angle DAB$.

**14.** The altitude to the hypotenuse of a right triangle separates the hypotenuse into segments having lengths 15 and 5. Find the length of the altitude and the lengths of the legs of the triangle. **Altitude is $5\sqrt{3}$, legs are 10 and $10\sqrt{3}$**

**15.** Given the figure as marked, find $v$, $w$, $x$, $y$, and $z$.
$z(z+9) = 20^2$; $z = 16$
$x = \sqrt{9 \cdot 16} = 12$
$y = \sqrt{9 \cdot 25} = 15$
$\frac{v}{8} = \frac{15}{20}$; $v = 6$
$w = 10$

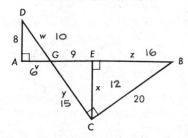

**16.** If $\triangle ABC \sim \triangle DEF$ and $\triangle DEF \sim \triangle ACB$, what kind of a triangle is $\triangle DEF$? **$\triangle DEF$ is isosceles with $DE = DF$**

**17.** A tennis ball is served from a height of 2 m and just clears a net 0.9 m high. If the ball is served from a line 12 m from the net and travels in a straight path, how far from the net does it hit the court?

$\frac{x}{12} = \frac{a}{b}$, and since $\triangle ACB \sim \triangle AEF$, $\frac{a+b}{a} = \frac{2}{0.9}$, or $\frac{a}{b} = \frac{0.9}{1.1}$.

Therefore $\frac{x}{12} =$ $\frac{0.9}{1.1}$ and $x =$ 9.8 m.

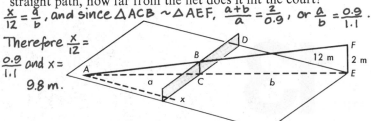

**18.** Given the triangles $\triangle PQR$ and $\triangle STV$ as shown, what is the ratio of their areas? $\frac{a \triangle STV}{a \triangle PQR} = \left(\frac{2}{5}\right)^2 = \frac{4}{25}$

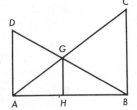

**19.** $\triangle ABC$ is an isosceles right triangle with $\angle A$ the right angle. $E$ and $D$ are points on opposite sides of $\overleftrightarrow{AC}$, with $E$ on the same side of $\overleftrightarrow{AC}$ as $B$, such that $\triangle ACD$ and $\triangle BCE$ are both equilateral. Find the ratio of the areas of $\triangle ACD$ and $\triangle BCE$. $\frac{a \triangle BCE}{a \triangle ACD} = \left(\frac{\sqrt{2}}{1}\right)^2 = \frac{2}{1}$

**20.** A side of one equilateral triangle is congruent to an altitude of another equilateral triangle. What is the ratio of the areas of the triangles? $\frac{4}{3}$

**21.** Given the figure with $\overline{AD}$, $\overline{HG}$, and $\overline{BC}$ each perpendicular to $\overline{AB}$. Prove:

(a) $AH \cdot GB = HB \cdot DG$.

(b) $AH \cdot GC = HB \cdot AG$.

(c) $AH \cdot BC = HB \cdot AD$.

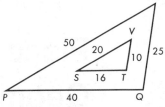

**22.** Given that no three of the points $P$, $Q$, $R$, and $X$ are collinear, and that $X$ is in the exterior of $\triangle PQR$. Draw the segments $\overline{XP}$, $\overline{XQ}$, and $\overline{XR}$. Let $A$ be any point of $\overline{XR}$ and let the line through $A$ parallel to $\overleftrightarrow{PR}$ intersect $\overline{XP}$ at $B$. Let the line through $B$ parallel to $\overleftrightarrow{PQ}$ intersect $\overline{XQ}$ at $C$. Draw $\overline{AC}$. Prove that $\triangle ABC \sim \triangle RPQ$.

## HONORS PROBLEM

Explain how two triangles can have five parts (sides and angles) of one congruent to five parts of the other triangle and still not be congruent.

---

### Answers to Chapter Review Problems

**21.** (a) Since $\overline{GH} \parallel \overline{AD}$ in $\triangle ABD$, $AH/HB = DG/GB$, or $AH \cdot GB = HB \cdot DG$.

(b) Since $\overline{GH} \parallel \overline{BC}$ in $\triangle ABC$, $AH/HB = AG/GC$, or $AH \cdot GC = HB \cdot AG$.

(c) Since $\triangle AHG \sim \triangle ABC$, $AH/AB = GH/BC$, or $AH \cdot BC = AB \cdot GH$. Since $\triangle BHG \sim \triangle BAD$, $HB/AB = GH/AD$, or $HB \cdot AD = AB \cdot GH$. Therefore $AH \cdot BC = HB \cdot AD$.

**22.**

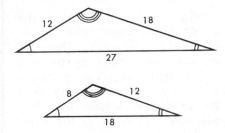

Since $\overline{BA} \parallel \overline{PR}$ and $\overline{BC} \parallel \overline{PQ}$, $\angle ABC \cong \angle RPQ$. Since $\overline{BA} \parallel \overline{PR}$, $BA/PR = BX/PX$. Similarly, since $\overline{BC} \parallel \overline{PQ}$, $BC/PQ = BX/PX$. Therefore, $BA/PR = BC/PQ$. Therefore, $\triangle ABC \sim \triangle RPQ$ by the SAS Similarity Theorem.

### Answer to Honors Problem

Of the five congruent pairs of parts, three must be angles, for if three were sides the triangles would be congruent. Hence the triangles are similar. Neither of the two pairs of congruent sides can be *corresponding* sides, or the triangles would be congruent by ASA. The remaining possibility can best be shown by an example.

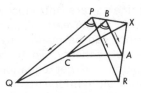

## Plane Coordinate Geometry

In Chapter 9 we studied parallel lines and quadrilaterals from a synthetic point of view. In Chapter 13 we gain some perspective by briefly looking at the same topic from an analytic point of view. Sections 13–2, 13–3, 13–4, 13–9 and 13–10 review material usually discussed in first year algebra courses.

ˎ Coordinates are introduced, in this book, at the earliest point at which they can be made a part of the geometric theory. To introduce coordinates and get equations of lines in a straightforward fashion, we need to know about similarity.

It has been claimed that coordinate systems are very helpful as a method of proof, in elementary geometry. This claim is grossly exaggerated; the only really notable example of the effective use of coordinate systems at an elementary level is in the proof of the median concurrence theorem (see page 514). Other illustrations of the use of this method are both scarce and unimpressive, and some of them are actually delusive. Consider the following example.

**Theorem.** If two lines $L_1$ and $L_2$ are both perpendicular to the same line $L$, then $L_1$ and $L_2$ are parallel.

"*Proof.*" Let $m_1, m_2$, and $m$ be the slopes of the lines. Then $m_1 = -1/m$ and $m_2 = -1/m$. Therefore $m_1 = m_2$, and $L_1$ and $L_2$ are parallel.

Note that this proof is incomplete: it assumes that all three of the lines have slopes, and thus assumes that none of them are vertical. Note also that the synthetic proof of the same theorem is trivial: if $L_1$ intersected $L_2$ at $P$, then there would be two perpendiculars to $L$ through $P$, which is impossible.

# Plane Coordinate Geometry

## Objectives...

- Explore relationships between algebra and geometry in terms of coordinate geometry.
- Apply the concept of slope to parallel and perpendicular lines.
- Derive the Distance Formula as a consequence of the Pythagorean Theorem.
- Prove theorems in the context of coordinate geometry.
- Develop coordinate formulas for linear relations.

## 13–1 INTRODUCTION

Mathematics is, in one way, quite different from the other sciences: it is the only science in which practically nothing ever has to be discarded. Of course, mathematicians are people, and being people, they make mistakes. But in mathematics, the mistakes of individuals are usually detected pretty quickly. The result is that when one generation has discovered something about mathematics, the next generation can go on to discover some more, without having to stop to correct serious errors in the things that were supposed to be known.

The first big step forward in geometry, after the Greeks, was the development of a new method, called *coordinate geometry*. This method was discovered in the seventeenth century by René Descartes (1596–1650). As we shall see, what Descartes did was to explore the relations between geometry and algebra and show how each of them could throw light on the other. In this chapter, we shall give a short introduction to coordinate geometry, so that you can see what it is and how it works.

## 13–2 COORDINATE SYSTEMS IN A PLANE

We already know, from Chapter 2, how coordinate systems work on a line.

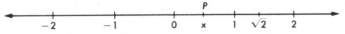

Once we have set up a coordinate system on a line, every number corresponds to a point, and every point corresponds to a number.

We shall now do the same sort of thing in a *plane.* In a plane, a point will correspond not to a single number, but to a *pair* of numbers.

**403**

Indeed, if you do not know that perpendiculars are unique, then you cannot set up a coordinate system in the first place, because you cannot explain what is meant by the x-coordinate of a point.

Thus, when coordinates are introduced for the first time, we are not making very significant use of them in the study of the underlying geometry. Primarily, we are investigating *the relation between the underlying geometry and the algebraic apparatus.* It is useful, for example, to know that lines are graphs of linear equations; but this does not give us any new information about the geometry of lines.

There are, however, substantial reasons for introducing coordinate systems early. Algebraic skills, and the art of using variables, need to be maintained. Geometry can help in improving intuitive understanding of algebra. (See, for example, the graph of $y = |x|$ on page 443.)

We believe that deductive synthetic geometry needs to have the field mainly to itself, for a period of many months. But once this has been done, a geometry course may well profit from a change of style and methodology.

**Planning the Chapter**

Because this chapter is long, we provide a chart below to facilitate planning.

| Section | Average Class | Above-average Class |
|---|---|---|
| 13–1 | } 1 | } 1 |
| 13–2 | | |
| 13–3 | 1 | |
| 13–4 | 2 | 2 |
| 13–5 | 1 | 1 |
| 13–6 | 1 | 1 |
| 13–7 | 2 | 1 |
| 13–8 | 2 | 2 |
| 13–9 | 1 | 1 |
| 13–10 | 2 | 2 |
| Review/Test | 1 | 1 |

Most students will have been introduced to cartesian coordinates in
their first year algebra course.
Thus, Sections 13–1, 13–2, and 13–3
may be given as a reading assignment so that the students may
concentrate on Sections 13–4, 13–8
and 13–10.    Note also that coordinate systems are used in the
latter part of Chapter 17.

## 13–2 COORDINATE SYSTEMS
    IN A PLANE

### Classroom Notes

Sections 13–2 and 13–3 develop the
idea of a coordinate system for a
plane.  Note that we develop a coordinate system for a plane in
terms of the coordinate system
developed for a line in Chapter 2.
Most students have encountered
the idea of a coordinate system for
the plane in first-year algebra; you
can draw on their experience and
cover Sections 13–2 and 13–3
rapidly, concentrating on Problems
1 through 12 of Problem Set 13–3.

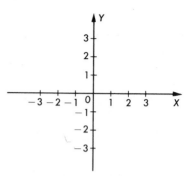

The scheme works like this.  First we
take a line $X$ in the plane, and set up a
coordinate system on $X$.  This line will
be called the *x-axis*.    In drawing
figures, we usually put an arrowhead
on the $x$-axis, to emphasize the positive direction on $X$.
    Now we let $Y$ be the perpendicular
to the $x$-axis through the point with
coordinate 0.  On $Y$ we set up a coordinate system in such a way that the
zero point on $Y$ is the zero point on $X$.  (By the Ruler Placement Postulate, this can be done.)  The line $Y$ will be called the *y-axis*.  As before,
we indicate the positive direction with an arrowhead.  The point where
the line $X$ intersects the line $Y$ is called the *origin*.  The origin is denoted
by 0, to remind us that it is the zero point on each of the axes.

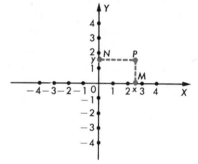

    We can now describe any point of
the plane by a pair of numbers, as
follows.  Given a point $P$, we drop a
perpendicular to the $x$-axis.  Let the
foot of the perpendicular be the point
$M$.  Let $x$ be the coordinate of $M$ on
the line $X$.  The number $x$ is called the
*x-coordinate* of $P$.  (In the figure, it
looks as if $x = 2\frac{1}{2}$.)
    We then drop a perpendicular to
the $y$-axis.  Let the foot of the perpendicular be the point $N$.  Let $y$ be
the coordinate of $N$ on the line $Y$.
The number $y$ is called the *y-coordinate* of $P$.  In the figure,
it looks as if $y = 1\frac{1}{2}$.  For
short, we indicate that $P$ has
these coordinates by writing
$P(2\frac{1}{2}, 1\frac{1}{2})$.
    Let us look at some more
examples.  From the figure,
we can read off the following:

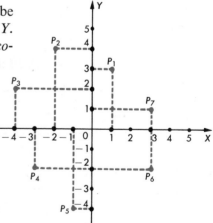

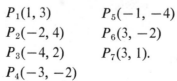

$P_1(1, 3)$            $P_5(-1, -4)$
$P_2(-2, 4)$          $P_6(3, -2)$
$P_3(-4, 2)$          $P_7(3, 1)$.
$P_4(-3, -2)$

Note that the order in which the coordinates are written makes a difference. The point with coordinates (1, 3) is $P_1$, and this point is different from $P_7$, which has coordinates (3, 1). Thus, the coordinates of a point form an *ordered* pair of real numbers, and you can't tell where the point is unless you know which number comes first.

We sum all this up in the following definitions.

### Definitions

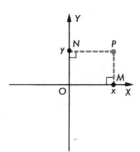

The *x-coordinate* of a point $P$ is the coordinate of the foot of the perpendicular from $P$ to the $x$-axis. The *y-coordinate* of $P$ is the coordinate of the foot of the perpendicular from $P$ to the $y$-axis. If $P$ has coordinates $x$ and $y$, then we write $P(x, y)$.

Just as a single line separates the plane into two pieces (each of which is a half-plane), so the two axes separate the plane into four parts, called *quadrants*. The four quadrants are identified by numbers.

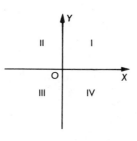

We have shown that under the scheme we have set up, every point $P$ determines an ordered pair of real numbers. Does it work in reverse? That is, does every ordered pair $(a, b)$ of real numbers determine a point? It is easy to see that the answer is "Yes."

At the point of the $x$-axis with coordinate $x = a$, we set up a perpendicular. We do the same at the point of the $y$-axis with coordinate $y = b$. The point where these perpendiculars intersect is the point with coordinates $(a, b)$.

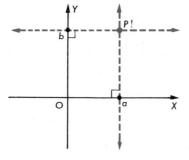

Thus we have a one-to-one correspondence between the points of the plane and the ordered pairs of real numbers. Such a correspondence is called a *coordinate system*. To describe a coordinate system, we need to choose (1) a line $X$, to be the $x$-axis, (2) a line $Y$, to be the $y$-axis, and (3) a positive direction on each of the axes. Once we have made these three choices, the coordinate systems on both axes are determined, and they in turn determine the coordinates of all points of the plane.

In this book, we shall rarely be talking about two coordinate systems at the same time. So long as we stick to a single coordinate system, every point $P$ determines an ordered pair $(a, b)$, and every ordered pair $(a, b)$ determines a point. It will therefore do no harm to ignore the difference between points and number pairs. This will enable us to use such convenient phrases as "the point $(2, 3)$" and "$P = (3, 4)$."

### Problem Set 13–2

1. (a) Give the coordinates of each point $P$ of the figure as an ordered pair of numbers.

   (b) Which three points are collinear? What are their coordinates? $P_1, P_3, P_6$ and $P_5, P_7, P_8$

   (c) Name the points in Quadrant I; in Quadrant IV. I : $P_1$
            IV : $P_3, P_5, P_6$

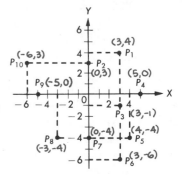

2. What are the coordinates of the origin? $(0, 0)$

3. What is the $y$-coordinate of the point $(3, \boxed{-5})$? of the point $(5, \boxed{-3})$? of the point $(-5 \boxed{3})$?

4. Consider the point $C(4, 7)$. What are the coordinates of its projection, $A$, into the $x$-axis? What are the coordinates of its projection, $B$, into the $y$-axis? $A(4, 0)$, $B(0, 7)$

5. Answer the questions of Problem 4 for the point $D(-4, 7)$. $(-4, 0)$ $(0, 7)$

6. Name the point which is the projection of the point $(0, 6)$ into the $x$-axis. $(0, 0)$

7. Name the point which is the projection of the point $(-1, 0)$ into the $y$-axis. $(0, 0)$

8. Complete: The $x$-coordinate of every point on the $y$-axis is $\underline{\quad 0 \quad}$.

9. Complete: The $y$-coordinate of every point on the $x$-axis is $\underline{\quad 0 \quad}$.

10. Consider the points

     $A(5, 2)$,     $B(4, -3)$,     $C(-4, 4)$,     and     $D(-3, -5)$.

   (a) Write their names, $A$, $B$, $C$, $D$, in the order (from left to right) of their projections into the $x$-axis. C, D, B, A

   (b) Arrange them in the order (from bottom to top) of their projections into the $y$-axis. D, B, A, C

**11.** The lines through $P(5, 7)$ which are perpendicular to the $x$-axis and to the $y$-axis form a rectangle with the two axes. Find the perimeter of the rectangle. **24**

**12.** Find the perimeter of the rectangle formed by the axes and the perpendiculars to the axes through the point $(-4, -2)$. **12**

**13.** Do as directed in Problem 11 for the point $P(-\frac{7}{2}, 3)$; for the point $P(-\sqrt{2}, \frac{3}{2})$; for the point $P(a, b)$, where $a$ and $b$ are any real numbers.
**13; 3 + 2√2 , 2a + 2b**

**14.** In which of the following pairs of points are the points closer together: (3, 0) and (7, 0), or (3, 0) and $(-2, 0)$?

**15.** In which of the following pairs of points are the points closer together: (2, 1) and (1, 2), or (2, 1) and (2, 0)?

---

**16.** *A three-dimensional coordinate system.* If we take a line perpendicular to the $x$-axis and to the $y$-axis at their intersection, we can set up a coordinate system in space. In this system we have a one-to-one correspondence between the points of space and ordered triples of real numbers. In the figure, the arrowheads indicate the positive direction on each axis and the dashed line segments are the perpendiculars which project each point $P$ into the respective axes. The projection of a point into an axis is its coordinate for that axis. Thus a point is completely described by its three coordinates, and we write $P(x, y, z)$.

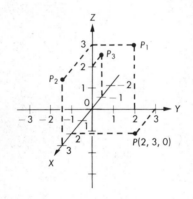

In the figure above, $P$ is a point in the $xy$-plane, so that its projection into the $z$-axis (*not* indicated) is 0. Its projection into the $x$-axis is 2 and into the $y$-axis is 3. Therefore we write $P(2, 3, 0)$.

(a) $P_1$ is a point in the $yz$-plane. Write its coordinates as an ordered triple of real numbers. **$P_1$(0,2,3)**

(b) $P_2$ and $P_3$ are points in the $xz$-plane. Write their coordinates as ordered triples. **$P_2$(3,0,3) , $P_3$(-1,0,2)**

(c) Which two points are in a plane parallel to the $xy$-plane? Can you prove it? What do you observe about their coordinates? **$P_1$ and $P_2$   z-coordinate is 3 in each case**

**17.** If a point $P$ is described by $P(x, y, z)$, on which axis is each of the points $A(0, 3, 0)$, $B(-2, 0, 0)$, and $C(0, 0, 5)$?
**y-axis     x-axis          z-axis**

**18.** If a point $P$ is described by $P(x, y, z)$, in which plane is each of the following points: $R(4, 0, 2)$, $S(3, -2, 0)$, and $T(0, 1, 5)$?
**xz-plane   xy-plane   yz-plane**

19. In representing a point in a sketch of a three-dimensional coordinate system, it is customary to consider first its projection into the *xy*-plane. In the figure, $P'$ is the projection of $P(2, 3, 4)$ into the *xy*-plane. What are the coordinates of $P'$? **P′(2,3,0)**

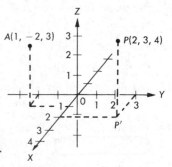

(a) What is the distance of point $P$ from the *xy*-plane? **4** from the *xz*-plane? **3** from the *yz*-plane? **2**

(b) What is the distance of point $A$ from the *xy*-plane? **3** from the *xz*-plane? **2** from the *yz*-plane? **1**

20. (a) What is the distance of the point $(3, 2, -2)$ from the *xy*-plane? **2** from the *xz*-plane? **2** from the *yz*-plane? **3**

(b) Answer part (a) for the point $(x, y, z)$, where $x$, $y$, $z$ are any real numbers. **|z|, |y|, |x|**

René Descartes (1596–1650)

Descartes is a famous man in two quite separate domains: he is known among philosophers as a great philosopher and among mathematicians as a great mathematician.

His greatest contribution to mathematics was the discovery of coordinate systems and their application to problems of geometry. Ever since then algebra and geometry have worked together, to the advantage of both. To this day, coordinate systems of the sort used in this book are referred to as

Cartesian coordinate systems, in honor of their inventor. The concept of coordinates was the first really fundamental contribution to geometry after the Greeks. (The word *Cartesian* comes from *Cartesius*, which is the Latin form of Descartes' name.)

Part of the credit for Descartes' discovery should go to Pierre Fermat, who had much the same ideas at about the same time. Fermat was one of the few great amateur mathematicians. He worked for the French government, and pursued mathematics in his spare time. He wrote letters to his friends about his discoveries, and never published them in any other form. But the material in Fermat's letters is now included in all the standard books on the theory of numbers.

The development of coordinate systems laid the foundation for the development of calculus, soon thereafter, by Newton and Leibniz. Thus Descartes must have been one of the men that Newton had in mind when he said that he had stood on the shoulders of giants.

## 13-3    HOW TO DRAW PICTURES OF COORDINATE SYSTEMS ON GRAPH PAPER

In drawing pictures of coordinate systems, it is convenient to use ready-made graph paper. On graph paper, the horizontal and vertical lines are printed, but we still have to draw everything else for ourselves.

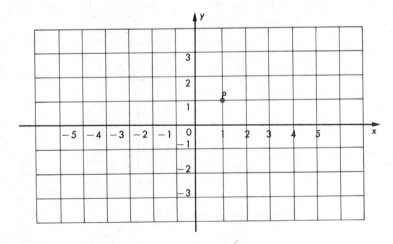

In the figure above, the lines in color represent the lines that are ordinarily printed on the paper. Everything else is drawn with a pen or pencil. Note that the *x*-axis is labeled *x* rather than *X*. This is customary. Here the symbol *x* is not the name of anything; it is merely a reminder that the coordinates on this axis are going to be denoted by the letter *x*; and similarly for the *y*-axis.

**Classroom Notes**

We speak of "drawing pictures of coordinate systems" on graph paper to remind the student that the coordinate system and the picture are different things. A coordinate system is not a graphic but a mathematical object, namely, a one-to-one correspondence between the points of a plane and the ordered pairs of real numbers.

You may wish to call attention to the discussion of the orientation of coordinate axes.

Remember that before we started discussing coordinate systems, we were free to draw figures to any scale we wanted. In the same way, and for the same reason, we can indicate any scale we want to on printed graph paper. For example, we might have marked the same sheet of paper like this:

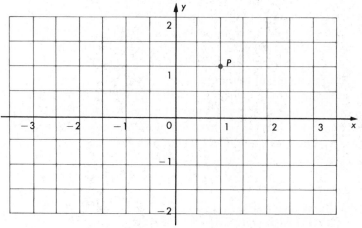

Because we have this freedom of choice, it is absolutely necessary to indicate what choice we made, by writing number labels on the axes to show the scale. If we hadn't done this in the figure above, no one would be able to tell whether *P* was supposed to be the point (1, 1) or the point (2, 2) or the point ($\pi$, $\pi$).

*To repeat:* to show a coordinate system on graph paper, we draw the axes and indicate the scale.

Note that we can draw axes in any of the following (or other) positions on a sheet of paper.

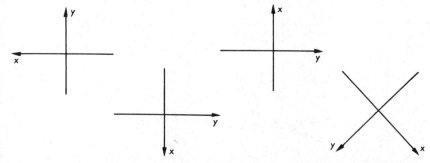

*None of these drawings are logically wrong.* But people find it much easier to read each other's graphs if they agree at the outset to draw the *x*-axis horizontally, with the coordinates increasing from left to right, and to draw the *y*-axis vertically, with coordinates increasing from bottom to top.

**Quiz**

A triangle has its vertices at $(-3, 0)$, $(13, 0)$, and $(-3, 8)$. How long is the median to the longest side?
(ans: $4\sqrt{5}$)

*A final word of caution:* You have probably seen many graphs on which the horizontal and vertical scales could be chosen independently of each other.

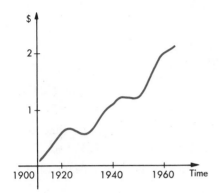
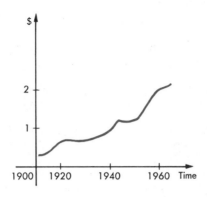

For example, if you want to draw a graph showing how the price of cheese (in dollars per kilogram) increased in the period from 1900 to 1960, there doesn't need to be any connection between the scales on the horizontal and vertical axes. (The scales measure different kinds of things, anyway.)

On the other hand, when you are drawing a coordinate system to do geometry, your picture will be distorted if the scales on the axes are different. The reason is that the scales will be used to measure distances.

In the figure, the scales tell us that $PQ = 2$ and $PR = 2$. Therefore $\triangle PQR$ must be isosceles. But it certainly doesn't look isosceles; and $\angle Q$ and $\angle R$ certainly don't look congruent. This means that we have drawn a distorted picture. To avoid such distortions, we use the same scale on each axis.

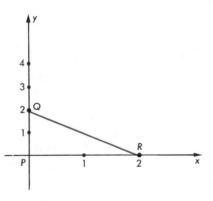

## Problem Set 13–3

[*Note:* In this problem set you will find that printed graph paper will be helpful, though not essential. In Problems 1 through 12 draw one set of axes for each problem.]

1. Choose a suitable scale on a set of axes and plot each of the following points: $A(2, 3)$, $B(3, 2)$, $C(4, -3)$, $D(-3, -4)$. In which quadrant is each point?

2. Plot each of the points $A(0, 0)$, $B(5, 0)$, $C(5, 3)$, $D(0, 3)$. Find
   (a) the perimeter of $\square ABCD = 16$   (b) $a\square ABCD = 15$

3. Plot each of the points $P(0, 0)$, $Q(3, 0)$, $R(0, 4)$. Find
   (a) the perimeter of $\triangle PQR = 12$   (b) $a\triangle PQR = 6$

4. Plot each of the points $F(0, 0)$, $G(8, 0)$, $H(8, -6)$.
   (a) Find $a\triangle FGH = 24$          (b) How long is $\overline{FH}$? $FH = 10$

5. Given that $\triangle ABC$ has its vertices at the points $(0, 1)$, $(0, 6)$, and $(12, 1)$, find $a\triangle ABC$ and the perimeter of $\triangle ABC$. $a\triangle ABC = 30$, $p\triangle ABC = 30$

6. Plot each of the points $A(1, 0)$, $B(7, 0)$, $C(10, 4)$, $D(4, 4)$. Find the perimeter and the area of $\square ABCD$. $p\square ABCD = 22$, $a\square ABCD = 24$

7. What is the area of a triangle whose vertices are the points $(0, 5)$, $(4, 0)$, and $(-4, 0)$? $20$

8. Plot each of the points $K(-2, 5)$, $M(-2, -3)$, $L(4, -3)$. Find $a\triangle KML$. How long is $\overline{KL}$? $a\triangle KML = 24$, $KL = 10$

9. A triangle has vertices at $(0, 0)$, $(0, 12)$, and $(10, 0)$. Find the length of the median to the shortest side. $13$

10. Plot each of the points $A(-3, -4)$, $B(-3, 6)$, $C(4, 6)$. Find the coordinates of a point $D$ such that $\square ABCD$ is a rectangle. $D(4, -4)$

---

11. The vertices of a triangle are the points $(1, 8)$, $(4, 1)$, and $(7, 1)$. Find the area of the triangle. $10.5$

12. The ends of the base of an isosceles triangle are the points $(3, 0)$ and $(-3, 0)$. Find the coordinates of the other vertex so that the area of the triangle will be 15. $(0, 5)$ or $(0, -5)$

13. "When is a square not a square?" In the figures below, the scale on each $x$-axis is purposely different from the scale on the corresponding $y$-axis, in order to give a distorted picture of the figure intended. What figure was intended in each case?

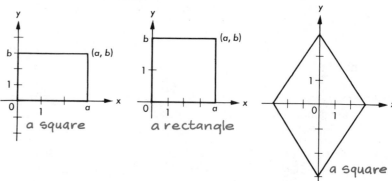

**14.** Given the figure on the left below, find the perimeter of $\square ABCD$.
p□ ABCD=36

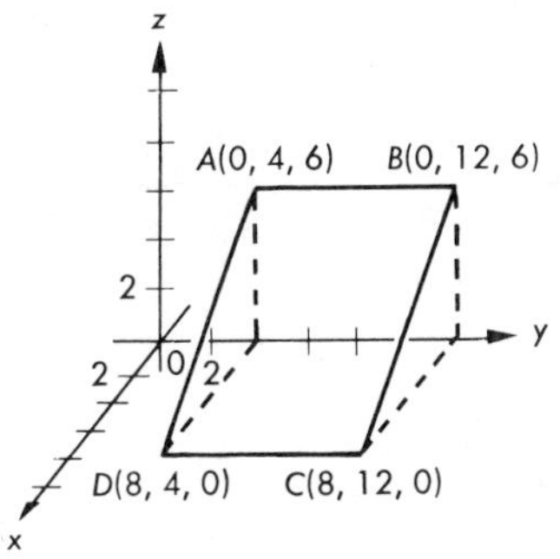
z
A(0, 4, 6)
B(0, 12, 6)
2
2
0
2
y
D(8, 4, 0)
C(8, 12, 0)
x

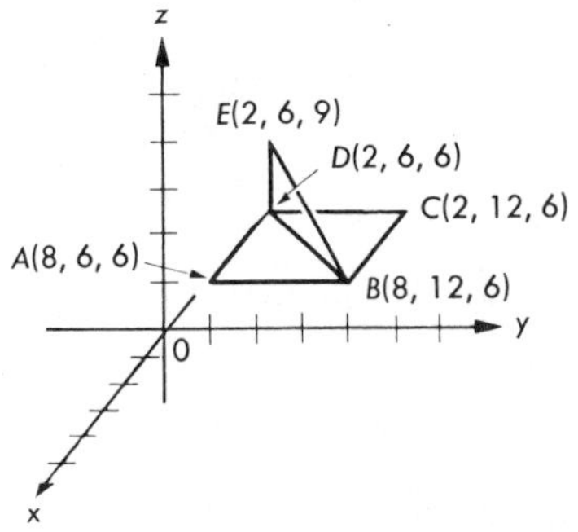
z
E(2, 6, 9)
D(2, 6, 6)
C(2, 12, 6)
A(8, 6, 6)
B(8, 12, 6)
0
y
x

**15.** In Problem 14, how long is the projection of $\overline{AC}$ into the $xy$-plane? $8\sqrt{2}$

**16.** Given the figure on the right above, as marked, find $BE$. BE=9

**17.** Draw a three-dimensional coordinate system. Mark off the same scale on the $y$-axis and on the $z$-axis. On the $x$-axis (the one which comes "toward" you) use a scale which is about 0.7 of the scale on the other two axes. Locate the point $A(1, 3, 2)$ and the point $B(1, -3, 2)$. Draw $\overline{AB}$. How long is $\overline{AB}$? AB=6

[*Hint:* See Problem 19 of Problem Set 13–2.]

**18.** Draw the figure of Problem 19 of Problem Set 13–2, but, instead of projecting $P$ into the $xy$-plane first,

(a) project $P$ into the $yz$-plane. $P''(0,3,4)$

(b) project $P$ into the $xz$-plane. $P'''(2,0,4)$

## 13–4 THE SLOPE OF A NONVERTICAL LINE

The $x$-axis and all lines parallel to it are called *horizontal*. The $y$-axis and all lines parallel to it are called *vertical*.

In the figure, it is easy to see that all points of the horizontal line $L_1$ have the same $y$-coordinate $a$, because the point $(0, a)$ is the common foot of all perpendiculars to the $y$-axis from points of $L_1$. Similarly, all points of the vertical line $L_2$ have the same $x$-coordinate $b$.

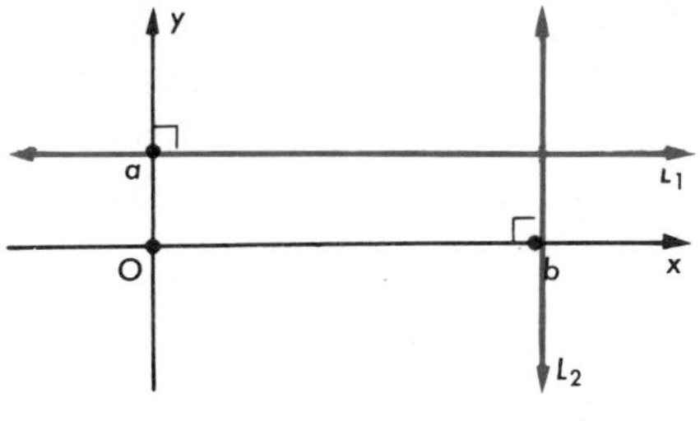
y
a
L1
O
b
x
L2

Of course, a segment is called horizontal if the line containing it is horizontal; and a segment is called vertical if the line containing it is vertical.

**Answers to Problems**

**16.** In right $\triangle ABD$, $AB = 6$ and $AD = 6$, so $BD = 6\sqrt{2}$. In right $\triangle BDE$, $BD = 6\sqrt{2}$ and $DE = 3$, so $BE^2 = BD^2 + DE^2 = (6\sqrt{2})^2 + (3)^2 = 72 + 9 = 81$. Therefore $BE = 9$.

## 13–4 THE SLOPE OF A NONVERTICAL LINE

### Classroom Notes

The idea of slope should not be new to the student. Most first course algebra books include at least a rudimentary discussion of the slope of a line. Even so, it is sometimes best to treat slope as a new topic, since many students will not remember it accurately.

You may wish to accompany the definition with a discussion of slope in intuitive terms. The figure at the top of page 414 in the student text and Problem 3 in the problem set are suitable for such a discussion. It is best to emphasize that it is the *numerator* of the slope fraction which represents the *rise* and that it is the *denominator* which represents the *run*. Try to give the student an idea of how the slope of a segment varies with its "inclination," that is, what a segment with a slope of 0.3, of 1.0, of 2.5, and so on, looks like. The student may not readily use the definition of *slope* to compute the slope of a segment, and may not readily estimate the slope of a particular segment. Hence it is valuable to give practice in these processes in class discussion.

Note that we first define the slope of a segment and then, having proved that on a nonvertical line all segments have the same slope (Theorem 13–1), we define the slope of a nonvertical *line* to be the slope of every segment on that line. It is possible to *first* define the slope of a *line* to be the ratio $(y_2 - y_1)/(x_2 - x_1)$ where $P_1(x_1, y_1)$ and $P_2(x_2, y_2)$ are *any* two points on the line, and then, after establishing the basic facts about slope, eventually prove that our definition is independent of our choice of points $P_1$ and $P_2$ on L. The mathematical objection to this procedure is that we would be talking, for quite a while, about "the slope of a line," before showing that the slope is determined when the line is named. Thus Theorem 13–1, when we finally stated it, would take the form of a claim that we had not been talking nonsense. It is more orderly to justify the term "slope of a line" before we start using it.

The idea of the *slope* of a segment is suggested by the following figures.

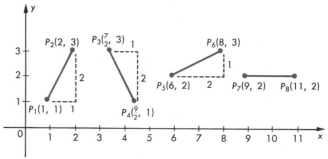

The slope of the first segment is 2; the slope of the second is $-2$; the slope of the third is $\frac{1}{2}$, and the slope of the fourth is 0. To be exact, the following definition is given.

**Definition**

If $P_1 = (x_1, y_1)$ and $P_2 = (x_2, y_2)$, and $\overline{P_1P_2}$ is nonvertical, then the slope of $\overline{P_1P_2}$ is

$$m = \frac{y_2 - y_1}{x_2 - x_1}.$$

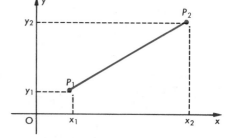

Some facts about slopes are obvious from the definition.

(1) If the points $P_1$ and $P_2$ are interchanged, the slope is the same as before, because

$$\frac{y_1 - y_2}{x_1 - x_2} = \frac{y_2 - y_1}{x_2 - x_1} = \frac{-(y_1 - y_2)}{-(x_1 - x_2)}.$$

In other words, the slope of a segment does not depend on the order in which its end points are named.

(2) On the other hand, it is important to name the coordinates in the same order in the numerator and denominator. The formula

$$\frac{y_1 - y_2}{x_2 - x_1}$$

is not a correct formula for the slope.

(3) For nonvertical segments, the slope formula always gives us a number, because the denominator $x_2 - x_1$ cannot be 0.

(4) For vertical segments, the slope formula *never* gives us a number, because in this case the denominator $x_2 - x_1$ is equal to 0. In fact, there is no such thing as the slope of a vertical segment.

(5) If a segment is horizontal, its slope is 0. (The numerator $y_2 - y_1$ is 0, and the denominator $x_2 - x_1$ is not 0.)

(6) If a segment is not horizontal (or vertical), then its slope is not 0.

(7) If a segment rises from left to right, its slope is positive. If the segment descends from left to right, its slope is negative. (See the figure on the left below.)

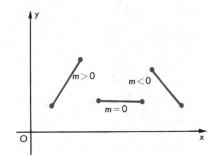 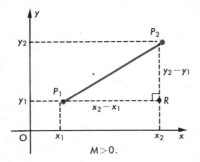

If a segment has positive slope, then its slope is the ratio of two distances as in the figure on the right above. Here, with $x_1 < x_2$ and $y_1 < y_2$, we have $P_1R = x_2 - x_1$ and $RP_2 = y_2 - y_1$. (Why?) Therefore

$$m = \frac{y_2 - y_1}{x_2 - x_1} = \frac{RP_2}{P_1R}.$$

If a segment has negative slope, then its slope is the *negative* of the ratio of two distances.

Here, with $x_1 < x_2$ and $y_2 < y_1$, we have

$$P_1R = x_2 - x_1$$

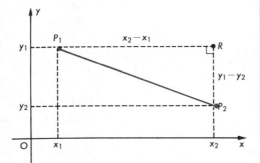

as before, but

$$RP_2 = y_1 - y_2 = -(y_2 - y_1).$$

Therefore

$$m = \frac{y_2 - y_1}{x_2 - x_1} = -\frac{RP_2}{P_1R}.$$

These ideas relate slopes to our geometry, and make it easy to see why the following theorem is true.

### Theorem 13–1

*On a nonvertical line, all segments have the same slope.*

**Proof.**    If the line is horizontal, this statement is obvious, because all segments on the line must have slope equal to 0.  The interesting cases are indicated by the following figures:

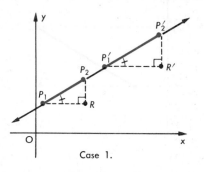 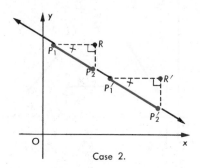

Case 1.                                    Case 2.

In Case 1, we have

$$\triangle P_1 R P_2 \sim \triangle P_1' R' P_2'$$

so that

$$\frac{RP_2}{R'P_2'} = \frac{P_1R}{P_1'R'},$$

$$\frac{RP_2}{P_1R} = \frac{R'P_2'}{P_1'R'}.$$

Therefore $\overline{P_1P_2}$ and $\overline{P_1'P_2'}$ have the same slope.

In Case 2, we also have

$$\triangle P_1 R P_2 \sim \triangle P_1' R' P_2'.$$

This gives, as before,

$$\frac{RP_2}{P_1R} = \frac{R'P_2'}{P_1'R'}.$$

This result is what we wanted, because the slopes of our two segments are the *negatives* of these two ratios.

Now that we have Theorem 13–1, we can talk not only about the slopes of segments but also about the slopes of lines.

### Definition

The *slope* of a nonvertical line is the number which is the slope of every segment of the line.

Thus, in the figure, the slope of $L$ is

$$\frac{1 - 3}{5 - 2} = -\frac{2}{3}.$$

Any other segment of the same line would give the same answer.

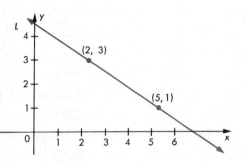

### Problem Set 13–4

**1.** Answer the questions below for each figure.

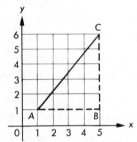

    (a) What are the coordinates of $A$, $B$, and $C$?  A(0,0), B(4,0), C(4,5)

    (b) What is $BC$? What is $AB$?    (c) What is the slope of $\overline{AC}$?
      BC=5        AB=4             Slope of $\overline{AC}$ = 5/4

**2.** Draw a set of coordinate axes. Locate four points, $A$, $B$, $C$, $D$, that have an x-coordinate of 3. Locate four points, $P$, $Q$, $R$, $S$, that have a y-coordinate of −2. Label each point with its coordinates.

**3.** Give the slope of each segment shown in the figure.

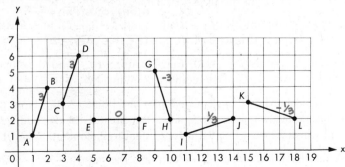

**13.** Integral answers include $(1, -2)$, $(2, 0)$, $(3, 2)$, $(4, 4)$, $(5, 6)$, $(6, 8)$, and $(7, 10)$.

**4.** Which pairs of points given below will determine horizontal lines? Which ones vertical lines? Horizontal: $(a), (d), (e), (j)$; vertical : $(b), (g), (i)$

(a)  $(5, 7)$  and  $(-3, 7)$ (b)  $(2, 4)$  and  $(2, -1)$

(c)  $(5, 2)$  and  $(-3, 5)$ (d)  $(0, -1)$  and  $(4, -1)$

(e)  $(3, 3)$  and  $(-3, 3)$ (f)  $(4, 7)$  and  $(-2, 6)$

(g)  $(0, 0)$  and  $(0, 5)$ (h)  $(0, 6)$  and  $(3, 0)$

(i)  $(a, b)$  and  $(a, c)$ (j)  $(a, b)$  and  $(c, b)$

**5.** Find the slope of each line which contains each pair of points listed below.

(a)  $(0, 0)$  and  $(8, 4)$ $m = \frac{1}{2}$  (b)  $(10, 5)$  and  $(6, 8)$ $m = -\frac{3}{4}$

(c)  $(2, -2)$  and  $(4, 2)$ $m = 2$  (d)  $(0, 3)$  and  $(-2, 3)$ $m = 0$

(e)  $(-2, 0)$  and  $(0, 6)$ $m = 3$  (f)  $(15, 6)$  and  $(-2, 23)$ $m = -1$

**6.** Find the slopes of the lines that contain each of the pairs of points listed below.

(a)  $(-5, 7)$   and   $(3, -8)$ $m = -\frac{15}{8}$

(b)  $(\frac{5}{2}, \frac{4}{3})$   and   $(-\frac{13}{2}, \frac{16}{3})$ $m = -\frac{4}{9}$

(c)  $(5\sqrt{2}, 6\sqrt{3})$   and   $(\sqrt{8}, \sqrt{12})$ $m = \frac{2\sqrt{6}}{3}$

(d)  $(63, 49)$   and   $(-7, 9)$ $m = \frac{4}{7}$

(e)  $(2a, 3b)$   and   $(-a, b)$ $m = \frac{2b}{3a}$

(f)  $(0, n)$   and   $(n, 0)$ $m = -1$

**7.** The vertices of a triangle are the points $A(-2, 3)$, $B(5, -4)$, and $C(1, 8)$. Find the slope of each side. $s(\overline{CA}) = \frac{5}{3}$, $s(\overline{BC}) = -3$, $s(\overline{AB}) = -1$

**8.** The vertices of a parallelogram are the points $R(1, 4)$, $S(3, 2)$, $T(4, 6)$, $V(2, 8)$. Find the slope of each side. $s(\overline{RS}) = -1$, $s(\overline{ST}) = 4$, $s(\overline{TV}) = -1$, $s(\overline{VR}) = 4$

**9.** Find the slope of each side of the quadrilateral whose vertices are $A(5, 6)$, $B(13, 6)$, $C(11, 2)$, $D(1, 2)$. Can you tell what kind of a quadrilateral it is? $s(\overline{AB}) = 0$, $s(\overline{BC}) = 2$, $s(\overline{CD}) = 0$, $s(\overline{DA}) = 1$, $\square ABCD$ is a trapezoid.

**10.** A quadrilateral has as vertices the points $M(a, b)$, $N(c, b)$, $O(c + d, e)$, $P(a + d, e)$. Find the slope of each side. $s(\overline{MN}) = 0$, $s(\overline{NO}) = \frac{e-b}{d}$, $s(\overline{OP}) = 0$, $s(\overline{PM}) = \frac{e-b}{d}$

**11.** $C$ is the midpoint of $\overline{AB}$, $A$ is the point $(-3, -2)$, and $B$ is the point $(2, 8)$. What is the slope of $\overline{BC}$? $s(\overline{BC}) = s(\overline{AB}) = 2$

**12.** Given the points $D(-4, 6)$, $E(1, 1)$, $F(4, -6)$. Find the slopes of $\overline{DE}$ and $\overline{EF}$. Are $D$, $E$, and $F$ collinear? Why? No, $s(\overline{DE}) = -1$ and $s(\overline{EF}) = -\frac{7}{3}$

**13.** Draw a coordinate system and plot the point $(2, 0)$. Now plot three other points whose $x$-coordinates are greater than 0 and less than 8 and which lie on a line with slope equal to 2, containing $(2, 0)$.

**14.** A line having a slope of $-1$ contains the point $(-2, 5)$. What is the $y$-coordinate of the point on the line whose $x$-coordinate is 8? $-5$

15. Draw a coordinate system. Draw the line through the origin which will pass through the point (93000000, 62000000). Name three points of this line whose x-coordinates are less than 10. $(1, \frac{2}{3}), (2, \frac{4}{3}), (3, 2), (4, \frac{8}{3}),$ $(5, \frac{10}{3}), (6, 4), (7, \frac{14}{3}), (8, \frac{16}{3}), (9, 6)$

16. Draw a coordinate system and plot the point $(-3, 1)$. Now plot three other points whose x-coordinates are greater than 0 and less than 10, and which lie on a line with slope equal to $-\frac{1}{3}$ and containing $(-3, 1)$. $(3, -1), (6, -2), (9, -3),$ etc.

## 13–5 PARALLEL AND PERPENDICULAR LINES

Using slopes, we can rather easily tell whether two nonvertical lines are parallel.

(1) If two nonvertical lines are parallel, then they have the same slope.

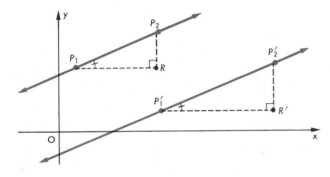

This follows from the fact that $\triangle P_1 R P_2 \sim \triangle P_1' R' P_2'$.

(2) If two different nonvertical lines intersect, then their slopes are different.

If the two lines intersect at $P_1$, as in the figure, then the slopes are

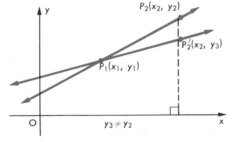

$$m = \frac{y_2 - y_1}{x_2 - x_1}$$

$$m' = \frac{y_3 - y_1}{x_2 - x_1}.$$

Here $m \neq m'$, because the denominators are the same and the numerators are different.

(3) If two non-vertical lines have the same slope, then they are parallel.

If the lines were intersecting, then their slopes would be different.

Combining statements (1) and (3), we get the following theorem.

## 13–5 PARALLEL AND PERPENDICULAR LINES

**Classroom Notes**

Theorems 13–2 and 13–3 are stated *after* the proof rather than before; in this way, the theorem appears as a summation of what has, in fact, just been proved.

The proofs of Theorem 13–2 and 13–3 are meant to be read; they leave several details to be filled in by the reader:

(1) Each theorem is an "if and only if" statement, and thus has two parts. Theorem 13–2 has the following two parts:

  (a) If two nonvertical lines are parallel, then they have the same slope.

  (b) If two nonvertical lines have the same slope, then they are parallel.

Note that the proof of (b) is an indirect proof; we show that if two nonvertical lines intersect, then their slopes are different.

Theorem 13–3 has the following two parts:

  (a) If two nonvertical lines are perpendicular, then their slopes are negative reciprocals.

  (b) If the slopes of the two nonvertical lines are negative reciprocals, then the lines are perpendicular.

Note that both parts of Theorem 13–3 are proved directly.

(2) The constructions in the proofs of the two parts of Theorem 13–3 are different. You should note in what way they are different and how this determines the way in which we prove $\triangle PRQ \cong \triangle Q'R'P$.

We begin the proof of Part (a) by taking the horizontal line through $P$ (Theorem 9–3 and the Parallel Postulate) and complete the two triangles by dropping perpendiculars (Theorems 6–3 and 6–4). It is then easy to show that $\angle RQP \cong \angle R'PQ'$

(vertical angles are congruent and complements of the same angle are congruent), making $\triangle PRQ \cong \triangle Q'R'P$ by SAA.

The construction for the proof of Part (b) is slightly different. As before, we take the horizontal line through $P$ and complete $\triangle PRQ$. Appealing to the equations of part (l) (page 420), we see that $m' = -1/m$ if and only if

$$\frac{Q'R'}{R'P} = \frac{PR}{RQ},$$

where $R'$ is some point of the ray opposite to $\overrightarrow{PR}$ and $Q'$ is on the line $L'$, such that $\overleftrightarrow{R'Q'} \perp \overleftrightarrow{R'R}$. Examining this latter proportion, we see that if we make $R'P = RQ$, then $Q'R'$ must equal $PR$. This is what we want, because now $\triangle PRQ \cong \triangle Q'R'P$ by SAS. Finally, since $\angle 2$ is congruent to its vertical angle and $\angle 2$ is complementary to $\angle 1$, we have $L \perp L'$.

**Theorem 13–2**

*Two nonvertical lines are parallel if and only if they have the same slope.*

Suppose now that we have two perpendicular lines, intersecting at $P$. Suppose that neither of our lines is vertical.

We take a point $Q$, on one of the lines, above and to the right of $P$, and complete the right triangle $\triangle PRQ$. We then take a point $Q'$, on the other line, above and to the left of $P$ such that $PQ' = PQ$. We complete the right triangle $\triangle Q'R'P$.

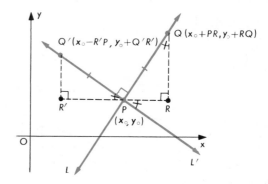

As indicated in the figure, $\angle PQR \cong \angle Q'PR'$, because both are complementary to $\angle QPR$. And $\angle PRQ \cong \angle Q'R'P$, because both are right angles. By Corollary 12–4.1, it follows that

$$\triangle PRQ \sim \triangle Q'R'P.$$

Therefore

$$\frac{RQ}{PR} = \frac{R'P}{Q'R'}.$$

By the slope formula, the slope of $L$ is

$$m = \frac{(y_0 + RQ) - y_0}{(x_0 + PR) - x_0} = \frac{RQ}{PR},$$

and the slope of $L'$ is

$$m' = \frac{(y_0 + Q'R') - y_0}{(x_0 - R'P) - x_0} = -\frac{Q'R'}{R'P} = -\frac{1}{m}.$$

**Quiz**

**1.** $\triangle ABC$ has vertices $A(-1, 4)$, $B(6, -3)$, and $C(10, 13)$. Determine the slope of the altitude to side $\overline{AC}$.
   (ans: $-\frac{11}{9}$)

**2.** Determine the smallest positive integers $a$ and $b$, such that if $A = (-6, 12)$, $B = (-4, 3)$, $C = (0, b)$, and $D = (a, 0)$, then $\overleftrightarrow{AB} \parallel \overleftrightarrow{CD}$.
   (ans: $a = 2$ and $b = 9$)

The same scheme works in reverse.

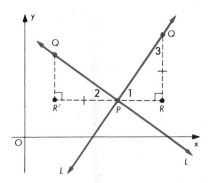

Given that $m' = -1/m$, we construct $\triangle PRQ$ and $\triangle Q'R'P$ as before, with $PR' = RQ$. We have

$$m = \frac{RQ}{PR}, \qquad m' = -\frac{Q'R'}{RP}.$$

Since $m' = -1/m$, it follows that

$$\frac{Q'R'}{R'P} = \frac{PR}{RQ}.$$

Therefore

$$\frac{Q'R'}{PR} = \frac{R'P}{RQ}.$$

By the SAS Similarity Theorem,

$$\triangle PRQ \sim \triangle Q'R'P.$$

Therefore $\angle 2 \cong \angle 3$, $\angle 1$ and $\angle 2$ are complementary, and $L \perp L'$.

**Theorem 13–3**

*Two nonvertical lines are perpendicular if and only if their slopes are negative reciprocals of each other.*

Neither of the last two theorems applies to the case where one of the two given lines is vertical. But for vertical lines, the facts are plain. If $L$ is vertical, then the lines parallel to $L$ are simply the other vertical lines. And the lines perpendicular to a vertical line are simply the horizontal lines.

**6.** The slope of $\overline{AB} = -1$, and the slope of $\overline{CD} = -1$; therefore $\square ABCD$ is a trapezoid. $\overline{AC}$ is horizontal, and $\overline{BD}$ is vertical; therefore the diagonals of $\square ABCD$ are perpendicular.

**12.** $\dfrac{3-1}{k-(-2)} = \dfrac{k-0}{5-1}$; $\dfrac{2}{k+2} = \dfrac{k}{4}$;

$k^2 + 2k - 8 = 0$; $(k+4)(k-2) = 0$;

$k + 4 = 0$ or $k - 2 = 0$; $k = -4$ or $k = 2$.

**13.** $\dfrac{3-1}{k-(-2)} = -\dfrac{5-1}{k-0}$; $\dfrac{2}{k+2} = \dfrac{-4}{k}$;

$k = -\dfrac{4}{3}$.

**14.** The slope of $\overleftrightarrow{QP} = -2$, and the slope

of $\overleftrightarrow{QR} = \dfrac{b+6}{b-5}$. If $\overleftrightarrow{QP} \perp \overleftrightarrow{QR}$, then

$\dfrac{b+6}{b-5} = -\left(\dfrac{1}{-2}\right)$. Therefore, $2b + 2 =$

$b - 5$, and $b = -17$.

## Problem Set 13–5

**1.** $L_1$, $L_2$, $L_3$, and $L_4$ are lines with slopes $\frac{2}{3}$, $-4$, $-1\frac{1}{2}$, $\frac{1}{4}$, respectively. Which pairs of lines are perpendicular? $L_1 \perp L_3$ , $L_2 \perp L_4$

**2.** Consider the points $A(-1, 5)$, $B(5, 1)$, $C(6, -2)$, $D(0, 2)$. Find the slopes of $\overleftrightarrow{AB}$, $\overleftrightarrow{BC}$, $\overleftrightarrow{CD}$, and $\overleftrightarrow{AD}$. Is $\square ABCD$ a parallelogram? Yes

**3.** Without plotting the points, determine which of the quadrilaterals whose vertices are given here are parallelograms.

(a) $A(-2, -2)$, $B(4, 2)$, $C(9, 1)$, $D(3, -3)$

(b) $K(-5, -2)$, $L(-4, 2)$, $M(4, 6)$, $N(3, 1)$ s($\overline{KL}$) = 4 , s($\overline{MN}$) = 5

(c) $P(5, 6)$, $Q(7, -3)$, $R(-2, -12)$, $S(-4, -3)$

**4.** The vertices of a triangle are $A(16, 0)$, $B(9, 2)$, and $C(0, 0)$.

(a) What are the slopes of its sides? s($\overline{AB}$) = $-\frac{2}{7}$, s($\overline{BC}$) = $\frac{2}{9}$, s($\overline{CA}$) = 0

(b) What are the slopes of its altitudes? $\frac{7}{2}$ , $-\frac{9}{2}$ , and slope of altitude from B is undefined.

**5.** Given the points $E(-4, 0)$, $G(3, 5)$, and $K(8, -2)$. Show that the product of the slope of $\overleftrightarrow{EG}$ and the slope of $\overleftrightarrow{GK}$ is $-1$. s($\overleftrightarrow{EG}$) · s($\overleftrightarrow{GK}$) = $\frac{5}{7} \cdot \frac{-7}{5} = -1$

**6.** Prove that the quadrilateral with vertices $A(-2, 2)$, $B(2, -2)$, $C(4, 2)$, and $D(2, 4)$ is a trapezoid with perpendicular diagonals.

**7.** Consider the points $W(0, 3)$, $X(6, 4)$, $Y(12, -3)$, $Z(-2, -12)$. Which two lines determined by these points are perpendicular? Prove your answer. s($\overleftrightarrow{XZ}$) = 2 , s($\overleftrightarrow{YW}$) = $-\frac{1}{2}$ , therefore, $\overleftrightarrow{XZ} \perp \overleftrightarrow{YW}$

**8.** Four points taken in pairs determine six segments. For each set of four points given below, find out which segments are parallel.

(a) $A(3, 6)$, $B(8, 2)$, $C(5, 9)$, $D(6, -1)$ $\overline{BC}$ ‖ $\overline{AD}$, $\overline{AC}$ ‖ $\overline{BD}$

(b) $P(0, -8)$, $Q(3, -2)$, $R(4, 0)$, $S(7, 6)$ P, Q, R, S are collinear s($\overline{PQRS}$) = 2

**9.** Prove that the triangle whose vertices are $H(-12, 1)$, $K(9, 3)$, and $M(11, -18)$ is a right triangle. s($\overline{HK}$) = $\frac{2}{21}$, s($\overline{KM}$) = $-\frac{21}{2}$ , $\overline{KM} \perp \overline{HK}$ and $\triangle HKM$ is a right triangle

**10.** Show that the line through $(3n, 0)$ and $(0, 7n)$ is parallel to the line through $(0, 21n)$ and $(9n, 0)$. Slope of 1st line = $-\frac{7}{3}$ = Slope of 2nd line

**11.** If the line containing points $(-8, m)$ and $(2, 1)$ is parallel to the line containing points $(11, -1)$ and $(7, m + 1)$, what must be the value of $m$? m = -4

**12.** What values of $k$ will make the line containing points $(k, 3)$ and $(-2, 1)$ parallel to the line through $(5, k)$ and $(1, 0)$? k = 2 or k = -4

**13.** In Problem 12, what values of $k$ will make the lines perpendicular? k = $-\frac{4}{3}$

**14.** Given the points $P(1, 2)$, $Q(5, -6)$, and $R(b, b)$, determine the value of $b$ so that $\angle PQR$ is a right angle. b = -17

**15.** Find the slopes of the six lines determined by the points $A(-5, 4)$, $B(3, 5)$, $C(7, -2)$, $D(-1, -3)$. Prove that $\square ABCD$ is a rhombus.

**16.** A ray $\overrightarrow{PQ}$ makes an angle of 30° with the $x$-axis. $\overline{QR} \perp \overrightarrow{PQ}$. If $P, Q, R$ are the points $P(-4, 0)$, $Q(5, 3\sqrt{3})$, and $R(x, 0)$, find the perimeter and area of $\triangle PQR$. $p\triangle PQR = 18 + 6\sqrt{3}$

$$a \triangle PQR = 18\sqrt{3}$$

## 13-6   THE DISTANCE FORMULA

If we know the coordinates of two points $P_1$ and $P_2$, then the points are determined. Therefore the distance between them is determined (Chapter 2, the Distance Postulate). We shall now find a way to *calculate* this distance $P_1P_2$ in terms of the coordinates $(x_1, y_1)$ and $(x_2, y_2)$.

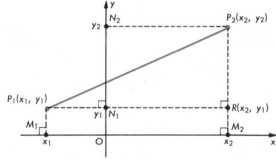

Let the feet of the perpendiculars from $P_1$ and $P_2$ be $M_1, N_1, M_2$, $N_2$, as indicated in the figure. Let $R$ be the point where the horizontal line through $P_1$ intersects the vertical line through $P_2$. Then

$$(P_1P_2)^2 = (P_1R)^2 + (RP_2)^2,$$

by the Pythagorean Theorem. $P_1R = M_1M_2$, because opposite sides of a rectangle are congruent. $RP_2 = N_1N_2$, for the same reason. Therefore, by substitution,

$$(P_1P_2)^2 = (M_1M_2)^2 + (N_1N_2)^2.$$

But we know by the Ruler Postulate that

$$M_1M_2 = |x_2 - x_1|$$

and

$$N_1N_2 = |y_2 - y_1|.$$

**Answers to Problems**

**15.** Since the slope of $\overline{AB}$ and the slope of $\overline{CD}$ each equal $\frac{1}{8}$, and the slope of $\overline{BC}$ and $\overline{DA}$ each equal $-\frac{7}{4}$, $\square ABCD$ is a parallelogram. Since the slope of $\overline{AC}$ equals $-\frac{1}{2}$, and the slope of $\overline{BD}$ equals 2, $\overline{AC} \perp \overline{BD}$. If the diagonals of a parallelogram are perpendicular, the parallelogram is a rhombus.

**16.** Since the slope of $\overrightarrow{PQ} = \sqrt{3}/3$, the slope of $\overline{RQ}$ must equal $-3/\sqrt{3}$. Substituting into the slope formula we find

$$-\frac{3}{\sqrt{3}} = \frac{0 - 3\sqrt{3}}{x - 5},$$

$$-3x + 15 = -9,$$

$$x = 8.$$

The coordinates of $R$ are $(8, 0)$. The distance $PR = 12$. Since $\overline{PR}$ is the hypotenuse of a 30-60-90 triangle, $PQ = 6\sqrt{3}$ and $QR = 6$. Therefore $p\triangle PQR = PQ + QR + RQ = 12 + 6 + 6\sqrt{3} = 18 + 6\sqrt{3}$, and $a\triangle PQR = \frac{1}{2}PQ \cdot RQ = \frac{1}{2}(6\sqrt{3})(6) = 18\sqrt{3}$.

**13-6 THE DISTANCE FORMULA**

**Classroom Notes**

The Distance Formula is important, and the students should be held responsible for its derivation. The generalized formula for the distance between two points in space (Problems 16 and 17 of Problem Set 13-6) is easily derived.

One technical point: In Chapter 2 we learned that the distance between two points on a horizontal (or vertical) line can be computed by means of the Ruler Postulate. For the points $P_1$ and $P_2$ in the figure below, $P_1P_2 = |x_2 - x_1|$.

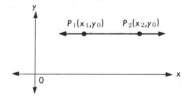

This distance can also be computed

by means of the Distance Formula:

$$P_1P_2 = \sqrt{(x_2 - x_1)^2 + (y_0 - y_0)^2}$$
$$= \sqrt{(x_2 - x_1)^2} = |x_2 - x_1|.$$

Students often write $\sqrt{(x_2 - x_1)^2} = x_2 - x_1$, which is, of course, incorrect. Remember that $\sqrt{a^2}$ equals $|a|$, not $a$, unless $a$ happens to be positive.

Some teachers prefer to teach the Midpoint Formula before teaching the Distance Formula. Since Sections 13–6 and 13–7 are not dependent on each other, they can be taught in either order.

Therefore

$$(P_1P_2)^2 = |x_2 - x_1|^2 + |y_2 - y_1|^2.$$

Since the square of a number is the same as the square of its absolute value, this expression can be written in the form

$$(P_1P_2)^2 = (x_2 - x_1)^2 + (y_2 - y_1)^2.$$

We are now almost done. Since $P_1P_2 \geq 0$, we get

$$P_1P_2 = \sqrt{(x_2 - x_1)^2 + (y_2 - y_1)^2}.$$

This is the formula that we were looking for. In deriving it, we have proved the following theorem.

**Theorem 13–4.** The Distance Formula

*The distance between the points $(x_1, y_1)$ and $(x_2, y_2)$ is*

$$\sqrt{(x_2 - x_1)^2 + (y_2 - y_1)^2}.$$

For example, if $P_1 = (3, 4)$ and $P_2 = (-2, 1)$, the formula tells us that

$$P_1P_2 = \sqrt{(-2 - 3)^2 + (1 - 4)^2}$$
$$= \sqrt{(-5)^2 + (-3)^2}$$
$$= \sqrt{25 + 9}$$
$$= \sqrt{34}.$$

Note that we could have read off this result from a figure, without using the formula. We have $a = 5$, $b = 3$. By the Pythagorean Theorem,

$$P_1P_2 = \sqrt{a^2 + b^2}$$
$$= \sqrt{5^2 + 3^2}$$
$$= \sqrt{34}.$$

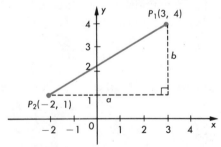

Note, however, that to see this we have to go through the same line of reasoning that we used in deriving the formula. The whole point of deriving general formulas is that we can go through a line of reasoning only *once*, and then apply the results whenever we need them, instead of repeating the same reasoning process over and over again.

## Problem Set 13-6

1. Use the distance formula to find the distance between the following points.

   (a) $(0, 0)$    and    $(3, 4)$ 5      (b) $(0, 0)$    and    $(3, -4)$ 5

   (c) $(1, 2)$    and    $(6, 14)$ 13      (d) $(8, 11)$    and    $(15, 35)$ 25

   (e) $(3, 8)$    and    $(-5, -7)$ 17      (f) $(-2, 3)$    and    $(-1, 4)$ $\sqrt{2}$

   (g) $(5, -1)$    and    $(-3, -5)$ $4\sqrt{5}$      (h) $(-6, 3)$    and    $(4, -2)$ $5\sqrt{5}$

2. Find the perimeter of a triangle whose vertices are $A(5, 7)$, $B(1, 10)$, and $C(-3, -8)$. $p\triangle ABC = 22 + 2\sqrt{85}$

3. $\triangle PQR$ has vertices $P(8, 0)$, $Q(-3, 2)$, and $R(10, 2)$.

   (a) Find the length of each side.      (b) Find $a\triangle PQR$.

   $PQ = \sqrt{125} = 5\sqrt{5}$, $QR = 13$, $RP = 2\sqrt{2}$      $a\triangle PQR = \frac{1}{2}(QR)h = \frac{1}{2} \cdot 13 \cdot 2 = 13$

4. The vertices of a quadrilateral are $D(4, -3)$, $E(7, 10)$, $F(-8, 2)$, $G(-1, -5)$. Find the length of each diagonal. $DF = 13$; $EG = 17$

5. Prove that the triangle whose vertices are $A(2, 3)$, $B(-1, -1)$, $C(3, -4)$ is isosceles. $AB = 5$, $BC = 5$, therefore $\triangle ABC$ is isosceles

6. A triangle has vertices $G(0, 7)$, $H(5, -5)$, and $K(10, 7)$. Find the length of the altitude to the shortest side. Altitude from H to $\overline{GK}$ is 12

7. Given the points $A(-1, 6)$, $B(1, 4)$, and $C(7, -2)$. Find $AB$ and $BC$. Prove that $B$ is between $A$ and $C$. $AB = 2\sqrt{2}$, $BC = 6\sqrt{2}$, $AC = 8\sqrt{2}$
   Since $AB + BC = AC$, $B$ is, by definition, between $A$ and $C$.

8. Given points $D(-4, -6)$, $E(-1, -2)$, and $F(3, 1)$. Show that $E$ is not between $D$ and $F$. $DE = 5$, $EF = 5$, $DF = 7\sqrt{2}$. $DE + EF \neq DF$;
   E is not between D and F by definition.

9. $\triangle KLM$ has vertices $K(-5, 18)$, $L(10, -2)$, and $M(-5, -10)$.
   $KL = 25$, $LM = 17$, $MK = 28$   h to $\overline{MK} = 15$
   (a) Find the perimeter of $\triangle KLM$.      (b) Find $a\triangle KLM$.
   $p\triangle KLM = 70$                 $a\triangle KLM = 210$

10. A triangle has vertices $M(-6, 0)$, $P(0, 6)$, and $Q(2, -2)$.

    (a) Find the perimeter of $\triangle MPQ$. $p\triangle MPQ = 6\sqrt{2} + 4\sqrt{17}$

    (b) Find the length of the altitude to the longest side. $QF = 5\sqrt{2}$

    (c) Find the area of the triangle. $a\triangle MPQ = \frac{1}{2}(6\sqrt{2})(5\sqrt{2}) = 30$

## Answers to Problems

**11.** Designate the points as follows: $A(-6, 0)$, $C(0, 6)$, $B(b, -b)$. Then since $AC = 6\sqrt{2}$, $AB$ must equal $6\sqrt{2}$. Therefore, $AB^2 = [-6 - b]^2 + [0 - (-b)]^2 = (b^2 + 12b + 36) + b^2 = 2b^2 + 12b + 36 = (6\sqrt{2})^2$. Hence, $b^2 + 6b - 18 = 0$. By the quadratic formula, $b = -3 \pm 3\sqrt{3}$. Therefore the coordinates of vertex $B$ are $B(-3 + 3\sqrt{3}, 3 - 3\sqrt{3})$ or $B(-3 - 3\sqrt{3}, 3 + 3\sqrt{3})$. It is easy to check that $BC = 6\sqrt{2}$.

**12.** You must travel 6 blocks to the east and 8 blocks north, a total of 14 blocks. There are obviously many different routes between your starting point and destination, each of which is 14 blocks long. In contrast, the shortest distance between your starting point and destination is

$$\sqrt{(6-12)^2 + (2-10)^2}$$
$$= \sqrt{6^2 + 8^2} = \sqrt{100}$$
$$= 10 \text{ blocks.}$$

The shortest distance, however, lies along the straight line between the two points and since this line runs through houses, you cannot drive a taxi over it.

**14.** (b) In right $\triangle ADC$, $AD^2 = AC^2 + CD^2$. And in right $\triangle ABC$, $AC^2 = AB^2 + BC^2$. Therefore, by substitution, $AD^2 = AB^2 + BC^2 + CD^2$. Since $A$ and $B$ lie on a line parallel to one of the coordinate axes, it is easy to compute $AB = (5 - 0)$. Similarly, $BC = 8 - (-4) = 8 + 4$, and $CD = 4 - (-2) = 4 + 2$. Therefore, $AD^2 = (5 - 0)^2 + (8 + 4)^2 + (4 + 2)^2$.

**16.** Let $R$ be the point whose coordinates are $R(x_2, y_1, z_1)$, and let $S$ be the point whose coordinates are $S(x_2, y_2, z_1)$. Then, in the horizontal right $\triangle PRS$, $PS^2 = PR^2 + RS^2 = (x_1 - x_2)^2 + (y_1 - y_2)^2$. And, in the vertical right $\triangle PSQ$, $PQ^2 = PS^2 + QS^2 = (x_1 - x_2)^2 + (y_1 - y_2)^2 + (z_1 - z_2)^2$. Therefore,
$$PQ = \sqrt{(x_1 - x_2)^2 + (y_1 - y_2)^2 + (z_1 - z_2)^2}.$$

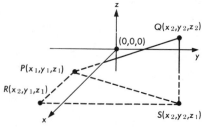

---

**11.** Find the values of $b$ such that the triangle whose vertices are $(-6, 0)$, $(0, 6)$, and $(b, -b)$ is equilateral. $b = -3 \pm 3\sqrt{3}$

**12.** In a very carefully planned city the streets are laid out with numbered avenues running north-south and numbered streets running east-west, as in the diagram at right in such a way that they form congruent squares. If you get into a taxi at the corner of 2nd Street and 6th Avenue and direct the driver to take you to 10th Street and 12th Avenue by the shortest possible route, what is the distance (in number of blocks) you travel? Is this the shortest distance between the two points? Explain. 14 blocks

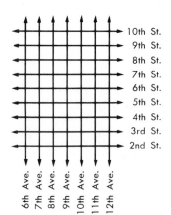

---

**13.** In the rectangular solid on the left below, one corner is at the origin and $A$, $B$, and $C$ are on the x-, y-, and z-axes, respectively. $P'$ is the projection of $P$ into the xy-plane. $(OP)^2 = (OP')^2 + (PP')^2$

(a) Find $OP'$. $= 10$   (b) Find $OP$. $= 5\sqrt{5}$   (c) Find $CP'$. $= OP = 5\sqrt{5}$

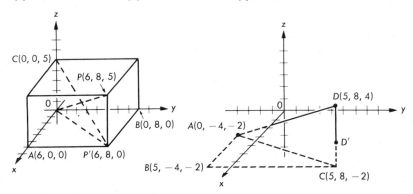

**14.** For the figure on the right above

(a) Find $AB$, $BC$, $AC$, $DC$, and $AD$.   $\overset{5}{AB}$, $\overset{12}{BC}$, $\overset{13}{AC}$, $\overset{6}{DC}$   $\sqrt{205}$

(b) Show that $AD^2 = (5 - 0)^2 + (8 + 4)^2 + (4 + 2)^2$.

**15.** Find the distance from the origin to the point $P(a, b, c)$. Does the resulting formula change if $a$, $b$, or $c$ is a negative number? [*Hint:* Use the figure of Problem 14 above to help you.] $OP = \sqrt{a^2 + b^2 + c^2}$

**16.** Show with a diagram similar to the figure of Problem 15 above that the distance $PQ$ between $P(x_1, y_1, z_1)$ and $Q(x_2, y_2, z_2)$ is given by the formula $PQ = \sqrt{(x_1 - x_2)^2 + (y_1 - y_2)^2 + (z_1 - z_2)^2}$.

**Answers to Problems**

20. (b) We cannot immediately conclude that figure ABCD is a parallelogram, since we do not
know that the four points are
coplanar. [In fact, the four
points are coplanar. This can
be ascertained by observing
that diagonals $\overline{AC}$ and $\overline{BD}$ have
the same midpoint.]

**17.** Find the distance $PQ$ if the coordinates of $P$ and $Q$ are given by the following.

(a) $P(4, -1, -5)$, $Q(7, 3, 7)$  PQ = 13

(b) $P(0, 4, 5)$,  $Q(-6, 2, 3)$  PQ = $2\sqrt{11}$

(c) $P(3, 0, 7)$,  $Q(-1, 3, 7)$  PQ = 5

(d) $P(-3, 4, -5)$, $Q(6, -8, 3)$  PQ = 17

.  (e) $P(1, 2, 3)$,  $Q(2, 3, 4)$  PQ = $\sqrt{3}$

**18.** Prove that the triangle with vertices $A(2, 0, 8)$,  $B(8, -4, 6)$, and $C(-4, -2, 4)$ is isosceles. By distance formula in Problem 16
AB = $\sqrt{56}$, AC = $\sqrt{56}$ (BC = $\sqrt{152}$) and △ABC is isosceles.

**19.** Show that $\triangle ABC$ is a right triangle if its vertices are
AB = 15, AC = 20, BC = 25
$A(2, 4, 1)$,  $B(11, -8, 1)$,  and  $C(2, 4, 21)$.
(AB)² + (AC)² = (BC)² so △ABC is a right triangle

**20.** The figure $ABCD$ has vertices $A(3, 2, 5)$, $B(1, 1, 1)$, $C(4, 0, 3)$, and $D(6, 1, 7)$.

(a) Show that its opposite sides are congruent. AB = CD = $\sqrt{21}$, BC = DA = $\sqrt{14}$

(b) Is $ABCD$ necessarily a parallelogram? No

## 13–7 THE MIDPOINT FORMULA

### Classroom Notes

While the proof of Theorem 13–5 is easy, and the theorem is easy to apply, the proof of Theorem 13–6 is difficult and the formula is easily forgotten. The exercises on the application of Theorem 13–6 (Problems 3, 4, and 5 of Problem Set 13–7) can be done as readily by common-sense reasoning as by the use of Theorem 13–6. Thus, it is not very important for the student to remember this theorem.

## 13–7   THE MIDPOINT FORMULA.   THE POINT DIVIDING A SEGMENT IN A GIVEN RATIO

Consider a segment $\overline{P_1P_2}$, on the $x$-axis:

Let $P$ be the midpoint, let the coordinates of these three points be as shown in the figure, and suppose that $x_1 < x_2$. It is then rather easy to see how to express $x$ in terms of $x_1$ and $x_2$. We want

$$P_1P = PP_2.$$

Since

$$P_1P = |x - x_1| = x - x_1$$

and

$$PP_2 = |x_2 - x| = x_2 - x,$$

our first equation means that

$$x - x_1 = x_2 - x \quad \text{or} \quad x = \frac{x_1 + x_2}{2}.$$

This formula also works when $x_2 < x_1$. (Proof? If we interchange $x_1$ and $x_2$, the problem is unchanged and so is the formula.)

**1.** If $R = (-1, -6)$ and $S = (5, 9)$, what are the coordinates of the two points of trisection of $\overline{RS}$?

(ans: $(1, -1)$ and $(3, 4)$)

**2.** Using coordinates prove that the medians to the congruent sides of an isosceles triangle are congruent.

(ans: Select a coordinate system so that for the isosceles triangle $\triangle ABC$, vertices $A$, $B$, and $C$ have coordinates $(a, 0)$, $(-a, 0)$, and $(0, c)$, respectively. The coordinates of $M$ and $N$, where $M$ and $N$ are midpoints of $\overline{AC}$ and $\overline{BC}$, respectively, are $(a/2, c/2)$ and $(-a/2, c/2)$. Then,

$$AN = \sqrt{\left(a - \left(\frac{-a}{2}\right)\right)^2 + \left(\frac{-c}{2}\right)^2}$$

$$= \sqrt{\left(\frac{3a}{2}\right)^2 + \left(\frac{c}{2}\right)^2}$$

and

$$BM = \sqrt{\left(\frac{a}{2} - (-a)\right)^2 + \left(\frac{c}{2}\right)^2}$$

$$= \sqrt{\left(\frac{3a}{2}\right)^2 + \left(\frac{c}{2}\right)^2}.$$

This shows that $AN = BM$.)

---

Once we have a midpoint formula for segments on the $x$-axis, it is easy to pass to the general case.

Here, if $P$ is the midpoint of $\overline{P_1P_2}$, then $M$ is the midpoint of $\overline{M_1M_2}$. (Why?) Therefore

$$x = \frac{x_1 + x_2}{2}.$$

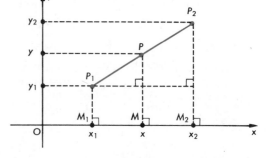

In the same way, we get

$$y = \frac{y_1 + y_2}{2}.$$

To sum up we state the following theorem.

**Theorem 13-5.** The Midpoint Formula

*Given $P_1 = (x_1, y_1)$ and $P_2 = (x_2, y_2)$. The midpoint of $\overline{P_1P_2}$ is the point*

$$P = \left(\frac{x_1 + x_2}{2}, \frac{y_1 + y_2}{2}\right).$$

Consider now a more general problem. Given a segment $\overline{P_1P_2}$ on the $x$-axis, and a positive real number $r$.

We want to find the coordinate of the point $P$ which divides $P_1P_2$ in the ratio $r$ to 1. That is, we want

$$\frac{P_1P}{PP_2} = r, \quad \text{or} \quad P_1P = rPP_2.$$

If $x_1 < x_2$, as in the figure, this means that

$$x - x_1 = r(x_2 - x), \quad \text{or} \quad x + rx = x_1 + rx_2,$$

or

$$x = \frac{x_1 + rx_2}{1 + r}.$$

Note that for $r = 1$, this ought to give the coordinate of the midpoint. (Does it?)

**Explanation for Problems**

After a discussion of Problem 15, you may wish to have the students generalize the formula for the coordinates of the midpoint $M$ of the segment joining $P(x_1, y_1, z_1)$ and $Q(x_2, y_2, z_2)$.

ans:

$$M = \left(\frac{x_1 + x_2}{2}, \frac{y_1 + y_2}{2}, \frac{z_1 + z_2}{2}\right)$$

For the case $x_2 < x_1$, the formula is exactly the same, but its derivation is slightly different. (We use $P_1P = x_1 - x$, $PP_2 = x - x_2$, and get the same answer.)

As in the case of the midpoint, we can easily pass to the general case. If

$$\frac{P_1P}{PP_2} = r,$$

then

$$\frac{M_1M}{MM_2} = r,$$

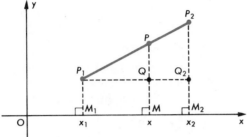

because $\triangle P_1PQ \sim \triangle P_1P_2Q_2$. Therefore it follows that

$$x = \frac{x_1 + rx_2}{1 + r}.$$

In exactly the same way, we obtain

$$y = \frac{y_1 + ry_2}{1 + r}.$$

Thus we have the following theorem.

**Theorem 13–6**

*If $P$ is between $P_1$ and $P_2$, and $\dfrac{P_1P}{PP_2} = r$, then*

$$P = \left(\frac{x_1 + rx_2}{1 + r}, \frac{y_1 + ry_2}{1 + r}\right).$$

**Problem Set 13–7**

**1.** Find the coordinates of the midpoint of each segment in the figure.

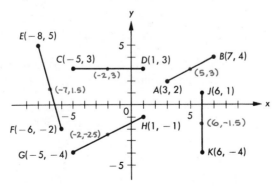

**7.** The midpoint of diagonal $\overline{AC}$ is (3.5, 2). The midpoint of diagonal $\overline{BD}$ is (3.5, 2). Since the diagonals of $\square ABCD$ have the same midpoint, they bisect each other. And by Theorem 9–21, if the diagonals of a quadrilateral bisect each other, the quadrilateral is a parallelogram.

**2.** Use the midpoint formula to find the coordinates of the midpoint of the segment joining each pair of the following points.

(a)  (6, 0)          and   (10, 2) (8,1)          (b)  (5, 7)    and   (11, 17) (8,12)

(c)  (12, 3)         and   (3, 2) (7.5,2.5)       (d)  (−5, 6)   and   (6, −5) (0.5,0.5)

(e)  $(\sqrt{2}, -\sqrt{3})$  and  $(\sqrt{18}, \sqrt{75})$ (2√2,2√3)     (f)  $(\frac{5}{4}, -\frac{5}{3})$  and  $(\frac{3}{4}, \frac{2}{3})$ (1,-0.5)

(g)  (a, 0)          and   (0, b) (a/2,b/2)       (h)  (a, b)    and   (c, d) ($\frac{a+c}{2}$, $\frac{b+d}{2}$)

**3.** If $A(3, 15)$ and $C(13, 0)$ are the end points of a segment and $B$ is a point of $\overline{AC}$, find the coordinates of $B$ given that the ratio $AB/BC$ equals the following.

(a) 4 (11,3)     (b) $\frac{2}{3}$ (7,9)

(c) $\frac{1}{4}$ (5,12)     (d) $\frac{3}{2}$ (9,6)

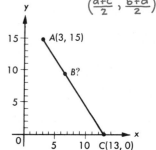

**4.** Given the points $P(5, 2)$ and $R(20, 14)$, and $Q$ between $P$ and $R$. Find the coordinates of $Q$ if $PQ/QR$ equals

(a) $\frac{1}{2}$. (10,6)     (b) 2. (15,10)     (c) $\frac{1}{3}$. (8.75,5)     (d) 4. (17,11.6)

**5.** What are the coordinates of the two points that trisect the segment having end points $(2, -3)$ and $(8, 9)$? $Q_1$ (4,1) , $Q_2$ (6,5)

**6.** If the vertices of a triangle are $A(5, -1)$, $B(1, 5)$, and $C(-3, 1)$, what are the lengths of its medians? AM=√52, BN=5, CP=√37

**7.** The vertices of a quadrilateral are $A(0, 0)$, $B(5, 1)$, $C(7, 4)$ and $D(2, 3)$. Show that the two diagonals have the same midpoint. Is the quadrilateral a parallelogram? Why? M (3.5,2) , Yes

---

**8.** Given $P(-3, -4)$, $M(b, -1)$, and $Q(7, b)$. Find $b$ so that $M$ will be the midpoint of $\overline{PQ}$. b=2   (b,-1)=($\frac{-3+7}{2}$, $\frac{-4+b}{2}$)

**9.** Given $G(-5, 8)$, $K(2, a)$, and $H(b, 1)$. Find $a$ and $b$ so that $K$ will be the midpoint of $\overline{GH}$. a=4.5,b=9   (2,a)=($\frac{-5+b}{2}$, $\frac{8+1}{2}$)

**10.** A segment has midpoint $M(3, -5)$, and one end point is $A(2, -4)$. What are the coordinates of $B$, the other end point? B (4,-6)

**11.** Given the quadrilateral whose vertices are $A(3, -2)$, $B(-3, 4)$, $C(1, 8)$, and $D(7, 4)$. $W$, $X$, $Y$, $Z$ are the midpoints of $\overline{AB}$, $\overline{BC}$, $\overline{CD}$, and $\overline{DA}$, respectively.

(a) Find the coordinates of $W$, $X$, $Y$, $Z$. W(0,1), X(-1,6), Y(4,6), Z(5,1)

(b) Find the perimeter of $\square WXYZ$. WX=√26, XY=5, YZ=√26, ZW=5 ; p□WXYZ = 10+ 2√26

(c) Find the slopes of $\overline{WX}$ and $\overline{YZ}$. s(WX)=-5 , s(YZ)=-5

**12.** Using coordinates, prove that two of the medians of the triangle with vertices at $(m, 0)$, $(-m, 0)$, and $(0, 3m)$ are perpendicular to each other.

$$s(\overline{AE}) = \frac{\frac{3m}{2} - 0}{\frac{m}{2} - (-m)} = 1$$

$$s(\overline{BD}) = -1$$

$\overline{AE} \perp \overline{BD}$ by Theorem 13-3

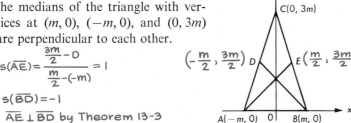

**13.** $A(-3, 2)$ and $B(5, 12)$ are two of the vertices of $\triangle ABC$. A line through $G$, the midpoint of $\overline{AB}$, and parallel to $\overline{AC}$, intersects $\overline{BC}$ at $H(10, 2)$. Find the coordinates of $C$, the third vertex. $C(15, -8)$

**14.** Given the figure, determine the coordinates of the midpoint of each of the segments $\overline{AO}$, $\overline{BO}$, $\overline{CO}$, $\overline{AB}$, $\overline{BC}$, and $\overline{AC}$.

The mid-point of $\overline{AO}$ is $(3,0,0)$
of $\overline{BO}$ is $(0,2,0)$
of $\overline{CO}$ is $(0,0,2)$
of $\overline{AB}$ is $(3,2,0)$
of $\overline{BC}$ is $(0,2,2)$
of $\overline{CA}$ is $(3,0,2)$

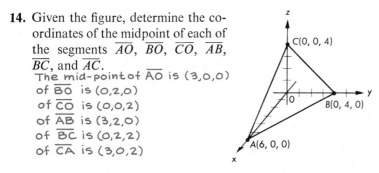

**15.** In the figure, $\overline{P'Q'}$ is the projection of $\overline{PQ}$ into the $xy$-plane, $\overline{PK} \parallel \overline{P'Q'}$, $\overline{P'A} \parallel y$-axis, $\overline{AQ'} \parallel x$-axis, $M$ is the midpoint of $\overline{PQ}$, $M'$ is the projection of $M$, $H$ is the midpoint of $\overline{QK}$, and $B$ and $C$ are midpoints of $\overline{AP'}$ and $\overline{AQ'}$, respectively.

(a) Why is $\overline{PP'} \parallel \overline{MM'} \parallel \overline{QQ'}$? Theorem 10-4

(b) Why is $M'$ the midpoint of $\overline{P'Q'}$?

(c) Find the coordinates of $P'$, $Q'$, $A$, and $K$. $P'(7,-3,0), Q'(1,9,0), A(7,9,0), K(1,9,3)$

(d) Find the coordinates of $B$, $C$, $H$, and $M'$. $B(7,3,0), C(4,9,0), H(1,9,6)$

(e) Find the coordinates of $M$, the midpoint of $\overline{PQ}$.
$M'(4,3,0)$
$M(4,3,6)$

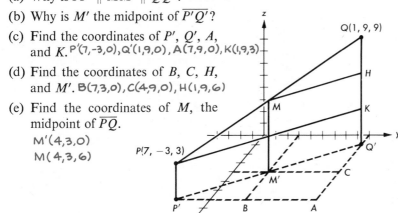

**13.** The coordinates of $G$, the midpoint of $\overline{AB}$, are $(1, 7)$. Since $\overline{GH}$ bisects one side, $\overline{AB}$, of $\triangle ABC$ and is parallel to a second side, $\overline{AC}$, $\overline{GH}$ bisects the third side, $\overline{BC}$; therefore, $H$ is the midpoint of $\overline{BC}$. Let the coordinates of $C$ be $(x, y)$. Then by the midpoint formula, the coordinates of $H$ are $\left(\dfrac{5 + x}{2}, \dfrac{12 + y}{2}\right)$. But since it is given that the coordinates of $H$ are $(10, 2)$, we have the equations: $\dfrac{5 + x}{2} = 10$, and $\dfrac{12 + y}{2} = 2$. Therefore $x = 15$, and $y = -8$. The coordinates of $C$ are $(15, -8)$.

**15.** (b) Since the three parallel lines $\overleftrightarrow{PP'}$, $\overleftrightarrow{MM'}$, and $\overleftrightarrow{QQ'}$ intercept congruent segments on transversal $\overleftrightarrow{PQ}$, they intercept congruent segments on transversal $\overleftrightarrow{P'Q'}$.

**18.** Since $BM' = 3$ and $MM' = 6$, we can conclude that $BM = \sqrt{45} = 3\sqrt{5}$, and that $p\triangle BMM' = 9 + 3\sqrt{5}$. Since $AQ' = 6$, and $QQ' = 9$, we can conclude that $AQ = 3\sqrt{13}$, and that $p\triangle AQQ' = 15 + 3\sqrt{13}$. However, the corresponding sides of $\triangle BMM'$ and $\triangle AQQ'$ are not proportional: $BM'/AQ' \neq MM'/QQ'$. Therefore it is not true that $\triangle BMM' \sim \triangle AQQ'$.

## 13–8 THE USE OF COORDINATE SYSTEMS IN PROVING GEOMETRIC THEOREMS

### Classroom Notes

The first step in applying coordinate methods is to choose a coordinate system in such a way as to make the algebra as simple as possible. For example, if we are given an isosceles triangle, we may place the axes as in the figure below and then use the properties of an isosceles triangle to determine the coordinates of the vertices.

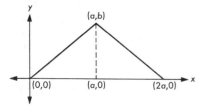

The student should be encouraged to draw on his knowledge of synthetic geometry and use the fact that the altitude to the base of an isosceles triangle bisects the base. Hence, the x-coordinate of the vertex should be half the x-coordinate of the end point of the base that is not at the origin. On the other hand the y-coordinate of the vertex is not determined by the coordinates of the other vertices and is an arbitrary positive number.

---

**16.** Find the coordinates of the midpoint of a segment joining the points:

(a) $(3, 5, 0)$ and $(1, 1, 8)$. $(2,3,4)$

(b) $(8, 5, 3)$ and $(0, 0, -5)$. $(4,2.5,-1)$

(c) $(-6, 2, 4)$ and $(6, -2, -4)$. $(0,0,0)$

(d) $(3\sqrt{2}, 2\sqrt{15}, -5\sqrt{3})$ and $(-\sqrt{2}, 0, \sqrt{27})$. $(\sqrt{2}, \sqrt{15}, -\sqrt{3})$

**17.** In Problem 15, find the coordinates of the two points which trisect $\overline{PQ}$. $T_1(5,1,5)$ and $T_2(3,5,7)$

**18.** In Problem 15, find the perimeters of $\triangle BMM'$ and $\triangle AQQ'$. Is $\triangle BMM' \sim \triangle AQQ'$? $p\triangle BMM' = 9 + 3\sqrt{5}$
$p\triangle AQQ' = 15 + 3\sqrt{13}$

## 13–8   THE USE OF COORDINATE SYSTEMS IN PROVING GEOMETRIC THEOREMS

We shall now see how coordinate systems can be put to work in proving geometric theorems. The main purpose of this section is to illustrate a certain method of working on geometry. The method will be easier to understand if the first illustrations that we deal with are simple ones. For this reason, we shall first apply the method to some theorems we already know.

### Theorem A

*The midpoint of the hypotenuse of a right triangle is equidistant from the vertices.*

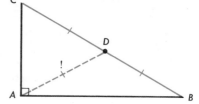

The first step in applying coordinate methods is to choose the coordinate system in such a way as to make the algebra as simple as possible. A good choice for this problem is the one shown in the figure below. That is, we put the origin at $A$, with $B$ and $C$ on the positive ends of the two axes. Thus $B = (a, 0)$, $C = (0, b)$, as in the figure. Therefore $D = (a/2, b/2)$, by the Midpoint Formula. Now

$$AD = \sqrt{\left(\frac{a}{2} - 0\right)^2 + \left(\frac{b}{2} - 0\right)^2},$$

and

$$BD = \sqrt{\left(a - \frac{a}{2}\right)^2 + \left(0 - \frac{b}{2}\right)^2}.$$

Therefore $AD = BD$. This proves the theorem, because $BD = CD$ by definition of the midpoint.

Our choice of axes was not the only good choice. The following figures suggest schemes which are just as easy.

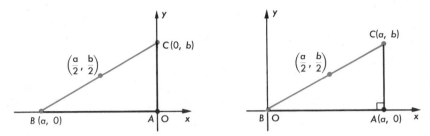

However, if you take the axes simply at random, you may turn an easy problem into a very hard one.

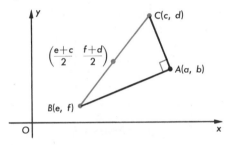

To start a proof, on the basis of this figure, you have to find a way to say, *algebraically*, that $\triangle ABC$ has a right angle at $A$. This can be done, but it doesn't look very easy or very pleasant.

In using coordinate systems to prove things about parallelograms, we nearly always place the axes as shown below at the right. Given a parallelogram $\square ABCD$, we put the origin at $A$, with $B$ on the positive end of the $x$-axis and $C$ and $D$ in the upper half-plane. Now the slope of $\overline{AB}$ is 0, and $\overline{AB} \parallel \overline{CD}$. Therefore the slope of $\overline{CD}$ is 0. This gives

$$\frac{e - c}{d - b} = 0.$$

Therefore we can replace $e$ by $c$ in the figure. (Why?) We also claim that

$$d = a + b.$$

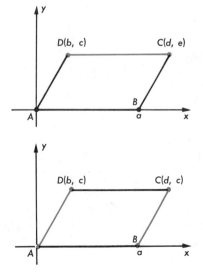

We might, alternatively, place the axes like this with the vertex on the $y$-axis:

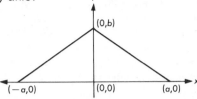

Then, since the altitude bisects the base, it divides the base into congruent segments, and therefore the end points of the base may be indicated by $(a, 0)$ and $(-a, 0)$.

*Caution:* Note that it is the figure which we are given and it is the coordinate system which we choose; we do not first set up a coordinate system and then place the figure on the coordinate system. See Problem 6 of Problem Set 13-8.

After having chosen a set of axes for the plane of the given figure, we still have to give names to the coordinates of the vertices of the figure, and there are some restrictions on how we can name them. Consider the parallelogram $\square ABCD$ on page 433 of the text. We designate the coordinates of $A$, $B$, and $D$ as $A(0, 0)$, $B(a, 0)$, and $D(b, c)$. The only fact about parallelograms that we have used to designate the coordinates of $C$ is the fact that the opposite sides of a parallelogram are, by definition, parallel. We can obtain the coordinates of $C$ more readily by using the fact that the opposite sides of a parallelogram are congruent. In the proof of Theorem B on page 434, it does not make any difference which approach we take to obtain the coordinates of $C$. But note that if we want to prove by coordinate methods that the opposite sides of parallelogram $\square ABCD$ are congruent, we can obviously not use *this* fact to obtain the coordinates of $C$. In general, when designating the coordinates of the vertices of a figure, use the definition of the figure or, when this is impractical, the basic properties of the figure. Caution students against using that property which is to be proved.

*A second word of caution:* The above discussion is based on the fact that it is *given* in the problem that the quadrilateral is a parallelogram.

If the problem is to *prove* that a quadrilateral is a parallelogram, then we obviously cannot use this fact in designating the coordinates of its vertices.

If class time is limited, you can use Problem Set 13–8 to conclude your work on proving theorems by coordinate methods. The equation of a line is a standard topic in algebra courses.

**Answers to Problems**

**1.** Compute $AC$ and $BD$ by the distance formula: $AC = \sqrt{(a - 0)^2 + (b - 0)^2} = \sqrt{a^2 + b^2}$. $BD = \sqrt{(a - 0)^2 + (0 - b)^2} = \sqrt{a^2 + b^2}$.

**2.** By the midpoint formula, the coordinates of $D$ and $E$ are $D(b, c)$ and $E(a + b, c)$. Since $D$ and $E$ have the same $y$-coordinate, $\overline{DE}$ is parallel to the $x$-axis, on which $\overline{AB}$ lies. Note $DE = a$, and $AB = 2a$.

**3.** Place the axes so that one vertex of the rhombus is the origin and one side lies along the positive $x$-axis. The vertices of the rhombus can then be designated by the coordinates: $A(0, 0)$, $B(a, 0)$, $C(a + b, c)$, and $D(b, c)$. Let $m_1$ be the slope of diagonal $\overline{AC}$, and $m_2$ be the slope of diagonal $\overline{BD}$. By the slope formula, $m_1 = \dfrac{c}{a + b}$, and $m_2 = \dfrac{-c}{a - b}$. Observe that

$$m_1 \cdot m_2 = \frac{c}{a + b} \cdot \frac{-c}{a - b} = \frac{-c^2}{a^2 - b^2}.$$

However, since the sides of a rhombus are congruent, $AB = AD$; and since by the distance formula, $AB^2 = a^2$, and $AD^2 = b^2 + c^2$, we can conclude that $a^2 = b^2 + c^2$. Therefore

$$m_1 \cdot m_2 = \frac{-c^2}{a^2 - b^2} = \frac{-c^2}{c^2} = -1,$$

and so $\overline{AC} \perp \overline{BD}$.

If $\overline{AD}$ and $\overline{BC}$ are not vertical, then they have slopes, and their slopes are the same. Thus

$$\frac{c - 0}{b - 0} = \frac{c - 0}{d - a},$$

$b = d - a$, and $d = a + b$. If $\overline{AD}$ and $\overline{BC}$ are vertical, then

$$b = 0, \quad d = a, \quad \text{and} \quad d = a + 0 = a + b,$$

as before.

We can therefore label our figure as shown on the right.

Once we know about this scheme, many theorems about parallelograms become very easy.

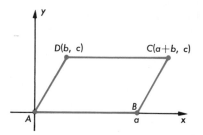

**Theorem B**

*If the diagonals of a parallelogram are congruent, then the parallelogram is a rectangle.*

**Proof.** In the notation of the figure above, we have given that $AC = BD$. By the Distance Formula, this says that

$$\sqrt{(a + b - 0)^2 + (c - 0)^2} = \sqrt{(a - b)^2 + (0 - c)^2},$$

or

$$(a + b)^2 + c^2 = (a - b)^2 + c^2,$$

or

$$a^2 + 2ab + b^2 + c^2 = a^2 - 2ab + b^2 + c^2.$$

Therefore

$$4ab = 0.$$

Since $a > 0$, it follows that $b = 0$, and this means that $D$ is on the $y$-axis. Therefore $\angle DAB$ is a right angle, and $\square ABCD$ is a rectangle.

The following problem set is designed to give you some practice in the use of coordinate systems. In solving these problems, therefore, you should try to make the algebra do most of the work, using the illustrative examples of this section as a model.

## Problem Set 13-8

Prove the following theorems using the methods of coordinate geometry.

**1.** The diagonals of the rectangle on the left below are equal in length.

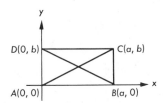 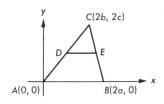

**2.** The segment between the midpoints of two sides of the triangle on the right above is parallel to the third side, and its length is one-half the length of the third side. [*Hint:* Since we will be finding the coordinates of midpoints and one-half of the base, it is convenient, although not necessary, to let the coordinates of $A$, $B$, and $C$ be as in the figure.]

**3.** The diagonals of a rhombus are perpendicular to each other. [*Hint:* Let the vertices be $(0, 0)$, $(a, 0)$, $(a + b, c)$, and $(b, c)$, Verify that the slopes are negative reciprocals.]

**4.** The median of a trapezoid is parallel to the bases, and its length is one-half the sum of the lengths of the bases.

**5.** The segment between the midpoints of the diagonals of a trapezoid is parallel to the bases and its length is one-half the difference of the lengths of the bases.

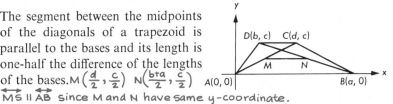

$M\left(\frac{d}{2}, \frac{c}{2}\right)$  $N\left(\frac{b+a}{2}, \frac{c}{2}\right)$

$\overleftrightarrow{MS} \parallel \overleftrightarrow{AB}$ since M and N have same y-coordinate.

**6.** The segments joining, in order, the midpoints of consecutive sides of a quadrilateral form a parallelogram. [*Note:* We can select our axes so that one vertex is $(0, 0)$ and a side of the figure is along the x-axis, no matter how "tipped" the figure may be.]

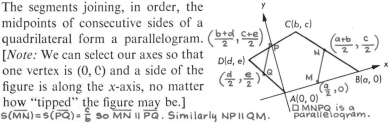

$s(\overline{MN}) = s(\overline{PQ}) = \frac{c}{b}$ so $\overline{MN} \parallel \overline{PQ}$. Similarly $\overline{NP} \parallel \overline{QM}$.

□ MNPQ is a parallelogram.

**7.** The segments joining, in order, the midpoints of consecutive sides of an isosceles trapezoid form a rhombus.

**8.** In $\triangle ABC$, if $\overline{CM}$ is the median to $\overline{AB}$, then

$$AC^2 + BC^2 = \frac{1}{2}AB^2 + 2CM^2.$$

[*Hint:* Choose the midpoint of $\overline{AB}$ at $(0, 0)$.]

---

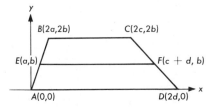

**8.** Place the axes so that the origin is the midpoint $M$ of $\overline{AB}$ and $\overline{AB}$ lies on the $x$-axis. Designate the coordinates of the vertices by $A(-a, 0)$, $B(a, 0)$ and $C(c, d)$. Then by direct application of the distance formula we can compute: $AC^2 = (c + a)^2 + d^2$, $BC^2 = (c - a)^2 + d^2$, $\frac{1}{2}AB^2 = \frac{1}{2}(2a)^2 = 2a^2$, and $2CM^2 = 2(c^2 + d^2)$. Observe that $AC^2 + BC^2 = \frac{1}{2}AB^2 + 2CM^2$.

**9.** It is easy to compute by the distance formula: $AC^2 = a^2 + c^2$, $AB^2 = (a - b)^2 = a^2 - 2ab + b^2$, $BC^2 = b^2 + c^2$, and $-2AB \cdot DB = -2(b - a)b = 2ab - 2b^2$. Then observe that $AC^2 = AB^2 + BC^2 - 2AB \cdot DB$.

**10.** Designate the coordinates of the vertices of the parallelogram as $A(0, 0)$, $B(a, 0)$, $C(a + b, c)$, and $D(b, c)$. Then compute by the distance formula that $AB^2 = CD^2 = a^2$, $AD^2 = BC^2 = b^2 + c^2$, $AC^2 = (a + b)^2 + c^2$ and $BD^2 = (a - b)^2 + c^2$. Then observe that $AB^2 + BC^2 + CD^2 + DA^2 = AC^2 + BD^2$.

**11.** Select a coordinate system as indicated below. Then, $M = (b, c)$, $N = (a + d, e)$.

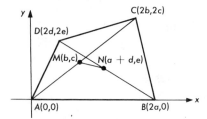

$AB^2 = 4a^2$.
$BC^2 = 4(a - b)^2 + 4c^2$.
$CD^2 = 4(b - d)^2 + 4(c - e)^2$.
$DA^2 = 4d^2 + 4e^2$.
$AC^2 = 4b^2 + 4c^2$.
$BD^2 = 4(a - d)^2 + 4e^2$.
$MN^2 = (a + d - b)^2 + (e - c)^2$.

From these expressions the given equation can be verified. Note that

$(a + d - b)^2 = a^2 + d^2 + b^2 + 2ad - 2ab - 2bd$.

**12.** Recall that if $R = (a_1, b_1, c_1)$ and $S = (a_2, b_2, c_2)$, then $RS^2 = (a_1 - a_2)^2 + (b_1 - b_2)^2 + (c_1 - c_2)^2$, and the midpoint of $\overline{RS}$ has the coordinates

$$\left( \frac{a_1 + a_2}{2}, \frac{b_1 + b_2}{2}, \frac{c_1 + c_2}{2} \right).$$

**9.** In any triangle, the square of a side opposite an acute angle is equal to the sum of the squares of the other two sides minus twice the product of one of those sides and the projection of the other on it. To prove: $AC^2 = AB^2 + BC^2 - 2AB \cdot DB$. At what point in the calculation do you need the hypothesis that $\angle B$ is acute? **Not necessary to proof.**

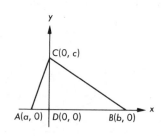

**10.** The sum of the squares of the sides of a parallelogram is equal to the sum of the squares of the diagonals.

**11.** In any quadrilateral the sum of the squares of the sides is equal to the sum of the squares of the diagonals plus four times the square of the length of the segment between the midpoints of the diagonals.

**12.** Prove that the four diagonals of a rectangular solid are congruent and intersect at a common midpoint. **Proof follows from distance and midpoint formulas in three dimensions.**

## 13-9   THE GRAPH OF A CONDITION

By a *graph* we mean a figure lying in the plane, that is, a set of points. Thus angles, triangles and half-planes are graphs, and so are segments, rays and lines.

The term "graph" is usually used when we are describing a figure by stating a condition which is satisfied by all points of the given figure, and by no other points. Here are some examples.

| Condition | Graph |
|---|---|
| 1. $y > 0$. | 1. The half plane above the $x$-axis |
| 2. $x > 0$. | 2. The half plane to the right of the $y$-axis |
| 3. $x = 0$. | 3. The $y$-axis |
| 4. $x > 0$ and $y > 0$. | 4. The first quadrant |
| 5. $x = 1$. | 5. The vertical line through $(1, 0)$ |
| 6. $x = 3$. | 6. The vertical line through $(3, 0)$ |
| 7. $1 < x < 3$. | 7. The infinite strip lying between the lines described by Conditions 5 and 6 |

The seven graphs are shown on p. 437.

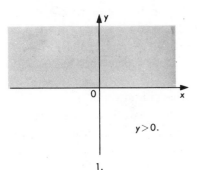

$y > 0.$

1.

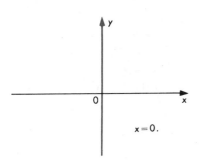

$x = 0.$

3.

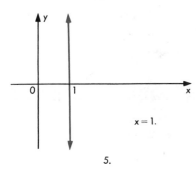

$x = 1.$

5.

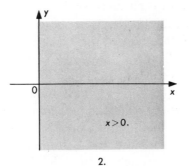

$x > 0.$

2.

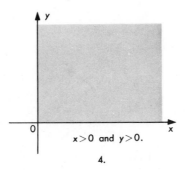

$x > 0$ and $y > 0.$

4.

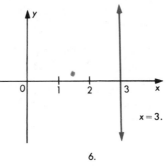

$x = 3.$

6.

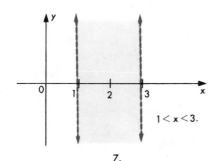

$1 < x < 3.$

7.

## 13-9 THE GRAPH OF A CONDITION

### Background Material

One of the dangers, in the intro-duction to coordinate geometry, is that the student will learn cookbook rules for drawing the graphs of linear equations without properly grasping the relation between an equation (or an inequality) and its graph. Hence this introductory sec-tion, in which the idea of the graph of a condition stands alone, apart from techniques which might en-cumber it or which might actually *replace* it in the mind of the student.

### Classroom Notes

Since most students will have at least encountered the idea of a graph of a condition in their first year algebra, you may wish to cover this section rapidly.

### Quiz

Given: $A = \{(x, y): 1 \leq x \leq 5\}$ and
    $B = \{(x, y): |y| \leq 3\}$.
1. Sketch the graph of $A \cap B$.
   (ans: The graph is the set of points in the rectangular region with vertices (1, 3), (1, −3), (5, 3), and (5, 3).)
2. Sketch the graph of $A \cup B$.
   (ans: The graph is the set of points in two infinite rectangular strips. One strip is bounded by the lines $x = 1$ and $x = 5$, and the other is bounded by the lines $y = 3$ and $y = −3$.)

## Answers to Problems

1. (a) The vertical line with an x-intercept equal to 5
   (b) The half-plane lying to the left of the vertical line, $x = -2$
   (c) The half-plane, together with its edge, lying above the horizontal line, $y = 4$
   (d) The x-axis
2. (a) Two vertical lines, $x = 2$ and $x = -2$
   (b) An infinitely long "strip" lying between the horizontal lines $y = 1$ and $y = -1$
   (c) The union of (1) the half-plane to the right of the vertical line $x = 3$, together with its edge, and (2) the half-plane to the left of the vertical line $x = -3$, together with its edge
3. The union of the two graphs is the set of all points which are on the vertical line $x = 3$, or on the horizontal line, $y = 2$. The intersection of the two graphs is the point $P(3, 2)$.
5. The intersection is a rectangular region lying in the first quadrant whose vertical edges are contained in the lines $x = 0$ and $x = 6$ and whose horizontal edges are contained in the lines $y = 0$ and $y = 4$.
7. A rectangular region with vertical edges contained in the vertical lines $x = -1$ and $x = 3$, and with horizontal edges contained in the horizontal lines $y = -2$ and $y = 5$. The area of the region is 28.
8. $\sqrt{(x-1)^2 + (y-0)^2}$
   $\qquad = \sqrt{(x-7)^2 + (y-0)^2}$,

or on simplification, $x = 4$. There are infinitely many points satisfying this equation. The set of all such points is the perpendicular bisector of $\overline{AB}$, that is, the vertical line $x = 4$.

10.

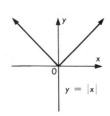

$y = |x|$

---

In each of these cases, we say that the figure is the *graph* of the condition that describes it. Thus each of the seven figures on p. 437 is the *graph* of the indicated condition.

*To repeat:* the *graph of a condition* is the set of all points that satisfy the condition.

This term is most often used when the condition is stated algebraically in terms of coordinates, as in the above examples. When the condition is stated in the form of an equation, we naturally speak of the figure as the graph of the equation. For example, the vertical line through $(1, 0)$ is the graph of the equation $x = 1$. Similarly, the first of the seven figures is called the graph of the inequality $y > 0$.

### Problem Set 13–9

1. On the same set of axes, sketch the graphs of the following conditions.
   (a) $x = 5$.　　(b) $x < -2$.　　(c) $y \geq 4$.　　(d) $y = 0$.

2. Sketch on one pair of axes the sets of points described by the following conditions:
   (a) $|x| = 2$.　　(b) $|y| < 1$.　　(c) $|x| \geq 3$.

3. Sketch the union of the graphs of $x = 3$ and $y = 2$. What is their intersection?

4. Given the conditions: (i) $x$ is a positive number and (ii) $y$ is a positive number.
   (a) Sketch the union of their graphs. The union is Quadrants I, II and IV, and the positive x- and y-axis.
   (b) Sketch the intersection of their graphs. The intersection is Quadrant I.

5. Sketch the intersection of the graphs of these four conditions:
   $$x \geq 0, \qquad x \leq 6, \qquad y \geq 0, \qquad y \leq 4.$$
   Describe the intersection in words.

6. State the conditions which describe the region sketched on the right.
   $R = \{(x, y) \mid -2 \leq x \leq 5 \text{ and } -3 \leq y \leq 0\}$

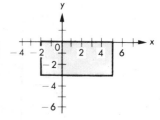

7. Sketch the graphs of the following conditions, and find the area of the intersection of the two graphs.
   $$-1 \leq x \leq 3 \qquad \text{and} \qquad -2 \leq y \leq 5.$$

8. The distance from a point $P(x, y)$ to $A(1, 0)$ is equal to the distance from $P$ to $B(7, 0)$. Write an equation which expresses this condition. How many such points $P$ are there? Sketch the set of all such points $P$.

9. Write an equation for the set of all points $P(x, y)$ which are equidistant from the points $A(0, 6)$ and $B(6, 0)$. Sketch the graph.

$\sqrt{(x-0)^2 + (y-6)^2} = \sqrt{(x-6)^2 + (y-0)^2}$ or $x=y$

10. Sketch the graph of $y = |x|$.

11. Sketch the graph of $y = -|x|$.

12. A point $P(x, y)$ is between the point $A(1, 3)$ and the point $B(8, 6)$. Use the distance formula and the definition of "between" to write an equation expressing this condition on $P$. $AP + PB = AB$

13. If $P = (x, y)$, $A = (a, c)$, and $B = (b, d)$, what condition on the points $P$, $A$, and $B$ is expressed by $AP + PB = AB$ by distance formula.

A-P-B by the definition of between.

$\sqrt{(x - a)^2 + (y - c)^2} + \sqrt{(x - b)^2 + (y - d)^2}$

Since A, B satisfy the given            $= \sqrt{(a - b)^2 + (c - d)^2}$ ?
equation, P is a point on $\overline{AB}$.

14. On the same set of axes, sketch the set of all points $P(x, y)$ satisfying the conditions:

(a) $\sqrt{(x - 3)^2 + (y + 2)^2} + \sqrt{(x - 7)^2 + (y - 1)^2} = 5$.

(b) $\sqrt{(x - 3)^2 + (y + 2)^2} = \sqrt{(x - 7)^2 + (y - 1)^2}$.

15. In the figure, $E$ is a plane parallel to the $xz$-plane and $F$ is a plane parallel to the $yz$-plane. $E$ and $F$ intersect in $\overleftrightarrow{AB}$. $\overleftrightarrow{CG}$ is in $E$, $\overleftrightarrow{CH}$ is in $F$, and both lines are in the $xy$-plane.

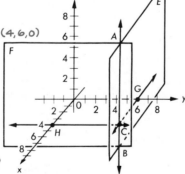

(a) What are the coordinates of $C$? $C(4, 6, 0)$

(b) What equation gives the condition whose graph is $E$? whose graph is $F$? $E: y=6$, $F: x = 4$

(c) $\overleftrightarrow{AB}$ is the graph of what condition? $x= 4$ and $y=6$

(d) Point $C$ is the graph of what condition? $x=4, y=6$ and $z=0$

16. In a three-dimensional coordinate system what are the graphs of each of the following conditions?

(a) $z = 0$. $xy$-plane   (b) $x = 0$. $yz$-plane   (c) $y = 0$. $xz$-plane

(d) $y = 3$.              (e) $z = 5$.              (f) $|y| = 2$.

(g) $x = 0$  and  $y = 0$.   (h) $x = 3$  and  $z = 0$.

(i) $|y| = 2$  and  $z = 0$.   (j) $x = 3$  and  $y = 2$.

---

11.

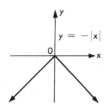

$y = -|x|$

12. By the distance formula,

$$AP = \sqrt{(x - 1)^2 + (y - 3)^2},$$
$$PB = \sqrt{(x - 8)^2 + (y - 6)^2},$$

and $AB = \sqrt{58}$. Therefore,

$$\sqrt{(x - 1)^2 + (y - 3)^2}$$
$$+ \sqrt{(x - 8)^2 + (y - 6)} = \sqrt{58}.$$

14. (a) Let $A = (3, -2)$, $B = (7, 1)$ and $P = (x, y)$. Note first that the coordinates of $A$ and $B$ each satisfy the given equation. Hence, the equation

$$\sqrt{(x - 3)^2 + (y + 2)^2}$$
$$+ \sqrt{(x - 7)^2 + (y - 1)^2} = 5$$

implies that $P = A$ or $P = B$, or that $AP + PB = AB$. But, by the definition of between, the equation $AP + PB = AB$ means that $P$ is between $A$ and $B$. Therefore, the set of all points $P$ satisfying condition (a) is the union (1) $A$ and $B$, and (2) the set of all points between $A$ and $B$. Thus the graph of condition (a) is $\overline{AB}$.

(b) By the distance formula, condition (b) means that $AP = PB$. The set of all points $P$ which are equidistant from $A$ and $B$ is the perpendicular bisector of $\overline{AB}$. Since the midpoint of $\overline{AB}$ is $M = (5, -\frac{1}{2})$ and the slope of $\overline{AB}$ is $\frac{3}{4}$, the equation of the perpendicular bisector of $\overline{AB}$ is

$$y + \frac{1}{2} = \frac{-4}{3}(x - 5).$$

16. (d) A vertical plane parallel to the $xz$-plane with a $y$-intercept of 3

(e) A horizontal plane with a $z$-intercept of 5

(f) Two vertical planes, each parallel to the $xz$-plane with $y$-intercepts of 2 and $-2$, respectively

(g) The $z$-axis

**16.** (h) A line in the xy-plane parallel to the y-axis and with an x-intercept of 3

    (i) Two lines in the xy-plane, each parallel to the x-axis, and with y-intercepts of 2 and −2

    (j) A vertical line which intersects the xy-plane at (3, 2)

## 13–10 HOW TO DESCRIBE A LINE BY AN EQUATION

### Background Material

In this section we establish two important forms for the equation of a line: the point-slope form and the slope-intercept form. Note that we do not establish a special form for the equation of the line which contains two given points. As a practical matter this problem can best be handled by use of the slope formula and the point-slope form for the equation of a line.

### Classroom Notes

Advanced students will have encountered the general equation of a line in a first-course in algebra. For most students, however, the material is new and thus must be carefully taught. You may wish to discuss several examples before assigning the problem set. Theorem 13–9 is the most important of the chapter.

## 13–10 HOW TO DESCRIBE A LINE BY AN EQUATION

It is easy to describe a vertical line by an equation.

    If the line intersects the x-axis at $(a, 0)$, then it is the graph of the equation $x = a$.

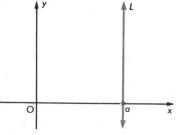

For nonvertical lines, we need to use the slope. Suppose that the line $L$ passes through the point $P_1 = (x_1, y_1)$, and has slope $m$. If $P = (x, y)$ is any *other* point of $L$, then

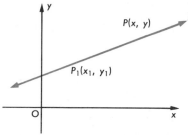

$$\frac{y - y_1}{x - x_1} = m,$$

because all segments of $L$ have slope $m$. Of course, this equation is not satisfied when $x = x_1$ and $y = y_1$, because in this case the fraction on the left becomes the nonsensical expression $0/0$, which is not equal to $m$ (or equal to anything else). But this is easily fixed: multiplying by $x - x_1$, we get

$$y - y_1 = m(x - x_1).$$

This operation *adds a point to the graph:* the new equation is satisfied for every point of $L$ other than $P_1$, because the old one was. And the new equation is also satisfied for $P_1$ itself, because when $x = x_1$ and $y = y_1$ we get $0 = m \cdot 0$, which is a true statement.

    We write this result as a theorem.

### Theorem 13–7

> *Let L be a line with slope m, passing through the point $(x_1, y_1)$. Then every point $(x, y)$ of L satisfies the equation*
>
> $$y - y_1 = m(x - x_1).$$

Note that this theorem does *not* say that $L$ is the graph of the equation. And in fact, we haven't proved this yet; we have proved only half of it.  When we say that $L$ is the graph of the equation, this means two things:

(1)   every point of $L$ satisfies the equation, and

(2)   every point that satisfies the equation is on $L$.

So far, we have proved (1).  We shall now prove (2).

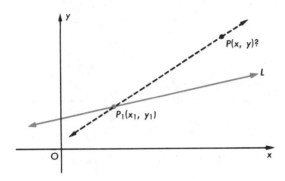

Suppose that $P(x, y)$ is a point for which

$$y - y_1 = m(x - x_1).$$

If $x = x_1$, then $y = y_1$, and $P$ is on $L$.  If $x \neq x_1$, then $\overline{P_1P}$ is not vertical, and its slope is

$$\frac{y - y_1}{x - x_1} = m.$$

Therefore $\overleftrightarrow{P_1P}$ and $L$ have the same slope.  Therefore these lines are parallel or the same.  They cannot be parallel, because $(x_1, y_1)$ is on both of them.  Therefore $\overleftrightarrow{P_1P}$ is $L$, and $P$ lies on $L$.

This gives us a theorem which is simpler and also says more than the preceding theorem.

### Theorem 13–8

**The graph of the equation**

$$y - y_1 = m(x - x_1)$$

**is the line which passes through the point $(x_1, y_1)$ and has slope $m$.**

The equation given in this theorem is called the *point-slope* form of the equation of the line.

If we know the coordinates of two points of a line, it is easy to find an equation for it.

Suppose, for example, that the line passes through the points

$P_1(2, 1)$     and     $P_2(5, 3)$.

Then its slope is

$$m = \frac{3 - 1}{5 - 2} = \frac{2}{3}.$$

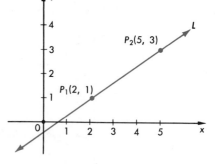

Using $P_1(2, 1)$ and $m = \frac{2}{3}$, in the point-slope form, we get

(1)     $y - 1 = \frac{2}{3}(x - 2)$.

We can simplify, obtaining an equivalent equation:

$$3y - 3 = 2x - 4,$$
(2)     $2x - 3y = 1$.

Note, however, that although equation (2) is "simpler" than equation (1), it is not as easy to interpret. Using Theorem 13-8, we can tell immediately that the graph of (1) is the line through (2, 1) with slope $\frac{2}{3}$. This is not so obvious for the simplified form (2).

Given an equation in the point-slope form, it is easy to draw its graph. Take, for example,

$$y - 3 = 2(x + 1).$$

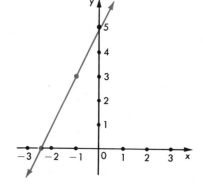

You can see immediately that the graph contains the point $(-1, 3)$. To draw the line, we merely need to know one more point of it. (Why?) Setting $x = 0$, we get

$$y - 3 = 2(0 + 1),$$

or

$$y = 5.$$

Therefore (0, 5) is on the graph. We can now use a ruler, because we knew at the start that the graph had to be a line. As a practical matter, however, it is a very good idea to check our work by calculating the coordinates of a third point. For example, setting $y = 0$, we get $0 - 3 = 2(x + 1)$, which gives $x = -\frac{5}{2}$. Therefore $(-\frac{5}{2}, 0)$ is on the graph, just as the figure suggests.

The following theorem is an easy consequence of Theorem 13–8.

**Theorem 13–9**

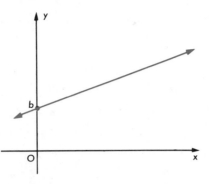

*The graph of the equation*

$$y = mx + b$$

*is the line which passes through the point $(0, b)$ and has slope m.*

The reason is that our equation can be written in the form

$$y - b = m(x - 0).$$

The equation $y = mx + b$ is called the *slope-intercept* form.  For many purposes, it is the most convenient form.

We can now draw the graph of the equation $y = |x|$ by the following method.  First we draw on the left below the graphs of the equations $y = x$ and $y = -x$.

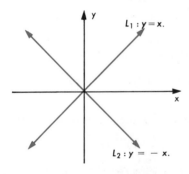
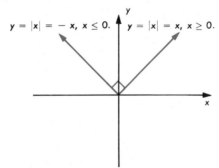

We remember that $|x|$ is defined by the following conditions:

(1)  For $x \geq 0$,      $|x| = x$.
(2)  For $x \leq 0$,      $|x| = -x$.

This means that to the right of the $y$-axis, our graph lies on the line $L_1$ but not on $L_2$.  To the left of the $y$-axis, our graph is on the line $L_2$ but not on $L_1$.  The graph therefore looks like the one on the right above.

It is easy to see that the two rays are perpendicular.  Therefore the graph of $y = |x|$ is a right angle.

**1.** Write an equation of the line through the point (4, 2) and perpendicular to the line whose equation is $3x + 12y = 8$.
(ans: $4x - y = 14$.)

**2.** Write an equation of the line which is parallel to $3x - 2y = 4$ and has a $y$-intercept of $-3$.
(ans: $3x - 2y = 6$.)

**Explanation for Problems**

Problems 1 through 9 of Problem Set 13–10 provide ample practice with the equation of a line. Problem 12 develops the useful intercept form for the equation of a line.

**Problem Set 13–10**

**1.** The equations below are written in point-slope form. For each equation find the slope and the coordinates of two points of its graph, and sketch the graph.

(a) $y - 3 = 2(x - 4)$. m=2;(0,-5)(4,3)  (b) $y - 1 = \frac{2}{3}(x - 6)$. m=⅔;
(c) $y + 6 = -\frac{1}{4}(x - 8)$. m=-¼; (0,-4),(8,-6)  (d) $y - 5 = 3x$. m=3; (0,5),(-5/3,0)  (6,1),(0,-3)
(e) $y = -2(x + 3)$. m=-2 ; (-3,0),(0,-6)

**2.** Write an equation of the line through point $P$, having slope equal to $m$, given that
y-1=3(x-4)          y+4=-2(x-½)
(a) $P = (4, 1)$   and  $m = 3$.   (b) $P = (\frac{1}{2}, -4)$  and  $m = -2$.
(c) $P = (8, 2)$   and  $m = \frac{3}{4}$.   (d) $P = (-4, 0)$  and  $m = \frac{5}{4}$.
y-2=¾(x-8)          y=⁵⁄₄(x+4)
(e) $P = (-6, 5)$  and  $m = 0$.
y=5

**3.** For each pair of points, first find the slope of the line which contains them, and then write an equation of the line.

(a) (5, 2)   and  (2, 8)   m=-2, y-2=-2(x-5)
(b) (2, 4)   and  (4, 5)   m=½, y-4=½(x-2)
(c) (0, 0)   and  (1, 5)   m=5, y=5x
(d) (2, 7)   and  (-8, 5)  m=⅕, y-7=⅕(x-2)
(e) (-6, 0)  and  (0, 4)   m=⅔, y=⅔(x+6)
(f) (9, -15) and  (12, -18)  m=-1, y+15=-1(x-9)
(g) (-4, -13) and  (19, 33)  m=2, y+13=2(x+4)
(h) $(\sqrt{2}, \sqrt{8})$  and  $(-\sqrt{8}, -\sqrt{2})$  m=1 y-√8=1(x-√2)

**4.** Joan and Al were comparing their solutions to homework problems. The problem was:

"Write an equation of the line through the points (2, -5) and (8, 7)."

Joan had the equation $y + 5 = 2(x - 2)$ and Al had $y - 7 = 2(x - 8)$. Whose answer was correct? Explain.
Both are correct; each used a different point in the equation.

**5.** For each of the equations below, written in slope-intercept form, determine the slope and the $y$-intercept, and sketch the graph.

(a) $y = 2x + 6$. 2,6          (b) $y = -2x + 6$. -2,6
(c) $y = \frac{2}{3}x$. ⅔,0          (d) $y = 2x - 6$. 2,-6
(e) $y = \frac{2}{3}x - 6$. ⅔,-6

**6.** Find an equation of the line with slope equal to $-5$ and containing the point (0, 4). y-4=-5(x-0) or y=-5x+4

**7.** Write an equation of the line through the point (7, -6) and parallel to the line whose equation is y+6=½(x-7)

$$y = \tfrac{1}{2}x + 1.$$

**8.** Write an equation of the line through the point $(-2, 0)$ and perpendicular to the line whose equation is $y = -\frac{2}{3}x + 6$.   $y = \frac{3}{2}(x+2)$

---

**9.** On one set of axes draw the graphs of the equations

$$y = 3, \qquad y = x + 3, \qquad y - 3 = -\frac{5}{3}(x - 8).$$

(a) What are the coordinates of the three points at which the lines intersect? $(0,3), (8,3)$ and $(5,8)$

(b) Find the area of the triangular region bounded by the three lines.
$A = \frac{1}{2} bh = \frac{1}{2} \, 8 \cdot 5 = 20$

**10.** On one set of axes draw the graphs of the equations $y = -\frac{1}{2}x + 4$, $y = \frac{3}{4}x + 4$, $y + 1 = -\frac{4}{3}(x - 10)$.

(a) What are the coordinates of the three points at which the lines intersect? $P(0,4), Q(4,7), R(10,-1)$

(b) Find the area of the triangular region bounded by the three lines.
$a\triangle PQR = 25$

**11.** Sketch the graph of $x = |y|$.

**12.** Using the point-slope form of the equation of a line, prove that the equation of the line through the points $(a, 0)$ and $(0, b)$ can be written

$$\frac{x}{a} + \frac{y}{b} = 1 \qquad (a, b \neq 0)$$

Explain why this form is referred to as the "intercept form."

**13.** Use Problem 12 to write an equation of the line whose $x$-intercept is 5 and whose $y$-intercept is 3. Check your equation by using the slope-intercept form or the point-slope form. $\frac{x}{5} + \frac{y}{3} = 1$

**14.** Sketch the graph of $|x| + |y| = 4$.

---

**15.** In a three-dimensional coordinate system, $3x + 6y + 2z = 12$ is the equation of a plane which intersects each axis. What are the coordinates of the intercepts? $(4,0,0), (0,2,0)$ and $(0,0,6)$

**16.** In the figure on the right, plane $K$ intersects the axes at the points shown. The equation of $K$ is

$$6x + 4y + 9z = 36.$$

(a) Find the equations of the intersections of $K$ with each coordinate plane.

(b) Show that the equation of $K$ may be written as $\begin{array}{c}\text{Divide}\\\text{equation by 36.}\end{array}$

$$\frac{x}{6} + \frac{y}{9} + \frac{z}{4} = 1.$$

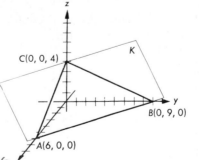

$C(0, 0, 4)$   $K$

$B(0, 9, 0)$

$A(6, 0, 0)$

---

## Answers to Problems

**10.** (b) Since the slopes of $\overline{PQ}$ and $\overline{QR}$ are negative reciprocals, $\overline{PQ} \perp \overline{QR}$, and $a\triangle PQR = \frac{1}{2}(PQ)(QR)$. By the distance formula, $PQ = 5$ and $QR = 10$. Therefore $a\triangle PQR = 25$.

**11.**

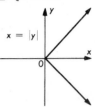

$x = |y|$

**12.** By the slope formula, $m = \dfrac{0 - b}{a - 0} = \dfrac{-b}{a}$. The point-slope form of the equation of a line is $y - y_1 = m(x - x_1)$, so $y - 0 = \dfrac{-b}{a}(x - a)$. This equation simplifies to $\dfrac{x}{a} + \dfrac{y}{b} = 1$. This form is called the "intercept form" because the denominator, $a$, of the $x$ term is the abscissa of the point at which the line intercepts the $x$-axis, and the denominator, $b$, of the $y$-term is the ordinate of the point at which the line intercepts the $y$-axis.

**14.**

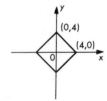

$(0,4)$

$(4,0)$

**16.** (a) $K$ intersects the $xy$-plane in

$$\overleftrightarrow{AB}: \ \frac{x}{6} + \frac{y}{9} = 1.$$

$K$ intersects the $yz$-plane in

$$\overleftrightarrow{BC}: \ \frac{y}{9} + \frac{z}{4} = 1.$$

$K$ intersects the $xz$-plane in

$$\overleftrightarrow{AC}: \ \frac{x}{6} + \frac{z}{4} = 1.$$

Using the Area Addition Postulate, we find $a\triangle ABC = a\square AMPC + a\square BNPC + a\square AMNB$. We then use the areas of the trapezoids. See Solution Section for a complete solution.

17. Write an equation of the plane determined by the three points.

   (a) $(5, 0, 0)$, $(0, 3, 0)$, and $(0, 0, 4)$  $\frac{x}{5} + \frac{y}{3} + \frac{z}{4} = 1$

   (b) $(12, 0, 0)$, $(0, 4, 0)$, and $(0, 0, -3)$  $\frac{x}{12} + \frac{y}{4} - \frac{z}{3} = 1$

   (c) $(5, 0, 0)$, $(0, -3, 0)$, and $(0, 0, 10)$  $\frac{x}{5} - \frac{y}{3} + \frac{z}{10} = 1$

   [*Hint:* See Problems 12 and 16 above. You need not prove that your equations are correct.]

18. For each of the following equations determine the intercepts. Sketch the three-dimensional graph of each equation.

   (a) $4x + 3y + 2z = 12.$ $(3,0,0),(0,4,0),(0,0,6)$

   (b) $14x + 35y + 10z = 70.$ $(5,0,0),(0,2,0),(0,0,7)$

   (c) $9x - 7y + 21z = 63.$ $(7,0,0),(0,-9,0),(0,0,3)$

   (d) $6x + 5z = 30.$ $(5,0,0),$ no y intercept $, (0,0,6)$

19. In the figure $\overleftrightarrow{AB}$, $\overleftrightarrow{CD}$, and $\overleftrightarrow{EF}$ are the projections of $\overleftrightarrow{PQ}$ into the $xy$-plane, the $yz$-plane, and the $xz$-plane, respectively.

   (a) Find the coordinates of $A$, $B$, $C$, $D$, $E$, $F$.

   (b) Find the equations of $\overleftrightarrow{AB}$, $\overleftrightarrow{CD}$, and $\overleftrightarrow{EF}$ in their respective coordinate planes. $\overleftrightarrow{AB}: 4x + y = 10$, $\overleftrightarrow{CD}: y - 2z = -8$, $\overleftrightarrow{EF}: 2x + z = 9$

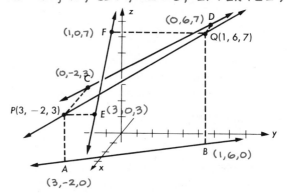

**HONORS PROBLEM**

Given $\triangle ABC$ with vertices $A(a, a')$, $B(b, b')$, and $C(c, c')$ such that $0 < a < c < b$ and $0 < a' < b' < c'$.

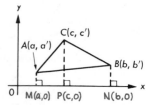

Prove that

$$a\triangle ABC = \tfrac{1}{2}[a(b' - c') + b(c' - a') + c(a' - b')].$$

What happens to the formula on the right if $A$ and $B$ are interchanged? $A$ and $C$? $B$ and $C$? See Solution Section.

## CHAPTER REVIEW

1. What are the coordinates of the projection of the point $(5, 2)$ into the $x$-axis? into the $y$-axis? $(5,0)$ and $(0,2)$

2. What is the fourth vertex of a rectangle that has three vertices at $(-1, -1)$, $(3, -1)$, and $(3, 5)$? $(-1,5)$

3. Find the perimeter and area of a triangle whose vertices are $(3, 2)$, $(3, -4)$, and $(9, -4)$. $p = 12 + 6\sqrt{2}$, $a = 18$

4. Given $\triangle ABC$ with vertices $A(-3, -5)$, $B(3, 3)$, and $C(13, -9)$.
   (a) Find the coordinates of the midpoint of each side.
   (b) Find the length of each median. $AN = 5\sqrt{5}$, $BP = 2\sqrt{26}$, $CM = \sqrt{233}$
   (c) Write the equation of the line containing each median, in the point-slope form. $\overleftrightarrow{AN}$: $y + 5 = \frac{2}{11}(x+3)$ $\overleftrightarrow{BP}$: $y - 3 = -5(x-3)$
   $\overleftrightarrow{CM}$: $y + 9 = -\frac{8}{13}(x-13)$

5. The vertices of a quadrilateral are $A(-1, 1)$, $B(4, 3)$, $C(6, -2)$, $D(1, -4)$.
   (a) Prove that $\square ABCD$ is a parallelogram.
   (b) Show that its diagonals are perpendicular and congruent.

6. A line having slope $\frac{2}{3}$ contains the point $(0, -6)$. What is the $y$-coordinate of the point on the line whose $x$-coordinate is 12?
   $y$-coordinate is 2

7. Using the methods of coordinate geometry, prove that the diagonals of an isosceles trapezoid are congruent.

8. Prove that the triangle whose vertices are $A(-3, 7)$, $B(2, -2)$, and $C(11, 3)$ is an isosceles right triangle.

9. One end point of a segment is the point $(-1, 8)$, and the midpoint of the segment is $(4, 2)$. Find the coordinates of the other end point. $(9, -4)$

10. A triangle has vertices $A(5, 7)$, $B(2, 0)$, and $C(5, -3)$. Find the altitude to the longest side. Find the area of the triangle. Altitude $\overline{BD}$ to $\overline{AC}$ is 3 units, $a\triangle ABC = \frac{1}{2} AC \cdot BD = \frac{1}{2} 10 \cdot 3 = 15$

11. A segment has end points $(4, -2)$ and $(13, 13)$. Find the coordinates of the points that trisect the segment. $(7, 3)$ and $(10, 8)$

12. Write an equation for the set of all points $P(x, y)$ that are equidistant from the points $A(0, 8)$ and $B(12, -8)$. $3x - 4y = 18$

13. Write the equation of the line through the point $(0, 5)$ and parallel to the line $y = 2x - 13$. $y - 5 = 2(x-0)$

14. Write the equation of the line through the point $(6, -1)$ that is perpendicular to the line $y = 3x + 1$. $y + 1 = -\frac{1}{3}(x-6)$

15. On one set of axes draw the graphs of the equations $x = 9$, $y = x$, $y - 1 = -\frac{1}{2}(x - 1)$.
   (a) Find the coordinates of the intersections of the lines. $A(1,1)$, $B(9,-3)$, $C(9,9)$
   (b) Find the area of the triangular region bounded by the lines.
   $a\triangle ABC = 48$

## Answers to Chapter Review Problems

4. (a) The midpoint of $\overline{AB}$ is $M(0, -1)$.
   The midpoint of $\overline{BC}$ is $N(8, -3)$.
   The midpoint of $\overline{CA}$ is $P(5, -7)$.

5. (a) Compute by the slope formula that the slopes of $\overline{AB}$ and $\overline{CD}$ are each $\frac{2}{5}$, and that the slopes of $\overline{BC}$ and $\overline{AD}$ are each $-\frac{5}{2}$. Therefore $\square ABCD$ is a parallelogram. Note that since the slopes of $\overline{AB}$ and $\overline{BC}$ are negative reciprocals, $\overline{AB} \perp \overline{BC}$ and $\square ABCD$ is therefore a rectangle.
   (b) Observe that the slope of $\overline{AC}$ is $-\frac{3}{7}$, and that the slope of $\overline{BD}$ is $\frac{7}{3}$. Therefore, $\overline{AC} \perp \overline{BD}$. This means that rectangle $\square ABCD$ is a square. $AC = BD = \sqrt{58}$.

7. Place the axes so that one vertex of the trapezoid is the origin, and one of the parallel sides lies on the positive $x$-axis. Since the quadrilateral is an isosceles trapezoid, the coordinates of its vertices can be designated: $A(0, 0)$, $B(a, 0)$, $C(a - b, c)$, and $D(b, c)$. Then by the distance formula, $AC^2 = (a - b)^2 + c^2$, and $BD^2 = (a - b)^2 + c^2$. Therefore $\overline{AC} \cong \overline{BD}$.

8. The slope of $\overline{AB}$ is $-\frac{9}{5}$, and the slope of $\overline{BC}$ is $\frac{5}{9}$, so $\overline{AB} \perp \overline{BC}$ and $\triangle ABC$ is a right triangle. Since $AB = BC = \sqrt{74}$, $\triangle ABC$ is an isosceles right triangle.

12. The midpoint $M$ of $\overline{AB}$ is $M(6, 0)$. The slope of $\overline{AB}$ is $-\frac{4}{3}$, so the slope of the perpendicular bisector of $\overline{AB}$ is $\frac{3}{4}$. Therefore the equation of the perpendicular bisector of $\overline{AB}$ is $y - 0 = \frac{3}{4}(x - 6)$, or $3x - 4y = 18$.

## Circles and Spheres

The material in this chapter is in two parts: Sections 14–1 through 14–3 deal with incidence properties of lines and circles and the analogous incidence properties of planes and spheres. Sections 14–4 through 14–7 deal with the metric topics, namely, the measures of the angles and segments formed when two intersecting lines intersect a circle.

The material in this chapter is standard. Our presentation is new only in the following ways: (1) The definitions are carefully stated. (2) After developing the incidence properties of lines and circles, we establish the corresponding incidence properties of planes and spheres. (3) We prove Theorems 14–9 and 14–12; these are important.

### Planning the Chapter

| Section | Average Class | Above-average Class |
|---|---|---|
| 14–1 | 1 | 1 |
| 14–2 | 3 | 2 |
| 14–3 | 1 | 1 |
| 14–4 | 2 | 2 |
| 14–5 | 2 | 2 |
| 14–6 | 2 | 2 |
| 14–7 | 3 | 2 |
| 14–8 | 1 | 1 |
| Review/ Test | 2 | 1 |

CHAPTER **14**

# Circles and Spheres

## Objectives...

- Review definitions of basic terms related to circles and spheres: diameter, radius, chord, secant, tangent, arc.
- Develop and use the theorems expressing relations of circles and lines, spheres and planes in space.
- Prove and use theorems about measurement of angles and arcs of circles.
- Apply coordinate geometry to circles.

**Classroom Notes**

It is not necessary to preview Section 14–1 with your students. They can read Section 14–1 and do Problems 1 through 9 of Problem Set 14–1 on their own. Then, after discussing their work, you can devote most of your first class day to Section 14–2.

## 14–1  BASIC DEFINITIONS

Roughly speaking, a circle is the boundary of a round region in a plane; and a sphere is the surface of a round ball in space.

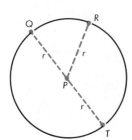 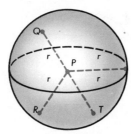

The following definitions state the same ideas in more precise language.

### Definition

Let $P$ be a point in a given plane, and let $r$ be a positive number. The *circle with center P and radius r* is the set of all points of the plane whose distance from $P$ is equal to $r$.

### Definition

Let $P$ be a point, and let $r$ be a positive number. The *sphere with center P and radius r* is the set of all points of space whose distance from $P$ is equal to $r$.

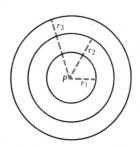

Two or more spheres or two or more coplanar circles with the same center are called *concentric*. In the figure, $P$ is the common center of the three concentric circles.

A *chord* of a circle is a segment whose end points lie on the circle.

In the figure, $\overline{AB}$ is a chord.

A line which intersects the circle in two points is called a *secant* of the circle.

In the figure, $\overleftrightarrow{AB}$ is a secant.

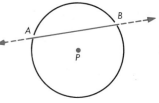

Thus every chord determines a secant, and every secant contains a chord.

Similarly, a *chord* of a sphere is a segment whose end points lie on the sphere. And a *secant* of a sphere is a line which intersects the sphere in two points.

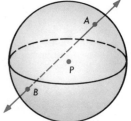

A *diameter* of a circle or sphere is a chord containing the center.

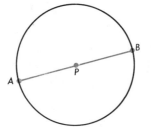
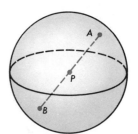

A *radius* of a circle is a segment from the center to a point of the circle. (Similarly for spheres.) The point $A$ is called the *outer end* of the radius $\overline{PA}$.

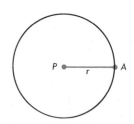

Note that we are using the word *radius* in two senses, to mean either a segment or a number, but it ought to be clear from the context which meaning is intended. Similarly, if a circle has radius $r$, we shall speak of the number $2r$ as *the diameter* of the circle. Of course, the number $2r$ is the length of every chord through the center.

To repeat: In the figure on the right, $r$ is *the radius;* $\overline{PB}$ is *a radius;* $\overline{PA}$ is *a radius;* $2r$ is *the diameter;* $\overline{AB}$ is *a diameter;* and $\overline{PC}$ is *a radius* with $C$ as its *outer end.*

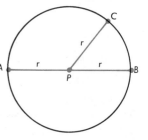

## Theorem 14–1

*The intersection of a sphere with a plane through its center is a circle with the same center and the same radius.*

To see why this is so, we merely need to recall the definition of a sphere and the definition of a circle. Given a sphere $S$ with center $P$ and radius $r$, and a plane $E$. Then $S$ is the set of all points of space whose distance from $P$ is equal to $r$. The intersection of $S$ and $E$ is the set of all points of $E$ whose distance from $P$ is equal to $r$. This is a circle with the same center $P$ and the same radius $r$.

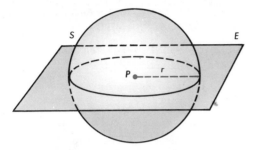

Knowing this, we can state the following definition.

## Definition

The intersection of a sphere with a plane through its center is called a *great circle* of the sphere.

There is another reason for this term: the great circles are the *largest* circles that lie on the sphere. For example, if we draw meridians and parallels in the usual way, as on globes, then the equator is a great circle, but the other parallels of latitude are not. The other parallels of latitude are all smaller than the equator, becoming very small near the North and South Poles.

**Quiz**

Prove that the intersection of any two diameters of a circle is the center of the circle.

    (ans: From the definition of diameter, two diameters intersect in at least one point—namely, the center of the circle. The desired conclusion follows by noting that two line segments intersect in no more than one point.)

**4.** The word "radius" is used in the sense of length (a positive real number) rather than in the sense of a segment.

**5.** Since $\triangle AOC \cong \triangle BOD$ by SAS, $\overline{AC} \cong \overline{BD}$ and $\angle ACO \cong \angle BDO$. We can then conclude by the AIP Theorem that $\overline{AC} \parallel \overline{BD}$. Note that by Theorem 9–20, $\square ACBD$ is a parallelogram. Note secondly that since the length of median $\overline{CO}$ in $\triangle ACB$ is one-half of $AB$, we can conclude by Problem 9, Section 9–7 that $\triangle ACB$ is a right triangle and therefore $\square ACBD$ is a rectangle.

**12.** Given: $\overline{AB}$ is a diameter of circle $C$ with center at $P$. $\overline{AD}$ and $\overline{AE}$ are congruent chords of $C$, with $D$ and $E$ lying on opposite sides of $\overline{AB}$.
Prove: $\angle DAP \cong \angle EAP$.
Proof: Since $\overline{AD} \cong \overline{AE}$ by hypothesis, and $\overline{AP} \cong \overline{AP}$ and $\overline{PD} \cong \overline{PE}$, $\triangle DAP \cong \triangle EAP$ by SSS, and therefore $\angle DAP \cong \angle EAP$.

---

## Problem Set 14–1

**1.** Can a chord of a circle be a secant of the same circle? Why?
No, a chord is a line segment and a secant is a line.

**2.** Given the figure, what name applies to each of the following.

(a) $\overline{MK}$ diameter   (b) $\overleftrightarrow{RK}$ secant

(c) $P$ center   (d) $\overline{PR}$ radius

(e) $\overline{RK}$ chord   (f) $R$ outer end of $\overline{PR}$

(g) $\overline{PM}$ radius   (h) $M$ outer end of $\overline{PM}$

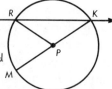

**3.** Why are a circle and a secant of the circle coplanar?
The plane of the circle contains two points of the secant and contains the secant by Postulate 6.

**4.** In the statement of Theorem 14–1, what does "radius" mean?

**5.** Prove that if $\overline{AB}$ and $\overline{CD}$ are two diameters of a circle, then $\overline{AC} \cong \overline{BD}$ and $\overline{AC} \parallel \overline{BD}$.

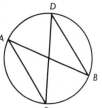

**6.** Indicate whether each statement is true or false.

(a) Every diameter of a circle is a secant of the circle. F

(b) All radii of a sphere are congruent. T

(c) Every diameter of a sphere is the diameter of a great circle. T

(d) Every radius of a circle is a chord of the circle. F

(e) Every secant of a sphere intersects the sphere in exactly one point. F

(f) Every chord of a circle contains exactly two points of the circle. T

(g) A sphere and a great circle of the sphere have the same center and the same radius. T

**7.** Which of the following statements do you think are true?

(a) If a radius bisects a chord of a circle, then it is perpendicular to the chord. F

(b) The intersection of a line with a circle may be empty. T

(c) Two circles may intersect in exactly three points. F

(d) A line may intersect a circle in exactly one point. T

(e) Two spheres may intersect in exactly one point. T

(f) Two spheres may intersect in a circle. T

(g) The secant which is the perpendicular bisector of a chord of a circle contains the center of the circle. T

(h) If a line intersects a circle in one point, then it intersects the circle in two points. F

**Classroom Notes**

The definition of a tangent to a circle uses the term "intersects" rather than the more colorful word "touches." It is important for the students to realize that a circle and a tangent to it have *exactly one* point in common.

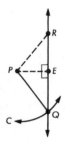

The proof of Theorem 14–2 is easy; the proof of its converse, Theorem 14–3, is hard. The proof of Theorem 14–3 is an indirect proof: we suppose that $L$ is not perpendicular to $\overline{PQ}$ at $Q$, and show, on the basis of this assumption, that $L$ intersects the circle at a second point. Since we are showing that $L$ intersects the circle at a second point, it is helpful to sketch the figure in such a way that we cannot read this conclusion from the figure.

Problems 4, 11, 16, and 18 of Problem Set 14–2A are particularly interesting.

---

8. Given a sphere $S$ with center $P$ and a plane $E$. If $P$ lies in $E$ then $E \cap S$ is a _____circle_____.

9. The sentence below contains the word "diameter" twice. Explain how "diameter" is used each time.
First: length of any chord of the circle containing the center
Although a circle may have only one diameter, a circle actually does have infinitely many diameters.
Second: a chord containing the center

---

10. Prove that the diameters of a circle are the longest chords of the circle. [*Hint:* If $c$ is the length of any other chord, is $c < 2r$?]
c < r + r = 2r by the triangle inequality

11. If $AB$ and $CD$ are two diameters of a sphere, then prove that the figure $ACBD$ is a rectangle.
Figure ACBD lies in the plane determined by the intersecting segments $\overline{AB}$ and $\overline{CD}$. See Problem 5.

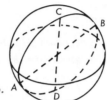

12. Prove: If each of two congruent chords of a circle has an end point in common with a diameter and they intersect the circle on opposite sides of the diameter, then the chords determine congruent angles with the diameter.

## 14–2 TANGENT LINES TO CIRCLES

Throughout this section, we shall be talking about circles in a fixed plane.

### Definitions

The *interior* of a circle is the set of all points of the plane whose distance from the center is less than the radius. The *exterior* of a circle is the set of all points of the plane whose distance from the center is greater than the radius.

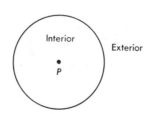

Thus every point of the plane is in the interior, or in the exterior, or on the circle. Frequently we shall say for short that a point is *inside* the circle, or *outside* the circle. (Remember that $0 < r$ because $r > 0$. Therefore the center is automatically in the interior.)

**1.** A tangent line intersects a circle at (3, 4). If the circle has its center at the origin, what is the equation of the tangent line?

(ans: $4y + 3x = 25$.)

**2.** In a plane, the perpendicular bisector of a chord $\overline{AB}$ intersects the chord at $C$ and the circle at $D$ and $E$. If $AB = 16$ and $CD = 3$, what is the radius of the circle?

(ans: 73/6)

**3.** Two chords of a circle are perpendicular at a common end point. Prove that the product of the lengths of the chords is four times the product of their distances from the center of the circle.

Proof: Let $\overline{PQ}$ and $\overline{QR}$ be the two chords perpendicular at $Q$. The shortest distance between the center $S$ of the circle and $\overline{PQ}$ is $ST$, and between $S$ and $\overline{QR}$ is $SW$, where $\overline{ST} \perp \overline{PQ}$, $\overline{SW} \perp \overline{QR}$, $T \in \overline{PQ}$, and $W \in \overline{QR}$. Since all of the angles of quadrilateral $\square STQW$ are right angles, $ST = QW$ and $SW = TQ$. By Theorem 14–4, $PQ = 2TQ$ and $QR = 2QW$. This shows that $PQ \cdot QR = 2TQ \cdot 2QW = 4SW \cdot ST$.

## Definitions

A *tangent* to a circle is a line (in the same plane) which intersects the circle in one and only one point. This point is called the *point of tangency*, or *point of contact*. We say that the line and the circle are *tangent* at this point.

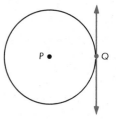

Every circle has a tangent at each of its points. We can see this from the following theorem.

## Theorem 14–2

> *A line perpendicular to a radius at its outer end is tangent to the circle.*

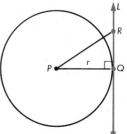

**Proof.** Let $L$ be perpendicular to the radius $\overline{PQ}$ at $Q$. We need to show that no other point of $L$ lies on the circle.

Let $R$ be any other point of $L$. By the First Minimum Theorem (Theorem 7–7), the shortest segment from $P$ to $L$ is the perpendicular segment. Therefore $PR > PQ$. Therefore $PR > r$, and $R$ is not on the circle; $R$ is in the exterior.

The converse is also true.

## Theorem 14–3

> *Every tangent to a circle is perpendicular to the radius drawn to the point of contact.*

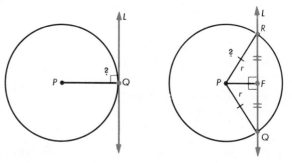

The figure on the left shows the situation as it actually occurs. The figure on the right illustrates the indirect proof which we give on the next page.

**Answers to Problems**

  **2.** Simply construct a line perpendicular, at the given point, to the radius drawn to the given point.

**Proof.** Given that $L$ is tangent to the circle $C$ at the point $Q$. Suppose $L$ is not perpendicular to $\overline{PQ}$. We shall show that this assumption leads to a contradiction.

Let $F$ be the foot of the perpendicular from $P$ to $L$. Then $F \neq Q$. Let $R$ be a point on the ray opposite to $\overrightarrow{FQ}$, such that $FR = FQ$. Then $\triangle PFR \cong \triangle PFQ$. (Why?) Therefore $PR = PQ = r$, and $R$ lies on the circle. Therefore $L$ intersects the circle in two points instead of in one. This is impossible, because $L$ is a tangent line. Therefore our supposition is false, and $L \perp \overline{PQ}$ at $Q$, which was to be proved.

In the figure on the left below, the two circles are *internally tangent*. In the figure on the right, the two circles are *externally tangent*.

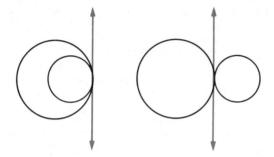

### Definition

Two circles are *tangent* if they are tangent to the same line at the same point. If two tangent circles are coplanar, and their centers are on the same side of their common tangent, then they are *internally tangent*. If two tangent circles are coplanar, and their centers are on opposite sides of their common tangent, then they are *externally tangent*.

### Problem Set 14–2A

1. Draw a circle with center $P$ and radius $PQ = 4$ cm. Locate a point $A$ such that $PA = 5$ cm, and a point $B$ such that $PB = 2.5$ cm. Now complete the following statements:
   - (a) $A$ lies in the ___exterior___ of the circle because ___PA > PQ___.
   - (b) $B$ lies in the ___interior___ of the circle because ___PB < PQ___.
   - (c) The circles with radii $\overline{PA}$, $\overline{PQ}$, and $\overline{PB}$ are called __concentric__.

2. Explain how you can construct a tangent to a circle at a given point of the circle if you are given the center of the circle.

3. $E$ is a point in the exterior of a circle. How many tangents to the circle contain $E$? Make a sketch. ᴛᴡᴏ

**4.** Since $\overline{AB}$ is tangent to the smaller circle at $Q$, $\overline{AB}$ is, by Theorem 14–3, perpendicular to the radius to the point of contact: $\overline{PQ} \perp \overline{AB}$. $PA = PB$ since they are radii, and $\triangle PAB$ is isosceles. $AQ = QB$ since the altitude of an isosceles triangle bisects the base.

**8.** By Theorem 14–3, $m\angle PBC = 90$ so $\angle PBC \cong \angle BPA$. Also $AP = PB$, since both are radii of the same circle, and $PB = BC$ by hypothesis; therefore $\triangle APB \cong \triangle PBC$ by SAS and $AB = PC$. Also $\angle ABP \cong \angle CPB$, so $\overline{AB} \parallel \overline{PC}$ by the AIP Theorem.

**11.** Since the circles with center at $P$ and $P'$ are tangent at $Q$, each is, by definition, tangent to the common tangent line at $Q$. Hence by Theorem 14–3, $\overleftrightarrow{PQ}$ and $\overleftrightarrow{P'Q}$ are each perpendicular to the common tangent at $Q$. But Theorem 6–1 implies that $\overleftrightarrow{PQ} = \overleftrightarrow{P'Q}$. Therefore $P$, $Q$, and $P'$ are collinear.

**4.** Prove: Given two concentric circles, every chord of the greater circle which is tangent to the smaller circle is bisected at its point of tangency. [*Hint:* Draw $\overline{PA}$, $\overline{PQ}$, and $\overline{PB}$.]

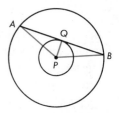

**5.** Prove that the tangents to a circle at the end points of a diameter are parallel. Use Theorem 14-3 and Theorem 9-2.

**6.** One arrangement of three circles having different radii so that each circle is tangent to the other two is shown in this figure. Make sketches showing at least three other arrangements. (1) All circles inside C, (2) C" inside C', (3) C" outside and tangent to C and C' at two points.

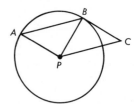

**7.** $\overline{PS}$ is a radius of the given circle to the left below and $\overline{SK}$ is a segment tangent to the circle. If $SK = 6$ and the diameter of the circle is 18, how far is the point $K$ from the center of the circle? $\sqrt{117} = 3\sqrt{13}$

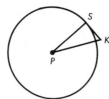

**8.** In the figure to the right above, $\overline{CB}$ is tangent to the circle at $B$, $m\angle APB = 90$, and $BC = PB$. Prove that $AB = PC$ and that $\overline{AB} \parallel \overline{PC}$. Use Theorem 14-3

**9.** The distance of a point $E$ from the center, $A$, of a circle is 20. The radius of the circle is 5. A line through $E$ is tangent to the circle at $B$. Find $EB$. $EB = 5\sqrt{15}$

**10.** Two concentric circles have diameters of 10 and 26. Tangents to the smaller circle pass through the ends of a diameter of the larger circle. Find the length of the segment along each tangent which has an end point on each circle. 12

**11.** Prove the following theorem:

> If two circles are tangent, then their centers are collinear with their point of tangency. Use Theorem 14-3 and Theorem 6-1.

[*Hint:* Consider the common tangents in the two cases below.]

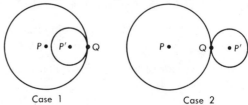

Case 1                                    Case 2

12. Prove that if two circles having congruent radii are externally tangent, then any point equidistant from their centers is on their common tangent.
   Common tangent is perpendicular bisector of segment joining
   centers. Conclusion follows from Theorem 6-2.

13. In the figure, each of the circles with centers A, B, and C is tangent to the other two. If $AB = 10$, $AC = 14$ and $BC = 18$, find the radius of each circle. [*Hint:* Let the radius of one circle equal $x$].
   Let $AR = AT = x$, $RB = BS = 10-x$, $CS = CT = 18-(10-x)$
   $= 8+x$. $AT + CT = AC$; $x+8+x = 14$ and $x = 3$
   $AR = 3$, $BR = 7$, $CT = 11$

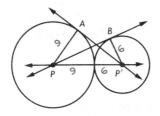

14. Given the figure in which the circles are tangent, $P$ and $P'$ are the centers of the circles, and $\overrightarrow{PB}$ and $\overrightarrow{P'A}$ are tangents at $B$ and $A$, respectively. Given that the radii are 9 and 6, find $PB$ and $P'A$.
   Use Pythagorean Theorem.
   $PB = 3\sqrt{21}$, $P'A = 12$

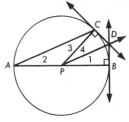

15. Three concentric circles have radii of 5, 10, and 15. Chords of the two larger circles are tangent to the two smaller circles, respectively, and the points of tangency lie on the same radius of the largest circle. Find the area of the quadrilateral region determined by the end points of the chords.
   $A = \frac{1}{2}h(b_1+b_2)$; $h = 5$, $b_1 = 10\sqrt{5}$, $b_2 = 10\sqrt{3}$   $A = 25(\sqrt{3}+\sqrt{5})$

16. Given: In the figure on the left below, $\overline{AB}$ is a diameter of the circle with center $P$. $L$ is tangent to the circle at $T$. $\overline{AD}$ and $\overline{BC}$ are each perpendicular to $L$. Prove: $PD = PC$.

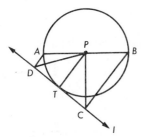
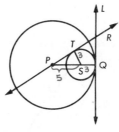

17. In the figure on the right above, the circles with centers $P$ and $S$ are both tangent to line $L$ at $Q$. A secant of the larger circle passes through $P$, is tangent to the smaller circle at $T$, and intersects $L$ at $R$. Given that the radii of the circles are 8 and 3, find $QR$. By Pythagorean Theorem $PT = 4$
   $\triangle PTS \sim \triangle PQR$ (AA) and $\frac{QR}{ST} = \frac{PQ}{PT}$, $QR = 6$

18. In a circle with center $P$, $\overline{AB}$ is a diameter and $\overline{AC}$ is any other chord. A secant through $P$ parallel to $\overline{AC}$ intersects the tangent at $C$ in a point $D$. Prove that $\overrightarrow{DB}$ is tangent to the circle at $B$. [*Hint:* Introduce $\overline{PC}$.]

## Classroom Notes

The average student should be asked to write proofs for these theorems.

The proof of Theorem 14–4 depends on introducing the radii $\overline{PQ}$ and $\overline{PR}$ and showing that $\triangle PFQ \cong \triangle PFR$ by the Hypotenuse Leg Theorem.

The proof of Theorem 14–5 again depends on introducing the radii $\overline{PQ}$ and $\overline{PR}$ and showing that $\triangle PSQ \cong \triangle PSR$ by SSS.

Theorem 14–6 can be proved by using either Theorem 14–4 or Theorem 14–5 and the uniqueness of the perpendicular bisector. More simply, it follows directly from Theorem 6–2.

The following theorems are easy to prove.

### Theorem 14–4

*The perpendicular from the center of a circle to a chord bisects the chord.*

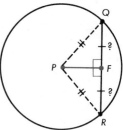

### Theorem 14–5

*The segment from the center of a circle to the midpoint of a chord which is not a diameter is perpendicular to the chord.*

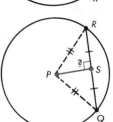

### Theorem 14–6

*In the plane of a circle, the perpendicular bisector of a chord passes through the center.*

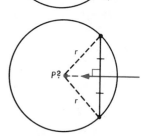

Proof?  (If you don't see how to prove any of the preceding theorems, try using Theorem 6–2.)

### Corollary 14–6.1

*No circle contains three different collinear points.*

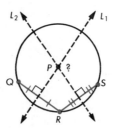 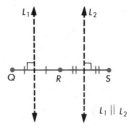

**Proof.** If three points $Q$, $R$, $S$ of the circle were collinear, then the perpendicular bisectors of the chords $\overline{QR}$ and $\overline{RS}$ would be parallel. This is impossible, because both of these lines pass through the center.

In Theorems 14–7 and 14–8, the triangles are congruent by the Hypotenuse Leg Theorem.

Note that Corollary 14–6.1 tells us that a line cannot intersect a circle in three or more points.

### Definition

Circles with congruent radii are called *congruent*.

Note that this definition of *congruent circles* fits in with the use of the word *congruent* for segments, angles, and triangles. The underlying idea, in each case, is that two figures are congruent if they have the same size and shape.

### Theorem 14–7

**In the same circle or in congruent circles, chords equidistant from the center are congruent.**

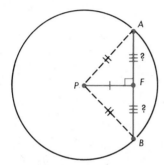 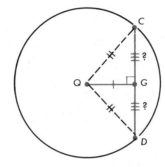

Proof? (In the figures above, some of the marks are based on Theorem 14–4.)

### Theorem 14–8

**In the same circle or in congruent circles, any two congruent chords are equidistant from the center.**

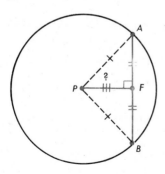 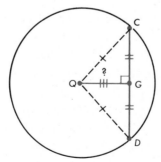

Proof?

Finally, we observe the following theorem.

The Line-Circle Theorem (Theorem 14–9) is written in the text as a characterization theorem (see the comments for Section 15–1). The intersection of $L$ and $C$ is the set of all points on $L$ which are at a distance $\sqrt{r^2 - s^2}$ from $F$, the foot of the perpendicular from $P$ to $L$. Let $G$ be the intersection of $L$ and $C$, and let $H$ be the set of all points on $L$ which are at a distance $\sqrt{r^2 - s^2}$ from $F$, the foot of the perpendicular from $P$ to $L$. In Part (1) of the proof we show that if $X$ is in $G$, then $X$ is in $H$, and in Part (2) we show that if $X$ is in $H$, then $X$ is in $G$. This means that $G \subset H$ and $H \subset G$ and hence that $G = H$.

The Line-Circle Theorem is intrinsically hard for students to grasp. Furthermore, it is written in the style of a characterization theorem, and the text does not explicitly take up characterization theorems until Chapter 15. Finally, the characterization of the set $H$ is essentially algebraic, and this does not contribute to making the theorem easy *even as a characterization theorem*. Consequently, we recommend that you assign the proof of this theorem only to honors students.

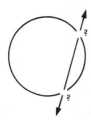

The Line-Circle Theorem is noteworthy mathematically because to prove it we had to use the Euclidean Completeness Postulate (every positive number has a positive square root) for the first time. This fact should not surprise us, because the theorem itself describes a completeness property of the plane. If the plane "had holes in it," and

---

**Theorem 14–9**  The Line-Circle Theorem.

> *If a line and a circle are coplanar, and the line intersects the interior of the circle, then it intersects the circle in two and only two points.*

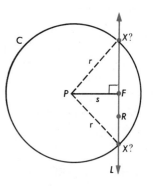

**Proof.** As in the figure, let $C$ be a circle of radius $r$, let $L$ be a line, and suppose that $L$ contains a point $R$ of the interior of $C$. Then $PR < r$. Let $F$ be the foot of the perpendicular from $P$ to $L$, and let $PF = s$.

(1) If $X$ is on both $L$ and $C$, then $\triangle PFX$ has a right angle at $F$, and so

$$r^2 = s^2 + FX^2.$$

Therefore

$$FX = \sqrt{r^2 - s^2}.$$

(2) If $X$ is a point of $L$, and $FX = \sqrt{r^2 - s^2}$, then $X$ is on $C$. The reason is that

$$\begin{aligned} PX^2 &= PF^2 + FX^2 \\ &= s^2 + (r^2 - s^2) \\ &= r^2. \end{aligned}$$

But $r^2 - s^2 > 0$, because $r > s$. Thus, by the Point-Plotting Theorem, there are exactly two points $X$ of $L$ such that $FX = \sqrt{r^2 - s^2}$. Therefore exactly two points of $L$ are on $C$, which was to be proved.

### Problem Set 14–2B

1. State the theorem or corollary which justifies each conclusion below. $P$ is the center of the circle and $Q$ is a point of tangency.

   (a) If $\overline{PN} \perp \overline{CD}$, then $CN = ND$. Theorem 14-4

   (b) Points $A$, $Q$, and $B$ are noncollinear. Corollary 14-6.1

   (c) If $PM = PN$, $\overline{PM} \perp \overline{AB}$, and $\overline{PN} \perp \overline{CD}$, then $\overline{AB} \cong \overline{CD}$. Theorem 14-7

   (d) If $\overline{AB} \cong \overline{CD}$, $\overline{PM} \perp \overline{AB}$, and $\overline{PN} \perp \overline{CD}$, then $PM = PN$. Theorem 14-8

   (e) If $\overleftrightarrow{RT}$ is a tangent, $\overleftrightarrow{RT} \perp \overline{PQ}$. Theorem 14-3

   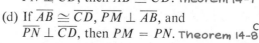

   (f) If $M$ is in the interior of the circle, then $\overleftrightarrow{MQ}$ intersects the circle in exactly one point other than $Q$. Theorem 14-9

2. In a circle whose radius is 10 cm, a chord is 6 cm from the center. How long is the chord? 16cm

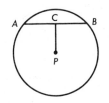

3. A diameter and a chord of a circle have a common end point. If the length of the diameter is 40 and the length of the chord is 24, how far is the chord from the center of the circle? 16

4. A chord 16 cm long is 15 cm from the center of a circle. What is the radius of the circle? 17 cm

5. In the figure, $P$ is the center of the circle,

$$\overline{PD} \perp \overline{AC}, \qquad \overline{PE} \perp \overline{BC},$$

and

$$PD = PE.$$

Prove that $\angle DBA \cong \angle EAB$.

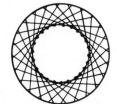

6. Prove: In any circle, the midpoints of all chords congruent to a given chord form a circle concentric with the given circle and with a radius equal to the distance of any one of the chords from the center. Use Theorems 14-5, 14-7, and 14-2.

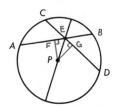

7. Prove: In a circle, if two chords which have a common end point determine congruent angles with a diameter from the same point, then the chords are congruent.

8. Given an arc of a circle, as in the figure at the right, explain how you could find the center and radius of the circle. Construct two chords in the arc; construct the perpendicular bisectors of each.

9. In a circle a chord 12 cm long is parallel to a tangent and bisects the radius drawn to the point of tangency. How long is the radius? $4\sqrt{3}$cm

10. A chord 18 cm long is perpendicular to a radius of a circle. The distance from the intersection of chord and radius to the outer end of the radius is 3 cm. Find the length of the radius. Let r = radius, then $(r-3)^2 + 9^2 = r^2$ and r = 15 cm

11. Prove: If two congruent chords (not diameters) of a circle intersect on a diameter, they determine congruent angles with the diameter.

---

"some points that ought to be there were missing," then the theorem would fail.

In the present treatment, this sort of thing is ruled out by the Euclidean Completeness of the real number system. In a purely synthetic treatment, the Line-Circle Theorem should be taken as a postulate.

**Answers to Problems**

5. Since the chords $\overline{AC}$ and $\overline{CB}$ are equidistant from the center of the circle, we can conclude by Theorem 14–7 that $\overline{AC} \cong \overline{CB}$, and then by the Isosceles Triangle Theorem that $\angle CAB \cong \angle CBA$. Since the perpendicular from the center of a circle bisects a chord, we conclude that $AD = \frac{1}{2}AC$ and $BE = \frac{1}{2}BC$, and thus that $AD = BE$. Since, trivially, $\overline{AB} \cong \overline{AB}$, $\triangle DBA \cong \triangle EAB$ by SAS, and thus $\angle DBA \cong \angle EAB$.

6. By Theorem 14–5 the segment joining a midpoint of a chord to the center is perpendicular to the chord. By Theorem 14–7 these segments all have equal lengths. By the definition of a circle, all points equidistant from a point lie on the circle having the point as center and its radius equal to the distance. By Theorem 14–2 the chords are all tangent to the inner circle.

7. Given: $\overline{AB}$ is a diameter of a circle $C$ with center at $P$. $\overline{AD}$ and $\overline{AE}$ are chords of $C$ such that $\angle DAB \cong \angle EAB$. Prove: $\overline{AD} \cong \overline{AE}$.
Proof: Let $\overline{PF}$ be the perpendicular segment from $P$ to $\overline{AD}$, and let $\overline{PG}$ be the perpendicular segment from $P$ to $\overline{AE}$. Then $\triangle PAF \cong \triangle PAG$ by SAA, and thus $PF = PG$, that is, the chords $\overline{AD}$ and $\overline{AE}$ are equidistant from the center of $C$. Therefore $\overline{AD} \cong \overline{AE}$ by Theorem 14–7.

11. Let $\overline{PF}$ be the perpendicular segment from $P$ to $\overline{AB}$, and let $\overline{PG}$ be the perpendicular segment from $P$ to $\overline{CD}$. Since the chords $\overline{AB}$ and $\overline{CD}$ are congruent, they are equidistant from the center of the circle; thus $\overline{PF} \cong \overline{PG}$. Therefore $\triangle PEF \cong \triangle PEG$, by HL, and thus $\angle PEF \cong \angle PEG$.

**13.** Let the three noncollinear points be A, B, and C. Introduce two segments $\overline{AB}$ and $\overline{BC}$ and construct their perpendicular bisectors. Let P be the point of intersection of these perpendicular bisectors. Since P is on the perpendicular bisector of $\overline{AB}$, P is equidistant from A and B: $PA = PB$. Since P is on the perpendicular bisector of $\overline{BC}$, P is equidistant from B and C: $PB = PC$. Thus $PA = PB = PC$, and therefore A, B, and C each lie on the circle with center at P and radius PA.

**14.** Introduce $\overline{PG}$, the perpendicular segment from P to $\overleftrightarrow{AB}$; introduce $\overline{P'H}$, the perpendicular segment from P' to $\overleftrightarrow{AB}$. Since $\overline{PG}$, $\overline{MR}$, $\overline{P'H}$ are each perpendicular to $\overline{AB}$, $\overline{PG} \parallel \overline{MR} \parallel \overline{P'H}$. Since these parallel lines intercept congruent segments on the transversal $\overleftrightarrow{PP'}$, they intercept congruent segments on the transversal $\overleftrightarrow{AB}$; hence $GR = RH$. But a radius perpendicular to a chord bisects the chord, and so $AR = 2GR$ and $BR = 2RH$. Therefore $AR = BR$.

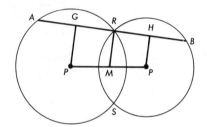

**12.** For each part of this problem answer in the following way.

> Write "extra" if more information is given than is needed to get a numerical answer. Write "not enough" if not enough information is given. Write "OK" if just enough information is given to allow a numerical solution. Write "contradictory" if the given information is contradictory.

[*Note:* You do not need to solve; just decide whether or not you can.]

In the figure P is the center of the circle and $\overline{AB} \perp \overline{CD}$.

(a) $AF = 5$, $AB = ?$ OK (b) $PB = 7$, $CD = ?$ OK (c) $AC = 9$, $PB = ?$ N.E.

(d) $CF = 3$, $FP = 2$, $PD = 6$, $CD = ?$ Cont.

(e) $PB = 13$, $PF = 5$, $AB = ?$ OK

(f) $AB = 16$, $CD = 20$, $CF = 4$, $PB = ?$ Extra

(g) $CF = 7$, $PB = 17$, $FB = 10$, $CD = ?$ Cont.

(h) $CD = 30$, $AB = 24$, $AC = ?$ OK

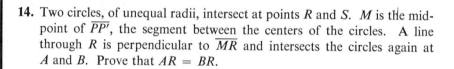

**13.** Prove the following theorem.

> Any three noncollinear points lie on a circle.

**14.** Two circles, of unequal radii, intersect at points R and S. M is the midpoint of $\overline{PP'}$, the segment between the centers of the circles. A line through R is perpendicular to $\overline{MR}$ and intersects the circles again at A and B. Prove that $AR = BR$.

## 14–3 TANGENT PLANES

If you have really learned the preceding section, you will have no trouble with this one. The reason is that the relation between spheres and planes in space is very much like the relation between circles and lines in a plane. There is, therefore, a very close analogy between the definitions and theorems in the preceding section and the definitions and theorems in this one.

### Definitions

The *interior* of a sphere is the set of all points of space whose distance from the center is less than the radius. The *exterior* of a sphere is the set of all points of space whose distance from the center is greater than the radius.

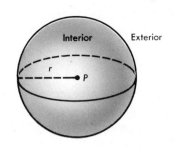

Thus every point of space is in the interior, or in the exterior, or on the sphere. Frequently we shall say for short that a point is *inside* the sphere, or *outside* the sphere.

(Remember that $0 < r$ because $r > 0$. Therefore the center is automatically in the interior.)

## Definitions

A *tangent plane* to a sphere is a plane which intersects the sphere in exactly one point. This point is called the *point of tangency*, or *point of contact*. We say that the plane and the sphere are *tangent* at this point.

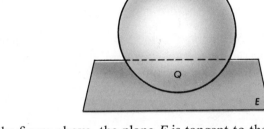

In the figure above, the plane $E$ is tangent to the sphere at $Q$. Note that $Q$ does not appear to be on the "edge" of the sphere. (When a round ball rests on a table, and we look at it from above, we can't see the point on which it is resting.)

Every sphere has a tangent plane at each of its points. We can see this from the following theorem.

### Theorem 14–10

> *A plane perpendicular to a radius at its outer end is tangent to the sphere.*

**Proof.** Let $E$ be perpendicular to the radius $\overline{PQ}$ at $Q$. We need to show that no other point of $E$ lies on the sphere.

Let $R$ be any other point of $E$. By the Second Minimum Theorem (Theorem 8–10) the shortest segment from $P$ to $E$ is the perpendicular segment. Therefore $PR > PQ$. Therefore $PR > r$, and $R$ is not on the sphere; $R$ is in the exterior.

**Classroom Notes**

The definitions and theorems for tangent planes to spheres are so closely analogous to those for tangent lines to circles that it is reasonable to appeal to the student's capacity for generalizing from two to three dimensions and to develop these definitions and theorems in an informal class discussion.

Note that Theorem 14–12 (the Plane-Sphere Theorem) is analogous to Theorem 14–9 (the Line-Circle Theorem), and is also written up as a characterization theorem.

The converse is also true.

### Theorem 14–11

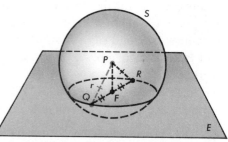

***Every tangent plane to a sphere is perpendicular to the radius drawn to the point of contact.***

**Proof.** Given that *E* is tangent to *S* at the point *Q*. Suppose that *E* is not perpendicular to $\overrightarrow{PQ}$. We shall show that this assumption leads to a contradiction. The figure illustrates the indirect proof.

Let *F* be the foot of the perpendicular from *P* to *E*. Then $F \ne Q$. Let *R* be a point on the ray opposite to $\overrightarrow{FQ}$, such that $FR = FQ$. Then $\triangle PFR \cong \triangle PFQ$. (Why?) Therefore $PR = PQ = r$, and *R* lies on the sphere. Therefore *E* intersects the sphere in a point other than *Q*. This is impossible, because *E* is a tangent plane.

In this proof, and several times before, we have drawn figures in which the intersection of a plane and a sphere appears to be a circle. Before proceeding with our investigation of tangent planes, we show that these figures are right.

### Theorem 14–12  The Plane-Sphere Theorem

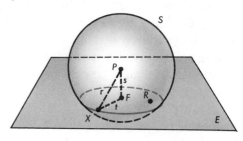

***If a plane intersects the interior of a sphere, then the intersection of the plane and the sphere is a circle. The center of this circle is the foot of the perpendicular from the center of the sphere to the plane.***

**Proof.** The notation is that of the figure. Given that the plane *E* intersects the interior of the sphere *S* in a point *R*. Let *F* be the foot of the perpendicular from *P* to *E*. We need to show that the intersection of *E* and *S* is a circle with center at *F*.

Now $PR < r$, because *R* is in the interior. By the Second Minimum Theorem, $PF \le PR$. Therefore $PF < r$. Let $PF = s$.

(1) Let *X* be any point in the intersection of *E* and *S*. Then $\triangle PFX$ has a right angle at *F*. Therefore

$$s^2 + FX^2 = r^2, \quad \text{and} \quad FX = \sqrt{r^2 - s^2}.$$

Therefore *X* lies on the circle with center *F* and radius $t = \sqrt{r^2 - s^2}$.

Therefore the intersection of $E$ and $S$ *lies in* the circle with center $F$ and radius $t = \sqrt{r^2 - s^2}$.

This doesn't necessarily mean that the intersection *is* the circle. To complete the proof, we need to show that every point of the circle lies in the intersection.

(2) Let $X$ be any point of the circle in $E$ with center $F$ and radius $t = \sqrt{r^2 - s^2}$. By the Pythagorean Theorem,

$$\begin{aligned} PX^2 &= t^2 + s^2 \\ &= (r^2 - s^2) + s^2 \\ &= r^2. \end{aligned}$$

Therefore $PX = r$, and $X$ lies on the sphere.

### Theorem 14–13

**The perpendicular from the center of a sphere to a chord bisects the chord.**

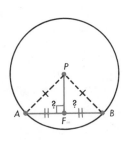

Proof? (It is the same as the proof of Theorem 14–4.)

### Theorem 14–14

**The segment from the center of a sphere to the midpoint of a chord is perpendicular to the chord.**

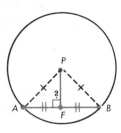

The proof is like that of Theorem 14–5.

### Problem Set 14–3

1. Complete: If a plane intersects a sphere, the intersection is either a ___circle___ or a ___point___.

2. Complete: If a line intersects a sphere, the intersection is either ___two points___ or ___one point___.

3. Can three points of a sphere ever be collinear? Explain. No

4. In a sphere having a radius of 15, the distance of a chord from the center is 9. How long is the chord? 24

5. A chord of a sphere is 12 in. long and is 6 in. from the center of the sphere. Find the radius of the sphere. $6\sqrt{2}$ cm

## Answers to Problems

**6.** By Theorem 14–11, every tangent plane to a sphere is perpendicular to the radius drawn to the point of contact. Therefore, $\overleftrightarrow{PA} \perp E$. But, by definition, if a line, $\overleftrightarrow{PA}$, is perpendicular to a plane, $E$, at a point $A$, it is perpendicular to every line in $E$ through $A$. Therefore, $\overleftrightarrow{PA} \perp \overleftrightarrow{AB}$, and so on.

**7.** By Problems 5 and 11, Section 14–1, the figure formed by joining, in succession, the end points of two diameters of a sphere is a rectangle. It is easy to see that if the diagonals of a rectangle are perpendicular, the rectangle is a square.

**9.** Let the three points be $A$, $B$, $C$. To find the center of the circle, in the plane $ABC$, construct the perpendicular bisectors of any two of the three segments $\overline{AB}$, $\overline{BC}$, $\overline{AC}$. The bisectors intersect at the center, $Q$, of the circle. $\overline{QA}$, $\overline{QB}$, and $\overline{QC}$ are radii of the circle. Construct the line perpendicular to plane $ABC$ at $Q$. This line meets the sphere in two points, $X$ and $Y$. Determine the midpoint, $P$, of $\overline{XY}$. $P$ is the center of the sphere. $\overline{PA}$, $\overline{PB}$, and $\overline{PC}$ are radii of the sphere.

**10.** By definition, a great circle lies in a plane through the center of the sphere. The intersection of the two planes must contain the center of the sphere, so the segment in the intersection which is a chord of the sphere is also a diameter of the sphere, and hence of each circle.

**11.** Let $\overline{PA}$ be the perpendicular segment from $P$ to $E$, and let $\overline{PB}$ be the perpendicular segment from $P$ to $F$. Let $G$ be a plane containing points $P$, $A$, and $B$, and let circle $C$ be the intersection of plane $G$ and sphere $S$. Let $\overline{HJ}$ be the chord of $C$ which lies in plane $E$, and $\overline{KL}$ be the chord of $C$ which lies in plane $F$. Proof: The above considerations enable us to simplify a spatial problem to a planar problem. Since $PA = PB$ by hypothesis, the chords $\overline{HJ}$ and $\overline{KL}$ of $C$ are equidistant from the center of $C$. We can therefore conclude by Theorem 14–7 that $HJ = KL$. But this obviously implies that $AH = BK$, which means that the circle formed by the intersection of $E$ and $S$ is congruent to the circle formed by the intersection of $F$ and $S$.

**6.** Sphere $S$ is tangent to plane $E$ at $A$. $P$ is the center of $S$, and $B$, $C$, $D$ lie in $E$. What is the relationship of $\overrightarrow{PA}$ to $\overleftrightarrow{AB}$, $\overleftrightarrow{AC}$, and $\overleftrightarrow{AD}$? Explain. $\overrightarrow{PA} \perp \overleftrightarrow{AB}, \overleftrightarrow{AC}, \overleftrightarrow{AD}$

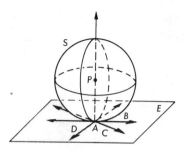

**7.** Prove: If two diameters of a sphere are perpendicular, then the figure formed by the segments joining their end points in succession is a square.

**8.** Find the radius of the circle formed by a plane 4 cm from the center of a sphere whose diameter is 10 cm. **3 cm**

---

**9.** Given a sphere and three points on it. Explain how to determine the center and the radius of the circle which contains the points. Explain how to determine the center and radius of the sphere.

**10.** Explain why any two great circles of a sphere intersect at the end points of a diameter of the sphere.

**11.** Prove the following theorem.

If two planes intersect a sphere and their distances from the center are equal, then the intersections are either two points or two congruent circles.

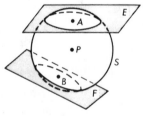

---

$MA = MB$, $\triangle AMB$ is rt. isosceles and $AM = 5\sqrt{2}/2$. $\overline{PM} \perp \overline{MA}$, $\triangle AMP$ is rt. isosceles and $AP = 5$. $\triangle AMP \cong \triangle AMB$ and $AB = AP = BP$ and thus $m\angle APB = 60$.

**12.** Given: Plane $E$ intersects sphere $S$. $P$ is the center of $S$. $A$, $B$, $C$, $M$ are in $E$. $A$ and $B$ are in $S$. $PC$ is altitude of equilateral triangle $\triangle APB$ and $PC = 5\sqrt{3}/2$.

$\overline{PM} \perp E$.

$\overline{AM} \perp \overline{MB}$.

$AC = BC$.

$AM = PM$.

$AB = 5$.

Find: The radius of the sphere, $m\angle APB$, and $PC$.

**13.** Two great circles are said to be perpendicular if they lie in perpendicular planes. Show that for every two great circles there is one other great circle perpendicular to both. If two great circles on the earth are meridians (through the poles), what great circle is their common perpendicular?

**14.** In the figure, $P$ and $P'$ are the centers of spheres $S$ and $S'$. $A$ and $B$ are two points of the intersection of the two spheres. $\overleftrightarrow{AB}$ and $\overleftrightarrow{PP'}$ intersect at $M$. $\overrightarrow{PA}$ is tangent to $S'$ at $A$.

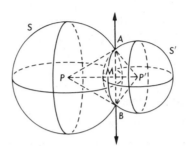

(a) Describe the intersection of spheres $S$ and $S'$.

(b) If the radius of $S$ is 12 and $PA = AB$, find the radius of $S'$ and the distance between the centers of the spheres.

## 14–4 ARCS OF CIRCLES

We started this chapter with a discussion of circles, and then proceeded to give an analogous discussion of spheres. In the rest of the chapter, however, we shall be concerned only with circles, because the corresponding theory for spheres is too hard for a first course in geometry.

In the figure on the left below, $\angle APB$ is a *central angle* of the circle $C$.

### Definition

A *central angle* of a circle is an angle whose vertex is the center of the circle.

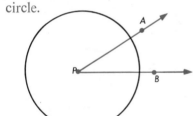 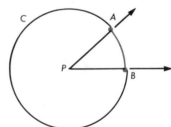

In the figure on the right above, the curve in color is the *minor arc $\overparen{AB}$*, and the black curve is the *major arc $\overparen{AB}$*. In each case, $A$ and $B$ are the *end points* of the arc.

### Definitions

Let $C$ be a circle with center $P$, and let $A$ and $B$ be points which lie on $C$ but are not the end points of the same diameter. Then the *minor arc $\overparen{AB}$* is the union of $A$, $B$ and all points of $C$ that are in the interior of $\angle APB$. The *major arc $\overparen{AB}$* is the union of $A$, $B$ and all points of $C$ that lie in the exterior of $\angle APB$. In each case, $A$ and $B$ are the *end points* of the arc $\overparen{AB}$, and $P$ is the *center* of the arc $\overparen{AB}$.

serious disadvantage which may not be obvious. Effective teaching of geometry requires pictures, and these ought to be accurate pictures of the mathematical objects that they are supposed to describe. If an angle is defined as a region, then any accurate picture of an angle would have to use shading to show what region is meant. In any but the very simplest figures, it is hopelessly tedious to shade enough regions to show all the angles correctly. In practice, nobody would do it. Therefore, if we defined angles as regions, our pictures would cease to be accurate.

Under the definition used in this book, it is easy to draw an accurate picture of an angle. The arrowheads make it plain that the figure is the union of two rays.

The definition of degree measure also tells us that the degree measure of a circle is 360. More precisely: If $A$ and $B$ are any two points on the circle $C$, and $X$ and $Y$ are two other points of $C$ on opposite sides of $\overleftrightarrow{AB}$, then $m\widehat{AXB} + m\widehat{AYB} = 360$.

## Background Material

The proof of Theorem 14–15 is tedious, because we must discuss five cases, but each of the five cases is easy. We describe them, give the figures, and leave the verifications to the reader.

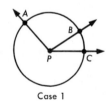

Case 1

CASE 1. $\widehat{ABC}$ is a minor arc. The conclusion follows from the Angle Addition Postulate.

If $A$ and $B$ are the end points of a diameter, then we get two arcs, each of which is called a *semicircle*.

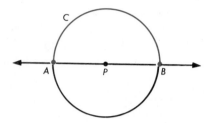

## Definition

Let $C$ be a circle, and let $A$ and $B$ be the end points of a diameter. A *semicircle* $\widehat{AB}$ is the union of $A$, $B$, and the points of $C$ that lie in a given half-plane with $\overleftrightarrow{AB}$ as edge. The points $A$ and $B$ are the *end points* of the semicircle.

Note that the notation $\widehat{AB}$ for arcs is always ambiguous, because every two points $A$ and $B$ of a circle are the end points of two different arcs of the circle. The easiest way to avoid this ambiguity is to pick another point $X$ of the arc, and denote the arc by $\widehat{AXB}$. For example, in the figure to the right, $\widehat{AXB}$ is the minor arc, drawn in color, and $\widehat{AYB}$ is the major arc, drawn black. When it is clear from the context which arc is meant, we may simply write $\widehat{AB}$.

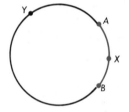

We now want to define the *degree measures* of arcs, in the way suggested by the labels in the following figures.

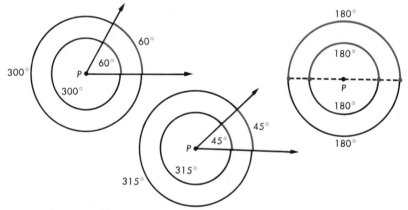

Note that the degree measure of an arc does not depend on the size of the circle. On the pairs of concentric circles above, corresponding arcs have the same measure. Note also that as an arc gets longer (on the fixed circle) its measure gets bigger. Thus a major arc always has measure greater than 180.

These ideas are conveyed by the following definition.

## Definition

(1) The *degree measure* of a minor arc is the measure of the corresponding central angle.

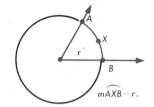

$m\widehat{AXB} = r.$

(2) The *degree measure* of a semicircle is 180.

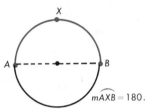

$m\widehat{AXB} = 180.$

(3) The *degree measure* of a major arc is equal to 360 minus the measure of the corresponding minor arc.

Hereafter, the degree measure of an arc will be referred to simply as its measure. The measure of an arc $\widehat{AB}$ will be denoted by $m\widehat{AB}$.

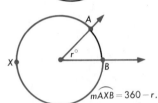

$m\widehat{AXB} = 360 - r.$

The following theorem looks reasonable. The proof, however, is unusually tedious. Note that when $\widehat{ABC}$ is a minor arc, the formula follows directly from the Angle Addition Postulate. When $\widehat{ABC}$ is not a minor arc there are several cases to consider. The practical value of the formula should be obvious, at any rate, and so we agree here to use it without going through the details of the proof.

**Theorem 14–15.** The Arc Addition Theorem

*If B is a point of $\widehat{AC}$, then*

$$m\widehat{ABC} = m\widehat{AB} + m\widehat{BC}.$$

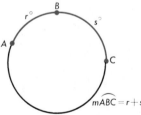

$m\widehat{ABC} = r + s.$

## Problem Set 14–4

**1.** In the figure, $A$ and $B$ are the end points of a diameter.

(a) Name the semicircles. $\widehat{ACB}$ and $\widehat{ADB}$

(b) Name the minor arcs. $\widehat{AC}, \widehat{CB}, \widehat{BD}, \widehat{DA}$, and $\widehat{DC}$

(c) Name the major arcs. $\widehat{ABD}, \widehat{ABC}, \widehat{DBC}, \widehat{BDC}$, and $\widehat{BCD}$

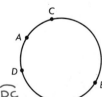

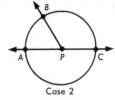

Case 2

CASE 2. $\widehat{ABC}$ is a semicircle. The conclusion follows from the Supplement Postulate.

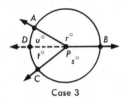

Case 3

CASE 3. $\widehat{ABC}$ is a major arc, and $A$ and $C$ are on opposite sides of the diameter that contains $B$. (What are the equations relating $r$, $u$, $s$, and $t$?)

Case 4

CASE 4. $\widehat{ABC}$ is a major arc, and $A$ and $C$ are on the same side of the diameter that contains $B$.

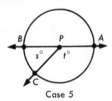

Case 5

CASE 5. $\widehat{ABC}$ is a major arc, and one of the arcs $\widehat{AB}$, $\widehat{BC}$ is a semi-circle. (Here $m\widehat{ABC} = 360 - t = 180 + 180 - t = 180 + s = m\widehat{AB} + m\widehat{BC}$.)

### Quiz

Two points on a circle determine a minor arc and a major arc. If the measure of the major arc is 39 less than 12 times the measure of the minor arc, what is the measure of the minor arc?

(ans: $3\frac{9}{13}$)

## Answers to Problems

**5.** Since $\angle GPK$ and $\angle HPM$ are vertical angles, $m\angle GPK = m\angle HPM$. Since $\angle GPK$ and $\angle HPM$ are central angles, $m\widehat{GK} = m\angle GPK$ and $m\widehat{HM} = m\angle HPM$. Therefore, $m\widehat{GK} = m\widehat{HM}$.

**7.** Let $\overline{PC}$ be the bisector of central angle $\angle BPA$ where $P$ is the center of the circle and $\widehat{AB}$ is the minor arc corresponding to the central angle $\angle BPA$. $m\angle APC = m\angle CPB$, by the definition of angle bisector. Since $m\angle APC = m\widehat{AC}$ and $m\angle BPC = m\widehat{BC}$, $m\widehat{AC} = m\widehat{BC}$ and $\overline{PC}$ bisects $\widehat{AB}$ by the definition of bisect.

**8.** Since $\overline{DC} \perp \overline{CF}$, $m\angle DCF = 90$, and so $m\angle ACD + m\angle BCF = 90$. Since $m\angle DCF = m\angle ECF + m\angle DCE$, by the AAP we can conclude that $m\angle ACD + m\angle BCF = m\angle ECF + m\angle DCE$. But since $\angle ACD$ and $\angle ECF$ are central angles of the large circle and $\angle BCF$ and $\angle DCE$ are central angles of the small circle, we conclude by the definition of the measure of an arc that $m\widehat{AD} + m\widehat{QT} = m\widehat{EF} + m\widehat{RS}$.

**10.** (See diagram for Case 3 in Background Material.) Let $\overline{BD}$ be the diameter containing $B$. Since $A$ and $C$ are on opposite sides of $\overleftrightarrow{BD}$, the arc $\widehat{ADC}$ is the minor arc corresponding to the major arc $\widehat{ABC}$. Therefore $m\widehat{AD} + m\widehat{DC} = m\widehat{ADC}$ by the AAP. Let $P$ be the center of the circle. Then $\angle APD$ and $\angle APB$ form a linear pair, so $m\angle APD + m\angle APB = 180$ and $m\widehat{AD} + m\widehat{BA} = 180$. Similarly $m\widehat{BC} + m\widehat{CD} = 180$, so $m\widehat{AB} + m\widehat{BC} = 180 - m\widehat{AD} + 180 - m\widehat{CD} = 360 - (m\widehat{AD} + m\widehat{CD}) = 360 - m\widehat{ADC} = m\widehat{ABC}$ by the definition of the degree measure of a major arc.

**2.** In the figure $M$ is the center of the circle.

(a) Name a central angle. $\angle GMK$ or $\angle IMK$

(b) Name a chord not a diameter. $\overline{GH}$

(c) Name a major arc. $\widehat{GKH}, \widehat{KGH}, \widehat{HGI}, \widehat{IGK}$, etc.

(d) If $m\angle KMI = 70$, what is $m\widehat{KGI}$?
$m\widehat{KGI} = 290$

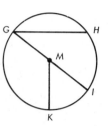

**3.** In the figure on the left below, $P$ is the center of the circle and $RQ = PS$. Find $m\widehat{RQ}, m\widehat{RS}, m\widehat{SRQ}, m\widehat{RSQ}$.
60      120      180      300

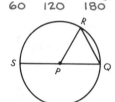

$m\angle BPC = 100$
$m\widehat{BC} = 100$
$m\widehat{AD} = 100$
$m\angle APC = 80$
$m\widehat{AC} = 80$
$m\widehat{BD} = 80$

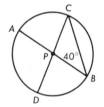

**4.** In the figure on the right above, diameters $\overline{AB}$ and $\overline{CD}$ intersect at $P$. If $m\angle ABC = 40$, find the measure of each minor arc of the circle.

**5.** Prove: If $\overline{GH}$ and $\overline{MK}$ are two diameters of a circle, then $m\widehat{GK} = m\widehat{HM}$.

**6.** In this figure, $P$ is the center of each arc. Which arc has the greatest measure? $\widehat{CD}$

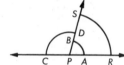

**7.** Prove: The bisector of a central angle of a circle bisects the corresponding minor arc.

**8.** Given: $\widehat{AB}$ is a semicircle with center $C$.

$\widehat{PQ}$ is concentric with $\widehat{AB}$.

$\overline{EC} \perp \overline{AB}$ and $\overline{DC} \perp \overline{CF}$.

Prove: $m\widehat{AD} + m\widehat{QT} = m\widehat{EF} + m\widehat{RS}$.

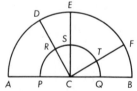

**9.** Two points on a circle determine a minor arc and a major arc. If the measure of the major arc is 40 less than 4 times the measure of the minor arc, find the measure of each arc. 80 and 280

**10.** Prove the Arc Addition Theorem for the following case:

$\widehat{ABC}$ is a major arc and $A$ and $C$ are on opposite sides of the diameter containing $B$.

Assume any other cases necessary to the proof.

## 14-5   INSCRIBED ANGLES AND INTERCEPTED ARCS

In each of the figures below, $\angle x$ is said to be *inscribed* in the arc which is drawn in color.

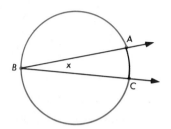 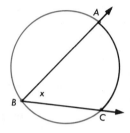

This idea can be described in words, quickly and easily.

### Definition

An angle is *inscribed* in an arc if
(1) the sides of the angle contain the end points of the arc and
(2) the vertex of the angle is a point, but not an end point, of the arc.

Of course, if $D$ is any point of $\overset{\frown}{ABC}$ other than $A$ or $C$, then $\overset{\frown}{ABC} = \overset{\frown}{ADC}$, and so $\angle ADC$ is also inscribed in the same arc. In the figure on the right, all the angles shown are inscribed in the arc $\overset{\frown}{AC}$ which is drawn in color. The figure looks as though these angles were all congruent, and in fact, this is always the case, as we shall soon see.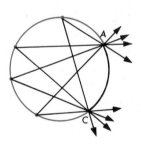

In the first two figures below, the angle *intercepts* the arc or arcs drawn in color; but this is not the case in the third figure.

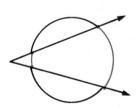  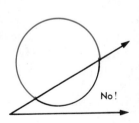

### Definition

An angle *intercepts* an arc if
(1) the end points of the arc lie on the angle,
(2) all other points of the arc are in the interior of the angle, and
(3) each side of the angle contains an end point of the arc.

## 14-5 INSCRIBED ANGLES AND INTERCEPTED ARCS

**Classroom Notes**

It is important to make clear the definition of *an angle inscribed in an arc* and the definition of *an angle which intercepts an arc;* students tend to find these difficult. In Sections 14-5 and 14-6 we establish the classical theorems about the angles formed by two lines which intersect a circle: Theorem 14-16, Theorem 14-19, and the theorems in Problems 10, 12, and 14 of Problem Set 14-6.

**Theorem 14–16.**    The Inscribed Angle Theorem

> *The measure of an inscribed angle is half the measure of its intercepted arc.*

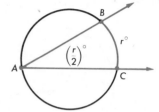

**Restatement.**    Let $\angle A$ be inscribed in an arc $\overset{\frown}{BAC}$ of a circle, intercepting the arc $\overset{\frown}{BC}$. Then

$$m\angle A = \tfrac{1}{2}m\overset{\frown}{BC}.$$

**Proof.**    *Case* 1.   We consider first the case in which $\angle A$ contains a diameter of the circle. By Corollary 9–13.3,

$$r = s + t.$$

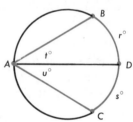

By the Isosceles Triangle Theorem, $t = s$. Therefore

$$s = \frac{r}{2}.$$

This proves the theorem, in Case 1, because $s = m\angle A$ and $r = m\overset{\frown}{BC}$.

Now we know that the theorem holds in Case 1. We shall use this fact to show that it holds in every case.

*Case* 2.   Suppose that $B$ and $C$ are on opposite sides of the diameter through $A$ like this:

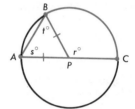

We know by Case 1 that

$$t = \frac{r}{2} \quad \text{and} \quad u = \frac{s}{2}.$$

Therefore, by addition $t + u = \tfrac{1}{2}(r + s)$. But $t + u = m\angle A$ and $r + s = m\overset{\frown}{BDC}$.

(Reason, in each case?) Therefore $m\angle A = \tfrac{1}{2}m\overset{\frown}{BC}$, as before.

*Case* 3.   Suppose, finally, that $B$ and $C$ are on the same side of the diameter through $A$. Then

$$r + s = m\overset{\frown}{BCD}$$

and

$$t + u = m\angle BAD.$$

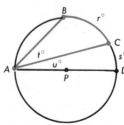

By Case 1,

$$t + u = \tfrac{1}{2}(r + s),$$

and

$$u = \tfrac{1}{2}s.$$

Therefore

$$t = \tfrac{1}{2}r,$$

and $m\angle A = \tfrac{1}{2}m\widehat{BC}$, as before. (Reasons, for each step?)

    Theorem 14–16 has two important corollaries.

### Corollary 14–16.1

*Any angle inscribed in a semicircle is a right angle.*

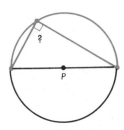

    The proof is obvious: such an angle always *intercepts* a semicircle, and $90 = \tfrac{1}{2} \cdot 180$.

### Corollary 14–16.2

*Every two angles inscribed in the same arc are congruent.*

Again this is obvious: they intercept the same arc.

### Definitions

A triangle is *inscribed in* a circle if the vertices of the triangle lie on the circle. If each side of the triangle is tangent to the circle, then the triangle is *circumscribed about* the circle.

A quadrilateral is *inscribed in* a circle if the vertices of the quadrilateral lie on the circle. If each side of the quadrilateral is tangent to the circle, then the quadrilateral is *circumscribed about* the circle.

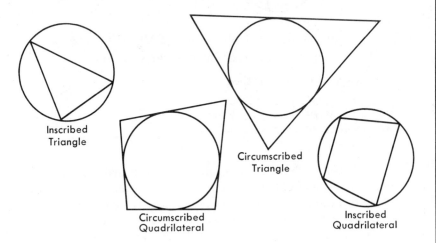

Inscribed Triangle

Circumscribed Triangle

Circumscribed Quadrilateral

Inscribed Quadrilateral

**Quiz**

**1.** $\overline{AB}$ is a diameter of a circle and chords $\overline{AC}$ and $\overline{BD}$ intersect at $E$. If $m\widehat{AD} = 85$ and $m\widehat{BC} = 70$, what is $m\angle AEB$?
    (ans: $102\tfrac{1}{2}$)

**2.** Prove: Given two circles externally tangent, such that the diameter of one of the circles is twice the diameter of the other. Then for any secant that contains the point of tangency, its chord in the larger circle will be twice as long as its chord in the smaller circle.

    Proof: Let $B$ be the point of tangency, and $\overline{AB}$, $\overline{BC}$, $E$, and $D$ the diameters and the points of intersection of the secant line with the larger and smaller circles, respectively. By Corollary 14–16.1, $\angle AEB$ and $\angle BDC$ are right angles. $\angle ABE \cong \angle DBC$ (vertical angles). Thus, $\triangle ABE \sim \triangle CBD$ (AAA). This implies that $EB/BD = AB/BC = 2$. Hence, $EB = 2BD$.

## Answers to Problems

**8.** One drawing appears below.

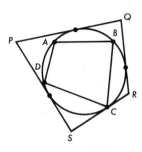

**9.** Since $\angle ACB$ and $\angle ADB$ are each inscribed in a semicircle, $\angle ACB$ and $\angle ADB$ are each right angles by Corollary 14–16.1. Therefore $\triangle ABC \cong \triangle ABD$ by HL.

**10.** Since $\angle ACB$ is inscribed in a semicircle, $\angle ACB$ is a right angle and $AC \perp CB$. By Theorem 14–5, a segment from the center of a circle to the midpoint of a chord is perpendicular to the chord. Thus $\overline{PQ} \perp \overline{CB}$, and therefore, by Theorem 9–2 $\overline{AC} \parallel \overline{PQ}$. Finally, since $R$ is the midpoint of $\overline{AC}$, $\overline{PR} \perp \overline{AC}$. But if a line is perpendicular to one of two parallel lines, it is perpendicular to the other. Hence $\overline{PR} \perp \overline{PQ}$.

---

### Problem Set 14–5

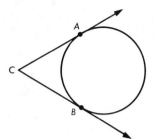

**1.** Show that, according to definition, both major arc $\overset{\frown}{AB}$ and minor arc $\overset{\frown}{AB}$ of this figure are intercepted arcs of $\angle C$.
Both arcs meet all three conditions.

**2.** Given the figure with $\overrightarrow{AS}$ tangent at $S$.

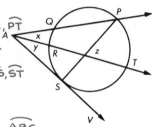

(a) Name the arc(s) intercepted by $\angle x$. $\overset{\frown}{OR}, \overset{\frown}{PT}$
(b) Name the arc(s) intercepted by $\angle z$. $\overset{\frown}{PT}$
(c) Name the arc(s) intercepted by $\angle y$. $\overset{\frown}{RS}, \overset{\frown}{ST}$

**3.** Given the figure.

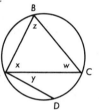

(a) Name the arc in which $\angle z$ is inscribed. $\overset{\frown}{ABC}$
(b) Name the arc which $\angle x$ intercepts. $\overset{\frown}{BC}$
(c) Name the arc which $\angle z$ intercepts. $\overset{\frown}{ADC}$
(d) Name the angle inscribed in $\overset{\frown}{BCA}$. $\angle BCA$
(e) Name the arc which $\angle BAD$ intercepts. $\overset{\frown}{BCD}$
(f) Name the angle inscribed in $\overset{\frown}{CBD}$. $\angle CAD$

**4.** In the figure on the left, $P$ is the center of the circle. If $m\angle B = 35$, find $m\angle A$ and $m\angle P$.
35     70

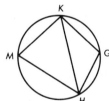

$m\overset{\frown}{KGH}=150$
$m\overset{\frown}{KG}=80$
$m\overset{\frown}{MH}=120$
$m\angle MKH=60$
$m\angle GKH=35$
$m\angle KGH=105$
$m\angle GHK=40$
$m\angle KHM=45$

**5.** In the figure on the right above, if $m\angle M = 75$, $m\overset{\frown}{MK} = 90$, and $m\overset{\frown}{GH} = 70$, find the measures of all other arcs and angles.

**6.** If $m\angle RQS = 45$ and $P$ is the center of $\overset{\frown}{QRS}$, prove that $\overline{RP} \perp \overline{SP}$.
Since $m\angle RQS=45$, $m\overset{\frown}{RS}=90$ and $m\overset{\frown}{RS}=m\angle RPS=90$, therefore $\overline{RP} \perp \overline{SP}$

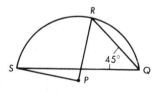

**7.** Prove: If two circles are tangent internally such that the smaller circle contains the center of the larger circle, then any chord of the larger circle having one end point at the point of tangency is bisected by the smaller circle. Use Corollary 14–16.1 and Theorem 14–4

**8.** Draw a circle. Next draw $\square ABCD$ inscribed in the circle. Finally draw $\square PQRS$ circumscribed about the circle.

**9.** $\overline{AB}$ is a diameter of the circle on the left below and $C$ and $D$ are points of the circle on opposite sides of $\overline{AB}$ such that $BC = BD$. Prove that $\triangle ABC \cong \triangle ABD$. Use HL

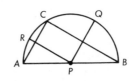

**10.** Given: $P$ is the center of semicircle $\overset{\frown}{AB}$ in the figure to the right above; $\overline{PR}$ bisects $\overline{AC}$ and $\overline{PQ}$ bisects $\overline{BC}$.

Prove: $\overline{PR} \perp \overline{PQ}$.

**11.** Given the figure with $m\overset{\frown}{AG} = m\overset{\frown}{BG}$. Prove that

$$\triangle MHB \sim \triangle MAG.$$

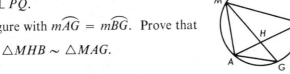

**12.** Given a circle with parallel chords $\overline{AB}$ and $\overline{CD}$. $A$ and $C$ are on the same side of the perpendicular bisector of $\overline{AB}$. Prove that $m\overset{\frown}{AC} = m\overset{\frown}{BD}$.

**13.** Prove: If an angle inscribed in an arc is a right angle, the arc is a semi-circle.

**14.** Prove the following theorem.
$m\angle Q = \frac{1}{2} m\overset{\frown}{PSR},\ m\angle S = \frac{1}{2} m\overset{\frown}{PQR}$ (Th. 14-16)
The opposite angles of an inscribed quadrilateral are supplementary.
$m\overset{\frown}{PQR} + m\overset{\frown}{PSR} = 360$ so $m\angle Q + m\angle S = 180$

**15.** In the figure, if $m\angle P = 60$ and $m\overset{\frown}{PSR} = 128$, what is $m\angle Q$, $m\angle R$, and $m\angle S$?
64    120
116

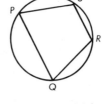

*Figure for Problems 14 and 15*

---

**16.** In semicircle $\overset{\frown}{ACB}$, $\overline{CD} \perp \overline{AB}$ at $D$. Prove that $CD$ is the geometric mean of $AD$ and $DB$. Use Corollary 14-16.1 and Theorem 12-8

**17.** Given that

(a) $AD = 9$ and $DB = 4$, find $CD$. 6

(b) $AB = 25$ and $AD = 5$, find $CD$. 10

(c) $AD = 32$ and $CD = 8$, find $DB$. 2

(d) $AD = 3$ and $DB = 1$, find $CD$. $\sqrt{3}$

(e) $AB = 25$ and $CD = 12$, find $AD$ and $DB$. 16, 9

*Figure for Problems 16 and 17*

**18.** In a circle, if diameter $\overline{AB}$ is perpendicular to chord $\overline{CD}$ at $E$, prove that $CD^2 = 4AE \cdot BE$.

**22.** Let $F$ be the intersection of $\overline{AE}$ and $\overline{BC}$, $G$ the intersection of $\overline{CD}$ and $\overline{AB}$, and $H$ the intersection of $\overline{AE}$ and $\overline{CD}$. Then since two angles of $\triangle GAH$ are congruent respectively to two angles of $\triangle FCH$ we can conclude that the third pair of angles are congruent: $\angle BAE \cong \angle DCB$. But since $\angle BAE$ and $\angle DCB$ are inscribed angles, this means that $m\widehat{BE} = m\widehat{BD}$.

**23.** Since $\overrightarrow{PQ}$ is parallel and congruent to $\overrightarrow{SR}$, $\square PQRS$ is a parallelogram. This much is easy; but it is moderately difficult to show that $\square PQRS$ is a rhombus. Let $A$ and $B$ be respectively the centers of the circles which have $\overline{PQ}$ and $\overline{SR}$ as diameters, and introduce $\overline{PT}$, $\overline{AT}$, and $\overline{QT}$, and $\overline{ST}$, $\overline{BT}$, and $\overline{RT}$. (Although it appears that $P$, $T$, and $R$ are collinear and that $\overline{PR}$ is thus a diagonal of the parallelogram, we must prove it.) Since the two circles are tangent at $T$, $\overline{AT}$ and $\overline{BT}$ are each perpendicular to the common tangent at $T$, and so $A$, $T$, and $B$ are collinear. Since $\triangle PTA \cong \triangle RTB$ by SAS, $m\angle PTA = m\angle RTB$ and hence by the Angle Construction Postulate, $\overrightarrow{TP}$ and $\overrightarrow{TR}$ are opposite rays, which means that $P$, $T$, and $R$ are collinear. Similarly we can show that $Q$, $T$, and $S$ are collinear. Therefore, the diagonals $\overline{PR}$ and $\overline{QS}$ of parallelogram $\square PQRS$ do intersect at $T$, the point of tangency of the two congruent circles. Since $\angle PTQ$ is inscribed in a semicircle, $\angle PTQ$ is a right angle, and therefore the diagonals of $\square PQRS$ are perpendicular, and thus, $\square PQRS$ is a rhombus.

## 14–6 CONGRUENT ARCS

### Classroom Notes

This section is relatively easy. You may wish to assign proofs of the theorems to the students, and then discuss them in class.

The three cases of Theorem 14–18 should at least be drawn and the proofs outlined before assigning the problem set.

**19.** In the figure on the left below, $\overline{AB}$ is a diameter of the smaller of two concentric circles. $\overline{AP}$ and $\overline{BQ}$ are tangent to the smaller circle at $A$ and $B$, respectively. Prove that $\overline{AB}$ and $\overline{PQ}$ intersect at the center of the circles.

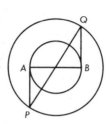 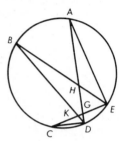

**20.** Given the figure on the right above, prove that $AG \cdot GD = EG \cdot GC$.

**21.** Prove: If a parallelogram is inscribed in a circle, the parallelogram is a rectangle. Opposite angles are equal (Th. 9-15) and supplementary (Problem 14 above) and thus each angle is a rt. angle (Th. 4-4)

**22.** $\triangle ABC$ is inscribed in a circle. $\overline{AE}$ and $\overline{CD}$ are chords, $\overline{AE} \perp \overline{BC}$, and $\overline{CD} \perp \overline{AB}$. Prove that $m\widehat{BD} = m\widehat{BE}$.

**23.** Two congruent circles are tangent externally at $T$. Diameter $\overline{PQ}$ is parallel to diameter $\overline{SR}$, with $S$ and $Q$ on opposite sides of $\overleftrightarrow{PR}$. Prove that $\square PQRS$ is a rhombus.

## 14–6    CONGRUENT ARCS

### Definition

In the same circle, or in congruent circles, two arcs are called *congruent* if they have the same measure.

### Theorem 14–17

> *In the same circle or in congruent circles, if two chords are congruent, then so are the corresponding minor arcs.*

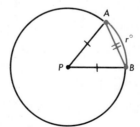 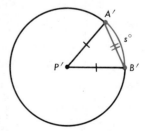

**Proof.** The notation of the proof is that of the figure. We need to show that $r = s$. By SSS,

$$\triangle APB \cong \triangle A'P'B'.$$

Therefore $m\angle APB = m\angle A'P'B'$. Since $m\widehat{AB} = m\angle APB$ and $m\widehat{A'B'} = m\angle A'P'B'$, we have $r = s$, and $\widehat{AB} \cong \widehat{A'B'}$.

### Theorem 14–18

*In the same circle or in congruent circles, if two arcs are congruent, then so are the corresponding chords.*

In the proof, there are three cases to consider, because the two congruent arcs may be minor arcs, major arcs, or semicircles. The following figure suggests the proof for the second of these cases.

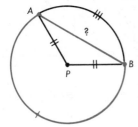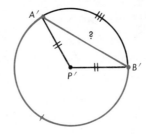

We get $AB = A'B'$, by using SAS to prove $\triangle APB \cong \triangle A'P'B'$.

In the figure for the next theorem $\overrightarrow{BC}$ is called a *tangent ray* and $\overrightarrow{BA}$ is called a *secant ray*. You should be able to state definitions for these terms for yourself.

### Theorem 14–19. The Tangent-Secant Theorem

*Given an angle with its vertex on a circle, formed by a secant ray and a tangent ray. The measure of the angle is half the measure of the intercepted arc.*

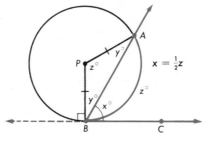

**Proof.** In the notation of the figure, we have $x + y = 90$, $2y + z = 180$; and we want to show that $x = \frac{1}{2}z$. This is easy, because $x = 90 - y$ and $z = 180 - 2y$.

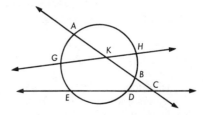
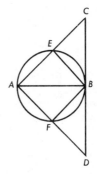

**1.** Since $\overline{AB} \cong \overline{CD}$, we can conclude by Theorem 14–17 that $m\widehat{ACB} = m\widehat{CBD}$. But by the Arc Addition Theorem, $m\widehat{ACB} = m\widehat{AC} + m\widehat{CB}$, and $m\widehat{CBD} = m\widehat{CB} + m\widehat{BD}$. Therefore, by subtraction, $m\widehat{AC} = m\widehat{BD}$, which means that $\widehat{AC} \cong \widehat{BD}$.

**5.** By Problem 4, $m\angle KHG = m\angle KGH$, and by Theorem 9–13 the sum of the measures of the angles of $\triangle GHK$ equals 180. Therefore, $m\angle HGK = 60$, and so by Theorem 14–19, $m\widehat{GH} = 120$. By subtraction, the measure of major arc $\widehat{GH} = 240$, so that the measure of major arc $\widehat{GH}$ equals twice the measure of minor arc $\widehat{GH}$.

**6.** Use the figure for Problem 3. Since by Problem 4, $\angle KHG \cong \angle KGH$, we conclude by the Converse of the Isosceles Triangle Theorem that $\overline{KG} \cong \overline{KH}$.

**7.** $m\widehat{AB} = 80$, $m\widehat{CD} = 40$; $m\angle BEA = m\angle CED = 60$, $m\angle BEC = m\angle AED = 120$, $m\angle BAC = 85$, $m\angle CAD = 20$, $m\angle BAD = 105$, $m\angle DAP = 35$, $m\angle ABD = 35$, $m\angle DBC = 20$, $m\angle ABC = 55$, $m\angle BCA = 40$, $m\angle ACD = 35$, $m\angle BCD = 75$, $m\angle ADB = 40$, $m\angle BDC = 85$, $m\angle ADC = 125$, $m\angle CDS = 20$, $m\angle ADP = 35$, $m\angle APD = m\angle RPQ = 110$, $m\angle CAP = 55$, $m\angle BDP = 75$.

**8.** Since $\widehat{AD} \cong \widehat{CB}$, $\angle ACD \cong \angle CDB$, and therefore $\overline{AC} \parallel \overline{BD}$, so that $\square ADBC$ is a trapezoid. Since $\widehat{AD} \cong \widehat{CB}$ we can also conclude by Theorem 14–18 that $\overline{AD} \cong \overline{CB}$, and that therefore $\square ADBC$ is an isosceles trapezoid. [Note: The problem assumes that $\overleftrightarrow{DA}$ and $\overleftrightarrow{BC}$ intersect. Otherwise, $\square ADBC$ may not be an isosceles trapezoid.]

**9.** Since $\overline{AD} \cong \overline{DC} \cong \overline{CB}$, we can conclude by Theorem 14–17 that $\widehat{AD} \cong \widehat{DC} \cong \widehat{CB}$, and then by Theorem 14–16 that $\angle APD \cong \angle DPC \cong \angle CPB$, that is $\overrightarrow{PC}$ and $\overrightarrow{PD}$ trisect $\angle APB$.

**Problem Set 14–6**

**1.** In the figure on the left below, $\overline{AB} \cong \overline{CD}$. Prove that $\widehat{AC} \cong \widehat{BD}$.

 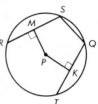

**2.** In the circle on the right above with center $P$, $PM = PK$ and $\overline{PM}$ and $\overline{PK}$ are perpendicular to chords $\overline{RS}$ and $\overline{QT}$, respectively. Prove that $\widehat{RS} \cong \widehat{QT}$. Use Theorem 14-7 and then Theorem 14-17

**3.** $\overrightarrow{KH}$ and $\overrightarrow{KG}$ are tangent to the circle at $H$ and $G$. If the measure of the major arc $\widehat{GH}$ is 242, find $m\angle DGH$ and $m\angle GHK$. 121, 59

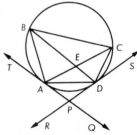

**4.** In the figure for Problem 3, why is $\angle KHG \cong \angle KGH$? $m\angle KHG = \frac{1}{2} m\widehat{GH} = m\angle KGH$ (Th. 14-19)

**5.** In the figure for Problem 3, if $m\angle K = 60$, show that the measure of major arc $\widehat{GH}$ is twice the measure of minor arc $\widehat{GH}$.

**6.** Prove: If two tangents to a circle intersect each other, then they form an isosceles triangle with the chord joining the points of tangency.

**7.** In the figure, $\overleftrightarrow{PA}$ and $\overleftrightarrow{PD}$ are tangents at $A$ and $D$, respectively. If

$$m\widehat{AD} = 70, \qquad m\widehat{BC} = 170$$

and

$$m\angle TAB = 40,$$

find the measure of each angle and each minor arc of the figure.

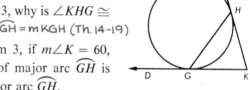

**8.** In the figure on the left below, $\widehat{AD} \cong \widehat{CB}$. Prove that $\square ADBC$ is an isosceles trapezoid.

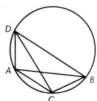 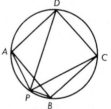

**9.** In the figure on the right above, $\square ABCD$ is a square, inscribed in a circle, and $P$ is any point of $\widehat{AB}$ other than $A$ or $B$. Prove that $\overline{PC}$ and $\overline{PD}$ trisect $\angle APB$.

10. Prove the following theorem. $m\angle DKB = m\angle B + m\angle C = \frac{1}{2}m\widehat{DB} + \frac{1}{2}m\widehat{AC}$
    Use Exterior Angle Theorem

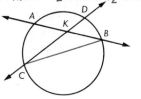

The measure of an angle formed by two secants of a circle intersecting at a point in the interior of the circle is one-half the sum of the measures of the arcs intercepted by the angle and its vertical angle.

[*Hint:* Prove $m\angle DKB = \frac{1}{2}(m\widehat{DB} + m\widehat{AC})$. First introduce $\overline{BC}$.]

11. In the figure for Problem 10, given that
    (a) $m\widehat{DB} = 40$ and $m\widehat{AC} = 90$, find $m\angle AKC$. **65**
    (b) $m\widehat{AD} = 100$ and $m\widehat{BC} = 170$, find $m\angle BKC$. **135**
    (c) $m\widehat{AC} = 130$ and $m\angle DKB = 75$, find $m\widehat{DB}$. **20**
    (d) $m\widehat{ACD} = 310$ and $m\widehat{BC} = 200$, find $m\angle AKC$. **55**
    (e) $m\widehat{BAC} = 180$ and $m\angle DKB = 57$, find $m\widehat{AD}$. **66**

12. Prove the following theorem. $m\angle K = |m\angle BCD - m\angle ABC| = |\frac{1}{2}m\widehat{BD} - \frac{1}{2}m\widehat{AC}| = \frac{1}{2}|m\widehat{BD} - m\widehat{AC}|$

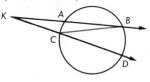

The measure of an angle formed by two secants of a circle intersecting at a point in the exterior of the circle is one-half the absolute value of the difference of the measures of the intercepted arcs.

[*Hint:* Prove $m\angle K = \frac{1}{2}(m\widehat{BD} - m\widehat{AC})$. First introduce $\overline{BC}$.]

13. In the figure for Problem 12, given that
    (a) $m\widehat{BD} = 70$ and $m\widehat{AC} = 30$, find $m\angle K$. **20**
    (b) $m\widehat{BD} = 126$ and $m\widehat{AC} = 18$, find $m\angle K$. **54**
    (c) $m\widehat{AC} = 50$ and $m\angle K = 22$, find $m\widehat{BD}$. **94**
    (d) $m\widehat{AB} = 80$, $m\widehat{BD} = 80$, and $m\widehat{CD} = 190$, find $m\angle K$. **35**
    (e) $m\angle K = 28$, $m\widehat{ABD} = 166$, and $m\widehat{ACB} = 290$, find $m\widehat{CD}$. **154**

14. Verify that the theorem of Problem 12 holds if the words "two secants" are replaced by "a secant and a tangent" or by "two tangents."

$m\angle K = m\angle BCD - m\angle CBK$
$= \frac{1}{2}(m\widehat{BD} - m\widehat{BC})$

$m\angle K = m\angle DBC - m\angle BCK$
$= \frac{1}{2}m\widehat{BCE} - \frac{1}{2}m\widehat{BC}$

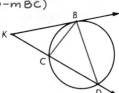
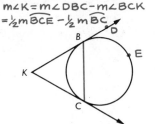

15. Two tangents to a circle form an angle whose measure is 72. What is the number of degrees in each intercepted arc? **108, 252**

16. A tangent ray $\overrightarrow{BC}$ is a ray contained in the tangent line to the circle at $B$.
A secant ray $\overrightarrow{BA}$ is a ray containing a chord of the circle with $B$ as an end point.
17. Given: $\angle STR$ formed by tangent ray $\overrightarrow{TR}$ and secant ray $\overrightarrow{TS}$ with $S$ on the circle.
Proof: Let $M$ be the midpoint of the intercepted arc $\widehat{TS}$. Introduce $\overline{TM}$, and $\overline{MA}$, the perpendicular segment from $M$ to $\overrightarrow{TR}$, and $\overline{MB}$, the perpendicular segment from $M$ to $\overrightarrow{TS}$. Then since $m\angle MTR = \frac{1}{2}m\widehat{TM}$ by Theorem 14–19, and $m\angle MTS = \frac{1}{2}m\widehat{MS}$ by Theorem 14–16, and $m\widehat{TM} = m\widehat{MS}$, by hypothesis, we conclude that $m\angle MTR = m\angle MTS$. Therefore $\triangle MTA \cong \triangle MTB$ by SAA, so that $MA = MB$; that is, $M$ is equidistant from $\overrightarrow{TR}$ and $\overrightarrow{TS}$.
19. Since the arcs in which the angles are inscribed are congruent, the arcs which the angles intercept are congruent. But it follows from Theorem 14–16 that angles which intercept congruent arcs are congruent.
20. By Theorem 14–17, the corresponding minor arcs have the same degree measure $r$, so the corresponding major arcs have the same degree measure $360 - r$; thus corresponding major arcs are congruent.
21. (a) $m\widehat{BE} = 64, m\widehat{AE} = m\widehat{AD} = 116$; $m\angle EAB = m\angle DAB = 32, m\angle AEB = m\angle ADB = 90, m\angle EBA = m\angle DBA = 58, m\angle AEG = m\angle ADG = 58, m\angle BEG = m\angle BDG = 32$, etc. $m\angle ACB = 58$.
24. There are two cases to consider, but the proof is the same in each case. Introduce the common tangent at $T$. Then the angle formed by the tangent at $A$ and line $L$ is congruent to the angle formed by the common tangent and line $L$ by Theorem 14–19. Similarly, the angle formed by the tangent at $B$ and line $L$ is congruent to the angle formed by the common tangent and line $L$. Therefore the tangents at $A$ and $B$ are parallel in the case (a) of the internally tangent circles by corresponding angles, and in case (b) of the externally tangent circles by alternate interior angles.

480

16. Write formal definitions of *tangent ray* and *secant ray*.

17. Given an angle with its vertex on a circle, formed by a secant ray and a tangent ray. Prove that the midpoint of the intercepted arc is equidistant from the sides of the angle.

18. In the figure, $\overleftrightarrow{PR}$ and $\overleftrightarrow{QS}$ are tangents and $\overline{PQ}$ is a diameter. Given that

$$m\widehat{MQ} = 120 \quad \text{and} \quad RQ = 8,$$

find the radius of the circle. $2\sqrt{3}$

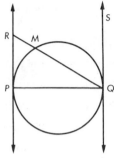

19. Prove the following theorem.

> If two arcs are congruent, then any angle inscribed in one of the arcs is congruent to any angle inscribed in the other arc.

20. Prove: In the same circle or in congruent circles, if two chords are congruent, then so are the corresponding major arcs.

21. $\overline{AB}$ is a diameter of the circle, and chord $\overline{DE}$ is parallel to tangent $\overleftrightarrow{CB}$.

(a) Given $m\widehat{BD} = 64$. Find the measure of each angle and each minor arc of the figure.

(b) Given that $AE = 16$ and the radius of the circle is 10, find the length of each segment.

(c) Using the information of part (b), find the area of $\square ADBE$. 192

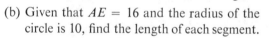
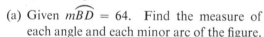

22. Given that $\overleftrightarrow{KS}$ is tangent to the circle at $T$ and secant $\overleftrightarrow{KR}$ contains $P$, the center of the circle. If $m\angle K = 35$, find $m\widehat{QT}$ and $m\angle STR$. $m\,\widehat{QT} = 55$
$m\angle STR = 62\frac{1}{2}$

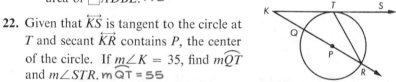

23. Given two tangents to a circle intersecting at $K$. If the measure of one of the intercepted arcs is four times the measure of the other arc, what is the measure of $\angle K$? $m\angle K = 108$

24. Two noncongruent circles are tangent at a point $T$. A secant, $L$, through $T$ intersects the larger circle at $A$ and the smaller circle at $B$. Prove that the tangents at $A$ and $B$ are parallel. [*Note:* There are two cases: (a) the circles are internally tangent; (b) the circles are externally tangent.]

**25.** In the figure on the left below, if $m\widehat{BD} = 70$ and $m\angle DMB = 4m\angle K$, find $m\widehat{AC}$ and $m\angle K$.

$m\angle K = \frac{1}{2}(70-x),\ m\angle DMB = \frac{1}{2}(70+x)$
$\text{and } \frac{1}{2}(70+x) = 4 \cdot \frac{1}{2}(70-x)$
$m\widehat{AC} = 42 \quad m\angle K = 14$

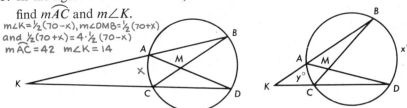

**26.** Given the figure on the right above, find the ratio of $x$ to $y$ which will make $m\angle DMB = 2m\angle K$. $\quad m\angle K = \frac{1}{2}(x-y) \quad m\angle DMB = \frac{1}{2}(x+y)$
$$\frac{x}{y} = \frac{3}{1}$$

**27.** Given a circle and a point $P$ in its exterior. A line through $P$ is tangent to the circle at $T$. A secant containing $P$ intersects the circle at $Q$ and $R$, with $Q$ between $R$ and $P$. The bisector of $\angle QTR$ intersects $\overline{RQ}$ at $S$. Prove that $PT = PS$.

**28.** Given: $\overline{AD}$ and $\overline{DB}$ are diameters of congruent, tangent circles. $\overleftrightarrow{BC}$ is a tangent at $C$. $\quad m\angle ADC = m\angle DCB +$
$m\angle CBD$ by Exterior
Prove: $m\widehat{AC} = m\widehat{DC} + m\widehat{DE}.$ Angle Theorem.
The conclusion follows from Ths. 14-16 and 14-19 and transitivity.

**29.** From a point $P$ in the exterior of a circle a secant intersects the circle at $A$ and $B$, with $P$-$A$-$B$. Another secant through $P$ intersects the circle at $C$ and $D$, with $P$-$C$-$D$. $\overleftrightarrow{BC}$ intersects a line through $P$ and parallel to $\overline{AD}$ at a point $R$. Prove that $PR^2 = CR \cdot BR$.

## 14–7 THE POWER THEOREMS

### Definition

If $\overleftrightarrow{QA}$ is tangent to a circle at $A$, then $\overline{QA}$ is called a *tangent segment* from $Q$ to the circle.

**Theorem 14–20.** The Two-Tangent Theorem

*The two tangent segments to a circle from a point of the exterior are congruent and determine congruent angles with the segment from the exterior point to the center.*

# 14–7 THE POWER THEOREMS

## Classroom Notes

Theorems 14–21, 14–22, and 14–23 are standard. In traditional texts they were formulated somewhat differently; for example, Theorem 14–22 was usually stated:

> Given a tangent and a secant to a circle from the same external point, the square of the tangent is equal to the product of the secant and its external segment.

Although the meaning is clear, the statement is not quite accurate, since it fails to distinguish between a tangent segment and the length of the tangent segment; hence the statements in the text, using distances. Before defining the power of a point $Q$ with respect to a circle $C$, we must first show that it exists: the product $QR \cdot QS$ depends only on $C$ and $Q$ and not on the choice of the secant line $L$.

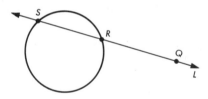

And we are thereby able to point up the essential idea underlying these three theorems.

**Restatement.** Given a circle $C$ with center $P$, and a point $Q$ of the exterior of $C$. If $\overline{QA}$ and $\overline{QB}$ are tangent to $C$ at $A$ and $B$, then $QA = QB$ and $\angle PQA \cong \angle PQB$.

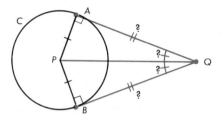

**Proof.** $PA = PB$, because $A$ and $B$ are on the circle; and $PQ = PQ$. By Theorem 14–3, $\angle A$ and $\angle B$ are right angles. By the Hypotenuse-Leg Theorem (Theorem 7–4) we have $\triangle PQA \cong \triangle PQB$. Therefore $QA = QB$ and $\angle PQA \cong \angle PQB$, which was to be proved.

Consider now the case of two *secant* lines to a circle, through the same point of the exterior.

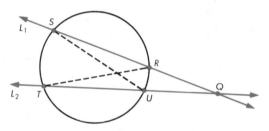

In the figure, $\overline{QS}$ and $\overline{QT}$ are called *secant segments* to the circle. To be exact, we have the following definition.

## Definition

If a segment intersects a circle in two points, and exactly one of these is an end point of the segment, then the segment is called a *secant segment* to the circle.

The next theorem says that in the figure above we always have

$$QR \cdot QS = QU \cdot QT.$$

That is, the product of the "two distances" from $Q$ to the circle is completely determined by the given circle and the point $Q$, and does not change when we choose different secant lines.

**Theorem 14–21.** The Two-Secant Power Theorem

> *Given a circle $C$, and a point $Q$ of its exterior. Let $L_1$ be a secant line through $Q$, intersecting $C$ in points $R$ and $S$; and let $L_2$ be another secant line through $Q$, intersecting $C$ in points $U$ and $T$. Then*
>
> $$QR \cdot QS = QU \cdot QT.$$

**Looking Ahead**

In proving that *M* is equidistant from the tangent segments in Problem 9, the student may notice that any point on $\overrightarrow{QP}$, the bisector of $\angle Q$, is equidistant from the sides of the angle. This is Theorem 15–3.

**Proof.** Consider the triangles $\triangle QSU$ and $\triangle QTR$. They have $\angle Q$ in common. And $\angle QSU \cong \angle QTR$, because they are inscribed in the same arc $\widehat{RSU} = \widehat{RTU}$. By the AA Corollary (12–4.1), we have $\triangle QSU \sim \triangle QTR$. Therefore

$$\frac{QS}{QT} = \frac{QU}{QR},$$

and

$$QR \cdot QS = QU \cdot QT,$$

which was to be proved.

Thus the product $QR \cdot QS$ is determined when the circle $C$ and the exterior point $Q$ are named. This number is called the *power of Q with respect to C.*

Theorem 14–22 is going to say that in the figure below, in which $\overline{QT}$ is a tangent segment, we have

$$QR \cdot QS = QT^2.$$

This equation means that

$$QT = \sqrt{QR \cdot QS}.$$

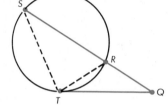

Thus $QT$ is the geometric mean of $QR$ and $QS$. The theorem is easier to state than the preceding one.

**Theorem 14–22.**    The Tangent-Secant Power Theorem

    *Given a tangent segment $\overline{QT}$ to a circle, and a secant line through $Q$, intersecting the circle in points $R$ and $S$. Then*

$$QR \cdot QS = QT^2.$$

In other words, the square of the length of a tangent segment is the power of its outer end point with respect to the circle.

**Proof.** $\widehat{TR}$ is the arc intercepted by $\angle QST$ and $\angle QTR$ in the figure above. The main steps in the proof are as follows:

(1)   $m\angle QST = \frac{1}{2}m\widehat{TR}.$      (5)   $\triangle QST \sim \triangle QTR.$

(2)   $m\angle QTR = \frac{1}{2}m\widehat{TR}.$      (6)   $\dfrac{QS}{QT} = \dfrac{QT}{QR}.$

(3)   $\angle QST \cong \angle QTR.$

(4)   $\angle Q \cong \angle Q.$           (7)   $QR \cdot QS = QT^2.$

What are the reasons for each step?

**1.** □*ABCD* is circumscribed about a circle. $AB = 13$ and $DC = 18$. What is the perimeter of the quadrilateral?

(ans: 62)

**2.** A secant segment and a tangent segment to a circle have a common end point in the exterior of the circle. If the secant segment is 15 cm long and its chord is 5 cm long, how long is the tangent segment?

(ans: $5\sqrt{6}$ cm)

**3.** The power of an exterior point *P* with respect to a circle *C* of radius 5 is 144. How far is *P* from the center of the circle?

(ans: 13)

**Answers to Problems**

**1.** By Problem 4, Section 14-6, the two tangent segments to a circle from an exterior point form congruent angles with chord joining the points of tangency. We can therefore conclude from Theorem 9-13 that the triangle formed is equiangular and consequently equilateral.

The next theorem states that in the figure below we have

$$QR \cdot QS = QU \cdot QT.$$

**Theorem 14-23.** The Two-Chord Power Theorem

*Let $\overline{RS}$ and $\overline{TU}$ be chords of the same circle, intersecting at Q. Then*

$$QR \cdot QS = QU \cdot QT.$$

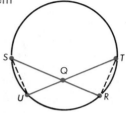

Again we give only the main steps in the proof:

(1) $\angle U \cong \angle R$.

(2) $\angle SQU \cong \angle TQR$.

(3) $\triangle SQU \sim \triangle TQR$.

(4) $\dfrac{QS}{QT} = \dfrac{QU}{QR}$.

(5) $QR \cdot QS = QU \cdot QT$.

This theorem enables us to define the power of a point with respect to a circle for the case in which the point lies *inside* the circle. We have found that the product $QR \cdot QS$ is determined when the circle *C* and the point *Q* are named; this number does not change when we choose different chords containing *Q*. We can therefore define the *power of Q with respect to C* as the number $QR \cdot QS$.

**Problem Set 14-7**

**1.** Prove: If the measure of the angle determined by two tangent segments to a circle from a point of the exterior is 60, then the tangent segments form an equilateral triangle with the chord joining the points of tangency.

**2.** A point *P* is 13 cm from the center of a circle with a 10-cm diameter. How long are the tangent segments from the point *P*? 12 cm

**3.** The sum of the lengths of two tangent segments to a circle from the same exterior point is equal to the diameter of the circle. Find the measure of the angle determined by the tangent segments. 90

**4.** Two chords of a circle intersect. The segments of one chord have lengths 4 and 6. If the length of one segment of the other chord is 3, find the length of the remaining segment. 8

**5.** Given: Circles $C$ and $C'$ are both tangent to $L$ at $T$. $P$ is any point (except $T$) of $L$. $\overline{PA}$ and $\overline{PB}$ are tangent segments.

Prove: $PA = PB$. By Theorem 14-20, PA=PT and PT=PB. Therefore, PA = PB.

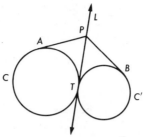

**6.** The sides of $\square ABCD$ are tangent to the circle, as shown in the figure. Prove that

$$AB + DC = AD + BC.$$

Use Theorem 14-20 and

AP+PB+DS+SC = AT+RB+TD+RC
              = AT+TD+ RB+RC

AB + DC = AD + BC

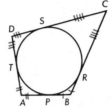

**7.** Two tangent segments to a circle from a point in the exterior determine an angle of 60°. If the diameter of the circle is 10, how long are the tangent segments? 5√3

**8.** If the tangent segments of Problem 7 determine an angle of 120°, how long are the tangent segments? $\frac{5\sqrt{3}}{3}$

**9.** In the figure, $\overline{QR}$ and $\overline{QS}$ are tangent segments to the circle whose center is $P$. $\overline{QP}$ intersects the circle at $M$. Prove that $M$ is equidistant from the tangent segments.

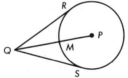

**10.** Find the power of $Q$ (see figure) with respect to $C$ given that

  (a)   $QS = 9$   and   $QR = 5.$ 45
  (b)   $QS = 3$   and   $SR = 12.$ 27
  (c)   $QU = 7$   and   $QT = 5.$ 35
  (d)   $QT = 1$   and   $TU = 13.$ 12
  (e)   $QR = 4$   and   $SR = 14.$ 40

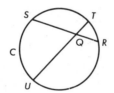

**11.** Two and one half centimetres from the end of a 95-cm diameter of a circle, the diameter intersects a chord 10 cm from one end of the chord. How long is the chord? 33.13 cm

**12.** In the figure, if $PA = 6$, $PB = 15$, and $PC = 8$, what is $PD$? PD=11¼

**13.** In the figure, if $PB = 24$, $AB = 16$, and $PD = 16$, what is $PC$? PC=12

**14.** In the figure, if $PD = 20$, $CD = 12$, and $AB = 27$, what is $PB$? PB=32

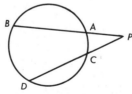

Figure for Problems 12, 13, 14

# Answers to Problems

**20.** Applying Theorem 14–22 to tangent segment $\overline{AT}$ and secant segment $\overline{AE}$ in the large circle we conclude $AB \cdot AE = AT^2$. Applying Theorem 14–22 to tangent segment $\overline{AT}$ and secant segment $\overline{AD}$ in the small circle we conclude $AC \cdot AD = AT^2$. Therefore, $AB \cdot AE = AC \cdot AD$, or $AB/AD = AC/AE$.

**24.** $\triangle PCR \sim \triangle QDR$ by AA, and since $PC/QD = \frac{2}{1}$, $PR/RQ = \frac{2}{1}$; and since $PQ = 18$ we can conclude that $PR = 12$ and $RQ = 6$. Since $\triangle PCR$ and $\triangle QDR$ are 30–60–90 triangles we can conclude that $CR = 6\sqrt{3}$ and $RD = 3\sqrt{3}$ and thus that $CD = 9\sqrt{3}$.

**25.** Given: Two circles, $C(P, r_1)$ and $C(Q, r_2)$ with $r_1 > r_2$. $\overline{AB}$ and $\overline{DE}$ are common external tangent segments. Prove: $\overline{AB} \cong \overline{DE}$.

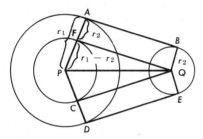

Proof: Introduce $\overline{QF}$, the perpendicular segment from $Q$ to $\overline{PA}$, and $\overline{QG}$, the perpendicular segment from $Q$ to $\overline{PD}$. First observe that $\triangle PFQ \cong \triangle PGQ$ by HL and consequently that $\overline{FQ} \cong \overline{GQ}$. Secondly observe that $\square AFQB$ and $\square DGQE$ are rectangles, so $\overline{AB} \cong \overline{FQ}$ and $\overline{DE} \cong \overline{GQ}$, and so, in turn, $\overline{AB} \cong \overline{DE}$.

---

486                                    14–7 | THE POWER THEOREMS

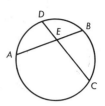

**15.** In the figure, $AB = 25$, $AE = 18$, and $DC = 27$. Find $EB$, $DE$, and $EC$.
$EB = 7$, $DE = 6$, $EC = 21$ or
$EB = 7$, $DE = 21$, $EC = 6$

**16.** Find the power of $Q$ (see figure) with respect to $C$ given that:

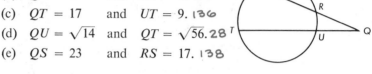

  (a) $QR = 4$     and    $QS = 13$. $52$

  (b) $QR = 6$     and    $RS = 8$. $84$

  (c) $QT = 17$    and    $UT = 9$. $136$

  (d) $QU = \sqrt{14}$ and    $QT = \sqrt{56}$. $28$

  (e) $QS = 23$    and    $RS = 17$. $138$

**17.** In the figure, $\overline{QT}$ is a tangent segment. Find the power of $Q$ with respect to $C$ given that

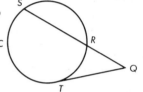

  (a) $QR = 4$, $QS = 9$, and $QT = 6$. $36$

  (b) $QS = 13$    and    $RS = 9$. $52$

  (c) $QT = 8$     and    $RS = 12$. $64$

  (d) $QR = \sqrt{6}$    and    $QS = \sqrt{54}$. $18$

  (e) $QS = \sqrt{17}$ and    $QT = \sqrt{13}$. $13$

**18.** In the figure, find $QS$ given that

  (a) $QR = 5$ and $QT = 10$. $20$

  (b) $QT = 8$ and $QR = 7$. $9\frac{1}{7}$

  (c) $QT = 16$ and $RS = 24$. $32$

  Let $QR = x$ then $QR \cdot QS = QT^2$ or $x(x+24) = 256$ or $x = 8$

---

**19.** Given the figure on the right below with both circles tangent to $L$ at $T$. $P$ is any point of $L$ other than $T$. Prove that $PM \cdot PR = PK \cdot PS$.

$PT^2 = PM \cdot PR$ } by Theorem 14–22
$PT^2 = PK \cdot PS$
conclusion follows by transitivity

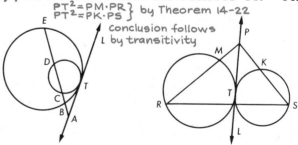

**20.** In the figure on the left above, $A$ is any point of $L$ except $T$, the common point of tangency of the circles. Prove that

$$\frac{AB}{AD} = \frac{AC}{AE}.$$

**21.** If a common tangent of two circles intersects the line through their centers at a point between the centers, it is called a *common internal tangent*. If it does not intersect the line through their centers at a point between the centers, it is called a *common external tangent*. (In this figure, $\overleftrightarrow{AB}$ is a common external tangent, and $\overleftrightarrow{CD}$ is a common internal tangent.)

Given two circles, how many common external tangents and how many common internal tangents are there if

(a) the circles do not intersect as in the figure? *2 external, 2 internal*

(b) the circles are externally tangent? *2 external, 1 internal*

(c) the circles intersect in two points? *2 external, 0 internal*

(d) the circles are internally tangent? *1 external, 0 internal*

(e) the circles are concentric? *0 external, 0 internal*

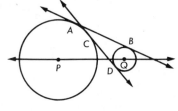

**22.** Two circles have radii 5 and 17 and a common external tangent segment of length 16. What is the distance between their centers? *20*

**23.** The radii of the two circles below left are 3 and 8, and the distance between their centers is 13. Find the length of their common external tangent segment. [*Hint:* Introduce a line through $Q$ perpendicular to $\overline{AP}$.]

*Use Pythagorean Theorem and AB = 12*

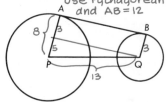

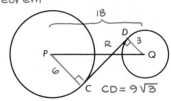

*CD = 9√3*

**24.** The distance between the centers of the two circles above right, having radii of 3 and 6, is 18. How long is the common internal tangent segment.

**25.** Prove that the common external tangent segments of two circles are congruent.

---

**26.** Prove: The common internal tangents of two nonintersecting circles and the line through the centers of the circles meet at the same point.

[*Hint:* Use an indirect proof. Draw radii. Use similarity and proportions.]

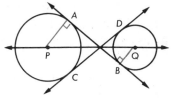

**27.** Prove that the common internal tangent segments of two nonintersecting circles are congruent.

**28.** $\overline{DB}$ is a diameter of a circle. A tangent through $D$ and a secant through $B$ intersect at a point $A$. The secant also intersects the circle at $C$. Prove that $DB^2 = AB \cdot BC$.

**Answers to Problems**

**26.** Let $\overline{AB}$ intersect $\overline{PQ}$ at $R$. $m\angle A = m\angle B = 90$, and $m\angle ARP = m\angle BRQ$ by vertical angles. Therefore $\triangle ARP \sim \triangle BRQ$ by AA. This gives $PR/QR = PA/QB$. Now suppose $\overline{DC}$ meets $\overline{PQ}$ at point $R'$. Then, by a similar argument, we get $PR'/QR' = PA/QB$. Hence $PR'/QR' = PR/QR$, and $R$ and $R'$ are both between $P$ and $Q$. Therefore $R' = R$.

**27.** Suppose the common internal tangent segments $\overline{AB}$ and $\overline{CD}$ intersect at a point $R$. By Theorem 14–20, $AR = CR$ and $RB = RD$ so by addition $AR + RB = CR + RD$ or $AB = CD$.

**28.** By Theorem 14–22, $AD^2 = AB \cdot AC$. By the Pythagorean Theorem,
$$DB^2 = AB^2 - AD^2$$
$$= AB^2 - AB \cdot AC$$
$$= AB(AB - AC)$$
$$= AB \cdot BC.$$

**29.** Case 1: By Theorem 14–20, $AM = MT$ and $MT = MB$, so $AM = MB$. Therefore $L$ bisects $\overline{AB}$ and similarly $L$ bisects $\overline{CD}$. Case 2: Applying Theorem 14–22 we conclude that $AM^2 = MR \cdot MS$ and that $BM^2 = MR \cdot MS$. Therefore $AM^2 = BM^2$, so $AM = BM$. Similarly, $CN = DN$.

**30.** $a\square QRST = a\triangle TQR + a\triangle STR = (\frac{1}{2})(RS \cdot QR + RS \cdot ST) = (\frac{1}{2})(RS)(QR + ST)$. But by Theorem 14–20, $QR = QP$ and $ST = PT$. Therefore, $a\square QRST = \frac{1}{2}RS(QP + PT) = \frac{1}{2}RS \cdot QT$.

## 14–8 CIRCLES IN A COORDINATE PLANE

### Classroom Notes

The study of circles by coordinate methods is, of course, based on the assumption that Chapter 13, "Plane Coordinate Geometry," has been covered. In teaching this section, it is important to teach proficiency in the practical procedure of converting from the form $x^2 + y^2 + Ax + By + C = 0$ to the form $(x - a)^2 + (y - b)^2 = r^2$, in cases where the conversion is possible. And it is important to stress that the conversion is not always possible.

**29.** Prove: If two circles and a line intersect in the same point, or points, then the line bisects each common external tangent segment of the circles.

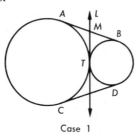 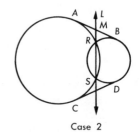

Case 1　　　　　　Case 2

**30.** $\overline{RS}$ is a diameter of a circle. $L_1$ is the tangent to the circle at $R$, and $L_2$ is the tangent at $S$. A line through $Q$, any point of $L_1$ other than $R$, is tangent to the circle at $P$ and intersects $L_2$ at $T$. Prove that

$$a\square QRST = \tfrac{1}{2}RS \cdot QT.$$

**31.** In the figure, $\overline{AB}$ is a diameter and $\overleftrightarrow{CD}$ is the tangent at $B$. Prove that

$$AC \cdot AG = AD \cdot AH.$$

By Problem 30, AC·AG=AB² and AD·AH=AB². Therefore AC·AG=AD·AH

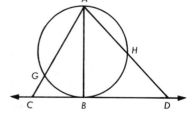

## 14–8 CIRCLES IN A COORDINATE PLANE

If we set up a coordinate system in the plane, it is easy to see what the equation of a circle is. Take first the case where the center is the origin. The circle with center at $O$ and radius $r$ is defined by the condition

$$OP = r.$$

Letting $P$ have coordinates $(x, y)$, we use the distance formula, and write our equation algebraically as

$$\sqrt{(x - 0)^2 + (y - 0)^2} = r,$$

or

$$x^2 + y^2 = r^2.$$

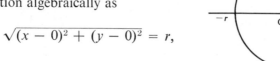

If the center is the point $Q(a, b)$, then the circle is defined by the condition $QP = r$.

Algebraically, we have

$$\sqrt{(x - a)^2 + (y - b)^2} = r,$$

or

$$(x - a)^2 + (y - b)^2 = r^2.$$

**Theorem 14–24**

*The graph of the equation*

$$(x - a)^2 + (y - b)^2 = r^2$$

*is the circle with center (a, b) and radius r.*

We can apply this theorem forward or backward.

(1) If we know the center and the radius, we can write an equation for the circle. For example, the circle with center $(3, 1)$ and radius 2 is the graph of the equation

$$(x - 3)^2 + (y - 1)^2 = 4.$$

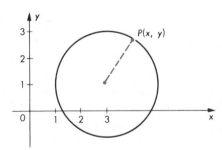

(2) Given an equation of the type dealt with in Theorem 14–24, we can tell what the center and radius of the circle must be. For example, given

$$(x + 1)^2 + (y - 2)^2 = 9,$$

we know that the center is $(-1, 2)$ and the radius is 3.

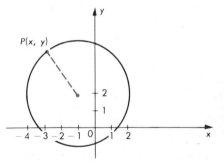

So far, so good. But suppose that our second equation for the circle has fallen into the hands of somebody who likes to "simplify" every equation that he sees. He would have "simplified" the standard form, getting

$$x^2 + 2x + 1 + y^2 - 4y + 4 = 9,$$

and then

$$x^2 + y^2 + 2x - 4y - 4 = 0.$$

Sometimes we will find equations of circles given in forms like this. To find out what their graphs are, we need to "unsimplify" them to get back to the standard form

$$(x - a)^2 + (y - b)^2 = r^2.$$

The method is that of completing the square. First we rearrange the terms so as to bring together the terms involving $x$ and those involving $y$, and we move the constant terms to the other side of the equals sign. This gives

$$x^2 + 2x \quad + y^2 - 4y \quad = 4.$$

We now want to add something to the first two terms to complete a perfect square. That is, we want

$$x^2 + 2x + (?) = (x - a)^2.$$

Since

$$(x - a)^2 = x^2 - 2ax + a^2,$$

we must have $a = -1$, $a^2 = 1$. What we need to add, therefore, is 1. (The rule is simple: we take half the coefficient of $x$, and square the result.) In the same way, we see that to get a perfect square, we should add 4 to the terms involving $y$.

Since we are adding a total of 5 on the left, we should also add a total of 5 on the right. This gives

$$x^2 + 2x + 1 + y^2 - 4y + 4 = 4 + 5,$$

or

$$(x + 1)^2 + (y - 2)^2 = 9,$$

which is in the standard form. From the standard form we can tell that the graph is the circle with center at $(-1, 2)$ and radius 3.

If in the standard form $(x - a)^2 + (y - b)^2 = r^2$ we multiply out and rearrange the terms, we obtain

$$x^2 + y^2 - 2ax - 2by + a^2 + b^2 - r^2 = 0.$$

This has the form

$$x^2 + y^2 + Ax + By + C = 0,$$

where

$$A = -2a, \qquad B = -2b, \qquad C = a^2 + b^2 - r^2.$$

Thus we have the following theorem.

### Theorem 14–25

*Every circle is the graph of an equation of the form*

$$x^2 + y^2 + Ax + By + C = 0.$$

It might seem reasonable to suppose that the converse is also true. That is, we might think that the graph of an equation of this form is always a circle. But this is not true at all. Consider, for example, the equation $x^2 + y^2 = 0$. Here $A = B = C = 0$. If $x$ and $y$ satisfy this equation, then $x$ and $y$ are both zero. Therefore the graph contains only one point, namely, the origin.

Consider next the equation $x^2 + y^2 + 1 = 0$. Here $A = B = 0$ and $C = 1$. Since $x^2 \geq 0$ and $y^2 \geq 0$ for every $x$ and $y$, it follows that $x^2 + y^2 + 1 \geq 1$ for every $x$ and $y$. Therefore $x^2 + y^2 + 1$ is never equal to 0 for any $x$ and $y$. Therefore the graph of our equation *contains no points at all; the* graph is the empty set.

The next theorem tells us that, in fact, the only possible graphs are the circle that we would normally expect and the two peculiar possibilities that we have just discussed.

### Theorem 14–26

*The graph of the equation*

$$x^2 + y^2 + Ax + By + C = 0$$

*is (1) a circle, (2) a point, or (3) the empty set.*

**Proof.** In our general equation, we shall complete the square for the terms involving $x$, and also for the terms involving $y$, just as we did in the example we worked out above. This gives

$$x^2 + Ax \qquad + y^2 + By \qquad = -C,$$

$$x^2 + Ax + \left(\frac{A}{2}\right)^2 + y^2 + By + \left(\frac{B}{2}\right)^2 = -C + \left(\frac{A}{2}\right)^2 + \left(\frac{B}{2}\right)^2,$$

$$\left(x + \frac{A}{2}\right)^2 + \left(y + \frac{B}{2}\right)^2 = \frac{A^2 + B^2 - 4C}{4}.$$

There are now three possibilities.

**Looking Ahead**

Problem 26 contains a system of linear and quadratic equations. Most students will not be familiar with this type of system. In the system

$$\begin{cases} x + y = -6 \\ x^2 + y^2 = 72 \end{cases}$$

suggest that the students solve the first equation for $x$ (or $y$), then substitute in the second equation, and finally solve the resulting equation by the quadratic formula.

This problem and Problems 31 and 32 should be assigned to honors students.

**Quiz**

**1.** A diameter of a certain circle is the segment whose end points are $(-1, 7)$ and $(9, -3)$. Write the equation of the circle.

(ans: $x^2 + y^2 - 8x - 4y = 30$)

**2.** The equation of a circle is

$$x^2 + y^2 + 6x - 12y = 15.$$

Find the coordinates of the center and the length of a radius of the circle.

(ans: center: $(-3, 6)$; radius: $2\sqrt{15}$)

(1) If the fraction on the right is positive, then it has a square root. The graph is then the circle with center

$$(a, b) = \left(-\frac{A}{2}, -\frac{B}{2}\right)$$

and radius

$$r = \tfrac{1}{2}\sqrt{A^2 + B^2 - 4C}.$$

(2) If the fraction on the right is 0, then the graph is the point

$$\left(-\frac{A}{2}, -\frac{B}{2}\right).$$

(3) If the fraction on the right is negative, then the graph is the empty set, because the left-hand side can never be negative.

**Problem Set 14–8**

[*Note:* Problems in this problem set should be solved by the methods of coordinate geometry when a choice of methods exists.]

**1.** Write the equation of the circle whose center is at the origin and whose radius is as follows.

(a) 4  $x^2+y^2=16$     (b) 7  $x^2+y^2=49$     (c) $\frac{2}{3}$  $x^2+y^2=\frac{4}{9}$

(d) 11  $x^2+y^2=121$     (e) $\sqrt{15}$  $x^2+y^2=15$     (f) $\pi$  $x^2+y^2=\pi^2$

**2.** Given the circle whose equation is $x^2 + y^2 = 25$, which of the following points are points of the circle?

(a) $(0, -5)$     (b) $(3, -4)$     (c) $(3, 2)$

(d) $(24, 1)$     (e) $(\sqrt{8}, -\sqrt{17})$     (f) $(2\sqrt{3}, \sqrt{13})$

**3.** Given the circle whose equation is $x^2 + y^2 = 36$. Which of the following points are in its interior, which are in its exterior, which are on the circle?

(a) $(3, 3\sqrt{3})$ I     (b) $(4, -5)$ E     (c) $(-6, 0)$ C     (d) $(5, -3)$ I

(e) $(-4, -4)$ I     (f) $(2\sqrt{2}, 2\sqrt{7})$ C     (g) $(\frac{9}{2}, \frac{7}{4})$ I     (h) $(-2\sqrt{6}, 4)$ E

**4.** Find the radius and write the equation of the circle whose center is at the origin and which contains the point

(a) $(0, -4)$     (b) $(3, 5)$     (c) $(-2, 7)$     (d) $(2, \sqrt{17})$

    $x^2+y^2=16$     $x^2+y^2=34$     $x^2+y^2=53$     $x^2+y^2=21$

**5.** Write the equation of each circle with center and radius as given.

(a) $(2, 5)$, 4                  (b) $(-3, 0)$, 6

(c) $(--4, -6)$, $\sqrt{21}$         (d) $(0, 7)$, $\frac{5}{3}$

**Answers to Problems**
5. (a) $(x - 2)^2 + (y - 5)^2 = 16$.
   (b) $(x + 3)^2 + y^2 = 36$.
   (c) $(x + 4)^2 + (y + 6)^2 = 21$.
   (d) $x^2 + (y - 7)^2 = \frac{25}{9}$.
10. (c) $C(3, 7)$, $r = 2\sqrt{2}$.
    (d) $C(-4, 5)$, $r = 6$.
    (e) $r = \sqrt{13}$.
    (g) $r = \frac{5}{3}$.

6. A circle whose center is the point $(2, 3)$ contains the point $(6, 6)$. Write its equation. $(x-2)^2 + (y-3)^2 = 35$

7. A circle with center at $(-4, 0)$ passes through the point $(2, -1)$. Write its equation. $(x+4)^2 + y^2 = 37$

8. The end points of a diameter of a circle are $(-6, 2)$ and $(6, -2)$. Find its center and its radius, and write its equation. $x^2 + y^2 = 40$

9. Write the equation of the circle having a diameter with end points $(5, 8)$ and $(-1, -4)$. $(x-2)^2 + (y-2)^2 = 45$

10. Determine the center and radius of each circle:

(a) $x^2 + y^2 = 16$. $c(0,0)$, $r=4$   (b) $x^2 + y^2 - 9 = 0$. $c(0,0)$, $r=3$

(c) $(x - 3)^2 + (y - 7)^2 = 8$.   (d) $(x + 4)^2 + (y - 5)^2 = 36$.

(e) $(x - 2)^2 + y^2 = 13$. $c(2,0)$   (f) $4x^2 + 4y^2 = 36$. $c(0,0)$, $r=3$

(g) $9x^2 + 9y^2 - 25 = 0$. $c(0,0)$   (h) $3x^2 + 3(y - 1)^2 = 12$. $c(0,1)$, $r=2$

(i) $2(x + 5)^2 + 2(y - 4)^2 - 14 = 0$. $c(-5,4)$, $r=\sqrt{7}$

(j) $5x^2 + 5y^2 - 7 = 0$. $c(0,0)$, $r=\sqrt{7/5} = \frac{1}{5}\sqrt{35}$

11. Find the center and radius of the circle whose equation is
$C(3,4)$, $r=2$        $x^2 - 6x + 9 + y^2 - 8y + 16 = 4$.

12. Find the center and radius of the circle whose equation is
$C(-4,1)$, $r=5$        $x^2 + y^2 + 8x - 2y - 8 = 0$.

13. Sketch the graph of the equation $x^2 + y^2 - 8x + 6y = 11$.
$C(4,-3)$, $r=6$
14. Sketch the graph of the equation $x^2 + y^2 - 4x + 8y + 4 = 0$.
$C(2,-4)$, $r=4$
15. Sketch the graph of the equation $x^2 + y^2 + 6x - 2y = -10$.
The graph is the point $(-3,1)$.

---

16. Write the equation of the circle with center at $(-3, 4)$ which is tangent to the $x$-axis. $(x+3)^2 + (y-4)^2 = 16$

17. Write the equation of the circle tangent to both the $x$- and $y$-axes, given that its radius is 3 and its center is in the fourth quadrant.
$(x-3)^2 + (y+3)^2 = 9$
18. Identify the geometric figures described by the following equations:

(a) $x^2 + y^2 = 15$. circle: center$(0,0)$, $r=\sqrt{15}$

(b) $x^2 + y^2 + 14x - 16y + 104 = 0$. circle: center$(-7,8)$, $r=3$

(c) $x^2 + 6x - 2y - x^2 + 2 = 0$. straight line: $y$-intercept $(0,1)$, slope $= 3$

(d) $x^2 + y^2 + 10x - 4y + 33 = 0$. $\emptyset$

(e) $2x^2 + 2y^2 + 12x + 9 = 0$. circle: center$(-3,0)$, $r=\frac{3}{2}\sqrt{2}$

(f) $x^2 + y^2 + 4x - 10y + 29 = 0$. Point $(-2,5)$

**20.** The midpoint of the segment has the coordinates $\left(\dfrac{a}{2}, \dfrac{a}{2}\right)$. Since the slope of the segment is $-1$, the slope of the perpendicular bisector is 1. Therefore, the equation of the perpendicular bisector is, in point-slope form, $y - \dfrac{a}{2} = x - \dfrac{a}{2}$. Since the coordinates of the origin satisfy this equation, this line contains the center of the circle whose equation is $x^2 + y^2 = a^2$.

**22.** (b) The equation of the circle can be transformed into $(x - 4)^2 + (y - 2)^2 = 25$, so its center is $P(4, 2)$. The midpoint $M$ of $\overline{DE}$ is $M(\tfrac{7}{2}, \tfrac{7}{2})$, and the slope of $\overline{DE}$ is $\tfrac{1}{3}$ so the slope of the perpendicular bisector of $\overline{DE}$ is $-3$. Therefore the equation of the perpendicular bisector of $\overline{DE}$ is, in point-slope form, $y - \tfrac{7}{2} = -3(x - \tfrac{7}{2})$. Since the coordinates of $P(4, 2)$ satisfy this equation we conclude that the perpendicular bisector of $\overline{DE}$ contains the center of the circle.

**26.** It is easy to see from a diagram that the $x$ and $y$ intercepts of the tangent to the smaller circle at $(-3, -3)$ are $(-6, 0)$ and $(0, -6)$. Therefore the equation of the tangent is $\dfrac{x}{-6} + \dfrac{y}{-6} = 1$, or $x + y = -6$. To find the points of intersection of this line with the larger circle we must solve the system consisting of $x + y = -6$ and $x^2 + y^2 = 72$. By substitution we obtain $x^2 + 6x - 18 = 0$, so $x = -3 \pm 3\sqrt{3}$ by the quadratic formula. Therefore the end points of the chord are $(-3 - 3\sqrt{3}, -3 + 3\sqrt{3})$ and $(-3 + 3\sqrt{3}, -3 - 3\sqrt{3})$.

**28.** Note that the radius of the circle is 10 and the distance from the center to the point $(16, 12)$ is 20. Therefore, a tangent segment from the exterior point, the radius to the point of tangency, and the segment from the exterior point to the center form a right triangle in which the hypotenuse is twice the shorter leg. Therefore we conclude by Theorem 9–28 that the triangle is a 30–60–90 triangle. But by Theorem 11–12, in a 30–60–90 triangle, the longer leg is $\tfrac{1}{2}\sqrt{3}$ times as long as the hypot-

---

**19.** In the circle whose equation is $x^2 + y^2 = 49$, a chord is perpendicular to a diameter at the point $(0, 4)$. Find the length of the chord and determine the coordinates of its end points. Length of chord is $2\sqrt{33}$ and the end points are $(-\sqrt{33}, 4)$ and $(\sqrt{33}, 4)$

**20.** Prove that the perpendicular bisector of the segment with end points $(a, 0)$ and $(0, a)$ contains the center of the circle whose equation is $x^2 + y^2 = a^2$.

**21.** Given the circle whose equation is $x^2 + y^2 = 225$ and the points $A(-15, 0)$ and $B(9, 12)$. Points A and B satisfy the equation of the circle

(a) Show that $\overline{AB}$ is a chord of the circle.

(b) Find the midpoint of $\overline{AB}$. M($-3, 6$)

(c) Find the equation of the perpendicular bisector of $\overline{AB}$. $y - 6 = -2(x + 3)$

(d) Show that the perpendicular bisector of $\overline{AB}$ contains the center of the circle. Coordinates of origin satisy equation of perpendicular bisector

**22.** Given the circle whose equation is $x^2 + y^2 - 8x - 4y - 5 = 0$ and the points $D(-1, 2)$ and $E(8, 5)$.

(a) Show that $\overline{DE}$ is a chord of the circle. Points D and E satisfy the equation of the circle.

(b) Show that the perpendicular bisector of $\overline{DE}$ contains the center of the circle.

(c) Find the distance from the center of the circle to $\overline{DE}$. PM $= \tfrac{1}{2}\sqrt{10}$, where M is midpoint of $\overline{DE}$ and P is center of circle.

**23.** Find the area of a square inscribed in the circle whose equation is $x^2 + y^2 = 144$. $A = \tfrac{1}{2}d^2$ ($d =$ diagonal $=$ diameter of circle) $A = 288$

**24.** Find the area of a square inscribed in the circle whose equation is $x^2 + y^2 + 8x - 10y + 5 = 0$. $(x+4)^2 + (y-5)^2 = 36$. As in Problem 23 $A = \tfrac{1}{2}d^2 = \tfrac{1}{2}(12)^2 = 72$

**25.** A chord of the circle $x^2 + y^2 = 72$ is tangent to the circle $x^2 + y^2 = 18$. Find the length of the chord. $6\sqrt{6}$

**26.** If the chord of Problem 25 is tangent to the smaller circle at the point $(-3, -3)$, find the equation of the line determined by the chord and find the coordinates of the end points of the chord.

**27.** Find the length of the tangent segments from the point $(13, 0)$ to the circle whose equation is $x^2 + y^2 = 25$. 12 (Note triangle formed is a 5-12-13 right triangle.)

**28.** Find the length of the tangent segments from the point $(16, 12)$ to the circle whose equation is $x^2 + y^2 = 100$.

---

**29.** Find the length of the tangent segments from the point $(-8, 3)$ to the circle whose equation is $x^2 + y^2 - 14x + 10y + 10 = 0$.

**30.** Given the circle whose equation is $x^2 + y^2 = 36$. For what values of $a$ is the point $(a, a + 4)$ in the interior of the circle?

**31.** Show that the two circles whose equations are $x^2 + y^2 = 16$ and $x^2 + y^2 - 20x + 64 = 0$ are externally tangent. What are the coordinates of their point of tangency? Eliminate 2nd degree terms and circles intersect at (4,0)

**32.** Show that the two circles whose equations are $x^2 + y^2 + 8x + 6y = 0$ and $x^2 + y^2 - 16x - 12y = 0$ are externally tangent. Find the equation of the line through their point of contact which is their common tangent.

**33.** Given the circle whose equation is $x^2 + y^2 + 16x + 12y = 125$.

(a) Find the equation of the circle with radius 5 which is internally tangent to the given circle at (4, 3). $x^2 + y^2 = 25$

(b) Find the equation of their common tangent. Since slope of line through centers and (4,3) is ¾, Slope of tangent = -⁴⁄₃; y-3 = -⁴⁄₃(x-4).

**34.** Find the equation of the circle which is tangent to all four of the circles characterized by these four equations: $x^2 + y^2 = 100$

$$x^2 + y^2 + 10x = 0.$$
$$x^2 + y^2 - 10x = 0.$$
$$x^2 + y^2 + 10y = 0.$$
$$x^2 + y^2 - 10y = 0.$$

**35.** Using a scale of about 3 centimetres = 1 unit, make a careful sketch of the circles having the following equations:

$$(x - 1)^2 + (y - 1)^2 = 1.$$
$$(x + 1)^2 + (y - 1)^2 = 1.$$
$$(x - 1)^2 + (y + 1)^2 = 1.$$
$$(x + 1)^2 + (y + 1)^2 = 1.$$

(a) Find the equation of the circle which has each of the given circles as an internally tangent circle. $x^2 + y^2 = (1 + \sqrt{2})^2$

(b) Find the equation of the circle which has each of the given circles as an externally tangent circle. $x^2 + y^2 = (\sqrt{2} - 1)^2$

## CHAPTER REVIEW

m∠A=38, m∠ABD=116, m∠FBD=64, m∠DCE=19,

**1.** In the figure, $\overleftrightarrow{AB}$ is tangent to the circle. If $m\widehat{BD} = 128$, $m\widehat{DE} = 38$, and $m\widehat{CE} = 104$, what are the measures of the six angles? m∠DCA=161, m∠D=45

**2.** In the figure, $\overleftrightarrow{AB}$ is tangent to the circle. If $AC = 9$ and $CE = 7$, what is $AB$? AB=12

**3.** In the figure, if $BD = CD = 15$ and $m\widehat{BC} = 120$, what is the radius of the circle? r=5√3

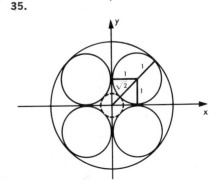

enuse. Therefore, the length of each tangent segment is $10\sqrt{3}$.

**29.** The equation of the circle is $(x - 7)^2 + (y + 5)^2 = 64$, so its radius is 8 and the distance from the center $(7, -5)$ to the point $(-8, 3)$ is 17. In a right triangle with hypotenuse of length 17 and a leg of length 8, the other leg is of length 15. Therefore, the length of each of the tangent segments is 15.

**30.** For the point $(a, a + 4)$ to be in the interior of the circle $x^2 + y^2 = 36$, we must have $a^2 + (a + 4)^2 < 36$. This gives $a^2 + 4a - 10 < 0$. By the quadratic formula $a = -2 - \sqrt{14}$ or $a = -2 + \sqrt{14}$. Since $a$ must satisfy the inequality $a^2 + 4a - 10 < 0$, it follows that $-2 - \sqrt{14} < a < -2 + \sqrt{14}$.

**32.** Eliminating the second degree terms and substituting, we discover that the two circles intersect at the single point $(0, 0)$ and are therefore tangent. The equation of the first circle is $(x + 4)^2 + (y + 3)^2 = 25$ and the equation of the second circle is $(x - 8)^2 + (y - 6)^2 = 100$. Therefore the slope of the line through their centers $(-4, -3)$ and $(8, 6)$ and the point of tangency $(0, 0)$ has a slope of $\frac{3}{4}$. Therefore, the slope of the common tangent is $-\frac{4}{3}$ and the equation of the common tangent is $y = -\frac{4}{3}x$.

**34.**

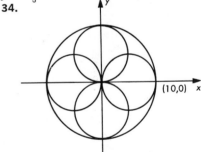

(10,0)  x

**35.**

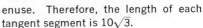

**Answers to Chapter Review Problems**

**8.** By the Pythagorean Theorem, $AD =$ 9. If $r$ is the radius of the circle, then $OD = r - 9$ and $OC = r$. Therefore, in $\triangle DOC$, $r^2 = (r - 9)^2 + 12^2$ so $18r = 225$ and $r = 12.5$. The diameter is 25.

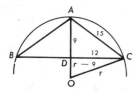

**4.** In the figure, if $RP = 8$, $MP = 6$ and $PQ = 3$, what is $KQ$?  $KQ = 19$

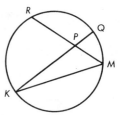

**5.** In the figure, if $MR = MK$, $m\widehat{MK} = 140$ and $m\widehat{MQ} = 26$, what is $m\angle RPK$?

$m\angle RPQ = \frac{1}{2}(m\widehat{MK} + m\widehat{RQ}) = 127$

so $m\angle RPK = 53$

**6.** Indicate for each of the statements below whether it is true or false.

(a) The measure of a central angle is equal to the measure of its intercepted arc.  T

(b) If two arcs are congruent, an inscribed angle of one arc is congruent to an inscribed angle of the other arc.  T

(c) If two angles which are inscribed in two arcs are congruent, then the arcs are congruent.  F

(d) A point which is the midpoint of two chords of a circle is the center of the circle.  T

(e) In a circle, if $m\widehat{AB} = \frac{1}{2}m\widehat{AC}$, then the chord of $\widehat{AB}$ is one-half as long as the chord of $\widehat{AC}$.  F

(f) A secant which bisects two chords of a circle is perpendicular to each of the chords.  F

(g) If a line bisects a chord of a circle, then it bisects the minor arc of the chord.  F

(h) If two chords of a circle are not congruent, the shorter chord is closer to the center.  F

(i) A tangent to a circle at the midpoint of an arc is parallel to the chord of the arc.  T

(j) The center of an arc is the point that bisects the arc.  F

(k) Two tangents to a circle at the ends of a diameter are parallel.  T

(l) Two tangents to the same circle may be perpendicular to each other.  T

**7.** Given the circle with center $P$ and $\overline{CB} \parallel \overline{PQ}$. If $m\angle BCP = 55$, what is $m\widehat{BQ}$ and $m\widehat{AD}$?

$m\widehat{BQ} = 55$,  $m\widehat{AD} = 70$

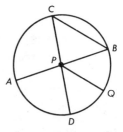

**8.** In searching an ancient ruin an archeologist found a piece of the rim of an old wheel. In order to restore the wheel he needed the diameter. He marked three points, $A$, $B$, $C$, on the rim so that $\overline{AB}$ was congruent to $\overline{AC}$. If $AB = 15$ and $BC = 24$, what was the diameter of the wheel?

25

**9.** If $\overline{AB}$ is a diameter of a circle with center $P$, and $X$ and $Y$ are points of the circle such that $\overrightarrow{XY}$ bisects $\angle AXB$, prove that $\overline{PY} \perp \overline{AB}$.

**10.** Prove that it is impossible for the lengths of the segments of two intersecting chords of a circle to be four consecutive integers. (See figure to the left below.)

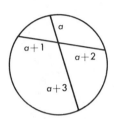

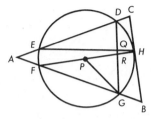

**11.** Given the figure on the right above. $P$ is the center of the circle. $\overline{CB}$ is tangent at $H$. $ED = FG$, $m\widehat{ED} = 96$, and $m\angle DEH = 30$. Find the measure of each arc and each angle in the figure.

**12.** In the figure $\square ABCD$ is circumscribed about the circle. The vertices of $\triangle PQR$ are points of tangency for $\square ABCD$. $\overline{PQ} \parallel \overline{AB}$. If $m\angle RPQ = 72$ and $m\angle RQP = 54$, find the measure of each arc and each angle in the figure.

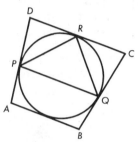

**13.** A quadrilateral is inscribed in a circle. If the measures of two of its angles are 68 and 143, what are the measures of the other two angles?
112 and 37

---

**14.** Write the equation of the circle with center at $(0, 0)$ and radius 4.
$x^2 + y^2 = 16$

**15.** Find the center and radius of the circle whose equation is $x^2 + 10x + y^2 + 16 = 0$. Center $(-5,0)$, radius $= 3$ .

**16.** In the figure, $\triangle ABC$ is equilateral, $\overline{AB}$ is a diameter of the circle, and the circle intersects the other two sides of $\triangle ABC$ at $D$ and $E$. If the diameter of the circle is 16, find the area of the inscribed quadrilateral $\square ABED$.
$a\square ABED = 48\sqrt{3}$

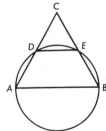

**17.** A circular hole 40 cm in diameter is cut in a sheet of plywood and a spherical globe 50 cm in diameter is set into the hole. How far below the top surface of the plywood will the sphere extend? 10 cm

**Answers to Chapter Review Problems**

**9.** Since $\overrightarrow{XY}$ bisects $\angle AXB$, $m\widehat{AY} = m\widehat{BY}$ by Theorem 14–16. But since $\angle APY$ and $\angle BPY$ are central angles, this means that $\angle APY \cong \angle BPY$ and therefore $\overline{PY} \perp \overline{AB}$.

**10.** By Theorem 14–23 it must be true that $a(a+3) = (a+1)(a+2)$, $a^2 + 3a = a^2 + 3a + 2$, or $0 = 2$. Since this is impossible, it is impossible for the lengths of the segments of two intersecting chords of a circle to be four consecutive integers.

**11.** $m\angle A = 60$, $m\widehat{FE} = 24$, $m\widehat{ED} = 96$, $m\widehat{DH} = 60$, $m\widehat{HG} = 84$, $m\widehat{GF} = 96$, $m\angle DEH = 30$, $m\angle EDQ = 60$, $m\angle CDQ = 120$, $m\angle C = 72$, $m\angle CHQ = 78$, $m\angle QHR = 12$, $m\angle RHB = m\angle DQH = m\angle HQR$ $= m\angle RQE = m\angle EQR = 90$, $m\angle B = 48$, $m\angle BGR = 120$, $m\angle RGP = 18$, $m\angle PGF = 42$, $m\angle PFG = 42$, $m\angle FPG = 96$, $m\angle RPG = 84$, $m\angle PRG = m\angle HRQ = 78$, $m\angle GRH = m\angle PRQ = 102$.

**12.** $m\widehat{PR} = 108$, $m\widehat{RQ} = 144$, $m\widehat{QP} = 108$, $m\angle DRP = m\angle PRQ$ $= m\angle RQP = m\angle PQB = m\angle QPA$ $= m\angle DPR = 54$, $m\angle RQC = m\angle QRC = m\angle RPQ$ $= m\angle D = 72$, $m\angle A = m\angle B = 126$, $m\angle C = 36$

**19.** $\angle P \cong \angle P'$ and $\angle Q \cong \angle Q'$ by Corollary 14–16.2, so $\triangle PAQ \sim \triangle P'A'Q'$ by AA; therefore $\angle PAQ \cong \angle P'A'Q'$, since corresponding angles of similar triangles are congruent.

**20.** $m\angle x = m\angle z + m\angle CBP$ and $m\angle y = m\angle z + m\angle CAP$ by Corollary 9–13.3. Also $m\angle x + m\angle CAP = m\angle APB = m\angle y + m\angle CBP$ and $m\angle APB = 2m\angle z$ by Theorem 14–16. Therefore $6m\angle z = (m\angle x + m\angle CAP) + (m\angle y + m\angle CBP) + (m\angle x - m\angle CBP) + (m\angle y - m\angle CAP) = 2m\angle x + 2m\angle y$.

**22.** By Theorem 14–22, $\angle PCB \cong \angle A$ and $m\angle PCD = m\angle PCB + n$ by the AAP. Also $m\angle PDC = n + m\angle A$ by Corollary 9–13.3. Thus $m\angle PCD = m\angle PCB + n = m\angle A + n = m\angle PDC$, so $\triangle PCD$ is isosceles by Theorem 5–4.

**24.** The angle measures can be determined as shown below. Hence, $\triangle PAR$

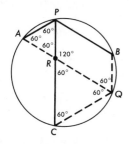

and $\triangle QCR$ are equilateral triangles and $\square PRQB$ is a parallelogram.

$$PC = PR + RC = AR + RQ.$$

But

$$AR = AP$$

and

$$RQ = PB.$$

Therefore,

$$PC = PA + PB.$$

**25.** $AP^2 = PQ \cdot PR = 1(8 + 1) = 9$, by Theorem 14–22. $AP = PX = XB = 3$ so $QX = 2$ and $XR = 6$. Then by Theorem 14–23, $AX \cdot XB = QX \cdot XR$, so $AX \cdot 3 = 2 \cdot 6$ and thus $AX = 4$.

**18.** Given a line $L$ containing the two points $P$ and $Q$, and all circles tangent to $L$ at $Q$. Prove that the tangent segments from $P$ to all these circles are congruent. By Th. 14-20, two tangent segments to any of these circles are congruent and length=PQ. Thus all are congruent.

**19.** Two coplanar circles intersect at the points $A$ and $B$. Secant segments $\overline{PQ}$ and $\overline{P'Q'}$ intersect at $B$. Prove that $\angle PAQ \cong \angle P'AQ'$.

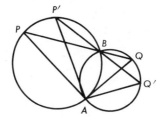
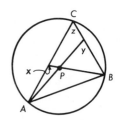

**20.** In the figure above right, $P$ is the center of the circle through points $A$, $B$, and $C$. With the figure as marked, prove that $m\angle x + m\angle y = 3m\angle z$.

**21.** A square is circumscribed around a circle of radius 8, while an equilateral triangle is inscribed in the same circle. Find the difference between the area of the square and the area of the triangle. $256 - 48\sqrt{3}$

**22.** In the figure, $\overline{PC}$ is a tangent segment and $\overrightarrow{CD}$ bisects $\angle ACB$. Prove that $\triangle PCD$ is isosceles.

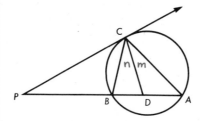
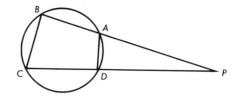

**23.** Secant segments $\overline{PB}$ and $\overline{PC}$ intersect a circle at $A$ and $D$ respectively. Prove that $\triangle PAD \sim \triangle PCB$. By Th. 14-21, PA·PB=PD·PC so $\frac{PA}{PC} = \frac{PD}{PB}$. Since $\angle P \cong \angle P$, $\triangle PAD \sim \triangle PCB$ by Theorem 13-5.

**24.** Given that $A$, $B$, $C$ are points of a circle such that $m\widehat{AB} = m\widehat{AC} = m\widehat{BC} = 120$. $P$ is any point of $\widehat{AB}$. Prove that $PA + PB = PC$. [*Hint:* Introduce a line through $A$ and parallel to $\overline{PB}$.]

**25.** In the figure, $\overrightarrow{PA}$ is tangent to the circle at $A$. $AP = PX = XB$. If $PQ = 1$ and $QR = 8$, what is $AX$? $AX=4$

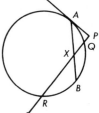

**26.** Given a circle with center $P$ and a point $A$ in its exterior. $\overline{AB}$ and $\overline{AC}$ are tangent segments, and $\overline{CD}$ is a diameter. Prove that $\overline{DB} \parallel \overline{PA}$.

**27.** In the figure, $\overline{AB}$ is a diameter of the circle. If $AB = 8$, $AQ = 4$, and $PQ = 12$, what are $PB$ and $PR$?
$\triangle ABR \cong \triangle APR$ (HL) and $RB = PR$.
By Theorem 14-21 $AP \cdot PQ = PR \cdot PB$.
$8 \cdot 12 = 2 PR \cdot PR$, $PR = 4\sqrt{3}$, $PB = 8\sqrt{3}$.

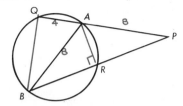

**28.** On a semicircle with center $P$ take chords $\overline{AB}$ and $\overline{AC}$ such that $m\widehat{AB} = 3m\widehat{AC}$ and $C$ is a point of minor arc $\widehat{AB}$. Radius $\overline{PC}$ intersects $\overline{AB}$ at $E$. Prove that $\triangle ACE$ is isosceles.

## HONORS PROBLEMS

(a) One of the first facts that a student of astronomy learns is that the latitude of a position on the earth is the same as the angle of Polaris (the North Star) above the horizon when observed from that position. Show why this is so by proving the following theorem. The physical situation is described by the following symbolism: $\overleftrightarrow{NS}$ is the earth's axis, the circle is a meridian, $C$ is the center, $E$ is on the equator, $O$ is the observer, $\overrightarrow{OH}$ is the horizon, and $m\angle POH$ is the elevation of Polaris.
Let $m\widehat{OE} = r$, then $m\angle POC = 180 - (90-r) = 90 + r$

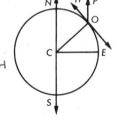

Given: The circle with center $C$.
$\quad\quad\quad\quad\quad\quad m\angle POH$
Radius $\overline{CE} \perp \overleftrightarrow{NS}$. $= m\angle POC - 90$
$\quad\quad\quad\quad\quad\quad = 90 + r - 90$
$\overleftrightarrow{OH}$ is tangent at $O$. $= r$ and
$\quad\quad\quad\quad\quad\quad m\widehat{OE} = m\angle POH$
$\overrightarrow{OP} \parallel \overleftrightarrow{NS}$.

Prove: $m\widehat{OE} = m\angle POH$.

(b) Two noncongruent circles intersect in two points, $X$ and $Y$. A secant through $X$ intersects the larger circle at $A$ and the smaller circle at $B$. A secant through $Y$ intersects the larger circle at $C$ and the smaller circle at $D$. Prove that $\overline{AC} \parallel \overline{BD}$.

(c) On the bridge of a ship at sea, the captain asked the new, young officer standing next to him to determine the distance to the horizon. The officer took pencil and paper, and in a few moments came up with an answer. On the paper he had written the formula $d = 3.6\sqrt{h}$. Show that this formula is a good approxima- tion of the distance, in kilometres, to the horizon, if $h$ is the height, in metres, of the observer above the water. (Assume the radius of the earth to be 6500 km.) If the bridge was 27 m above the water, what was the distance to the horizon? $d \doteq \sqrt{13h} \doteq 18.7$ km

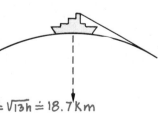

---

## Answers to Chapter Review Problems

**26.** Choose $E$ such that $E$–$B$–$A$. Then $m\angle EBD = \frac{1}{2}m\angle BPD$ by Theorem 14–19. Also $m\angle BPD + m\angle BPC = 180$, since $\angle BPD$ and $\angle BPC$ form a linear pair. By Theorem 14–20, $\angle BAP \cong \angle CAP$ so $\angle BPA \cong \angle CPA$ by Theorem 4–7. But $m\angle BPC = m\angle BPA + m\angle CPA$ by the AAP, so that $m\angle BPA = \frac{1}{2}m\angle BPD$ and $m\angle BAP = 90 - m\angle BPA = 90 - \frac{1}{2}m\angle BPC = 90 - \frac{1}{2}(180 - m\angle BPD) = \frac{1}{2}m\angle BPD = m\angle EBD$. Thus, $\overline{DB} \parallel \overline{PA}$ by AIP.

**28.** $m\angle CAE = \frac{1}{2}m\angle CPB$ by Theorem 14–16 and $\frac{1}{2}m\widehat{CB} = \frac{1}{3}m\widehat{AB} = m\widehat{AC}$ by hypothesis. Thus $\frac{1}{2}m\angle CPB = m\angle CPA$ and $\angle CAE \cong \angle CPA$. Also $\angle ACE \cong \angle PCA$, so $\triangle CAE \sim \triangle CPA$ by the AA corollary. Finally, $\dfrac{AC}{AE} = \dfrac{PC}{PA} = 1$, since $PA$ and $PC$ are radii of the same circle. Thus $\triangle ACE$ is isosceles.

### Answers to Honors Problem

(b) Introduce $\overline{XY}$. (1) Then $\angle ACY$ and $\angle AXY$ are supplementary, since they are a pair of opposite angles of an inscribed quadrilateral. (2) $\angle AXY$ and $\angle BXY$ are supplementary by the Supplement Postulate. $\angle BXY$ and $\angle BDY$ are supplementary, since they are a pair of opposite angles of an inscribed quadrilateral. Hence $\angle ACY$ and $\angle BDY$ are supplementary, and this implies that $\overline{AC} \parallel \overline{BD}$.

(c) Let $d$ be the required distance. By Theorem 14–22,

$$d^2 = \frac{h}{1000}\left(13\,000 + \frac{h}{1000}\right).$$

$$d^2 = 13h + \left(\frac{h}{1000}\right)^2.$$

Now since $h$ is very small compared to 1000, $\left(\dfrac{h}{1000}\right)^2$ is exceedingly small, and is not significant. So approximately, $d = \sqrt{13h} \doteq 3.6\sqrt{h}$. Hence, $d$ is roughly $3.6\sqrt{27} \doteq 18.7$ km.

## Characterizations and Constructions

The first part of the chapter deals with characterization or *locus* problems and is largely descriptive in nature; the only characterization theorems we actually prove are the Perpendicular Bisector Theorem and the Angle Bisector Characterization Theorem.

The second part of the chapter deals with straightedge and compass constructions. In a course on metric geometry the restriction to straightedge and compass is rather artificial; all the elementary straightedge and compass constructions can be done much more readily with ruler and protractor. Straightedge and compass constructions have, on the other hand, always interested high-school students, and, what is more, they have been important historically in stimulating significant advances in mathematics. Hence we have included them in this text.

### Planning the Chapter

Planning this chapter will depend on the significance you attach to this topic. Note that the material of this chapter is not essential to the mathematical logic of the course. In this sense it may be treated as supplementary. Students, however, usually enjoy the change of pace this chapter provides.

One day may be spent on each section and two days spent on Section 15–8. It is worthwhile to teach the optional Section 15–10; the students are usually challenged by the ideas of impossibility, especially after they have worked many constructions themselves.

# Characterizations and Constructions

## Objectives...

- Apply characterizations in the plane and in space, and in coordinate geometry.
- Prove the concurrence theorems and identify the centers of concurrency: centroid, orthocenter, incenter, circumcenter.
- Learn the classical constructions with straightedge and compass.
- Study the three impossible construction problems of Greek geometry.

## 15–1  CHARACTERIZATIONS

You will remember that in Chapter 6 we proved a characterization theorem for the perpendicular bisector of a segment in a plane.

### Theorem 6–2

*The perpendicular bisector of a segment, in a plane, is the set of all points of the plane that are equidistant from the end points of the segment.*

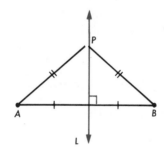

Briefly, we say that the points of the perpendicular bisector $L$ are *characterized* by the condition $PA = PB$. By this we mean that (1) every point of $L$ satisfies the condition $PA = PB$, and (2) every point of the plane that satisfies the condition $PA = PB$ is on $L$.

Similarly, we showed in Chapter 8 that the perpendicular bisecting plane of a segment $\overline{AB}$ is characterized by the condition $PA = PB$. (Here, of course, $P$ can be any point in space.)

Characterizations appear not only in theorems but also in definitions. For example, the sphere with center $P$ and radius $r$ is, by definition, the set of all points $Q$ such that $PQ = r$. Thus we say that the sphere is characterized by the condition

$$PQ = r.$$

**Background Material**

To *characterize* a figure, that is, a set of points, means to state a condition which is satisfied by all the points of the given figure and by no other points. For example, we can characterize the perpendicular bisector of a segment in a plane by saying that it is the set of all points of the plane which are equidistant from the end points of the segment. In practice we frequently turn the problem around: we state a characterization of a point set, that is, a set of conditions which the points of the set must satisfy, and *then* inquire what the set we have characterized "looks like."

Characterization theorems are often called *locus* theorems. The Perpendicular Bisector Theorem, for example, can be stated as follows:

> The perpendicular bisector of a segment, in a plane, is the *locus* of all points of the plane that are equidistant from the end points of the segment.

The word *locus* is the Latin for *place*. In geometry, it came to be used in the sense of "the *location* of all points satisfying a given condition." Thus every locus is a set of points and every set of points is a locus. Hence the word does not describe a particular kind of geometric figure, as one might expect. Rather, it gives the reader a cue: we speak of a figure as a *locus* if we are about to regard it as a set of points. In modern geometry (except in projective geometry) we *always* regard figures as sets of points, and so no such cue word is needed. Note also that various mathematical idioms involving the word *locus* have now been superseded by the phrase "the set of all points $P$ such that . . ."

To show that a certain set is characterized by a given condition, we must show that (1) each point of the set satisfies the given condition and (2) each point satisfying the condition is a point of the set.

We can gain some insight into characterization theorems, by looking at what we are doing from a set theoretic point of view. In a characterization theorem we establish that two sets $R$ and $S$ are in fact the same. There is a standard procedure for showing that two sets are the same: if $R$ is a subset of $S$, and $S$ is a subset of $R$, then $R = S$.

**Explanation for Problems**

Problem Set 15–1 deals with characterizations on an intuitive level; the student is not asked to prove any characterization theorems. Note that in Problems 1 through 8 we provide the student with a description of the set which we have just characterized; all he has to do is to decide whether the description is correct, and if it is not, correct it. In Problems 9 through 26, however, he has to come up with his own descriptions. The most common error is to fail to sketch the *complete* figure; that is, every point of the figure which he sketches will satisfy the given condition, but it will not be true that every point which satisfies the given condition will be in the figure he has sketched. Consider the following examples:

*Problem.* What is the set of all points in a plane that are equidistant from two intersecting lines? A student might answer that it is the line $L_3$, as shown in the figure at the top of page 503. But this is incorrect: all points of $L_3$ are equidistant from $L_1$ and $L_2$, but $L_3$ is not the set of *all* such points.

*A word of caution:* In the plane figure below, every point of $\overline{CD}$ is equidistant from $A$ and $B$.

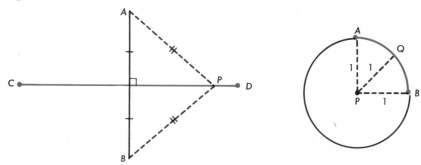

But the segment $\overline{CD}$ is *not* characterized by the condition $PA = PB$, because this condition is satisfied by many points that are not on $\overline{CD}$, namely, all points of the line $\overleftrightarrow{CD}$. Similarly, in the following figure, every point of $\overarc{AB}$ lies at a distance 1 from $P$. But $\overarc{AB}$ is not characterized by the condition $PQ = 1$, because all other points of the circle satisfy the same condition.

This is why the restatement of a characterization theorem usually appears in two parts:

(1) Every point of the given set satisfies the given condition.
(2) Conversely, every point that satisfies the given condition is in the given set.

See, for example, the restatements of Theorems 6–2 and 8–6.

**Problem Set 15–1**

In Problems 1–8 a characterization statement is accompanied by a representative sketch. You are to decide whether each statement is really a characterization. If it is, answer "true." If it is not, write a corrected statement and make a corrected sketch. In the sketches, the required set of points is a solid figure, whereas the dashed figures are those contained in the given conditions or necessary in the explanation.

**1.** The set of all points in a plane $E$ which are equidistant from each of two
T parallel lines in $E$ is the perpendicular bisector, in $E$, of any segment perpendicular to the two lines and having an end point in each of them.

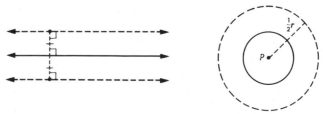

**2.** The set of all points which are midpoints of radii of a given circle is a
T circle concentric with the given circle and with a radius equal to one-half the radius of the given circle. (See figure below Problem 1.)

**3.** The set of all points in a plane which are 1 cm from a given line is a line
F parallel to the given line at a distance of 1 cm.

*The set of all points is two lines parallel to the given line.*

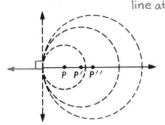

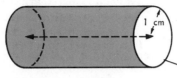

**4.** In space the set of all points which are 1 cm from a given line is a cylin-
T drical surface with 1-cm radius and the given line as axis.

**5.** In a plane, the set of all points which are centers of circles tangent to a
F given line at a given point of the line is a ray perpendicular to the line at the given point. *The set of points is a line perpendicular to the line at the given point.*

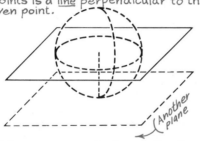

**6.** In space the set of all points which are centers of spheres of radius $r$,
F tangent to a given plane is a plane parallel to the given plane at a distance equal to $r$. *The set of points is two planes parallel to given plane.*

**7.** The set of all points in a plane which are
T vertices of the right angles of right triangles having the same segment as hypotenuse is a circle with the hypotenuse as its diameter without the end points of the diameter.

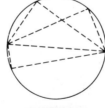

**8.** The set of all points in a plane whose distance
F from a given point is less than 2 cm is a circle, with center the given point and radius of 2 cm, plus its interior. *Interior only*

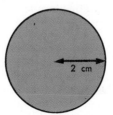

In Problems 9 through 20 make a sketch and describe the required set of points. *See Solution Section for Sketches.*

**9.** In a given plane the set of all points equidistant from two given points.

**10.** The set of all points which are the midpoints of chords of a circle having a given length.

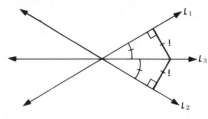

In fact, the set of *all* such points is the union of the two lines $L_3$ and $L_4$.

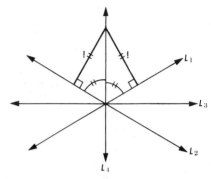

*Problem.* Given two points $A$ and $B$, what is the set of all points $C$ such that $\triangle ABC$ is a right triangle?

At first glance one might recall that any angle inscribed in a semicircle is a right angle, and give the following as a picture of the set:

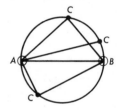

Note that the points $A$ and $B$ are not in the set; there is no such thing as $\triangle AAB$ or $\triangle ABB$. However, the problem did not require that the right angle be at $C$. The right angle might equally well be at $A$ or at $B$, and so the complete set looks like this:

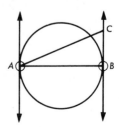

Here again the points $A$ and $B$ are not in the set. The set consists of all points on the circle with $\overline{AB}$ as diameter, *and* all points on the lines perpendicular to this diameter at $A$ and $B$, except for the points $A$ and $B$.

### Quiz

**1.** Describe completely the set of points characterized by the following conditions: The set of all points in a plane which are centers of circles tangent to a given line at a given point of the line.

(ans: A point belongs to this set if and only if it is not the point of tangency, and it is on a line passing through the given point of tangency and perpendicular to the given line.)

**2.** Describe completely the set of all points $K$ in a plane such that $K$ is the vertex of the right angle of a right triangle whose hypotenuse is the segment $\overline{MP}$.

(ans: A point belongs to this set if and only if it is not $P$ or $M$, and it is on a circle with the midpoint of $\overline{MP}$ as center and radius $MP/2$.)

### Answers to Problems

**9.** The perpendicular bisector of the segment between the given points of the plane

**10.** A circle concentric with the given circle and radius $r' = \sqrt{r^2 - \left(\dfrac{a}{2}\right)^2}$, where $r$ = radius of the given circle, and $a$ = length of each of the chords

[Note: There is a special case. If the given congruent chords happen to be diameters, then the set of all midpoints of these congruent chords is obviously just the center of the given circle.]

**11.** Let $C$ be the given circle, with center at $O$, and let $A$ be the given point of $C$. Let $S$ be the set characterized by the conditions of the problem. Let $P$ be the midpoint of $\overline{AO}$, and let $C'$ be the circle with center at $P$, containing $A$ and $O$. Then $S = C' - \{A\}$; that is, $S$ consists of all points of $C'$, except for the point $A$.

**11.** The set of all points which are midpoints of chords of a circle having a given point of the circle as an end point.

**12.** The set of all points, in a plane, which are 1 cm from a given segment 4 cm long and also are 2 cm from the midpoint of the segment. There are 4 points satisfying these conditions.

**13.** The set of all points $A$, in a plane, for which $\triangle ABC$, with a given segment $\overline{BC}$ as base, has a given area. 2 lines parallel to $\overline{BC}$. The distance from $\overline{BC}$ to either line is $2k/BC$ where $k = a \triangle ABC$.

**14.** The set of all points in a plane which are centers of circles tangent to a given circle at a given point of the circle. All points on line through center and given point with the exception of these two points.

**15.** The set of all points in the exterior of a circle of diameter 6 which are end points of tangent segments of length 4. A circle concentric with given circle and with a radius of 5.

**16.** The set of all points in a plane which are $\frac{1}{2}$ cm from a segment, $\overline{AB}$, of length 2 cm.

**17.** The set of all points which are $\frac{1}{2}$ cm from a segment, $\overline{AB}$, of length 2 cm.

**18.** The set of all points in a plane which are centers of circles of a given radius that contain a given point. A circle with given point as center and given distance as radius.

**19.** The set of all points in a plane which are 3 cm from each of two points 5 cm apart. Two points, which are the intersection of two circles having given points as centers and radii of 3 cm

**20.** The set of all points which are 3 cm from a given plane and also are 5 cm from a given point of the plane.

**21.** Given a circle $C$ with center $P$, and a point $A$ in the plane of $C$. Let $B$ be that point of the intersection of $\overleftrightarrow{AP}$ and $C$ such that $P$ is not between $A$ and $B$. Then $AB$ is the *distance of the point $A$ from the circle $C$.* Describe the set of all points in a plane whose distance from a circle equals the radius of the circle. Union of circle concentric with C, radius equal to twice PB and P, the center of the circle.

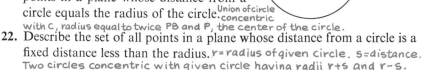

**22.** Describe the set of all points in a plane whose distance from a circle is a fixed distance less than the radius. r = radius of given circle. s = distance. Two circles concentric with given circle having radii r+s and r−s.

**23.** Describe the set of all points in a plane equidistant from two given points and equidistant from two given parallel lines.

**24.** Describe the set of all points in a plane at a given distance from a given point and at a given distance from a given line.

**25.** Describe the set of all points in a plane which are centers of circles tangent to a given line at a given point of the line and are centers of circles of a given radius tangent to the same given line.

**26.** Describe the set of all points which are at a given distance from a given plane and are at a given distance from a given point of the given plane.

**27.** Sometimes the solution to a characterization problem requires a discussion of various cases. Consider, for example, the following problem and its solution, which you should complete by filling in the blanks.
Describe the set of all points in a plane at a given distance from a given point and equidistant from two given parallel lines.

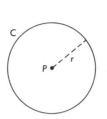
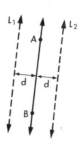

**Solution**

(1) The set of all points at a distance $r$ from point $P$ is the __circle__ $C$ with center $P$ and radius $r$.

(2) The set of all points equidistant from parallel lines $L_1$ and $L_2$ is $\overleftrightarrow{AB}$, the __perpendicular bisector__ of a segment between $L_1$ and $L_2$ perpendicular to both of them.

(3) The required set is the intersection of $C$ and $\overleftrightarrow{AB}$.

   (i) If $C$ and $\overleftrightarrow{AB}$ do not intersect, the required set is __the null set__.

   (ii) If $C$ and $\overleftrightarrow{AB}$ are __tangent__, the required set contains exactly one point.

   (iii) If $\overleftrightarrow{AB}$ contains a point in the __interior__ of $C$, the required set contains exactly __two__ points.

## 15–2  THE USE OF CHARACTERIZATIONS IN COORDINATE GEOMETRY

In coordinate geometry, we use characterizations continually.  For example, in the figure the line $L$ is the graph of the equation

$$x + y = 1.$$

(Why?)  This means that the line is *characterized* by the condition $x + y = 1$; every point $(x, y)$ of $L$ satisfies this condition, and no other point $(x, y)$ satisfies it.

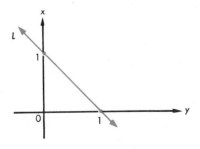
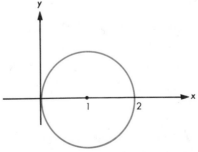

Similarly, in the next figure, the circle is characterized by the condition $(x - 1)^2 + y^2 = 1$.

---

**12.**

![figure for problem 12]

**16.** A figure consisting of two segments each 2 cm long parallel to the given segment and 0.5 cm from it, together with two semicircular "ends" which have the end points of the given segment as centers and radii of 0.5 cm.

**17.** A surface consisting of a 2-cm section of a cylindrical surface which has the given segment as an axis and a 0.5 cm radius, together with two hemispherical "ends" which have the end points of the given segment as centers and radii of 0.5 cm.

**20.** Let $E$ be the given plane, and let $P$ be the given point. Let $A$ be the set of all points which are 3 cm from $E$. Then $A$ is the union of two planes $E_1$ and $E_2$, each parallel to $E$ at a distance of 3 cm from $E$. Let $B$ be the set of all points at a distance of 5 cm from $P$. Then $B$ is a sphere with center at $P$ and radius 5 cm. The desired set $S$ is the intersection of $A$ and $B$. This is the union of two circles $C_1$ and $C_2$, lying in $E_1$ and $E_2$. The centers of these circles are the intersections of $E_1$ and $E_2$ with the perpendicular line to $E$ through $P$. Each of them has radius 4 cm.

**23.** The set $R$ of all points in a plane equidistant from two given points is the perpendicular bisector of the segment between the two points. The set $S$ of all points in a plane equidistant from two parallel lines is a line parallel to the two given lines and "midway" between them. Since $R$ is a line and $S$ is a line, the intersection of $R$ and $S$ can be either (1) the empty set, (2) a point or (3) a line, all depending, of course, on the relative locations of the two given points and the two given lines.

**24.** The set of all points in a plane at a given distance from a given point is a circle with the given point as center and the given distance as radius. The set of all points in a plane at a given distance from a given line is the union of two lines each parallel to the given line and at the given distance from the given line. The intersection of these two sets, a circle and two parallel lines, can be either (1) one point, (2) two points, (3) three points, (4) four points, or (5) the empty set, all of course depending on the relative locations of the given point and given line and on the given distances.

**25.** The set of all points in a plane which are centers of circles tangent to a given line at a given point of the line is the set of all points on the line perpendicular to the given line at the given point, with the exception of the point of intersection itself; and the set of all points in a plane which are centers of circles of a given radius tangent to the same given line is the union of two lines, each parallel to the given line and at the given distance from the given line. The intersection of these two sets consists of two points.

**26.** The set of all points which are at a given distance from a given plane is the union of two planes, each parallel to the given plane and at the given distance from the given plane. The set of all points at a given distance from a given point (of the given plane) is a sphere with the given point as center and the given distance as radius. The intersection of these two sets, the two parallel planes and the sphere can be either: (1) the empty set, (2) two points or (3) the union of two congruent circles, one lying in each of the parallel planes.

## 15-2 THE USE OF CHARACTERIZATIONS IN COORDINATE GEOMETRY

**Classroom Notes**

In Section 13-10 we proved that the line $L$ which passes through the point $P(x_1, y_1)$ and has slope $m$ is characterized by the equation $y - y_1 = m(x - x_1)$. To prove this, we needed to prove two things:

(1) If $P(x_1, y_1)$ is a point on $L$, then $P$ satisfies the equation $y - y_1 = m(x - x_1)$.

(2) If $P(x_1, y_1)$ satisfies the equation $y - y_1 = m(x - x_1)$, then $P$ is on $L$.

(Why?) In fact, every time we say that a figure is the graph of a certain equation, this means that the equation is a characterization of the graph. Most of the time, our work in coordinate geometry depends on the fact that the figures we are working with are characterized by simple equations.

### Problem Set 15-2

**1.** Sketch each of the following sets (that is, sketch the graphs).

(a) $\{(x, y) \mid x = 3\}$

(b) $\{(x, y) \mid y = -2\}$

(c) $\{(x, y) \mid y = x - 2\}$

(d) $\{(x, y) \mid x + y = 0\}$

**2.** Sketch each of the following sets.

(a) $\{(x, y) \mid x > -1\}$

(b) $\{(x, y) \mid y \leq 0\}$

(c) $\{(x, y) \mid x < y\}$

(d) $\{(x, y) \mid x + y \geq 1\}$

**3.** Make a sketch and describe by an equation the set of all points $P(x, y)$ which are equidistant from $A(5, 0)$ and $B(1, 0)$. $\{(x,y) \mid x=3\}$

**4.** Make a sketch and describe by an equation the set of all points $P(x, y)$ which are equidistant from $C(2, 2)$ and $D(2, -8)$. $\{(x,y) \mid y=-3\}$

**5.** Make a sketch and describe by an equation the set of all points $P(x, y)$ which are equidistant from the lines given by $x = -3$ and $x = 7$. $\{(x,y) \mid x=2\}$

**6.** Sketch each of the following sets.

(a) $\{(x, y) \mid x^2 + y^2 = 25\}$

(b) $\{(x, y) \mid x^2 + y^2 = 8\}$

(c) $\{(x, y) \mid (x - 1)^2 + y^2 = 4\}$

(d) $\{(x, y) \mid x^2 + (y + 1)^2 = 9\}$

**7.** Sketch and describe the set of all points $P(x, y)$ which are equidistant from the points $A(0, 5)$ and $B(5, 0)$. $\{(x,y) \mid y=x\}$

**8.** Sketch each of the following sets and describe each in the briefest way possible.

(a) $\{(x, y) \mid x = 3 \text{ and } y = 6\}$ $\{(3,6)\}$

(b) $\{(x, y) \mid x = y \text{ and } x = 5\}$ $\{(5,5)\}$

(c) $\{(x, y) \mid x^2 + y^2 = 16 \text{ and } x = -4\}$ $\{(-4,0)\}$

(d) $\{(x, y) \mid x^2 + y^2 = 25 \text{ and } y = 3\}$ $\{(4,3),(-4,3)\}$

(e) $\{(x, y) \mid y = -2 \text{ and } |x| = 7\}$ $\{(7,-2),(-7,-2)\}$

(f) $\{(x, y) \mid |x| = 3 \text{ and } |y| = 5\}$ $\{(3,5),(3,-5),(-3,5),(-3,-5)\}$

---

**9.** What is the difference between the following two sets?

(a) $\{(x, y) \mid x = 4 \text{ and } y = 5\}$

(b) $\{(x, y) \mid x = 4 \text{ or } y = 5\}$

10. Make a sketch and describe by an equation the set of all points $P(x, y)$ which are twice as far from $(8, 0)$ as from $(2, 0)$.

11. Sketch the following set: $\{(x, y)\} \mid -1 \leq x \leq 5$ and $0 \leq y \leq 4\}$.

12. Sketch the following set:

$$\{(x, y) \mid (x - 3)^2 + y^2 = 25 \text{ or } (x + 6)^2 + y^2 = 52\}.$$

13. Let $A = \{(x, y) \mid 3 < |x| < 6\}$, $B = \{(x, y) \mid 2 < |y| < 5\}$, and $C = \{(x, y) \mid 2y > x > y\}$. Sketch each of the following sets:

(a) $A \cup B$              (b) $A \cap B$

(c) $\{(x, y) \mid (x, y) \subset A$    and    $(x, y) \subset B\}$

(d) $A \cap C$              (e) $B \cap C$

## 15–3   CONCURRENCE THEOREMS

We recall from Section 9–9 the definition of concurrent lines.

### Definition

Two or more lines are *concurrent* if there is a single point which lies on all of them. The common point is called the *point of concurrency*.

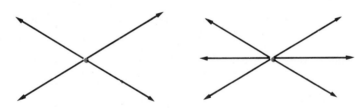

We remarked then that the chances of three or more lines being concurrent are very slight. It is even more surprising then that four sets of three lines related to triangles each turn out to be sets of concurrent lines. One of these is the three medians of a triangle, first discussed in Theorem 9–31 of Section 9–9.

In this section we prove the concurrency of the perpendicular bisectors of the sides of any triangle, and the concurrency of the three altitudes of a triangle. In the two following sections we give a proof of the concurrency of the bisectors of the three angles of any triangle and we give an alternative proof, based on methods of coordinate geometry, for the concurrency of the three medians.

Later in this chapter we learn that some of these points of concurrency are important centers for geometric constructions.

## Quiz

Describe by an equation the set of all points in a plane which are equidistant from the points $(5, 9)$ and $(11, -3)$.
   (ans: $x - 2y = 2$.)

## Answers to Problems

1. (a) A vertical line with $x$-intercept of 3
   (b) A horizontal line with $y$-intercept of $-2$
   (c) A line with a slope $m = 1$, and a $y$-intercept $b = -2$
   (d) A line through the origin with a slope $m = -1$

2. (a) The half-plane to the right of the vertical line $x = -1$
   (b) The union of the $x$-axis and the half-plane "below" the $x$-axis
   (c) The half-plane "above" the line $y = x$
   (d) The union of the line $y = -x + 1$ and the half-plane "above" this line

6. (a) A circle with center at $(0, 0)$ and $r = 5$
   (b) A circle with center at $(0, 0)$ and $r = 2\sqrt{2}$
   (c) A circle with center at $(1, 0)$ and $r = 2$
   (d) A circle with center at $(0, -1)$ and $r = 3$

7. A line with slope $m = 1$, and $y$-intercept $b = 0$.

9. The set in (a) consists of the single point $(4, 5)$. The set in (b) is the union of two sets: a vertical line through $(4, 5)$ and a horizontal line through $(4, 5)$.

10. By the distance formula,

$$\sqrt{(x - 8)^2 + y^2} = 2\sqrt{(x - 2)^2 + y^2}.$$

This equation can be simplified to $x^2 + y^2 = 16$. Therefore, the set of all such points is the circle with center at the origin and radius 4.

11.

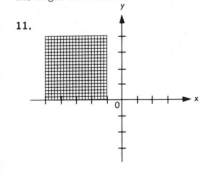

**12.**

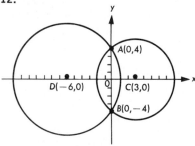

**13.** (a)

(b, c)

(d)

(e)

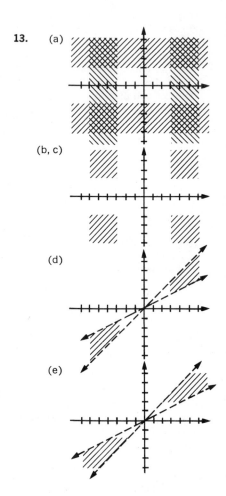

**Theorem 15–1.**   The Perpendicular Bisector Concurrence Theorem

*The perpendicular bisectors of the sides of a triangle are concurrent.   Their point of concurrency is equidistant from the vertices of the triangle.*

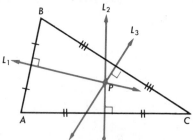

**Proof.**   Given $\triangle ABC$. Let $L_1$, $L_2$, and $L_3$ be the perpendicular bisectors of $\overline{AB}$, $\overline{AC}$, and $\overline{BC}$. If $L_1$ and $L_2$ were parallel, then $\overleftrightarrow{AB}$ and $\overleftrightarrow{AC}$ would be parallel. (Why?) But $\overleftrightarrow{AB}$ intersects $\overleftrightarrow{AC}$. Therefore $L_1$ intersects $L_2$ at a point $P$.

By the characterization theorem for perpendicular bisectors (Theorem 6–2), we have $PA = PB$, because $P$ is on $L_1$. By the same theorem, $PA = PC$, because $P$ is on $L_2$. Therefore $PB = PC$. By the same theorem, this means that $P$ is on $L_3$.

Thus the perpendicular bisectors are concurrent, and their point of intersection is equidistant from the vertices.

**Corollary 15–1.1**

*Every three different noncollinear points lie on one and only one circle.*

(They lie on the circle with center $P$ and radius $PA = PB = PC$.)

**Corollary 15–1.2**

*Two different circles can intersect in at most two points.*

(In the proof, you need Corollaries 14–6.1 and 15–1.1.)

So far we have used the term *altitude* (for a triangle) in two senses: it may mean (1) a perpendicular segment from a vertex of the triangle to the opposite side, or (2) the length of such a perpendicular segment. In the following theorem, we use the word altitude in yet a third sense: here it means (3) a *line* through one vertex of the triangle, perpendicular to the opposite side.

**Theorem 15–2.**   The Altitude Concurrence Theorem

*The three altitudes of a triangle are always concurrent.*

**Proof.** Given $\triangle ABC$, through each vertex we draw a line parallel to the opposite side. No two of these three lines are parallel. (Why?) Therefore they determine a triangle $\triangle DEF$.

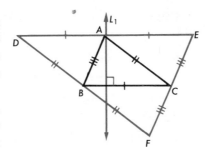

We know that opposite sides of a parallelogram are congruent. By two applications of this theorem, we get $AD = BC = AE$. Therefore *the altitude through A to $\overleftrightarrow{BC}$ is the perpendicular bisector of $\overline{DE}$*. For the same reasons, the other two altitudes of $\triangle ABC$ are the perpendicular bisectors of the other two sides of $\triangle DEF$. By Theorem 15–1, these three lines are concurrent.

Note that this theorem would become false if we interpreted the word *altitude* in the old sense to mean a segment. The perpendicular *segments* do not necessarily intersect at all. It is the *lines* that are always concurrent.

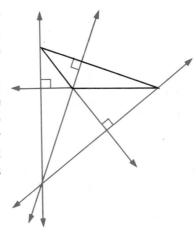

### Definition

The point of concurrency of the altitudes of a triangle is called the *orthocenter*.

### Problem Set 15–3

1. Draw a scalene, an isosceles, and a right triangle on your paper and construct the three perpendicular bisectors of the sides and the three altitudes of each triangle, showing the points of concurrency. Right triangle

2. (a) In what kind of triangle is the orthocenter a vertex of the triangle?

   (b) In what kind of triangle does the orthocenter coincide with the point of concurrency of the perpendicular bisectors? Equilateral triangle

3. Three points lie on a circle. The points are joined with segments forming a triangle. Where will the perpendicular bisectors of the segments be concurrent? At the center of the circle

---

## 15-3 CONCURRENCE THEOREMS

### Classroom Notes

The concurrence theorems are interesting and quite easy to prove. Some of the students may notice that the point of concurrency of the perpendicular bisectors of a triangle is the center of the circle which contains the vertices of the triangle. (Problem 3 of the problem set also elicits this conclusion.) You could anticipate Section 15–8 and mention the names of each of the points of concurrency of the triangle: the orthocenter is the intersection of the altitudes; the circumcenter is the intersection of the perpendicular bisectors; and the incenter is the intersection of the angle bisectors (which will be studied in the next section).

### Looking Ahead

Problem 8 anticipates the statement of Theorem 15–3. A discussion of this problem leads directly to Section 15–4 and a proof of the theorem.

### Quiz

**1.** Given three noncollinear points. Describe a method of locating the point in their plane equidistant from all three points.

    (ans: Construct the perpendicular bisectors, $L$ and $M$, of $\overline{AB}$ and $\overline{BC}$, respectively, where $A$, $B$, and $C$ are the three given noncollinear points. Then the required point is $P$, where $\{P\} = L \cap M$.)

**2.** Under what conditions will the altitudes of a triangle be concurrent in the exterior of the triangle?

    (ans: One angle of the triangle must be obtuse.)

### Answers to Problems

  **4.** At the point of intersection of the perpendicular bisectors of any two of the three segments joining the points in pairs. The points must be noncollinear if the perpendicular bisectors are to intersect.

**5.** The line perpendicular to the plane of the three points at the point of intersection of the perpendicular bisectors, in that plane, of the segments between the given points. [Note: This line can also be described as the line of intersection of the perpendicular bisecting planes of the three segments determined by the given points.]

**8.** The set of all points in the interior of $\angle BAC$ which are equidistant from the sides of the angle is the bisector of $\angle BAC$ minus its end point $A$.

**10.** The midpoint $D$ of $\overline{AB}$ has coordinates (4, 6). The slope of $\overline{AB}$ is 2, so the slope of $L$, the perpendicular bisector of $\overline{AB}$, is $-\frac{1}{2}$. Therefore the equation of $L$ is $y - 6 = -\frac{1}{2}(x - 4)$, or $x + 2y = 16$. Similarly, the equation of $M$, the perpendicular bisector of $\overline{BC}$, is $3x - y = -3$, and the equation of $N$, the perpendicular bisector of $\overline{AC}$, is $2x - 3y = -19$. The lines $L$ and $M$ intersect at a point $P = (\frac{10}{7}, \frac{51}{7})$ and it is easy to check by substitution that $P$ lies on the line $N$.

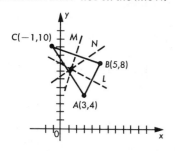

**11.** Let $\overline{AE}$ be the altitude to $\overline{BC}$, and let $\overline{BF}$ be the altitude to $\overline{AC}$. Then the equation of $\overleftrightarrow{AE}$ is $y = \frac{4}{5}(x + 4)$ and the equation of $\overleftrightarrow{BF}$ is $y = -\frac{2}{5}(x - 8)$. The coordinates of the point of intersection of $\overleftrightarrow{AE}$ and $\overleftrightarrow{BF}$ are $(0, \frac{16}{5})$ so the altitudes $\overline{AE}$ and $\overline{BF}$ of $\triangle ABC$ do intersect on the $y$-axis.

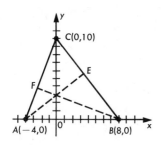

**4.** Given three noncollinear points, where is the point in their plane equidistant from all three? Why must the points be noncollinear?

**5.** Sketch and describe the set of all points equidistant from three noncollinear points.

**6.** Given a right triangle, where is the point in its plane equidistant from its vertices? *At the midpoint of the hypotenuse*

**7.** The altitude to the hypotenuse of an isosceles right triangle has length 7. What is the area of the triangle? *49*

**8.** Given any angle $\angle BAC$. Describe the set of all points of the interior which are equidistant from the sides of the angle. You should be able to prove your answer. (Warning: this set is neither a ray nor a line.)

**9.** A quadrilateral is *cyclic* if its four vertices lie on a circle. Prove that the perpendicular bisectors of the four sides and the perpendicular bisectors of the two diagonals of a cyclic quadrilateral are concurrent. *Each side and diagonal are chords of the circle; hence the perpendicular bisector of each passes through the center.*

**10.** Find equations for the perpendicular bisectors of the sides of $\triangle ABC$ and show that they are concurrent, given $A(3, 4)$, $B(5, 8)$, and $C(-1, 10)$.

**11.** Given $A(-4, 0)$, $B(8, 0)$, and $C(0, 10)$, find equations for the altitudes through $A$ and $B$ of $\triangle ABC$ and show that they intersect on the $y$-axis.

## 15–4 THE ANGLE BISECTORS OF A TRIANGLE

The next thing we want to prove is that the angle bisectors of a triangle are always concurrent.

To get this result, however, we first need to learn some more about angle bisectors. What we need is a characterization. This is given in the following theorem.

### Theorem 15–3

> *The bisector of an angle, minus its end point, is the set of all points of the interior of the angle that are equidistant from the sides.*

**Restatement.** (1) If $P$ is in the interior of $\angle BAC$, and $P$ is equidistant from $\overleftrightarrow{AB}$ and $\overleftrightarrow{AC}$, then $P$ is on the bisector of $\angle BAC$.

(2) If $P$ is on the bisector of $\angle BAC$, and $P \neq A$, then $P$ is in the interior of $\angle BAC$ and is equidistant from $\overleftrightarrow{AB}$ and $\overleftrightarrow{AC}$.

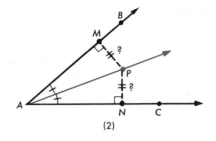

(1)    (2)

The figures illustrate the two parts of the restatement. The notation of the proofs is that of the figures.

### Proof of (1)

| STATEMENTS | REASONS |
|---|---|
| 1. $P$ is in the interior of $\angle BAC$. | 1. Given |
| 2. $\overline{PM} \perp \overrightarrow{AB}$ and $\overline{PN} \perp \overrightarrow{AC}$. | 2. Definition of the distance from a point to a line |
| 3. $\angle M$ and $\angle N$ are right angles. | 3. Definition of perpendiculars |
| 4. $\angle M \cong \angle N$. | 4. Right angles are congruent. |
| 5. $PM = PN$. | 5. Given |
| 6. $\triangle AMP \cong \triangle ANP$. | 6. Hypotenuse-Leg Theorem |
| 7. $\angle PAM \cong \angle PAN$. | 7. Definition of congruent triangles |
| 8. $\overrightarrow{AP}$ is the bisector of $\angle BAC$. | 8. Definition of the bisector of an angle |

### Proof of (2)

| STATEMENTS | REASONS |
|---|---|
| 1. $P$ lies on the bisector of $\angle ABC$, and $P \neq A$. | 1. Given |
| 2. $P$ lies in the interior of $\angle BAC$. | 2. Definition of angle bisector |
| 3. $\angle PAM \cong \angle PAN$. | 3. Definition of angle bisector |
| 4. $\overline{PM} \perp \overrightarrow{AB}$ and $\overline{PN} \perp \overrightarrow{AC}$. | 4. Definition of distance from a point to a line |
| 5. $\angle M \cong \angle N$. | 5. Right angles are congruent |
| 6. $PA = PA$. | 6. Identity |
| 7. $\triangle AMP \cong \triangle ANP$. | 7. The SAA Theorem |
| 8. $MP = NP$. | 8. Definition of congruent triangles |

## 15–4 THE ANGLE BISECTORS OF A TRIANGLE

### Classroom Notes

To write a complete proof of Theorem 15–4, we first need to prove that the bisectors $\overrightarrow{AD}$ and $\overrightarrow{BE}$, of $\angle A$ and $\angle B$, really do intersect.

(1) By the definition of *bisector*, $D$ is in the interior of $\angle A$. By the Crossbar Theorem, $\overrightarrow{AD}$ intersects $\overline{BC}$ in a point $F$.

(2) Similarly, $E$ is in the interior of $\angle B$, and so $\overrightarrow{BE}$ intersects $\overline{AF}$ in a point G.

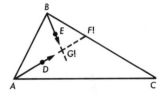

### Answers to Problems

**2.** (a) Construct the angle bisector of $\angle DAB$ and the perpendicular bisector of $\overline{CD}$. Their point of intersection is equidistant from $\overleftrightarrow{AD}$ and $\overleftrightarrow{AB}$ and also equidistant from $D$ and $C$.

(b) Construct the angle bisectors of $\angle DAB$ and $\angle ADC$. Their point of intersection is equidistant from $\overleftrightarrow{AB}$, $\overleftrightarrow{AD}$, and $\overleftrightarrow{DC}$.

**4.** The two intersecting lines form two pairs of vertical angles. The set of all points in the plane of these two lines which are equidistant from each of these intersecting lines is the union of the (four) bisectors of each of the angles formed. Note that these four rays form a pair of perpendicular lines.

**5.** The set of all points in the plane which are equidistant from two intersecting lines is, by Problem 4, the set consisting of the four rays which bisect, individually, each of the four angles formed by the two intersecting lines. The set of all points in this plane which are 2 cm from the point of intersection is a circle with the point of intersection as center and 2-cm radius. The four rays and the circle intersect at four points, which, by the way, separate the circle into four congruent arcs.

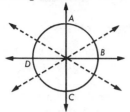

**6.** The set of all points which are equidistant from two intersecting planes is the union of their line of intersection and the four half-planes which bisect respectively each of the four dihedral angles formed by the two given intersecting planes. These four half-planes, with their common edge form two perpendicular planes.

**7.** The angle bisectors of a quadrilateral are not necessarily concurrent. They are, however, concurrent in a square or rhombus. The angle bisectors are concurrent if and only if the point of concurrency is equidistant from all four sides of the quadrilateral. This means that the angle bisectors of a quadrilateral are concurrent if and only if a circle can be inscribed in the quadrilateral. See Construction 10, Section 15-9.

**8.** The set of all points in a plane which are equidistant from the sides of an angle in that plane is the bisector of the given angle. The set of all points in this plane which are at a given distance from a given line in this plane is the union of two lines, each parallel to the given line and at the given distance from the given line. The intersection of these two sets, a ray and two parallel lines can be either (1) the empty set, (2) one point, (3) two points, or (4) a ray.

**9.** Given: $\Box ABCD$ is a parallelogram, $\overrightarrow{AP}$ bisects $\angle A$, $\overrightarrow{BP}$ bisects $\angle B$, $\overline{PE}$, $\overline{PF}$, and $\overline{PG}$ are the perpendicular segments to $\overline{AD}$, $\overline{AB}$ and $\overline{BC}$ respectively.
Prove: $PE = PG$.
Proof: Since $P$ is on the bisector of $\angle A$, and $P$ is on the bisector of $\angle B$; $PE = PF$ and $PF = PG$ by Theorem 15-3. Therefore $PE = PG$, which was to be proved.

**10.** Let $P$ be the point of intersection of the bisectors of $\angle ECB$ and $\angle CBD$. Since $P$ is on the bisector of $\angle ECB$, $P$ is equidistant from $\overleftrightarrow{CE}$ and $\overleftrightarrow{CB}$. Since $P$ is on the bisector of $\angle CBD$, $P$ is equidistant

Now we can prove our concurrence theorem:

**Theorem 15-4.** The Angle Bisector Concurrence Theorem

*The angle bisectors of a triangle are concurrent in a point which is equidistant from the three sides.*

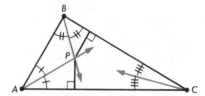

**Proof.** Given $\triangle ABC$, let $P$ be the intersection of the bisectors of $\angle A$ and $\angle B$. Then $P$ is in the interior of $\angle A$, and in the interior of $\angle B$, and is therefore in the interior of $\angle C$. Hence

(1)  $P$ is equidistant from $\overleftrightarrow{AC}$ and $\overleftrightarrow{AB}$;

(2)  $P$ is equidistant from $\overleftrightarrow{AB}$ and $\overleftrightarrow{BC}$;

(3)  $P$ is equidistant from $\overleftrightarrow{AC}$ and $\overleftrightarrow{BC}$;

(4)  $P$ is on the bisector of $\angle C$.

Reasons? Theorem 15-3 and transitivity

**Problem Set 15-4**

**1.** A line intersects the sides of $\angle BAC$ in points $P$ and $Q$. Locate a point of $\overleftrightarrow{PQ}$ which is equidistant from $\overrightarrow{AB}$ and $\overrightarrow{AC}$. The intersection of the bisector of $\angle BAC$ and $\overleftrightarrow{PQ}$ is equidistant from $\overrightarrow{AB}$ and $\overrightarrow{AC}$.

**2.** $\Box ABCD$ is any convex quadrilateral.

(a) Explain how to find a point which is equidistant from $\overleftrightarrow{AD}$ and $\overleftrightarrow{AB}$ and also equidistant from $D$ and $C$.

(b) Explain how to find a point which is equidistant from $\overleftrightarrow{AB}$, $\overleftrightarrow{AD}$, and $\overleftrightarrow{DC}$.

(c) Do the points of part (a) and part (b) coincide? Only in the special case that $\Box ABCD$ is a square.

**3.** Describe the set of all points that are centers of circles tangent to both sides of a given angle. The bisector of the given angle, minus its end point.

**4.** Describe the set of all points in a plane which are equidistant from two intersecting lines.

**5.** Describe the set of all points in a plane which are equidistant from two intersecting lines and are 2 cm from the point of intersection.

**6.** Describe the set of all points which are equidistant from two intersecting planes.

7. Make sketches of several different convex quadrilaterals and carefully sketch in the bisectors of the angles. Are the four bisectors in each quadrilateral concurrent? In what special type of quadrilateral are the angle bisectors concurrent? Is there a general way of describing all quadrilaterals whose angle bisectors are concurrent?

8. Describe the set of all points of the interior of an angle which are equidistant from the sides of the angle and are at a given distance from a given line.

9. Prove that the bisectors of two consecutive angles of a parallelogram intersect at a point equidistant from a pair of opposite sides.

10. Prove the following theorem.

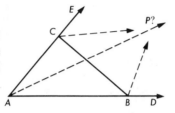

Given $\angle DAE$ and $A$-$C$-$E$ and $A$-$B$-$D$. Then the bisectors of the angles $\angle DAE$, $\angle DBC$, and $\angle ECB$ are concurrent.

11. Describe the set of all points in space which are equidistant from all three of the lines determined by the sides of a triangle.

12. Given a pair of coordinate axes, show that the set of all points equidistant from the two axes is

$$\{(x, y) \mid y = x \text{ or } y = -x\}.$$

## HONORS PROBLEM

*See Solution Section for complete answer.*

The following instructions were found on an old map.

"Start from the crossing of King's Road and Queen's Road. Proceed due north on King's Road and find a large pine tree and then a maple tree. Return to the crossroads. Due west on Queen's Road there is an elm, and due east on Queen's Road there is a spruce. One magical point is the intersection of the elm-pine line with the maple-spruce line. The other magical point is the intersection of the spruce-pine line with the elm-maple line. The treasure lies where the line through the two magical points meets Queen's Road."

A search party found the elm 4 km from the crossing, the spruce 2 km from the crossing, and the pine 3 km from the crossing, but could find no trace of the maple. Nevertheless, they were able to locate the treasure from the instructions. Show how they could do this. *Treasure is 8 km east of crossroads on Queen's Road.*

One member of the party remarked on how fortunate they were to have found the pine still standing. The leader laughed and said, "We didn't need the pine tree." Show that he was right. *Use coordinates (o,p) for pinetree and use same equations.*

from $\overleftrightarrow{CB}$ and $\overleftrightarrow{BD}$. Therefore, $P$ is equidistant from $\overleftrightarrow{CE}$ and $\overrightarrow{BD}$, that is, $P$ is equidistant from the sides of $\angle DAE$; and since $P$ is obviously in the interior of $\angle DAE$ this means that $P$ is on the bisector of $\angle DAE$. Therefore the bisectors of $\angle DAE$, $\angle DBC$, and $\angle ECB$ are concurrent.

11. There are four points which are equidistant from all three of the lines determined by the sides of the triangle. This follows by applying Theorem 15–4 and Problem 10 to the bisectors of the interior and exterior angles of the triangle.

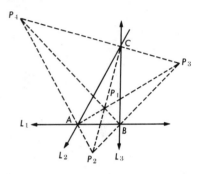

12. Part (1) Prove: If $P(x, y)$ is equidistant from each of the axes then $P$ is on the line $y = x$, or the line $y = -x$. Proof: Since $P(x, y)$ is equidistant from each of the axes, $|x| = |y|$. This means that either $x = y$ or $x = -y$.

Part (2) Prove: If $P(x, y)$ is on either the line $y = x$ or the line $y = -x$, then $P$ is equidistant from both axes. Proof: If $P$ is on the line $y = x$, then the distance of $P$ from the $x$-axis is $|y|$, and the distance of $P$ from the $y$-axis is $|x|$. Since $y = x$, $|y| = |x|$, which means that $P$ is equidistant from both axes. A similar argument holds if $P$ is on the line $y = -x$.

### Answer to Honors Problem

Use the sketch below to start students on this problem.

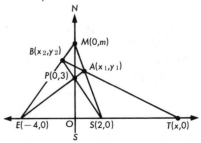

# 15-5 THE MEDIAN CONCURRENCE THEOREM

## Classroom Notes

In the text, the Median Concurrence Theorem is proved by coordinate techniques. Here is an alternative proof which depends on the introduction of an auxiliary figure and on the fact that the diagonals of a parallelogram bisect each other.

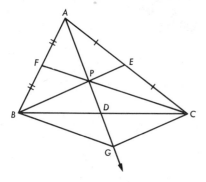

*Proof.* Let $P$ be the point of intersection of the medians $\overline{BE}$ and $\overline{CF}$; let $D$ be the point at which $\overrightarrow{AP}$ intersects $\overline{BC}$, and let $G$ be the point of $\overrightarrow{AP}$, beyond $P$ from $A$, such that $PG = PA$. Then introduce $\overline{BG}$ and $\overline{CG}$. Since $F$ is the midpoint of $\overline{AB}$ and $P$ is the midpoint of $\overline{AG}$, we conclude that $\overleftrightarrow{FP} \parallel \overline{BG}$. Similarly, $\overleftrightarrow{PE} \parallel \overline{GC}$. Therefore $\square BGCP$ is a parallelogram, and so $D$ is the midpoint of $\overline{CB}$. This means that $\overline{AD}$ is the median to $\overline{BC}$, and it follows that the three medians of the triangle are concurrent.

To show that $BP = \frac{2}{3}BE$, we note that $PE = \frac{1}{2}GC$ and that $BP = GC$. Therefore $BP = 2PE$, and so $BP = \frac{2}{3}(BE)$.

The orthocenter, the centroid, and the circumcenter of a triangle are collinear, and, what is more, the centroid is a point of trisection of the segment between the orthocenter and the circumcenter. For a proof of this, see the solution of Problem 9 of the Chapter Review in the Solution Section.

---

## 15-5   THE MEDIAN CONCURRENCE THEOREM

In Section 9–9 we proved Theorem 9–31 on the intersection of the medians of a triangle by using Theorem 9–30, involving parallel lines. The figure should remind you that the medians of a triangle are concurrent, and that the point of concurrency is two-thirds of the way long each median.

What follows is an alternative proof of Theorem 9–31 making use of coordinate geometry. It is a good example of how coordinate geometry provides easier proofs of some theorems. Because we have restated the theorem in new terminology, as used in this chapter, we assign it a new number.

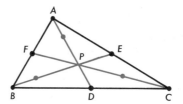

**Theorem 15–5.**   The Median Concurrence Theorem

> *The medians of every triangle are concurrent. And their point of concurrency is two-thirds of the way along each median, from the vertex to the opposite side.*

**Proof.** We take the axes as indicated in the figure. We use $6a$, $6b$, $6c$ to avoid fractions later. $E$ is the midpoint of $\overline{AC}$; we get its coordinates by the Midpoint Theorem (Theorem 13–5).

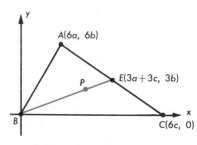

Now let $P$ be the point of the median $\overline{BE}$ such that $BP = 2PE$. By Theorem 13–6 we get

$$P = \left( \frac{0 + 2(3a + 3c)}{3}, \frac{0 + 2 \cdot 3b}{3} \right) = (2a + 2c, 2b).$$

Now let $Q$ be the point of the median $\overline{AD}$ from $A$ to $\overline{BC}$ such that $AQ = 2QD$. Since $D = (3c, 0)$, we have

$$Q = \left( \frac{6a + 2 \cdot 3c}{3}, \frac{6b + 2 \cdot 0}{3} \right) = (2a + 2c, 2b).$$

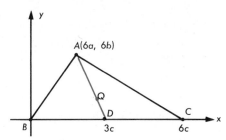

This means that $P = Q$, because a point is determined by its coordi-nates.

Similarly, it follows that the corresponding point of the median from $C$ to $\overline{AB}$ is the same point $P$. This proves the theorem.

## Definition

The point of concurrency of the medians is called the *centroid* of the triangle.

## Problem Set 15–5

**1.** In the figure on the left below, medians $\overline{AE}$, $\overline{BF}$, and $\overline{CD}$ are concurrent at $Q$.

    (a) If $AE = 9$, what is $AQ$? 6    (b) If $QD = 5$, what is $CD$? 15

    (c) If $BQ = 12$, what is $QF$? 6    (d) If $QE = 4$, what is $AQ$? 8

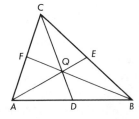 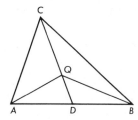

**2.** Given: The figure on the right above, with median $\overline{CD}$ and $Q$ the centroid of $\triangle ABC$. $\triangle QED \sim \triangle CFD$ (AA). Since $\frac{QD}{CD} = \frac{1}{3}$ (Th. 15-5), $QE/CF = 1/3$.
Prove: The altitude from $Q$ to $\overline{AB}$ is one-third the altitude from $C$ to $\overline{AB}$.

**3.** Using the figure for Problem 1, prove that $a\triangle AQB = a\square CEQF$.

**4.** In $\triangle GKM$, centroid $Q$ is on median $\overline{GR}$, and $\overline{GH}$ is an altitude. Given that $QR = 4$ and $HR = 6$, what is $GH$? $6\sqrt{3}$

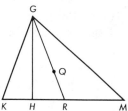

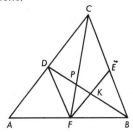

**6.** The coordinates of $M$, the midpoint of $\overline{AB}$, are $(3, 5)$, and therefore by the Median Concurrence Theorem the coordinates of the centroid $P$ of $\triangle ABC$ are $(2, \frac{10}{3})$. The distance from the orthocenter $C(0, 0)$ to the centroid $P(2, \frac{10}{3})$ is $CP = \frac{2}{3}\sqrt{34}$.

**7.** The coordinates of $M$, the midpoint of $\overline{PQ}$, are $(-2, 0)$ and therefore the coordinates of the centroid are $C(-\frac{4}{3}, 2)$.

The coordinates of the midpoint $N$ of $\overline{QR}$ are $(1, 3)$ and since the slope of $\overline{QR}$ is $-3$, the slope of the perpendicular bisector of $\overline{QR}$ is $\frac{1}{3}$. Therefore, the equation of the perpendicular bisector of $\overline{QR}$ is $y - 3 = \frac{1}{3}(x - 1)$. Trivially, the equation of the perpendicular bisector of $\overline{PQ}$ is $x = -2$. Therefore the coordinates of the circumcenter $D$ of $\triangle PQR$, that is, the point of concurrency of the perpendicular bisectors of the sides, are $(-2, 2)$. Therefore the distance between the centroid and the circumcenter is $CD = \frac{2}{3}$.

**8.** Since the slope of $\overline{QR}$ is $-3$, the slope of the altitude from $P$ to $\overline{QR}$ is $\frac{1}{3}$, and the equation of the altitude is $y = \frac{1}{3}(x + 6)$. The equation of the altitude from $R$ to $\overline{PQ}$ is, trivially, $x = 0$. Therefore the coordinates of the orthocenter $E$ are $(0, 2)$. Hence the distance from the orthocenter to the centroid is $EC = \frac{4}{3}$. Observe that in $\triangle PQR$ of Problems 7 and 8, the orthocenter $E$, the centroid $C$, and the circumcenter $D$ are collinear and that the centroid separates $\overline{ED}$ into two segments whose lengths are in a ratio of 1:2.

**5.** Given $\triangle ABC$ with vertices $A(6, 0)$, $B(0, 10)$, and $C(0, 0)$.

(a) Find the coordinates of the point of concurrency of the perpendicular bisectors of the sides. M(3,5)

(b) Find the coordinates of the orthocenter. C(0,0)

(c) Find the distance from the orthocenter to the point of concurrency of the perpendicular bisectors. CM = √34

---

**6.** Given $\triangle ABC$ of Problem 5, find the coordinates of the centroid, and the distance from the centroid to the orthocenter. $\frac{2}{3}\sqrt{34}$

**7.** Given $\triangle PQR$ with vertices $P(-6, 0)$, $Q(2, 0)$, and $R(0, 6)$. Find the distance between the centroid and the point of concurrency of the perpendicular bisectors of the sides. $\frac{2}{3}$

**8.** Given $\triangle PQR$ of Problem 7, find the coordinates of the orthocenter and the distance from the orthocenter to the centroid. (0,2), $\frac{4}{3}$

## 15–6  CONSTRUCTIONS WITH STRAIGHTEDGE AND COMPASS

Up to now, we have been doing geometry with a ruler and a protractor. In effect, our postulates tell us that we have an infinitely long ruler, with number labels on it. We use this "ruler" to draw lines and measure distances. We also have a protractor. With this we can measure angles, and we can also lay off angles with a given measure, starting at a given ray.

Probably this is the simplest way of doing geometry. There is another very important way, however. This is geometry with straightedge and compass. Under this scheme, we do not have a ruler with marks on it but only a straightedge (infinitely long, of course), so that, although we can draw straight lines, we cannot measure distances at all. We also have a compass. With this we can draw circles, with any given point as center and passing through any other given point. But we can't measure angles any more than we can measure distances.

This is the scheme developed by the Greek geometers of antiquity. (As a matter of fact, distance and angular measure are not mentioned in Euclid's *Elements* at all.) This scheme has considerable mathematical interest today and leads to some curious problems, when we try to find out what sort of figures we can draw with our straightedge and compass. The solutions to some of these problems are of practical value in mechanical drawing; and so professional draftsmen know them.

No matter which way we do geometry, we have certain physical drawing instruments and a corresponding mathematical theory. In each case, the mathematical theory is exact, but the results obtained with the physical drawing instruments are only approximate.

To justify our constructions with straightedge and compass, we need a theroem describing the way in which circles intersect each other. Suppose we have given two circles of radius $a$ and $b$, with $c$ as the distance between their centers.

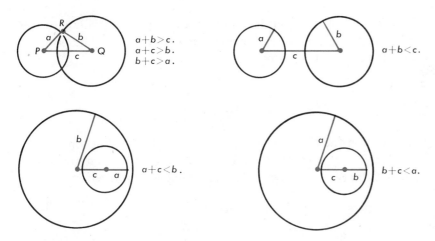

If the circles intersect in two points, as in the figure at the upper left, then each of the numbers $a$, $b$, and $c$ is less than the sum of the other two. We get these three inequalities by applying the Triangle Inequality (Theorem 7-8) to $\triangle PQR$ in three ways. On the other hand, if any one of these three inequalities works in the opposite way, the circles don't intersect at all, as the other three figures illustrate. And if the sum of two of our numbers is *equal* to the third, then the circles are tangent.

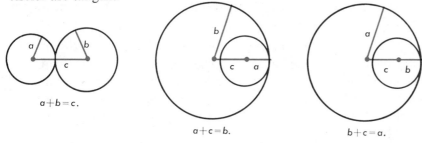

This situation is described in the following theorem.

**Background Material**

The postulates we have used so far fall into seven groups:

(1) The ruler postulates (Postulates 1, 2, 3);

(2) The incidence postulates (Postulates 4, 5, 6, 7, 8);

(3) The separation postulates (Postulates 9, 10);

(4) The protractor postulates (Postulates 11, 12, 13, 14);

(5) The congruence postulates (Postulates 15, 16, 17);

(6) The parallel postulate (Postulate 18);

(7) The area postulates (Postulates 19, 20, 21, 22).

Our treatment of incidence and separation has been quite standard; and so also was our treatment of parallelism. In fact, where these topics are concerned, the differences between one book and another are mainly in the style of exposition.

The ruler and protractor postulates, however, are another matter. These were invented rather recently (by G. D. Birkhoff), and the mathematical spirit reflected by them is quite different from the mathematical spirit of the Greeks. The basic difference, roughly speaking, is that rulers and protractors are used for measuring things; we place them on geometric figures and we read off real numbers from the scales that are marked on them. Birkhoff's metric postulates tell us, in effect, that we have an "ideal ruler" and an "ideal protractor," with which we can measure segments and angles exactly. The Greeks, on the other hand, considered that measurement was merely one of the practical arts. It was not considered to deserve the attention of mathematicians and philosophers. Just as we have described the metric treatment in terms of two drawing instruments, the marked ruler and protractor, so we can describe Greek geometry in terms of two different drawing instruments—the *unmarked* ruler and the compass. The Greeks thought about geometry in terms of these two instruments; and they investigated at length the question of what figures could be constructed by means of them.

Before we proceed to consider problems of construction with ruler and compass, several warnings are in order.

(1) When we speak of a ruler and a compass, we mean an "ideal ruler" and an "ideal compass," which draw straight lines and circles exactly. The thickness of pencil marks and the approximations involved in draftsmanship will not concern us.

(2) The Euclidean ruler has no marks on it. We can use it to draw the line through two given points, but that is *all* we can use it for. We cannot use it to measure distances between points, or even to tell whether two segments are congruent.

(3) In Euclid, the compass was "collapsible." Given two points $P$ and $Q$, you could draw the circle with center at $P$, containing $Q$, but you could *not* use the compass to lay off a segment congruent to $\overline{PQ}$, on a ray $\overrightarrow{AB}$. The latter had to be done by a more complicated construction, using both the compass and the ruler (see *EGAS*, Section 19–1).

In the present elementary treatment, we do not raise this delicate question: it is taken for granted, without comment, that the compass can be used as a pair of dividers, to lay off a segment congruent to a

**Theorem 15–6.**    The Two-Circle Theorem

*Given two circles of radius a and b, with c as the distance between their centers. If each of the numbers a, b, and c is less than the sum of the other two, then the circles intersect in two points, on opposite sides of the line through the centers.*

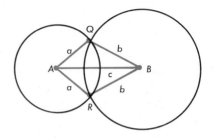

This is a theorem because it can be proved if we are willing to work hard enough. In the present chapter, however, we omit the proof and regard the statement as a postulate.

## 15–7   ELEMENTARY CONSTRUCTIONS

In this section and the next we shall show how the simplest constructions are done. All of these will, of course, be carried out in a given plane. They will appear later as steps in more difficult constructions.

CONSTRUCTION 1.   To bisect a given angle.

Given $\angle A$.

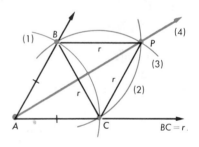

STEP 1.   Using $A$ as center, draw any circle. The circle will intersect the sides of $\angle A$ in points $B$ and $C$. Obviously $AB = AC$, as the marks on the figure indicate.

STEP 2.   Draw the circle with center at $B$ and radius $r = BC$.

STEP 3.   Draw the circle with center at $C$ and the same radius $r = BC$.

By the Two-Circle Theorem, these circles intersect in two points, lying on opposite sides of $\overleftrightarrow{BC}$. (The hypothesis of the Two-Circle Theorem must be satisfied, because each of the numbers $r$, $r$, and $r$ is less than the sum of the other two.) Let $P$ be the intersection point which is on the opposite side of $\overleftrightarrow{BC}$ from $A$, as in the figure.

STEP 4.   Draw $\overrightarrow{AP}$.

By SSS we have $\triangle PAB \cong \triangle PAC$. Therefore $\angle PAB \cong \angle PAC$, and $\overrightarrow{AP}$ is the bisector.

(In drawing our two circles, in Steps 2 and 3, we could have used any radius greater than $\frac{1}{2}BC$. We cannot get into trouble unless we use a radius so small that the circles do not intersect at all.)

CONSTRUCTION 2. To copy a given angle on a given side of a given ray.

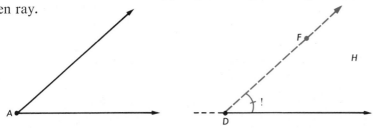

Given $\angle A$, a ray with end point $D$, and a half-plane $H$, with the given ray on its edge. We want to construct a ray $\overrightarrow{DF}$, with $F$ in $H$, so as to get a second angle which is congruent to the first.

STEP 1. Draw a circle with center at $A$, and with any radius $r$. The circle will intersect the sides of $\angle A$ in points $B$ and $C$.

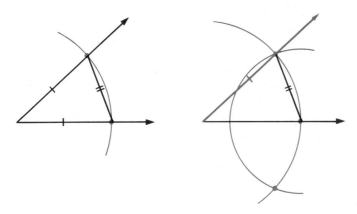

STEP 2. Draw the circle with center at $D$ and radius $r = AB = AC$. This circle will intersect the given ray in a point $E$.

STEP 3. Draw the circle with center at $E$ and radius $s = BC$.

These two circles will intersect in two points $F$ and $G$, on opposite sides of $\overleftrightarrow{DE}$. [*Query:* How do we know that each of the numbers $r$, $s$, and $r$ is less than the sum of the other two? This condition is what we need to apply the Two-Circle Theorem.] Let $F$ be the intersection point which lies in $H$, as in the figure.

STEP 4. Draw $\overrightarrow{DF}$.

This is the ray we wanted. By SSS, $\triangle FDE \cong \triangle BAC$. Therefore $\angle FDE \cong \angle BAC$, as desired.

given segment, anywhere we like.

(4) In studying ruler and compass constructions, we shall not attempt to build the foundations of geometry all over again. In proving that our constructions work, we shall freely use the theorems of metric plane geometry. In particular, we shall make continual use of the two-circle theorem.

The validity of the Two-Circle Theorem depends on the existence of a certain triangle, and the proof of the Two-Circle Theorem is easier to follow if we first establish this preliminary theorem. If $a$, $b$, and $c$ are the lengths of the sides of a triangle, then each of the numbers $a$, $b$, $c$ is less than the sum of the other two. (We know this by three applications of the triangle inequality.) We shall prove the converse.

**The Triangle Theorem.** Given three positive numbers $a$, $b$, $c$. If each of these numbers is less than the sum of the other two, then there is a triangle whose sides have length $a$, $b$, $c$.

*Proof.* Without loss of generality, let us suppose that $a \geq b \geq c$. Take a segment $\overline{BC}$, of length $a$. We want to find a point $A$ such that $AB = c$ and $AC = b$. We shall start by *assuming* that there is a triangle $\triangle ABC$, of the sort that we are looking for, and then find out where the point $A$ must be. Of course, this procedure will not prove anything in itself, because we are starting by assuming the very thing that we are supposed to be proving. But once we have found the exact location of the points that *might* work, it will be easy to check that they really *do* work.

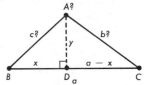

Suppose, then, that $\triangle ABC$ is given, with sides of the desired length, as indicated in the figure above. Let $D$ be the foot of the perpendicular from $A$ to $\overleftrightarrow{BC}$. Then $B$-$D$-$C$, because $\overline{BC}$ is a longest side of $\triangle ABC$. Therefore, if $BD = x$, then $DC = a - x$. Let $AD = y$. Then by two applications of the Pythagorean Theorem, we have

$$y^2 = c^2 - x^2, \qquad (1)$$
$$x^2 = b^2 - (a - x)^2. \qquad (2)$$

Therefore

$$c^2 - x^2 = b^2 - (a - x)^2,$$

so that

$$c^2 - x^2 = b^2 - a^2 + 2ax - x^2,$$

and

$$2ax = a^2 + c^2 - b^2.$$

Therefore

$$x = \frac{a^2 + c^2 - b^2}{2a}; \qquad (3)$$

and from (1), we get

$$y = \sqrt{c^2 - x^2}. \qquad (4)$$

What we have proved so far is that if $x$ and $y$ satisfy (1) and (2), then $x$ and $y$ satisfy (3) and (4). We shall check, conversely, that if $x$ and $y$ satisfy (3) and (4), then $x$ and $y$ satisfy (1) and (2). Half of this is trivial. If (4) holds, then so also does (1). Suppose then, that (3) is satisfied. Reversing the steps in the derivation, we get

$$c^2 - x^2 = b^2 - (a - x)^2.$$

Since (1) is known to hold, it follows that $y^2 = b^2 - (a - x)^2$, which is Eq. (2).

We can summarize this by writing

(1) and (2) $\Leftrightarrow$ (3) and (4).

Now that we know what triangle to look for, let us start all over again. We have three positive numbers $a$, $b$, $c$, with $a \geq b \geq c$. Let

$$x = \frac{a^2 + c^2 - b^2}{2a}.$$

CONSTRUCTION 3. To copy a given triangle on a given side of a given ray.

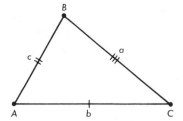
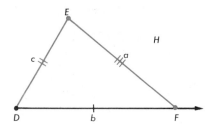

Given triangle $\triangle ABC$. We also have given a ray with end point $D$, and a half-plane $H$ containing the ray in its edge. We want to construct $\triangle DEF$, with $F$ on the given ray and $E$ in $H$, so that $\triangle DEF \cong \triangle ABC$.

STEP 1. First we draw a circle with center at $D$ and radius $b = AC$. This circle intersects our ray in a point $F$, and $DF = AC$.

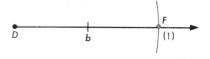

STEP 2. Draw a circle with center $D$ and radius $c$.

STEP 3. Draw a circle with center $F$ and radius $a$. These two circles ought to intersect, as in the figure, in two points on opposite sides of $\overleftrightarrow{DF}$. And by the Two-Circle Theorem they *do* intersect in this way, because each of the numbers $a$, $b$, and $c$ is less than the sum of the other two. (Why?) As indicated in the figure, let $E$ be the intersection point that lies in $H$.

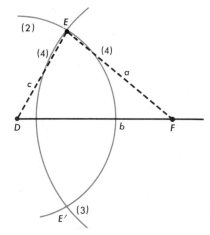

STEP 4. Now draw the segments $DE$ and $\overline{EF}$. By SSS we have $\triangle DEF \cong \triangle ABC$, which is what we wanted.

If you look again at Section 6–6, you will see that in the proof of SSS we had much the same problem as in Construction 3, namely, the problem of copying a given triangle on a given side of a given ray. It is worthwhile to compare the two methods. (In Section 6–6 we were using a ruler and a protractor instead of a straightedge and a compass. And we used SAS, instead of SSS, to show that our construction worked.)

## Problem Set 15-7

(*Note:* The problems of this set should be done with straightedge and compass.)

1. Draw a line horizontally across the top of your homework paper. Using the length of the segment $\overline{AB}$ below, mark off a scale (with a compass) at least 10 units long. Use this scale, whenever necessary in solving the problems that follow.

$$A \text{———} B$$

Construct triangles with sides of the lengths given below.

(a) 5, 6, 8    (b) 3, 5, 7    (c) 4, 4, 5    (d) 6, 10, 8

2. Draw any obtuse triangle and construct the bisector of each of its angles.

3. Draw any scalene triangle $\triangle ABC$. Copy the triangle, on a given side of a given ray, by a method which depends on the ASA Postulate.

4. Construct an equilateral triangle with a side of length 5.

5. Construct an isosceles triangle having a base of length 8 and two congruent sides of length 5.

6. Prove that it is always possible to construct an equilateral triangle having a given segment as one of its sides. *The distances satisfy the Two Circle Theorem.*

7. Two lengths, $a$ and $b$, are given for the congruent sides and base, respectively, of an isosceles triangle to be constructed. What conditions on $a$ and $b$ are necessary to make the construction possible? *b < 2a*

8. Draw any convex quadrilateral. Copy it on a given side of a given ray.

## 15-8   ELEMENTARY CONSTRUCTIONS (CONTINUED)

CONSTRUCTION 4. To construct the parallel to a given line through a given external point.

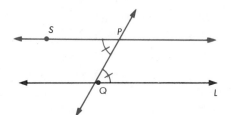

Given the line $L$, and the external point $P$. Let $Q$ and $R$ be any two points of $L$.

STEP 1.   Draw $\overleftrightarrow{PQ}$.

STEP 2.   By Construction 2, draw $\angle QPS$ congruent to $\angle PQR$, with $S$ on the opposite side of $\overleftrightarrow{PQ}$ from $R$. Then $\angle QPS$ and $\angle PQR$ are alternate interior angles. Then $\overleftrightarrow{PS} \parallel \overleftrightarrow{QR}$, which is what we wanted.

Then $x > 0$, because $a^2 \geq c^2 > 0$. We want to set $y = \sqrt{c^2 - x^2}$, but first we have to prove that $c > x$, to make sure that the radicand is positive. Obviously it will be sufficient to show that $c - x > 0$. Now

$$c - x = c - \frac{a^2 + c^2 - b^2}{2a}$$

$$= \frac{2ac - a^2 - c^2 + b^2}{2a}$$

$$= \frac{b^2 - (a^2 - 2ac + c^2)}{2a}$$

$$= \frac{b^2 - (a - c)^2}{2a}.$$

We now know that $a < b + c$. Therefore $a - c < b$. Since both $a - c$ and $b$ are greater than or equal to 0, it follows that $(a - c)^2 < b^2$; and this means that $c - x > 0$, or $c > x$.

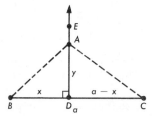

We are now ready to construct our triangle. Let $\overline{BC}$ be a segment of length $a$. Let $D$ be the point of $\overline{BC}$ such that

$$BD = x = \frac{a^2 + c^2 - b^2}{2a}. \qquad (3')$$

Let $\overrightarrow{DE}$ be a ray starting at $D$, perpendicular to $\overline{BC}$, and let $A$ be a point of $\overrightarrow{DE}$ such that

$$AD = y = \sqrt{c^2 - x^2}. \qquad (4')$$

Since $x$ and $y$ satisfy (3) and (4), it follows that $x$ and $y$ satisfy (1) and (2). Thus

$$x^2 + y^2 = c^2 \qquad (1')$$
$$(a - x)^2 + y^2 = b^2. \qquad (2')$$

But $x^2 + y^2 = AB^2$, and $(a - x)^2 + y^2 = AC^2$. Therefore $AB^2 = c^2$ and $AC^2 = b^2$. Since $b$ and $c$ are positive, this means that $AB = c$ and $AC = b$. Therefore $\triangle ABC$ is a triangle of the sort that we were looking for.

On the basis of the Triangle Theorem, it is easy to prove the Two-Circle Theorem. We have given a circle C, with center P and radius a, and a circle C', with center M and radius b:

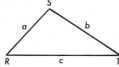

The distance PM between the centers is c, and each of the numbers a, b, c is less than the sum of the other two. Therefore there is a triangle $\triangle RST$, with $RS = a$, $ST = b$, and $RT = c$:

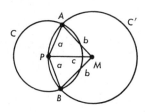

Let A be a point in the plane of our two circles such that $\angle APM \cong \angle R$ and $AP = a = RS$. By SAS, $\triangle RST \cong \triangle PAM$, so that $AM = ST = b$. Thus A is on both C and C'. Let B be a point on the opposite side of $\overleftrightarrow{PM}$ from A, such that $\angle BPM \cong \angle R$ and $BP = a = RS$. By SAS, $\triangle RST \cong \triangle PBM$, so that B is on both C and C'. It is not hard to check that these points A and B are the only points where the two circles intersect.

The Two-Circle Theorem should have been stated as a postulate in Euclid's *Elements*, but the necessity of this was overlooked.

**Classroom Notes**

We suggest that you establish, for your students, some rules of procedure for writing up construction problems, such as the following.

Step 1. Draw segments and angles to serve as the given segments and angles.

**CONSTRUCTION 5.** To divide a segment into a given number of congruent segments.

Given $\overline{AB}$, we want to divide $\overline{AB}$ into $n$ congruent segments. (The figure shows the case $n = 5$.)

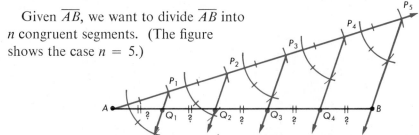

STEP 1. Starting at A, draw any ray at all which does not lie on $\overleftrightarrow{AB}$.

STEP 2. On this ray, lay off $n$ congruent segments $\overline{AP_1}$, $\overline{P_1P_2}$, ..., $\overline{P_{n-1}P_n}$ end to end. (The length of these segments does not matter, so long as they have the same length. We can therefore choose $P_1$ at random and lay off the rest of the segments with the compass, one at a time.)

STEP 3. Draw $\overline{P_nB}$.

STEP 4. Through the other points $P_1$, $P_2$, ..., $P_{n-1}$, draw rays parallel to $\overleftrightarrow{P_nB}$, intersecting $\overline{AB}$ in the points $Q_1$, $Q_2$, ..., $Q_{n-1}$.

Since our parallel lines intercept congruent segments on the transversal $\overleftrightarrow{AP_n}$, they also intercept congruent segments on the transversal $\overleftrightarrow{AB}$. (This is Corollary 9–30.1.) Therefore the points $Q_1$, $Q_2$, ..., $Q_{n-1}$ divide $\overline{AB}$ into $n$ congruent segments end to end.

**CONSTRUCTION 6.** To construct the perpendicular bisector of a given segment.

Given $\overline{AB}$.

STEP 1. Draw the circle with center at A and radius $r = AB$.

STEP 2. Draw the circle with center at B and radius $r = AB$.

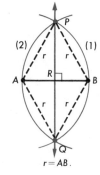

The Two-Circle Theorem now applies, because each of the numbers $r$, $r$, and $r$ is less than the sum of the other two. Therefore the circles intersect in two points P and Q.

STEP 3. Draw $\overleftrightarrow{PQ}$.

Since P is equidistant from A and B, P lies on the perpendicular bisector of $\overline{AB}$. For the same reason, Q lies on the perpendicular bisector. But two points determine a line. Therefore $\overleftrightarrow{PQ}$ is the perpendicular bisector of $\overline{AB}$.

Of course, there was no need to use circles of radius $r = AB$. Any larger radius would have worked as well. In fact, any radius greater than $\frac{1}{2}AB$ would have worked. (Reasons?)

Obviously, if we can construct the perpendicular bisecting line of a segment, we can construct the bisecting point. (This is the point $R$ in the preceding figure.) We note this as a sort of "corollary construction."

**CONSTRUCTION 7.** To construct the midpoint of a given segment.

The perpendicular bisector automatically gives us the midpoint.

**CONSTRUCTION 8.** To construct a perpendicular to a given line through a given point.

*Case 1.* Given a line $L$ and a point $P$. Suppose first that $P$ is an external point. Let $Q$ be any point of $L$.

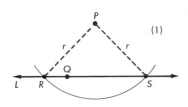
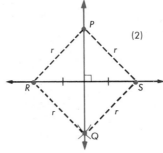

STEP 1. Draw a circle with center $P$ and radius $r > PQ$. Since $Q$ lies in the interior of the circle, it follows by Theorem 14–9 that $L$ intersects the circle in two points $R$ and $S$.

STEP 2. Construct the perpendicular bisector of $\overline{RS}$. This line passes through $P$, because $P$ is equidistant from $R$ and $S$.

Note that to draw the perpendicular bisector, we don't need to go through *all* of Construction 6; we only need to draw enough of each of our two circles to get an intersection point $Q$ different from $P$.

Therefore $\overleftrightarrow{PQ}$ must be the perpendicular bisector, because it contains two points which are equidistant from $R$ and $S$.

*Case 2.* If the point $P$ lies on the line $L$, the construction is easier.

STEP 1. Draw any circle with center at $P$, intersecting $L$ in points $R$ and $S$.

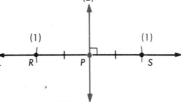

STEP 2. Draw the perpendicular bisector of $\overline{RS}$.

This bisector is the required line.

Step 2. Sketch the figure as it will look when completed and indicate the given parts.

Step 3. Analyze the figure and try to discover a sequence of elementary constructions by which the figure can be constructed. Construct the figure, and state, in order, the steps used.

The important part of a construction problem lies in discovering a sequence of steps by which the figure can be constructed. You should insist that the student write out these steps, because otherwise you will be faced with the impossible task of deciphering his completed figure. In writing out the steps, the student should, however, be allowed some liberty, especially in the use of metric terminology. After constructing the figure, he should reflect on two questions: (1) Can the figure always be constructed or must some restrictions be placed on the given parts? (2) Does there remain anything to be proved before we can conclude that the construction actually yields a figure with all the prescribed properties? The authors do not believe that it is necessary to insist on a detailed proof that the construction "works"; but probably some teachers would not agree.

**Quiz**

**1.** With straightedge and compass only, divide a given segment into six congruent segments.

   (ans: Given the segment $\overline{AB}$, draw any ray $\overrightarrow{AP}$ which does not lie on $\overleftrightarrow{AB}$. On this ray lay off seven congruent segments $\overline{AP_1}$, $\overline{P_1P_2}$, $\overline{P_2P_3}$, ..., $\overline{P_6P_7}$ end to end. Draw $\overline{P_7B}$. Through the other points $P_1$, $P_2$, $P_3$, ..., $P_6$, draw rays parallel to $\overline{P_7B}$, intersecting $\overline{AB}$ in the points $Q_1$, $Q_2$, $Q_3$, ..., $Q_6$. These points divide $\overline{AB}$ into seven congruent segments end to end.)

**2.** With straightedge and compass only, construct a segment of length $\sqrt{7}$ times the length of a given segment.

(ans: Given the segment $\overline{AB}$. On a line, mark off $\overline{AC}$ so $AC = 7AB$, and $\overline{CD}$, so $CD = AB$. Draw a semicircle with $\overline{AD}$ as diameter and construct a line perpendicular to $\overline{AD}$ at C. This perpendicular intersects the semicircle at E. Then, $CE = \sqrt{7}\, AB$.)

## Explanation for Problems

In Problem Sets 15–8 and 15–9, we have sometimes found it convenient to use the terminology of measurement and length in discussing construction problems. There is nothing wrong in this, because all our geometry has been described in such terms. It is important, however, to emphasize to your classes that these are *straightedge* and compass constructions, not *ruler* and compass constructions. We may use lengths in stating a constructions problem, and in showing that our construction works, but we cannot use measurement to carry out the construction.

In the answers below, only the key steps of the constructions are given. See the Solution Section for figures, complete details, and some of the more difficult proofs that various constructions work.

### Answers to Problems

**3.** On one ray of the given angle $\angle RAS$, construct a segment $\overline{AB}$ of the given length. Construct the line parallel to the other side of $\angle RAS$, through B. Construct the circle with center at A, with radius equal to the length of the given diagonal. The circle and the parallel intersect at the opposite vertex.

**6.** Construct a line L perpendicular to the given altitude $\overline{PF}$ at F. At P, construct two 30° angles, on either side of $\overrightarrow{PF}$. The sloping sides of these angles intersect L at the other two vertices of the desired equilateral triangle $\triangle ABP$.

**11.** Construct collinear points R, S, and T, with R-S-T, $RS = a$, and $ST = b$. Construct a semicircle with $\overline{RT}$ as diameter.

---

**Problem Set 15–8** See Solution Section for complete solution of more difficult constructions.

(*Note:* The problems of this set should be done with straightedge and compass.)

1. Construct an isosceles right triangle. Construct rt. angle $\angle BAC$ and locate P on $\overline{AB}$, Q on $\overline{AC}$ such that $AP = AQ$.
2. Construct a rhombus, given the lengths of its diagonals. Construct diagonals ⊥ at their midpoints.
3. Construct a parallelogram, given one of its angles, the length of a shorter side, and the length of the longer diagonal.

4. Construct the following angles.
   (a) 60° Construct equilateral triangle (b) 30° Bisect 60° (c) 75° Use fact 75° = 45+30 =60+15 =90−15 (d) 15° Bisect 30°

5. Construct an isosceles triangle, given the base and the altitude to the base. Use ⊥ bisector of base. Measure altitude on ⊥ bisector.
6. Construct an equilateral triangle, given its altitude.

7. Given the vertex angle of an isosceles triangle, construct a base angle. Bisect vertex angle and construct complement of that angle.
8. Construct an isosceles triangle, given a base angle and the altitude to the base. Construct angle and line parallel to one ray at a distance of the altitude. Intersection with other ray will be vertex of triangle.
9. Trisect a given segment. Apply construction 5.

10. Given a segment of length $a$, construct a segment of length
    (a) $a\sqrt{2}$. hypotenuse of 45-45-90 △ (b) $a\sqrt{3}$. long leg of 30-60-90 △ (c) $a\sqrt{6}$. Use lengths 2a and 3a in procedure for Prob
11. Given two segments of lengths $a$ and $b$, construct a segment whose length is the geometric mean of $a$ and $b$. [*Hint:* See Problem 16 of Problem Set 14–5.] See Theorem 12-9.

12. Construct a right triangle, given one acute angle and
    (a) the length of the hypotenuse.
    (b) the altitude upon the hypotenuse.

13. Construct a triangle, given the lengths of two sides and the length of the median to the longer side. See Solution Section for further explanation.
14. Construct a parallelogram, given one angle, one side, and the altitude to that side. Construct parallel to one ray of angle at a distance of the altitude. Parallel intersects other ray. Mark off length of given side from vertex and from point of intersection.

15. Construct two circles internally tangent, given the radius of each circle.

16. Construct a circle tangent to both sides of an angle, given the angle and the radius of the circle.

17. Given the radius, construct three congruent circles each tangent to the other two.

18. Construct an equilateral triangle, given a segment whose length equals the perimeter of the triangle. Trisect given segment x. Construct equilateral triangle with side x/3.

**19.** Construct a tangent to a circle from a point in the exterior of the circle. [*Hint:* Use Corollary 14–16.1.]

**20.** Construct an isosceles trapezoid, given the bases and a diagonal. *An isosceles trapezoid is symmetric with respect to the perpendicular bisector of bases. See Solution Section for further explanation.*

**21.** Construct an isosceles triangle, given the base and the altitude to one of the congruent sides. [*Hint:* Problem 19 should help.]

**22.** Construct a right triangle, given one acute angle and a segment whose length is the sum of the lengths of the legs. [*Hint:* How can you use a 45° angle?]

**23.** Given two points, *A* and *B*, of a line *L*. At *A*, a circle, *C*, is tangent to *L*. Construct a circle tangent to *L* at *B* and also tangent to *C*. [*Hint:* Analyze the diagram in which *Q* is the center of the required circle.]

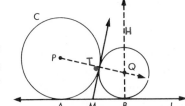

**24.** Construct a triangle, given the lengths of two sides and the length of the median to the third side.

**25.** Given a segment $\overline{AB}$ and an angle $\angle C$. Construct the set of all points *P* in a plane such that $\angle APB \cong \angle C$.

*Angle intercepts arc of twice m∠C. See Solution Section for construction of circles.*

## 15–9   INSCRIBED AND CIRCUMSCRIBED CIRCLES

In the figure, the circle $C_1$ is *inscribed in* $\triangle ABC$, and the circle $C_2$ is *circumscribed about* $\triangle ABC$.

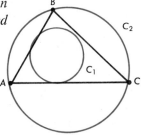

### Definitions

If a circle is tangent to all three sides of a triangle, then we say that the circle is *inscribed in* the triangle, and that the triangle is *circumscribed about* the circle. If a circle contains all three of the vertices of a triangle, then we say that the circle is *circumscribed about* the triangle, and that the triangle is *inscribed in* the circle.

It is a fact that every triangle is circumscribed about one circle and inscribed in another. One way to see, roughly, why this is true is to

---

Construct the perpendicular to $\overline{RT}$ intersecting $\overline{RT}$ at *S* and the semicircle at *P*. Then $\overline{SP}$ has the required length.

**12.** (a) On one side of the acute angle $\angle A$, construct a segment $\overline{AB}$ congruent to the hypotenuse. Drop a perpendicular to the other side of $\angle A$, ending at *C*. This gives $\triangle ABC$, with a right angle at *C*.

(b) Let *h* be the given altitude. Construct the line *L*, parallel to one side of the angle, at a distance *h*, and intersecting the other side at a point *C*. Now construct the perpendicular to $\overleftrightarrow{AC}$ at *C*. This intersects the other side of $\angle A$ at a point *B*.

**13.** From the midpoint of the longer side, construct a circle with radius equal to the median. At one end of the longer side, construct a circle with radius equal to the length of the other side. These intersect at the third vertex of the triangle.

**15.** On the first radius $\overline{AB}$ construct a segment $\overline{BC}$ congruent to the second radius. Use *A* as the center of the first circle and *C* as the center of the second.

**16.** Construct the bisector $\overrightarrow{AP}$ of the given $\angle ABC$. Construct the line *L* parallel to one side of $\angle ABC$, at a distance equal to the given radius, and intersecting the bisector at a point *E*. Construct the perpendicular from *E* to either side of $\angle ABC$, ending at *G*, and construct the circle with center at *E*, containing *G*.

**17.** Construct an equilateral triangle with sides of length 2*r*. Use the vertices as centers for the three circles of radius *r*.

**19.** Given the circle *O*, with center *C*, and the point *P*. Construct a circle *O′*, with $\overline{PC}$ as diameter, intersecting *O* at *T* and *S*. $\overleftrightarrow{QT}$ and $\overleftrightarrow{QS}$ are tangents.

**20.** Given $b_1$ and $b_2$ ($b_1 > b_2$) as the lengths of the bases, and *d* as the length of a diagonal. Construct $\overline{AB}$ of length $b_1$. Construct $\overline{AE}$ on $\overline{AB}$, of length $(b_1 - b_2)/2$. Construct the perpendicular, *L*, to $\overline{AB}$ at *E*. Construct the circle with center at *B* and radius *d*. This will intersect *L* at two points, either of which will do as a third vertex of the trapezoid. Construct the fourth vertex similarly.

**21.** Given the altitude $\overline{CD}$, construct the perpendicular line *L* at *D*. Construct the circle with center at *C* and radius equal to the base. This intersects $L$ in two points. Let $A$ be one of these. We now have one base angle, $\angle A$. Copy this angle at $B$ to get the third side.

**22.** Given $\angle A$, and the sum $a + b$ of the lengths of the legs. On one side of $\angle A$ construct $\overline{AD}$, of length $a + b$. Construct a 45° angle at $D$, intersecting the other side of $\angle A$ at $B$. Construct a perpendicular from $B$ to a point $C$ of $\overline{AD}$. Now we have $\triangle ABC$.

**23.** Construct the tangent to $C$ from $M$, the midpoint of $\overline{AB}$. Construct the perpendicular $\overrightarrow{BH}$. The intersection of $\overrightarrow{PT}$ and $\overrightarrow{BH}$ is the center of the required circle with radius $QB$.

**24.** Given: Segments of length $b$, $c$, and $m_a$.
  (1) Construct $\triangle ACR$ with $AC = b$, $CR = c$ and $AR = 2m_a$.
  (2) Locate the midpoint $M$ of $\overline{AR}$.
  (3) On $CM$ locate a point $B$ such that $MB = MC$.

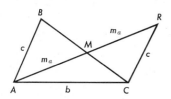

Then $\triangle ABC$ is the required triangle. Since $\triangle AMB \cong \triangle RMC$ by SAS, $AB = CR = c$.

**Quiz**

Match the names on the left below with the descriptions on the right:
  (i) incenter    (a) concurrency of medians
  (ii) centroid    (b) concurrency of perpendicular bisectors
  (iii) orthocenter    (c) concurrency of altitudes
  (iv) circumcenter    (d) concurrency of angle bisectors
  (ans: i, d; ii, a; iii, c; iv, b)

think of a little circle in the interior of a triangle, gradually swelling up. At the stage where it can't swell up any more, it must be inscribed. Similarly, think of an adjustable steel hoop, gradually closing in on the triangle from the outside. At the stage where it can't close in any further, it must be circumscribed.

We shall now prove not only that the inscribed and circumscribed circles exist, but also that they can be drawn with straightedge and compass.

CONSTRUCTION 9. To circumscribe a circle about a given triangle.

Given $\triangle ABC$.

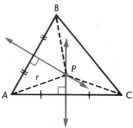

STEP 1. Construct the perpendicular bisectors of $\overline{AB}$ and $\overline{AC}$. These lines intersect in a point $P$. By Theorem 15–1, $P$ is equidistant from $A$, $B$, and $C$.

STEP 2. Draw the circle with center at $P$ and radius $r = PA$. Since $PB = PC = PA = r$, the circle contains not only $A$ but also $B$ and $C$.

**Definition**

The point of concurrency of the perpendicular bisectors of the sides of a triangle is called the *circumcenter* of the triangle.

We can also draw the inscribed circle.

CONSTRUCTION 10. To inscribe a circle in a given triangle.

Given $\triangle ABC$.

STEP 1. Bisect $\angle A$.

STEP 2. Bisect $\angle B$.

By Theorem 15–4, these bisectors meet in a point which is equidistant from all three sides of the triangle.

STEP 3. Drop a perpendicular from $P$ to $\overline{AC}$. Let $D$ be the foot of the perpendicular.

STEP 4. Draw the circle with center $P$ and radius $r = PD$.

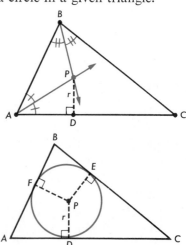

Now the circle is tangent to $\overleftrightarrow{AC}$ at $D$ because $\overleftrightarrow{AC}$ is perpendicular to the radius $\overline{PD}$. For the same reason, the circle is also tangent to the other two sides. We have therefore constructed the required circle.

### Definition

The point of concurrency of the angle bisectors of a triangle is called the *incenter* of the triangle.

### Problem Set 15-9

(*Note:* The problems of this set should be done with straightedge and compass.)

1. Construct an equilateral triangle. Then construct its circumscribed circle and its inscribed circle. Intersection of medians is center of both circles.
2. Construct an isosceles right triangle. Then construct its inscribed circle. Median to hypotenuse and one angle bisector intersect at center of circle.
3. Given any scalene triangle, construct its circumscribed circle. Center is intersection of perpendicular bisectors of the sides.
4. Given any scalene triangle, construct its inscribed circle. Construct angle bisectors, perpendicular to side from intersection point is radius.
5. Circumscribe a circle about a given square.

6. Given a rhombus, construct its inscribed circle. Construct diagonals. Intersection is center of inscribed circle.
7. Answer the following question by doing the construction. Then prove your answer.

   How many chords will fit end to end in a circle if each chord is congruent to a radius of the circle? Six equilateral triangles formed by the radii to end points of the chords.
8. Construct a right triangle, given one acute angle and the radius of the circumscribed circle.

9. Construct an isosceles triangle, given the base and the radius of the inscribed circle.

10. Construct an isosceles right triangle, given the radius of the circumscribed circle.

---

11. Construct an equilateral triangle, given the radius of the inscribed circle.

12. Construct a right triangle, given a leg and the radius of the inscribed circle.

13. Construct an isosceles triangle, given the vertex angle and the radius of the inscribed circle.
   See Solution Section for further explanation.
14. Prove that the perimeter of a right triangle equals the sum of the diameter of its inscribed circle and twice the diameter of its circumscribed circle.

### Answers to Problems

8. Construct a semicircle using the given distance as radius. Construct the given angle at one end of the diameter. The intersection of the ray and the semicircle is the vertex of the right angle. (Corollary 14-16.1)
9. Construct the perpendicular bisector of $\overline{AB}$, the base, at a point $M$. Construct a circle with center $P$ on the bisector and radius $PM$ equal to the given radius. Construct the tangents to the circle from $A$ and $B$. Their intersection is the third vertex. ( Alternatively: Construct the tangent from $A$ to circle. The intersection with $\overrightarrow{MP}$ is the third vertex.)
10. From the midpoint of a segment of twice the given length, construct a semicircle with the given radius, and then the perpendicular bisector of the segment. The intersection will be the vertex of the right angle.
11. Construct three radii of a circle with the given radius, such that each segment forms an angle of 120° with each of the others. Construct the tangents at the end points of the radii. The intersection points of these tangents are the vertices of the required equilateral triangle.
12. Construct a circle with the given radius, tangent to both the sides of a right angle $\angle ABC$. Construct $D$ on $\overrightarrow{BC}$ such that $BD$ is the given distance. From $D$, construct the other tangent $L$ to the circle. $L$ intersects $\overrightarrow{BA}$ at the third vertex of the desired triangle.
13. Construct the bisector $\overrightarrow{AY}$ of the given angle $\angle A$. Construct a line $L$, parallel to one side of $\angle A$, at a distance equal to the given radius, and intersecting $\overrightarrow{AY}$ at $P$. $P$ is the center of the inscribed circle $C$. $C$ intersects $\overrightarrow{AY}$ in two points. Let $R$ be the intersection point farthest from $A$. Construct the tangent to $C$ at $R$. This tangent intersects the sides of $\angle A$ in the other two vertices of the triangle.

**14.** Let the lengths of the sides of the right triangle be $a$, $b$, and $c$; and let the diameters of the inscribed and circumscribed circles be $d_1$ and $d_2$ respectively. Using the Area Addition Postulate and algebra, we find $d_1 = \dfrac{2ab}{a+b+c}$. Since $d_2 = c$,

$$d_1 + 2d_2$$

$$= \frac{2ab}{a+b+c} + 2c$$

$$= \frac{2ab + 2bc + 2ac + 2c^2}{a+b+c}$$

$$= \frac{2ab + 2ac + 2bc + a^2 + b^2 + c^2}{a+b+c}$$

$$= \frac{(a+b+c)^2}{a+b+c} = a+b+c$$

Q.E.D.

## 15–10 THE IMPOSSIBLE CONSTRUCTION PROBLEMS OF ANTIQUITY

**Classroom Notes**

Impossible problems always seem to stimulate the imaginations of students and you will probably receive many "proofs" of at least the angle trisection problem from now until the end of the school year.

Of course the proofs of the impossibility of these problems are far beyond the scope of an elementary course. The proofs involve ideas which are remote from elementary geometry; and this is why they remained undiscovered for over two thousand years. For a full exposition of them, see Chapter 19 of *EGAS*.

## 15–10 THE IMPOSSIBLE CONSTRUCTION PROBLEMS OF ANTIQUITY

The ancient Greeks discovered all the constructions you have studied so far, together with many others which are more difficult. There were some problems, however, that the best Greek mathematicians worked on for years without success.

To get an idea of how hard a construction problem can be, consider the problem of dividing a circle into 17 congruent arcs, end to end, with straightedge and compass.

When you draw in the corresponding chords, you get a figure called a *regular polygon of 17 sides*, or, briefly, a *regular 17-gon*. This problem was well known, but remained unsolved, for over two thousand years. Finally the required construction was discovered, in the last century, by K. G. Gauss.

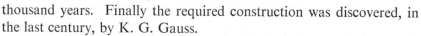

But some of the ancient Greek problems turned out to be harder than very hard: they were actually impossible.

**(1) THE ANGLE TRISECTION PROBLEM**
Given any angle $\angle BAC$, we want to construct rays $\overrightarrow{AD}$ and $\overrightarrow{AE}$ (with $D$ and $E$ in the interior of $\angle BAC$) so that

$$\angle BAD \cong \angle DAE \cong \angle EAC.$$

In this construction we are to use only a straightedge and a compass.

The first thing that most people try is to take $AB = AC$, draw $\overline{BC}$, and then trisect $\overline{BC}$, as shown on the right. This doesn't work; $\angle BAD$ and $\angle EAC$ can be shown to be congruent, but neither of these angles is congruent to $\angle DAE$. In fact, nobody has ever found a method that works, because this construction has been proved to be impossible. The proof is very difficult and will not be included here.

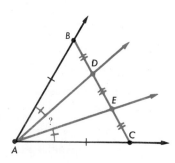

**(2) THE DUPLICATION OF THE CUBE.** A cube of edge $a$ has volume $a^3$. Given a segment of length $a$, we want to construct a segment of length $b$, such that a cube of edge $b$ has twice the volume of a cube of edge $a$. Algebraically, of course, this means that

$$b^3 = 2a^3, \quad \text{or} \quad b = a\sqrt[3]{2}.$$

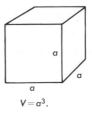

$V = a^3.$

Nobody had any luck with this problem either. There is a curious myth in connection with it. The story goes that the people of a certain Greek town were dying in large numbers from a plague, so they consulted the oracle at Delphi to find out which god was angry and why. The oracle told them that the angry god was Apollo. The altar to Apollo, in the town, was a cube of solid gold. Apollo wanted his altar to be twice as big.

When the people got home from Delphi, they made a new altar, with edges twice as long as the edges of the old one. The plague then got worse instead of better, and the people realized that Apollo must have been thinking about the *volume* of his altar. (Of course, when the edge was doubled, the volume was multiplied by eight instead of two.) This raised the problem of the duplication of the cube, but the local mathematicians were unable to solve it. Thus the first attempt to apply mathematics to the problems of public health was a total failure.

(3) SQUARING THE CIRCLE.       Given a circle, we want to construct a square which has the same area.

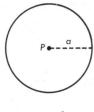

$A = \pi a^2.$

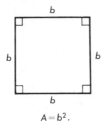

$A = b^2.$

Algebraically, this means that $b = a\sqrt{\pi}$.

For over two thousand years, the best mathematicians tried to find ways to carry out these three constructions with straightedge and compass. Finally it was discovered in modern times that all three problems were *impossible*.

*Impossibility* in mathematics does not mean the same thing as "impossibility" in everyday life, and so it calls for some explanation.

Frequently, when we say that something is impossible, we merely mean that it is very difficult, like finding a needle in a haystack. Often we mean that we don't *see* how to do it, and doubt that it can be done. Thus people used to say that flying machines were impossible, and people went right on saying this until somebody built an airplane and flew in it.

Mathematical impossibility is not like this. In mathematics, there are some things that really can't be done, and it is possible to *prove* that they can't be done.

No matter how clever you are, you can't find a whole number between 2 and 3, because there isn't any such number.

Starting with a segment $\overline{AB}$, we find that there are certain segments that we can construct, and other segments that are impossible to construct, with straightedge and compass. For example, there are constructible segments of lengths $2AB$, $\frac{1}{2}AB$, $\sqrt{2}AB$, and $\frac{1}{10}AB$. But there is no constructible segment $\overline{CD}$ for which

$$CD^3 = 2AB^3.$$

This is what we mean when we say that the duplication of the cube with straightedge and compass is impossible.

The angle-trisection problem deserves some further discussion.

(1) *Some* angles can easily be trisected with straightedge and compass. For example, a right angle can be so trisected. And this means that trisection is possible for 45° angles, $22\frac{1}{2}°$ angles, and many others. When we say that the angle-trisection problem is impossible, we mean that there are *some* angles for which the trisecting rays cannot be constructed.

(2) The angle-trisection problem becomes solvable if we relax the rules very slightly by allowing ourselves to make two marks on the straightedge.

Given $\angle B$, and a straightedge with two marks on it. Let $r$ be the distance between the two marks. We first draw a circle with center at $B$ and radius $r$. This intersects our angle in two points $A$ and $C$.

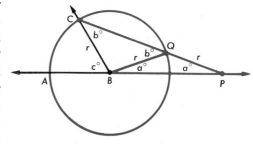

We now lay down the straightedge so that (a) it passes through $C$. We then slide and rotate it in such a way that (b) one of the marks falls on a point $Q$ of the circle, and (c) the other mark falls on a point $P$ of the ray opposite to $\overrightarrow{BA}$.

We then have the situation shown in the figure. Since $\triangle QBP$ is isosceles with $QB = QP = r$, its base angles have the same measure $a$, as indicated; and similarly for $\triangle BCQ$.

Now the measure of an exterior angle of a triangle is the sum of the measures of the remote interior angles. Applying this theorem to $\triangle QBP$, we get $b = a + a = 2a$. Applying the same theorem to $\triangle BCP$,

we get $c = b + a$. Therefore $c = 3a$. That is, $m\angle P = \frac{1}{3}m\angle ABC$.
We now copy $\angle P$ twice in the interior of $\angle ABC$:

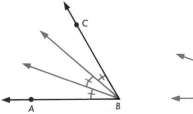 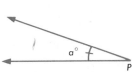

We have now trisected $\angle ABC$.

Of course, this procedure is not allowed by the old Greek rules for constructions with straightedge and compass.

## Problem Set 15–10

1. (a) What is the number such that the sum of 5 and the number equals 5 times the number? Prove your answer. $x+5 = 5x$, $x = \frac{4}{5}$

 (b) What is the number such that 4 times the number divided by the number equals 5? Prove your answer. $\frac{4x}{x} = 5$. There is no solution.

2. Explain how to trisect a 135° angle with straightedge and compass.

3. Prove that it is impossible to construct a triangle two of whose sides are 2 cm and 3 cm long, such that the altitude to the third side is 4 cm.

4. Given a square $\square ABCD$. $M$ and $N$ are the midpoints of $\overline{DC}$ and $\overline{BC}$, respectively. $\overline{AM}$ and $\overline{AN}$ intersect $\overline{BD}$ at $R$ and $S$. Prove that $\overline{AM}$ and $\overline{AN}$ trisect $\overline{BD}$ but do *not* trisect $\angle DAB$.

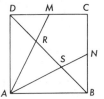

5. A carpenter is able to trisect any angle by using an instrument, called a *carpenter's square*, shown in the figure at the right. All the angles are right angles and $EF = CD = \frac{1}{2}AB$. To trisect an angle $\angle PRQ$ with the carpenter's square, the carpenter first uses the longest edge to draw a ray $\overrightarrow{ST}$ parallel to $\overrightarrow{RP}$ at distance $EF$. Then placing the carpenter's square so that $\overline{DE}$ contains $R$, $A$ is on $\overrightarrow{ST}$, and $B$ is on $\overrightarrow{RQ}$, the carpenter knows that $\overrightarrow{RD}$ and $\overrightarrow{RA}$ trisect $\angle PRQ$. Prove that this is so.

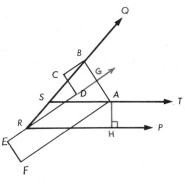

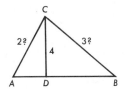

**4.** The set of all points in $E$ which are $d$ units from the given line is the union of two lines each parallel to the given line and $d$ units from the given line. The set of all points in $E$ which are $r$ units from the given point is a circle with the given point as center and the distance $r$ as radius. The intersection of these two sets, the two parallel lines and the circle, is either (1) the empty set, (2) one point, (3) two points, (4) three points, or (5) four points.

**5.** The set of all points which are at a given distance $r$ from a given point $Q$ is a circle $C(P, r)$. The set of all points which are equidistant from $P$ and $Q$ is the perpendicular bisector, $L$, of $\overline{PQ}$. If $PQ < 2r$, then the midpoint $M$ of $\overline{PQ}$ is in the interior of the circle $C(P, r)$, and so $L$ intersects $C$ at two points. If $PQ = 2r$, then $M$ is on $C$ and $L$ intersects $C$ at one point, $M$. If $PQ > 2r$, then $M$ is in the exterior of $C$ and $L$ does not intersect $C$.

**6.** (a) A vertical line with $x$-intercept $c = -1$
  (b) A line through the origin with a slope $m = 1$
  (c) A horizontal line with $y$-intercept $b = 2$

**9.** The construction itself is obvious. It is, however, an important fact that the orthocenter, the centroid, and the circumcenter of a triangle are all collinear and that the centroid is a point of trisection of the segment between the orthocenter and the circumcenter. (See the Solution Section for proof.)

**15.** There exists a point $P$, in the plane of trapezoid $\square ABCD$, which is equidistant from $A$, $B$, $C$, and $D$ if and only if the trapezoid is isosceles.

**16.** (1) Any point equidistant from $L_1$ and $T$ must lie on one of the two lines $G$ and $H$ which bisect the angles formed by $L_1$ and $T$.
  (2) Similarly, any point equidistant from $L_2$ and $T$ must lie on one of the two lines $J$ and $K$ which bisect the angles formed by $L_2$ and $T$.
  (3) Therefore, any point which is equidistant from $L_1$, $L_2$ and $T$ must lie on the intersection of set $A$ consisting of lines $G$ and $H$, and set $B$ consisting of lines $J$ and $K$. The intersection of

---

## CHAPTER REVIEW

**1.** Describe the set of all points in a plane which are equidistant from two given parallel lines. Line parallel to the two lines and "midway between them".

**2.** Describe the set of all points in a plane which are centers of circles tangent to a given circle at a given point of the circle. Line through center of given circle and given point excepting these two points.

**3.** Describe the set of all points in space which are at a given distance from a given point. Sphere with given point as center and given distance as radius.

**4.** Given a line and a point not on the line in plane $E$. Describe the set of all points in $E$ which are a distance $d$ from the given line and also a distance $r$ from the given point.

**5.** Describe the set of all points which are at a given distance from a given point $P$, and equidistant from $P$ and another point $Q$.

**6.** Sketch each of the following sets.

  (a) $\{(x, y) \mid x = -1\}$       (b) $\{(x, y) \mid y = x\}$
  (c) $\{(x, y) \mid y = 2\}$       (d) $\{(x, y) \mid y < x\}$ half-plane below line in part(b)

**7.** Sketch and describe with an equation the set of all points equidistant from the points $A(-5, 0)$ and $B(3, 0)$. $\{(x,y)\mid x=-1\}$, vertical line with x-intercept of -1.

**8.** Sketch and describe with an equation the set of all points at distance 3 from the graph of the equation $y = 0$. (Use of the $\pm$ sign is not allowed). $\{(x,y)\mid |y|=3\}$, two horizontal lines, one with y-intercept of 3, the other with -3.

**9.** Construct a fairly large scalene triangle. Then find by construction the orthocenter, the centroid, and the incenter of the triangle.

**10.** Construct a rhombus, given one angle and a segment whose length equals the perimeter of the rhombus. Divide given segment in 4. Measure this new distance on both rays of angle. At these end points, strike arcs with distance as radius. Intersection is 4th vertex.

**11.** Given $\triangle ABC$ with vertices $A(-4, 6)$, $B(0, -3)$, and $C(4, 6)$.

  (a) Prove that $\triangle ABC$ is isosceles.
  (b) Determine the coordinates of its centroid. (0, 3)

  y-axis is perpendicular bisector of $\overline{AC}$ and that B is on the y-axis.

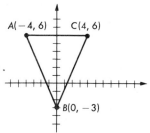

**12.** Given $\triangle PQR$ with vertices $P(-4, 7)$, $Q(8, 7)$, and $R(8, 2)$, find the coordinates of its orthocenter. Q(8,7) [$\triangle PQR$ is right triangle.]

13. Given $\triangle EFG$ with vertices $E(-2, 0)$, $F(4, 6)$, and $G(10, 0)$. [$\triangle EFG$ is isosceles rt. triangle.]

    (a) Find the coordinates of the circumcenter. $(4,0)$. Midpoint of hypotenuse

    (b) Write an equation of the circumscribed circle. $(x-4)^2 + y^2 = 36$

14. Let $A$ be the center of a circle with radius $a$, and let $B$ be the center of a circle with radius $b$, both circles lying in the same plane. If $a + b > AB$, must the circles intersect? No Why? If $a + AB < b$ or $b + AB < a$, one circle will be in the interior of the other.

15. $\square ABCD$ is a trapezoid with bases $\overline{AB}$ and $\overline{DC}$. Under what conditions will there exist a point $P$, in the plane of the trapezoid, equidistant from $A$, $B$, $C$, and $D$?

16. Given two parallel lines $L_1$ and $L_2$ and a transversal $T$. Describe the set of all points equidistant from $L_1$, $L_2$, and $T$.

---

17. Find the coordinates of the centroid of the triangle whose vertices are $A(-5, 0)$, $B(9, 0)$, and $C(5, 8)$.

18. Construct a parallelogram, given one side, one acute angle, and the longer diagonal.

19. Construct a right triangle, given one acute angle and the radius of the inscribed circle.

20. Given a segment whose length is the sum of the lengths of a diagonal and a side of a square. Construct the square.

21. Given a segment whose length is the difference of the lengths of a diagonal and a side of a square. Construct the square.

18-21. See Solution Section for further explanation.

---

sets $A$ and $B$ is the two points $X$ and $Y$, as indicated in the diagram.

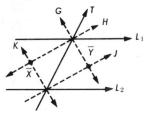

17. The midpoint of $\overline{AB}$ is $(2, 0)$. By Theorem 15–5 and 13–6 the centroid is $(2 + \frac{1}{3}(5 - 2),\ 0 + \frac{1}{3}8) = (3, \frac{8}{3})$. It is useful to know that the coordinates of the centroid of a triangle are the averages of the coordinates of the vertices. If the coordinates of the vertices are $A(x_1, y_1)$, $B(x_2, y_2)$ and $C(x_3, y_3)$, then the coordinates of the centroid are

$$G\left(\frac{x_1 + x_2 + x_3}{3},\ \frac{y_1 + y_2 + y_3}{3}\right).$$

18. Construct the side $\overline{AB}$ on one side of the given $\angle A$. Construct the line $L$, through $B$, parallel to the other side of $\angle A$. Construct the circle $O$ with center at $A$ and radius equal to the diagonal. $O$ intersects $L$ at the vertex opposite to $A$.

19. Construct the bisector of the given $\angle A$. Construct a line $L$, parallel to one side of $\angle A$, at the given distance, intersecting the bisector at $P$. $P$ is the center of the inscribed circle $C$. Construct $C$. $L$ intersects $C$ in two points. Let $H$ be the intersection point farthest from $A$. Construct the perpendicular to $L$ at $H$. This intersects the sides of $\angle A$ in two points, which are the other two vertices of the triangle.

20. Let $d$ and $a$ be the lengths of the diagonal and side. Construct $\angle A$, with measure $22\frac{1}{2}°$. Construct $\overline{AB}$, on one side of $\angle A$, so that $AB = a + d$. Construct the perpendicular to $\overline{AB}$ at $B$, intersecting the other side of $\angle A$ at $P$. Then $\overline{BP}$ is a side of the square.

21. Let $d - a$ be the given difference. Construct $\angle A$, with measure $67\frac{1}{2}°$ $(45° + 22\frac{1}{2}°)$. Construct $\overline{AB}$ on one side of $\angle A$, so that $AB = d - a$. Construct the perpendicular to $\overline{AB}$ at $B$, intersecting the other side of $\angle A$ at $P$. Then $\overline{BP}$ is a side of the square.

In this chapter we study the circumference and area of a circle, the length of a circular arc, and the area of a circular sector. The necessary treatment of limits is left at an intuitive level. We study the measurement of a circle in the familiar way by means of inscribed regular polygons, and so the chapter begins by discussing the idea of a polygon. The notion of a (simple closed) polygon was not introduced earlier because the idea of a polygonal region was the one which was needed for our development, in Chapter 11, of the area formulas.

In this chapter it was not possible to maintain the level of explicitness and rigor of the preceding portion of the text. We have not attempted to explain (1) to what sort of plane figures areas can be assigned in a reasonable fashion, (2) how area is defined for those figures for which it *can* be defined, or (3) why a circular region belongs to the class of figures that we can measure. Thus (to put it bluntly) we have not presented a theory in which the formula $A = \pi r^2$ appears as a theorem.

The reason for this is that the underlying theory is too sophisticated to be presented at this level. (For a full exposition of it, see Chapters 21 and 22 of *EGAS*.) We should bear in mind, however, that the theory of measure was not set in order, by modern standards, until the nineteenth century. It therefore seems reasonable to extract from the theory its crucial ideas, and explain these on an intuitive level. On the basis of the intuitive exposition, we believe that the student will feel that he knows, of his own knowledge, why the area formulas are correct; and we believe that in feeling this way, he will be essentially

CHAPTER 16

# Areas of Circles and Sectors

Objectives...

- Learn the definition of a polygon and the angle sum formulas.
- Develop the formula for the circumference of a circle and use it in problems.
- Develop the formula for the area of a circle and use it in problems.
- Develop and use formulas for arc length and area of sectors and segments of circles.

## 16–1 POLYGONS

A polygon is a figure formed by fitting together segments end to end. This idea is formally stated in the following definition.

### Definitions

Let $P_1, P_2, \ldots, P_n$ be a sequence of $n$ distinct points in a plane, with $n \geq 3$. Suppose that the $n$ segments $\overline{P_1 P_2}, \overline{P_2 P_3}, \ldots, \overline{P_{n-1} P_n}, \overline{P_n P_1}$ have the following properties:

(1) No two of the segments intersect except at their end points.

(2) No two segments with a common end point are collinear.

Then the union of the $n$ segments is called a *polygon*. The points $P_1, P_2, \ldots, P_n$ are called the *vertices* of the polygon, and the segments $\overline{P_1 P_2}, \overline{P_2 P_3}, \ldots, \overline{P_{n-1} P_n}, \overline{P_n P_1}$ are called its *sides*. The *angles* of the polygon are $\angle P_n P_1 P_2$, $\angle P_1 P_2 P_3$, and so on. For short, we often denote the angles by $\angle P_1$, $\angle P_2$, and so on. The sum of the lengths of the sides is called the *perimeter*. A segment whose end points are two nonconsecutive vertices of the polygon is called a *diagonal*.

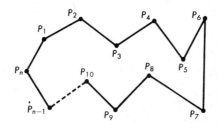

A polygon with $n$ sides is called an *n-gon*. Thus we might refer to triangles and quadrilaterals as 3-*gons* and 4-*gons*, although these terms are seldom used. Similarly, 5-gons are called *pentagons*, 6-gons are *hexagons*, 8-gons are *octagons*, and 10-gons are *decagons*. Some of the other *n*-gons (for small numbers *n*) also have special names taken from Greek, but these are not very commonly used.

right. This chapter also has a collateral purpose, that of furnishing a concrete example of a limiting process.

An often-heard "rule of pedagogy" is that within a course the standard of rigor should be uniform. It is hard to believe that the people who propose this rule have thought of what it would mean if anybody followed it. In this book, it would require that we omit the discussion of the area of a circle.

### Planning the Chapter

The average class will usually spend about two days on each section of this chapter. For the above-average class one day each on Sections 16–1 and 16–3 and two days each on the other sections should suffice.

An average class can spend the remainder of the year studying for the final examination or working on topics from Chapters 17, 18, and 19. You may wish to assign parts of these chapters without requiring that the students be responsible for the material.

## 16–1 POLYGONS

### Classroom Notes

We do not want a definition of a *polygon* to allow a polygon to cross itself. Condition (1) in the definition takes care of this, since it prevents two segments from crossing. Condition (2) is included for simplicity of treatment. For example, suppose $P_2$, $P_3$, and $P_4$ were allowed to be collinear. Then, by condition (1), $\overline{P_2 P_3}$ and $\overline{P_3 P_4}$ would be collinear segments, end to end, which means that we did not need to mention $P_3$ at all. Moreover, if we allowed superfluous vertices, every triangle would also be a 4-gon.

Polygons and polygonal regions are related ideas, but the distinction between them is important. In a plane, every polygon is the boundary of a polygonal region (although the proof is difficult), but a polygonal region does not necessarily have a polygon as its boundary. See the commentary on Section 11–1.

In this section, we have given a definition for polygons in general. In the rest of the chapter, however, we shall be dealing only with convex polygons, and in fact with regular convex polygons.

## Explanation for Problems

The familiar theorem on the sum of the measures of the angles of a convex polygon and the theorem on the sum of the measures of the exterior angles of a convex polygon are stated in Problems 8 and 13 of this problem set.

The four figures below satisfy our definition of polygon.

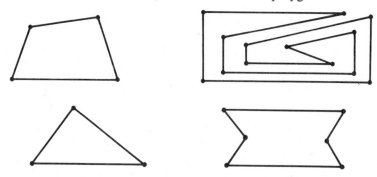

But these do not:

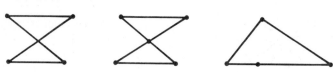

Each side of a polygon lies on a line, and each line, of course, separates the plane into two half-planes.

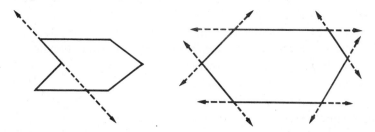

It can easily happen (as in the figure on the left) that each of these half-planes contains points of the polygon. If this does *not* happen for any side of the polygon (as in the figure on the right), then the polygon is called *convex*. We repeat this briefly as a definition.

## Definition

A polygon is *convex* if no two points of it lie on opposite sides of a line containing a side of the polygon.

This use of the term "convex" is natural: if a polygon is convex, then the polygon plus its interior forms a *convex set* in the sense defined in Chapter 3. When we speak of the area of a convex polygon we mean the area of the corresponding convex polygonal region.

**Quiz**

**1.** What is the sum of the measures of the angles of a convex polygon of 13 sides?

(ans: 1980)

**2.** The sum of the measures of the angles of a convex polygon is 4320. How many sides does it have?

(ans: 26)

## Problem Set 16-1

**1.** In this figure, no two segments intersect except at their end points, and no two segments with a common end point are collinear. Yet the figure is not a polygon. Why? *Points A,B,C,D,E are not all distinct.*

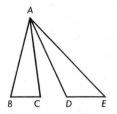

**2.** Which of the figures below are hexagons? Which are convex hexagons?

(a) *(a),(b),(d),and (g)*  (b)   (c)   (d) *(a) and (d)*

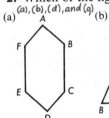   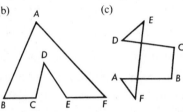   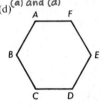

*Note that figures (c),(e) and (f) are not polygons*

(e)   (f)   (g)   (h)

   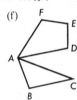      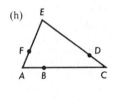

**3.** Give a precise explanation of why this figure is not a convex polygon. *Points P and Q lie on opposite sides of $\overleftrightarrow{SR}$.*

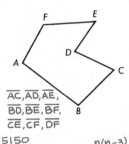

**4.** Is a polygon that has all its sides congruent and all its angles right angles necessarily a square? *No, consider the figure* ⊹.

**5.** (a) Name all the diagonals of each of the polygons shown at the right.

*$\overline{AC}, \overline{AD}, \overline{BD}, \overline{BE}, \overline{CE}$*

*$\overline{AC}, \overline{AD}, \overline{AE}, \overline{BD}, \overline{BE}, \overline{BF}, \overline{CE}, \overline{CF}, \overline{DF}$*

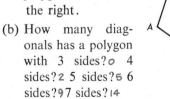   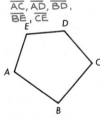

(b) How many diagonals has a polygon with 3 sides? *o* 4 sides? *2* 5 sides? *5* 6 sides? *9* 7 sides? *14*

(c) How many diagonals has a polygon with 103 sides? *5150* *n* sides? *$\frac{n(n-3)}{2}$*

**6.** In a convex polygon all the diagonals from *one* vertex are drawn. How many triangles result if the polygon has 4 sides? *2* 5 sides? *3* 6 sides? *4* 11 sides? *9* 35 sides? *33* *n* sides? *n-2*

**8.** Since the polygon is convex, its diagonals lie in the interior of each angle, so the Angle Addition Postulate can be applied to show that the sum of the measures of the angles of the polygon equals the sum of the measures of the angles of the triangles. Consider the point from which the diagonals are drawn as the vertex of each triangle and the opposite side as the base. An $n$-gon then has $n - 2$ such bases, and therefore there are $n - 2$ triangles. Since the sum of the measures of the angles of each if 180, the sum of the measures of the angles of the polygon is $(n - 2)180$.

**13.** The measure of each exterior angle is 180 minus the measure of the corresponding interior angle. Therefore the sum of the measures of the exterior angles of a convex $n$-gon is equal to $n \cdot 180$ minus the sum of the measures of the interior angles, which is equal to $n \cdot 180 - (n - 2)180 = 2 \cdot 180 = 360$.

**15.** By the definition of a convex polygon, given any side of the polygon, the entire polygon, except for that one side, lies entirely in one of the half-planes determined by that side. The intersection of all such half-planes is the *interior* of the polygon.

Alternatively:

The intersection of the interiors of all the angles of the polygon is the *interior* of the polygon.

**16.** (a) By introducing a sufficient number of segments in the interior of the polygon, we can decompose or separate the polygon and its interior into a finite number of triangular regions such that if any two of these intersect the intersection is either a segment or a point.

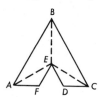

(b) The boundary of the polygonal region *ABCDEFGH* is not a polygon. It is the union of two polygons.

---

**7.** Calculate the sum of the measures of the angles of a convex pentagon; of a convex hexagon. [*Hint:* Draw all the diagonals from *one* vertex.]

**540, 720**

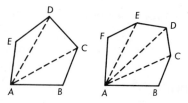

**8.** Verify the following generalization.

> The sum of the measures of the angles of a convex polygon of $n$ sides is $(n - 2)180$.

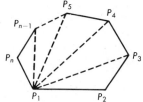

**9.** Find the sum of the measures of the angles of a convex octagon; decagon; 12-gon; 15-gon; 20-gon. **1080, 1440, 1800, 2340, 3240**

**10.** What is the number of sides of a convex polygon if the sum of the measures of its angles is 900? 1260? 1980? 2700? 4140?

**7    9    13    17    25**

**11.** Using the figure on the right, verify the statement of Problem 8.

The number of triangles with vertex Q is equal to the number of sides. The sum of the angles of all triangles is 180n. The sum of the angles at Q is 360. Sum of angles of polygon = 180n − 360 = 180(n−2)

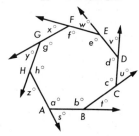

**12.** Determine the sum of the measures of the exterior angles (one at each vertex) of a convex pentagon; of a convex octagon. **360, 360**

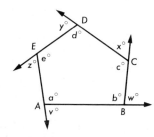

**13.** Verify the following generalization.

> The sum of the measures of the exterior angles (one at each vertex) of a convex polygon of $n$ sides is 360.

**14.** What is the sum of the measures of all the exterior angles of a convex 15-gon? If the 15-gon is equiangular, what is the measure of each exterior angle? **360, 24**

---

**15.** State a definition of the *interior* of a convex polygon. (See the definition of interior of a triangle.)

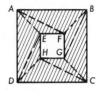

**16.** Discuss the truth or falsity of the following statements.

(a) The union of any convex polygon with its interior is a polygonal region.T

(b) The boundary of every polygonal region is a polygon.F

**17.** Given a correspondence $P_1P_2P_3 \cdots P_n \leftrightarrow Q_1Q_2Q_3 \cdots Q_n$ between two polygons. If the corresponding sides are congruent and the corresponding angles are congruent, must the two polygons be similar? No Must their perimeters be equal? Yes Must they enclose regions having equal areas? No

Support your answer with logical reasoning and/or examples.

## HONORS PROBLEM

That a polygon separates the points of the plane into two sets, called the interior and exterior of the polygon, seems a rather obvious fact. It is, however, provable from our postulates, though its proof is quite difficult. Show that this theorem is important to the solution of the following popular puzzle. Three houses, $A$, $B$, $C$, are each to be connected to three outlets, one for gas, $G$, one for water, $W$, and one for electricity, $E$.

The challenge is to draw paths, one from each house to each outlet, without letting any two paths intersect. The whole figure is to lie in a plane. See Solution Section.

     $A$      $B$      $C$

     ·      ·      ·

     $G$      $W$      $E$

     ·      ·      ·

## 16–2 REGULAR POLYGONS

### Definition

A polygon is *regular* if (1) it is convex, (2) all of its sides are congruent, and (3) all of its angles are congruent.

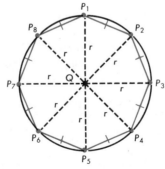

For example, an equilateral triangle is a regular 3-gon, and a square is a regular 4-gon.

We can construct regular $n$-gons with any number of sides by the following method. We begin with a circle, with center $Q$ and radius $r$. We first divide the circle into $n$ congruent arcs, end to end. Each of the arcs then has measure $360/n$. (The figure shows the case $n = 8$.) For each little arc, we draw the corresponding chord. This gives us a polygon, with vertices $P_1, P_2, \ldots, P_n$. It is easy to see that the polygon is convex. The sides are all congruent because the small arcs are.

If we draw the radii from $Q$ to the vertices, we get a set of isosceles triangles. By SSS, all these triangles are congruent. Therefore all the

---

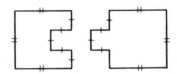

**17.** The perimeters are necessarily equal, but the two polygons are not necessarily congruent, and they do not necessarily enclose regions having equal areas.

**Answer to Honors Problem**

In a plane, it is not possible to draw paths from each outlet to each house, in such a way that the paths do not intersect. This is the simplest example of a nonplanar network. See the Solution Section for diagrams and a complete explanation.

## 16–2 REGULAR POLYGONS

### Classroom Notes

We speak of dividing a circle into $n$ congruent arcs, end to end. This is *not* supposed to be a ruler-and-compass construction; and in fact, for some integers $n$, no such construction is possible. We are merely using angular measure to draw rays, starting at the center, forming $n$ congruent angles, each of measure $360/n$. The points where these rays intersect the circle are the end points of the arcs that we wanted.

## Quiz

**1.** What is the measure of each angle of a regular seven-sided polygon?

    (ans: $128\frac{4}{7}$)

**2.** A side of a regular hexagon inscribed in a circle is 8. What is the apothem, and what is the area of the hexagonal region?

    (ans: $4\sqrt{3}$, $96\sqrt{3}$)

**3.** A quadrilateral is circumscribed about a circle whose diameter is 12. If the perimeter of the quadrilateral is 52, what is the area of the quadrilateral?

    (ans: 156)

**Answers to Problems**

**3.** A polygon is inscribed in a circle if all of its vertices lie on the circle.

---

angles of the polygon are congruent. (The measure of each angle is twice the measure of each base angle of each of the isosceles triangles.) Therefore the polygon is regular.

It is a fact that every regular polygon can be constructed by this method. That is, every regular polygon is inscribed in a circle. We shall not stop to prove this statement because we won't need it. We shall be using regular polygons only in the study of circles, and all the regular polygons we talk about will be constructed by the method we have just described.

The center $Q$ of the circle in which the polygon is inscribed is called the *center* of the polygon. Since all the small isosceles triangles in the figure above are congruent, they have the same base $e$ and the same altitude $a$. The number $a$ is the distance from the center to each of the sides.

### Definition

The distance $a$ from the center of a regular polygon to each of the sides is called the *apothem* of the polygon.

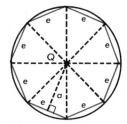

The perimeter is denoted by $p$. Obviously $p = ne$. It is easy to calculate the area of the region formed by the polygon plus its interior. Each isosceles triangle has area $\frac{1}{2}ae$. There are $n$ triangles. Therefore the area is $A_n = n \cdot \frac{1}{2}ae = \frac{1}{2}ap$.

### Problem Set 16–2

**1.** What quadrilateral, if any, is equilateral but not regular? equiangular but not regular? A rhombus, a rectangle

**2.** Sketch a polygon that has congruent sides and all right angles, but is not regular. See figure for answer to Problem 4, page 537.

**3.** Write a definition of an inscribed polygon.

**4.** Polygon $ABCDEF$ is a regular hexagon inscribed in a circle of diameter 8. $P$ is the center of the circle.

    (a) What is $m\angle FPE$? 60

    (b) How long is $\overline{FE}$? 4

    (c) What is the perimeter of the hexagon? 24

    (d) What is $m\angle ABC$? 120

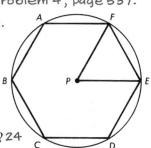

**5.** How would you construct a regular hexagon with only a compass and an unmarked straightedge? *Construct six equilateral triangles with common vertex.*

**6.** Determine the area of a regular hexagon which has a side 10 cm long.
$A = \frac{1}{2}ap = \frac{1}{2}(5\sqrt{3})(60) = 150\sqrt{3}\ cm^2$

**7.** A side of a regular hexagon inscribed in a circle is 4. Find the lengths of the radius of the circle and the apothem of the hexagon. $T=4,\ a=2\sqrt{3}$

**8.** Prove that the area of a regular hexagon of side $s$ is $\frac{3}{2}\sqrt{3}\ s^2$.

**9.** The figure represents part of a regular $n$-gon inscribed in a circle with center $Q$.

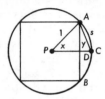

   (a) What is $m\angle P_5QP_6$? $= \frac{360}{n}$

   (b) What is $m\angle QP_5P_6 + m\angle QP_6P_5$? $180 - \left(\frac{360}{n}\right)$

   (c) Why is $\angle QP_6P_5 \cong \angle QP_5P_4$? $\triangle QP_6P_5 \cong \triangle QP_5P_4$ *by SSS.*

   (d) Why is $m\angle P_4P_5P_6 = m\angle P_4P_5Q + m\angle QP_5P_6$? *Angle Addition Postulate*

   (e) Show that $m\angle P_4P_5P_6 = 180 - \dfrac{360}{n}$.

**10.** Determine the measure of each angle of a regular polygon of 5 sides; 9 sides; 12 sides; 15 sides; 17 sides; 24 sides. (See Problem 9.) $108$
$140 \qquad 150 \qquad 156 \qquad 158\frac{14}{17} \quad 165$

**11.** How many sides has a regular polygon if the measure of an exterior angle is 72? 45? 36? 24? $17\frac{1}{7}$?
     $5 \qquad 8 \qquad 10 \qquad 15 \qquad 21$

**12.** How many sides has a regular polygon if the measure of one of its angles is $128\frac{4}{7}$? 140? 144? 160?
   $7 \qquad\quad 9 \qquad 10 \qquad 18$

**13.** The perimeter of a regular polygon is 48 and its apothem is 6. What is the area of the polygon? $A = \frac{1}{2}ap = \frac{1}{2}\cdot 6 \cdot 48 = 144$

**14.** The area of a regular polygon is 144 and its apothem is 6. What is its perimeter? Can you tell how many sides it has? $p=48$,
*It has 4,8,6,12,16, or 24 sides (any factor of 48).*

**15.** How would you construct a regular octagon with only a compass and an unmarked straightedge?

---

**16.** $\square ABCD$ is any quadrilateral having each of its sides tangent to a circle of diameter 9. If the perimeter of $\square ABCD$ is 56, what is $a\square ABCD$?
*If P is center of circle, $a\square ABCD =$ $a\triangle ABP + a\triangle BCP + a\triangle CDP + a\triangle DAP$ $= \frac{1}{2}r(AB+BC+CD+DA) = \frac{1}{2}rp = 126$.*

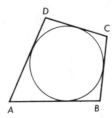

**17.** Prove that each side of a regular octagon inscribed in a circle of radius 1 has a length of $\sqrt{2 - \sqrt{2}}$.

**18.** The area of a regular octagon is $200\sqrt{2}$ and each side of the octagon is $200 - 100\sqrt{2}$. Find the apothem of the octagon. $\frac{\sqrt{2}(2+\sqrt{2})}{4} = \frac{1+\sqrt{2}}{2}$

---

**Answers to Problems**

**8.** The area of each of the triangles is $\left(\dfrac{\sqrt{3}}{4}\right)s^2$, so the area of the hexagon is

$$6 \cdot \left(\frac{\sqrt{3}}{4}\right)s^2 = \left(\frac{3\sqrt{3}}{2}\right)s^2.$$

**9.** (e) $m\angle P_4P_5P_6$
$$= m\angle P_4P_5Q + m\angle QP_5P_6$$
$$= m\angle QP_6P_5 + m\angle QP_5P_6$$
$$= 180 - \frac{360}{n}.$$

**15.** Construct two perpendicular lines at a point $P$. Then construct the bisectors of the angles formed by these lines. Then locate on each of the eight rays points which are equidistant from $P$. The figure formed by joining these points in sequence is a regular octagon.

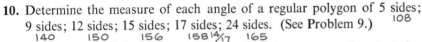

**17.** The length of each side of an inscribed square is obviously equal to $\sqrt{2}$. Therefore $AD = \sqrt{2}/2$. Let $FD = x$, $DC = y$, and $AC = s$. Since $\triangle APD$ is a right triangle,

$$x = \sqrt{1^2 - \left(\frac{\sqrt{2}}{2}\right)^2} = \sqrt{\frac{1}{2}} = \frac{\sqrt{2}}{2}.$$

Therefore $y = 1 - x = 1 - \sqrt{2}/2$. Then since $\triangle ACD$ is a right triangle, $s^2 = AD^2 + y^2 = (\sqrt{2}/2)^2 + (1 - \sqrt{2}/2)^2 = 2 - \sqrt{2}$, so that $s = \sqrt{2 - \sqrt{2}}$.

## 16–3 THE CIRCUMFERENCE OF A CIRCLE. THE NUMBER $\pi$

### Classroom Notes

The proofs of Theorem 16–1 and Theorem 16–2 in the next section make use of limit arguments. You should try to give the student an intuitive grasp of the limit concept for sequences; to go beyond this would be very hard, and would in any case take a great deal of time. (See Section 21.3, *"Limits of Sequences,"* in EGAS.)

*A suggestion:* in response to questions from a very sophisticated class, you may want to use the idea that the perimeter $p$ approaches a limit, because (1) it increases as $n$ increases and (2) it is bounded above. Both statements are true, of course, but they are much easier to verify if we use a $2^n$-gon. (This way, the number of sides doubles at each stage.) To verify (2), inscribe the circle in a square; the perimeter of the square is then an upper boundary for the perimeter $p$.

$\pi$ is defined as the ratio $C/2r$. Since $C$ is, by definition, the limit of the perimeter of a regular inscribed $n$-gon, we can assert that the ratio $p/2r \to \pi$, and we can use this fact to obtain a decimal approximation of $\pi$. You should inscribe, successively, in a circle of radius 1, a regular 4-gon, 8-gon, and 16-gon, and compute in each case the ratio $p/2r$.

### 16–3    THE CIRCUMFERENCE OF A CIRCLE. THE NUMBER $\pi$

In this section and the next one, we shall consider regular $n$-gons for various values of $n$. As usual, we denote the side, apothem, and perimeter of a regular $n$-gon inscribed in a circle of radius $r$ by $e$, $a$, and $p$.

Let $C$ be the circumference of a circle. It seems reasonable to suppose that if you want to measure $C$ approximately, you can do it by inscribing a regular polygon with a large number of sides and then measuring the perimeter of the polygon. That is, the perimeter $p$ ought to be a good approximation of $C$ when $n$ is large. In other words, once we decide how close to $C$ we want $p$ to be, we should be able to get $p$ this close to $C$ merely by making $n$ large enough. We describe this situation in symbols by writing

$$p \to C,$$

and we say that $p$ approaches $C$ as a limit.

We cannot prove this, however; and the reason why we cannot prove it is rather unexpected. The reason is that so far, we have no mathematical definition of what is meant by the circumference of a circle. (We can't get the circumference merely by adding the lengths of segments, the way we did to get the perimeter of a polygon, because a circle doesn't contain any segments, even very short ones. In fact, Corollary 14–6.1 tells us that no circle contains even *three* points which are collinear.)

But the remedy is easy: we take the statement

$$p \to C$$

as our definition of $C$.

### Definition

The *circumference* of a circle is the limit of the perimeters of the inscribed regular polygons.

We now want to define the number $\pi$, in the usual way, as the ratio of the circumference to the diameter. But to be sure that this definition makes sense, we first need to know that the ratio $C/2r$ is the same for all circles, regardless of their size. In fact, this is true.

**Theorem 16–1**

*The ratio of the circumference to the diameter is the same for all circles.*

**Proof.**  Given a circle with center $Q$ and radius $r$, and a circle with center $Q'$ and radius $r'$.  In each circle we inscribe a regular $n$-gon.

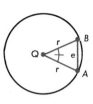
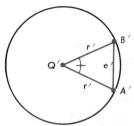

In the figure, we show only one side of each $n$-gon, with the corresponding isosceles triangle.  The two central angles are congruent, as the marks indicate, because the measure of each is $360/n$.  Also, the sides are proportional: $r'/r = r'/r$.  By the SAS Similarity Theorem,

$$\triangle BQA \sim \triangle B'Q'A'.$$

Therefore

$$\frac{e'}{r'} = \frac{e}{r}, \qquad \frac{ne'}{r'} = \frac{ne}{r}, \qquad \text{and} \qquad \frac{p'}{r'} = \frac{p}{r},$$

where $p$ and $p'$ are the perimeters of the two $n$-gons.  Now

$$p \to C \qquad \text{and} \qquad p' \to C',$$

by definition.  Therefore

$$\frac{p}{r} \to \frac{C}{r} \qquad \text{and} \qquad \frac{p'}{r'} \to \frac{C'}{r'}.$$

Since $\dfrac{p}{r}$ and $\dfrac{p'}{r'}$ are equal, their limits are the same:

$$\frac{C}{r} = \frac{C'}{r'} \qquad \text{and} \qquad \frac{C}{2r} = \frac{C'}{2r'},$$

which was to be proved.

The ratio $C/2r$ is denoted by $\pi$.  Since this is the same for all circles, the formula

$$C = 2\pi r$$

holds for all circles.

The number $\pi$ is not rational.  In fact, it cannot be calculated exactly by any of the ordinary methods of algebra.  On the other hand, it can be approximated, as closely as we please, by rational numbers. Some of the useful approximations are

$$3, \quad 3.14, \quad 3\tfrac{1}{7}, \quad 3.1416, \quad \tfrac{355}{113}, \quad 3.14159265358979.$$

It is not hard to convince yourself, by making physical measurements, that $\pi$ is a little more than 3. But to get a very close approximation requires the use of very advanced mathematics.

## Problem Set 16-3

1. A regular polygon is inscribed in a circle, then another regular polygon with one more side than the first is inscribed, and so on endlessly, each new polygon having one more side than the previous one.

   (a) What is the limit of the apothem? **Radius of the circle**

   (b) What is the limit of the length of a side? **0**

   (c) What is the limit of the measure of an angle of the polygon? **180**

   (d) What is the limit of the perimeter of the polygon? **Circumference**

2. Find the missing numbers:

   | Diameter | Radius | Circumference |
   |---|---|---|
   | 12 | **? 6** | $12\pi$ |
   | **? 16** | 8 | **? $16\pi$** |
   | 14.6 | **? 7.3** | **? $14.6\pi$** |
   | **? 36** | **? 18** | $36\pi$ |
   | $2\pi$ | **? $\pi$** | **? $2\pi^2$** |
   | **? $5\pi$** | **? $\frac{5\pi}{2}$** | $5\pi^2$ |
   | **? $2\sqrt{2}$** | $\sqrt{2}$ | **? $2\sqrt{2}\,\pi$** |

3. The diameter of a wheel is 28 cm. How far does the wheel travel with each revolution? (Which approximation of $\pi$ makes the computation easiest?)     **88 cm ($3\tfrac{1}{7}$)**

4. Which is the closer approximation to $\pi$, 3.14 or $\boxed{3\tfrac{1}{7}}$?     **$3\tfrac{1}{7} \doteq 3.142857$**

5. The circumference of a log is 62.8 cm. How long is the side of a cross section of the largest square beam that can be cut from the log? (Use 3.14 for $\pi$.) **$r = \dfrac{c}{2\pi} = 10\,cm$**
   **The side $= 10\sqrt{2}$ cm**      **10**, **$10\sqrt{2}$**, **10**

6. What is the radius of a circle whose circumference is $\pi$? **$r = \tfrac{1}{2}$**

7. A circular swimming pool 20 metres in diameter is to be enclosed by a fence in the shape of a square. The total length of the fence is to be twice the circumference of the pool. How long will the fence be along one side of the square? **$C = \pi d = 62.8$; $P = 125.6$ and $S = 31.4$ m**

8. The earth is approximately 150,000,000 km from the sun. The path of the earth around the sun is nearly circular. Calculate how far we travel each year "in orbit" with respect to the sun. What is a close estimate of our speed (in kilometres per hour) in this orbit? $c = 2\pi r = 2(3.14)(150 \times 10^6) = 9.42 \times 10^8$ km. Velocity is approximately 107 500 km/h.

9. The radius of the earth is approximately 6450 km. As the earth rotates, objects on its surface are constantly traveling at various speeds with respect to the earth's axis, depending upon the latitude of each object. What is the approximate speed, in kilometres per hour, of an object near the equator? What is the speed of an object at latitude 45°N? 1690 km/h, 1190 km/h

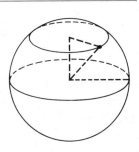

10. The side of a square is 8 cm long. Find the circumference of its inscribed circle; of its circumscribed circle. $8\pi$ cm, $8\pi\sqrt{2}$ cm

11. The length of a side of an equilateral triangle is 12. What is the circumference of its inscribed circle? of its circumscribed circle? $4\pi\sqrt{3}$, $8\pi\sqrt{3}$

12. A side of a regular hexagon is 6. What is the circumference of its circumscribed circle? of its inscribed circle? $12\pi$, $6\pi\sqrt{3}$

13. The radii of three circles are 1 m, 10 m, and 10 000 m. The radius of each circle is increased by 1 m, so that the new radii are, respectively, 2 m, 11 m, and 10 001 m. Determine the increase in the circumference of each circle, due to the increase of the radius. Increase in circumference is $2\pi$ in each case.

14. Two concentric circles each contain an inscribed square. The larger square is also circumscribed about the smaller circle. If the circumference of the larger circle is $12\pi$, what is the circumference of the smaller circle, and what is the difference of the areas of the two squares? $6\sqrt{2}\pi$, 36

## 16–4  THE AREA OF A CIRCLE

### Definition

A *circular region* is the union of a circle and its interior.

When we speak of "the area of a circle," we mean the area of the corresponding circular region. (This is the same sort of abbreviation we use when we speak of "the area of a triangle," meaning the area of the corresponding triangular region.) We shall now get a formula for the area of a circle.

## 16–4 THE AREA OF A CIRCLE

### Classroom Notes

In the proof of Theorem 16–2 it is asserted that $A_n \to A$, $a \to r$, and that $p \to C$. These facts are intuitively obvious; you can, however, make these assertions more meaningful by actually computing $A_n$, using the formula $A_n = \frac{1}{2}ap$ for $n = 3, 4, 6$.

Note that the areas $A_n$ increase and are bounded above. (See the commentary on Section 16–3.) As in the case of the perimeters, this is easiest to verify if we use a $2^n$-gon.

**1.** The circumference of a circle is $6\pi$. What is its area?

(ans: $9\pi$)

**2.** Two circles have radii of 12 and 16, respectively. What is the ratio of their areas?

(ans: 9/16)

**3.** The circumference of a circle and the perimeter of a square are each 28. Which has the greater area, the circle or the square?

(ans: the circle)

Given a circle of radius $r$, we inscribe in it a regular $n$-gon. As usual, the area of the $n$-gon is denoted by $A_n$; the perimeter is $p$ and the apothem is $a$. In Section 16–2, p. 540, we found that

$$A_n = \tfrac{1}{2}ap.$$

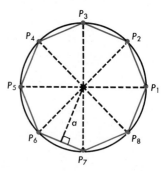

In this situation there are three quantities involved, each depending on $n$. These are $p$, $a$, and $A_n$. To get our formula for the area of a circle, we must find out what limits these quantities approach as $n$ becomes very large.

*What happens to $A_n$?* $A_n$ is always slightly less than the area $A$ of the circle, because there are always some points that lie inside the circle but outside the regular $n$-gon. However, the difference between $A_n$ and $A$ is very small when $n$ is very large, for, when $n$ is very large, the polygon almost fills up the interior of the circle. Thus, we expect that

$$A_n \to A. \tag{1}$$

But just as in the case of the circumference of the circle, this can never be proved, since we have not yet given any definition of the area of a circle. Here also, the remedy is easy:

**Definition**

The *area of a circle* is the limit of the areas of the inscribed regular polygons.

Thus, $A_n \to A$ by definition.

*What happens to $a$?* The apothem $a$ is always slightly less than $r$, because either leg of a right triangle is shorter than the hypotenuse. But the difference between $a$ and $r$ is very small when $n$ is very large. Thus

$$a \to r. \tag{2}$$

*What happens to $p$?* By definition of $C$, we have

$$p \to C. \tag{3}$$

9. The area of the circle is greater. $C = 2\pi r = 20$, so $r = \dfrac{10}{\pi}$ and the area of the circle equals $\dfrac{100}{\pi} \doteq 31.85$. But $s = \dfrac{20}{4} = 5$, so the area of the square is 25.00. The area of the circle is 6.85 greater than the area of the square.

Fitting together results (2) and (3), we get $\frac{1}{2}ap \to \frac{1}{2}rC$. Therefore, since $A_n = \frac{1}{2}ap$, we have $A_n \to \frac{1}{2}rC$. But we knew from (1) that $A_n \to A$. Therefore $A = \frac{1}{2}rC$. Since $C = 2\pi r$, this gives

$$A = \tfrac{1}{2}r \cdot 2\pi r = \pi r^2.$$

Thus the familiar formula has finally become a theorem.

**Theorem 16–2**

*The area of a circle of radius r is $\pi r^2$.*

**Problem Set 16–4**

1. Find the circumference and the area of a circle whose radius is 3; 5; $\sqrt{2}$; $\pi$. 6$\pi$, 9$\pi$; 10$\pi$, 25$\pi$; 2$\pi\sqrt{2}$, 2$\pi$; 2$\pi^2$, $\pi^3$

2. Find the circumference and the area of a circle whose diameter is 6; 9; 2; $\pi\sqrt{12}$. 6$\pi$, 9$\pi$; 9$\pi$, $\dfrac{81\pi}{4}$; 2$\pi$, $\pi$; 2$\pi^2\sqrt{3}$, 3$\pi^3$

3. What is the radius of a circle whose area is $49\pi$? $20\pi$? 25? 16? $18\pi^3$? 7   2$\sqrt{5}$   $\frac{5}{\sqrt{\pi}}$   $\frac{4}{\sqrt{\pi}}$   3$\pi\sqrt{2}$

4. What is the area of a circle whose circumference is $6\pi$? $16\pi$? 12? $2\pi$? 9$\pi$   64$\pi$   $\frac{36}{\pi}$   $\pi$

5. Compute the area of one face of an iron washer, given that its diameter is $1\frac{1}{4}$ cm and the diameter of the hole is $\frac{1}{2}$ cm. (Use $3\frac{1}{7}$ for $\pi$.) $A = \pi r_1{}^2 - \pi r_2{}^2 = \frac{33}{32}$ cm$^2 \doteq 1.031$ cm$^2$

6. Prove the following theorem.

    The ratio of the areas of two circles is equal to the square of the ratio of their radii. $\dfrac{A_1}{A_2} = \dfrac{\pi r_1{}^2}{\pi r_2{}^2} = \left(\dfrac{r_1}{r_2}\right)^2$

7. Two circles have radii of 3 and 12, respectively. What is the ratio of their areas? 1:16

8. The circumferences of two circles are 7 and $4\pi$. What is the ratio of the areas of the circles? 49 : 16$\pi^2$

9. The circumference of a circle and the perimeter of a square are each 20 cm. Which has the greater area, the circle or the square? How much greater? 6.85cm$^2$

10. Given a square with a side of length 10, find the area of the region bounded by its inscribed and circumscribed circles. 25$\pi$

**12.** Let $p$ be the perimeter of the square and the circumference of the circle. Then $A_s = s^2 = \left(\dfrac{p}{4}\right)^2 = \dfrac{p^2}{16}$. But $r = \dfrac{p}{2\pi}$, so that $A_c = \pi r^2 = \pi\left(\dfrac{p}{2\pi}\right)^2 = \dfrac{p^2}{4\pi}$.

Therefore
$$\dfrac{As}{Ac} = \dfrac{p^2/16}{p^2/4\pi} = \dfrac{4\pi}{16} = \dfrac{\pi}{4}.$$

**16.** $A = \pi \cdot PC^2 - \pi \cdot PM^2$
$= \pi[PC^2 - PM^2]$.

But by the Pythagorean Theorem, $PC^2 - PM^2 = MC^2$. Therefore $A = \pi \cdot MC^2 = \frac{1}{4}\pi \cdot BC^2$.

**17.** $\qquad AC^2 + BC^2 = AB^2.$
$$\dfrac{\pi}{8}\cdot AC^2 + \dfrac{\pi}{8}\cdot BC^2 = \dfrac{\pi}{8}\cdot AB^2.$$
$$(x + m) + (y + n) = z + m + n$$
$$x + y = z.$$

**19.**

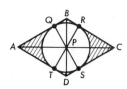

$a\square ABCD = a\triangle ABP + a\triangle BCP$
$\qquad\qquad + a\triangle CDP + a\triangle DAP.$

Since the circle is inscribed in the rhombus, $\overline{PQ} \perp \overline{AB}$, and so $a\triangle ABP = \frac{1}{2}AB \cdot PQ = \frac{1}{2}AB \cdot r$. Therefore $a\square ABCD = \frac{1}{2}r(AB + BC + CD + DA) = \frac{1}{2}rp = 20$. The area of the shaded region is the area of the rhombus minus the area of the circle. $20 - 4\pi \doteq 7.44$.

---

**11.** In the figure, the diameter of each small semicircle equals the radius of the large semicircle. If the radius of the large semicircle is 2, what is the area of the shaded region? $2\pi - 2\left(\dfrac{\pi}{2}\right) = \pi$

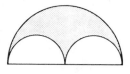

**12.** The perimeter of a square is equal to the circumference of a circle. Which has the greater area? Find the ratio of the area of the square to the area of the circle.   ↖ The circle

**13.** $\square ABCD$ is a square whose side is $s$. $X$ and $Z$ are midpoints of $\overline{AD}$ and $\overline{BC}$, respectively. Circular arc $\overarc{DY}$ and $\overarc{BY}$ have centers $X$ and $Z$, respectively. Determine the area of the shaded region. $\dfrac{s^2}{2}$

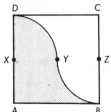

**14.** In a sphere of radius 10 cm, sections are made by planes 4 cm and 5 cm from the center. Which section will have the greater area? Compute the ratio of the areas of the two sections.
Section nearer the center.
Areas equal $84\pi$ cm² and $75\pi$ cm².
Ratio of areas is $84/75$.

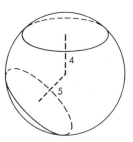

**15.** An *annulus* is a region bounded by two concentric circles. Find the area of the annulus bounded by the inscribed and circumscribed circles of an equilateral triangle with a side of length 6. $A = \pi r_1{}^2 - \pi r_2{}^2$
$= \pi[(2\sqrt{3})^2 - (\sqrt{3})^2] = 9\pi$

**16.** Given two concentric circles and a chord of the larger circle tangent to the smaller circle. Prove that the area of the annulus formed by the circles is equal to one-fourth the product of $\pi$ and the square of the length of the chord.

---

**17.** The semicircles drawn in the figure have as diameters the sides of right triangle $\triangle ABC$. $x$, $y$, $z$, $m$, and $n$ are the areas of the regions, as shown. Prove that $x + y = z$.

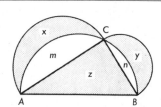

**18.** The 12-gon shown here, with 8 of its vertices on a circle, has all sides congruent, and all its angles are right angles. Given that the length of each side is 4, find the area of the part of the circular region which is outside the polygon.

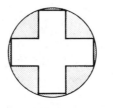

*Area of circle = 40, Area of polygon = 80, Shaded region ≐ 45.6*

**19.** A circle with circumference $4\pi$ is inscribed in a rhombus with perimeter 20. Compute the total area of the regions bounded by the circle and the rhombus. *Area of rhombus = 20, Area of circle = 4π, Area of region ≐ 7.44*

**20.** An isosceles trapezoid whose bases are 2 cm and 6 cm is circumscribed about a circle. Determine the area of that part of the trapezoid region which lies outside the circle. *Approximately 4 cm²*

**21.** A target on which an amateur can be expected to hit the bullseye as often as he can hit any of the rings is constructed in the following way. Let the distance between two parallel rays, $\overrightarrow{PM}$ and $\overrightarrow{AN}$, be $PA = r$, the radius of the bullseye. The circle with radius $r$ and center $P$ intersects $\overrightarrow{PM}$ at $Q$. Let the perpendicular to $\overrightarrow{PM}$ at $Q$ intersect $\overrightarrow{AN}$ at $B$. Then draw the circle with radius $PB = r_1$ and center $P$. This process is repeated, drawing perpendiculars at $R$ and $S$ and concentric circles with radii $PC = r_2$ and $PD = r_3$. Of course, more rings can be constructed.

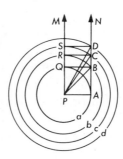

(a) Express $r_1$, $r_2$, and $r_3$ in terms of $r$.

(b) Show that the areas of the bullseye and the three rings, namely, $a$, $b$, $c$, and $d$, are equal.

## 16–5  LENGTHS OF ARCS AND AREAS OF SECTORS

To define the length of a circular arc, we use the same sort of scheme that we used to define the circumference of the whole circle. First we cut up the given arc $\widehat{AB}$ into $n$ congruent arcs, end to end. Then we draw the corresponding chords. Just as before, all the chords have the same length $e$, and the sum of their lengths is

$$p = ne.$$

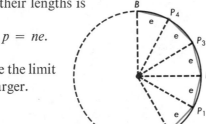

The *length* of $\widehat{AB}$ is defined to be the limit of $p$ as $n$ becomes larger and larger.

---

**Answers to Problems**

**20.** From the second figure, $4^2 - 2^2 = 12$, and so the altitude of the trapezoid is $2\sqrt{3}$. In the first figure, since the bases are parallel and tangent to the circle, we see that $\overline{FH}$ (altitude of the trapezoid) must be a diameter, so the radius is $\sqrt{3}$. Therefore the area of the circle is $3\pi$. The area of the trapezoid is $8\sqrt{3}$. The area outside the circle is $(8\sqrt{3} - 3\pi)$ cm². This is approximately 4 cm².

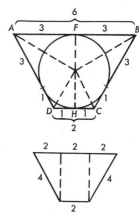

**21.** (a) (1) In the right triangle $\triangle PAB$, $PA = r$, $AB = r$, and $PB = r_1$. Therefore $r_1{}^2 = r^2 + r^2$ or $r_1 = r\sqrt{2}$.

(2) In the right triangle $\triangle PAC$, $PA = r$, $AC = PR = PB = r_1 = r\sqrt{2}$, and $PC = r_2$. Therefore, since $PC^2 = PA^2 + AC^2$, we have $r_2{}^2 = r^2 + (r\sqrt{2})^2 = 3r^2$, so $r_2 = r\sqrt{3}$.

(3) Proceeding in this way we find that $r_1 = r\sqrt{2}, r_2 = r\sqrt{3}$, $r_3 = r\sqrt{4}, \ldots$

(b) Now, using the area formula for a circle, we have
$a = \pi r^2$;
$b = \pi(r\sqrt{2})^2 - a = \pi r^2$;
$c = \pi(r\sqrt{3})^2 - (a + b)$
$\qquad = 3\pi r^2 - 2\pi r^2 = \pi r^2$;
$d = \pi(2r)^2 - (a + b + c)$
$\qquad = 4\pi r^2 - 3\pi r^2 = \pi r^2$.

## 16–5 LENGTHS OF ARCS AND AREAS OF SECTORS

### Classroom Notes

The formulas for the length of an arc and the area of a sector are easy to derive, learn, and use. Be careful to point out the distinction between arc measure and arc length.

In the following discussion, it will be convenient to consider an entire circle as an arc of measure 360. The circumference can then be regarded as the length of an arc of measure 360.

### Theorem 16–3

*If two arcs have equal radii, then their lengths are proportional to their measures.*

$$\frac{\text{length } \widehat{AB}}{m\widehat{AB}} = \frac{\text{length } \widehat{A'B'}}{m\widehat{A'B'}}.$$

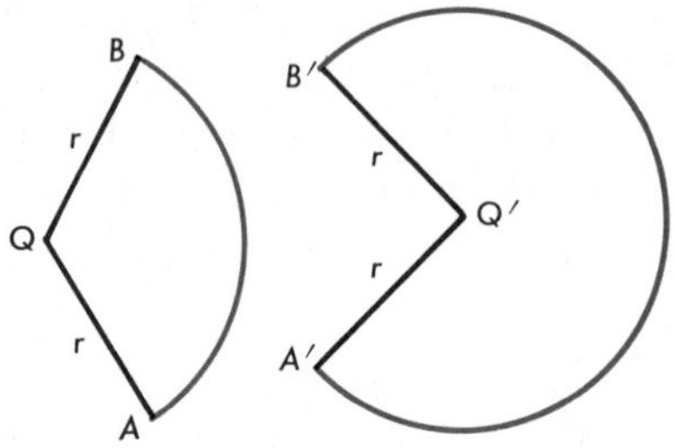

In simple cases, it is easy to see why this is true. If you double the measure of an arc, this doubles the length; if you divide the measure by 7, this divides the length by 7, and so on. But a complete proof of the theorem is too difficult for this course. We shall therefore regard the theorem as a new postulate.

On the basis of this theorem, we can calculate the lengths of arcs.

### Theorem 16–4

*If an arc has measure q and radius r, then its length is*

$$L = \frac{q}{180} \cdot \pi r.$$

**Proof.** Let $C$ be the circumference of a circle of radius $r$. By Theorem 16–3,

$$\frac{L}{q} = \frac{C}{360}.$$

But $C = 2\pi r$. Therefore

$$\frac{L}{q} = \frac{2\pi r}{360},$$

and

$$L = \frac{q}{180} \cdot \pi r.$$

A *sector* is a region like one of these:

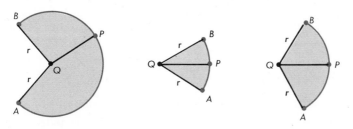

## Definitions

Let $\overset{\frown}{AB}$ be an arc of a circle with center $Q$ and radius $r$. The union of all segments $\overline{QP}$, where $P$ is any point of $\overset{\frown}{AB}$, is called a *sector*. $\overset{\frown}{AB}$ is called the *arc* of the sector, and $r$ is called its *radius*.

We define the area of a sector by the same sort of scheme that we used to define the area of a circle. Using the same type of proofs, we obtain the following theorem.

### Theorem 16–5

**The area of a sector is half the product of its radius and the length of its arc.**

Briefly, $A = \frac{1}{2}rL$. There is an easy way to remember this formula. The area of a sector in a circle of fixed radius $r$ ought to be proportional to the length of its arc. (In fact, this is true.) When the arc is the whole circle, the area is $\pi r^2 = \frac{1}{2}Cr$, where $C = 2\pi r$. Therefore, for a sector with arc length $L$ and area, $A$ we must have

$$\frac{A}{L} = \frac{\frac{1}{2}Cr}{C}, \quad \text{and} \quad A = \frac{1}{2}rL.$$

Using the formula for $L$ in Theorem 16–4, we get:

### Theorem 16–6

**If a sector has radius $r$ and its arc has measure $q$, then its area is**

$$A = \frac{q}{360} \cdot \pi r^2.$$

Note that for $q = 360$ the theorem says that $A = \pi r^2$, which is what it ought to say.

**6.** "Arc measure" means "degree measure of the arc." The degree measure of an arc equals

    (1) the measure of the corresponding central angle, if the arc is a minor arc

    (2) 180, if the arc is a semicircle

    (3) 360 minus the measure of the corresponding minor arc, if the arc is a major arc

Hence, the degree measure of an arc is a real number $r$, with $0 < r < 360$. Note that the degree measure of an arc does not depend on the radius of the arc.

    Arc length is defined as the limit of a sum. Specifically, partition the arc $\widehat{AB}$ into $n$ congruent arcs by points $A = P_0$, $P_1, P_2 \ldots, P_n, P_{n+1} = B$, and define $s_n = P_0P_1 + P_1P_2 + \cdots + P_nP_{n+1}$. Then $\widehat{L_{AB}} = \lim\limits_{n\to\infty} s_n$. For practical purposes the formula $L = \dfrac{q}{180}\pi r$, Theorem 16–4, is more useful. Note that the length of an arc is a positive real number, $L$, associated with the arc, which does depend on the radius of the arc.

**15.** The region between the circle and the octagon consists of eight circular segments whose area is easily computed. See Problem 13(a).

$$\text{Area of the sector} = (q/360)\pi r^2$$
$$= \tfrac{45}{360}\pi 6^2 = \tfrac{9}{2}\pi$$
$$\text{Area of } \triangle APB = \tfrac{1}{2}bh = \tfrac{1}{2}(6)(3\sqrt{2})$$
$$= 9\sqrt{2}.$$

Therefore, the area of each segment is $9\pi/2 - 9\sqrt{2}$, and so the area of eight of these segments is $36(\pi - 2\sqrt{2}) \doteq 11.204$.

**16.** The area of each petal is twice the area of a segment of a circle in which the radius $r = 1$ and the arc measure $q = 60$.

$$\text{Area of the sector} = (q/360)\pi r^2$$
$$= \tfrac{60}{360}\pi 1^2 = \pi/6.$$

$$\text{Area of the equilateral triangle}$$
$$= r^2\sqrt{3}/4 = \sqrt{3}/4.$$

Therefore, the area of each segment is $\dfrac{\pi}{6} - \dfrac{\sqrt{3}}{4}$, and the area of the given figure is $12\left(\dfrac{\pi}{6} - \dfrac{\sqrt{3}}{4}\right) = 2\pi - 3\sqrt{3}.$

---

## Problem Set 16–5

**1.** The radius of a circle is 18. How long is an arc of 60°? of 90°? of 120°? of 150°? of 180°? of 270°?
    $6\pi$    $9\pi$    $12\pi$
    $15\pi$    $18\pi$    $27\pi$

**2.** What is the radius of a circle if the length of a 45° arc is $3\pi$?  $r=12$

**3.** What is the radius of a circle if the length of a 72° arc is $4\pi$?  $r=10$

**4.** Both $\widehat{AB}$ and $\widehat{CD}$ are arcs of 60°, but their lengths are not equal. $P$ is the center of both arcs. If $PA = 6$ and $AC = 3$, how long is $\widehat{AB}$ and how long is $\widehat{CD}$?  $2\pi$ and $3\pi$

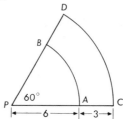

**5.** The length of a 60° arc is 1 cm. Find the radius of the arc and the length of the chord of the arc.  radius is $\frac{3}{\pi}$ cm, chord is $\frac{3}{\pi}$cm

**6.** Explain the difference between arc measure and arc length.

**7.** The radius of a circle is 10. What is the area of a sector having an arc of 90°? of 72°? of 180°? of 216°? of 324°?
    $25\pi$   $20\pi$   $50\pi$   $60\pi$   $90\pi$

**8.** In a circle with radius 2, a sector has area $\pi$. What is the measure of the arc of the sector?  $q=90$

**9.** In a circle with radius 6, a sector has area $15\pi$. What is the length of the arc of the sector?  $L=5\pi$

**10.** The minute hand of a large clock on the tower of a public building is 6 decimetres long. Find the distance traveled by the tip of the minute hand in 5 min. How many centimetres does the tip of the minute hand travel in 1 min?  $L=\frac{30}{180}\cdot\pi\cdot 6=\pi dm$;  $L=\frac{10}{5}\pi=2cm$

**11.** In designing very tall buildings engineers must allow for the swaying motion which is typical of skyscraper structures. The height of the Empire State Building at the 102d floor is 381 metres. If the building, at this height, describes an arc of $\frac{1}{2}$°, how far does it sway back and forth?  $L=\frac{0.5}{180}\cdot\pi\cdot 381 \doteq 3.32m$

**12.** A *segment of a circle* is a region bounded by an arc of the circle and the chord of the arc. Describe a method of determining the area of a segment of a circle.  Area$_{segment}=A_{sector}-A_{triangle}$

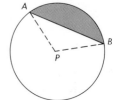

13–14. $A_s$ = Area of sector, $A_t$ = Area of triangle, $A_g$ = Area of segment

**13.** Find the area of a segment of a circle given that the radius, $r$, of the circle and the measure of the arc, $m\widehat{AB}$, are:

(a) $r = 12$; $m\widehat{AB} = 60$.      $A_s = 24\pi$,
     $A_t = 36\sqrt{3}$, $A_g \doteq 13.04$

(b) $r = 6$; $m\widehat{AB} = 120$.      $A_s = 12\pi$
     $A_t = 9\sqrt{3}$, $A_g \doteq 22.11$

**14.** Find the area of a segment of a circle given that the radius, $r$, of the circle and the measure of the arc, $m\widehat{AB}$, are:

(a) $r = 8$; $m\widehat{AB} = 45$.      $A_s = 8\pi$,
     $A_t = 16\sqrt{2}$, $A_g \doteq 2.51$

(b) $r = 10$; $m\widehat{AB} = 30$.      $A_s = 25\pi/3$
     $A_t = 25$, $A_g = 25\pi/3 - 25$

**15.** A regular octagon is inscribed in a circle of radius 6. Find the area of that part of the circular region that is outside the octagon.    $36(\pi - 2\sqrt{2}) \doteq 11.2$

**16.** The radius of each circular arc which makes up this six-petal design is the same as the radius of the circle which contains the outer tips of all the petals. If the radius is 1, what is the area of the figure? $2\pi - 3\sqrt{3}$

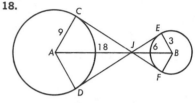

**17.** A continuous belt runs around two wheels as shown. The wheels have radii of 3 cm and 15 cm and the distance between their centers is 24 cm. Find the length of the belt. $24\sqrt{3} + 22\pi$ cm $\doteq 110.6$ cm

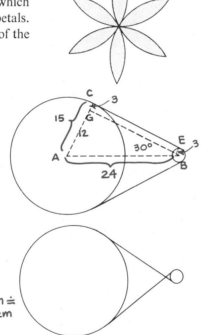

**18.** A continuous belt runs around two wheels so that the wheels will turn in opposite directions. The wheels have radii of 3 cm and 9 cm, and the distance between their centers is 24 cm. Find the length of the belt. $24\sqrt{3} + 16\pi$ cm $\doteq 91.8$ cm

## HONORS PROBLEM

Derive a formula for the area of an oval. Construct an oval in the following way. Let $\overline{AB}$ and $\overline{CD}$ be perpendicular diameters of a circle having radius $r$. With $A$ as center and $AB$ as radius swing an arc from $B$ intersecting $\overleftrightarrow{AC}$ at $G$. Similarly, with $B$ as center and $AB$ as radius, let $\widehat{AH}$ intersect $\overleftrightarrow{BC}$ at $H$. Finally, with $C$ as center and $CG$ as radius, draw $\widehat{GH}$. Find the area of the oval $ADBGH$. $r^2[(3 - \sqrt{2})\pi - 1]$

### Answers to Problems

**17.** Introduce $\overline{BG} \perp \overline{AC}$. Then $AG = AC - GC = 15 - 3 = 12$. Since the length of the hypotenuse of the right triangle $\triangle ABG$ is twice that of the leg $\overline{AG}$, we conclude by Theorem 9–28 that $\triangle ABG$ is a 30–60–90 triangle and consequently that $CE = GB = 12\sqrt{3}$. The length of the major arc $\widehat{CD} = (q/360)2\pi r = \frac{240}{360} \cdot 30\pi = 20\pi$. The length of the minor arc $\widehat{EF} = (q/360)2\pi r = \frac{120}{360}6\pi = 2\pi$. Therefore, the total length of the belt is $24\sqrt{3} + 22\pi \doteq 110.6$ cm.

**18.**

By Problem 29, Section 14–7, the two common internal tangents $\overline{CF}$ and $\overline{ED}$ and the line $\overline{AB}$ of centers are concurrent at a point $J$. Since $\triangle ACJ \sim \triangle BFJ$ by AA, the ratio $\dfrac{AJ}{JB} = \dfrac{AC}{FB} = \dfrac{3}{9} = \dfrac{1}{3}$. Therefore $J$ separates $\overline{AB}$ into two segments whose lengths are in a ratio of 3:1. Since $AB = 24$, $AJ = 18$, and $JB = 6$. Since the hypotenuse of the right $\triangle ACJ$ is twice the leg $\overline{AC}$, we can conclude that $\triangle ACJ$ is a 30–60–90 triangle and consequently that $CJ = 9\sqrt{3}$. Similarly $JF = 3\sqrt{3}$. The length of the major arc $\widehat{CD} = q/360(2\pi r) = \frac{240}{360} \cdot 18\pi = 12\pi$. The length of the major arc $\widehat{EF} = q/360(2\pi r) = \frac{240}{360} \cdot 6\pi = 4\pi$. Therefore, the length of the belt is $24\sqrt{3} + 16\pi$ cm $= 91.8$ cm.

### Answer to Honors Problem

$a$(Oval $ADBGH$)

     $= a$(Semicircular region $ADB$)
         $= \frac{1}{2}\pi r^2$

     $+ a$(Sector $A$, $\widehat{BG}$)
         $= \frac{1}{8}4\pi r^2$

     $+ a$(Sector $B$, $\widehat{AH}$)
         $= \frac{1}{8}4\pi r^2$

     $- a$(Triangle $ABC$)
         $= -r^2$

     $+ a$(Sector $C$, $\widehat{GH}$)
         $= \frac{1}{4}\pi[r(2 - \sqrt{2})]^2$

     $\therefore a$(Oval $ADBGH$)
         $= r^2[(3 - \sqrt{2})\pi - 1]$.

See sketch on page 554.

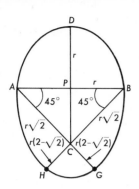

**Answers to Chapter Review Problems**

**19.** $a(\text{Fig } PQR)$
$$= a(\triangle ABC) - 3a(\text{Sector } A, PR)$$
$$= \frac{s^2\sqrt{3}}{4} - 3\left(\frac{q}{360}\right)\pi r^2$$
$$= \frac{6^2\sqrt{3}}{4} - 3\left(\frac{60}{360}\right)\pi 3^2.$$
$$= 9\left(\sqrt{3} - \frac{\pi}{2}\right).$$
$p(\text{Fig } PQR)$
$$= 3\pi.$$

**20.** Duplicate the figure in the other three quadrants. Then
$$A = \tfrac{1}{4}[\pi r^2 - \tfrac{1}{2}d_1 d_2] = \tfrac{1}{4}[\pi r^2 - \tfrac{1}{2}(2r)(2r)]$$
$$= \frac{r^2}{4}(\pi - 2).$$

**21.** $a(\text{Fig } ABC)$
$$= 3a(\text{Sector } A, \overset{\frown}{BC}) - 2a(\triangle ABC).$$
$$= 3 \cdot \tfrac{1}{6} \cdot \pi r^2 - 2\frac{r^2\sqrt{3}}{4}$$
$$= \frac{r^2}{2}(\pi - \sqrt{3}).$$
$p(\text{Fig } ABC)$
$$= \pi r.$$

## CHAPTER REVIEW

1. Is a convex polygon a convex set? No

2. A hexagon is circumscribed about a circle of diameter 10. If the perimeter of the hexagon is 38, what is the area of the hexagon? $A = \frac{1}{2}ap = 95$

3. Compare the apothem of a regular polygon and the radius of the inscribed circle. (That is, which is larger?) $a = r_i$. They are equal.

4. Compare the apothem of a regular polygon and the radius of the circumscribed circle. $a < r_c$

5. A convex polygon has 13 sides. What is the sum of the measures of its 13 exterior angles? 360

6. How many sides does a convex polygon have if the sum of the measures of its angles is 1080? 8

7. What is the measure of each angle of a regular pentagon? hexagon? octagon? decagon?
108   120   135   144

8. What is the apothem of a regular polygon having area 225 and perimeter 60? 7.5

9. If the circumference of a circle is $C$ and its radius is $r$, what is the value of $C/r$? $2\pi$

10. What is the radius of a circle if its circumference is equal to its area? $r = 2$

11. The area of a circle is 6 times its circumference. What is its radius? $r = 12$

12. Two concentric circles have radii of 5 and 13. Find the radius of a circle whose area equals the area of the annulus bounded by the two given circles. $r = 12$

13. If the radius of one circle is 4 times the radius of another, what is the ratio of their diameters? of their circumferences? of their areas?
4:1   4:1   16:1

14. The circumferences of two circles are $6\pi$ and $10\pi$. What is the ratio of their areas? 9 : 25

---

15. Compare the areas of an equilateral triangle circumscribed about a circle and an equilateral triangle inscribed in the circle. 4:1

16. Show that the area of a circle is given by the formula $\frac{1}{4}\pi d^2$, where $d$ is the diameter of the circle. $A = \pi r^2 = \pi\left(\frac{d}{2}\right)^2 = \frac{1}{4}\pi d^2$

17. Will more water flow through three 2.5-cm pipes or one 7.5-cm pipe? Prove your answer. (A pipe is measured by its inside diameter.)
$A = \pi\left(\frac{7.5}{2}\right)^2 \doteq 14.1\,\pi$, but $3\left[\pi\left(\frac{2.5}{2}\right)^2\right] \doteq 4.69\,\pi$

18. The area of a square equals the area of a circle with diameter 2. How long is a side of the square? $A_c = \pi = s^2 = A_s$. $s = \sqrt{\pi}$

**19.** Given that the length of a side of the equilateral triangle $\triangle ABC$ is 6 and $P$, $Q$, $R$ are midpoints of the sides. $\overset{\frown}{PQ}$, $\overset{\frown}{PR}$, and $\overset{\frown}{QR}$ have the vertices of the triangle as their centers. Find the area and the length of the boundary of the shaded region $PQR$.
$$a(PQR) = 9\left(\sqrt{3} - \frac{\pi}{2}\right)$$
$$p(PQR) = 3\pi$$

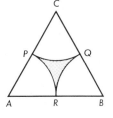

**20.** The square is inscribed in a 90° sector of radius $r$. Derive a formula for the area of the shaded regions. $\frac{r^2}{4}(\pi - 2)$

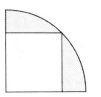

**21.** Each vertex of figure $ABC$ is the center of the opposite arc. The figure has the interesting property that when rolled between two parallel lines which just touch it, it will always touch both lines, just as a circle will. (A figure having this property is said to be of *constant width*.) Let the radius of each arc be $r$ and derive a formula for the area of figure $ABC$ and a formula for the perimeter of figure $ABC$. $a(ABC) = \frac{r^2}{2}(\pi - 3)$,
$$p(ABC) = \pi r$$

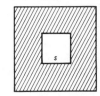

## HONORS PROBLEM

A problem commonly faced in architectural design is that of covering a surface with regular polygonal regions. For example, a plane can be covered by congruent square regions placed four at a vertex, as shown here.

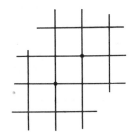

(a) How many equilateral triangular regions must be placed at a vertex to cover a plane? 6

(b) What other class of regular polygonal regions can be used to cover a plane? How many would be needed at a vertex? 3
    Regular hexagonal regions

(c) Two regular octagons and one square will exactly cover the part of a plane around a point when arranged as shown. What other combinations of three regular polygonal regions (two of which are alike) will accomplish this? You should be able to find two other combinations.

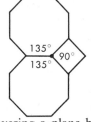

(d) Investigate whether there are other possibilities of covering a plane by regular polygonal regions. A table of measures of angles of regular polygons would be helpful in discovering workable combinations.

**Explanation for Problems**

The figure in Problem 21 is also called a Reuleaux Triangle, named after Franz Reuleaux (1829–1905). Because the triangle has constant width, it can rotate in a square hole. The students could attempt to construct and design a drill based on the Reuleaux triangle.

Construct an equilateral triangle of cardboard having a side the same length as the side of a square cut in the middle of another piece of cardboard. With a compass, and using the triangle's vertices as centers, draw the necessary arcs. Cut out this Reuleaux triangle. It will rotate in the hole and will always maintain contact with each side of the square. Designing the actual drill is up to the student.

Such a drill was designed in 1914 by Harry J. Watts. The Watts Brothers Tool Works of Wilmerding, Penn. supplies drills for the machine boring of squares, hexagons, and octagons.

If the students are interested in knowing more about curves of constant width, as well as other related problems, you should refer them to Martin Gardner's "Mathematical Games" in *Scientific American*, February 1963, and the chapter on such curves in *The Enjoyment of Mathematics* by Rademacher and Toeplitz.

This chapter serves as an introduction to trigonometry and so it is a supplemental chapter. It may be omitted or covered at the end of the year. A minimum study of the chapter would include only Sections 17–1, 17–2, and 17–3.

The first three sections introduce the basic trigonometric ratios, their traditional uses, and a few fundamental identities. The remainder of the chapter is devoted to the more modern study of analytic trigonometry, using coordinate systems, directed angles, and the winding function. The winding function is the first and simplest example of the periodic functions which will appear, in more difficult forms, in future mathematics courses.

## Planning the Chapter

Although most continuing mathematics students will study trigonometry later, this chapter provides a good introduction to the subject.

An average class may spend one day each on the first three sections of this chapter. The rest of the chapter contains more difficult concepts and can be omitted.

An above-average class should spend two days each on Sections 17–6 and 17–8 and one day on each of the other sections.

CHAPTER **17**

# Trigonometry

Objectives...

- Develop the basic trigonometric ratios.
- Develop skill with using tables to evaluate trigonometric ratios.
- Relate the ratios to the winding function.
- Develop identities involving trigonometric functions.

This section is not difficult for it is based on similar triangles. Since similarity was studied in Chapter 12, the students may need a quick review of ratios before attempting the special ratios of right triangles.

Note that no restriction is needed for the denominators of the three ratios, since the sides of a triangle have positive lengths. When the three ratios are defined as functions, as in Section 17–6, the tangent is not defined in the cases where its denominator becomes zero.

## 17–1   THE TRIGONOMETRIC RATIOS

Consider two right triangles with a pair of congruent acute angles. By the AA Corollary 12–4.1, we know that $\triangle ABC \sim \triangle A'B'C'$. Therefore

$$\frac{a}{a'} = \frac{b}{b'} = \frac{c}{c'}.$$

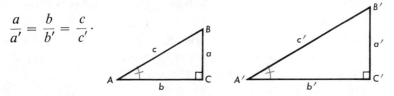

(Here we follow the convention that the length of the side opposite $\angle A$ is $a$, the length of the side opposite $\angle B$ is $b$, and so forth.)

From this proportionality we have the following equations:

$$\frac{a}{b} = \frac{a'}{b'}, \qquad \frac{b}{c} = \frac{b'}{c'}, \qquad \frac{a}{c} = \frac{a'}{c'}.$$

Therefore the ratios $a/c$, $b/c$, and $a/b$ do not depend on the *size* of the triangle; once we know $m\angle A$, these ratios are determined. They are called the *trigonometric ratios*.

The ratio $a/c$ is called the *sine* of $\angle A$, and we write

$$\sin \angle A = \frac{a}{c}.$$

If $m\angle A = r$, then we may write

$$\sin r° = \frac{a}{c}.$$

This makes sense, because $a/c$ is determined if we know either $\angle A$ or $r$.

**1.** Simplify the following expression.

$$\left(\frac{\tan 45°}{\cos 60°} \div \cos 30°\right) + \sin 60°$$

(ans: $11\sqrt{3}/6$)

**2.** Determine whether the following statements are true or false. If your answer is "false" correct the sentence so the resulting statement is true.

(a) $(\tan \angle A)(\sin \angle A) = \cos \angle A$.

(b) $(-\sin \angle A)^2 = (\cos \angle A)^2 - 1$.

(ans: False $(\tan \angle A)(\cos \angle A) = \sin \angle A$; false $(-\sin \angle A)^2 = 1 - (\cos \angle A)^2$.)

Similarly, $b/c$ is called the *cosine* of $\angle A$, and we write

$$\cos \angle A = \frac{b}{c} \quad \text{or} \quad \cos r° = \frac{b}{c}.$$

The ratio $a/b$ is called the *tangent* of $\angle A$, and we write

$$\tan \angle A = \frac{a}{b} \quad \text{or} \quad \tan r° = \frac{a}{b}.$$

To sum up:

$$\sin \angle A = \sin r° = \frac{a}{c},$$

$$\cos \angle A = \cos r° = \frac{b}{c},$$

$$\tan \angle A = \tan r° = \frac{a}{b}.$$

For some angles and some numbers $r$, the trigonometric ratios are easy to calculate. Take, for example, the case $r = 45$. Since the ratios do not depend on the size of the triangle, we can use *any* right triangle $\triangle ABC$ with a 45° angle at $A$. The triangle is then isosceles, with $a = b$. We take $a = b = 1$. By the Pythagorean Theorem, $c = \sqrt{2}$, as shown in the figure. We now have

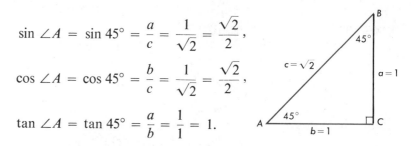

$$\sin \angle A = \sin 45° = \frac{a}{c} = \frac{1}{\sqrt{2}} = \frac{\sqrt{2}}{2},$$

$$\cos \angle A = \cos 45° = \frac{b}{c} = \frac{1}{\sqrt{2}} = \frac{\sqrt{2}}{2},$$

$$\tan \angle A = \tan 45° = \frac{a}{b} = \frac{1}{1} = 1.$$

[*Query:* If we had let $a = b = \sqrt{2}$, would the trigonometric ratios have changed? Why or why not?]

The case $r = 30$ is almost as easy. We know by Theorem 9–27 that $a = c/2$. Since the size of the triangle does not matter, we can choose any size we like. Thus, for example, if we take $c = 2$, then $a = 1$, as shown in the figure. The Py-

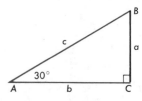

thagorean Theorem gives us $b^2 = c^2 - a^2 = 4 - 1 = 3$.) Thus we have $a = 1$, $b = \sqrt{3}$, and $c = 2$. We can now read off the values:

$$\sin 30° = \frac{a}{c} = \frac{1}{2},$$

$$\cos 30° = \frac{b}{c} = \frac{\sqrt{3}}{2},$$

$$\tan 30° = \frac{a}{b} = \frac{1}{\sqrt{3}} = \frac{\sqrt{3}}{3}.$$

*A word of caution:* Note that we have used the degree sign in the expressions $\sin r°$, $\cos r°$, $\tan r°$. The reason is that later you will be using another unit of measure for angles, called *radian measure*. To know what the sine of a number is, you have to know what unit is being used.

## Problem Set 17–1

**1.** Given this figure as marked,

(a) explain why AA corollary

$$\underset{12}{\triangle ABC} \sim \underset{9}{\triangle AB'C'} \sim \underset{6\frac{3}{4}\ \ 5\ \ 15}{\triangle AB''C''}.$$

(b) find $AB''$, $B''C''$, $B'C'$, $AC$, $AC''$.   $\frac{3}{5}$   $\frac{4}{5}$

(c) find $\sin \angle A$, $\cos \angle A$, $\sin \angle C$, $\frac{4}{5}$
 $\sin \angle C''$, $\sin \angle C'$.
 $\frac{4}{5}$    $\frac{4}{5}$

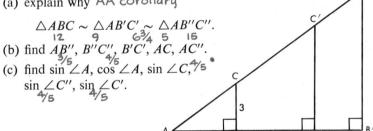

**2.** Complete each statement by referring to the figures.

(a) $\sin \angle X = \frac{x}{?z}$    (b) $\sin \angle B = \frac{?b}{a}$.

(c) $\cos \angle X = \frac{?4}{z}$.    (d) $\sin \angle ? \underset{C}{=} \frac{c}{a}$.

(e) $\sin \angle Y = \frac{?4}{z}$.    (f) $\underset{tan}{---} \angle B = \frac{b}{c}$.

(g) $\tan \angle Y = \frac{?}{?} \cdot \frac{y}{x}$    (h) $\tan \angle C = \frac{?}{?} \cdot \frac{c}{b}$

(i) $\cos \angle ? \underset{Y}{=} \frac{x}{z}$.    (j) $\underset{cos}{---} \angle B = \frac{c}{a}$.

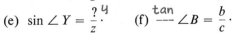
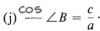
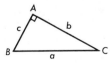

**Explanation for Problems**

Problems 18 and 19 look ahead to Section 17–3, where the first of the fundamental trigonometric identities is introduced. The Honors Problem asks the student to prove the law of cosines. This law, the law of sines, the inverse trigonometric functions, and related topics will appear in future mathematics courses.

**15.** sin $\angle A = a/c$, and $c = AB = 1$. Thus sin $\angle A = a$. Similarly cos $\angle A = b/c = b$. If $c = AB = k$, then sin $\angle A = a/c = a/k$ and $a = k$ sin $\angle A$. Similarly cos $\angle A = b/k$ and $b = k$ cos $\angle A$.

**16.** Consider a right triangle $\triangle PQR$ with the right angle at $R$, and recall that the acute angles of a right triangle are complementary. Since sin $\angle P = QR/PQ$ and cos $\angle Q = QR/PQ$ we can conclude that sin $\angle P = $ cos $\angle Q$.

**17.** Consider the triangle in Problem 16. Then tan $\angle P = QR/PR$ and tan $\angle Q = PR/QR$, and therefore

$$(\tan \angle P)(\tan \angle Q)$$
$$= QR/PR \cdot PR/QR = 1.$$

**18.** $\dfrac{\sin \angle A}{\cos \angle A} = \dfrac{a/c}{b/c} = \dfrac{a}{b} = \tan \angle A.$

**19.** $(\sin \angle A)^2 + (\cos \angle A)^2$

$$= \left(\frac{a}{c}\right)^2 + \left(\frac{b}{c}\right)^2 = \frac{a^2 + b^2}{c^2} = \frac{c^2}{c^2} = 1.$$

**21.** In $\triangle ABC$, sin $\angle A = h$ where $h$ is the length of the altitude from $C$ to $\overline{AB}$, and so $h = b$ sin $\angle A$. Thus $a\triangle ABC = \frac{1}{2}bc$ sin $\angle A$.

---

**3.**

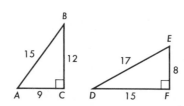
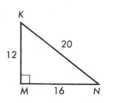
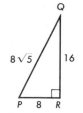

Given these right triangles with lengths of sides as indicated. Find the following trigonometric ratios.

(a) sin $\angle A$ $\frac{4}{5}$   (b) cos $\angle A$ $\frac{3}{5}$   (c) tan $\angle A$ $\frac{4}{3}$   (d) sin $\angle D$ $\frac{8}{17}$

(e) sin $\angle N$ $\frac{3}{5}$   (f) cos $\angle D$ $\frac{15}{17}$   (g) tan $\angle N$ $\frac{3}{4}$   (h) tan $\angle P$ $2$

(i) cos $\angle P$ $\frac{\sqrt{5}}{5}$   (j) cos $\angle N$ $\frac{4}{5}$   (k) tan $\angle D$ $\frac{8}{15}$   (l) sin $\angle E$ $\frac{15}{17}$

**4.**

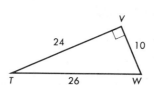
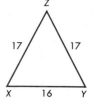

Given the triangles as marked, find the following trigonometric ratios.

(a) cos $\angle G$ $\frac{3}{5}$   (b) sin $\angle H$ $\frac{12}{13}$   (c) tan $\angle T$ $\frac{5}{12}$   (d) sin $\angle W$ $\frac{12}{13}$

(e) cos $\angle T$ $\frac{12}{13}$   (f) tan $\angle G$ $\frac{4}{3}$   (g) sin $\angle X$ $\frac{15}{17}$   (h) cos $\angle Y$ $\frac{8}{17}$

**5.** In the right triangle $\triangle ABC$, the hypotenuse $\overline{AB}$ is 25 in. long.

(a) If sin $\angle A = \frac{4}{5}$, how long is $\overline{BC}$? **20 in.**

(b) If cos $\angle A = 0.60$, what is tan $\angle A$ expressed as a decimal? **1.333**

(c) If tan $\angle A = 3\frac{3}{7}$, what are the lengths of $\overline{AC}$ and $\overline{BC}$? **AC=7, BC=24**

**6.** In $\triangle GKM$, $GM = 30$, $GK = 50$, and cos $\angle G = 0.80$. Find the altitude to $\overline{GK}$ and the area of $\triangle GKM$.
**Altitude MH =18**
**a$\triangle$GKM=450**

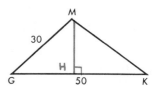

**7.** In the trapezoid $\square ABCD$, $\overline{DC} \parallel \overline{AB}$, $AD = 20$, and $BC = 26$. If sin $\angle A = .5$, what is the altitude of the trapezoid and what is sin $\angle B$?
**Altitude=10**
**sin $\angle$B=$\frac{5}{13}$**

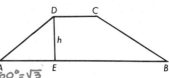

**8.** Find sin 60°, cos 60°, and tan 60°.
**sin 60°=$\frac{\sqrt{3}}{2}$, cos 60°=$\frac{1}{2}$, tan 60°=$\sqrt{3}$**

**9.** Show that sin 30° = cos 60°. **sin 30°=$\frac{1}{2}$= cos 60°**

**10.** What is the relationship of tan 60° and tan 30°? **They are reciprocals.**

11. In the parallelogram $\square ABCD$, diagonal $\overline{BD}$ is perpendicular to $\overline{AB}$. If $AB = 5$ and $\tan \angle A = 1$, what is $a\square ABCD$? a □ ABCD = 25

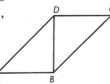

---

$m\angle P = 45$  $m\angle Q = 60$
12. If $\sin \angle P = \frac{1}{2}\sqrt{2}$, what is $m\angle P$? If $\sin \angle Q = \frac{1}{2}\sqrt{3}$, what is $m\angle Q$? If $\angle P$ and $\angle Q$ are angles of $\triangle PQR$, what is $m\angle R$? m∠R = 75

13. In $\triangle ABC$, $\tan \angle A = \sqrt{3}$ and $\tan \angle C = \sqrt{3}/3$. Find $m\angle B$. [*Hint:* This problem is similar to Problem 12.] m∠A = 60, m∠C = 30, m∠B = 90

14. In $\triangle GHK$, $\tan \angle H = 2 \cos \angle G = 1$. Find $m\angle K$. tan ∠H = 1, m∠H = 45, cos ∠G = ½, m∠G = 60, m∠K = 75

15. Given a right triangle $\triangle ABC$ in which the hypotenuse $\overline{AB}$ has length 1. Show that $a = \sin \angle A$ and that $b = \cos \angle A$. If $AB = k$, show that $a = k \sin \angle A$ and that $b = k \cos \angle A$.

16. Prove: The sine of an acute angle is equal to the cosine of its complement.

17. Prove: The product of the tangent of an acute angle and the tangent of the complement of the angle is 1.

18. Show that $\tan \angle A = \dfrac{\sin \angle A}{\cos \angle A}$ for every acute angle $\angle A$.

19. Show that $(\sin \angle A)^2 + (\cos \angle A)^2 = 1$ for every acute angle $\angle A$.

20. Show that the area of an equilateral triangle with a side of length 1 is given by $(\sin 60°)(\cos 60°)$. Observe that an altitude is equal to sin 60° and each side is equal to 2 cos 60°.

---

21. In $\triangle ABC$, let the altitude from $C$ intersect $\overline{AB}$ between $A$ and $B$. Prove that $a\triangle ABC$ is given by $\frac{1}{2}bc \sin \angle A$.

22. Let $e$ be the length of each side of a regular polygonal region of $n$ sides. Show that the area of the region is given by the formula

$$\frac{ne^2}{4} \tan \left(\frac{90(n-2)}{n}\right)^{\circ}$$

23. Check the formula of Problem 22 by finding the area of a regular hexagon with side of length 8. 96√3

24. Use trigonometric ratios to express the area of a regular polygon of 9 sides, each of length 8. 144 tan 70°

25. Use trigonometric ratios to express the area of a regular polygon of 15 sides, each of length 4. 60 tan 78°

---

**Answers to Problems**

22. A regular polygon of $n$ sides can be divided into $n$ congruent isosceles triangles with base $e$ and central or vertex angle $(360/n)°$. Call this typical triangle $\triangle PQR$.

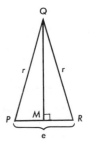

$\overline{QM}$, the altitude, is also the angle bisector of $\angle Q$. Thus $m\angle PQM = 180/n$ and

$$m\angle QPR = 90 - \frac{180}{n} = \frac{90(n-2)}{n}.$$

Since

$$\tan \angle QPR = \frac{QM}{\frac{1}{2}e},$$

$$QM = \tfrac{1}{2}e \tan \frac{90(n-2)}{n}.$$

$$a\triangle PQR = \tfrac{1}{2}e \left(\tfrac{1}{2}e \tan \frac{90(n-2)}{n}\right)$$

$$= \frac{e^2}{4} \tan \frac{90(n-2)}{n}.$$

Since there are $n$ of these triangles in the regular polygon, its area is

$$\frac{ne^2}{4} \tan \frac{90(n-2)}{n}.$$

## Answer to Honors Problem

For the first figure we have the following facts: (1) $h^2 = a^2 - y^2$, (2) $h^2 = b^2 - x^2$, (3) $y + x = c$, and therefore $y - x = c - 2x$, (4) $\cos \angle A = \frac{x}{b}$. Therefore, $a^2 - y^2 = b^2 - x^2$, and

$$\begin{aligned}
a^2 &= b^2 + (y^2 - x^2) \\
&= b^2 + (y + x)(y - x) \\
&= b^2 + c(c - 2x) \\
&= b^2 + c^2 - 2cx \\
&= b^2 + c^2 - 2cb \cos \angle A.
\end{aligned}$$

A similar proof can be used for the second figure.

## 17-2 NUMERICAL TRIGONOMETRY. THE USE OF TABLES

### Classroom Notes

Students welcome the opportunity to see how mathematics is used in a practical situation. A student may ask what happens when a surveyor finds an angle of $22\frac{1}{2}°$ instead of 22°. Instead of answering the question you could have the students guess what the tangent of $22\frac{1}{2}°$ should be. This discussion could lead naturally into the idea of interpolation introduced in Problems 12–14 of the problem set. The rest of the material in this section is not difficult.

## HONORS PROBLEM

Prove the following theorem.

Given $\triangle ABC$ with $\angle A$ acute, then $a^2 = b^2 + c^2 - 2bc \cos \angle A$.

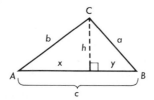
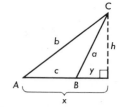

## 17-2 NUMERICAL TRIGONOMETRY. THE USE OF TABLES

In the preceding section, we calculated, the sine, cosine, and tangent of 30°, 45° and 60°. These were expressed in terms of $\sqrt{2}$ and $\sqrt{3}$. The decimal approximations, correct to three decimal places, are:

$$\sqrt{2} = 1.414, \qquad \frac{1}{\sqrt{2}} = \frac{\sqrt{2}}{2} = 0.707,$$

$$\sqrt{3} = 1.732, \qquad \frac{1}{\sqrt{3}} = \frac{\sqrt{3}}{3} = 0.577,$$

Therefore we have

$$\sin 30° = \frac{1}{2} = 0.500,$$

$$\cos 30° = \frac{\sqrt{3}}{2} = \frac{1.732}{2} = 0.866,$$

$$\tan 30° = \frac{1}{\sqrt{3}} = \frac{\sqrt{3}}{3} = 0.577.$$

Similarly we can calculate the trigonometric ratios for 45° and 60°. Thus we get the following table:

| Angle | Sine | Cosine | Tangent |
|-------|------|--------|---------|
| 30° | 0.500 | 0.866 | 0.577 |
| 45° | 0.707 | 0.707 | 1.000 |
| 60° | 0.866 | 0.500 | 1.732 |

These are the trigonometric ratios that we have learned to calculate. By advanced methods it is possible to calculate the sine, cosine, and tangent of *any* angle as accurately as you want. (In fact, the ancient Greeks computed such tables, because they needed them in their study of astronomy.) On p. 567 you will find a table of the values of the trigonometric ratios for angles whose measures are full degrees. The table is accurate to three decimal places, which is good enough for our present purposes.

Such tables have many important applications. Suppose, for example, that a surveyor wants to determine the distance between two points on opposite ends of a pond. He cannot measure $\overline{BC}$ directly. But he can measure $\overline{AB}$ and $\angle A$. Suppose he finds that $\overline{AB} = 305$ m and $r = 32$. Now

$$\sin r° = \frac{BC}{AB}.$$

Therefore

$$BC = AB \sin r°.$$

The surveyor looks in his tables and finds that $\sin 32° = 0.530$. Hence

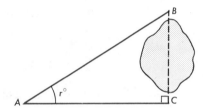

$$BC = 305 \times 0.530 = 161.65 \text{ m}.$$

Surveyors, who need to solve problems of this kind, solve them by the method described.

The tables can also be used for other types of indirect measurement. One way of measuring the height of a flagpole without climbing it would be to measure a certain distance, say 100 m, from the base, and then measure the angle marked $\angle A$ in the figure. In the figure, $\overline{BC}$ represents the flagpole, and $m\angle A = 22$. Since

$$\tan 22° = \frac{BC}{AC},$$

we have

$$BC = AC \tan 22°$$
$$= 100 \times 0.404$$
$$= 40.4 \text{ m}.$$

Note that in problems of this kind, we can always make sure that the arithmetic involved will be easy. We can measure off any distance we want, from the base of the pole, and so we choose a point $A$ for which $AC$ comes out to an even number of metres.

**Problem Set 17-2**

1. Using the table of trigonometric ratios, give the decimal form of:
   (a) sin 12°..208  (b) cos 35°..819  (c) tan 20°..364  (d) cos 66°..407
   (e) sin 50°..766  (f) cos 40°..643  (g) tan 82°.7.115  (h) sin 3°..052
   (i) tan 3°..052  (j) cos 60°..500

2. Find $m\angle A$ given that:
   (a) sin $\angle A$ = 0.309. m∠A=18      (b) cos $\angle A$ = 0.208. m∠A=78
   (c) tan $\angle A$ = 0.306. m∠A=17      (d) cos $\angle A$ = 0.961. m∠A=16
   (e) tan $\angle A$ = 2.904. m∠A=71      (f) sin $\angle A$ = 0.961. m∠A=74
   (g) sin $\angle A$ = 0.454. m∠A=27      (h) cos $\angle A$ = 0.731. m∠A=43
   (i) tan $\angle A$ = 8.144. m∠A=83      (j) tan $\angle A$ = 0.554. m∠A=29

3. Given that the hypotenuse $\overline{AB}$ of $\triangle ABC$
   is 20 m long and $m\angle A$ = 38, find $BC$
   and $AC$. BC= 12.32 m
                    AC= 15.76 m

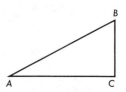

4. In $\triangle ABC$, $\angle C$ is a right angle, $m\angle A$ = 42, and $AC$ = 7. How long
   is $\overline{BC}$? BC=6.30

5. In $\triangle PQR$, $m\angle P$ = 54, $PR$= 15, and
   $PQ$ = 18. Find the length of the altitude to $\overline{PQ}$; to $\overline{PR}$.
       altitude to $\overline{PQ}$ =12.14
       altitude to $\overline{PR}$= 14.56

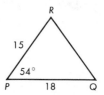

6. In $\triangle GHK$, $m\angle G$ = 70, $GK$ = 12, and $GH$ = 20. Find the altitude to
   $\overline{GH}$ and the area of $\triangle GHK$. altitude to $\overline{GH}$=GK·sin∠G= 11.28,
                                            a△GHK=112.8

7. Calculate the area of $\triangle ABC$, given

   $AB$ = 30,  $BC$ = 16,  and  $m\angle B$ = 47.
   a△ABC=(AB sin∠B)½ BC
        =21.93·½·16
        = 175.44

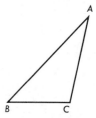

8. Determine the measures, to the nearest degree, of the acute angles of a
   3-4-5 triangle. 37°, 53°

9. Determine the measures, to the nearest degree, of the acute angles of an
   8-15-17 triangle. 28°, 62°

10. The base of an isosceles triangle is 8 m long, and the angle opposite the base has measure 30°. Calculate the lengths of the three altitudes of the triangle. 14.93m, 7.73m, 7.73m

11. In $\triangle ABC$, $\angle C$ is a right angle and $AB = 9$. Given also that tan $\angle A = 1.111$, find $BC$ and $AC$.

BC = AB sin∠A = 6.69
AC = AB cos∠A = 6.02

12. Examine the table of trigonometric ratios for sin 53°, sin 54°, sin 55°, sin 56°. Explain why a good estimate of sin 54°30′ is 0.814. What would be a good estimate of sin 55°30′? A good estimate of sin 54°12′ is 0.811. Why? Estimate sin 54°6′. Explain why each of the following is a good estimate:

sin 55°30′ = .824     sin 54°6′ = .810

$$\sin 30°30' = 0.508, \qquad \sin 76°30' = 0.972,$$
$$\sin 30°20' = 0.505, \qquad \sin 76°45' = 0.973.$$

This method of estimating values which do not appear explicitly in a table is called *interpolation*.

13. Interpolate in the table of trigonometric ratios to obtain estimates of the following (see Problem 12).

(a) sin 37°30′ .609 (b) sin 65°30′ .910 (c) sin 63.5° .895 (d) sin 56.3° .832

(e) sin 47°20′ .735 (f) sin 45°40′ .715 (g) sin 73.4° .958 (h) sin 20.5° .350

(i) sin 17°30′ .301 (j) sin 41°15′ .659

14. Interpolate in the table of trigonometric ratios to obtain estimates of the following (see Problem 12).

(a) cos 33°30′ .834 (b) cos 36.6° .803 (c) cos 18°24′ .949 (d) tan 31°30′ .613

(e) tan 42°20′ .911 (f) cos 61°40′ .474 (g) tan 58.5° 1.632 (h) cos 67°15′ .387

(i) tan 66°30′     (j) tan 63°45′ 2.028
     2.301

15. In surveying for a new highway, an engineer drove two large stakes, $A$ and $B$, on opposite banks of a river, to mark the sites of bridge abutments. Then from a point $O$, 100 m from $B$ and such that $\overleftrightarrow{OB} \perp \overleftrightarrow{AB}$, he measured the angle $\angle AOB$. If $m\angle AOB = 73$, what is the distance across the river from $A$ to $B$? AB = OB tan ∠O = 327.1m

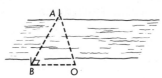

16. A ladder on a fire truck can be extended to a maximum length of 21 m when elevated to its maximum angle of 70°. The base of the ladder is mounted on the truck 2.15 m above the ground. How high above the ground will the ladder reach? h = 2.15 + 21 sin 70° ≐ 21.89 m

**Answers to Problems**

**22.**

A regular $n$-gon can be divided into $n$ congruent isosceles triangles. The radius of the inscribed circle is the altitude of each of these triangles, which is $\dfrac{e}{2}\tan\dfrac{90(n-2)}{n}$ by Problem 22 of Section 17–1. The area of the polygonal region is

$$\frac{\pi e^2}{4}\tan^2\frac{90(n-2)}{n}.$$

**Answers to Honors Problem**

(a) Let $DB = x$; then $AD = c - x$.

$$c\cdot\frac{\tan a° \tan b°}{\tan a° + \tan b°}$$

$$= c\cdot\frac{\dfrac{h}{c-x}\cdot\dfrac{h}{x}}{\dfrac{h}{c-x}+\dfrac{h}{x}}$$

$$= c\cdot\frac{h^2}{hx + hc - hx} = h.$$

(b) $h = 68\dfrac{(\tan 35°)(\tan 45°)}{\tan 35° + \tan 45°}$

$$= \frac{68(.700)(1.000)}{.700 + 1.000}$$

$$= \frac{(68)(.7)}{1.7} = 28.$$

---

**17.** A forest ranger watches for fires from a look-out tower built on a high hill. The site of the tower is 740 m above most of the surrounding land, and the tower itself is 24 m tall. If the ranger sights a fire at an angle of 7° from the horizontal, how far, to the nearest half-kilometre, is the fire from the tower?

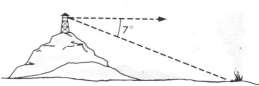

$\text{Sin } 7° = \dfrac{764}{x}$

$x \doteq 6.5\text{ km}$

**18.** An airplane is approaching an airport at an altitude of 6400 m. (Assume that the airport is close to sea level.) The pilot has orders to descend at a constant angle of 6° while coming in for a landing. How far from the runway should the pilot begin his descent? [Round your answer to the nearest tenth of a kilometre.] $\text{Sin } 6° = \dfrac{6400}{x}, x \doteq 61.0\text{ km}$

**19.** A tall radio tower is anchored by long cables called guy wires, such as $AB$ in the figure. If $A$ is 250 m from the base of the tower and if $m\angle BAC = 59$, how long is the guy wire? How far above the ground is it fastened to the tower? How tall is the tower, $\overline{DC}$, if $m\angle DAC = 71$?

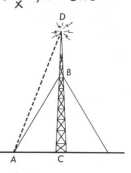

$AB = \dfrac{AC}{\cos\angle BAC} \doteq 485\text{ m}$

$BC = AC\tan\angle BAC \doteq 416\text{ m}$

$DC = AC\tan\angle DAC \doteq 726\text{ m}$

**20.** Get the best numerical approximation you can, using the table on p. 567, for the area of a regular 9-gon with sides of length 8. [See Problem 24 of Problem Set 17–1.] $\mathbf{395.57}$

**21.** Get a numerical approximation for the area of the circle inscribed in a regular 9-gon with sides of length 8. [Use 3.1416 for $\pi$.] $\mathbf{379.3}$

**22.** Derive a formula in terms of the trigonometric ratios for the area of the inscribed circle of any regular $n$-gon with sides of length $e$.

$\text{area inscribed circle} = \dfrac{\pi e^2}{4}\tan^2\dfrac{90(n-2)}{n}$

### HONORS PROBLEM

In $\triangle ABC$, $\overline{CD}$ is the altitude to $\overline{AB}$ and $AB = c$.

(a) Show that the altitude $h$ is given by the formula

$$h = c\,\frac{\tan a° \tan b°}{\tan a° + \tan b°}.$$

(b) Compute $h$ given that $c = 68$, $a = 35$, and $b = 45$. $h = 28$

## TABLE OF TRIGONOMETRIC RATIOS

| $r$ | $\sin r$ | $\cos r$ | $\tan r$ | $r$ | $\sin r$ | $\cos r$ | $\tan r$ |
|---|---|---|---|---|---|---|---|
| 1° | 0.017 | 1.000 | 0.017 | 46° | 0.719 | 0.695 | 1.035 |
| 2° | 0.035 | 0.999 | 0.035 | 47° | 0.731 | 0.682 | 1.072 |
| 3° | 0.052 | 0.999 | 0.052 | 48° | 0.743 | 0.669 | 1.111 |
| 4° | 0.070 | 0.998 | 0.070 | 49° | 0.755 | 0.656 | 1.150 |
| 5° | 0.087 | 0.996 | 0.087 | 50° | 0.766 | 0.643 | 1.192 |
| 6° | 0.105 | 0.995 | 0.105 | 51° | 0.777 | 0.629 | 1.235 |
| 7° | 0.122 | 0.993 | 0.123 | 52° | 0.788 | 0.616 | 1.280 |
| 8° | 0.139 | 0.990 | 0.141 | 53° | 0.799 | 0.602 | 1.327 |
| 9° | 0.156 | 0.988 | 0.158 | 54° | 0.809 | 0.588 | 1.376 |
| 10° | 0.174 | 0.985 | 0.176 | 55° | 0.819 | 0.574 | 1.428 |
| 11° | 0.191 | 0.982 | 0.194 | 56° | 0.829 | 0.559 | 1.483 |
| 12° | 0.208 | 0.978 | 0.213 | 57° | 0.839 | 0.545 | 1.540 |
| 13° | 0.225 | 0.974 | 0.231 | 58° | 0.848 | 0.530 | 1.600 |
| 14° | 0.242 | 0.970 | 0.249 | 59° | 0.857 | 0.515 | 1.664 |
| 15° | 0.259 | 0.966 | 0.268 | 60° | 0.866 | 0.5 | 1.732 |
| 16° | 0.276 | 0.961 | 0.287 | 61° | 0.875 | 0.485 | 1.804 |
| 17° | 0.292 | 0.956 | 0.306 | 62° | 0.883 | 0.469 | 1.881 |
| 18° | 0.309 | 0.951 | 0.325 | 63° | 0.891 | 0.454 | 1.963 |
| 19° | 0.326 | 0.946 | 0.344 | 64° | 0.899 | 0.438 | 2.050 |
| 20° | 0.342 | 0.940 | 0.364 | 65° | 0.906 | 0.423 | 2.145 |
| 21° | 0.358 | 0.934 | 0.384 | 66° | 0.914 | 0.407 | 2.246 |
| 22° | 0.375 | 0.927 | 0.404 | 67° | 0.921 | 0.391 | 2.356 |
| 23° | 0.391 | 0.921 | 0.424 | 68° | 0.927 | 0.375 | 2.475 |
| 24° | 0.407 | 0.914 | 0.445 | 69° | 0.934 | 0.358 | 2.605 |
| 25° | 0.423 | 0.906 | 0.466 | 70° | 0.940 | 0.342 | 2.747 |
| 26° | 0.438 | 0.899 | 0.488 | 71° | 0.946 | 0.326 | 2.904 |
| 27° | 0.454 | 0.891 | 0.510 | 72° | 0.951 | 0.309 | 3.078 |
| 28° | 0.469 | 0.883 | 0.532 | 73° | 0.956 | 0.292 | 3.271 |
| 29° | 0.485 | 0.875 | 0.554 | 74° | 0.961 | 0.276 | 3.487 |
| 30° | 0.5 | 0.866 | 0.577 | 75° | 0.966 | 0.259 | 3.732 |
| 31° | 0.515 | 0.857 | 0.601 | 76° | 0.970 | 0.242 | 4.011 |
| 32° | 0.530 | 0.848 | 0.625 | 77° | 0.974 | 0.225 | 4.331 |
| 33° | 0.545 | 0.839 | 0.649 | 78° | 0.978 | 0.208 | 4.705 |
| 34° | 0.559 | 0.829 | 0.675 | 79° | 0.982 | 0.191 | 5.145 |
| 35° | 0.574 | 0.819 | 0.700 | 80° | 0.985 | 0.174 | 5.671 |
| 36° | 0.588 | 0.809 | 0.727 | 81° | 0.988 | 0.156 | 6.314 |
| 37° | 0.602 | 0.799 | 0.754 | 82° | 0.990 | 0.139 | 7.115 |
| 38° | 0.616 | 0.788 | 0.781 | 83° | 0.993 | 0.122 | 8.144 |
| 39° | 0.629 | 0.777 | 0.810 | 84° | 0.995 | 0.105 | 9.514 |
| 40° | 0.643 | 0.766 | 0.839 | 85° | 0.996 | 0.087 | 11.430 |
| 41° | 0.656 | 0.755 | 0.869 | 86° | 0.998 | 0.070 | 14.301 |
| 42° | 0.669 | 0.743 | 0.900 | 87° | 0.999 | 0.052 | 19.081 |
| 43° | 0.682 | 0.731 | 0.933 | 88° | 0.999 | 0.035 | 28.636 |
| 44° | 0.695 | 0.719 | 0.966 | 89° | 1.000 | 0.017 | 57.290 |
| 45° | 0.707 | 0.707 | 1 | | | | |

## 17-3 RELATIONS AMONG THE TRIGONOMETRIC RATIOS

### Classroom Notes

The three theorems of this section are important, especially Theorem 17-1. Not only are many of the identities easily simplified by the use of these theorems, but important formulas, such as the angle addition and double angle formulas, are based in part on Theorem 17-1.

### Background Material

The word *cosine* is a contraction of the Latin phrase *complementi sinus,* meaning "sine of the complement." Theorem 17-3 states, in effect, that this term is correct.

### Quiz

**1.** Simplify the following expression. Assume that $\angle A$ and $\angle B$ are complementary angles.

$$(\sin \angle A + \sin \angle B - 1) \times (\sin \angle A + \sin \angle B + 1)$$

(ans: $2 \sin \angle A \sin \angle B$)

**2.** Write $\tan \angle A$ in terms of $\sin \angle A$. Assume that $\angle A$ is an acute angle.

(ans: $\sin \angle A/\sqrt{(1 - \sin^2 \angle A)}$)

**3.** Prove the following identity. Assume that $q$ is an acute angle.

$$\frac{\tan q + 1}{\cot q + 1} = \sin q \sec q.$$

(ans:

$$\frac{\tan q° + 1}{\cot q° + 1} = \frac{\tan q° + 1}{\dfrac{1}{\tan q°} + 1}$$

$$= \frac{\tan q° + 1}{\dfrac{1 + \tan q°}{\tan q°}}$$

$$= \frac{(\tan q° + 1) \tan q°}{1 + \tan q°}$$

$$= \tan q° = \sin q° \left(\frac{1}{\cos q°}\right)$$

$$= \sin q° \sec q°)$$

## 17–3  RELATIONS AMONG THE TRIGONOMETRIC RATIOS

In a right triangle, as in the figure, we have $a^2 + b^2 = c^2$. Dividing by $c^2$, we get

$$\left(\frac{a}{c}\right)^2 + \left(\frac{b}{c}\right)^2 = 1.$$

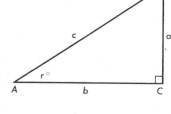

Since

$$\sin \angle A = \frac{a}{c} \quad \text{and} \quad \cos \angle A = \frac{b}{c},$$

we have the following theorem.

### Theorem 17–1

> *For every $\angle A$,  $(\sin \angle A)^2 + (\cos \angle A)^2 = 1.$*

We usually denote the square of the sine by $\sin^2 \angle A$, which is easier to write than $(\sin \angle A)^2$, and proceed similarly for the cosine. In this notation, the above equation takes the form

$$\sin^2 \angle A + \cos^2 \angle A = 1, \quad \text{or} \quad \sin^2 r° + \cos^2 r° = 1,$$

if $m \angle A = r$. All three of these equations say the same thing.

We read off from the triangle above that

$$\tan \angle A = \frac{a}{b}.$$

Since

$$\frac{a}{b} = \frac{a/c}{b/c},$$

we have the following theorem.

### Theorem 17–2

> *For every $\angle A$,*
>
> $$\tan \angle A = \frac{\sin \angle A}{\cos \angle A}.$$

In the notation of degree measures, the above statement says that for every $r$,

$$\tan r° = \frac{\sin r°}{\cos r°}.$$

Finally, looking at our right triangle sidewise, we observe that

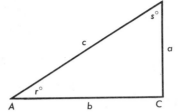

$$\sin \angle B = \frac{b}{c} = \cos \angle A$$

and

$$\cos \angle B = \frac{a}{c} = \sin \angle A.$$

Since the acute angles of a right triangle are complementary, we have

$$s = m\angle B = 90 - r.$$

## Theorem 17–3

**If $\angle A$ and $\angle B$ are complementary, then**

$$\sin \angle B = \cos \angle A$$

**and**

$$\cos \angle B = \sin \angle A.$$

For degree measures, these equations take the form

$$\sin (90 - r)° = \cos r°,$$
$$\cos (90 - r)° = \sin r°.$$

## Problem Set 17–3

Use the basic relations stated in Theorems 17–1, 17–2, and 17–3 to prove the following identities.

1. $\dfrac{\tan r°}{\tan s°} = \dfrac{\sin r° \cos s°}{\sin s° \cos r°} \cdot = \dfrac{\frac{\sin r°}{\cos r°}}{\frac{\sin s°}{\cos s°}}$

2. $\tan r° + \tan s° = \dfrac{\sin r° \cos s° + \cos r° \sin s°}{\cos r° \cos s°} \cdot = \dfrac{\sin r°}{\cos r°} + \dfrac{\sin s°}{\cos s°}$

3. $\tan r° = \dfrac{\sin r°}{\sqrt{1 - \sin^2 r°}} \cdot = \dfrac{\sin r°}{\cos r°}$

4. $1 - (\cos r° - \sin r°)^2 = 2 \sin r° \cos r°.$

5. The *cotangent* of an angle is the reciprocal of the tangent of that angle; that is,

$$\cot \angle A = \frac{1}{\tan \angle A}.$$

   (a) Prove that $\tan (90 - r)° = \cot r°.$
   (b) Prove that $\cot (90 - r)° = \tan r°.$

Answers to Problems

4. $1 - (\cos r° - \sin r°)^2$
   $= 1 - (\cos^2 r° - 2 \sin r° \cos r° + \cos^2 r°)$
   $= 1 - (1 - 2 \sin r° \cos r°)$
   $= 2 \sin r° \cos r°.$

5. (a) Consider a right triangle $\triangle RST$ with the right angle at $T$. Then

$$\cot \angle R = \frac{1}{\tan \angle R} = \frac{1}{\frac{ST}{RT}}$$

$$= \frac{RT}{ST} = \tan \angle S.$$

But $m\angle S = 90 - m\angle R$. Therefore, $\tan (90 - r°) = \cot r°.$

   (b) In the same way,

$$m\angle S = 90 - m\angle R$$

and hence

$$\cot \angle S = \frac{1}{\tan \angle S} = \frac{1}{\frac{RT}{ST}}$$

$$= \frac{ST}{RT} = \tan \angle R.$$

Therefore, $\cot (90 - r)° = \tan r°.$

6. $\dfrac{\cos r°}{1 + \sin r°} = \dfrac{\cos r°}{1 + \sin r°} \cdot \dfrac{1 - \sin r°}{1 - \sin r°}$

$$= \frac{\cos r° (1 - \sin r°)}{1 - \sin^2 r°}$$

$$= \frac{\cos r° (1 - \sin r°)}{\cos^2 r°}$$

$$= \frac{1 - \sin r°}{\cos r°}$$

8. $\dfrac{\sin r°}{1 - \cos r°} = \dfrac{\sin r°}{1 - \cos r°} \cdot \dfrac{1 + \cos r°}{1 + \cos r°}$

$$= \frac{\sin r° (1 + \cos r°)}{1 - \cos^2 r°}$$

$$= \frac{\sin r° (1 + \cos r°)}{\sin^2 r°}$$

$$= \frac{1 + \cos r°}{\sin r°}$$

11. $\sec r° - \cos r°$

$$= \frac{1}{\cos r°} - \cos r°$$

$$= \frac{1 - \cos^2 r°}{\cos r°} = \frac{\sin^2 r°}{\cos r°}$$

$$= \left(\frac{\sin r°}{\cos r°}\right) \sin r° = \tan r° \sin r°$$

**12.** Substitute $\dfrac{\sin r°}{\cos r°}$ for $\tan r°$ in each case in the expression on the left and reduce the resulting fraction to lowest terms. Then use Theorem 17–1.

**13.** Make the substitutions $\tan r° = \dfrac{\sin r°}{\cos r°}$ and $\tan s° = \dfrac{\sin s°}{\cos s°}$ in the expression on the left and reduce the resulting fraction to lowest terms.

**14.** $\dfrac{\sec r°}{\sin r°} - \dfrac{2\cos r°}{\sin r°}$

$= \dfrac{\sec r° - \cos r°}{\sin r°} - \dfrac{\cos r°}{\sin r°}$

$= \dfrac{\dfrac{1}{\cos r°} - \cos r°}{\sin r°} - \cot r°$

$= \dfrac{1 - \cos^2 r°}{\sin r° \cos r°} - \cot r°$

$= \dfrac{\sin^2 r°}{\sin r° \cos r°} - \cot r°$

$= \dfrac{\sin r°}{\cos r°} - \cot r° = \tan r° - \cot r°.$

**15.** $\dfrac{(\cos^2 r° - \sin^2 r°)^2}{\cos^4 r° - \sin^4 r°}$

$= \dfrac{(\cos^2 r° - \sin^2 r°)^2}{(\cos^2 r° - \sin^2 r°)(\cos^2 r° + \sin^2 r°)}$

$= \dfrac{\cos^2 r° - \sin^2 r°}{\cos^2 r° + \sin^2 r°}$

$= \dfrac{1 - \dfrac{\sin^2 r°}{\cos^2 r°}}{1 + \dfrac{\sin^2 r°}{\cos^2 r°}} = \dfrac{1 - \tan^2 r°}{1 + \tan^2 r°}$

Another method would be to observe the following:

$\dfrac{\cos^2 r° - \sin^2 r°}{\cos^2 r° + \sin^2 r°} = \cos^2 r° - \sin^2 r°;$

$\dfrac{1 - \tan^2 r°}{1 + \tan^2 r°} = \dfrac{1 - \tan^2 r°}{\sec^2 r°},$

$= \cos^2 r°(1 - \tan^2 r°),$

$= \cos^2 r° - \sin^2 r°.$

**16.** $\dfrac{\tan r°}{1 - \cot r°} + \dfrac{\cot r°}{1 - \tan r°}$

$= \dfrac{\tan r°}{1 - \dfrac{1}{\tan r°}} + \dfrac{\dfrac{1}{\tan r°}}{1 - \tan r°}$

---

**6.** $\dfrac{1 - \sin r°}{\cos r°} = \dfrac{\cos r°}{1 + \sin r°}$ · multiply by $\dfrac{1 - \sin r°}{1 - \sin r°}$

**7.** $\dfrac{2\sin r° \cos r°}{\cos^2 r° - \sin^2 r°} = \dfrac{2\tan r°}{1 - \tan^2 r°} \cdot = \dfrac{\dfrac{2\sin r°}{\cos r°}}{1 - \dfrac{\sin^2 r}{\cos^2 r}}$

**8.** $\dfrac{\sin r°}{1 - \cos r°} = \dfrac{1 + \cos r°}{\sin r°}$ · multiply by $\dfrac{1 + \cos r°}{1 + \cos r°}$

**9.** The *secant* of an angle is the reciprocal of the cosine of that angle; that is,

$$\sec \angle A = \dfrac{1}{\cos \angle A}.$$

Prove that $\tan r° = \sin r° \sec r°$.

$\tan r° = \dfrac{\sin r°}{\cos r°}$

$= \sin r° \cdot \dfrac{1}{\cos r°}$

$= \sin r° \cdot \sec r°$

**10.** $1 + \tan^2 r° = \sec^2 r°$. (See Problem 9.) Substitute $\dfrac{\sin r°}{\cos r°}$ for $\tan r°$ and reduce fraction to $\left(\dfrac{1}{\cos r°}\right)^2$ which is $\sec^2 r°$.

**11.** $\sec r° - \cos r° = \tan r° \sin r°$. (See Problem 9.)

**12.** $\dfrac{1 - \tan^2 r°}{1 + \tan^2 r°} = 1 - 2\sin^2 r°.$

**13.** $\dfrac{1 - \tan r° \tan s°}{\tan r° + \tan s°} = \dfrac{\cos r° \cos s° - \sin r° \sin s°}{\sin r° \cos s° + \cos r° \sin s°}.$

**14.** $\dfrac{\sec r°}{\sin r°} - \dfrac{2\cos r°}{\sin r°} = \tan r° - \cot r°.$

---

**15.** Show that $\dfrac{(\cos^2 r° - \sin^2 r°)^2}{\cos^4 r° - \sin^4 r°} = \dfrac{1 - \tan^2 r°}{1 + \tan^2 r°}.$

**16.** Show that $\dfrac{\tan r°}{1 - \cot r°} + \dfrac{\cot r°}{1 - \tan r°} = 1 + \tan r° + \cot r°.$

## 17–4   RADIAN MEASURE FOR ANGLES AND ARCS

We found, in Theorem 16–4, that if an arc has measure $q$ and radius $r$, then its length is

$$L = \dfrac{q}{180}\pi r,$$

It follows that

$$\dfrac{L}{r} = \dfrac{q}{180}\pi.$$

Thus the ratio $L/r$ depends only on $q$, the measure of the arc. It is the same for all arcs of measure $q$, regardless of the radius of the circle.

In the figure, we have

$$\frac{L_1}{r_1} = \frac{q}{180}\pi = \frac{L_2}{r_2},$$

and so

$$\frac{L_1}{r_1} = \frac{L_2}{r_2}.$$

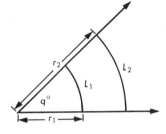

The ratio $L/r$ is called the *radian measure* of the arc. If $\widehat{AB}$ is a minor arc, then $L/r$ is also called the *radian measure of the central angle*. We denote the radian measure by $rm\widehat{AB}$ or $rm\angle BCA$. Thus, in the figure,

$$\frac{L}{r} = rm\widehat{AB} = rm\angle BCA.$$

The radian measure of an angle is usually denoted by the Greek letter $\theta$ (pronounced thāta). Thus if $m\angle C = q$, then

$$rm\angle C = \theta = \frac{q}{180}\pi.$$

Following is a table of corresponding values of $q$ and $\theta$, for various simple cases

| $q$ | 30 | 45 | 60 | 90 | 120 | 135 | 150 |
|---|---|---|---|---|---|---|---|
| $\theta$ | $\dfrac{\pi}{6}$ | $\dfrac{\pi}{4}$ | $\dfrac{\pi}{3}$ | $\dfrac{\pi}{2}$ | $\dfrac{2\pi}{3}$ | $\dfrac{3\pi}{4}$ | $\dfrac{5\pi}{6}$ |

Thus a protractor would be marked with radian measures in the following way.

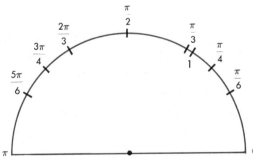

Note that the label 1 is in approximately the right place. Since $\pi$ is approximately 3.1416, we find that $\pi/3$ is approximately 1.0472, which is a little greater than 1. Therefore 1 is a little less than $\pi/3$, as the labels indicate.

---

$$= \frac{\tan^2 r°}{\tan r° - 1} + \frac{1}{\tan r°\,(1 - \tan r°)}$$

$$= \frac{\tan^3 r° - 1}{\tan r°\,(\tan r° - 1)}$$

$$= \frac{\tan^2 r° + \tan r° + 1}{\tan r°}$$

$$= \tan r° + 1 + \cot r°.$$

## 17–4 RADIAN MEASURE FOR ANGLES AND ARCS

### Classroom Notes

Here the essential fact is that the ratio $L/r$ depends only on the angle and not on the choice of the circle. This is what is needed to define radian measure.

### Background Material

For segments the unit of measure hardly matters, except for convenience, but this is not true of angles. In elementary mathematics, as in the preceding chapters of this book, any unit of angular measure will do. In higher mathematics, however, there is a "natural unit" for angles; this is the radian, and degrees are not used at all.

In this section we see the first examples of the advantage of radians: the formula for arc length takes the simple form $A = r\theta$, and the area of a sector is given by the formula $A = \frac{1}{2}r^2\theta$. In calculus, the advantage is greater, and the trigonometric functions are always defined in terms of radians. Therefore it is important to make the transition to radians in the present chapter.

**1.** If the measure of an angle is $13\pi/12$ radians, what is its measure in degrees?
(ans: 195)
**2.** What degree measure, to the nearest degree, is equivalent to 1 radian?
(ans: 57)
**3.** An angle has a measure of 135°. What is its radian measure?
(ans: $3\pi/4$)
**4.** Find the radian measure of a central angle of a circle of radius $k$ which subtends an arc of length $k$.
(ans: 1)

Working the other way around we can solve for $q$ in the formula

$$\theta = \frac{q}{180} \pi,$$

so that

$$q = \frac{180}{\pi} \theta.$$

We then set $\theta = 1$, and calculate $q = 57.296$. This is a little less than 60, as it should be.

To convert back and forth between degree and radian measure, the easiest formula is the following:

$$\frac{q}{180} = \frac{\theta}{\pi}.$$

This says that the measure of an arc, divided by the measure of a semicircle, is the same in degrees and in radians. That is, *the ratio does not depend on the unit of measure.*

**Problem Set 17–4**

**1.** In the figure, each of the arcs has measure $q$. If $r_1, r_2, r_3 \sim 2, 3, 4$, find

(a) $\dfrac{L_1}{L_3} \cdot \dfrac{1}{2}$   (b) $\dfrac{L_1}{L_2} \cdot \dfrac{2}{3}$   (c) $\dfrac{L_2}{L_3} \cdot \dfrac{3}{4}$

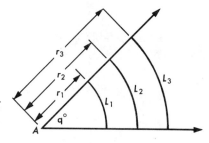

**2.** Why is the radian measure of a central angle defined only for central angles having minor arcs? Semicircles and major arcs do not have central angles

**3.** The circular protractor shown on page 571 may be thought of as a tool primarily for measuring arcs. The scale marked around the inside of the circle indicates degree measure. Copy this figure and mark the equivalent scale in radian measure around the outside of the figure.

**4.** Convert radian measure to degree measure for the following:

(a) $\dfrac{\pi}{2}$ 90°   (b) $\dfrac{\pi}{15}$ 12°   (c) $\dfrac{3\pi}{8}$ 67½°   (d) $\dfrac{4\pi}{3}$ 240°

(e) $\dfrac{6\pi}{5}$ 216°   (f) $\dfrac{9\pi}{8}$ 202½°   (g) $\dfrac{17\pi}{12}$ 255°   (h) $\dfrac{26\pi}{15}$ 312°

**5.** Convert degree measure to radian measure for the following:

(a) 60 $\dfrac{\pi}{3}$   (b) 36 $\dfrac{5}{\pi}$   (c) 84 $\dfrac{7\pi}{15}$   (d) 100 $\dfrac{5\pi}{9}$

(e) 150 $\dfrac{5\pi}{6}$   (f) 112½ $\dfrac{5\pi}{8}$   (g) 225 $\dfrac{5\pi}{4}$   (h) 330 $\dfrac{11\pi}{6}$

**6.** To the nearest degree, what is the degree measure equivalent to 3 radians?
$$172°$$

**7.** (a) What is the circumference of a circle whose radius is 1? (Leave answer in terms of $\pi$.) $2\pi$

   (b) What is the radian measure of an arc of 360°? $2\pi$

## 17–5  DIRECTED ANGLES AND THE WINDING FUNCTION

In Section 4–1 we defined an angle to be simply a set of points. If two rays have the same end point but do not lie on the same line, then their union is an angle. The rays $\overrightarrow{AB}$ and $\overrightarrow{AC}$ are the sides of $\angle BAC$. The order in which these rays are mentioned does not matter. Thus $\angle BAC$ and $\angle CAB$ are exactly the same angle.

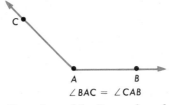
$\angle BAC = \angle CAB$

  From now on, however, we shall be dealing also with *directed angles*, in which the order of the sides really does make a difference. This idea is conveyed by the following figures.

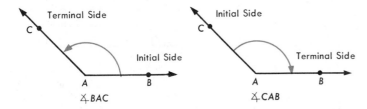

We use the symbol $\measuredangle$ to indicate a directed angle. Note that $\measuredangle BAC \neq \measuredangle CAB$. We make this idea official in the following definition:

### Definition

Let $\overrightarrow{AB}$ and $\overrightarrow{AC}$ be any two rays with the same endpoint. The *directed angle* $\measuredangle BAC$ is the ordered pair $(\overrightarrow{AB}, \overrightarrow{AC})$. The ray $\overrightarrow{AB}$ is called the *initial side* of $\measuredangle BAC$, and the ray $\overrightarrow{AC}$ is called the *terminal side*.

  Note that in this definition, the rays may be collinear. Thus a directed angle may turn out to be a "zero angle" or a "straight angle."

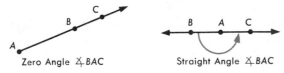

**17–5 DIRECTED ANGLES AND THE WINDING FUNCTION**

**Classroom Notes**

The meaning of directed angles becomes clearer when we use the winding function. An angle with measure $\pi/2$ is not the same as an angle with measure $-\pi/2$, because the terminal sides are in different quadrants of the coordinate system.

  The distinction between $\angle BAC$ for the undirected angle and $\measuredangle BAC$ for the directed angle need not be observed consistently if the context makes the meaning clear. It is important, however, to have a notation which avoids ambiguity when necessary.

Most first course algebra texts use the idea of a function, and so most students will be familiar with it. The description of a function by ordered pairs is easy to understand, and may already be familiar.

It is a fact that the winding function is periodic, with period equal to $2\pi$. That is, $W(\theta + 2\pi) = W(\theta)$, for every $\theta$. But at this stage there is no need to state this as a theorem in the text. The fact is observed naturally, when the student works on simple problems, such as Problem 6. For example, to locate $W(9\pi)$, we subtract multiples of $2\pi$ until we get a number between 0 and $2\pi$. Thus $W(9\pi) = W(\pi)$, and the point is now easy to locate. Similarly, in Problem 9, $W(101\pi) = W(\pi)$. After many such experiences, the student is ready to solve Problems 13 and 14 by making a generalization.

Consider now the circle $C$ in the $xy$-plane with center at the origin and radius equal to 1. $C$ is called the unit circle. [*Query:* What is the circumference of the unit circle?]

Let $W(0)$ be the point $(1, 0)$, as in the figures below. To each real number $\theta$ there corresponds a point of $C$, denoted $W(\theta)$, and determined according to the following rules.

(1) If $\theta > 0$, we start at $W(0)$ and move around $C$ in the *counterclockwise* direction until we have traced out a path whose total length is $\theta$. The point where our path ends is $W(\theta)$.

(2) If $\theta < 0$, we start at $W(0)$ and move around $C$ in the *clockwise* direction, until we have traced out a path whose total length is $|\theta|$. The point where our path ends is $W(\theta)$.

Since the circumference of the unit circle $C$ is $2\pi$, it follows that $W(2\pi) = W(0)$, for going around the circle once brings us back where we started. Going halfway around, we get to $W(\pi) = (-1, 0)$. Similarly, $W(\pi/2) = (0, 1)$ and $W(3\pi/2) = (0, -1)$. These points are shown in the figure on the left below.

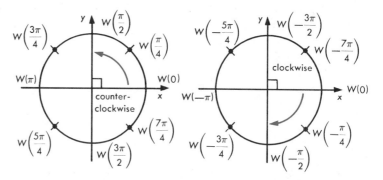

The figure on the right above shows that for negative values of $\theta$ we go clockwise, getting to the same points in different ways.

Under rules (1) and (2), as stated above, we have a correspondence $\theta \rightarrow W(\theta)$ between real numbers $\theta$ and points $W(\theta)$ of the unit circle. A correspondence of this sort is called a *function*. In particular, the correspondence $W$ is called the *winding function*.

Probably you have encountered the idea of a function before, in your study of algebra. There are essentially two ways to define a function.

Given a set $A$, called the domain, and a set $B$, called the range, we can state a rule under which to each element of $A$ there corresponds a unique element of $B$. We then have a function $f : A \rightarrow B$, mapping $A$ into $B$. This is the way we define the winding function. In this case, the domain $A$ is the set of all real numbers, and the range $B$ is the set of all points of the unit circle.

Another way to define a function is to use a collection of ordered pairs. For example, if $A = \{P, Q, R, S, T\}$ and $B = \{-2, -1, 0, 1, 2, 3, 4\}$, then the collection

$$\{(P, -1), (Q, 0), (R, 1), (S, 3), (T, 3)\}$$

defines a function $f : A \to B$. Under the action of this function, $P \to -1$, $Q \to 0$, $R \to 1$, $S \to 3$, and $T \to 3$. Thus the ordered pairs tell us what element of $B$ corresponds to each element of $A$. Note that the collection

$$\{(P, -1), (Q, 0), (R, 1), (Q, 3), (S, 3), (T, 4)\}$$

does *not* define a function. [Why?]

In fact, every function can be thought of as a collection of ordered pairs, if we allow the collection to be infinite. For example, the winding function can be thought of as the set of all ordered pairs of the form $(\theta, W(\theta))$.

A directed angle is in standard position, in a coordinate plane, if its initial side is the positive end of the $x$-axis.

In the figure, $\angle POA$, $\angle POB$, and $\angle POC$ are in standard position, but $\angle AOB$ is not. If $P = W(0)$ and $A = W(\theta)$, then we write: $\angle POA = \angle\theta$. That is, $\angle\theta$ is the angle in standard position determined by $\theta$.

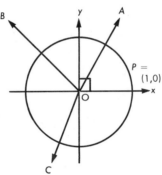

## Problem Set 17-5

1. Draw a set of perpendicular coordinate axes and a unit circle. Sketch some angle, called $\angle\theta$, in standard position for each of the following conditions.

   (a) $0 < \theta < \dfrac{\pi}{2}$  Quad I      (b) $-\dfrac{\pi}{2} < \theta < 0$  Quad IV

   (c) $\pi < \theta < \frac{3}{2}\pi$  Quad II      (d) $-\frac{3}{2}\pi < \theta < -\pi$  Quad II

2. For each angle of Problem 1 specify the quadrant that contains the point $W(\theta)$. See above.

3. Give the terminal side, for each angle named below, if possible.

   (a) $\angle ABC$ $\overrightarrow{BC}$      (b) $\angle GDF$ $\overrightarrow{DF}$      (c) $\angle BAC$ none

   (d) $\angle PQR$ $\overrightarrow{QR}$      (e) $\angle QPR$ none      (f) $\angle DKM$ $\overrightarrow{KM}$

4. (a) If $\angle\theta = \angle BCA$ and $\overrightarrow{CB} = \overrightarrow{CA}$, what is $\theta$? The zero-angle

   (b) If $\angle\theta = \angle BCA$ and $\overrightarrow{CB}$ and $\overrightarrow{CA}$ are opposite rays, what is $\theta$?
   The straight angle

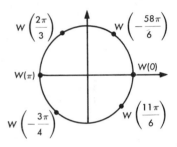
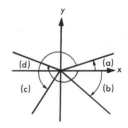

**10.** Since the circumference of the unit circle is $2\pi$, the distance around the circle from a point $W(\theta)$ to itself is $2\pi$ and thus $W(\theta) = W(\theta + 2\pi)$.

**5.** Given that $\sphericalangle \theta = \sphericalangle ABC$ in standard position. Name the quadrant that contains the point $C$ for each value of $\theta$.

(a) $\frac{5}{8}\pi$ **Quad II**     (b) $-\frac{1}{3}\pi$ **Quad IV**     (c) $\frac{6}{5}\pi$ **Quad III**

(d) $-\frac{23}{12}\pi$ **Quad I**     (e) $-\frac{4}{7}\pi$ **Quad III**     (f) $\frac{19}{10}\pi$ **Quad IV**

**6.** Let $A = W(0)$, $B = W\left(\frac{1}{2}\pi\right)$, $C = W(\pi)$, and $D = W\left(\frac{3}{2}\pi\right)$. Denote by the capital letters $A$, $B$, $C$, $D$ each of the following points.

(a) $W(2\pi)$ **A**    (b) $W(3\pi)$ **C**    (c) $W\left(\frac{7}{2}\pi\right)$ **D**    (d) $W\left(\frac{5}{2}\pi\right)$ **B**

(e) $W(9\pi)$ **C**    (f) $W\left(\frac{15}{2}\pi\right)$ **D**    (g) $W\left(\frac{21}{2}\pi\right)$ **B**    (h) $W(20\pi)$ **A**

**7.** Follow the directions of Problem 6.

(a) $W(-\pi)$ **C**    (b) $W\left(-\frac{7}{2}\pi\right)$ **B**    (c) $W(-11\pi)$ **C**    (d) $W\left(\frac{9}{2}\pi\right)$ **B**

(e) $W\left(\frac{17}{2}\pi\right)$ **B**    (f) $W\left(-\frac{5}{2}\pi\right)$ **D**    (g) $W(-16\pi)$ **A**    (h) $W\left(-\frac{13}{2}\pi\right)$ **D**

**8.** Copy this figure of a circle with 16 points marked as shown. Label each of the points except for $W(0)$ with the capital letters $A$ through $P$ corresponding to the following.

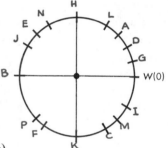

A. $W\left(\frac{1}{4}\pi\right)$    B. $W(-\pi)$    C. $W\left(\frac{5}{3}\pi\right)$

D. $W\left(\frac{13}{6}\pi\right)$    E. $W\left(\frac{11}{4}\pi\right)$    F. $W\left(\frac{10}{3}\pi\right)$

G. $W\left(\frac{49}{12}\pi\right)$    H. $W\left(\frac{9}{2}\pi\right)$    I. $W\left(-\frac{1}{6}\pi\right)$    J. $W\left(\frac{5}{6}\pi\right)$    K. $W\left(-\frac{13}{2}\pi\right)$

L. $W\left(\frac{19}{3}\pi\right)$    M. $W\left(-\frac{9}{4}\pi\right)$    N. $W\left(-\frac{4}{3}\pi\right)$    P. $W\left(\frac{13}{4}\pi\right)$

**9.** Some of the points named in Problem 8 are listed below. Identify each with the appropriate capital letter as specified in Problem 8.

(a) $W(101\pi)$ **B**    (b) $W\left(\frac{505}{2}\pi\right)$ **H**    (c) $W(999\pi)$ **B**    (d) $W\left(\frac{304}{3}\pi\right)$ **F**

**10.** Is it true for each real number $\theta$ that $W(\theta) = W(\theta + 2\pi)$? Explain. **Yes**

**11.** For what values of $\theta$ between 0 and $6\pi$ is it true that $W(\theta) = W(-\theta)$?
**$\pi$, $2\pi$, $3\pi$, $4\pi$, $5\pi$**

**12.** Given a point $R = W(\theta)$ of a circle. Explain the position of the point $S = W(\theta + \pi)$ with respect to $R$. **Opposite ends of a diameter**

---

**13.** For what values of $n$ is it true that $W(\theta) = W(\theta + 2n\pi)$? **All integers**

**14.** For what values of $n$ is it true that $W(\theta) = W(\theta - 2n\pi)$? **All integers**

**15.** Find a general formula for all the numbers $x$ such that $W(\theta) = W(x)$.
**$\{x \mid x = \theta + 2n\pi, \ n \ \text{any integer}\}$**

16. Let $A = \{K, L, M\}$, let $B = \{0, 1, 2\}$.

$$\text{Let } f: A \to B = \{(K, 1), (L, 0), (M, 2)\}.$$
$$\text{Let } g: A \to B = \{(K, 0), (L, 0), (M, 0)\}.$$

(a) Is $f$ a function? Yes (b) Is $g$ a function? Yes

(c) Is $f$ a one-to-one correspondence? Yes

(d) Is $g$ a one-to-one correspondence? No

17. Consider the correspondence $x \to 2x$, where $x$ is any real number. Some elements of this correspondence are the pairs (1, 2), (3, 6), $(\frac{1}{2}, 1)$, $(-\frac{2}{3}, -\frac{4}{3})$, $(\sqrt{3}, 2\sqrt{3})$, and so on.

(a) Is this correspondence a function? Yes

(b) Is this correspondence one-to-one? Yes

18. Consider the correspondence $t \to t^2$, where $t$ is any real number. Some elements of this correspondence are the pairs (0, 0), (2, 4), (3, 9), $(\sqrt{2}, 2)$, (−3, 9), (−1, 1), and so on.

(a) Is this correspondence a function? Yes

(b) Is this correspondence one-to-one? No

## 17-6 TRIGONOMETRIC FUNCTIONS OF ANGLES AND OF NUMBERS

In this section we will examine our concept of the trigonometric ratios in terms of our new concept of angle. First consider the following discussion, which is similar to the introduction to Section 17-1.

In the figure the innermost circle is a unit circle, $W(0) = (1, 0)$, and $W(\theta) = (x_1, y_1)$ is a point in the first quadrant. By dropping three perpendiculars to the $x$-axis we form three right triangles, each having $\angle\theta$ as an angle. Our previous definition of sine can be applied giving

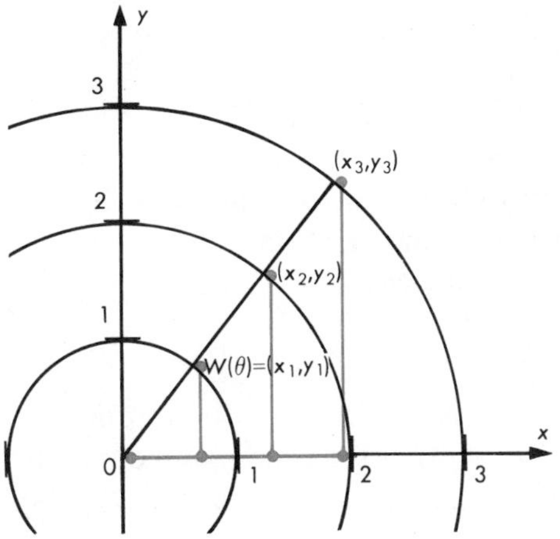


$$\sin \angle\theta = \frac{y_1}{1} = \frac{y_2}{2} = \frac{y_3}{3}.$$

These equations give

$$y_1 = \sin \angle\theta, \quad y_2 = 2 \sin \angle\theta = 2y_1, \quad y_3 = 3 \sin \angle\theta = 3y_1.$$

### 17-6 TRIGONOMETRIC FUNCTION OF ANGLES AND OF NUMBERS

**Classroom Notes**

In this section it is important to stress that the trigonometric functions are defined for numbers, not just for angles. (It is a common but unfortunate practice to refer to numbers as angles when trigonometric functions are being discussed. When this happens, it means that the idea of a trigonometric function of a number has not really been accepted.)

Problems 9 and 10 may form a good basis for an extended class discussion; they may be solved as a joint enterprise of you and the class. The resulting graphs will be more instructive than formulas and tables. One method the students could use to draw the graph would be the following: Draw a unit circle and a second graph of the same scale as shown below. On the circle mark points $W\left(\dfrac{n\pi}{4}\right)$, $0 \le n \le 8$ and $W\left(\dfrac{n\pi}{6}\right)$, $0 \le n \le 12$. Using the unit circle to measure the length of the $\sin\theta$, mark the points $(\theta, \sin\theta)$ on the second graph. Connect the points to finish the graph.

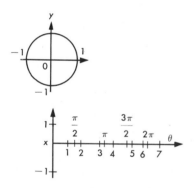

Some students may feel the need to draw more of the graph, say, on the interval from $-\pi$ to 0. If this happens, then the resulting disussion may bring out the fact that $\sin(-\theta) = -\sin\theta$, anticipating one of the theorems in the next section. Or the students may draw the extended graph simply by plotting more points, and then observe that $\sin(-\theta) = -\sin\theta$. Further extensions of the graph may bring out the identity $\sin(\theta + 2\pi) = \sin\theta$.

A discussion session along these lines may arouse keen interest, especially in a strong class. If so, it is well worth an hour.

Thus, regardless of the radius of the circle, we see that the sine of $\angle\theta$ can be expressed solely in terms of the unit circle. A similar result holds for the cosine of $\angle\theta$. With this in mind, the following figure makes sense.

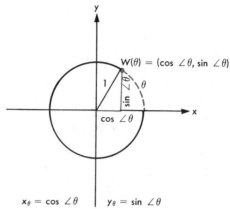

$$x_\theta = \cos\angle\theta \qquad y_\theta = \sin\angle\theta$$

Now consider the directed angle $\angle\theta$ shown in the figure, with $W(\theta)$, a point in the third quadrant. A perpendicular from this point to the $x$-axis forms a leg of a right triangle (shown in color) which is congruent to a triangle in the first quadrant. By comparing these two triangles, we see that the lengths of the sides of the triangle in the third quadrant should be $|\sin\angle\theta|$ and $|\cos\angle\theta|$, and that $W(\theta) = (\cos\angle\theta, \sin\angle\theta)$ as before. Thus we are led to begin our formal presentation with definitions for sine, cosine, and tangent of directed angles.

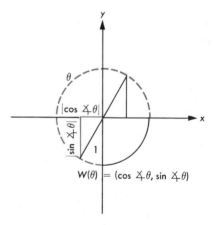

### Definition

Given a unit circle in a coordinate plane. Let $W(0) = (1, 0)$ and let $\theta \to W(\theta)$ be the winding function. For each real number $\theta$, let $W(\theta) = (x_\theta, y_\theta)$, and let $\angle\theta = \angle W(0)OW(\theta)$. Then

$$\sin\angle\theta = y_\theta$$
$$\cos\angle\theta = x_\theta$$
$$\tan\angle\theta = \frac{y_\theta}{x_\theta}, \quad \text{(whenever } x_\theta \ne 0\text{).}$$

The formulas of this definition apply for all possible locations of $W(\theta)$ on the unit circle. Observe that when $\theta = 5\pi/4$, $W(\theta)$ lies in the third quadrant, and the coordinates $x_\theta$ and $y_\theta$ are both negative numbers. Consequently, $\sin \sphericalangle 5\pi/4$ and $\cos \sphericalangle 5\pi/4$ are both negative numbers, but $\tan \sphericalangle 5\pi/4$ is a positive number, because the quotient of two negative numbers is a positive number. [*Query:* What is the sign of $\cos \sphericalangle 3\pi/4$? of $\sin \sphericalangle 3\pi/4$? of $\sin \sphericalangle (-\pi/6)$? of $\tan \sphericalangle (-\pi/6)$?]

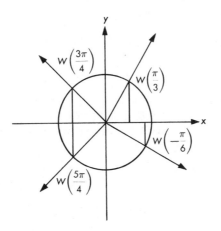

Since the new definitions work for every real number $\theta$, we can state the following.

### Definition

For every real number $\theta$, the correspondences

$$\theta \rightarrow \sin \sphericalangle \theta, \quad \theta \rightarrow \cos \sphericalangle \theta, \quad \theta \rightarrow \tan \sphericalangle \theta$$

are called the *trigonometric functions*.

Furthermore, since $\sphericalangle \theta$ is determined when $\theta$ is known, it follows that

$$\sin \theta = \sin \sphericalangle \theta,$$
$$\cos \theta = \cos \sphericalangle \theta,$$
$$\tan \theta = \tan \sphericalangle \theta.$$

That is, we have the following definition.

### Definition

A *trigonometric function of a number* $\theta$ is the same trigonometric function of the corresponding directed angle, $\sphericalangle \theta$.

We can now calculate numerical values of the trigonometric functions for various simple values of $\theta$. For example, since $W(0) = (1, 0)$, we get

$$\cos 0 = 1, \sin 0 = 0, \tan 0 = \frac{0}{1} = 0.$$

**Quiz** (closed book)

Evaluate each of the following.
1. $\sin 0$      (ans: 0)
2. $\cos (7\pi/6)$      (ans: $-\sqrt{3}/2$)
3. $\tan (-5\pi/3)$      (ans: $\sqrt{3}$)
4. $\cos \pi$      (ans: $-1$)
5. $\sin (-5\pi/4)$      (ans: $\sqrt{2}/2$)
6. $\tan (9\pi/2)$      (ans: undefined)
7. $\sin (11\pi/6)$      (ans: $-1/2$)
8. $\cot (-\pi/4)$      (ans: $-1$)
9. $\sec (5\pi/3)$      (ans: 2)
10. $\cos (15\pi/2)$      (ans: 0)
11. $\sin (4\pi/3)$      (ans: $-\sqrt{3}/2$)
12. $\cot (\pi/2)$      (ans: 0)
13. $\sin (-11\pi/6)$      (ans: 1/2)
14. $\cos (2\pi/3)$      (ans: $-1/2$)
15. $\sec (17\pi/6)$      (ans: $-2\sqrt{3}/3$)

Problems 11 and 12 look ahead to Section 17–8 and the addition formulas. These problems could be used as preparation exercises for this section and thus could be assigned after Section 17–7 has been read and discussed.

Similarly, $W(\pi) = (-1, 0)$ gives us

$$\cos \pi = -1, \quad \sin \pi = 0, \quad \tan \pi = \frac{0}{-1} = 0.$$

For $\theta = \pi/2$, $W(\theta) = (0, 1)$ gives us

$$\cos \frac{\pi}{2} = 0 \quad \text{and} \quad \sin \frac{\pi}{2} = 1.$$

(*Note:* We might start to write $1/0$ as the value for $\tan \pi/2$ until we realize that $1/0$ is not a number. This is why we define $\tan \measuredangle \theta$ by writing

$$\tan \measuredangle \theta = \frac{y_\theta}{x_\theta} \quad \text{(whenever } x_\theta \neq 0\text{)}.$$

Thus we conclude that $\tan \pi/2$ does not exist.)

We tabulate these results in a more compact form.

Table 1

| $\theta$ | $\sin \theta$ | $\cos \theta$ | $\tan \theta$ |
|---|---|---|---|
| $0$ | $0$ | $1$ | $0$ |
| $\dfrac{\pi}{2}$ | $1$ | $0$ | — |
| $\pi$ | $0$ | $-1$ | $0$ |
| $\dfrac{3\pi}{2}$ | $-1$ | $0$ | — |

We can calculate values of the trigonometric functions for some other values of $\theta$ by using the 30-60-90 and 45-45-90 triangles. First study the figure to make sure you understand all the labels. Then you can simply read the values of the sine and cosine functions from the figure and easily compute the values of the tangent function.

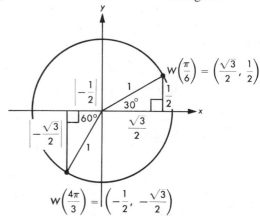

## Table 2

| $\theta$ | $\sin \theta$ | $\cos \theta$ | $\tan \theta$ |
|---|---|---|---|
| $\dfrac{\pi}{6}$ | $\dfrac{1}{2}$ | $\dfrac{\sqrt{3}}{2}$ | $\dfrac{\sqrt{3}}{3}$ |
| $\dfrac{4\pi}{3}$ | $-\dfrac{\sqrt{3}}{2}$ | $-\dfrac{1}{2}$ | $\sqrt{3}$ |

## Problem Set 17–6

1. On a unit circle let the point $W(\pi/4)$ be called $A$ and let $D$ be the foot of the perpendicular from $A$ to the $x$-axis. What are the lengths $OD$ and $AD$? What are the coordinates of the point $A$? What is $\sin \pi/4$? What is $\cos \pi/4$? What is $\tan \pi/4$? $OD = AD = \frac{\sqrt{2}}{2}$, $\left(\frac{\sqrt{2}}{2}, \frac{\sqrt{2}}{2}\right)$, $\frac{\sqrt{2}}{2}$, $\frac{\sqrt{2}}{2}$, $1$

2. On a unit circle let $W(7\pi/6) = B$ and let $D$ be the foot of the perpendicular from $B$ to the $x$-axis. What are the lengths $BD$ and $OD$? What are the coordinates of $B$? What is $\sin 7\pi/6$? $\cos 7\pi/6$? $\tan 7\pi/6$? $BD = \frac{1}{2}$
$OD = \sqrt{3}/2$, $(-\sqrt{3}/2, -\frac{1}{2})$, $-\frac{1}{2}$, $-\sqrt{3}/2$, $\sqrt{3}/3$

3. Following the pattern established in Problems 1 and 2, construct a figure and calculate the values of the three trigonometric functions for each of the following numbers.

(a) $\dfrac{\pi}{3}$   $\begin{aligned}\sin \pi/3 &= \sqrt{3}/2\\ \cos \pi/3 &= \frac{1}{2}\\ \tan \pi/3 &= \sqrt{3}\end{aligned}$    (b) $\dfrac{2\pi}{3}$   $\begin{aligned}\sin 2\pi/3 &= \sqrt{3}/2\\ \cos 2\pi/3 &= -\frac{1}{2}\\ \tan 2\pi/3 &= -\sqrt{3}\end{aligned}$    (c) $\dfrac{5\pi}{3}$   $\begin{aligned}\sin 5\pi/3 &= -\sqrt{3}/2\\ \cos 5\pi/3 &= \frac{1}{2}\\ \tan 5\pi/3 &= -\sqrt{3}\end{aligned}$

4. Do as directed in Problem 3 for each of the following numbers.

(a) $\dfrac{3\pi}{4}$   $\begin{aligned}\sin 3\pi/4 &= \sqrt{2}/2\\ \cos 3\pi/4 &= -\sqrt{2}/2\\ \tan 3\pi/4 &= -1\end{aligned}$    (b) $\dfrac{5\pi}{4}$   $\begin{aligned}\sin 5\pi/4 &= -\sqrt{2}/2\\ \cos 5\pi/4 &= -\sqrt{2}/2\\ \tan 5\pi/4 &= 1\end{aligned}$    (c) $\dfrac{7\pi}{4}$   $\begin{aligned}\sin 7\pi/4 &= -\sqrt{2}/2\\ \cos 7\pi/4 &= \sqrt{2}/2\\ \tan 7\pi/4 &= -1\end{aligned}$

5. Tabulate the results of Problems 1, 3, and 4 in a table similar to Tables 1 and 2 on pages 580 and 581.

6. Complete the sequence begun in Table 2, p. 581, and in Problem 2 above, by making any necessary calculations to find values of the three trigonometric functions for the number $n\pi/6$, $n = 1, 5, 7, 11$. Tabulate your results. Why is it not necessary to make calculations for other values of $n$?

7. Use the results of the previous problems, if possible, to find values of the trigonometric functions of the following numbers.

(a) $\dfrac{11\pi}{4}$   $\begin{aligned}\sin 11\pi/4 &= \sqrt{2}/2\\ \cos 11\pi/4 &= -\sqrt{2}/2\\ \tan 11\pi/4 &= -1\end{aligned}$    (b) $-\dfrac{4\pi}{3}$   $\begin{aligned}\sin -4\pi/3 &= \sqrt{3}/2\\ \cos -4\pi/3 &= -\frac{1}{2}\\ \tan -4\pi/3 &= -\sqrt{3}\end{aligned}$    (c) $\dfrac{19\pi}{2}$   $\begin{aligned}\sin 19\pi/2 &= -1\\ \cos 19\pi/2 &= 0\\ \tan 19\pi/2 &= \text{undefined}\end{aligned}$

8. Do as directed in Problem 7 for the following numbers.

(a) $\dfrac{31\pi}{6}$   $\begin{aligned}\sin 31\pi/6 &= -\frac{1}{2}\\ \cos 31\pi/6 &= -\sqrt{3}/2\\ \tan 31\pi/6 &= \sqrt{3}/3\end{aligned}$    (b) $-13\pi$   $\begin{aligned}\sin -13\pi &= 0\\ \cos -13\pi &= -1\\ \tan -13\pi &= 0\end{aligned}$    (c) $16\pi$   $\begin{aligned}\sin 16\pi &= 0\\ \cos 16\pi &= 1\\ \tan 16\pi &= 0\end{aligned}$

## Answers to Problems

5.

| $\theta$ | $\sin \theta$ | $\cos \theta$ | $\tan \theta$ |
|---|---|---|---|
| $\dfrac{\pi}{3}$ | $\dfrac{\sqrt{3}}{2}$ | $\dfrac{1}{2}$ | $\sqrt{3}$ |
| $\dfrac{2\pi}{3}$ | $\dfrac{\sqrt{3}}{2}$ | $-\dfrac{1}{2}$ | $-\sqrt{3}$ |
| $\dfrac{3\pi}{4}$ | $\dfrac{\sqrt{2}}{2}$ | $-\dfrac{\sqrt{2}}{2}$ | $-1$ |
| $\dfrac{5\pi}{4}$ | $-\dfrac{\sqrt{2}}{2}$ | $-\dfrac{\sqrt{2}}{2}$ | $1$ |
| $\dfrac{5\pi}{3}$ | $-\dfrac{\sqrt{3}}{2}$ | $\dfrac{1}{2}$ | $-\sqrt{3}$ |
| $\dfrac{7\pi}{4}$ | $-\dfrac{\sqrt{2}}{2}$ | $\dfrac{\sqrt{2}}{2}$ | $-1$ |

6.

| $\theta$ | $\sin \theta$ | $\cos \theta$ | $\tan \theta$ |
|---|---|---|---|
| $\dfrac{\pi}{6}$ | $\dfrac{1}{2}$ | $\dfrac{\sqrt{3}}{2}$ | $\dfrac{\sqrt{3}}{3}$ |
| $\dfrac{5\pi}{6}$ | $\dfrac{1}{2}$ | $-\dfrac{\sqrt{3}}{2}$ | $-\dfrac{\sqrt{3}}{3}$ |
| $\dfrac{7\pi}{6}$ | $-\dfrac{1}{2}$ | $-\dfrac{\sqrt{3}}{2}$ | $\dfrac{\sqrt{3}}{3}$ |
| $\dfrac{11\pi}{6}$ | $-\dfrac{1}{2}$ | $\dfrac{\sqrt{3}}{2}$ | $-\dfrac{\sqrt{3}}{3}$ |

**15.** In the figure, $\triangle OAB \cong \triangle OCD$ by SAA. Therefore $OB = OD$ and $CD = AB$. Now $OB = |x| = x$ because $x > 0$, and $OD = |x'| = -x'$ because $x' < 0$. Therefore $\cos(\theta + \pi) = x' = -x = -\cos\theta$. Similarly, $|y'| = |y|$, $y' = -y$, and

$$\sin(\theta + \pi) = -\sin\theta.$$

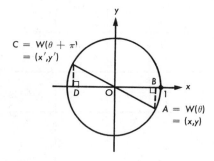

**18.** In the figure $\triangle OAB \cong \triangle COD$ by SAA. Therefore $OB = CD$ and $AB = OD$. Now $AB = |y| = y$ because $y > 0$, and $OD = |x'| = -x'$ because $x' < 0$. Therefore $x' = -y$, and $\cos(\theta + \pi/2) = -\sin\theta$. Similarly, $|y'| = |x|$, $y' = -x$, and

$$\sin(\theta + \pi/2) = -\cos\theta.$$

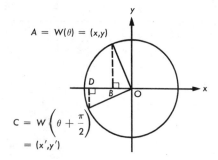

**9.** Explain why $\sin(\theta + 2n\pi) = \sin\theta$ for all integral values of $n$.

$W(\theta) = W(\theta + 2n\pi)$ for all integral values of $n$

**10.** Does $\cos(\theta + 2n\pi) = \cos\theta$ for all integers $n$? Why? Yes

$W(\theta) = W(\theta + 2n\pi)$

**11.** Verify the following equation by substituting numerical values for each trigonometric term.

$$\cos\frac{5\pi}{6} = \cos\frac{\pi}{3}\cos\frac{\pi}{2} - \sin\frac{\pi}{3}\sin\frac{\pi}{3}$$

How is $\frac{5\pi}{6}$ related to $\frac{\pi}{3}$ and $\frac{\pi}{2}$? $\frac{5\pi}{6} = \frac{\pi}{3} + \frac{\pi}{2}$

**12.** Verify the following equation by substituting numerical values for each trigonometric term.

$$\sin\frac{5\pi}{6} = \sin\frac{\pi}{3}\cos\frac{\pi}{2} + \cos\frac{\pi}{3}\sin\frac{\pi}{2}.$$

$\sin(a+b) = \sin a\cos b + \cos a + \sin b$

Letting $a = \frac{\pi}{3}$ and $b = \frac{\pi}{2}$, write a formula for $\sin(a + b)$. Does this formula hold if $a = \pi$ and $b = \frac{\pi}{2}$? Yes

**13.** Given that $\sin\theta = \frac{1}{2}\sqrt{3}$, use the figure to find $\sin(\theta + \pi)$. $-\frac{1}{2}\sqrt{3}$ If $0 < \theta < \frac{\pi}{2}$, what is $\theta$? $\frac{\pi}{3}$ If $2\pi < \theta < 5\pi/2$, what is $\theta$? $\frac{7\pi}{3}$

**14.** Given that $\cos\theta = \frac{1}{2}\sqrt{2}$, use the figure to find $\cos(\theta + \pi)$. $-\frac{1}{2}\sqrt{2}$ If $0 < \theta < \frac{\pi}{2}$, what is $\theta$? $\frac{\pi}{4}$ If $2\pi < \theta < 5\pi/2$, what is $\theta$? $\frac{9\pi}{4}$

**15.** On a figure like the one for Problems 13 and 14 demonstrate that for $\frac{3\pi}{2} < \theta < 2\pi$, $\sin(\theta + \pi) = -\sin\theta$ and that $\cos(\theta + \pi) = -\cos\theta$.

**16.** Given that $\sin\theta = \frac{1}{2}$, use the figure to find $\cos\left(\theta + \frac{\pi}{2}\right)$ and $\cos\left(\theta - \frac{\pi}{2}\right)$. $-\frac{1}{2}$     $\frac{1}{2}$

**17.** Given that $\cos\theta = \frac{1}{2}\sqrt{3}$, use the figure to find $\sin\left(\theta + \frac{\pi}{2}\right)$ and $\sin\left(\theta - \frac{\pi}{2}\right)$. $\frac{\sqrt{3}}{2}$     $-\frac{\sqrt{3}}{2}$

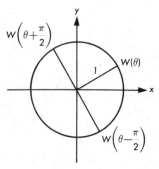

**18.** On a figure like the one for Problems 16 and 17 demonstrate that for $\frac{\pi}{2} < \theta < \pi$, $\sin\left(\theta + \frac{\pi}{2}\right) = \cos\theta$, and $\cos\left(\theta + \frac{\pi}{2}\right) = -\sin\theta$. Can you find an equivalent formula for $\sin\left(\theta - \frac{\pi}{2}\right)$ and $\cos\left(\theta - \frac{\pi}{2}\right)$?

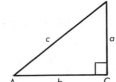

$\sin(\theta - \frac{\pi}{2}) = -\cos\theta \qquad \cos(\theta - \frac{\pi}{2}) = \sin\theta$

## 17-7  SOME BASIC TRIGONOMETRIC IDENTITIES

In Section 17–3 we studied ratios defined for the acute angles of a right triangle. We found that

$$\sin^2 \angle A + \cos^2 \angle A = 1, \quad \text{and}$$

$$\frac{\sin \angle A}{\cos \angle A} = \tan \angle A,$$

for every acute angle $\angle A$. One would expect, therefore, corresponding theorems for the trigonometric functions $\sin\theta$, $\cos\theta$, and $\tan\theta$. Note that $\sin^2\theta$ means $(\sin\theta)^2$ and $\cos^2\theta$ means $(\cos\theta)^2$.

**Theorem 17–4**

  ***For every real number $\theta$, $sin^2 \theta + cos^2 \theta = 1$.***

**Proof.** Let $W(\theta) = (x_\theta, y_\theta)$ be a point on the unit circle with center $O = (0, 0)$. $OW(\theta) = 1$. By the distance formula $\sqrt{x_\theta^2 + y_\theta^2} = 1$, so that $x_\theta^2 + y_\theta^2 = 1$. Since $x_\theta = \cos\theta$, and $y_\theta = \sin\theta$, substitution yields the desired result, $\cos^2\theta + \sin^2\theta = 1$.

**Theorem 17–5**

  ***If $\cos\theta \neq 0$, then $\dfrac{\sin\theta}{\cos\theta} = \tan\theta$.***

  You may supply a proof.

  Suppose now that $0 < \theta < \pi$ so that $W(\theta)$ is a point on the upper half of the unit circle. Then $W(-\theta)$ lies below $W(\theta)$ on the same vertical line. This implies that the coordinates of $W(\theta)$ and $W(-\theta)$, are related: $x_{-\theta} = x_\theta$, $y_{-\theta} = -y_\theta$ as the markings in the figure indicate. These formulas hold because we get to the

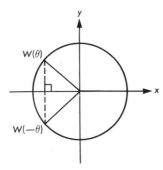

**17-7 SOME BASIC TRIGONOMETRIC IDENTITIES**

**Classroom Notes**

This section is closely related to Section 17–3 and to the problems in Problem Set 17–6. The identities take forms which are already familiar in various special cases. The new part is that we show that these identities hold for *all* values of $\theta$. This means that the proofs ought to be fairly easy, and many students can furnish them for themselves. But the difference between special results (as earlier) and general results (as in this section) is worth stressing in class.

**1.** If $\sin \theta = 6/7$ and $W(\theta)$ is in Quadrant III, find $\tan \theta$.

(ans: $6\sqrt{13}/13$)

**2.** If $\cos \theta = 3/11$ and $W(\theta)$ is in Quadrant IV, find $\sin (-\theta)$.

(ans: $4\sqrt{7}/11$)

**3.** If $\tan \theta = -15/8$, find the possible values of $\cos (\theta + \pi)$.

(ans: $8/17$ or $-8/17$)

**4.** Find all replacements of $\theta$ which make the following a true statement.

$\sin \theta \tan \theta = \cos \theta$ and $0 < \theta \leq 2\pi$.

(ans: $\theta \in \{\pi/4, 3\pi/4, 5\pi/4, 7\pi/4\}$)

points $W(\theta)$ and $W(-\theta)$ by travelling around the unit circle for the same distance $|\theta|$, but in opposite directions. Therefore, the points $W(\theta)$ and $W(-\theta)$ always lie symmetrically opposite one another across the $x$-axis. This gives us the following:

**Theorem 17–6**

> *For every $\theta$*
>
> $$\sin (-\theta) = -\sin \theta,$$
> $$\cos (-\theta) = \cos \theta,$$
> $$\tan (-\theta) = -\tan \theta \quad (\textbf{\textit{if}} \cos \theta \neq 0).$$

**Proof.** The first two formulas hold because $y_{-\theta} = -y_\theta$ and $x_{-\theta} = x_\theta$.

To get the third formula, observe that

$$\tan (-\theta) = \frac{y_{-\theta}}{x_{-\theta}} = -\frac{y_\theta}{x_\theta} = -\tan \theta$$

whenever $x_\theta \neq 0$.

**Problem Set 17–7**

**1.** Evaluate $\sin^2 \dfrac{3\pi}{4} + \cos^2 \dfrac{3\pi}{4}$.   1

**2.** Evaluate $1 - \sin^2 \dfrac{5\pi}{3}$.   $\frac{1}{4}$

**3.** Evaluate $\sin^2 \dfrac{5\pi}{4} + \cos^2 \dfrac{5\pi}{4}$.   1

**4.** If $\sin \theta = \dfrac{4}{5}$, find $\cos^2 \theta$. $\frac{9}{25}$

**5.** Evaluate $\sin^2 \dfrac{17\pi}{2} + \cos^2 \dfrac{17\pi}{2}$.   1

**6.** If $\cos \theta = \dfrac{2}{3}$, find $\sin^2 \theta$. $\frac{5}{9}$

**7.** Evaluate $1 - \cos^2 \dfrac{\pi}{3}$. $\frac{3}{4}$

**8.** If $\cos \theta = -\dfrac{7}{8}$, find $\sin^2 \theta$. $\frac{15}{64}$

**9.** If $\sin \theta = -\dfrac{5}{9}$, find $\cos^2 \theta$. $\frac{56}{81}$

**10.** If $\sin \theta = \dfrac{2}{3}$, and $\dfrac{\pi}{2} < \theta < \pi$, find:

(a) $\cos \theta$. $-\dfrac{\sqrt{5}}{3}$

(b) $\tan \theta$. $-\dfrac{2\sqrt{5}}{5}$

**11.** If $\cos \theta = -\dfrac{4}{9}$, and $\pi < \theta < \dfrac{3\pi}{2}$, find:

(a) $\sin \theta$. $-\dfrac{\sqrt{65}}{9}$

(b) $\tan \theta$. $\dfrac{\sqrt{65}}{4}$

**12.** If $\cos \theta = \dfrac{2}{5}$, and $\dfrac{3\pi}{2} < \theta < 2\pi$, find:

(a) $\sin \theta$. $-\dfrac{\sqrt{21}}{5}$

(b) $\tan \theta$. $-\dfrac{\sqrt{21}}{2}$

13. If $\sin \theta = \frac{3}{7}$, and $0 < \theta < \frac{\pi}{2}$, find:

   (a) $\cos \theta$. $\frac{2\sqrt{10}}{7}$              (b) $\tan \theta$. $\frac{3\sqrt{10}}{20}$

14. If $\tan \theta = \frac{1}{2}$, and $\pi < \theta < \frac{3\pi}{2}$, find:

   (a) $\sin \theta$. $-\frac{\sqrt{5}}{5}$            (b) $\cos \theta$. $\frac{-2\sqrt{5}}{5}$

15. If $\tan \theta = -\frac{4}{3}$, and $\frac{\pi}{2} < \theta < \pi$, find:

   (a) $\sin \theta$. $\frac{4}{5}$               (b) $\cos \theta$. $-\frac{3}{5}$

16. Let $W(\theta)$ be a point in Quadrant I on the unit circle with center $O$. $W(\theta)B$ is perpendicular to the $x$-axis at $B$, $OB$, $= 0.6$ and $W(\theta)B = 0.8$. Find:

   (a) $\sin \theta$. .8      (b) $\cos \theta$. .6      (c) $\sin(-\theta)$. $-.8$

   (d) $\cos(-\theta)$. .6      (e) $\tan(-\theta)$. $-1.33$      (f) $\sin\left(\theta + \frac{\pi}{2}\right)$. .6

   (g) $\cos\left(\theta + \frac{\pi}{2}\right)$. $-.8$      (h) $\sin(\theta + \pi)$. $-.8$      (i) $\cos(\theta + \pi)$. $-.6$

17. Let $W(\theta)$ be a point in Quadrant IV on the unit circle with center $O$. $W(\theta)E$ is perpendicular to the $x$-axis at $E$, $W(\theta)E = 0.6$ and $OE = 0.8$. Find:

   (a) $\sin \theta$. $-.6$      (b) $\cos \theta$. .8      (c) $\tan \theta$. $-.75$

   (d) $\sin(-\theta)$. .6      (e) $\cos(-\theta)$. .8      (f) $\cos(\theta + \pi)$. $-.8$

   (g) $\sin(\theta + \pi)$. .6      (h) $\sin\left(\theta - \frac{\pi}{2}\right)$. $-.8$      (i) $\cos\left(\theta - \frac{\pi}{2}\right)$. .6

18. If $\sin \theta = \frac{2}{5}$, and $W(\theta)$ lies in Quadrant II, find:

   (a) $\cos \theta$. $-\frac{\sqrt{21}}{5}$      (b) $\sin(-\theta)$. $-\frac{2}{5}$      (c) $\cos(-\theta)$. $-\frac{\sqrt{21}}{5}$

19. If $\sin \theta = \frac{3}{4}$, and $W(\theta)$ lies in Quadrant I, find:

   (a) $\cos \theta$. $\frac{\sqrt{7}}{4}$      (b) $\sin(-\theta)$. $-\frac{3}{4}$      (c) $\sin(\theta + \pi)$. $-\frac{3}{4}$

20. If $\sin \theta = \frac{3}{4}$, and $W(\theta)$ lies in Quadrant II, find:

   (a) $\cos \theta$. $-\frac{\sqrt{7}}{4}$      (b) $\cos(\theta + \pi)$. $\frac{\sqrt{7}}{4}$      (c) $\sin\left(\theta + \frac{\pi}{2}\right)$. $-\frac{\sqrt{7}}{4}$

---

21. If $\tan \theta = \sin \theta$, and $0 \leq \theta \leq 2\pi$, what is $\cos \theta$? What is $\theta$? 0 or 2π

22. If $\tan \theta = 2 \sin \theta$, and $0 \leq \theta \leq 2\pi$, what is $\cos \theta$? ½ What is $\theta$? $\frac{\pi}{3}$ or $\frac{5\pi}{3}$

23. If $\sin \theta = \cos \theta$, and $0 \leq \theta \leq 2\pi$, what is $\tan \theta$? 1 What is $\tan(-\theta)$? 1 What is $\theta$? $\frac{\pi}{4}$ or $\frac{5\pi}{4}$

**Explanation for Problems**

Problems 24 and 25 are of course examples of the addition formulas to be proved in the following section. They can be solved in several ways. Since the problems are very similar, we give solutions only for Problem 24.

**24.** *Distance Method:*

$A = W(0) = (1, 0)$, $B = (x, y) = W(\theta) =$ $(\cos \theta, \sin \theta)$, $C = W(\pi/6) = (\sqrt{3}/2, 1/2)$, $D = W(-\pi/4) = (\sqrt{2}/2, -\sqrt{2}/2)$. By the Angle Addition Postulate $B = W(\theta) = W(5\pi/12)$. Using the distance formula we find the distance $AB$ and $CD$.

$$AB^2 = (\cos \theta - 1)^2 + (\sin \theta - 0)^2$$
$$= \cos^2 \theta - 2 \cos \theta + 1 + \sin^2 \theta$$
$$= 2 - 2 \cos \theta$$

$$CD^2 = \left(\frac{\sqrt{3}}{2} - \frac{\sqrt{2}}{2}\right)^2 + \left(\frac{1}{2} + \frac{\sqrt{2}}{2}\right)^2$$
$$= 2 - \frac{\sqrt{6} - \sqrt{2}}{2}$$

Since $CD = AB$,

$$2 - 2 \cos \theta = 2 - \frac{\sqrt{6} - \sqrt{2}}{2},$$

and $\cos \theta = \dfrac{\sqrt{6} - \sqrt{2}}{4}$. Using Theorem 17–4, $\sin \theta = \dfrac{\sqrt{6} + \sqrt{2}}{4}$.

*Table Method:*

Since $W(5\pi/12) = W(75°)$, $(x, y) = (\cos 75°, \sin 75°) \doteq (.259, .966)$. Some students may decide to generalize Problems 11 and 12 of Section 17–6, to find that since $\theta = 5\pi/12 = \pi/4 + \pi/6$, the following formulas should work.

$$\cos 5\pi/12 = \cos \pi/6 \cos \pi/4$$
$$- \sin \pi/6 \sin \pi/4$$
$$= (\sqrt{6} - \sqrt{2})/4$$
$$\sin 5\pi/12 = \sin \pi/6 \cos \pi/4$$
$$+ \sin \pi/4 \cos \pi/6$$
$$= (\sqrt{6} + \sqrt{2})/4$$

However, you should caution students to be careful when generalizing relationships. Sometimes statements are true only for very specific cases. A simple example is the following. The statement "$n^2 - n + 41$ is a prime number when $n$ is a positive number" is true only for all positive numbers less than 41. Thus, the student should be extremely careful about generalizing.

---

**24.** Given the unit circle on the left below with the points $A, B, C, D$ as marked. What values of $x$ and $y$ will make $AB = CD$?

$$B(x,y) = W\left(\tfrac{5\pi}{12}\right) = \left(\cos \tfrac{5\pi}{12}, \sin \tfrac{5\pi}{12}\right) = \left(\tfrac{\sqrt{6}-\sqrt{2}}{4}, \tfrac{\sqrt{6}+\sqrt{2}}{4}\right)$$

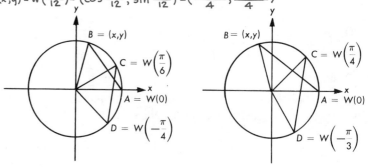

**25.** Given the unit circle on the right above with the points $A, B, C, D$ as marked. What values of $x$ and $y$ will make $AB = CD$?

$$B(x,y) = W\left(\tfrac{7\pi}{12}\right) = \left(-\cos \tfrac{5\pi}{12}, \sin \tfrac{5\pi}{12}\right) = \left(\tfrac{\sqrt{2}-\sqrt{6}}{4}, \tfrac{\sqrt{2}+\sqrt{6}}{4}\right)$$

## 17–8   MORE IDENTITIES.   THE ADDITION FORMULAS

It is easy to calculate the distance between $W(0) = (1, 0)$ and any point $W(\theta) = (\cos \theta, \sin \theta)$.

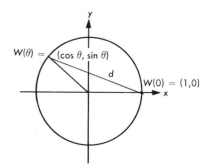

By the distance formula,

$$d^2 = (\cos \theta - 1)^2 + (\sin \theta - 0)^2$$
$$= \cos^2 \theta - 2 \cos \theta + 1 + \sin^2 \theta$$
$$= 2 - 2 \cos \theta.$$

This will be used in the proof of the following theorem.

**Theorem 17–7.**   The Addition Formula for the Cosine

*For all real numbers a and b,*

$$cos\,(a + b) = cos\,a \cos b - \sin a \sin b.$$

**Proof.** In the figure on the left, $P = W(0)$, $Q = W(a)$, and $R = W(a + b)$.

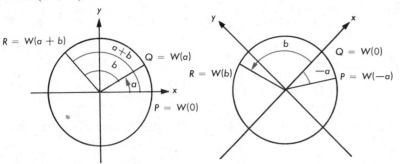

Setting $\theta = a + b$ in the distance formula result proved at the beginning of this section, we get

$$(1) \qquad d^2 = PR^2 = 2 - 2 \cos (a + b).$$

In the figure on the right, the points $P$, $Q$, and $R$ are the same as before, but the axes have been placed in a different position, so that $Q$ lies on the positive $x$-axis. Thus, in the figure on the right,

$$P = W(-a), \quad Q = W(0), \quad R = W(b),$$

as the labels indicate. This gives the following coordinates for $P$ and $R$:

$$P = (\cos (-a), \sin (-a)) = (\cos a, -\sin a),$$
$$R = (\cos b, \sin b).$$

By the distance formula,

$$
\begin{aligned}
(2) \quad PR^2 &= (\cos a - \cos b)^2 + (-\sin a - \sin b)^2 \\
&= \cos^2 a - 2 \cos a \cos b + \cos^2 b \\
&\quad + \sin^2 a + 2 \sin a \sin b + \sin^2 b \\
&= 2 - 2 (\cos a \cos b - \sin a \sin b).
\end{aligned}
$$

Formulas (1) and (2) give two different expressions for the unique distance $PR$, and these expressions must be equal. Therefore

$$2 - 2 \cos (a + b) = 2 - 2 (\cos a \cos b - \sin a \sin b),$$

and

$$\cos (a + b) = \cos a \cos b - \sin a \sin b,$$

which was to be proved.

**Classroom Notes**

If the class has discussed thoroughly Problems 24 and 25 of the preceding section, there should be little difficulty in generalizing the proof using the distance formula. The rest of the theorems in this section should be relatively easy since they have been encountered before in Problem Set 17–6. Theorem 17–8 occurs in Problem 15, Theorem 17–9 in Problem 18, and Theorem 17–11 in Problem 15.

The addition formula for the cosine can be used to give quick derivations of many of the formulas of the preceding section. The following two theorems are of special importance, because they are used in deriving an addition formula for the sine.

### Theorem 17–8

*For every real number $\theta$, $cos\ (\theta + \pi) = -cos\ \theta$.*

**Proof.** In the addition formula for the cosine, set $a = \theta$ and $b = \pi$. This gives

$$\cos (\theta + \pi) = \cos \theta \cos \pi - \sin \theta \sin \pi$$
$$= (\cos \theta)(-1) - (\sin \theta)(0)$$
$$= -\cos \theta.$$

### Theorem 17–9

*For every real number $\theta$,*

$$(1)\ \ cos \left( \theta + \frac{\pi}{2} \right) = -sin\ \theta,$$

*and*

$$(2)\ \ sin \left( \theta + \frac{\pi}{2} \right) = cos\ \theta.$$

**Proof.** In the addition formula for the cosine, set $a = \theta$, $b = \pi/2$. This gives

$$\cos \left( \theta + \frac{\pi}{2} \right) = \cos \theta \cos \frac{\pi}{2} - \sin \theta \sin \frac{\pi}{2}$$
$$= (\cos \theta) \cdot 0 - (\sin \theta) \cdot 1 = -\sin \theta.$$

Therefore (1) is true. To prove (2), we replace $\theta$ by $(\theta + \pi/2)$ in (1). This gives

$$\cos \left( \theta + \frac{\pi}{2} + \frac{\pi}{2} \right) = -\sin \left( \theta + \frac{\pi}{2} \right)$$

Now $\cos (\theta + \pi) = -\cos \theta$, by Theorem 17–10. Therefore

$$-\cos \theta = -\sin \left( \theta + \frac{\pi}{2} \right),$$

and so $\sin (\theta + \pi/2) = \cos \theta$, which was to be proved.

**Theorem 17–10.** The Addition Formula for the Sine

***For all real numbers a and b,***

$$\sin(a+b) = \sin a \cos b + \cos a \sin b.$$

**Proof.** In formula (1) of Theorem 17–9, we substitute $a + b$ for $\theta$. This gives

$$\cos\left(a + b + \frac{\pi}{2}\right) = -\sin(a+b).$$

Therefore

$$\begin{aligned}\sin(a+b) &= -\cos\left(a+b+\frac{\pi}{2}\right) = -\cos\left[a + \left(b + \frac{\pi}{2}\right)\right]\\ &= -\left[\cos a \cos\left(b+\frac{\pi}{2}\right) - \sin a \sin\left(b + \frac{\pi}{2}\right)\right]\\ &= -[(\cos a)(-\sin b) - \sin a \cos b]\\ &= \sin a \cos b + \cos a \sin b.\end{aligned}$$

(You should give the reasons for each of these steps.)

**Theorem 17–11**

***For every real number θ,***

$$\sin(\theta + \pi) = -\sin\theta.$$

You may supply a proof.

To get formulas for the sine and cosine of $a - b$, we merely replace $b$ by $-b$ in the addition formulas.

**Theorem 17–12**

***For all real numbers a and b,***

$$\begin{aligned}\cos(a-b) &= \cos a \cos b + \sin a \sin b, \quad \textit{and}\\ \sin(a-b) &= \sin a \cos b - \cos a \sin b.\end{aligned}$$

You may supply a proof.

Finally, we get two formulas for the tangent by applying Theorems 17–5, 17–7, and 17–10.

**Quiz**

**1.** Write each of the following as a trigonometric function of $\theta$.

(a) $\cos\left(\frac{\pi}{2} - \theta\right)$

(b) $\sin(\theta + \pi)$

(c) $\tan\left(\theta - \frac{3\pi}{2}\right)$, where $\theta$ is not a multiple of $\pi$.

(ans: $\sin\theta$, $-\sin\theta$, $-\cot\theta$)

**2.** If $\tan\theta = 2/3$, what is $\tan 2\theta$? (ans: 12/5)

**3.** Find $\cos(11\pi/12)$. (ans: $-(\sqrt{2}/4)(1+\sqrt{3})$)

**4.** Find replacements of $\theta$ which make the following statement true.

$$\sin 2\theta = \cos\theta \text{ and } 0 < \theta \leq 2\pi.$$

(ans: $\theta \in \{\pi/2, 3\pi/2, \pi/6, 5\pi/6\}$)

Notice that the answers to Problem 1 contain the final answers to Problem 24 of Problem Set 17–7.

**Answers to Problems**

**5.** $\cos(\theta - \pi/2) = \cos\theta\cos\pi/2 + \sin\theta\sin\pi/2 = \cos\theta\cdot 0 + \sin\theta\cdot 1 = \sin\theta$

**6.** $\sin(\theta - \pi/2) = \sin\theta\cos\pi/2 - \cos\theta\sin\pi/2 = \sin\theta\cdot 0 - \cos\theta\cdot 1 = -\cos\theta$

**7.** (a) $\tan\left(\theta + \dfrac{\pi}{2}\right) = \dfrac{\sin\left(\theta + \dfrac{\pi}{2}\right)}{\cos\left(\theta + \dfrac{\pi}{2}\right)}$

$= \dfrac{\cos\theta}{-\sin\theta} = -\dfrac{1}{\tan\theta}$

$\tan\left(\theta - \dfrac{\pi}{2}\right) = \dfrac{\sin\left(\theta - \dfrac{\pi}{2}\right)}{\cos\left(\theta - \dfrac{\pi}{2}\right)}$

$= \dfrac{-\cos\theta}{\sin\theta} = -\dfrac{1}{\tan\theta}$

when $\cos(\theta + \pi/2)$ and $\cos(\theta - \pi/2)$ do not equal zero.

---

**Theorem 17–13**

> *For all real numbers a and b,*
>
> $$\tan(a + b) = \frac{\tan a + \tan b}{1 - \tan a \tan b} \quad \textit{(whenever tan a tan b} \neq 1\textit{)}.$$

A simple substitution of $-b$ for $b$ in this last formula gives us the final theorem.

**Theorem 17–14**

> *For all real numbers a and b,*
>
> $$\tan(a - b) = \frac{\tan a - \tan b}{1 + \tan a \tan b} \quad \textit{(whenever tan a tan b} \neq -1\textit{)}.$$

**Problem Set 17–8**

1. Use the fact that $5\pi/12 = \pi/4 + \pi/6$ to find:
   (a) $\sin 5\pi/12.$ $\frac{\sqrt{6}+\sqrt{2}}{4}$   (b) $\cos 5\pi/12.$ $\frac{\sqrt{6}-\sqrt{2}}{4}$   (c) $\tan 5\pi/12.$ $2+\sqrt{3}$

2. Use the fact that $\pi/12 = \pi/3 - \pi/4$ to find:
   (a) $\sin\pi/12.$ $\frac{\sqrt{6}-\sqrt{2}}{4}$   (b) $\cos\pi/12.$ $\frac{\sqrt{6}+\sqrt{2}}{4}$   (c) $\tan\pi/12.$ $2-\sqrt{3}$

3. If $\theta = 7\pi/6$, what is $\sin\theta$? $-\frac{1}{2}$ What is $\cos\left(\theta + \dfrac{\pi}{2}\right)$? $\frac{1}{2}$

4. If $\theta = 5\pi/4$, what is $\cos\theta$? $-\frac{\sqrt{2}}{2}$ What is $\sin\left(\theta + \dfrac{\pi}{2}\right)$? $-\frac{\sqrt{2}}{2}$

5. Show that $\cos\left(\theta - \dfrac{\pi}{2}\right) = \sin\theta.$ Use Theorem 17–12.

6. Show that $\sin\left(\theta - \dfrac{\pi}{2}\right) = -\cos\theta.$ Use Theorem 17–12.

7. (a) Develop formulas for $\tan\left(\theta + \dfrac{\pi}{2}\right)$ and $\tan\left(\theta - \dfrac{\pi}{2}\right)$.

   (b) Show that $\tan\left(\theta + \dfrac{\pi}{2}\right) = \tan\left(\theta - \dfrac{\pi}{2}\right).$ Both equal $-\dfrac{1}{\tan\theta}$.

8. If $\tan\theta = 1/3$, what is $\tan\left(\theta + \dfrac{\pi}{2}\right)$? $-3$

9. If $\cos\left(\theta + \dfrac{\pi}{2}\right) = -5/13$ and $\sin\left(\theta + \dfrac{\pi}{2}\right) = 12/13$, what is $\tan\theta$? $\frac{5}{12}$

10. If $\cos(\theta + \pi) = -8/17$ and $\tan(\theta + \pi) = 15/8$, what is $\sin(\theta + \pi)$?   -15/17

11. If $\tan\theta_1 = 2.3$ and $\tan\theta_2 = 1.4$, find $\tan(\theta_1 + \theta_2)$; find $\tan(\theta_1 - \theta_2)$.   -1.67   .213

12. If $\tan\theta_1 = 7/9$ and $\tan\theta_2 = -4/9$, find $\tan(\theta_1 + \theta_2)$; find $\tan(\theta_1 - \theta_2)$.   $\frac{27}{109}$ , $\frac{99}{53}$

13. Prove that $\sin\left(\dfrac{\pi}{2} - \theta\right) = \cos\theta$. Use Theorem 17-12.

14. Prove that $\cos\left(\dfrac{\pi}{2} - \theta\right) = \sin\theta$. Use Theorem 17-12.

15. Which of the following are true statements for all numbers $\theta$?

(a) $\sin\left(\theta + \dfrac{\pi}{2}\right) = \sin\left(\theta - \dfrac{\pi}{2}\right)$ · cos θ $\overset{?}{=}$ -cos θ; False

(b) $\cos\left(\theta - \dfrac{\pi}{2}\right) = \cos\left(\dfrac{\pi}{2} - \theta\right)$ · sin θ $\overset{?}{=}$ sin θ; True

(c) $\cos\left(\theta + \dfrac{\pi}{2}\right) = \sin\left(\theta + \dfrac{\pi}{2}\right)$ · -sin θ $\overset{?}{=}$ cos θ; False

(d) $\sin\left(\dfrac{\pi}{2} - \theta\right) = \sin\left(\theta - \dfrac{\pi}{2}\right)$ · cos θ $\overset{?}{=}$ -cos θ; False

sin 2θ = sin θ cos θ + sin θ cos θ = 2 sin θ cos θ

16. Noting that $\theta + \theta = 2\theta$, prove that $\sin 2\theta = 2\sin\theta\cos\theta$.

17. If $\sin\theta = \sqrt{6}/3$ and $\pi/2 < \theta < \pi$, find $\sin 2\theta$.   $\dfrac{-2\sqrt{2}}{3}$

18. Prove that $\cos 2\theta = \cos^2\theta - \sin^2\theta$   cos 2θ = cos θ cos θ - sin θ sin θ
$$= 1 - 2\sin^2\theta$$ = cos²θ - sin²θ
     = (1 - sin²θ) - sin²θ
$$= 2\cos^2\theta - 1.$$ = cos²θ - (1 - cos²θ)

19. If $\cos\theta = \sqrt{5}/4$, find $\cos 2\theta$.   $-\dfrac{3}{8}$

20. If $\sin\theta = -0.2$, find $\cos 2\theta$.   0.92

21. Prove that $\tan 2\theta = \dfrac{2\tan\theta}{1 - \tan^2\theta}$.   tan 2θ = $\dfrac{\tan θ + \tan θ}{1 + \tan θ \tan θ} = \dfrac{2\tan θ}{1 - \tan² θ}$

22. If $\cos\theta = \sqrt{5}/3$ and $3\pi/2 < \theta < 2\pi$, find $\tan 2\theta$.   $-4\sqrt{5}$

23. Express $\sin 3\theta$ as a function of $\sin\theta$.   sin 3θ = 3 sin θ - 4 sin³θ

24. If $\sin\theta = \sqrt{5}/3$, find $\sin 3\theta$.   $\dfrac{7\sqrt{5}}{27}$

25. Find all values of $\theta$, $0 \le \theta \le 2\pi$ such that $\sin 3\theta = 0$.   0, π/3, 2π/3, π, 4π/3, 5π/3, 2π

26. Express $\cos 3\theta$ as a function of $\cos\theta$.   cos 3θ = 4 cos³θ - 3 cos θ

27. If $\sin\theta = 0.8$ and $\pi/2 < \theta < \pi$, find $\cos 3\theta$.   0.936

**Answers to Problems**

13. $\sin(\pi/2 - \theta)$
$$= \sin\pi/2\cos\theta - \cos\pi/2\sin\theta$$
$$= 1\cdot\cos\theta - 0\cdot\sin\theta = \cos\theta$$

14. $\cos(\pi/2 - \theta)$
$$= \cos\pi/2\cos\theta + \sin\pi/2\sin\theta$$
$$= 0\cdot\cos\theta + 1\cdot\sin\theta = \sin\theta$$

21. $\tan 2\theta = \dfrac{\sin 2\theta}{\cos 2\theta} = \dfrac{2\sin\theta\cos\theta}{\cos^2\theta - \sin^2\theta}$
$$= \dfrac{2\tan\theta}{1 - \tan^2\theta}$$

where $\cos 2\theta \ne 0$.

23. Use the sine addition formula twice.

26. Use the cosine addition formula twice.

**29.** $\tan (a+b) = \dfrac{\sin (a+b)}{\cos (a+b)}$

$= \dfrac{\sin a \cos b + \cos a \sin b}{\cos a \cos b - \sin a \sin b}$

$= \dfrac{\tan a + \tan b}{1 - \tan a \tan b}$

by dividing numerator and denominator by cos a cos b.

**31.** $W(\theta_1) = (x, y) = (\cos \theta_1, \sin \theta_1)$ and
$W(\theta_1 + \theta_2)$
$\quad = (x', y')$
$\quad = (\cos (\theta_1 + \theta_2), \sin (\theta_1 + \theta_2))$
$\cos (\theta_1 + \theta_2)$
$\quad = \cos \theta_1 \cos \theta_2 - \sin \theta_1 \sin \theta_2$
$\quad = x \cos \theta_2 - y \sin \theta_2$
$\sin (\theta_1 + \theta_2)$
$\quad = \sin \theta_1 \cos \theta_2 + \sin \theta_2 \cos \theta_1$
$\quad = y \cos \theta_2 + x \sin \theta_2$

**Answers to Chapter Review Problems**

**2.** In $\triangle TVS$, $\sin \angle S = \frac{1}{2}$ means $m \angle S = 30$ and $\triangle TVS$ is a 30-60-90 triangle. $VS = 10\sqrt{3}$ and $TV = 10$. In $\triangle PQR$, $QP = 10$ and $\cos \angle R = \frac{1}{2}$. $m \angle R = 60$, so $\triangle PQR$ is a 30-60-90 triangle and $RP = 10\sqrt{3}/3$. $a\square QRST = a\triangle PQR + a\square QTVP + a\triangle TVS = \frac{1}{2}\cdot10\sqrt{3}/3 \cdot 10 + 8\cdot10 + \frac{1}{2}\cdot 10\cdot10\sqrt{3} = 80 + 200\sqrt{3}/3$.

---

**28.** Find all values of $\theta$, $0 \le \theta \le 2\pi$, such that $\cos 3\theta = 0$. $\frac{\pi}{6}, \frac{\pi}{2}, \frac{5\pi}{6}, \frac{7\pi}{6}, \frac{3\pi}{2}$ $\frac{11\pi}{6}$

**29.** Prove Theorem 17–13.

**30.** Complete the solution of the following problem.
On a unit circle, $W(\theta) = (0.6, 0.8)$.
What are the coordinates of a second
point, $W\left(\theta + \dfrac{\pi}{6}\right)$ ? $(.3\sqrt{3}-.4, .4\sqrt{3}+.3)$

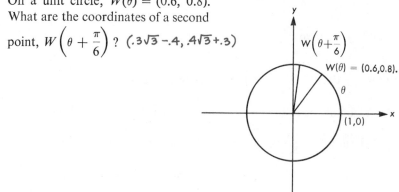

*Solution:*

For $W(\theta)$, $\cos \theta = 0.6$ and $\sin \theta = 0.8$. For $W\left(\theta + \dfrac{\pi}{6}\right)$, $\cos\left(\theta + \dfrac{\pi}{6}\right) =$

$\cos \theta \cos \pi/6 - \sin \theta \sin \pi/6$, by Theorem 17–7, and $\sin\left(\theta + \dfrac{\pi}{6}\right) =$

$\sin \theta \cos \pi/6 + \cos \theta \sin \pi/6$, by Theorem 17–10. Now, make the appropriate numerical substitutions and find the coordinates of

$W\left(\theta + \dfrac{\pi}{6}\right)$.

**31.** On a unit circle, $W(\theta_1) = (x, y)$ and $W(\theta_1 + \theta_2) = (x', y')$. Show that $x' = x \cos \theta_2 - y \sin \theta_2$ and $y' = y \cos \theta_2 + x \sin \theta_2$.
Use Addition Formulas since $x' = \cos(\theta_1 + \theta_2)$ and $y' = \sin(\theta_1 + \theta_2)$

## CHAPTER REVIEW

**1.** Given $\triangle ABC$ as marked, find the following trigonometric ratios.
(a) $\cos \angle A$  $8/17$       (b) $\sin \angle BCD$  $4/5$
(c) $\tan \angle A$  $15/8$       (d) $\tan \angle B$  $3/4$
(e) $\sin \angle B$  $3/5$        (f) $\cos \angle ACD$  $15/17$

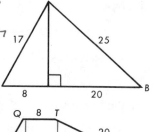

**2.** Given trapezoid $\square QRST$ as shown.
If $\sin \angle S = \cos \angle R = 0.5$, find
$a\square QRST$.  $80 + \dfrac{200\sqrt{3}}{3}$

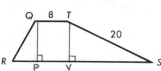

**Explanation for Chapter Review Problems**

3. Use the table of trigonometric ratios to find

(a) $\sin 47°$; $\cos 32°$; $\tan 54°$. $.731, .848, 1.376$

(b) $m \angle A$ if $\cos \angle A = 0.208$; if $\sin \angle A = 0.292$; if $\tan \angle A = 9.514$. $78, 17, 84$

4. A submarine at a depth of 28 m receives sonar reflections from a ship on the surface at an angle of 31° from the horizontal. To the nearest number of metres, how far is the ship from the surface position directly above the submarine? $47 m$

5. Convert degree measure to radian measure for each of the following.

(a) 240 $4\pi/3$ (b) 495 $11\pi/4$ (c) 129 $43\pi/60$

6. Convert radian measure to degree measure for each of the following.

(a) $\frac{7}{4}\pi$ $315°$ (b) $\frac{7}{8}\pi$ $157\frac{1}{2}°$ (c) $\frac{13}{45}\pi$ $52°$

7. For an isosceles triangle the two equal sides are each 5 and the base angles are each $\frac{\pi}{6}$. Find the area of the triangle. $\frac{25\sqrt{3}}{4}$

8. Given that $W(\theta)$ is a point on a unit circle, which quadrant contains $W(\theta)$ for the following values of $\theta$?

(a) $\frac{7}{6}\pi$ Quad III (b) $-\frac{3}{7}\pi$ Quad IV (c) $\frac{19}{3}\pi$ Quad I (d) $-\frac{37}{4}\pi$ Quad II

9. For the directed angle $\angle MAR$, which side is the initial side? Which side is the terminal side? $\overrightarrow{AM}, \overrightarrow{AR}$

10. For a point $W(\theta)$ of a unit circle, $\sin \theta = \frac{5}{13}$. What are the coordinates of $W(\theta)$ if $\frac{\pi}{2} < \theta < \pi$? $\left(-\frac{12}{13}, \frac{5}{13}\right)$

11. Find the values of the three trigonometric functions of each of the following numbers.

(a) $\frac{3\pi}{2}$ $\sin 3\pi/2 = -1$ $\cos 3\pi/2 = 0$ $\tan 3\pi/2 = $ undefined

(b) $\frac{5\pi}{3}$ $\sin 5\pi/3 = -\sqrt{3}/2$ $\cos 5\pi/3 = \frac{1}{2}$ $\tan 5\pi/3 = -\sqrt{3}$

(c) $\frac{13\pi}{4}$ $\sin 13\pi/4 = -\sqrt{2}/2$ $\cos 13\pi/4 = \sqrt{2}/2$ $\tan 13\pi/4 = 1$

12. If $\sin \theta = \frac{3}{8}$ and $W(\theta)$ lies in Quadrant II, find

(a) $\cos \theta. -\frac{\sqrt{55}}{8}$ (b) $\sin(-\theta). -\frac{3}{8}$ (c) $\cos(-\theta). -\frac{\sqrt{55}}{8}$

13. If $\sin \theta = \frac{5}{9}$ and $\tan \theta = \frac{-5\sqrt{14}}{28}$, what is $\cos \theta$? $-\frac{2\sqrt{14}}{9}$

14. Given that $\cos \theta = 0.6$, what is $\cos(\theta + \pi)$? $\cos(\theta + \frac{1}{2}\pi)$? $\cos(\theta - \frac{1}{2}\pi)$? $\sin \Theta > 0: -\frac{3}{5}, \frac{4}{5}, -\frac{4}{5}$; $\sin \Theta < 0: -\frac{3}{5}, -\frac{4}{5}, \frac{4}{5}$

15. Given $\cos \theta_1 = 0.8$, $\sin \theta_1 > 0$, $\cos \theta_2 = 0.6$, and $\sin \theta_2 < 0$, find $\cos(\theta_1 - \theta_2)$; $\sin(\theta_1 - \theta_2)$.

16. Given $\tan \theta_1 = 2.3$ and $\tan \theta_2 = -0.4$, find $\tan(\theta_1 + \theta_2)$; $\tan(\theta_1 - \theta_2)$. $0.99$ $33.8$

17. If $\sin \theta = 0.3$, what is $\cos 2\theta$? $0.82$

18. If $\cos \theta = \frac{\sqrt{6}}{4}$, what is $\cos 2\theta$? $-\frac{1}{4}$

---

**3.** Here the symbol $\angle A$ means that the angle is undirected and acute, as in the first sections of this chapter. Therefore the answers for 3(b) are as follows: If $\cos \angle A = .208$, then $m \angle A = 78$. If $\sin \angle A = .292$, then $m \angle A = 17$.

**14.** Since $\cos \theta = \frac{3}{5}$, $W(\theta)$ can be in either Quadrant I or Quadrant IV. If $W(\theta)$ is in Quadrant I, then (1) $\cos(\theta + \pi) = -\cos \theta = -\frac{3}{5}$ by Theorem 17-10. (2) $\cos(\theta + \frac{1}{2}\pi) = -\sin \theta$ by Theorem 17-11. $\sin \theta = \frac{4}{5}$ when $W(\theta)$ is in Quadrant I, so $\cos(\theta + \frac{1}{2}\pi) = -\frac{4}{5}$. (3) By Theorem 17-14, $\cos(\theta - \frac{1}{2}\pi) = \sin \theta = \frac{4}{5}$. If $W(\theta)$ is in Quadrant IV, then $\sin \theta = -\frac{4}{5}$ and (1) $\cos(\theta + \pi) = -\frac{3}{5}$, (2) $\cos(\theta + \frac{1}{2}\pi) = \frac{4}{5}$, and (3) $\cos(\theta - \frac{1}{2}\pi) = -\frac{4}{5}$.

**15.** We calculate $\sin \theta_1 = .6$ since $\sin \theta_1 > 0$; and $\sin \theta_2 = -.8$ since $\sin \theta_2 < 0$. Now substitute these values in Theorem 17-14, getting $\cos(\theta_1 - \theta_2) = (.8)(.6) + (.6)(-.8) = 0$, and $\sin(\theta_1 - \theta_2) = (.6)(.6) - (.8)(-.8) = 1$. (All the given information is needed to determine the answers.)

**16.** Since the addition formula for the tangent uses only the tangent, we simply substitute the given values; there are no double signs to worry about.

## Symmetry, Transformations, and Vectors

This supplementary chapter is a brief introduction to the topics mentioned in the title. Both point and line symmetry are covered, three types of rigid motions are introduced, and dilations are discussed when vectors are presented.

Since the material is designed primarily for the better than average students, average classes may wish to cover only the first three sections. The brief introduction to polar coordinates can be expanded with the use of any modern text in analytic geometry. Some of the more advanced students may wish for further discussion of this topic and vectors.

Transformations are important in later mathematics, especially abstract algebra. The set of all transformations of a plane form a group under the operation *composition* of transformations. This is an important example of an associative, non-commutative group.

### Planning the Chapter

An average class may wish to spend three days reading and discussing the first three sections of this chapter as an introduction to symmetry and simple types of transformations. An above-average class, however, will probably study the chapter thoroughly, concentrating on Sections 18–4 and 18–5 for two or three days and spending approximately one day on each of the other sections.

CHAPTER **18**

# Symmetry, Transformations, and Vectors

## Objectives . . .

- Analyze the concept of motion in geometric terms.
- Set up correspondence between congruent figures based on reflections, translations, and rotations.
- Apply the concept of vectors to the dilation transformation.
- Relate the idea of symmetry to reflections in the plane.

**Classroom Notes**

This section can be assigned as reading and discussed with Section 18–2. Most students have an intuitive understanding of symmetry and will have no trouble with the concepts in the forms in which they are presented in this section.

## 18–1   INTRODUCTION

So far in this book, in dealing with the idea of congruence, we have used the ideas of distance and angular measure. (Segments are congruent if they have the same length, angles are congruent if they have the same measure, and so on.) In some informal discussions, however, we have used the idea of *motion*. Thus we said informally that two geometric figures are congruent if one can be moved so as to coincide with the other.

In this chapter, we shall study the idea of motion in a mathematical way, using a class of correspondences between points, called *transformations*. One kind of transformation is a *rigid motion*, which is related to congruence. Another kind of transformation is a *dilation*, which is related to similarity.

The study of transformations begins with the idea of *symmetry*. In the figure below, the triangles marked I and II are *symmetric about* the line *L*.

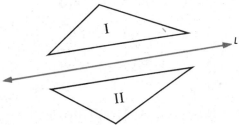

One way of expressing this is to observe that if the paper is folded along the line *L*, then the two triangles are made to coincide. Another way to describe the symmetry is to note that if a mirror is placed vertically, with its edge on the line *L*, then the image of II in the mirror will look just like I (except, of course, for the Roman numeral).

595

In the next figure there are many such symmetry relations.

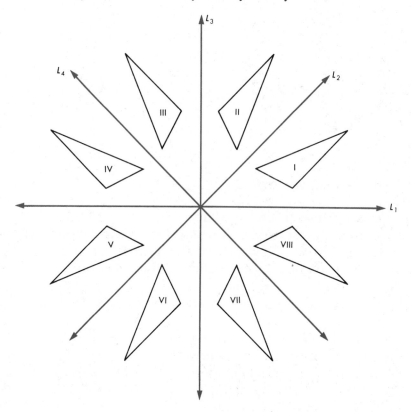

For example, I and II are symmetric about $L_2$. We abbreviate this by writing I-$L_2$-II. This can be checked either by paper-folding or by using a mirror. Similarly, I-$L_1$-VIII, I-$L_3$-IV, and I-$L_4$-VI. There are four more such symmetry relations in the figure.

In the following section, we shall deal with these relations mathematically. In later sections we shall study rigid motions and dilations.

## 18–2   REFLECTIONS AND SYMMETRIC FIGURES

In the figure, $P'$ is the *reflection of P across the line L.* The definition conveyed by the figure is as follows.

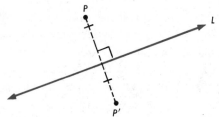

## Definition

One point is the *reflection* of another, across a line, if the line is the perpendicular bisector of the segment joining the two points. If the point lies on the line, the reflection is the point itself.

If $P'$ is the reflection of $P$, then $P$ is the reflection of $P'$. In the figure below, the irregular-looking curve is *symmetric* about the line $L$.

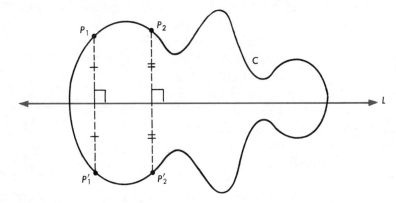

## Definitions

Let $C$ be a set of points, and let $L$ be a line. If $C$ contains the reflection across $L$ of each point of $C$, then $C$ is *symmetric about L*. The line $L$ is called the *axis of symmetry*, and the set $C$ is said to be *line-symmetric*.

This idea applies to a great variety of figures—curves, polygons, surfaces, solids, and many others. For example, a circle is symmetric about any line through its center. So also is the interior of the circle. A sphere is symmetric about any line through its center, and so also is the interior of the sphere. In this chapter we shall be dealing only with plane figures.

In the figure below, $P'$ is the *reflection of P across the point Q*.

## Definition

The *reflection of a point P across a point Q* is the point $P'$ such that $Q$ is the midpoint of the segment $\overline{PP'}$. We also say that the points $P$ and $P'$ are *symmetric* about $Q$.

**Classroom Notes**

Not much here is essentially new, but the distinction between point and line symmetry should be stressed. Since the proof of Theorem 18-1 is rather easy, one of the students in the class may present it to the rest of the class.

### Definition

Let $C$ be a set of points, and let $Q$ be a point. If for each point $P$ of $C$, $C$ contains the reflection of $P$ across $Q$, then $C$ is *symmetric about Q*. The point $Q$ is called the *center of symmetry* of $C$, and the set $C$ is said to be *point-symmetric*.

Every circle is symmetric in this sense, and its center of symmetry is the center of the circle. Similarly, a square is symmetric about the point where its diagonals intersect. Thus a square has a center, in the sense that we have just defined. In each of these cases the figure is symmetric about certain lines. The circle is symmetric about every line through its center. The square is symmetric about the lines containing its diagonals, and also about the lines through the midpoints of opposite sides.

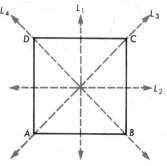

In a coordinate plane, there are simple formulas for the reflection of a point across the axes, and across the origin. The reflection of $P(x, y)$ across the $x$-axis is $P_1(x, -y)$. Across the $y$-axis it is $P_2(-x, y)$, and across the origin it is $P_3(-x, -y)$. These formulas are used in the proof of the following theorem.

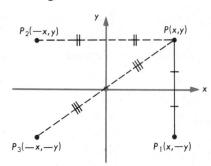

### Theorem 18-1

*If a plane figure is symmetric about each of two perpendicular lines, then it is symmetric about the point where the lines intersect.*

**Restatement.**  Let $C$ be a set of points in a plane $E$. Let $L$ and $L'$ be perpendicular lines in $E$, intersecting at a point $Q$. If $C$ is symmetric about both $L$ and $L'$, then $C$ is symmetric about $Q$.

**Proof.**  Set up a coordinate system, using $L$ as the $x$-axis and $L'$ as the $y$-axis. Let $P(x, y)$ be any point of $C$. We need to show that $C$ contains the reflection of $P$ across $Q$. Since $C$ is symmetric about $L$, $P_1$ belongs to $C$. Since $C$ is symmetric about $L'$, $P_2$ belongs to $C$. But $P_2$ is the reflection of $P$ across $Q$, and this is what we wanted to prove.

It can easily happen that a figure is symmetric about a point without being symmetric about any line at all. That is, a figure may be point-symmetric without being line-symmetric.

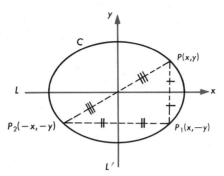

In the figure, the curve $C$ is the union of two semi-circles having the point $Q$ in common. $C$ is symmetric about $Q$, but is not symmetric about any line. Can a figure be symmetric about a line without being symmetric about any point? **Yes**

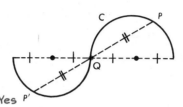

### Problem Set 18–2

**1.** In the figure, which point is the reflection of

(a) $A$ across $L_1$?  **B**

(b) $A$ across $L_2$?  **D**

(c) $C$ across $L_1$?  **G**

(d) $D$ across $L_2$?  **A**

(e) $F$ across $L_2$?  **G**

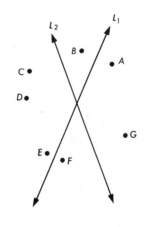

**2.** In the figure lines $L_1$ and $L_2$ intersect at $P$, the center of the circle. Which point is the reflection of

(a) $R$ across $L_1$?  **S**

(b) $R$ across $P$?  **V**

(c) $S$ across $P$?  **X**

(d) $S$ across $L_2$?  **W**

(e) $Y$ across $L_2$?  **R**

(f) $Y$ across $P$?  **T**

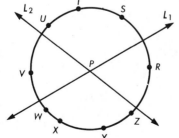

**3.** Which of the following types of quadrilaterals are symmetric about a diagonal: parallelogram, (rhombus,) rectangle, (square,) trapezoid?

**Quiz**

**1.** Find the reflection of the point $(4, 2)$ across the line $x = -3$.

(ans: $(-10, 2)$)

**2.** If the point $(2, 3)$ is the reflection of the point $(-4, 5)$ across the line $L$, state the equation of $L$.

(ans: $y = 3x + 7$.)

**3.** For what values of $n$ is a regular polygon of $n$ sides symmetric about a point? about a line?

(ans: for $n$ an even integer greater than two; for all integers greater than two)

**4.** Either prove or give a counterexample for the following statement. If $v(P)$ is the reflection of $P$ across the $x$-axis then $v(v(P)) = P$.

(ans: The statement is true. Proof: If $P = (x, y)$, then $v(v(x, y)) = v(x, -y) = (x, y)$.)

**6.** A rhombus is symmetric about each of its diagonals. Since the diagonals are perpendicular, the rhombus is symmetric about the intersection of the diagonals, by Theorem 18–1.

**4.** In this figure the triangles are congruent and each is isosceles. What is the reflection of

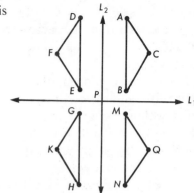

(a) $\overline{AC}$ across $L_2$? DF

(b) $\overline{BC}$ across $L_1$? MQ

(c) $\overline{DF}$ across $P$? NQ

(d) $\overline{GK}$ across $L_1$? EF

(e) $\overline{GK}$ across $P$? BC

**5.** Is this figure symmetric about a line? No Is it symmetric about a point? How does the shading effect the symmetry?

Yes, the intersection of $L_1$ and $L_2$. If the shading is ignored, the figure is symmetric about $L_1, L_2, L_3,$ and $L_4$.

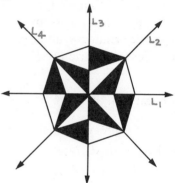

**6.** Prove that a rhombus is symmetric about a point.

**7.** Trace each figure below and sketch in each axis of symmetry. Mark each center of symmetry whenever one exists. Assume that segments that look congruent are congruent, and segments that look parallel are parallel.

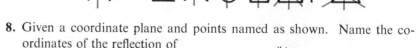

**8.** Given a coordinate plane and points named as shown. Name the coordinates of the reflection of

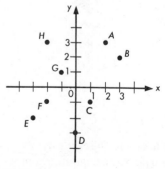

(a) $A$ across the $x$-axis. (2, -3)

(b) $B$ across the $y$-axis. (-3, 2)

(c) $C$ across the origin. (-1, 1)

(d) $D$ across the $x$-axis. (0, 3)

(e) $E$ across the origin. (3, 2)

(f) $F$ across the $y$-axis. (2, -1)

(g) $G$ across the $x$-axis. (-1, -1)

(h) $H$ across the origin. (2, -3)

9. Given a coordinate plane. For each point named below, give its reflection across (1) the x-axis, (2) the y-axis, (3) the origin.

(a) $(5, -3)$    (b) $(-8, 14)$    (c) $(6, -6)$    (d) $(3, 11)$

(5,3),(-5,-3),(-5,3)    (-8,-14),(8,14),(8,-14)    (6,6),(-6,-6),(-6,6)    (3,-11),(-3,11),(-3,-11)

10. Let $v(A)$ be the reflection of the point $A$ across the y-axis in a coordinate plane. Similarly, let $h(A)$ be the reflection of $A$ across the x-axis, and let $p(A)$ be the reflection of $A$ across the origin. The reflection $v$ followed by the reflection $h$ for the point $A$ is called the *product* of $v$ and $h$ and is denoted by $hv(A)$. For example, if $A = (3, -2)$, then $v(3, -2) = (-3, -2)$ and $hv(3, -2) = (-3, 2)$.

(a) Show that $hv(a, b) = p(a, b)$.    (b) Show that $hv(a, b) = vh(a, b)$.

(c) Show that $ph(a, b) = v(a, b)$.    (d) What is $phv(a, b)$?

11. For a set of points in space, define the concept of being symmetric about a plane.

12. A sphere is one example of a set which is symmetric about a plane. Give two more examples.    cube, line, segment, plane, isosceles triangle, square, rhombus, ellipsoid, cylinder, etc.

13. Is it possible for a non-coplanar set of points to be symmetric about a point but not symmetric about any plane? Yes

14. Is it possible for a non-coplanar set of points to be symmetric about a point but not symmetric about any line? Yes

## 18-3    RIGID MOTIONS: REFLECTIONS AND TRANSLATIONS

We have often used the idea of correspondences between sets of points in a plane. For example, when we described congruences between triangles, we used correspondences of the type $ABC \leftrightarrow A'B'C'$. This was a shorthand for the three matching pairs $A \leftrightarrow A'$, $B \leftrightarrow B'$, and $C \leftrightarrow C'$.

If $\triangle ABC \cong \triangle A'B'C'$, then the correspondence between the vertices describes a way of moving $\triangle ABC$ so as to make it coincide with $\triangle A'B'C'$. Reflections are correspondences, too. We use this idea in the next definition.

### Definition

Given a plane $E$ and a line $L$ in $E$. For each point $P$ of $E$, let $P'$ be the reflection of $P$ across $L$. The correspondence $P \leftrightarrow P'$ is called the *reflection of the plane $E$ across $L$.*

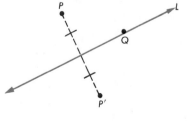

**Answers to Problems**

10. (a) $hv(a, b) = h(-a, b) = (-a, -b)$
$$= p(a, b)$$

(b) $hv(a, b) = h(-a, b) = (-a, -b)$
$$= v(a, -b) = vh(a, b)$$

(c) $ph(a, b) = p(a, -b) = (-a, b)$
$$= v(a, b)$$

(d) $phv(a, b) = ph(-a, b)$
$$= p(-a, -b) = (a, b)$$

11. The *reflection* of a point $P$ across a plane $E$ is the point $P'$ such that $E$ is a perpendicular bisector of the segment joining $P$ and $P'$. A set of points $C$ is said to be *symmetric* about the plane $E$ if $C$ contains the reflection across $E$ of every point of $C$.

13. Let $M$ be a set which is the union of three segments $S_1$, $S_2$, and $S_3$, such that (1) the segments are of lengths 1, 2, and 3, (2) they intersect in a common midpoint $P$, (3) no two of them are perpendicular, and (4) they are not coplanar. Obviously $M$ is symmetric about $P$. We shall show that $M$ is not symmetric about any plane. Suppose, then, that $M$ is symmetric about a plane $E$. For each $i$ (from 1 to 3) let $S_i'$ be the reflection of $S_i$ across $E$. Then $S_i'$ is a segment of the same length as $S_i$. Therefore $S_i' = S_i$, since different segments $S_i$ have different lengths. Therefore either $S_i$ lies in $E$ or $S_i$ is perpendicular to $E$ at $P$. Since the segments are not coplanar, at least one of them, say $S_1$, is perpendicular to $E$ at $P$. The other two must lie in $E$, since perpendicular lines are unique. Therefore $S_1$ must be perpendicular to both $S_2$ and $S_3$, which contradicts condition (3).

14. The set $M$ defined in the answer to Problem 13 is not symmetric about any line. If $M$ were symmetric about a line $L$, then the reflection $S_i'$ of $S_i$ across $L$ would be a segment of the same length, and therefore $S_i' = S_i$ for each $i$. This means that either $S_i$ lies on $L$ or that $S_i \perp L$ at $P$. The segments $S_1$, $S_2$, and $S_3$ cannot all be perpendicular to $L$, because they are not coplanar. Therefore one of them, say $S_1$, lies on $L$. The other two are perpendicular to $L$, and therefore perpendicular to $S_1$, which is impossible.

## 18–3 RIGID MOTIONS: REFLECTIONS AND TRANSLATIONS

### Classroom Notes

In this section the idea of a transformation is introduced and rigid motions are discussed. A transformation is called a rigid motion if it preserves distances. A translation is the easiest sort of transformation to deal with algebraically, since coordinate systems in a plane are already familiar.

The students could investigate other properties which are preserved under translation besides distance. The measures of angles are preserved. Consider the angle $\angle ABC$ of $\triangle ABC$. Under the translation $T$, $\overline{AB} \cong \overline{A'B'}$, $\overline{BC} \cong \overline{B'C'}$, and $\overline{AC} \cong \overline{A'C'}$. Therefore $\triangle ABC \cong \triangle A'B'C'$, by SSS, and $\angle ABC \cong \angle A'B'C'$. Hence the measure of an angle is preserved under translation. Parallelism is another property preserved under translation. (Every line is moved onto a line, and non-intersecting lines are moved onto non-intersecting lines because the transformation is one-to-one.)

Recall that according to our earlier definition of the reflection of $P$ across $L$, points on $L$ correspond to themselves; that is, if $P$ is on $L$ then $P' = P$. Thus our latest definition introduces the idea of a correspondence involving all the points of a plane.

Our next theorem describes an important property of reflections.

### Theorem 18–2

*Distance is preserved under reflections across a line.*

**Restatement.** Let $L$ be a line in a plane $E$. Let $P_1$ and $P_2$ be points of $E$, and let $P'_1$ and $P'_2$ be their reflections across $L$. Then $P'_1 P'_2 = P_1 P_2$.

**Proof.** An easy way to see this is to set up a coordinate system for $E$, using $L$ as the $x$-axis. Let

$$P_1 = (x_1, y_1), \qquad P_2 = (x_2, y_2).$$

Then

$$P'_1 = (x_1, -y_1), \qquad P'_2 = (x_2, -y_2).$$

Using the distance formula, we get $P'_1 P'_2 = P_1 P_2$.

We are now ready to consider two important ideas.

### Definitions

A one-to-one correspondence $P \leftrightarrow P'$, between the points of a plane and themselves, is called a *transformation*. A transformation which preserves distances is called a *rigid motion*.

Thus a reflection of a plane across a line is a transformation, and Theorem 18–2 says that every reflection is a rigid motion.

Another type of rigid motion is called a *translation*. In a plane $E$, set up a rectangular coordinate system, in any position. Let $(h, k)$ be any point of $E$. Now describe a transformation

$$P \leftrightarrow P',$$

or

$$(x, y) \leftrightarrow (x', y'),$$

by providing that $x' = x + h$ and $y' = y + k$, for all points $P$ of $E$.

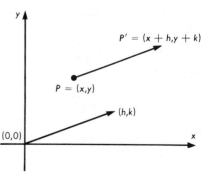

Thus $(0, 0) \leftrightarrow (h, k)$. We think of a translation as a way of moving the plane $E$, and so the arrows in the figure indicate the direction of the motion. [*Query:* What value of $k$ will give a translation in a direction parallel to the $x$-axis?]

We state these ideas as a definition.

## Definition

Let $P(x, y)$ and $(h, k)$ be any points of a coordinate plane $E$. Then the transformation $P \leftrightarrow P'$ such that $(x, y) \leftrightarrow (x + h, y + k)$ is called the *translation of the plane E by the point* $(h, k)$.

## Theorem 18–3

### *Every translation is a rigid motion.*

**Proof.** Let $P_1 = (x_1, y_1)$, and $P_2 = (x_2, y_2)$, so that

$$P'_1 = (x_1 + h, y_1 + k), \qquad P'_2 = (x_2 + h, y_2 + k).$$

Then, by the distance formula,

$$P'_1 P'_2 = \sqrt{[(x_2 + h) - (x_1 + h)]^2 + [(y_2 + k) - (y_1 + k)]^2}$$
$$= \sqrt{(x_2 - x_1)^2 + (y_2 - y_1)^2} = P_1 P_2.$$

If $P \leftrightarrow P'$, under a transformation, then $P'$ is called the *image* of $P$, and $P$ is called the *pre-image* of $P'$. Thus $(h, k)$ is the image of $(0, 0)$ under the translation of the plane by the point $(h, k)$, and $(0, 0)$ is the pre-image of $(h, k)$. In the figure below, the circle $C'$ is the image of the circle $C$ under the translation by $(2, 1)$, and $C$ is the pre-image of $C'$.

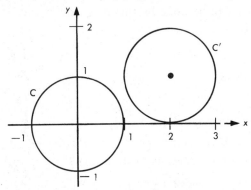

Thus the *image of a set of points* is the set of all images of points of the given set.

**Background Material**

Let G be the set of all translations of a coordinate plane. We allow the "identity translation" $I$: $(x, y) \leftrightarrow (x, y) = (x + 0, y + 0)$. We can define the *sum* of two translations $T_1$ and $T_2$ as the transformation under which we perform first $T_1$ and then $T_2$. (Thus we are defining the sum by composition of functions.) It is easy to see that $T_1 + T_2$ is always a translation. Given $T_1$: $(x, y) \leftrightarrow (x + h_1, y + k_1)$, and $T_2$: $(x', y') \leftrightarrow (x' + h_2, y' + k_2)$, we find that $T_1 + T_2$ is the translation under which $(x, y) \leftrightarrow (x + h_1 + h_2, y + k_1 + k_2)$. Under the operation $+$, the set G forms a *group* in the sense defined in abstract algebra. That is, G has the following properties. (1) G is closed under addition. That is, the sum of any two elements of G is an element of G. (2) Addition is associative. (3) There is a "zero element" 0 in G, such that $0 + T = T + 0$ for every $T$. (4) For each $T$ in G there is an element $-T$ in G such that $T + (-T) = -T + T = 0$. Also the group is commutative: $T_1 + T_2 = T_2 + T_1$ for every $T_1, T_2$ in G.

For a discussion of geometric transformations from this viewpoint, see *Geometry, A Perspective View*, by Rosskopf, Levine, and Vogeli (McGraw-Hill, 1969).

**1.** Let $P = (2, -5)$, $R$ be the image of $P$ under a reflection across the line $x = -3$, and $S$ the image of $P$ under the translation $(-5, -6)$. State the coordinates of $R$ and $S$.

(ans: $(-8, -5)$, $(-3, -11)$)

**2.** Given points $P = (0, 0)$, $Q = (3, 2)$, $R = (-5, 3)$, and $S = (-3, k)$. If a rigid motion maps $P$ onto $R$ and $Q$ onto $S$, evaluate $k$.

(ans: $k = 0$ or $k = 6$)

**3.** Let $R$ be the correspondence $(x, y) \leftrightarrow$ $(2x + 3, y - 5)$ for each point $(x, y)$ of a coordinate plane. Is $R$ a reflection across some line $L$? a translation?

(ans: No, in each case. Reflections and translations are rigid motions, and this correspondence is not. For example, take $P = (0, 0)$, $Q = (1, 0)$. Then $PQ = 1$. But $P \leftrightarrow P' = (3, -5)$, $Q \leftrightarrow Q' = (5, -5)$, $P'Q' = 2 \neq PQ$.)

Translations are easy to handle algebraically; we merely add $h$ to each $x$-coordinate and add $k$ to each $y$-coordinate. Reflections are often hard to deal with algebraically, but we can handle them graphically by paper-folding. Suppose, for example, that we are given a triangle $\triangle ABC$, and a point $A'$. There is a reflection, of the plane across a line, under which $A \leftrightarrow A'$.

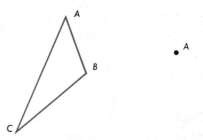

We want to draw the image of $\triangle ABC$ under this reflection. To do this, first trace $\triangle ABC$ and $A'$ on thin tracing paper. Fold the tracing paper so that $A$ falls on $A'$, and make a crease. This crease will determine the line of reflection, $L$. With the paper folded so that $\triangle ABC$ is on the outside, trace $\triangle ABC$ on the other side of the fold. This will be the image, $\triangle A'B'C'$. The process is illustrated by the figure on the left below. When the paper is opened up it will appear as in the figure on the right.

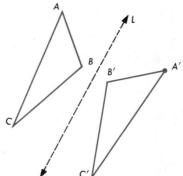

All reflections can be done by this method.

### Problem Set 18–3

**1.** In a coordinate plane let $P_1 = (3, 5)$ and $P_2 = (8, 11)$ and let $P_1'$ and $P_2'$ be their reflections across the $x$-axis.

(a) What are the coordinates of $P_1'$ and $P_2'$? $(3, -5)$, $(8, -11)$

(b) Use the distance formula to show that $P_1P_2 = P_1'P_2'$. $P_1P_2 = \sqrt{61}$

**2.** Follow the directions of Problem 1 for the points $P_1 = (-4, 5)$ and $P_2 = (7, -3)$. $P_1'(-4, -5)$, $P_2'(7, 3)$  $P_1P_2 = \sqrt{185}$

3. In a coordinate plane let $P_1 = (4, 7)$ and $P_2 = (-5, -6)$ and let $P_1'$ and $P_2'$ be their reflections across the $y$-axis.

(a) What are the coordinates of $P_1'$ and $P_2'$? $(-4,7), (5,-6)$

(b) Use the distance formula to show that $P_1P_2 = P_1'P_2'$. $P_1P_2 = 5\sqrt{10}$

4. How does the definition of a reflection across a line given in this section differ from the definition of a reflection across a line given in Section 18-2? **The definition of this section is stated in terms of correspondences.**

5. In a coordinate plane let $P_1 = (1, 8)$ and $P_2 = (4, 6)$ and let $P_1'$ and $P_2'$ be their reflections across the line whose equation is $y = x$.

(a) What are the coordinates of $P_1'$ and $P_2'$? $(8,1), (6,4)$

(b) Show that $P_1'P_2' = P_1P_2$. $P_1P_2 = \sqrt{13}$

6. Follow the directions of Problem 5 for the points $P_1 = (-1, 7)$ and $P_2 = (5, -5)$. $P_1'(7,-1), P_2'(-5,5)$   $P_1P_2 = \sqrt{5}$

7. Given the points $A$ and $B$ in a plane $E$. If $A'$ and $B'$ are the reflections of $A$ and $B$ across a line $L_1$, and $A''$ and $B''$ are the reflections of $A$ and $B$ across a line $L_2$, prove that $A'B' = A''B''$. **Use transitive property of equality**

8. Find the image of each of the following points under the translation by $(2, -3)$.

(a) $(4, 7)$ $(6,4)$      (b) $(-2, 1)$ $(0,-2)$      (c) $(-5, -4)$ $(-3,-7)$

9. For each of the following points find the image under the translation by $(-4, 8)$.

                                     $(\sqrt{3}-4, \sqrt{2}+8)$

(a) $(6, -6)$ $(2,2)$      (b) $(-4, 8)$ $(-8,16)$      (c) $(\sqrt{3}, \sqrt{2})$

10. Find the pre-image of each of the following points under the translation by $(3, 7)$.

(a) $(4, 9)$ $(1,2)$      (b) $(3, 2)$ $(0,-5)$      (c) $(1, -3)$ $(-2,-10)$

(d) $(-3, 4)$ $(-6,-3)$      (e) $(5, 0)$ $(2,-7)$      (f) $(-2, -1)$ $(-5,-8)$

11. Let $R$ be the correspondence under which $(a, b) \leftrightarrow (a + 3, b - 5)$, for each point $(a, b)$ of a coordinate plane. Show that $R$ is a rigid motion. **This is a transition by $(3,-5)$**

---

12. Prove the following theorem: Rigid motions preserve betweenness for points on a line. **If A-B-C, then AB+BC=AC, so A'B'+B'C'=A'C' and since rigid motion preserves distances, A'-B'-C'.**
*Restatement:* Given a rigid motion under which $A \leftrightarrow A'$, $B \leftrightarrow B'$, and $C \leftrightarrow C'$. If $A$-$B$-$C$, then $A'$-$B'$-$C'$.

13. Prove the theorem: Rigid motions preserve congruence for triangles. **Rigid motion preserves distances: Use SSS.**
*Restatement:* Given $\triangle ABC$ and a rigid motion under which $A \leftrightarrow A'$, $B \leftrightarrow B'$, and $C \leftrightarrow C'$, then $\triangle A'B'C' \cong \triangle ABC$.

14. For each figure below describe the rigid motion under which $A \leftrightarrow D$, $B \leftrightarrow E$, $C \leftrightarrow F$.

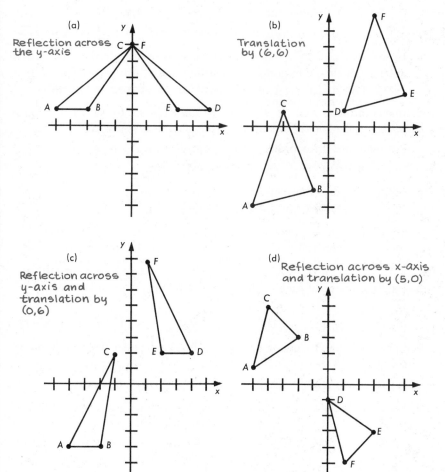

(a)
Reflection across the y-axis

(b)
Translation by (6,6)

(c)
Reflection across y-axis and translation by (0,6)

(d)
Reflection across x-axis and translation by (5,0)

15. In the figure, $\triangle A'B''C''$ is the reflection of $\triangle ABC$ across $L_1$, and $\triangle A'B'C'$ is the reflection of $\triangle A'B''C''$ across $L_2$. Trace $\triangle ABC$ and $\triangle A'B'C'$ on a sheet of paper, in exactly the same relative positions as in the figure. Then use the method of paper-folding to draw (1) the line $L_1$, (2) the dotted triangle, and (3) the line $L_2$.

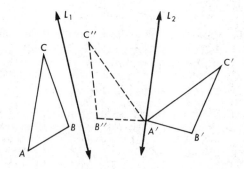

**Classroom Notes**

After a bit of practice with the conversion of rectangular coordinates to polar coordinates, it is clear that every rotation is a rigid motion. After proving that distance is preserved, the students may also wish to prove that measures of angles and parallelism of lines are also preserved.

16. Consider the reflection of a coordinate plane across the line whose equation is $y = x$. Describe this reflection by a formula of the type $(x, y) \leftrightarrow$ (?, ?). $(x,y) \leftrightarrow (y,x)$

17. Follow the directions in Problem 16 for the reflection of a coordinate plane across the line whose equation is $y = -x$. $(x,y) \leftrightarrow (-y,-x)$

## 18-4   ROTATIONS

Intuitively, a *rotation* is like the motion of a wheel about a fixed axle. In the figure, the radial segments represent the spokes of the wheel, and the arrows indicate that the wheel is rotated through the angle formed by two adjacent spokes.

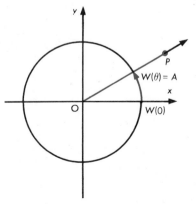

To get a better model of a rotation, think of a coordinate plane, represented by a sheet of paper, attached to a drawing board by a pin at the origin. We can rotate the paper through any angle that we want without removing the pin. In the figure the original position is shown in black, while the result of rotating through an angle $\angle a$ is shown in color.

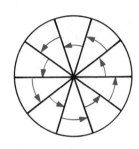

In the preceding section, we found that translations could be described by simple formulas $(x, y) \leftrightarrow (x + h, y + k)$. To get similar formulas for rotations we use the following scheme.

Every point $P$ in a coordinate plane lies in some ray $\overrightarrow{OA}$, and lies at a certain distance $r = OP$ from the origin. If $r$ and $\theta$ are known, then the point $P$ is determined. We then say that $P$ has *polar coordinates r* and $\theta$, and we write

$$P = [r, \theta].$$

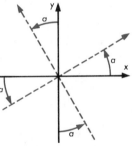

(The square brackets are used to distinguish the polar coordinates $[r, \theta]$ from the rectangular coordinates $(x, y)$ of the same point.) For example, if the rectangular coordinates of the point $P$ are $(\sqrt{3},1)$, then the polar coordinates are $[2, \pi/6]$ or $[2, 30°]$.

**1.** Let $R$ be a rotation about the origin under which $[r, \theta] \leftrightarrow [r, \theta - \pi/3]$. Find the image under $K$ of the point $(-2\sqrt{3}, -2)$.

(ans: $[4, 5\pi/6]$)

**2.** Let $T$ be the translation $(x, y) \leftrightarrow (x - 2, y + 3)$, and $R$ be a rotation about the origin under which $[r, \theta] \leftrightarrow [r, \theta + 3\pi/4]$. If $RT(P) = T(Q)$ and $P = (3, -3)$, find the coordinates of $Q$.

(ans: $((4 - \sqrt{2})/2, (-6 + \sqrt{2})/2)$)

**Answers to Problems**

**1.** (a) Since $x = \sqrt{3}$ and $y = 1$, $r = 2$ and $\tan \theta = 1/\sqrt{3}$ so $\theta = 30°$.

(b) $B = (-1, 1)$, $[\sqrt{2}, 135°]$;
$C = (1, \sqrt{3})$, $[2, 60°]$;
$D = (0, -1)$, $[1, 270°]$;
$E = (-\sqrt{3}, -1)$, $[2, 210°]$

Using polar coordinates, rotations can be defined in the following way.

**Definition**

Given a coordinate plane. The rotation of the plane about the origin, through an angle $\measuredangle a$, is the transformation $R_a$ under which

$$[r, \theta] \leftrightarrow [r, \theta + a].$$

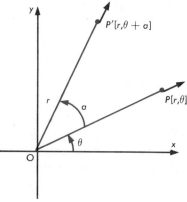

**Theorem 18-4**

*Every rotation is a rigid motion.*

**Proof.** Suppose that

$$P_1 \leftrightarrow P'_1, P_2 \leftrightarrow P'_2,$$

under a rotation through an angle $\measuredangle a$. We need to show that

$$P_1 P_2 = P'_1 P'_2.$$

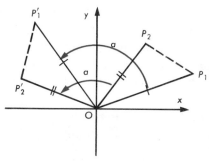

By the SAS Postulate, $\triangle OP_1 P_2 \cong \triangle OP'_1 P'_2$. Therefore $P_1 P_2 = P'_1 P'_2$. (The figure shows the case in which $O$, $P_1$, and $P_2$ are not collinear. If they are collinear, can you show that the equation $P_1 P_2 = P'_1 P'_2$ holds for a simpler reason?)

The definition of a rotation applies only to rotations about the origin. But any point of a plane can be taken as the origin. Therefore, to rotate a plane about a point $O'$, we set up a coordinate system with $O'$ as the origin, and use the formula $[r, \theta] \leftrightarrow [r, \theta + a]$. Then Theorem 18-4 applies, and says that the rotation is a rigid motion.

**Problem Set 18-4**

**1.** For the figure at the right

(a) explain why the point $A$ has rectangular coordinates $(\sqrt{3}, 1)$ and polar coordinates $[2, 30°]$.

(b) find both rectangular coordinates and polar coordinates for the points $B$, $C$, $D$, and $E$.

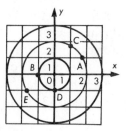

2. On a figure like that of Problem 1, plot each of the following points. Find polar coordinates of each point.

(a) $(1, 1)$ $[\sqrt{2}, 45°]$  (b) $\left(-\dfrac{\sqrt{3}}{2}, \dfrac{1}{2}\right)$ $[1, 150°]$(c) $(0, 1)$ $[1, 90°]$

(d) $\left(-\dfrac{1}{2}, -\dfrac{\sqrt{3}}{2}\right)$ $[1, 240°]$ (e) $\left(\dfrac{\sqrt{3}}{2}, -\dfrac{1}{2}\right)$ $[1, 330°]$(f) $(0, 0)$ $[0, 0°]$

(g) $(-1, -1)$ $[\sqrt{2}, 225°]$(h) $(-1, 0)$ $[1, 180°]$   (i) $(0, -1)$ $[1, 270°]$

3. On a figure like that of Problem 1 plot each of the following points. Find the rectangular coordinates of each point.                $\left(\dfrac{3\sqrt{3}}{2}, -\dfrac{3}{2}\right)$

(a) $\left[\sqrt{2}, \dfrac{3\pi}{4}\right]$ $(-1,1)$  (b) $[2, 240°]$ $(-1,-\sqrt{3})$(c) $[1, 2\pi]$ $(1,0)$   (d) $\left[3, \dfrac{11\pi}{6}\right]$

(e) $\left[2, -\dfrac{\pi}{4}\right]$ $(\sqrt{2},-\sqrt{2})$(f) $[3, -\pi]$ $(-3,0)$  (g) $[\tfrac{3}{2}, 30°]$ $\left(\dfrac{3\sqrt{3}}{4}, \dfrac{3}{4}\right)$(h) $\left[1, \dfrac{2\pi}{3}\right]$

$(-\tfrac{1}{2}, \sqrt{3}/2)$

4. In polar coordinates a point may be named by more than one ordered pair. For example, the point $(\sqrt{3}, 1)$ has at least the following names: $[2, 30°]$, $[2, 390°]$, $[2, -330°]$. Name each of the points of Problem 1 in at least two other ways. Use for example $[r, \theta + 2\pi]$ and $[r, \theta - 2\pi]$

5. Let $K$ be the rotation about the origin under which $[r, \theta] \leftrightarrow \left[r, \theta + \dfrac{\pi}{3}\right]$.

Find polar coordinates of the image under $K$ of each of the following points.

(a) $[1, 0°]$ $[1, 60°]$  (b) $[3, 45°]$ $[3, 105°]$

(c) $[2, 60°]$ $[2, 120°]$(d) $\left[2, \dfrac{\pi}{2}\right]$ $\left[2, \dfrac{5\pi}{6}\right]$

(e) $\left[3, -\dfrac{\pi}{3}\right]$ $[3, 0]$ (f) $\left[\dfrac{1}{2}, \dfrac{\pi}{4}\right]$ $\left[\dfrac{1}{2}, \dfrac{7\pi}{12}\right]$

6. Let $R$ be the rotation about the origin under which $[r, \theta] \leftrightarrow \left[r, \theta - \dfrac{\pi}{4}\right]$.

Find polar coordinates of the image under $R$ of each of the following points.                                             $\left[\sqrt{7}, \dfrac{5\pi}{12}\right]$

(a) $[1, 75°]$ $[1, 30°]$(b) $[5, 215°]$ $[5, 170°]$(c) $\left[4, -\dfrac{3\pi}{8}\right]$ $\left[4, -\dfrac{5\pi}{8}\right]$(d) $\left[\sqrt{7}, \dfrac{2\pi}{3}\right]$

7. Let $M$ be a rotation about the origin under which $[r, \theta] \leftrightarrow \left[r, \theta + \dfrac{3\pi}{4}\right]$.

Find polar coordinates of the pre-image under $M$ of each of the following points.                                    $\left[3, -\dfrac{\pi}{4}\right]$

(a) $(-1, 1)$ $[\sqrt{2}, 0]$  (b) $(-3, 0)$ $\left[3, \dfrac{\pi}{4}\right]$  (c) $\left[2, \dfrac{5\pi}{4}\right]$ $\left[2, \dfrac{\pi}{2}\right]$  (d) $\left[3, \dfrac{\pi}{2}\right]$

(e) $(0, -1)$ $\left[1, \dfrac{3\pi}{4}\right]$ (f) $\left[4, \dfrac{13\pi}{12}\right]$ $\left[4, \dfrac{\pi}{3}\right]$  (g) $\left[2, \dfrac{7\pi}{4}\right]$ $[2, \pi]$  (h) $(2, -2)$ $[2\sqrt{2}, \pi]$

8. Two or more rotations about the same origin can be performed successively. Find one rotation that is equivalent to performing first $T$ and then $R$.

(a) $T: [r, \theta] \leftrightarrow \left[r, \theta + \dfrac{\pi}{4}\right]$ and $R: [r, \theta] \leftrightarrow \left[r, \theta + \dfrac{\pi}{3}\right]$ $[r,\theta] \rightarrow [r,\theta + \frac{7\pi}{12}]$

(b) $T: [r, \theta] \leftrightarrow \left[r, \theta + \dfrac{\pi}{2}\right]$ and $R: [r, \theta] \leftrightarrow \left[r, \theta - \dfrac{3\pi}{4}\right]$ $[r,\theta] \rightarrow [r,\theta - \frac{\pi}{4}]$

(c) $T: [r, \theta] \leftrightarrow \left[r, \theta + \dfrac{5\pi}{6}\right]$ and $R: [r, \theta] \leftrightarrow \left[r, \theta - \dfrac{\pi}{3}\right]$ $[r,\theta] \rightarrow [\theta + \frac{\pi}{2}]$

9. In Problem 8, is the result the same for performing first $R$ and then $T$?
Yes

10. Let $R$ be a rotation about the origin through $\measuredangle\beta$ under which $A(x, y) \leftrightarrow A'(x', y')$. Also, let the point $A$ have polar coordinates $[r, \alpha]$. Recall, from Chapter 17, that $x = r \cos \alpha$ and $y = r \sin \alpha$.
Use addition formulas for sine and cosine in part (a). Use substitutions as shown for part (b).
(a) Show that

$\begin{cases} x' = \underline{r \cos \alpha} \cos \beta - \underline{r \sin \alpha} \sin \beta \text{ and} \\ y' = \underline{r \cos \alpha} \sin \beta + \underline{r \sin \alpha} \cos \beta. \end{cases}$

(over $x'$: $x$; over $y'$: $y$)

(b) Show that (a) gives

$x' = x \cos \beta - y \sin \beta$ and $y' = x \sin \beta + y \cos \beta.$

11. In Problem 10, let $(x, y) = (\sqrt{3}, 1)$ and $\measuredangle\beta = \dfrac{\pi}{6}$. Verify that $x' = 1$ and $y' = \sqrt{3}$. $x' = \sqrt{3} \cdot \sqrt{3}/2 - 1 \cdot \frac{1}{2} = 1$
$y' = \sqrt{3} \cdot \frac{1}{2} + 1 \cdot \sqrt{3}/2 = \sqrt{3}$

12. In Problem 10, let $(x, y) = (\sqrt{3}, 1)$ and $\measuredangle\beta = \dfrac{\pi}{4}$. Find $x'$ and $y'$.
$x' = (\sqrt{3} - 1)\frac{\sqrt{2}}{2}$  $y' = (\sqrt{3} + 1)\frac{\sqrt{2}}{2}$

13. In Problem 10, let $(x, y) = (1, 1)$ and $\measuredangle\beta = \dfrac{\pi}{3}$. Find $x'$ and $y'$.
$x' = \dfrac{1 - \sqrt{3}}{2}$  $y' = \dfrac{1 + \sqrt{3}}{2}$

14. In Problem 10, let $(x, y) = (1, \sqrt{3})$ and $\measuredangle\beta = \dfrac{2\pi}{3}$. Find $x'$ and $y'$.
$x' = -2$  $y' = 0$

15. Let $R$ be a rotation about the point $A(x, y)$ through $\measuredangle\beta$ under which $A'(x', y') \leftrightarrow A''(x'', y'')$. Show that

$x'' = (x' - x) \cos \beta - (y' - y) \sin \beta + x$
First translate by $(-x, -y)$, then use Problem 10 to rotate through $\measuredangle\beta$, then translate by $(x, y)$.
and

$y'' = (x' - x) \sin \beta + (y' - y) \cos \beta + y.$

**16.** In Problem 15, let $(x, y) = (5, 2)$, $(x', y') = (9, 9)$, and $\angle\beta = \dfrac{\pi}{6}$. Find $(x'', y'')$. $x'' = 2\sqrt{3} + \dfrac{3}{2}$   $y'' = 4 + \dfrac{7\sqrt{3}}{2}$

**17.** Let $S$ be a rotation about the point $A(1, \sqrt{3})$ through $\angle\theta$ where $\theta = \dfrac{\pi}{4}$.. Find the rectangular coordinates of the image under $S$ of the following points.

(a) $(4, 3\sqrt{3})$   (b) $(3, 1 + \sqrt{3})$   (c) $(-1, 2 + \sqrt{3})$

$\left(\dfrac{3\sqrt{2}}{2} - \sqrt{6} + 1, \dfrac{3\sqrt{2}}{2} + \sqrt{6} + \sqrt{3}\right)$   $\left(\dfrac{\sqrt{2}}{2} + 1, \dfrac{3\sqrt{2}}{2} + \sqrt{3}\right)$,   $\left(-2\sqrt{2} + 1, \sqrt{3}\right)$

**18.** Let $R$ be a rotation about the origin through $\angle\beta$ under which $A(x, y) \leftrightarrow A'(x', y')$ and $B(u, v) \leftrightarrow B'(u', v')$. Let $T$ be a translation by $(a, b)$ under which $A \leftrightarrow B$ and $A' \leftrightarrow A''(x'', y'')$.

(a) Show that  Use Problem 10 then translate.

$x'' = x \cos \beta - y \sin \beta + a$ and

$y'' = x \sin \beta + y \cos \beta + b$.

(b) Show that

Notice that u = x+a and then use Problem 10. $u' = (x + a) \cos \beta - (y + b) \sin \beta$ and

$v' = (x + a) \sin \beta + (y + b) \cos \beta$.

(c) Complete: If $T[R(x, y)] = A''$, then $R[T(x, y)] =$ ___B'___ .

(d) In general, does $T[R(x, y)] = R[T(x, y)]$? No

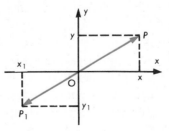

**19.** In Problem 18, let $(x, y) = (2, 1)$, $(a, b) = (6, 2)$ and $\angle\beta = \dfrac{\pi}{4}$.

(a) Find $x''$ and $y''$.   (b) Find $u'$ and $v'$.

$x'' = \dfrac{\sqrt{2}}{2} + 6$, $y'' = \dfrac{3\sqrt{2}}{2} + 2$   $u' = \dfrac{5\sqrt{2}}{2}$, $v' = \dfrac{11\sqrt{2}}{2}$

## 18-5   VECTORS

By a *vector* we mean an ordered pair of real numbers. Thus a vector is simply a point of a coordinate plane. One way to draw a picture of a vector $(x, y)$ is to draw the axes and then plot the point $P = (x, y)$. Another way to draw a picture of a vector is to draw the directed segment from the origin $O$ to the point $P = (x, y)$. This is sometimes considered a better picture because it re-minds us that every vector determines not only a magnitude (namely, the distance $OP$) but also a direction indicated by the arrowhead in the figure. (The zero vector $O = (0, 0)$ is an exception: it does not de-termine a direction.)

---

**Classroom Notes**

Vectors are relatively simple as presented in this section. Addition is defined as a translation and scalar multiplication introduces a new transformation, namely, dila-tion. The class should discuss the proof of the Parallelogram Law of Addition and carefully discuss the concept of dilation.

When we have defined the sum of two vectors and the scalar product, it is natural to ask how one vector can be multiplied by another. Later (though not in this book) we define the *inner product* of $(x, y)$ and $(x', y')$ by the formula $xx' + yy'$, Thus the inner product is a *number*. not a vector.

## Background Material

Since there is a zero vector and every vector has an inverse with respect to addition, an algebra of vectors can be defined. The usual properties of commutativity and associativity can be established. For further details see Chapter 14 of *Algebra and Trigonometry* by Johnson, et. al. (Addison Wesley, 1971)

Vectors are *added* in the following way.

### Definition

For every pair of vectors $(x_1, y_1)$, $(x_2, y_2)$, the vector sum $(x_1, y_1) + (x_2, y_2)$ is given by $(x_1 + x_2, y_1 + y_2)$.

The *zero vector* is $O = (0, 0)$. This vector works like 0, because $(x, y) + (0, 0) = (0, 0) + (x, y) = (x, y)$, for every $(x, y)$.

The following theorem shows that vector addition can be used to describe translations.

### Theorem 18–5

*In a plane E, let $P_0 = (h, k)$ be a vector in E, $P = (x, y)$ be any other vector in E, and $P' = P + P_0$. Then the correspondence $P \leftrightarrow P'$ is the translation of E by $P_0$.*

**Proof.** $P' = P + P_0 = (x, y) + (h, k) = (x + h, y + k)$. But this is the translation of $E$ by $P_0$, which is what we wanted to prove.

Another way to think of vector addition is geometrically, as explained in the following theorem.

### Theorem 18–6.  The Parallelogram Law of Addition

*Let $P_1 = (x_1, y_1)$ and $P_2 = (x_2, y_2)$, and suppose that $P_1$, $P_2$, and O are not collinear. Then $P_1 + P_2$ is the fourth vertex of the parallelogram determined by O, $P_1$, and $P_2$.*

**Proof.** Since $O$, $P_1$, and $P_2$ are not collinear, it follows that $P_1$ and $P_2$ are different from $O$ and from each other. By definition,

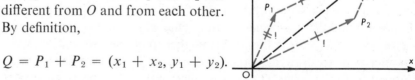

$$Q = P_1 + P_2 = (x_1 + x_2, y_1 + y_2).$$

(1) Under the translation $P \leftrightarrow P + P_1$, we have $O \leftrightarrow P_1$ and $P_2 \leftrightarrow Q$. Since every translation is a rigid motion (Theorem 18–3) it follows that $OP_2 = P_1Q$, as shown in the figure.

(2) Similarly, under the translation $P \leftrightarrow P + P_2$, we have $O \leftrightarrow P_2$, $P_1 \leftrightarrow Q$. Therefore $OP_1 = P_2Q$.

Since the opposite sides of $\square OP_1QP_2$ are congruent, it follows that $\square OP_1QP_2$ is a parallelogram (Theorem 9–19).

There is another algebraic operation performed on vectors. This is called *scalar multiplication*, and is defined as follows.

### Definition

For each vector $P = (x, y)$ and each real number $r$,

$$rP = r(x, y) = (rx, ry).$$

The vector $rP$ is called the *scalar product* of $r$ and $P$.

When we are discussing vectors, we refer to real numbers as *scalars*. Let $r$ be any scalar different from 0, and consider the correspondence

$$P \leftrightarrow P' = rP,$$
$$(x, y) \leftrightarrow r(x, y) = (rx, ry).$$

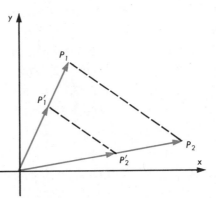

When $P$ is replaced by $P'$, the effect is to multiply all distance by $|r|$. To see this, take

$$P_1 = (x_1, y_1), \quad P_2 = (x_2, y_2),$$
$$P_1' = (rx_1, ry_1), \quad P_2' = (rx_2, ry_2).$$

Then

$$
\begin{aligned}
P_1'P_2' &= \sqrt{(rx_2 - rx_1)^2 + (ry_2 - ry_1)^2} \\
&= \sqrt{r^2(x_2 - x_1)^2 + r^2(y_2 - y_1)^2} \\
&= \sqrt{r^2} \sqrt{(x_2 - x_1)^2 + (y_2 - y_1)^2} \\
&= |r|P_1P_2.
\end{aligned}
$$

A transformation which has this property is called a *dilation*.

### Definition

Let $P \leftrightarrow P'$ be a one-to-one correspondence between the points of a plane and themselves. Suppose that there is a number $r \neq 0$ such that

$$P_1'P_2' = |r|P_1P_2,$$

for every pair of points $P_1$, $P_2$. Then the correspondence $P \leftrightarrow P'$ is called a *dilation*.

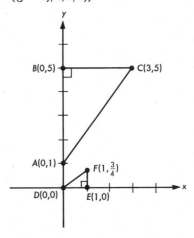

The use of the term *dilation* is more natural in the case $|r| > 1$, for all distances are increased under the transformation, and so the whole plane is stretched or dilated. For $|r| < 1$, all distances are diminished, and so the plane is shrunk. Thus for $|r| < 1$ the image of any figure in the plane is a scale model of the original figure, having exactly the same shape but a smaller size. Thus while rigid motions are like congruences, dilations are like similarities.

In the case $|r| = 1$, all distances are preserved, and so the dilation is a rigid motion.

### Problem Set 18–5

1. Draw two sets of rectangular coordinate axes. On one set draw a point as a picture of each of the following vectors. On the other set draw a directed segment from the origin as a picture of each vector.

   (a) (3, 2)  (b) (2, 3)  (c) (−2, 4)  (d) (2, −3)

2. Find each of the following vector sums.

   (a) $(-3, 4) + (10, -2)$ (7,2)  (b) $(0, -5) + (15, 8)$ (15,3)

   (c) $(8, -7) + (-3, -2)$ (5,-9)  (d) $3(1, 2) + (-2, -5)$ (1,1)

   (e) $(5, -4) + (-5, 4)$ (0,0)  (f) $(6, 3) - (-2, 8)$ (8,-5)

3. Find each scalar product.

   (a) $4(-5, 3)$ (-20,12)  (b) $\sqrt{2}(4, \sqrt{2})$ (4√2,2)  (c) $-3(2, -1)$ (-6,3)

4. Trace each of the following figures. Use the Parallelogram Law to draw a complete picture of each vector sum.

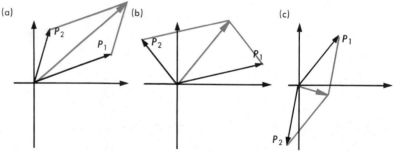

5. Subtraction for vectors is defined in terms of the additive inverse. For the vector $P = (x, y)$ the additive inverse is $(-x, -y)$. Sketch each one of the following vectors and its additive inverse as directed line segments from the origin.

   (a) (3, 4)  (b) (−2, 3)  (c) (4, −3)

6. From the following list identify which are scalars and which are vectors.

   $(4, -1)$, 7, $\sqrt{3}$, $(\sqrt{2}, 5)$, $\pi$, $(2, \pi)$, $(3, 0)$, 17  7,√3, π and 17 are scalars
   (4,-1), √2,5),(2π) and (3,0) are vectors

7. A transformation $T$ is defined by the correspondence $(r, s) \leftrightarrow 4(r, s)$. What name applies to $T$? Dilation

8. Given $\triangle ABC$ with $A(1, 4)$, $B(4, -3)$, and $C(-2, 1)$. Under a dilation $T$ from the origin, $A' = T(A) = (3, 12)$. If $B' = T(B)$ and $C' = T(C)$, what are the coordinates of $B'$ and $C'$? **B'=(12,-9), c'(-6,3)**

9. In Problem 8, what is the relation of $\triangle ABC$ and $\triangle A'B'C'$? **They are similar.**

10. In Problem 8, what is the ratio of $a\triangle ABC$ to $a\triangle A'B'C'$? **1:9**

11. Given a circle, $C$, with center at $(4, 3)$ and radius 5. A dilation $T$ is defined for the circle by the transformation $P' \leftrightarrow \sqrt{2} P$ for each point $P$ of $C$. Describe the set, $C'$, of all points $P$. **C' is the circle of radius $5\sqrt{2}$ with center $(4\sqrt{2}, 3\sqrt{2})$.**

12. For the set $C'$ of Problem 11, what is the circumference? What is the area of the region bounded by $C'$? **$10\sqrt{2}\pi$, $50\pi$**

---

13. A transformation can combine a dilation and a translation. For example, under the transformation $T: (x, y) \leftrightarrow 3(x, y) + (5, 8)$, the point $P(-5, 4)$ corresponds to the point $P'(-10, 20)$. Under $T$, what does the point $R(4, 3)$ correspond to? the point $S(2, -4)$? **R'(17,17) S'(11,-4)**

14. In Problem 13, sketch $\triangle PRS$ and $\triangle P'R'S'$ in a coordinate plane. What relations exist between corresponding sides of the triangles? between corresponding angles? **Corresponding angles are congruent**

15. Consider the transformation $K: P \leftrightarrow \frac{1}{2}P + P_0$ where $P = (x, y)$ and $P_0 = (3, -4)$. Find the image under $K$ of each of the following vectors.

$A = (12, 8)$ **A'=(9,0)**   $B = (-4, 6)$ **B'=(1,-1)**   $C = (8, -10)$ **C'=(7,-9)**

16. Consider the transformation $M: P \leftrightarrow 4P + P_0$, where $P = (x, y)$ and $P_0 = (-3, 5)$. Find the pre-image under $M$ of each of the following vectors.

$G'(5, 1)$ **G=(2,-1)**      $H'(9, 13)$ **H=(3,2)**      $J'(-7, 5)$ **J=(-1,0)**

17. Consider the transformation $S: P \leftrightarrow rP + \dfrac{1}{r} P_0$, where $r = 3, P = (x, y)$, and $P_0 = (6, 9)$.

(a) Find the image under $S$ of each of the following points.

$X(-1, -3)$      $Y(2, 6)$      $Z(5, 0)$
**X'(-1,-6)**      **Y'(8,21)**      **Z'(17,3)**

(b) Find the pre-image under $S$ of each of the points in part (a). **(-1,-2),(0,1),(1,-1)**

(c) Sketch, in a coordinate plane, the three triangles determined in parts (a) and (b).

---

18. Let $R$ be a rotation under which $P[r, \theta] \leftrightarrow P'[r, \theta + \beta]$. Let $D$ be a dilation under which $P(x, y) \leftrightarrow kP(x, y)$. Let $T$ be the transformation that combines $R$ and $D$, that is, $T = R(D)$.

(a) Show that under $T$, $(x, y) \leftrightarrow (kx \cos \beta - ky \sin \beta, kx \cos \beta + ky \sin \beta)$.

(b) Find the image under $T$ of $P(4, 3)$ if $\beta = \dfrac{\pi}{4}$. **$(k\frac{\sqrt{2}}{2}, 7k\frac{\sqrt{2}}{2})$**

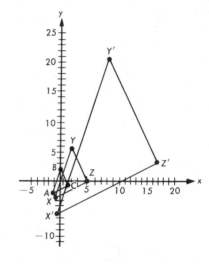

**Classroom Notes**

Now that the students are proficient with a variety of transformations, we can redefine congruence and similarity with the help of transformations. Theorems 18–9, 18–10, and 18–11 are the important ideas of this section.

## 18–6   A SECOND LOOK AT CONGRUENCE AND SIMILARITY

In this section, we shall show that if two triangles are congruent, in the same plane, then one can be moved onto the other by a rigid motion. Then we shall show that if two triangles are similar, then one can be moved onto the other by a rigid motion, followed by a dilation.

### Theorem 18–7

*Let P and P′ be any two points. Then there is a line-reflection under which P ↔ P′.*

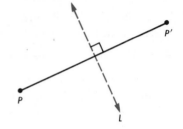

**Proof.** Reflect across the perpendicular bisector of $\overline{PP'}$.

### Theorem 18–8

*Let P and P′ be any two points, and let A be a point such that AP = AP′. Then there is a line-reflection under which A ↔ A and P ↔ P′.*

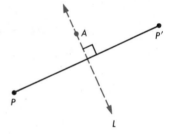

**Proof.** Let $L$ be the perpendicular bisector of $\overline{PP'}$, as before. Then $A$ lies on $L$. Now reflect across $L$.

### Theorem 18–9

*Let △ABC and △A′B′C′ be triangles in a plane. If △ABC ≅ △A′B′C′, then there is a rigid motion under which A ↔ A′, B ↔ B′, and C ↔ C′.*

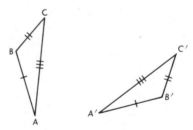

**Proof.**

*Step 1.* Let $R_1$ be a line-reflection under which $A \leftrightarrow A'$. (Theorem 18–7) Under $R_1$,

$$B \leftrightarrow D \quad \text{and} \quad C \leftrightarrow E.$$

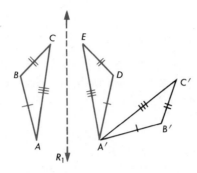

*Step 2.* Since $R_1$ is a rigid motion, $A'D = A'B'$, as indicated in the figure. By Theorem 18–8 there is a reflection under which $A' \leftrightarrow A'$ and $D \leftrightarrow B'$. Under $R_2$, $E \leftrightarrow F$.

The figure shows the case in which $F \neq C'$. It may happen that $F = C'$; in this case, we have $A \leftrightarrow A'$, $B \leftrightarrow B'$ and $C \leftrightarrow C'$ under Steps 1 and 2. If $F \neq C'$, as in the figure, we need one more step, as follows.

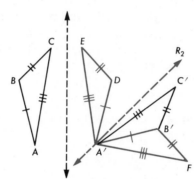

*Step 3.* If $F \neq C'$, then both $A'$ and $B'$ lie on the perpendicular bisector of $\overline{FC'}$. Let this line be $L$, and let $R_3$ be the reflection across $L$. Under $R_3$, $A' \leftrightarrow A'$, $B' \leftrightarrow B'$, and $F \leftrightarrow C'$. Now we are done.

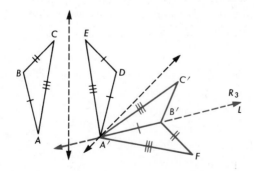

Theorem 18–9, as it stands, says only that the rigid motion takes the *vertices* of $\triangle ABC$ on the *vertices* of $\triangle A'B'C'$. The following theorem gives more information.

### Theorem 18–10

*Let $\triangle ABC$ and $\triangle A'B'C'$ be triangles in a plane. If $\triangle ABC \cong \triangle A'B'C'$, then there is a rigid motion under which $\triangle ABC$ is moved onto $\triangle A'B'C'$.*

That is, (1) if $P$ is a point of $\triangle ABC$, and $P \leftrightarrow P'$ under the rigid motion, then $P'$ is a point of $\triangle A'B'C'$. And (2) if $P'$ is a point of $\triangle A'B'C'$, and $P \leftrightarrow P'$, then $P$ is a point of $\triangle ABC$.

**Proof of (1).** We know that $A \leftrightarrow A'$, $B \leftrightarrow B'$, and $C \leftrightarrow C'$, under the rigid motion given by the preceding theorem. Each point of $\triangle ABC$ lies on one of the sides of $\triangle ABC$. Suppose, then, that $A$-$P$-$B$. Then $AP + PB = AB$. (Why?) Therefore $A'P' + P'B' = A'B'$, and so $A'$-$P'$-$B'$. Therefore $P'$ lies on $\overline{A'B'}$.

**Proof of (2).** If $A'$-$P'$-$B'$, then $A'P' + P'B' = A'B'$, $AP + PB = AP$, and $P$ lies on $\overline{AB}$.

All these ideas apply to similarities, in the following way.

### Theorem 18–11

*Let $\triangle ABC$ and $\triangle A'B'C'$ be triangles in a plane. If $\triangle ABC \sim \triangle A'B'C'$, then $\triangle ABC$ can be moved onto $\triangle A'B'C'$ by a rigid motion, followed by a dilation.*

**Proof.** Let $D$ and $E$ be points of $\overrightarrow{A'B'}$ and $\overrightarrow{A'C'}$, such that $\triangle ABC \cong \triangle A'DE$. By the preceding theorem, there is a rigid motion moving $\triangle ABC$ onto $\triangle A'DE$. It remains to show that there is a dilation moving $\triangle A'DE$ onto $\triangle A'B'C'$.

Since $\triangle A'DE \cong \triangle ABC$, and $\triangle ABC \sim \triangle A'B'C'$, it follows that $\triangle A'DE \sim \triangle A'B'C'$. Therefore

$$\frac{A'B'}{A'D} = \frac{A'C'}{A'E}.$$

Let $k = A'B'/A'D$. Then

$$A'B' = kA'D, \qquad A'C' = kA'E.$$

Now regard $A'$ as the origin, and consider the dilation

$$P \leftrightarrow P', \qquad (x, y) \leftrightarrow (kx, ky).$$

Then $D \leftrightarrow B'$, $E \leftrightarrow C'$, $\overline{A'D}$ is moved onto $\overline{A'B'}$, and $\overline{A'E}$ is moved onto $\overline{A'C'}$.

Finally, we need to check that $\overline{DE}$ is moved onto $\overline{B'C'}$. The proof is like that of Theorem 18–10. (1) Suppose that $D$-$P$-$E$. Then $DP + PE = DE$. Under the dilation, all distances are multiplied by $k$. Therefore

$$B'P' + P'C' = kDP + kPE = kDE = B'C',$$

and so $B'$-$P'$-$E'$.
(2) Suppose that $B'$-$P'$-$C'$. Then $B'P' + P'C' = B'C'$. Therefore

$$\frac{1}{k} B'P' + \frac{1}{k} P'C' = \frac{1}{k} B'C',$$

$$OP + PE = DE,$$

and $D$-$P$-$E$. Therefore $P$ lies on $\overline{DE}$.

The results of this section mean that the whole theory of congruence and similarity, developed in earlier chapters of this book, can be described in terms of geometric transformations. In fact, reflections and dilations are enough. (Recall that any congruence between triangles can be achieved by using either two or three reflections.)

The next and final chapter deals with solid mensuration, for which there is no advantage in using transformations. Thus we end our study of geometric transformations at this point.

## Quiz

**1.** If $AB = CD$, how many rigid motions will map $\overline{AB}$ onto $\overline{CD}$? Which theorems justify your conclusion?
  (ans: 2, Theorems 18–7 and 18–8)
**2.** The proof of Theorem 18–10 shows an important property of rigid motions, which is not explicitly stated in the theorem. What is this property?
  (ans: A rigid motion transforms lines onto lines.)
**3.** If $A = (-4, 4)$, $B = (-4, 0)$, $C = (-2, 0)$, $D = (0, 5)$, $E = (0, 4)$, and $F = (2, 4)$, find three or fewer lines such that the product of the reflections across these lines, followed by the dilation maps $\triangle ABC$ onto $\triangle FED$.
  (ans: There are several answers. One answer is as follows. Let $R$ be the reflection across the $y$-axis, $S$ be the reflection across the line $y = x$, $T$ be the reflection across the line $y = 4$, and $W$ be the dilation with origin $(0, 4)$ and scalar factor $\frac{1}{2}$. Then a transformation which maps $\triangle ABC$ onto $\triangle DEF$ is $WTSR$.)

The following answers are only suggestions of the transformations to use.
Students may have several different
answers, especially to the first two
problems.

1. (a) Reflect across the perpendicular
bisector of $\overline{AA'}$ to get $A \leftrightarrow A'$,
$C \leftrightarrow E$, $B \leftrightarrow D$, then reflect
across the perpendicular bi-
sector of $\overline{EC'}$ to get the required
position.

(b) Reflect across the perpendicular
bisector of $\overline{FF'}$ with $F \leftrightarrow F'$,
$E \leftrightarrow R$, $D \leftrightarrow T$, then rotate around
$F'$ through an angle of $m\angle RF'E'$
and reflect across $\overline{E'F'}$.

(c) Reflect across the perpendicular
bisector of $\overline{RR'}$ getting $R \leftrightarrow R'$,
$T \leftrightarrow Q$, $S \leftrightarrow P$, then rotate around
$R'$ through an angle of $m\angle QR'T$
getting the required position.

2. (a) Reflect across the perpendicular
bisector of $\overline{AA'}$ ($A \leftrightarrow A'$, $B \leftrightarrow$
$R$, $C \leftrightarrow S$) and rotate about $A'$
through an angle of $m\angle B'A'R$,
then reflect across $A'B'$. The
final step is the dilation $(x, y) \leftrightarrow$
$(kx, ky)$ where $k = \dfrac{A'B'}{AB}$.

(b) Reflect across the perpendicular
bisector of $\overline{DD'}$ ($D \leftrightarrow D'$, $E \leftrightarrow Q$,
$F \leftrightarrow S$) and rotate about $D'$
through an angle of $m\angle SD'F'$,
then dilate $(x, y) \leftrightarrow (kx, ky)$ where
$k = \dfrac{D'F'}{DF}$.

## Problem Set 18–6

1. Trace each of the following pairs of congruent triangles, in the same
relative positions shown below. Show that each triangle may be moved
onto its congruent mate by a rigid motion which is either (1) two or
three line reflections, (2) a rotation, or (3) a rotation and a line reflection,
by constructing the necessary axes of symmetry and the center of the
circle of rotation, whenever necessary.

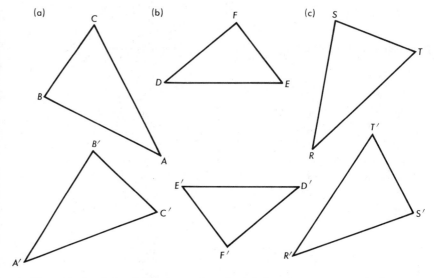

2. Trace each of the following pairs of triangles, in the same relative positions shown below. Show that the triangles in each pair are similar by
describing, or constructing, a rigid motion followed by a dilation that
matches $A$ to $A'$ and $D$ to $D'$.

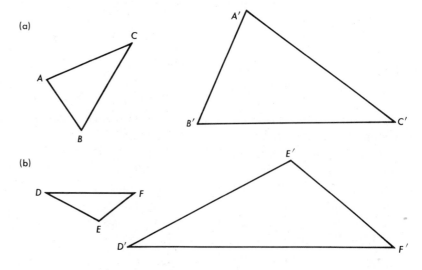

**3.** The following sequence of figures illustrates a method which uses a dilation to construct a required figure. Study this sequence and then devise similar methods to complete the required constructions.

Example: Inscribe a square in a given semi-circle.

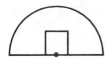 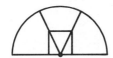 

(1) Construct any small square.

(2) Project from center of arc.

(3) Drop perpendiculars. Complete required square.

(a) Inscribe a rectangle in a semi-circle of radius 4 cm.

(b) Inscribe a rectangle in a circle of radius 4 cm.

(c) Inscribe a square in a quadrant of a circle.

(d) Inscribe a scalene triangle similar to the one shown here in a circle of radius 4 cm.

## CHAPTER REVIEW

**1.** Name three types of rigid motions. Translation, Reflection, Rotation

**2.** Name the transformation (in this chapter) which is not a rigid motion. Dilation

**3.** Complete: A square is both ___point___-symmetric and ___line___-symmetric.

**4.** Complete: An isosceles trapezoid is ___line___-symmetric, but is not ___point___-symmetric.

**5.** Complete: If a plane figure is symmetric about each of two perpendicular lines, then it is symmetric about their intersection point.

**6.** Complete: A (non-equilateral) isosceles triangle is ___line___-symmetric, but is not ___point___-symmetric.

**7.** Which of the following letters are line-symmetric? which are point-symmetric? E,T,X,I,V,H ; X,S,I,Z,H

ETXQSIVZFH

**Answers to Problems**

**3.** (a) Construct any rectangle similar to the given rectangle inside a semicircle of radius 4 cm with the midpoint of one edge at the center of the circle. The vertices not on the diameter are now projected outward to the circle from its center. Drop perpendiculars and complete the required rectangle.

(b) Construct any rectangle similar to the given one, with the midpoint of its diagonals at the center of the circle of radius 4 cm. Project the vertices to the circle from its center. Connect the vertices to complete the required rectangle.

(c) Construct any square with one vertex at the center of a given circle and two other vertices on the sides of a given quadrant of the circle. Project the fourth vertex from the center to the circle. Drop perpendiculars and complete the required square.

(d) Construct a triangle similar to the given triangle, so the center of a circle of radius 4 cm is the intersection point of the perpendicular bisectors of the three sides. Project the vertices from the center to the circle, connect the image points and complete the required triangle.

13. (a) $A = (1, \sqrt{3})$, [2, 60°],
$B = (0, 3)$, [3, 90°],
$C = (-1, \sqrt{3})$, [2, 120°],
$D = (-2, 0)$, [2, 180°],
$E = (-1, -1)$, [$\sqrt{2}$, 225°],
$F = (-1, -\sqrt{3})$, [2, 240°],
$G = (\sqrt{3}, -1)$, [2, 330°].

8. Given a coordinate plane. For each point named below give its reflection across (1) the x-axis, (2) the y-axis, and (3) the origin.

    (a) $(4, -3)$ **(4,3),(-4,-3),(-4,3)** (b) $(-2, 5)$ **(-2,-5),(2,5),(2,-5)**

    (c) $(-6, -8)$ **(-6,8),(6,-8),(6,8)** (d) $(9, 7)$ **(9,-7),(-7,9),(-9,-7)**

9. For each point named in Problem 8 give its reflection across line $y = x$.
    **(a) (-3,4), (b) (5,-2), (c) (-8,-6), (d) (7,9)**

10. Find the image of each of the following points under a translation by $(-2, 7)$.

    (a) $(3, -2)$ **(1,5)** (b) $(4, 6)$ **(2,13)** (c) $(-3, 11)$ **(-5,18)**

11. Let $T$ be the correspondence under which $(x, y) \leftrightarrow (x + 4, y - 1)$ for each point $(x, y)$ of a coordinate plane. Show that $T$ is a rigid motion.
    **T is a translation by (4,-1)**

12. Complete: Every point in a plane may be named by a set of **rectangular** coordinates, such as (1, 1), or by a set of ___**polar**___ coordinates, such as $\left[ \sqrt{2}, \dfrac{\pi}{4} \right]$.

13. Given the figure,

    (a) find both rectangular coordinates and polar coordinates for each of the points $A$-$G$.

    (b) Which points are symmetric about an axis? **A and C are symmetric about the y-axis.** Which are symmetric about the origin? **A and F are symmetric about the origin.**

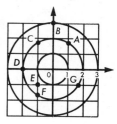

14. Find the rectangular coordinates of each of the following points.

    (a) [4, 300°]**(2,-2√3)** (b) $\left[ 12, \dfrac{3\pi}{4} \right]$**(-6√2,6√2)** (c) $\left[ 6, -\dfrac{\pi}{6} \right]$**(3√3,-3)**

15. Find polar coordinates of each of the following points.

    (a) $(0, -3)$**[3,270°]** (b) $(-5, 5)$**[5√2,135°]** (c) $(4, 4\sqrt{3})$**[8,60°]**

16. Give two other sets of polar coordinates for each of the following points.

    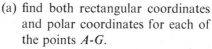

    (a) $\left[ 2, \dfrac{7\pi}{3} \right]$ **[2,π/3] [2,13π/3]** (b) $\left[ 4, -\dfrac{3\pi}{4} \right]$ **[4,5π/4] [4,13π/4]** (c) $\left[ 7, \dfrac{39\pi}{8} \right]$ **[7,23π/8] [7,7π/8]**

17. Let $S$ be a rotation about the origin under which $[r, \theta] \leftrightarrow \left[ r, \theta + \dfrac{\pi}{3} \right]$.

    Find polar coordinates of the image under $S$ of each of the following points.

    (a) $(1, 0)$**[1,π/3]** (b) $(-1, -\sqrt{3})$**[2,300°]** (c) $(-2\sqrt{3}, 2)$**[4,210°]**

    (d) $(-1, 0)$**[1,4π/3]** (e) $(0, 0)$**[0,0°]** (f) $(3, 3)$**[3√2,105°]**

    [Hint: first find the polar coordinates of each point.]

18. Find each vector sum.

   (a) $(3, 8) + (2, 4)$ **(5,12)**     (b) $(6, 0) + (13, -2)$ **(19,-2)**

   (c) $(5, 9) - (8, -2) + (0, -5)$    (d) $(7, -9) + (-7, 9)$ **(0,0)**
                         **(-3,6)**

19. Find each scalar product.

   (a) $6(4, -3)$ **(24,-18)**     (b) $-3(13, 4)$ **(-39,-12)**

20. Trace each of the following figures. Use the Parallelogram Law to draw a complete picture of each vector sum.

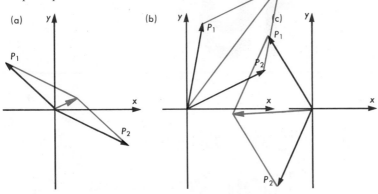

21. Given $\triangle ABC$ with $A(4, 0)$, $B(2, 8)$, and $C(-8, -4)$. Under a dilation $T$ from the origin, $A' = T(A) = (6, 0)$. What is $T(B)$ and $T(C)$?
   **T(B)=(3,12)   T(C)=(-12,-6)**

22. Given $\triangle D'E'F'$ with $D'(-2, 0)$, $E'(8, 16)$ and $F'(3, 1)$, the result of a dilation from the origin upon $\triangle DEF$. If $F(12, 4)$, what are the preimages of $D'$ and $E'$? **D=(-8,0), E=(32,64)**

23. For the triangles shown below describe a transformation which will effect the following correspondence.

   (a) $\triangle ABC \leftrightarrow \triangle A'B'C'$     (b) $\triangle ABC \leftrightarrow \triangle A''B''C''$

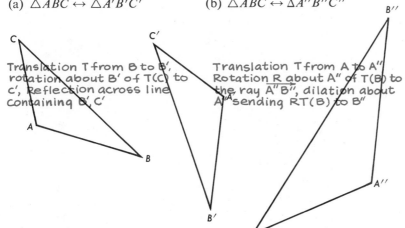

**Translation T from B to B', rotation about B' of T(C) to C', Reflection across line containing B', C'**

**Translation T from A to A", Rotation R about A" of T(B) to the ray A"B", dilation about A" sending RT(B) to B"**

## Solids and Their Volumes

The introductory comments on Chapter 16 apply with double emphasis to the present chapter, because the underlying theory is even more difficult. We have therefore not attempted to present this material on the same level of explicitness and rigor that was used in the first fifteen chapters. We have discussed mensuration intuitively, for particular solids, without attempting to explain what sort of figures in space can be regarded as "solids" and can be measured. In this style we develop the formulas for surface area, cross-section area, and volume for the familiar solids: prisms, pyramids, cylinders, cones, and spheres.

Note that we define a prism as a solid rather than a polyhedral surface. This approach is analogous to our earlier emphasis on polygonal regions rather than polygons, and is quite natural since our main object of study in this chapter is volumes of solids rather than areas of surfaces. If we used the alternative approach and defined a prism as a polyhedral surface, we would then be faced with the problem of defining the interior of this surface in order to get the volume of the corresponding solid.

### Planning the Chapter

This optional chapter can be introduced to an average class in approximately four days, covering only the first four sections superficially. An above-average class will spend two days on each section for an in-depth study of the solid geometry which began in Chapters 8 and 10.

CHAPTER **19**

# Solids and Their Volumes

## Objectives...

- Study the properties of solid figures: base areas, volumes, and surface areas.
- Analyze solid figures by examining their cross sections.
- Apply Cavalieri's Principle to find the volume of solid figures.
- Find the volume of a sphere by studying the volume of cylinders and cones.

**19–1 PRISMS**

**Classroom Notes**

This section introduces the idea of a prism and the different types of prisms. The proofs of the theorems and corollaries are easy and can be done by the students as part of their homework or in class.

## 19–1  PRISMS

Suppose we have given two parallel planes and a polygonal region in one of them.

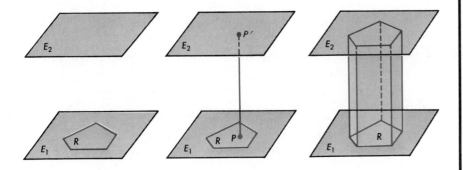

In the figures, the given region is $R$, lying in the plane $E_1$.

At each point $P$ of $R$, we set up a segment $\overline{PP'}$ perpendicular to $E_1$, joining $P$ to a point $P'$ of the second plane.  The union of all these segments is called a *right prism*.  The region $R$ is called its *lower base*, or simply its *base*.  We can think of a right prism as the solid that is swept out as the base moves vertically upward from $E_1$ to $E_2$.

A solid like this is called a *right* prism because the segments that we set up are perpendicular to the plane of the base.  We can form prisms of other kinds by setting up our segments in any fixed direction, which may or may not be perpendicular to the plane of the base.

We allow this possibility in the following definition.  Note however, that in this definition we can't allow $L$ to intersect $R$, because then no segment through the intersection point would be parallel to $L$.

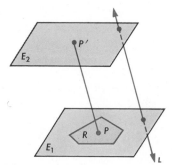 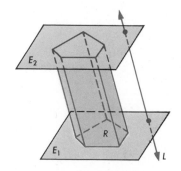

### Definition

Let $E_1$ and $E_2$ be two parallel planes, let $R$ be a polygonal region in $E_1$, and let $L$ be a line which intersects $E_1$ and $E_2$ but not $R$. For each point $P$ of $R$, let $\overline{PP'}$ be the segment which is parallel to $L$ and joins $P$ to a point $P'$ of $E_2$. The union of all the segments $\overline{PP'}$ is called a *prism*. The polygonal region $R$ is called the *base* of the prism. The distance between $E_1$ and $E_2$ is called the *altitude*. If $L$ is perpendicular to $E_1$ and $E_2$, then the prism is called a *right* prism.

Note that for right prisms the altitude is the distance $PP'$, but for nonright prisms the altitude is always less than $PP'$.

Prisms are described by their bases: a *triangular prism* is one whose base is a triangular region, and so on.

### Definition

A *cross section* of a prism is the intersection of the prism with a plane parallel to the plane of the base (provided that this intersection is not empty.)

### Theorem 19-1

*All cross sections of a triangular prism are congruent to the base.*

Of course the cross sections and the base are really triangular regions rather than triangles. When we say that they are congruent, we mean that the corresponding triangles are congruent.

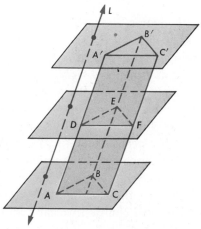

**Proof.** As in the figure, let the base be $\triangle ABC$ plus its interior, and let $D$, $E$, and $F$ be the points where the cross section intersects $\overline{AA'}$, $\overline{BB'}$, and $\overline{CC'}$. Then $\overline{AD} \parallel \overline{FC}$, because both these segments are parallel to $L$. And $\overline{DF} \parallel \overline{AC}$, by Theorem 10–1. Therefore $\square ADFC$ is a parallelogram. Therefore $DF = AC$.

In exactly the same way, we show that $DE = AB$ and $EF = BC$. By SSS we have $\triangle DEF \cong ABC$, which was to be proved.

### Corollary 19–1.1

***The upper and lower bases of a triangular prism are congruent.***

This is obvious, because the upper base is a cross section.

**Theorem 19–2.** The Prism Cross-Section Theorem

***All cross sections of a prism have the same area.***

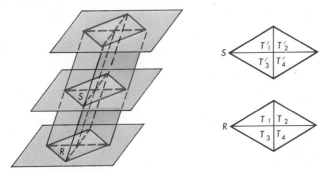

**Proof.** Let $R$ be the base, and let $S$ be a cross section. Then the area of $R$ is the sum of the areas of a finite set of triangular regions. The area of $S$ is the sum of the areas of the corresponding triangular regions in $S$. Since congruent triangles have the same area, the sum is the same for $R$ and $S$.

### Corollary 19–2.1

***The bases of a prism have the same area.***

This is because the upper base is a cross section.

Most of the time, we shall be concerned with prisms whose bases are convex polygonal regions.  By a *convex polygonal region* we mean a convex polygon plus its interior.  In such cases, we can speak of an *edge* or a *vertex* of the base.

The figure on page 627 reminds us of the definition of a prism.  In the figure, $A$ and $B$ are vertices of the base, and $\overline{AB}$ is an edge of the base.  The segments $\overline{AA'}$, $\overline{BB'}$ are called *lateral edges* of the prism.  The parallelogram region determined by $\square AA'B'B$ is called a *lateral face* of the prism.  We restate this in more exact language.

### Definition

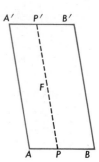

If $A$ is a vertex of the base of a prism, and $A'$ is the corresponding point of the upper base, then $\overline{AA'}$ is a *lateral edge* of the prism.  If $\overline{AB}$ is an edge of the base, and $F$ is the union of all segments $\overline{PP'}$ for which $P$ is in $\overline{AB}$ and $P'$ in $\overline{A'B'}$, then $F$ is a *lateral face* of the prism.

### Theorem 19–3

**The lateral faces of a prism are parallelogram regions.**

To prove this, show that $\overline{AA'} \parallel \overline{BB'}$ and $\overline{AB} \parallel \overline{A'B'}$.

### Corollary 19–3.1

**The lateral faces of a right prism are rectangular regions.**

Proof?  (We know that $L \perp E_1$ and $\overline{AA'} \parallel L$.)

### Definitions

The union of the lateral faces of a prism is called its *lateral surface*.  The union of its lateral faces and its two bases is called its *total surface*.

### Definitions

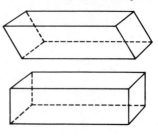

A *parallelepiped* is a prism whose base is a parallelogram region.
A *rectangular parallelepiped* is a right rectangular prism.

Thus all the faces of a parallelepiped (lateral, top, and bottom) are parallelogram regions. And all the faces of a rectangular parallelepiped are rectangular regions.

### Definition

A *cube* is a rectangular parallelepiped all of whose edges are congruent.

### Problem Set 19–1

1. (a) The prism shown here is called a *quadrilateral* _____ prism.

   (b) The region $ABCD$ is called *lower base of prism*.

   (c) $\overline{AA'}$ is called *a lateral edge of the prism*.

   (d) $\overline{HH'}$ is called *an altitude of the prism*.

   (e) If $\overline{AA'}$ were perpendicular to the plane of the base, then the prism would be called *a right prism*.

   (f) The parallelogram region $BB'C'C$ is called *a lateral face of the prism*.

   (g) The union of the lateral faces is called *the lateral surface of the prism*.

   (h) If $\square ABCD$ were a parallelogram, the prism would be called *parallelepiped* _____.

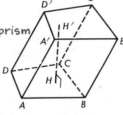

2. The figure on the left below, shows a right prism lying on a lateral face. Its bases are trapezoidal regions. The lengths of the parallel edges of the base are 4 and 9, the lengths of the nonparallel edges are 5 and 6, and $BF = 12$. Find the area of the lateral surface of the prism. *288*

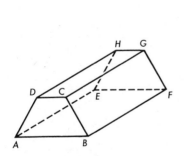 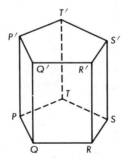

3. The altitude of the right pentagonal prism on the right above is 8 and the lengths of the edges of the base are 2, 5, 7, 7, and $8\frac{1}{2}$. Find the area of the lateral surface of the prism. *236*

4. A right prism has a lateral edge of 3 and the perimeter of its base is 34. What is the area of its lateral surface? *102*

---

**Quiz**

1. Complete each of the following so the resulting sentence is a true statement.
   (a) The minimum number of faces a prism must have is _____.
   (b) In a right prism the lateral faces are all _____.
   (c) A prism is triangular, quadrangular, pentagonal, and so on, depending on whether its _____ are triangular, quadrilateral, pentagonal regions, and so on.
   (d) The _____ of a prism is the perpendicular distance between the bases.
   (e) A cross section of a prism is the non-empty intersection of the prism with _____.
   (ans: 5, rectangular regions, bases, altitude, plane parallel to the plane of the base)

2. The base of a right prism is a rhombus with diagonals 6 and 12. Find the total surface area of the prism if its altitude is 20.
   (ans: $72 + 240\sqrt{5}$)

**9.** Prove: (1) $\overline{AA'}$ and $\overline{DD'}$ are coplanar, and (2) Region $ADD'A'$ is a parallelogram region.

Proof: (1) The lateral edges $\overline{AA'}$ and $\overline{DD'}$ are each parallel to the line $L$ used to generate the prism. If $L_1$, $L_2$, $L_3$ are three distinct lines, and $L_1 \parallel L_2$ and $L_2 \parallel L_3$, then $L_1 \parallel L_3$. Hence, $\overline{AA'} \parallel \overline{DD'}$. And since any two parallel lines determine a plane, $\overline{AA'}$ and $\overline{DD'}$ are coplanar. (2) By Theorem 19–3, the lateral faces of a prism are parallelogram regions, and since the opposite sides of a parallelogram are congruent, the lateral edge $\overline{AA'}$ is congruent to the lateral edge $\overline{BB'}$, where $\overline{BB'}$ is the lateral edge "next to" $\overline{AA'}$. In this manner we can establish a chain of congruences, $\overline{AA'} \cong \overline{BB'}$, $\overline{BB'} \cong \overline{CC'}$, ..., $\overline{CC'} \cong \overline{DD'}$. By the transitivity of congruence $\overline{AA'} \cong \overline{DD'}$. Since $\overline{AA'} \parallel \overline{DD'}$, and $\overline{AA'} \cong \overline{DD'}$, $\square ADD'A'$ is a parallelogram, and region $ADD'A'$ is a parallelogram region.

**14.** The area of the bases:
$$A = bh = 15 \cdot 6 = 90;$$
$$2A = 180$$
The area of the ends:
$$A = s^2 = 6^2 = 36;$$
$$2A = 72$$
The area of the sides:
$$A = bh = 15 \cdot 3\sqrt{3} = 45\sqrt{3};$$
$$2A = 90\sqrt{3}$$
Therefore, the total surface area $= 252 + 90\sqrt{3}$.

---

**5.** Prove that the area, $S$, of the lateral surface of a right prism is given by the formula $S = hp$, where $h$ is the altitude of the prism and $p$ is the perimeter of the base. Let $e_1, \ldots, e_n$ designate the lengths of edges, then $S = he_1 + he_2 \ldots he_n = h(e_1 + e_2 + \ldots + e_n) = hp$.

**6.** Find the altitude of a right prism for which the area of the lateral surface is 143 and the perimeter of the base is 13. $h = 11$

**7.** If a lateral face of a prism is a rectangle, does it follow that all of the lateral faces will be rectangles? No, they can be non-rectangular parallelograms.

**8.** The bases of this prism are equilateral triangles and its lateral faces are rectangular regions. Given that the length of an edge of the base is 6 and the altitude of the prism is 10, compute the area of the total surface of the prism. LSA = 180. Area of bases = $18\sqrt{3}$ Total surface area = $180 + 18\sqrt{3}$

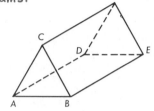

**9.** Prove that any two nonconsecutive lateral edges of a prism are coplanar and that the intersection of their plane with the prism is a parallelogram region. (First make a restatement in terms of the figure.)

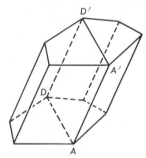

**10.** What is the area of the lateral surface of a cube with edge 5? What is the area of its total surface? LSA = 100, TSA = 150

**11.** The edges of a cross section of a triangular prism are 3, 6, and $3\sqrt{3}$. How long are the edges of another cross section? What geometric figure will it be? What are the measures of its angles? Compute the area of a cross section of this prism. $3, 6, 3\sqrt{3}$; Each cross section is a 30-60-90 triangle, the area of which is $9\sqrt{3}/2$.

**12.** The diagonal of a cube is $16\sqrt{3}$. Find the area of its total surface. $e = 16$   TSA = $6e^2 = 1536$

**13.** The dimensions of a rectangular parallelepiped are 4, 7, and 12. Compute its total surface area. 320

---

**14.** The base of a parallelepiped is a rectangular region 6 by 15. The end faces are square regions inclined 60° to the base. A plane perpendicular to a longer edge of the base intersects the parallelepiped in a rectangular region. Find the total surface area.

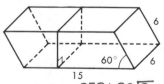

$252 + 90\sqrt{3}$

## 19–2 PYRAMIDS

The pyramid with base $R$ and vertex $V$ is the solid shown below.

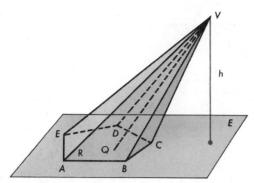

The pyramid is the union of all segments $\overline{VQ}$, where $Q$ is any point of the base. Thus:

### Definitions

Given a polygonal region $R$ in a plane $E$, and a point $V$ not in $E$. The *pyramid with base $R$ and vertex $V$* is the union of all segments $\overline{VQ}$ for which $Q$ belongs to $R$. The *altitude* of the pyramid is the (perpendicular) distance from $V$ to $E$.

Horizontal cross sections are defined in the same way for pyramids as for prisms. That is, a *horizontal cross section* of a pyramid is the intersection of the pyramid with a plane parallel to the plane of the base (providing, as before, that the plane must actually intersect the pyramid).

As a horizontal plane moves upward from the base toward the vertex, it is obvious that the area of the cross section steadily decreases, until it finally becomes zero at the vertex. In the following theorem, we obtain a formula which tells us exactly *how* the cross-sectional area changes when the base is triangular.

### Theorem 19–4

*Every cross section of a triangular pyramid, between the base and the vertex, is a triangular region similar to the base. If $h$ is the altitude, and $k$ is the distance from the vertex to the cross section, then the area of the cross section is equal to $k^2/h^2$ times the area of the base.*

**Classroom Notes**

In this section Theorem 19–4 establishes the important fact that for a triangular pyramid,

$$\frac{A_C}{A_B} = \left(\frac{h_C}{h_B}\right)^2.$$

Be sure students have grasped the proof of this important theorem before preceding with Theorems 19–5 and 19–6.

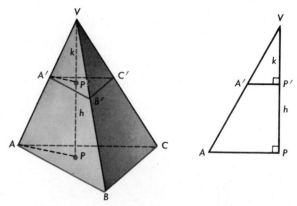

The notation of the proof is that of the figure. The base is the region determined by $\triangle ABC$. The triangle $\triangle A'B'C'$ is the corresponding triangle in the cross section. The segment $\overline{VP}$ is the perpendicular from $V$ to the plane of the base, with $VP = h$; and $\overline{VP'}$ is the perpendicular from $V$ to the plane of the cross section, with $\overline{VP'} = k$. The figure on the right shows $\triangle VAP$ and $\triangle VA'P'$ in their own plane. Note that $\angle P$ and $\angle P'$ (that is, $\angle VP'A'$) really are right angles, because $\overleftrightarrow{VP}$ is perpendicular to both of the two horizontal planes.

**Proof.** The main steps as are follows.

$$(1) \quad \triangle VA'P' \sim \triangle VAP.$$

Since $\angle P$ and $\angle P'$ are right angles, and $\angle V \cong \angle V$, the similarity follows from the **AA Corollary**.

$$(2) \qquad \frac{VA'}{VA} = \frac{k}{h},$$

because these are lengths of corresponding sides.

In exactly the same way, using $\triangle VP'B'$ and $\triangle VPB$, we can show that

$$(3) \qquad \frac{VB'}{VB} = \frac{k}{h}.$$

By the SAS Similarity Theorem, we get

$$(4) \quad \triangle VA'B' \sim \triangle VAB.$$

Therefore

$$(5) \qquad \frac{A'B'}{AB} = \frac{VA'}{VA} = \frac{k}{h}.$$

In this situation, there is nothing special about $\overline{AB}$ in the base and $\overline{A'B'}$ in the cross section; the edges $\overline{BC}$ and $\overline{B'C'}$ are related in the same way. Therefore we have

$$(6) \qquad \frac{B'C'}{BC} = \frac{k}{h},$$

and

$$(7) \qquad \frac{A'C'}{AC} = \frac{k}{h}.$$

By the SSS Similarity Theorem 12–7, we have

$$(8) \quad \triangle A'B'C' \sim \triangle ABC.$$

This proves half of our theorem. The other half now follows from Theorem 12–10, because the ratio of each pair of corresponding sides is $k/h$.

It isn't just for triangular pyramids that cross-sectional areas behave in this way; no matter what the shape of the base may be, the ratio is always $k^2/h^2$, as before.

### Theorem 19–5

*In any pyramid, the ratio of the area of a cross section to the area of the base is $k^2/h^2$, where $h$ is the altitude of the pyramid and $k$ is the distance from the vertex to the plane of the cross section.*

**Proof.** We cut up the base into little triangular regions $T_1, T_2, \ldots, T_n$, as in the definition of a polygonal region. Let their areas be $a_1, a_2, \ldots, a_n$. In the figure we show the case $n = 3$. Let the areas of the corresponding triangular regions in the cross section be $a'_1, a'_2, \ldots, a'_n$. Then the area of the base is

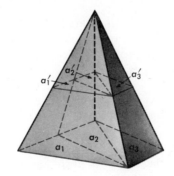

$$A = a_1 + a_2 + \cdots + a_n,$$

and the area of the cross section is

$$A_k = a'_1 + a'_2 + \cdots + a'_n.$$

**1.** Complete each of the following so the resulting sentence is true.

(a) The lateral surface of a pyramid consists of a number of _____.

(b) A regular tetrahedron is analogous to a _____ in two dimensional space.

(c) The areas of two sections parallel to the base of a pyramid are proportional to _____ of the sections from the vertex of the pyramid.

(ans: triangles, equilateral triangle, square of the distances)

**2.** The area of the base of a pyramid is 90. The altitude of the pyramid is 12. A plane section of the pyramid parallel to the base has an area of 10. How far from the base is this section?

(ans: 8)

**3.** In a certain square pyramid, the lateral faces are inclined 45° to the base. If the area of the base is 36, find the total surface area of the pyramid.

(ans: $36\sqrt{2} + 36$)

---

By the preceding theorem,

$$a'_1 = \frac{k^2}{h^2} a_1, \quad a'_2 = \frac{k^2}{h^2} a_2, \quad \ldots, \quad a'_n = \frac{k^2}{h^2} a_n.$$

Therefore

$$A_k = \frac{k^2}{h^2} (a_1 + a_2 + \cdots + a_n) = \frac{k^2}{h^2} A,$$

which was to be proved.

This theorem in turn enables us to prove the following.

**Theorem 19–6.**   The Pyramid Cross-Section Theorem

*If two pyramids have the same base area and the same latitude, then cross sections equidistant from the vertices have the same area.*

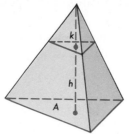 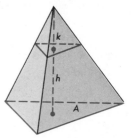

In the figure we show triangular pyramids, merely for the sake of simplicity. But the proof is not restricted to this case, and neither is the theorem.

**Proof.**   As indicated in the figure, let the base area of each pyramid be $A$; let $h$ be the altitude of each, and let $k$ be the distance from each cross section to the vertex. Then the cross-sectional areas are the same, because each of them is equal to $(k^2/h^2)A$.

**Problem Set 19–2**

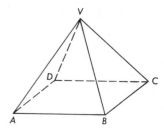

**1.** Like prisms, pyramids are named by the shapes of their bases. This is a sketch of a rectangular pyramid. Make sketches of triangular pyramids and square pyramids.

**2.** What is another name for a triangular pyramid? (See Chapter 3.)
Tetrahedron

**3.** Make formal definitions for *lateral edge* and *lateral face* of a pyramid.

**4.** In pyramid $V\text{-}ABC$, $\triangle ABC$ is equilateral. A plane parallel to the base intersects the lateral edges in $D$, $E$, and $F$, such that $VE = \frac{1}{2}EB$.

(a) What is $\dfrac{DV}{AV}$ ? $= \frac{1}{3}$

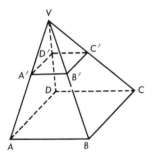

(b) What can you assert about $\triangle DEV$ and $\triangle ABV$? about $\triangle ABC$ and $\triangle DEF$?
$\triangle DEV \sim \triangle ABV$ by AA ; $\triangle ABC \sim \triangle DEF$ by SSS

(c) What is $\dfrac{DE}{AB}$ ? $= \frac{1}{3}$

(d) If $BC = 6$, what is $a\triangle DEF$?
$a\triangle DEF = s^2\sqrt{3}/4 = 2^2\sqrt{3}/4 = \sqrt{3}$

**5.** The altitude of a square pyramid is 10 and a side of the base is 15. Find the area of a cross section at a distance 6 from the vertex.   81

**6.** The area of the base of a pentagonal pyramid is 72 cm². The altitude of the pyramid is 12 cm. What is the area of a cross section 4 cm from the base?   $A_c = \left(\frac{k}{h}\right)^2 A_b = 32\,cm^2$

**7.** A cross section of area 108 cm² is 9 cm from the vertex of a pyramid whose base has an area of 180 cm². Find the altitude of the pyramid.   $h = 3\sqrt{15}\,cm$

**8.**

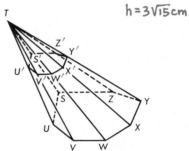

The two pyramids shown here, with the square pyramid on the left, have equal altitudes. Their bases are coplanar and the cross sections are coplanar. Given that $AB = 2\sqrt{6}$, $A'B' = 3\sqrt{2}$, and the area of the polygonal region $SUVWXYZ$ is 24, find the area of the cross section of the pyramid on the right.   Use Theorem 19–6 to conclude that the cross sections have equal areas:
$a\,S'U'V'W'X'Y'Z' = a\,\square A'B'C'D' = (3\sqrt{2})^2 = 18$

**9.** A pyramid whose base is a regular polygon and whose vertex is equidistant from each vertex of the base is called a *regular pyramid*.

Prove that the altitude from the vertex of a regular pyramid to its base intersects the base at its circumcenter (that is, at a point equidistant from each vertex of the base).

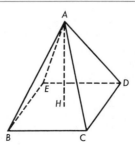

---

**Answers to Problems**

**3.** A *lateral edge* of a pyramid is a segment $\overline{VX}$, with $V$ the vertex of the pyramid and $X$ the vertex of the base of the pyramid.

A *lateral face* of a pyramid is the union of all segments $\overline{VY}$, with $V$ the vertex of the pyramid and $Y$ a point of a specific edge of the base of the pyramid.

**9.** All the triangles of the form $\triangle AHX$ when $X$ is a vertex of the base are congruent by HL. Consequently, $HB = HC = HD$, and so on, and so the vertices $B$, $C$, $D$, ... of the base are all equidistant from $H$. This means that $H$ is the circumcenter of the base.

**11.** Since the pyramid is regular, its base is a regular polygon and this means that the edges of the base are congruent. Again, since the pyramid is regular, its lateral edges are congruent. Consequently, the lateral faces of a regular pyramid are bounded by congruent isosceles triangles.

**12.** By Problem 11, the lateral faces of a regular pyramid are congruent triangles. The area of each of these triangles is given by the formula $A = \frac{1}{2}el$ when $e$ is the length of an edge of the base and $l$ is the slant height. Therefore, LSA $= n(\frac{1}{2}el) = \frac{1}{2}(ne)l = \frac{1}{2}pl$.

**14.** The area of the hexagonal base is $96\sqrt{3}$. Let $M$ be the midpoint of $\overline{BC}$. Since $\triangle BHC$ is equilateral, $MH = 4\sqrt{3}$. Then in $\triangle AMH$ since $MH = 4\sqrt{3}$ and $AH = 12$ we can conclude that $AM = 8\sqrt{3}$. Therefore, LSA $= \frac{1}{2}lp = \frac{1}{2}(8\sqrt{3})48 = 192\sqrt{3}$. Therefore, the total surface area is $288\sqrt{3}$.

**15.** Given a triangular pyramid $ABCD$. Let $M$ be the midpoint of $\overline{AC}$ and $N$ the midpoint of $\overline{BC}$. Then $\overline{MN} \parallel \overline{AB}$ and $MN = \frac{1}{2}AB$. Similarly, let $P$ be the midpoint of $\overline{BD}$ and $Q$ be the midpoint of $\overline{AD}$. Then $\overline{PQ} \parallel \overline{AB}$, and $PQ = \frac{1}{2}AB$. Therefore, $\overline{MN} \parallel \overline{PQ}$ and $\overline{MN} \cong \overline{PQ}$, and consequently $\square MNPQ$ is a parallelogram. It is easy to see that $M$, $N$, $P$, $Q$ can be determined by a weaker restriction: let $M$, $N$, $P$, $Q$ be points on $\overline{AC}$, $\overline{BC}$, $\overline{BD}$, and $\overline{AD}$ such that $\dfrac{AM}{AC} = \dfrac{BN}{BC} = \dfrac{BP}{BD} = \dfrac{AQ}{AD}$.

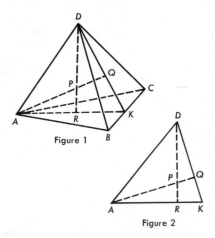

Figure 1

Figure 2

*Theorem:* The four altitudes of a regular tetrahedron are concurrent at a point $P$ such that the distance from any vertex to the point of concurrency is $\frac{3}{4}$ the length of the altitude from that vertex. Therefore,

$$\frac{\text{Area of Cross Section}}{\text{Area of the Base}} = \left(\frac{3}{4}\right)^2 = \frac{9}{16}.$$

Hence,

$$\text{Area of Cross Section} = \frac{9}{16}\left(\frac{s^2}{4}\sqrt{3}\right)$$
$$= 9\sqrt{3}.$$

*Proof:* Let $K$ be the midpoint of $\overline{BC}$, and observe that the altitudes $\overline{AQ}$ and $\overline{DR}$ of the regular tetrahedron $ABCD$ each lie in the plane of $\triangle ADK$. Let $P$ be the intersection of $\overline{AQ}$ and $\overline{DR}$. We can prove that $DP/DR = \frac{3}{4}$ by the following computations:

(1) Let $AB = s$. Then $DK = (s/2)\sqrt{3}$. And since $Q$ is the point of concurrency of the medians of $\triangle BCD$, this means that $DQ = \frac{2}{3}(DK) = (s/3)\sqrt{3}$. Similarly, since $R$ is the point of concurrency of the medians of $\triangle ABC$,

$$RK = \frac{1}{3}(AK)$$
$$= \frac{1}{3}\left(\frac{s}{2}\sqrt{3}\right)$$
$$= \frac{s}{6}\sqrt{3}.$$

Now apply the Pythagorean Theorem to $\triangle DRK$ to obtain $DR = s\sqrt{6}/3$.

10. One edge of the base of a regular square pyramid is 10 cm long, and the altitude of the pyramid is 12 cm. Find the area of the lateral surface of the pyramid. The slant height of the pyramid is 13 cm and LSA = $\frac{1}{2}\ell p$ = 260 cm². (See Problem 12 for definition of slant height.)

11. Prove that the lateral faces of a regular pyramid are bounded by congruent isosceles triangles.

12. The altitude of each lateral face of a regular pyramid is called the *slant height* of the pyramid. Show that the area of the lateral surface is one-half the product of the slant height and the perimeter of the base.

13. Find the area of the total surface of a regular pyramid whose altitude is 15 and whose base is a square with side 16. LSA = $\frac{1}{2}\ell p$ = 544
TSA = LSA + 16² = 800

14. Find the total surface area of a regular hexagonal pyramid given that an edge of the base is 8 and the altitude of the pyramid is 12. LSA = 192√3
TSA = 288√3

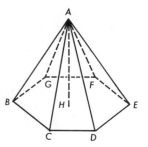

15. Given any triangular pyramid $ABCD$. Describe a plane whose intersection with the pyramid is a parallelogram region.

## HONORS PROBLEM

Given a regular tetrahedron (a triangular pyramid) with an edge of 8. Find the area of a cross section that contains the point of concurrency of the four altitudes of the pyramid. 9√3; see Solution Section for proof of interesting theorem related to this problem.

## 19-3 VOLUMES OF PRISMS AND PYRAMIDS. CAVALIERI'S PRINCIPLE

We shall now learn how to find the volumes of various solids. This process will involve many of the same ideas that we used in finding areas of polygonal regions. Our discussion, however, will be more informal than that in Chapter 11 and will not include a complete set of postulates adequate to justify everything we do, a step at a time. We shall, however, state the two main postulates which we use in getting numerical answers.

You remember that in Chapter 11 we took the area formula $A = e^2$ for squares, as a postulate, and then used a trick to get the area formula $A = bh$ for rectangles. For volumes of solids, our trick won't work, and so we use a stronger unit postulate.

**POSTULATE 23.** The Unit Postulate

*The volume of a rectangular parallelepiped is the product of the altitude and the area of the base.*

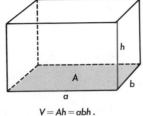

$V = Ah = abh$.

Of course, any face of a rectangular parallelepiped can be regarded as the base. We always get the same answer for the volume, because in each case $Ah$ is the product of the lengths of any three edges with a common end point.

To understand what is happening in our next postulate, let us first think of a physical model. We can make an approximate model of a square pyramid by forming a stack of thin square cards, cut to the proper size:

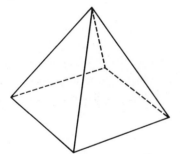

The figure on the left represents the exact pyramid, and the figure on the right is the approximate model made from cards.

Now suppose we drill a narrow hole in the model, from the top to some point of the base, and insert a thin rod so that it passes through every card in the model. We can then tilt the rod in any direction we want, keeping its bottom end fixed on the base. The shape of the model then changes, but its volume does not change. The reason is that its volume is simply the total volume of the cards, and this total volume does not change as the cards slide along each other.

The same principle applies more generally. Suppose we have two solids with bases in the same plane. We shall think of this plane as being horizontal. If all horizontal cross sections of the two solids at

(2) Since $\triangle DPQ \sim \triangle DKR$ by AA, $DP/DQ = DK/DR$. Therefore, $DP = \dfrac{DQ \cdot DK}{DR} = \dfrac{s\sqrt{6}}{4}$.

(3) Consequently, $\dfrac{DP}{DR} = \dfrac{\frac{s\sqrt{6}}{4}}{\frac{s\sqrt{6}}{3}} = \dfrac{3}{4}$.

## 19-3 VOLUMES OF PRISMS AND PYRAMIDS. CAVALIERI'S PRINCIPLE

**Classroom Notes**

In this section we begin to see how the study of volumes differs from the study of areas of polygonal regions in a plane. A pyramid is a rectilinear figure, but to find its volume we need to use Cavalieri's Principle. Thus we are really using a sort of limiting process, and this is very different from the methods which were adequate for the purposes of Chapter 11.

the same level have the same area, then the two solids have the same
volume.

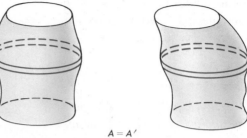

$A = A'$

This is true for the following reason. Let us again make a card model
of each of the solids. Then each card in the first model has exactly
the same volume as the corresponding card in the second model. By
using very thin cards, we can make card models that are very close
approximations to the given solids. In fact, we can make the approximation as close as we please, by using sufficiently thin cards. Therefore
the volumes of the two solids with which we started are the same.

The principle involved here is called *Cavalieri's Principle*. We surely
haven't proved it; we have merely been explaining why it is plausible.
We therefore state it in the form of a postulate.

**POSTULATE 24.**    Cavalieri's Principle

> *Given two solids and a plane. Suppose that every plane parallel to
> the given plane, intersecting one of the two solids, also intersects
> the other, and gives cross sections with the same area. Then the
> two solids have the same volume.*

Cavalieri's Principle is the key to the calculation of volumes, as we
shall soon see.

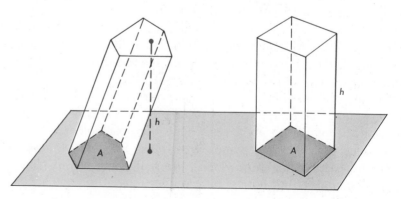

### Theorem 19–7

*The volume of any prism is the product of the altitude and the area of the base.*

**Proof.** Let $h$ and $A$ be the altitude and the base area of the given prism. Consider a rectangular parallelepiped with the same altitude $h$ and base area $A$, and with its base in the same plane as the base of the given prism. We know by the Prism Cross-Section Theorem that all cross sections, for both prisms, have the same area $A$. By Cavalieri's Principle, this means that they have the same volume. Since the volume of the rectangular parallelepiped is $Ah$ by Postulate 23, the theorem follows.

### Theorem 19–8

*If two pyramids have the same altitude and the same base area, and their bases lie in the same plane, then they have the same volume.*

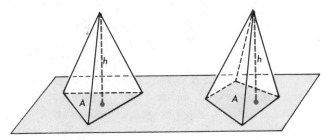

**Proof.** By the Pyramid Cross-Section Theorem, corresponding cross sections of the two pyramids have the same area. By Cavalieri's Principle, this means that the volumes are the same.

### Theorem 19–9

*The volume of a triangular pyramid is one-third the product of its altitude and its base area.*

**Proof.** Given a triangular pyramid, we form a triangular prism with the same base and altitude. (We are free to use a *right* triangular prism, as in the figure. It doesn't matter, one way or the other.)

We now cut up our prism into three pyramids, as shown in the figure on the right. We name these by naming their vertices, in any order.

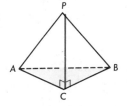
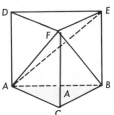

Thus our three new pyramids are *ADEF*, *ABEF*, and *AFBC*. Drawn separately, they look like this:

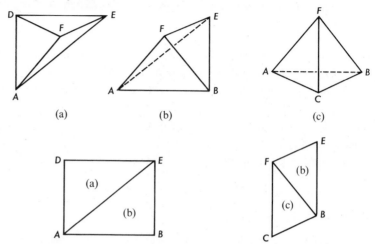

       (a)                   (b)                 (c)

(1) *ADEF and ABEF have the same volume.*

> **Proof.** We can regard *F* as the vertex of each of the pyramids. Their bases are then the triangular regions determined by △*ADE* and △*ABE*. Since these triangles are congruent, we know that *ADEF* and *ABEF* have the same base area; and they have the same altitude, because the altitude of each of them is the distance from *F* to the plane that contains their bases. Therefore they have the same volume.

(2) *ABEF and AFBC have the same volume.*

> **Proof.** We can regard *A* as the vertex of each of the pyramids. Their bases are then the triangular regions determined by △*BEF* and △*FBC*. Since these triangles are congruent, we know that *ABEF* and *AFBC* have the same base area. And they have the same altitude, because the altitude of each of them is the distance from *A* to the plane that contains their bases. Therefore they have the same volume.

(3) *AFBC and the original pyramid PABC have the same volume.* (The proof is obvious: they have the same base and the same altitude.)

We are now almost done. Let $a$ be the area of △*ABC*, and let $h$ be the altitude of *PABC*. Then the volume of our prism is $ah$. If

$V$ is the volume of each of our pyramids, then $3V = ah$. Therefore

$$V = \tfrac{1}{3}ah,$$

which was to be proved.

The same result holds for pyramids in general.

### Theorem 19–10

*The volume of a pyramid is one-third the product of its altitude and its base area.*

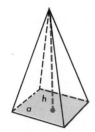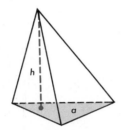

$$V = \tfrac{1}{3}ah$$

**Proof.** Given a pyramid of altitude $h$ and base area $a$. Take a triangular pyramid of the same altitude and base area, with its base in the same plane. By the Pyramid Cross-Section Theorem, cross sections at the same level have the same area. Therefore, by Cavalieri's Principle, the two pyramids have the same volume. Therefore the volume of each of them is $\tfrac{1}{3}ah$, which was to be proved.

### Problem Set 19–3

1. The altitude of a rectangular parallelepiped is 7, and the dimensions of the base are 4 and 5. Find its volume. **140**

2. A rectangular metal can, 1 dm by 1 dm by 1 dm, is filled with water. Given that 1 litre of liquid has a volume of 1000 cm³, how many litres of water does the can hold? **1 liter**

3. Certain silver ingots are cast in the shape of a right prism whose base (the end of the ingot) is a trapezoid. The bases of the trapezoid are 7.6 cm and 10 cm, and the height of the ingot is 5 cm. The length of the ingot is 30 cm. If the silver has a mass of 10.4 grams per cubic centimetre what is the mass of one ingot? **Mass = 13.728 Kg; A = 44 cm²; V = 1320 cm²**

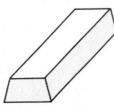

### Answers to Problems

**5.** The base of the prism consists of a rectangle which is 9.5 m by 42 m and a triangle with a base 42 m and a height 5.5 m. $A = (42)(9.5) + \tfrac{1}{2}(42)(5.5) = 514.5$ m² $V = Ah = (514.5)(130) = 66\,885$ m³.

**8.** Since the faces are equilateral triangles, the slant height is $(s/2)\sqrt{3}$. Then $\triangle AMH$ whose vertices are $A$ the vertex of the pyramid, $M$ the midpoint of a side of the base, and $H$ the foot of the altitude of the pyramid is a right triangle in which the hypotenuse $AM = \tfrac{3}{2}\sqrt{3}$ and $MH = s/2$. Therefore, the altitude $AH = (s/2)\sqrt{2}$, and

$$V = \frac{1}{3}\,AH = \frac{1}{3}\,(s^2)\left(\frac{s}{2}\sqrt{2}\right) = \frac{s^3\sqrt{2}}{6}.$$

**11.** As noted in Problem 9, a regular octahedron can be considered as two regular square pyramids with equilateral faces placed "base to base." Since these bases are squares, their area is given by the formula for the area of a rhombus, $A = \tfrac{1}{2}d_1 d_2$. Then the volumes of these two square pyramids is given by

$$V = 2(\tfrac{1}{3}Ah) = 2 \cdot (\tfrac{1}{3}\tfrac{1}{2}d_1 d_2 h) = \tfrac{1}{6}d_1 d_2 d_3.$$

**13.** Let $V_b$, $A_b$, and $h_b$ be the volume, area and height of the large pyramid and $V_c$, $A_c$, and $h_c$ be the corresponding dimensions of the smaller pyramid which has the given cross section as its base.

(a) By Theorem 19-5, $\dfrac{A_c}{A_b} = \left(\dfrac{h_c}{h_b}\right)^2$.

Therefore, $\dfrac{A_c}{64} = \left(\dfrac{6}{12}\right)^2 \cdot A_c = 16$.

(c) $\dfrac{V_b}{V_c} = \dfrac{\frac{1}{3}A_c h_c}{\frac{1}{3}A_b h_b} = \left(\dfrac{h_c}{h_b}\right)^2 \cdot \dfrac{h_c}{h_b} = \left(\dfrac{h_c}{h_b}\right)^3$.

Therefore, $\dfrac{V_c}{V_b} = \left(\dfrac{h_c}{h_b}\right)^3 = \left(\dfrac{1}{2}\right)^3 = \dfrac{1}{8}$.

**15. (a)** $\dfrac{A_c}{A_b} = \left(\dfrac{h_c}{h_b}\right)^2$; $\dfrac{20}{45} = \left(\dfrac{h_c}{6}\right)^2$;

$h_c^2 = 16$; $h_c = 4$.

**(b)** $\dfrac{V_c}{V_b} = \left(\dfrac{h_c}{h_b}\right)^2 = \left(\dfrac{4}{6}\right)^3 = \dfrac{8}{27}$.

**16. (a)** Let $\triangle AHM$ be the triangle whose vertices are: $A$, the vertex of the pyramid, $H$, the foot of the altitude of the pyramid, and $M$, the midpoint of a side of the base of the pyramid. Then since $AH = 16$ and $HM = 12$, $AM = 20$. And since $h_c/h_b = \frac{3}{4}$, we can conclude that the lateral faces of the frustum are trapezoids in which $b_1 = 24$, $b_2 = 18$ and $l = 5$. Therefore,

$$\text{LSA} = 4\left[\tfrac{1}{2}l(b_1 + b_2)\right] = 420.$$

**(b)** Note $V_f = V_b - V_c$.

$V_b = \tfrac{1}{3}A_b h_b = \tfrac{1}{3} \cdot 24^2 \cdot 16 = 3072$.

$V_c = \tfrac{1}{3} \cdot A_c \cdot h_c$

$\qquad = \tfrac{1}{3}(18)^2 \cdot 12 = 1296$.

Therefore, $V_f = V_b - V_c$

$\qquad\qquad = 1776$.

---

**4.** A lump of metal is submerged in a rectangular water tank 20 cm by 15 cm, raising the level of the water 0.35 cm. What is the volume of the metal? 105 cm³

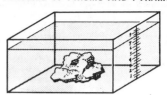

**5.** To calculate the cost of providing air-conditioning for a proposed construction project, a contractor has to compute the volume of air contained in a rectangular building as outlined in the figure. The building is 130 m long and 42 m wide. On both sides of the building the eaves are 9.5 m high, and the highest point of the roof is 15 m. Find the volume of the building. 66 885 m³

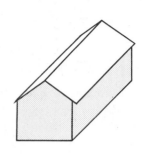

**6.** A right rectangular prism has an altitude of 18 cm and a base which measures 6 cm by 8 cm. A plane determined by a diagonal of the base and a vertex of the upper base forms a pyramid with the faces of the prism. Find the volume of the pyramid. $V = \frac{1}{3}(\frac{1}{2} \cdot 6 \cdot 8) \cdot 18 = 144$ cm³

**7.** Find the volume of a regular square pyramid whose altitude is 12 and whose base has an edge of 12. Also find the area of its lateral surface. $V = 576$; $\text{LSA} = \frac{1}{2}pl = 144\sqrt{5}$

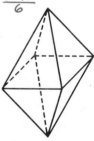

---

**8.** Derive a formula for the volume of a regular square pyramid whose lateral faces are equilateral triangles of side $s$. $V = \dfrac{s^3\sqrt{2}}{6}$

**9.** If two regular square pyramids whose lateral faces are equilateral triangles are placed base to base, the resulting 8-sided solid is called a *regular octahedron*. Prove that the volume, $V$, of the regular octahedron whose edge is $e$ is given by the formula $V = \frac{1}{3}\sqrt{2}e^3$. $V = 2\left(\dfrac{e^3\sqrt{2}}{6}\right) = \dfrac{e^3\sqrt{2}}{3}$ (See Problem 8)

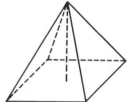

**10.** Compute the volume and the total surface area of a regular octahedron of edge 3. $V = 9\sqrt{2}$, $\text{TSA} = 18\sqrt{3}$

**11.** Prove that the volume of a regular octahedron is given by $V = \frac{1}{6}d_1 d_2 d_3$, where $d_1$, $d_2$, and $d_3$ are the lengths of its diagonals.

**12.** A cross section of a pyramid forms a small pyramid whose volume is 2 and whose altitude is 1. The volume of the large pyramid is 54. What is the altitude of this pyramid? $h = 3$

13. Pyramid $PABCDE$ is pentagonal, and the area of its base is 64. Altitude $PF$ equals 12. $V$, $W$, $X$, $Y$, and $Z$ are midpoints of the lateral edges, as shown in the figure. Find the area of the cross section $VWXYZ$. (Why is it a cross section?) Find the volume of the smaller pyramid. What is the ratio of the volumes of the two pyramids?
$A_c = 16$, $V_c = 32$, $\frac{V_c}{V_b} = \frac{1}{8}$

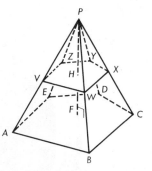

14. The part of a pyramid bounded by the base, a cross section, and the trapezoid regions of the lateral faces is called a *frustum* of a pyramid. In the figure for Problem 13, the vertices of the frustum are $A$, $B$, $C$, $D$, $E$, $V$, $W$, $X$, $Y$, and $Z$. Find the volume of this frustum. $V_b = 256$ and from Problem 13 $V_c = 32$. Thus $V_f = V_b - V_c = 224$

15. The area of a cross section of a pyramid is 20, and the area of the base of the pyramid is 45. If the altitude of the pyramid is 6, how far from the vertex is the cross section? What is the ratio of the volumes of the two pyramids? $h_c = 4$ $\frac{V_c}{V_b} = \frac{8}{27}$

16. A plane parallel to the base of a regular square pyramid intersects the altitude at a point three-fourths the distance from the vertex to the base. The altitude of the pyramid is 16, and the edge of the base is 24. Find the area of the lateral surface of the frustum and the volume of the frustum.
$LSA = 420$ $V_f = 1776$

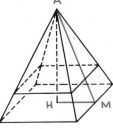

## HONORS PROBLEM

Show that the volume of a frustum is given by the formula

$$V = \tfrac{1}{3}h(B + B' + \sqrt{BB'}),$$

where $B$ and $B'$ are the areas of the bases and $h$ is the altitude of the frustum.

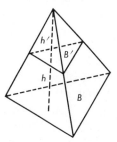

*Hint:* Let $h'$ be the altitude of the small pyramid. Get the volumes of the two pyramids. Note that

$$\frac{h + h'}{h'} = \frac{\sqrt{B}}{\sqrt{B'}}$$

so that

$$\frac{h}{h'} = \frac{\sqrt{B} - \sqrt{B'}}{\sqrt{B'}} \quad \text{and} \quad h' = \frac{h\sqrt{B'}}{\sqrt{B} - \sqrt{B'}}.$$

## Answer to Honors Problem

Let $V_F$ be the volume of the frustum, $V$ the volume of the large pyramid with base $B$, and $V'$ the volume of the small pyramid with base $B'$.

$$V_F = V - V'$$
$$= \tfrac{1}{3}B(h + h') - \tfrac{1}{3}B'h'$$
$$= \frac{1}{3}\left[B\left(h + \frac{h\sqrt{B'}}{\sqrt{B} - \sqrt{B'}}\right) - \frac{B'h\sqrt{B'}}{\sqrt{B} - \sqrt{B'}}\right]$$
$$= \frac{1}{3}h\left[\frac{B^{\frac{3}{2}} - (B')^{\frac{3}{2}}}{B^{\frac{1}{2}} - (B')^{\frac{1}{2}}}\right]$$
$$= \frac{1}{3}h\frac{(B^{\frac{1}{2}} - (B')^{\frac{1}{2}})(B + \sqrt{BB'} + B')}{B^{\frac{1}{2}} - (B')^{\frac{1}{2}}}$$
$$= \tfrac{1}{3}h(B + B' + \sqrt{BB'}).$$

When Archimedes calculated the volume of a sphere, he was using the idea expressed in Cavalier's Principle. This is, of course, a basic concept of integral calculus. For a more complete biography of Archimedes, see pp. 28–34 of *Men of Mathematics* by E. T. Bell (Simon and Schuster, 1965).

Archimedes (287-212 B.C.)

Archimedes is generally regarded as the greatest mathematician of antiquity, and one of the three or four greatest of all time. He was the first man to determine the volume of a sphere. He made a very accurate computation of $\pi$. And the methods that he devised for solving area and volume problems placed him many centuries ahead of his time. He was able to calculate the areas of regions bounded by very complicated curves; and his achievements in this kind of geometry stood almost alone for eighteen hundred years. The next major step forward in the computation of areas and volumes was the discovery of the calculus, by Newton and Leibniz, in the seventeenth century.

Unlike most of the Greek mathematicians, Archimedes was interested in applications. Legend has it that when the Romans attacked his native city of Syracuse, in Sicily, he played a leading part in the city's defense, terrorizing the invaders with weapons of his own invention. He is said to have bombarded the Roman ships with large stones, fired from the biggest catapults that anybody has ever seen. It is also reported that he set the Roman fleet on fire, using mirrors to focus the concentrated rays of the sun on the ships. When the attack settled down into a siege, Archimedes could no longer help; he returned to his study, and went back to work on mathematics.

He died on the job. When the Romans finally captured Syracuse, a soldier found him in his house, drawing geometric figures in the sand on the floor. *"Don't disturb my circles!"* said Archimedes. These turned out to be his last words. The Roman general had given orders that Archimedes was not to be harmed. But nobody knows whether the soldier knew or cared who his victim was.

## 19–4 CYLINDERS AND CONES

If you remember how we formed a prism with a given polygonal region as base, you will see that the same process works just as well for bases which are not polygonal regions. Suppose, for example, that we start with two parallel planes $E_1$ and $E_2$ as before, but use a *circular* region in $E_1$ as base.

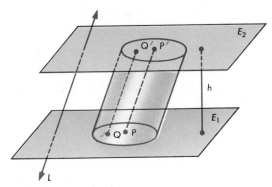

Exactly as before, we use a line $L$, intersecting $E_1$ and $E_2$ but not the base. And we form the union of all segments $\overline{QQ'}$, where $Q$ is in the base, $Q'$ is in $E_2$, and $\overline{QQ'} \parallel L$. The resulting solid is called a *circular cylinder*. There is no need to repeat the definitions of the altitude, cross sections, and so on, because these are exactly the same as the corresponding definitions for prisms. If $L \perp E_1$, then the cylinder is called a *right* cylinder.

Of course, you can get other kinds of cylinders by using other figures as bases. The circular cylinders, however, are the only ones that will be discussed in this book.

Similarly, the scheme that we used to form a pyramid can be used equally well when the base is not a polygonal region. If we use a circular region as base, the resulting solid is called a *circular cone*. Using the definition of a pyramid as your model, you should not have any trouble writing the definition of a circular cone.

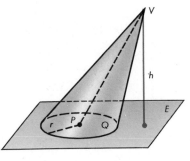

The following theorems on cylinders and cones are analogous to the corresponding theorems on prisms and pyramids. Their proofs are also very similar: the point is that the shape of the base never mattered very much in the first place. We therefore omit the details.

**Theorem 19–11**

> *Every cross section of a circular cylinder is a circular region congruent to the base.*

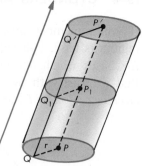

The proof is based on the fact that $P_1Q_1 = PQ = r$; this is true because $\overline{PQ}$ and $\overline{P_1Q_1}$ are opposite sides of the parallelogram $\square QQ_1P_1P$.

**Theorem 19–12**

> *Every cross section of a circular cylinder has the same area as the base.*

The next theorem is slightly more difficult.

**Theorem 19–13**

> *Given a cone of altitude h, and a cross section made by a plane at a distance k from the vertex. The area of the cross section is equal to $k^2/h^2$ times the area of the base.*

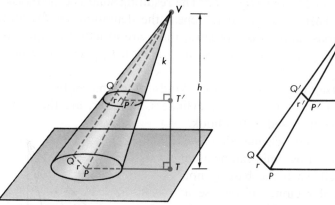

In the notation of the figure above, the main steps in the proof are as follows:

(1) $\triangle VPT \sim \triangle VP'T'$,

(2) $\dfrac{VP'}{VP} = \dfrac{VT'}{VT} = \dfrac{k}{h}$,

(3) $\triangle VP'Q' \sim \triangle VPQ$,

(4) $\dfrac{P'Q'}{PQ} = \dfrac{VP'}{VP} = \dfrac{k}{h}$   and   $P'Q' = \dfrac{k}{h} PQ$.

Thus, if $Q$ is on the circle with center $P$ and radius $r$ in the base, then $Q'$ is on the circle with center $P'$ and radius

$$r' = \frac{k}{h} PQ = \frac{k}{h} r$$

in the cross section. Therefore the cross section is a circular region of radius $r'$, and its area is

$$\pi \frac{k^2}{h^2} r^2.$$

This is equal to $k^2/h^2$ times the area of the base.

We can now calculate the volumes of cylinders and cones, using Cavalieri's Principle in the same way as we did for prisms and pyramids.

### Theorem 19–14

*The volume of a circular cylinder is the product of its altitude and the area of its base.*

The proof is like that of Theorem 19–7.

### Theorem 19–15

*The volume of a circular cone is one-third the product of its altitude and the area of its base.*

The proof is like that of Theorem 19–10.

### Problem Set 19–4

1. The base of a cylinder is a circular region of diameter 8. The altitude of the cylinder is also 8. What is the volume of the cylinder? $128\pi$

2. A drainage tile is a cylindrical shell 21 cm long. The inside and outside diameters are 4.5 and 5.1 cm. Find the volume of clay needed to make the tile. (Use $3\frac{1}{7}$ for $\pi$.) $95\,cm^3$

3. The two cylinders in the figure are identical. Compare the volume of the inscribed cone on the left with the volume of the two cones ("hourglass" figure) on the right. They have equal volumes.

**Quiz**

1. The areas of two cross sections of a cone, parallel to the base, are 100 and 16. If the distance between these sections is 6, how far from the vertex is the smaller section?
   (ans: 4)

2. The radius of the base of a cylinder is increased 20% and the altitude is increased 30%. By what percent is the volume increased?
   (ans: 87.2%)

3. A rectangle ☐ $ABCD$ is revolved 360° about the side $\overline{AD}$. If $AB = 4$ and $AD = 3$, find the volume determined by the revolution of triangle $\triangle DBC$.
   (ans: $32\pi$)

## Answers to Problems

**13.** The figure is a region bounded by two circles, one inside the other. Note, however, that the two circles are not necessarily concentric. Since the radius of the outer circle is 4 and the radius of the inner circle is 2, the area of the figure is given by

$$A = \pi r_1^2 - \pi r_2^2 = \pi(r_1^2 - r_2^2)$$
$$= \pi(4^2 - 2^2) = 12\pi.$$

**14.** Observe that the intersection is an annulus, that is, a region bounded by two concentric circles. Since the heights of the cones are in a ratio of $\frac{1}{3}$, the radii of the cones are in a ratio of $\frac{1}{3}$. Therefore, the inner radius of the annulus, that is, the radius of the base of the smaller cone, is 2. Therefore,
$A = \pi(r_1^2 - r_2^2) = \pi(6^2 - 2^2) = 32\pi$ cm².

**4.** How long must a 1 cm (inside diameter) pipe be to hold one litre of water? (The volume of one litre is 1000 cm³. Use $3\frac{1}{7}$ for $\pi$.)

**5.** Find the volume of a circular cone whose altitude is 12 and whose base has a radius equal to 3.2. $V = \frac{1}{3}\pi r^2 h \doteq 129$

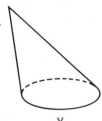

**6.** This figure represents a *right circular cone*. Define a right circular cone. Determine its altitude when its volume is $48\pi$ and the diameter of its base is 8. Given circle C, center P in plane E and point V not in E. A circular cone is the union of all segments $\overline{VX}$, X in the circle C. If $\overline{VP}$ is perpendicular to plane E, the cone is a right circular cone. Altitude = 9

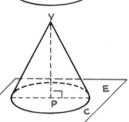

**7.** A conical tank is 115 cm deep and its circular top has a radius of 15 cm. How many litres of liquid will it hold? 27.1 liters

**8.** In a cone the altitude is 9. A plane parallel to the plane of the base intersects the cone, cutting off a smaller cone at the top. The distance between the planes is 5.

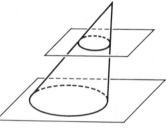

(a) What is the ratio of the altitudes of the two cones? $\frac{4}{9}$

(b) What is the ratio of the radii of the bases of the cones? $\frac{4}{9}$

(c) What is the ratio of the areas of the bases? $\frac{16}{81}$

(d) What is the ratio of the volumes of the two cones? $\frac{64}{729}$

**9.** The altitude of a cone is 5 cm. A plane 2 cm from the vertex of the cone is parallel to the base of the cone. If the volume of the smaller cone is 24 cm³, what is the volume of the larger cone? $\frac{V_1}{V_2} = \left(\frac{h_1}{h_2}\right)^3$ $V_1 = 375$ cm³

---

**10.** A square pyramid is inscribed in a circular cone such that they have the same vertex and the base of the pyramid is inscribed in the base of the cone. The common altitude is 18 and a side of the square is 15. Find the volume of each. Volume of square pyramid = 1350. Volume of circular pyramid = $\frac{1}{3}\pi\left(\frac{15\sqrt{2}}{2}\right)^2 \cdot 18 = 675\pi$.

**11.** A storage bin is shaped as in the figure. The radius of the cylindrical top is 2 m. The over-all height of the bin is 8 m and the altitude of the conical section is 360 cm. Find the capacity of the bin in cubic metres. 70.3 m³

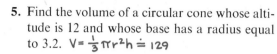

12. A conical surface stands inside a cylindrical surface. The base of the cone is the base of the cylinder, and the vertex of the cone lies in the upper base of the cylinder. Write a formula for the volume of the space bounded by the two surfaces and the upper base in terms of $r$, the radius of the base, and $h$, the altitude of the cylinder. $v = \frac{2}{3}\pi r^2 h$

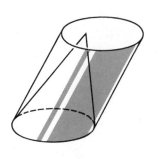

**Classroom Notes**

The method used to prove Theorem 19–16 is essentially the one used by Archimedes. The derivation of the formula for the surface area of a sphere (Theorem 19–17) is based on an approximation of the volume of a thin spherical shell. This sort of reasoning is often used in elementary calculus.

13. A plane intersects the figure of Problem 12 midway between the bases and parallel to them. Make a sketch of a top view of the intersection. If the radius of the cylinder is 4, what is the area of the intersection of the plane with the space between the two surfaces? $12\pi$

14. In the figure the right circular conical surface is inscribed in the right circular cylinder. Plane $E$ is parallel to the base of the cylinder 14 cm above the base. The altitude of the cone is 21 cm and the radius of the base is 6 cm. Find the area of the intersection of plane $E$ with the space between the two surfaces. $32\pi cm^2$

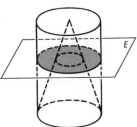

15. A frustum of a cone has an altitude of 8 and the radii of its upper and lower bases are 4 and 6. What is its volume? (See Problem 14 and the Honors Problem of Problem Set 19–3.)

$$v = \frac{1}{3}h\left(B + B' + \sqrt{BB'}\right) = \frac{608\pi}{3} \doteq 637$$

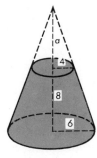

### 19–5   THE VOLUME AND THE SURFACE AREA
###          OF A SPHERE

By the volume of a sphere we mean, of course, the volume of the solid which is the union of the sphere and its interior.

So far, in our calculation of volumes, our best weapon has been Cavalieri's Principle. To use the Principle for the problem of the sphere, we shall need to find another solid with the same cross-sectional areas at every level. Therefore our first step should be to find the areas of the cross sections of our sphere. This is easy. Given a sphere of radius $r$, the horizontal cross sections are circular regions. If the cross section is at a distance $s$ from the center, and its radius is $t$, then we know by the Pythagorean Theorem that $t^2 = r^2 - s^2$. Therefore the area of the cross section at distance $s$ is

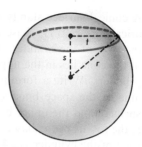

$$A_s = \pi t^2$$
$$= \pi(r^2 - s^2)$$
$$= \pi r^2 - \pi s^2.$$

This last formula has a geometric meaning: it is the area of the ring-shaped region lying inside a circle of radius $r$ and outside a circle of radius $s$, as shown on the right. A figure such as this is called an *annulus* (which is simply the Latin word for *ring*).

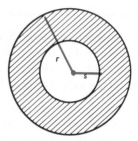

$$A = \pi r^2 - \pi s^2.$$

We shall now form a solid that has regions like this as its cross sections.

We take a horizontal plane $E$, tangent to the sphere. In this plane we take a circular region of radius $r$. Using this as base, we form a right circular cylinder of altitude $2r$.

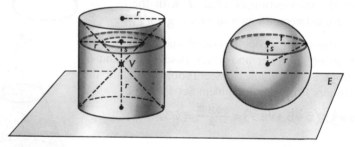

Let $V$ be the mid-point of the axis of the cylinders, that is, of the vertical segment joining the centers of the bases. We form two cones with $V$ as vertex, and with the top and bottom of the cylinder as bases.

The solid lying inside the cylinder and outside the cones is a solid of the sort we were looking for: each of its cross sections is an annulus, and the cross sections at distance $s$ from $V$ have area $\pi(r^2 - s^2)$. Therefore the volume of this solid is the same as the volume of the sphere.

But the volume of the new solid is easily calculated: it is equal to the volume of the cylinder minus the volumes of the cones. This gives

$$\pi r^2 \cdot 2r - 2 \cdot \tfrac{1}{3}\pi r^2 r$$
$$= 2\pi r^3 - \tfrac{2}{3}\pi r^3$$
$$= \tfrac{4}{3}\pi r^3.$$

Thus we have proved the following theorem.

## Theorem 19–16

*The volume of a sphere of radius r is $\frac{4}{3}\pi r^3$.*

There is a trick which enables us to use this result to find the area of the sphere itself, that is, of the surface. Given a sphere of radius $r$, we form a slightly larger sphere of radius $r + h$. The solid lying between the two spheres is called a *spherical shell*, and looks like the figure below. Let the surface area of the sphere be $A$, and let the volume of the shell be $V$. Then $V$ is approximately $Ah$, and if $h$ is small, the approximation is good. (For example, if you had a round ball of radius one foot, and painted it with a very thin coat of paint, say, one-hundredth of an inch thick, then the total volume of the paint you used would be about $\frac{1}{100}A$.) Thus $V/h$ is approximately $A$ when $h$ is small. And as $h \to 0$, we have $V/h \to A$.

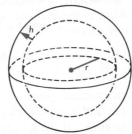

But we can calculate $V/h$ exactly, and see what it approaches as $h \to 0$. Now $V$ is the difference of the volumes of the two spheres. Therefore

$$
\begin{aligned}
V &= \tfrac{4}{3}\pi(r + h)^3 - \tfrac{4}{3}\pi r^3 \\
&= \tfrac{4}{3}\pi[(r + h)^3 - r^3] \\
&= \tfrac{4}{3}\pi[r^3 + 3r^2h + 3rh^2 + h^3 - r^3] \\
&= \tfrac{4}{3}\pi[3r^2h + 3rh^2 + h^3].
\end{aligned}
$$

[You should check that $(r + h)^3$ really is equal to $r^3 + 3r^2h + 3rh^2 + h^3$.] Therefore

$$
\begin{aligned}
\frac{V}{h} &= \tfrac{4}{3}\pi(3r^2 + 3rh + h^2) \\
&= 4\pi r^2 + h(4\pi r + \tfrac{4}{3}\pi h).
\end{aligned}
$$

As $h \to 0$, the entire second term approaches zero. Therefore

$$
\frac{V}{h} \to 4\pi r^2.
$$

Since we also know that $V/h \to A$, it follows that $A = 4\pi r^2$.
Thus we have proved the following theorem.

## Theorem 19–17

*The surface area of a sphere of radius r is $A = 4\pi r^2$.*

16.

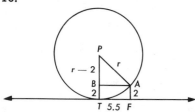

Observe that in the right triangle, $\triangle PAB$, $r^2 = (r-2)^2 + 5.5^2$. Therefore, $r = 8.56$ m, and $V = 2626$ m³. The tank holds 2626 kl, and the city uses 38 kl/h. Therefore, a full tank should last approximately 69.1 hours.

**17.** Let $A$ be the area of the lateral surface of the right circular cylinder, and let $V$ be the volume of the thin cylindrical shell. Then, for small values of $h$, $A \doteq V/h$ and as $h \to 0$ $V/h \to A$. But $V = \pi(r+h)^2 a - \pi r^2 a = \pi a(2rh + h^2)$, and thus $V/h = 2\pi ra + \pi ah$. Now as $h \to 0$, $V/h \to 2\pi ra$. But as $h \to 0$, $V/h \to A$. Therefore $A = 2\pi ra$.

**18.** Let $V_1$ and $S_1$ be the volume and surface area of the sphere. Let $V_2$ and $S_2$ be the volume and total surface area of the right circular cylinder. Since $V_1 = V_2$, $\frac{4}{3}\pi r^3 = \pi r^2 h$, and therefore $h = 4r/3$. Now, $S_1 = 4\pi r^2$ and $S_2 = 2(\pi r^2) + 2\pi rh = \frac{14}{3}\pi r^2$. Therefore the surface area of the sphere is less than the total surface area of the cylinder. Specifically,

$$\frac{S_1}{S_2} = \frac{4\pi r^2}{\frac{14}{3}\pi r^2} = \frac{6}{7}.$$

---

Note the rather interesting fact that the area of the sphere is exactly four times the area of a cross section through the center.

### Problem Set 19–5

1. Find the surface-area and the volume of a sphere whose radius equals 4.
   $S = 64\pi$, $V = 256\pi/3$

2. In a sphere of diameter 4 which is greater, its surface-area or its volume?
   $S = 16\pi$, $V = 32\pi/3$

3. In a sphere of diameter 10 which is greater, its surface-area or its volume?
   $S = 400\pi$, $V = 4000\pi/3$

4. What is the diameter of a sphere for which its volume is equal to its surface-area? $4\pi r^2 = \frac{4}{3}\pi r^3$, $r = 3$ and $d = 6$

5. A spherical storage tank has a radius of 2 m. How many litres will it hold? (Use $3\frac{1}{7}$ for $\pi$.) 32 524 liters

6. An ice cream cone is 13 cm deep and 5 cm across at the top. Two hemi-spherical scoops of ice cream, also of diameter 5 cm, are placed on top of the cone. If the ice cream is allowed to melt into the cone, will it overflow? Volume of cone = $27.1\pi$ cm³. Volume of ice cream = $20.8\pi$ cm³: No

7. A large storage building is in the shape of a hemisphere. If it took 13 $l$ of paint to cover the floor, how many litres can one expect to need to paint the exterior of the building? $\frac{\text{Surface Area}}{\text{area of floor}} = \frac{2}{1}$. Therefore 26 liters

8. The volumes of a sphere and a circular cylinder are equal and the diameter of the sphere equals the diameter of a base of the cylinder. Determine the altitude of the cylinder in terms of the diameter of the sphere. $\frac{4}{3}\pi r^3 = \pi r^2 h$, $h = \frac{4}{3}r = \frac{2}{3}d$

9. The diameter of a certain sphere is equal to the radius of a second sphere.
   (a) What is the ratio of their radii? $\frac{1}{2}$
   (b) What is the ratio of their surface-areas? $\frac{1}{4}$
   (c) What is the ratio of their volumes? $\frac{1}{8}$

---

10. The diameter of a certain sphere is one-third the radius of a second sphere. Answer the questions of Problem 9 by these spheres. $\frac{1}{6}$, $\frac{1}{36}$, $\frac{1}{216}$

11. The moon's diameter is approximately one-fourth the diameter of the earth. Compare the volumes of the moon and the earth. $\frac{1}{64}$

12. About three-fourths of the earth's surface is covered with water. How many millions of square kilometres of the earth's surface are land? (Use 12 870 km as the diameter and 3.14 as an approximation of $\pi$.) 1300 million km²

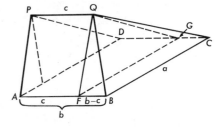

13. Archimedes (287–212 B.C.) showed that the volume of a sphere is two-thirds the volume of the smallest right circular cylinder that can contain it. Verify this.

$V_{cylinder} = \pi r^2 h = 2\pi r^3$

$V_{sphere} = \frac{4}{3}\pi r^3$

$\frac{V_{sphere}}{V_{cylinder}} = \frac{2}{3}$

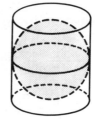

14. In the figure, the sphere is inscribed in the right circular cone. $\overline{AB}$ is a diameter of the base and $C$ is the vertex of the cone. $\triangle ABC$ is equilateral. Find the volume of the cone in terms of $r$, the radius of the sphere.

$h = 3r$ since $\triangle ABC$ equilateral and radius of base $r' = r\sqrt{3}$

$V = \frac{1}{3}\pi(r')^2 h = 3\pi r^3$

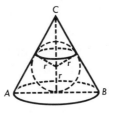

15. The volume of one sphere is one-half the volume of another sphere. What is the ratio of their radii?

$\frac{V_1}{V_2} = \left(\frac{r_1}{r_2}\right)^3 = \frac{1}{2}$ and $\frac{r_1}{r_2} = \frac{1}{\sqrt[3]{2}}$

16. The city engineer, who was 2 m tall, walked up to inspect the new spherical water tank. His head just touched the tank when he stood at a place 5.5 m from the point where the tank rested on the ground. Knowing that the city used 38 000 litres of water per hour, he immediately figured how many hours a full tank should last. How did he do it and what was his result? **69.1 hours**

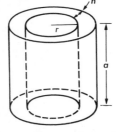

17. Using the method by which the formula for the surface-area of a sphere was derived (Theorem 19–17), show that the area of the lateral surface of a right circular cylinder is $2\pi ra$, where $r$ is the radius of a base and $a$ is the altitude.

18. A sphere and a right circular cylinder have equal volumes. The radius of the sphere equals the radius of the base of the cylinder. Compare the surface-area of the sphere with the area of the total surface of the cylinder.

## HONORS PROBLEM

Given a rectangle $\square ABCD$. $\overline{PQ}$ is a segment not in the plane of $\square ABCD$ such that $\overline{PQ} \parallel \overline{AB}$. Draw $\overline{PA}$, $\overline{PD}$, $\overline{QB}$, and $\overline{QC}$. The length of a perpendicular from any point on $\overline{PQ}$ to the plane of $\square ABCD$ is $h$. Let $AD = a$, $AB = b$, and $PQ = c$. Prove that the volume of the solid $ABCDPQ$ equals $\frac{1}{6}ah(2b + c)$.

In order to find a derivation, we first observe that the following statement is an immediate consequence of Theorem 11–6: If $R$ is a point of a line $L$ parallel to $\overline{PQ}$, then $a\triangle PQR$ is independent of the location of $R$ on $L$. This observation can be generalized: If $\overline{PQ}$ is a segment in a plane $E$ parallel to the plane of the rectangle $\square ABCD$ and $\overline{PQ} \parallel \overline{AB}$, then the volume of solid $ABCDPQ$ is independent of the location of $\overline{PQ}$ in $E$. We are consequently justified in assuming that $\overline{PQ}$ is located so that the plane of $\triangle PAD$ is perpendicular to the plane $\square ABCD$, as in the figure. Finally, let us assume that $c < b$. Introduce a point $F$ on $\overline{AB}$ such that $AF = c$, and a point $G$ on $\overline{DC}$ such that $DG = c$.

Then, the volume of the right prism with bases $\triangle APD$ and $\triangle FQG$ is $\frac{1}{2}ahc$. And, the volume of the rectangular pyramid $(Q, \square BCGF)$ is $\frac{1}{3}a(b - c)h$. Therefore, the volume of the solid $ABCDPQ$ is, by addition, $\frac{1}{6}ha(c + 2b)$.

It is easy to show that the formula holds for $c \geq b$ also. For $c = b$, the formula simplifies to $\frac{1}{2}abh$.

**1.** $V = Ah$, Volume of a prism

$V = abh$, Volume of a rectangular prism

$V = \pi r^2 h$, Volume of a circular prism

$V = \frac{1}{3}Ah$, Volume of a pyramid

$V = \frac{1}{3}\pi r^2 h$, Volume of a cone

$V = \frac{4}{3}\pi r^3$, Volume of a sphere

$V = \frac{1}{3}h(B + B' + \sqrt{BB'})$, Volume of a frustum of a pyramid

$A = ph$, Lateral surface area of a prism

$A = \frac{1}{2}pl$, Lateral surface area of a pyramid

$A = \pi rl$, Lateral surface area of a cone

$A = 4\pi r^2$, Surface area of a sphere

**5.** Let $V_s$ be the volume of the short jar with dimensions $(2r, h)$, and let $V_T$ be the volume of the tall jar with dimensions $(r, 2h)$. Then

$$\frac{V_s}{V_T} = \frac{\pi(2r)^2 h}{\pi r^2 (2h)} = \frac{4\pi r^2 h}{2\pi r^2 h} = \frac{2}{1}.$$

Therefore the short jar should cost twice as much as the tall jar. Since the tall jar cost 23¢, the short jar should cost 46¢. Since the short jar costs only 43¢, it is the better buy.

**17.** The volume of the cylinder is $3600\pi$ cm³. The volume of the sphere is $4000\pi/3$ cm³. Therefore the volume of water remaining in the can is $3600\pi - 4000\pi/3 = 2266.7\pi$ cm³.

**18.** We must first find the height of the parallelepiped. Since the base is 12 by 20, a diagonal of the base is

$$\sqrt{(12)^2 + (20)^2} = \sqrt{544} = 4\sqrt{34}.$$

Each diagonal of the parallelepiped is a diameter of the sphere and is therefore 25. Then in a triangle formed by a diagonal of the base, a diagonal of the parallelepiped and a "vertical" edge $h$ of the parallelepiped, we have

$$h^2 = (25)^2 - (4\sqrt{34})^2 = 81,$$

so that $h = 9$. Therefore the volume of the parallelepiped is

$$V = abh = (12)(20)(9) = 2160.$$

Since the volume of the sphere is $V = \frac{1}{6}\pi d^3 = 15625\pi/6 \doteq 8181$, we conclude that the volume of the part of the sphere outside of the parallelepiped is $8181 - 2160 \doteq 6021$.

---

## CHAPTER REVIEW

**1.** Without looking back through the chapter try to write down and identify all of the formulas for area and volume covered in this chapter.

**2.** Complete each sentence with the appropriate terms:

  (a) The bases of every prism are ___congruent___ and ___parallel___.

  (b) The lateral faces of a prism are ___parallelogram___ regions.

  (c) The lateral surface of a prism is the ___union___ of the ___lateral faces___ of the prism.

  (d) If the base of a prism is a parallelogram, the prism is called a ___parallelepiped___.

  (e) If two triangular pyramids have congruent bases, the volumes of the pyramids are proportional to the ___height___.

**3.** Complete each sentence with the appropriate terms:

  (a) In a right prism, each lateral edge is ___perpendicular___ to the base.

  (b) A cross-section of a pyramid is the ___intersection___ of the pyramid and a plane ___parallel___ to the base.

  (c) The areas of two cross-sections of a pyramid are proportional to the ___distances___ of their ___bases___ from the vertex of the ___pyramid___.

  (d) If a cone and a cylinder have congruent bases and equal altitudes, the volume of the cylinder is ___3 times___ the volume of the cone.

  (e) The volumes of two spheres are proportional to the ___cubes___ of their radii and the surface-areas are proportional to the ___squares___ of their radii.

**4.** The base of a right prism is a regular hexagonal region. An edge of the base is 2 cm long and a lateral edge of the prism is 7 cm long. Find the area of the lateral surface of the prism. Find the area of a cross-section 5 cm above the base. $LSA = 84\ cm^2$; $A = 6\sqrt{3}\ cm^2$

**5.** Two jars of the same brand of strawberry jam stand on a shelf in a supermarket. The taller jar is twice the height of the other jar, but its diameter is one-half as much as the diameter of the shorter jar. The taller jar costs 23 cents and the shorter jar costs 43 cents. Which is the better buy? _The shorter jar_

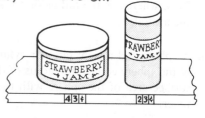

**6.** What is the volume of a cone if the altitude is 6 and the diameter of the base is 10? $50\pi$

**7.** The volume of a square pyramid is 384 cm³ and its altitude is 8 cm. How long is an edge of the base? What is the area of the lateral surface of the pyramid? (Assume that the projection of the vertex is the center of the base.) $LSA = 4(\frac{1}{2}l \cdot b) = 240\ cm^2$; $e = 12\ cm$

8. The bases of a hemisphere and
a cone are congruent circles and
are coplanar. A plane through
the vertex of the cone is parallel

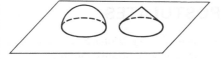

to the plane of the bases and is tangent to the hemisphere. What is the
ratio of the volume of the cone to the volume of the hemisphere? $\frac{1}{2}$

9. The base of a tetrahedron is a triangle whose sides have lengths 10, 24,
and 26. The altitude of the tetrahedron is 20. Find the area of a cross
section whose distance from the base is 15. 7.5

10. Given that the diameter of a sphere is 18, find its volume and surface-area.
$V = 972\pi$ , $A = 324\pi$

11. The volume of a cone is 400 cm³ and the radius of its base is 5 cm. Find
its altitude. $400 = \frac{1}{3}\pi 25 h$ , $h = \frac{48}{\pi} \doteq 15.28$ cm

12. A spherical ball of radius 3 cm has a hollow center of radius 2 cm. What
is the volume of the shell? $V = \frac{4}{3}\pi(r_1^3 - r_2^3) = \frac{76\pi}{3}$ cm³

13. Prove that the volume of a sphere is given by the formula $\frac{1}{6}\pi d^3$, where
$d$ is the diameter. $V = \frac{4}{3}\pi r^3 = \frac{4}{3}(\frac{d}{2})^3 = \frac{1}{6}\pi d^3$

14. The volume of a pyramid whose altitude is 12 cm is 432 cm³. Find the
area of a cross-section 3 cm above the base. $A_B = 108$ $\frac{A_c}{A_B} = (\frac{h_c}{h_B})^2$
$A_c = 60.75$ cm³

15. Given two cones. The altitude of the first is one-half that of the second
and the radius of the base of the first is one-half that of the second.
Compare their volumes. $\frac{1}{8}$

16. A sphere is inscribed in a right circular cylinder, such that it is tangent to
both bases. What is the ratio of the volume of the sphere to the volume
of the cylinder? $\frac{V_s}{V_c} = \frac{\frac{4}{3}\pi r^3}{\pi r^2 (2r)} = \frac{2}{3}$

17. A cylindrical can with radius 12 cm and height 25 cm is filled with water.
A sphere of diameter 20 cm is submerged in the can of water and then
removed. What volume of water remains in the can? 2266.7$\pi$ cm³

18. A rectangular parallelepiped whose base is 12 by 20 is inscribed in a
sphere of diameter 25. Find the volume of the part of the sphere outside
the parallelepiped. 6021

19. The base of a right circular cone has a diameter of 12 cm and the altitude
of the cone is 12 cm. The cone is filled with water. A sphere is lowered
into the cone until it fits snugly. Exactly one-half of the sphere remains
out of the water. After the sphere is removed, how much water remains
in the cone? 41$\pi \doteq 127$ cm³

20. The altitude of a right circular cone is 15 and the radius of its base is 8.
A cylindrical hole of diameter 4 is drilled through the cone, with its axis
along the axis of the cone, leaving a solid. What is the volume of this
solid? 270$\pi$

---

19.

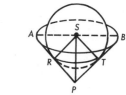

By the Pythagorean Theorem, $AP =$
$6\sqrt{5}$ in.; and therefore $RS(6\sqrt{5}) = 6(12)$
so that $RS = 12/\sqrt{5} = 12\sqrt{5}/5$ cm. The
volume of the cone is $V_c = \frac{1}{3}\pi r^2 h =$
$\frac{1}{3}\pi(6^2)12 = 144\pi$ cm³. The volume of the
sphere is

$$V_s = \frac{4}{3}\pi(RS)^3$$
$$= \frac{4}{3}\pi(12\sqrt{5}/5)^3 \doteq 206\pi \text{ cm}^3,$$

and thus the volume of the water dis-
placed is approximately $103\pi$ cm³.
Therefore the volume of the water remaining in the cone is approximately
$41\pi \doteq 127$ cm³.

20.

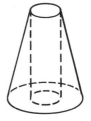

The volume of the original cone is
$V = \frac{1}{3}\pi r^2 h = \frac{1}{3}\pi(8^2)15 = 320\pi$. The volume of the small cone cut off at top is
$V = \frac{1}{3}\pi r^2 h = \frac{1}{3}\pi(2^2)\frac{15}{4} = 5\pi$. Therefore the
volume of the frustum of the cone is
$315\pi$. The volume of the cylinder removed from the frustum is $V = \pi r^2 h =$
$\pi(2^2)\frac{45}{4} = 45\pi$. Therefore the volume of
the solid remaining is $370\pi$.

# POSTULATES

***Postulate 1.*** *The Distance Postulate.* To every pair of different points there corresponds a unique positive number.

***Postulate 2.*** *The Ruler Postulate.* The points of a line can be placed in correspondence with the real numbers in such a way that
   (1) to every point of the line there corresponds exactly one real number;
   (2) to every real number there corresponds exactly one point of the line; and
   (3) the distance between any two points is the absolute value of the difference of the corresponding numbers.

***Postulate 3.*** *The Ruler Placement Postulate.* Given two points $P$ and $Q$ of a line, the coordinate system can be chosen in such a way that the coordinate of $P$ is zero and the coordinate of $Q$ is positive.

***Postulate 4.*** *The Line Postulate.* For every two points there is exactly one line that contains both points.

***Postulate 5.*** *The Plane-Space Postulate.*
   (a) Every plane contains at least three noncollinear points.
   (b) Space contains at least four noncoplanar points.

***Postulate 6.*** *The Flat Plane Postulate.* If two points of a line lie in a plane, then the line lies in the same plane.

***Postulate 7.*** *The Plane Postulate.* Any three points lie in at least one plane, and any three noncollinear points lie in exactly one plane.

***Postulate 8.*** *Intersection of Planes Postulate.* If two different planes intersect, then their intersection is a line.

***Postulate 9.*** *The Plane Separation Postulate.* Given a line and a plane containing it. The points of the plane that do not lie on the line form two sets such that
   (1) each of the sets is convex, and
   (2) if $P$ is in one of the sets and $Q$ is in the other, then the segment $\overline{PQ}$ intersects the line.

***Postulate 10.*** *The Space Separation Postulate.* The points of space that do not lie in a given plane form two sets, such that
   (1) each of the sets is convex, and
   (2) if $P$ is in one of the sets and $Q$ is in the other, then the segment $\overline{PQ}$ intersects the plane.

***Postulate 11.*** *The Angle Measurement Postulate.* To every angle there corresponds a real number between 0 and 180.

***Postulate 12.*** *The Angle Construction Postulate.* Let $\overrightarrow{AB}$ be a ray on the edge of the half-plane $H$. For every number $r$ between 0 and 180 there is exactly one ray $\overrightarrow{AP}$, with $P$ in $H$, such that $m\angle PAB = r$.

***Postulate 13.*** *The Angle Addition Postulate.* If $D$ is in the interior of $\angle BAC$, then $m\angle BAC = m\angle BAD + m\angle DAC$.

*Postulate 14.* *The Supplement Postulate.* If two angles form a linear pair, then they are supplementary.

*Postulate 15.* *The SAS Postulate.* Every SAS correspondence is a congruence.

*Postulate 16.* *The ASA Postulate.* Every ASA correspondence is a congruence.

*Postulate 17.* *The SSS Postulate.* Every SSS correspondence is a congruence.

*Postulate 18.* *The Parallel Postulate.* Through a given external point there is only one parallel to a given line.

*Postulate 19.* *The Area Postulate.* To every polygonal region there corresponds a unique positive real number.

*Postulate 20.* *The Congruence Postulate.* If two triangles are congruent, then the triangular regions determined by them have the same area.

*Postulate 21.* *The Area Addition Postulate.* If two polygonal regions intersect only in edges and vertices (or do not intersect at all), then the area of their union is the sum of their areas.

*Postulate 22.* *The Unit Postulate.* The area of a square region is the square of the length of its edge.

*Postulate 23.* *The Unit Postulate.* The volume of a rectangular parallelepiped is the product of the altitude and the area of the base.

*Postulate 24.* *Cavalieri's Principle.* Given two solids and a plane. Suppose that every plane parallel to the given plane, intersecting one of the two solids, also intersects the other, and gives cross sections with the same area. Then the two solids have the same volume.

## THEOREMS

*Theorem 2–1.* If $a - b > 0$, then $a > b$.

*Theorem 2–2.* If $a = b + c$ and $c > 0$, then $a > b$.

*Theorem 2–3.* Let $A$, $B$, and $C$ be points of a line, with coordinates $x$, $y$, and $z$ respectively. If $x < y < z$, then $A$-$B$-$C$.

*Theorem 2–4.* If $A$, $B$, and $C$ are three different points of the same line, then exactly one of them is between the other two.

*Theorem 2–5.* *The Point-Plotting Theorem.* Let $\overrightarrow{AB}$ be a ray, and let $x$ be a positive number. Then there is exactly one point $P$ of $\overrightarrow{AB}$ such that $AP = x$.

*Theorem 2–6.* *The Mid-Point Theorem.* Every segment has exactly one mid-point.

*Theorem 3–1.* If two different lines intersect, their intersection contains only one point.

*Theorem 3–2.* If a line intersects a plane not containing it, then the intersection contains only one point.

*Theorem 3–3.* Given a line and a point not on the line, there is exactly one plane containing both.

*Theorem 3–4.* Given two intersecting lines, there is exactly one plane containing both.

*Theorem 4–1.* Congruence between angles is an equivalence relation.

*Theorem 4–2.* If the angles in a linear pair are congruent, then each of them is a right angle.

*Theorem 4–3.* If two angles are complementary, then both are acute.

*Theorem 4–4.* Any two right angles are congruent.

*Theorem 4–5.* If two angles are both congruent and supplementary, then each is a right angle.

*Theorem 4–6. The Supplement Theorem.* Supplements of congruent angles are congruent.

*Theorem 4–7. The Complement Theorem.* Complements of congruent angles are congruent.

*Theorem 4–8. The Vertical Angle Theorem.* Vertical angles are congruent.

*Theorem 4–9.* If two lines are perpendicular, they form four right angles.

*Theorem 5–1.* Congruence for segments is an equivalence relation.

*Theorem 5–2.* Congruence for triangles is an equivalence relation.

*Theorem 5–3. The Angle Bisector Theorem.* Every angle has exactly one bisector.

*Theorem 5–4. The Isosceles Triangle Theorem.* If two sides of a triangle are congruent, then the angles opposite these sides are congruent.

*Theorem 5–5.* If two angles of a triangle are congruent, then the sides opposite them are congruent.

*Theorem 6–1.* In a given plane, through a given point of a given line, there is one and only one line perpendicular to the given line.

*Theorem 6–2. The Perpendicular Bisector Theorem.* The perpendicular bisector of a segment, in a plane, is the set of all points of the plane that are equidistant from the end points of the segment.

*Theorem 6–3.* Through a given external point there is at least one line perpendicular to a given line.

*Theorem 6–4.* Through a given external point there is at most one line perpendicular to a given line.

*Theorem 6–5.* If $M$ is between $A$ and $C$ on a line $L$, then $M$ and $A$ are on the same side of any other line that contains $C$.

***Theorem 6–6.*** If $M$ is between $B$ and $C$, and $A$ is any point not on $\overleftrightarrow{BC}$, then $M$ is in the interior of $\angle BAC$.

***Theorem 7–1.*** *The Parts Theorem.*
 (1) If $D$ is a point on $\overline{AB}$ between $A$ and $B$, then $\overline{AB} > \overline{AD}$ and $\overline{AB} > \overline{DB}$.
 (2) If $D$ is a point in the interior of $\angle ABC$, then $\angle ABC > \angle ABD$ and $\angle ABC > \angle DBC$.

***Theorem 7–2.*** *The Exterior Angle Theorem.* An exterior angle of a triangle is greater than each of its remote interior angles.

***Theorem 7–3.*** *The SAA Theorem.* Every SAA correspondence is a congruence.

***Theorem 7–4.*** *The Hypotenuse-Leg Theorem.* Given a correspondence between two right triangles. If the hypotenuse and one leg of one of the triangles are congruent to the corresponding parts of the second triangle, then the correspondence is a congruence.

***Theorem 7–5.*** If two sides of a triangle are not congruent, then the angles opposite them are not congruent, and the larger angle is opposite the longer side.

***Theorem 7–6.*** If two angles of a triangle are not congruent, then the sides opposite them are not congruent, and the longer side is opposite the larger angle.

***Theorem 7–7.*** *The First Minimum Theorem.* The shortest segment joining a point to a line is the perpendicular segment.

***Theorem 7–8.*** *The Triangle Inequality.* The sum of the length of any two sides of a triangle is greater than the length of the third side.

***Theorem 7–9.*** *The Hinge Theorem.* If two sides of one triangle are congruent, respectively, to two sides of a second triangle, and the included angle of the first triangle is larger than the included angle of the second, then the third side of the first triangle is longer than the third side of the second.

***Theorem 7–10.*** *The Converse Hinge Theorem.* If two sides of one triangle are congruent respectively to two sides of a second triangle, and the third side of the first triangle is longer than the third side of the second, then the included angle of the first triangle is larger than the included angle of the second.

***Theorem 8–1.*** If $B$ and $C$ are equidistant from $P$ and $Q$, then every point between $B$ and $C$ is equidistant from $P$ and $Q$.

***Theorem 8–2.*** If a line is perpendicular to each of two intersecting lines at their point of intersection, then it is perpendicular to the plane that contains them.

***Theorem 8–3.*** Through a given point of a given line there passes a plane perpendicular to the given line.

***Theorem 8–4.*** If a line and a plane are perpendicular, then the plane contains every line perpendicular to the given line at its point of intersection with the given plane.

***Theorem 8–5.*** Through a given point of a given line there is only one plane perpendicular to the line.

*Theorem 8–6.* *The Perpendicular Bisecting Plane Theorem.* The perpendicular bisecting plane of a segment is the set of all points equidistant from the end points of the segment.

*Theorem 8–7.* Two lines perpendicular to the same plane are coplanar.

*Theorem 8–8.* Through a given point there passes one and only one *plane* perpendicular to a given *line*.

*Theorem 8–9.* Through a given point there passes one and only one *line* perpendicular to a given *plane*.

*Theorem 8–10.* *The Second Minimum Theorem.* The shortest segment to a plane from an external point is the perpendicular segment.

*Theorem 9–1.* Two parallel lines lie in exactly one plane.

*Theorem 9–2.* In a plane if two lines are perpendicular to the same line, then they are parallel.

*Theorem 9–3.* Let $L$ be a line and let $P$ be a point not on $L$. Then there is at least one line through $P$, parallel to $L$.

*Theorem 9–4.* If two lines are cut by a transversal, and one pair of alternate interior angles are congruent, then the other pair of alternate interior angles are also congruent.

*Theorem 9–5.* Given two lines cut by a transversal. If a pair of alternate interior angles are congruent, then the lines are parallel.

*Theorem 9–6.* Given two lines cut by a transversal. If a pair of corresponding angles are congruent, then a pair of alternate interior angles are congruent.

*Theorem 9–7.* Given two lines cut by a transversal. If a pair of corresponding angles are congruent, then the lines are parallel.

*Theorem 9–8.* Given two lines cut by a transversal. If a pair of interior angles on the same side of the transversal are supplementary, the lines are parallel.

*Theorem 9–9.* If two parallel lines are cut by a transversal, each pair of corresponding angles are congruent.

*Theorem 9–10.* In a plane, if a line intersects one of two parallel lines in only one point, then it intersects the other.

*Theorem 9–11.* In a plane, if two lines are each parallel to a third line, then they are parallel to each other.

*Theorem 9–12.* In a plane, if a line is perpendicular to one of two parallel lines it is perpendicular to the other.

*Theorem 9–13.* For every triangle, the sum of the measures of the angles is 180.

*Theorem 9–14.* Each diagonal separates a parallelogram into two congruent triangles.

*Theorem 9–15.* In a parallelogram, any two opposite sides are congruent.

*Theorem 9–16.* In a parallelogram, any two opposite angles are congruent.

*Theorem 9–17.* In a parallelogram, any two consecutive angles are supplementary.

*Theorem 9–18.* The diagonals of a parallelogram bisect each other.

*Theorem 9–19.* Given a quadrilateral in which both pairs of opposite sides are congruent. Then the quadrilateral is a parallelogram.

*Theorem 9–20.* If two sides of a quadrilateral are parallel and congruent, then the quadrilateral is a parallelogram.

*Theorem 9–21.* If the diagonals of a quadrilateral bisect each other, then the quadrilateral is a parallelogram.

*Theorem 9–22.* The segment between the mid-points of two sides of a triangle is parallel to the third side and half as long.

*Theorem 9–23.* If a parallelogram has one right angle, then it has four right angles, and the parallelogram is a rectangle.

*Theorem 9–24.* In a rhombus, the diagonals are perpendicular to one another.

*Theorem 9–25.* If the diagonals of a quadrilateral bisect each other and are perpendicular, then the quadrilateral is a rhombus.

*Theorem 9–26.* The median to the hypotenuse of a right triangle is half as long as the hypotenuse.

*Theorem 9–27.* The *30-60-90 Triangle Theorem.* If an acute angle of a right angle has measure 30, then the opposite side is half as long as the hypotenuse.

*Theorem 9–28.* If one leg of a right triangle is half as long as the hypotenuse, then the opposite angle has measure 30.

*Theorem 9–29.* If three parallel lines intercept congruent segments on one transversal $T$, then they intercept congruent segments on every transversal $T'$ which is parallel to $T$.

*Theorem 9–30.* If three parallel lines intercept congruent segments on one transversal, then they intercept congruent segments on any other transversal.

*Theorem 9–31.* *The Median Concurrence Theorem.* The medians of every triangle are congruent. Their point of concurrency is two-thirds of the way along each median, from the vertex to the opposite side.

*Theorem 10–1.* If a plane intersects two parallel planes, then it intersects them in two parallel lines.

*Theorem 10–2.* If a line is perpendicular to one of two parallel planes it is perpendicular to the other.

*Theorem 10–3.* Two planes perpendicular to the same line are parallel.

*Theorem 10–4.* Two lines perpendicular to the same plane are parallel.

*Theorem 10–5.* Parallel planes are everywhere equidistant.

*Theorem 10–6.* All plane angles of the same dihedral angle are congruent.

*Theorem 10–7.* If a line is perpendicular to a plane, then every plane containing the line is perpendicular to the given plane.

*Theorem 10–8.* If two planes are perpendicular, then any line in one of them, perpendicular to their line of intersection, is perpendicular to the other plane.

*Theorem 10–9.* If a line and a plane are not perpendicular, then the projection of the line into the plane is a line.

*Theorem 11–1.* The area of a rectangle is the product of its base and its altitude.

*Theorem 11–2.* The area of a right triangle is half the product of its legs.

*Theorem 11–3.* The area of a triangle is half the product of any base and the corresponding altitude.

*Theorem 11–4.* The area of a trapezoid is half the product of its altitude and the sum of its bases.

*Theorem 11–5.* The area of a parallelogram is the product of any base and the corresponding altitude.

*Theorem 11–6.* If two triangles have the same base $b$ and the same altitude $h$, then they have the same area.

*Theorem 11–7.* If two triangles have the same altitude $h$, then the ratio of their areas is equal to the ratio of their bases.

*Theorem 11–8. The Pythagorean Theorem.* In a right triangle, the square of the hypotenuse is equal to the sum of the squares of the legs.

*Theorem 11–9.* If the square of one side of a triangle is equal to the sum of the squares of the other two sides, then the triangle is a right triangle, with its right angle opposite the longest side.

*Theorem 11–10. The Isosceles Right Triangle Theorem.* In an isosceles right triangle, the hypotenuse is $\sqrt{2}$ times as long as each of the legs.

*Theorem 11–11.* If the base of an isosceles triangle is $\sqrt{2}$ times as long as each of the two congruent sides, then the angle opposite the base is a right angle.

*Theorem 11–12.* In a 30-60-90 triangle, the longer leg is $\sqrt{3}/2$ times as long as the hypotenuse.

*Theorem 12–1.* Proportionality between sequences is an equivalence relation.

*Theorem 12–2. The Basic Proportionality Theorem.* If a line parallel to one side of a triangle intersects the other two sides in distinct points, then it cuts off segments which are proportional to these sides.

*Theorem 12–3.* If a line intersects two sides of a triangle, and cuts off segments proportional to these two sides, then it is parallel to the third side.

*Theorem 12–4. The AAA Similarity Theorem.* Given a correspondence between two triangles. If corresponding angles are congruent, then the correspondence is a similarity.

*Theorem 12–5.* Similarity between triangles is an equivalence relation.

***Theorem 12–6.*** *The SAS Similarity Theorem.* Given a correspondence between two triangles. If two pairs of corresponding sides are proportional, and the included angles are congruent, then the correspondence is a similarity.

***Theorem 12–7.*** *The SSS Similarity Theorem.* Given a correspondence between two triangles. If corresponding sides are proportional, then the correspondence is a similarity.

***Theorem 12–8.*** In any right triangle, the altitude to the hypotenuse separates the triangle into two triangles which are similar to each other and to the original triangle.

***Theorem 12–9.*** Given a right triangle and the altitude to the hypotenuse.
(1) The altitude is the geometric mean of the segments into which it separates the hypotenuse.
(2) Each leg is the geometric mean of the hypotenuse and the segment of the hypotenuse adjacent to the leg.

***Theorem 12–10.*** If two triangles are similar, then the ratio of their areas is the square of the ratio of any two corresponding sides.

***Theorem 13–1.*** On a nonvertical line, all segments have the same slope.

***Theorem 13–2.*** Two nonvertical lines are parallel if and only if they have the same slope.

***Theorem 13–3.*** Two nonvertical lines are perpendicular if and only if their slopes are negative reciprocals of each other.

***Theorem 13–4.*** *The Distance Formula.* The distance between the points $(x_1, y_1)$ and $(x_2, y_2)$ is $\sqrt{(x_2 - x_1)^2 + (y_2 - y_1)^2}$.

***Theorem 13–5.*** *The Midpoint Formula.* Given $P_1 = (x_1, y_1)$ and $P_2 = (x_2, y_2)$. The midpoint of $\overline{P_1P_2}$ is the point $P = \left( \dfrac{x_1 + x_2}{2}, \dfrac{y_1 + y_2}{2} \right)$.

***Theorem 13–6.*** If $P$ is between $P_1$ and $P_2$, and $\dfrac{P_1P}{PP_2} = r$, then

$$P = \left( \frac{x_1 + rx_2}{1 + r}, \frac{y_1 + ry_2}{1 + r} \right).$$

***Theorem 13–7.*** Let $L$ be a line with slope $m$, passing through the point $(x_1, y_1)$. Then every point $(x, y)$ of $L$ satisfies the equation $y - y_1 = m(x - x_1)$.

***Theorem 13–8.*** The graph of the equation $y - y_1 = m(x - x_1)$ is the line which passes through the point $(x_1, y_1)$ and has slope $m$.

***Theorem 13–9.*** The graph of the equation $y = mx + b$ is the line which passes through the point $(0, b)$ and has slope $m$.

***Theorem 14–1.*** The intersection of a sphere with a plane through its center is a circle with the same center and the same radius.

***Theorem 14–2.*** A line perpendicular to a radius at its outer end is tangent to the circle.

***Theorem 14–3.*** Every tangent to a circle is perpendicular to the radius drawn to the point of contact.

*Theorem 14–4.* The perpendicular from the center of a circle to a chord bisects the chord.

*Theorem 14–5.* The segment from the center of a circle to the midpoint of a chord which is not a diameter is perpendicular to the chord.

*Theorem 14–6.* In the plane of a circle, the perpendicular bisector of a chord passes through the center.

*Theorem 14–7.* In the same circle or in congruent circles, chords equidistant from the center are congruent.

*Theorem 14–8.* In the same circle or in congruent circles, any two congruent chords are equidistant from the center.

*Theorem 14–9. The Line-Circle Theorem.* If a line and a circle are coplanar and the line intersects the interior of a circle, then it intersects the circle in two and only two points.

*Theorem 14–10.* A plane perpendicular to a radius at its outer end is tangent to the sphere.

*Theorem 14–11.* Every tangent plane to a sphere is perpendicular to the radius drawn to the point of contact.

*Theorem 14–12.* If a plane intersects the interior of a sphere, then the intersection of the plane and the sphere is a circle. The center of this circle is the foot of the perpendicular from the center of the sphere to the plane.

*Theorem 14–13.* The perpendicular from the center of a sphere to a chord bisects the chord.

*Theorem 14–14.* The segment from the center of a sphere to the midpoint of a chord is perpendicular to the chord.

*Theorem 14–15. The Arc Addition Theorem.* If $B$ is a point of $\overarc{AC}$, then

$$m\overarc{ABC} = m\overarc{AB} + m\overarc{BC}.$$

*Theorem 14–16. The Inscribed Angle Theorem.* The measure of an inscribed angle is half the measure of its intercepted arc.

*Theorem 14–17.* In the same circle or in congruent circles, if two chords are congruent, then so are the corresponding minor arcs.

*Theorem 14–18.* In the same circle or in congruent circles, if two arcs are congruent, then so are the corresponding chords.

*Theorem 14–19. The Tangent-Secant Theorem.* Given an angle with its vertex on a circle, formed by a secant ray and a tangent ray. The measure of the angle is half the measure of the intercepted arc.

*Theorem 14–20. The Two-Tangent Theorem.* The two tangent segments to a circle from a point of the exterior are congruent and determine congruent angles with the segment from the exterior point to the center.

*Theorem 14–21. The Two-Secant Power Theorem.* Given a circle $C$, and a point $Q$ of its exterior. Let $L_1$ be a secant line through $Q$, intersecting $C$ in points $R$ and $S$; and let $L_2$ be another secant line through $Q$, intersecting $C$ in points $U$ and $T$. Then $QR \cdot QS = QU \cdot QT$.

*Theorem 14–22.* *The Tangent-Secant Power Theorem.* Given a tangent segment $\overline{QT}$ to a circle, and a secant line through $Q$, intersecting the circle in points $E$ and $S$. Then $QR \cdot QS = QT^2$.

*Theorem 14–23.* *The Two-Chord Power Theorem.* Let $\overline{RS}$ and $\overline{TU}$ be chords of the same circle, intersecting at $Q$. Then $QR \cdot QS = QU \cdot QT$.

*Theorem 14–24.* The graph of the equation $(x - a)^2 + (y - b)^2 = r^2$ is the circle with center $(a, b)$ and radius $r$.

*Theorem 14–25.* Every circle is the graph of an equation of the form

$$x^2 + y^2 + Ax + By + C = 0.$$

*Theorem 14–26.* The graph of the equation $x^2 + y^2 + Ax + By + C = 0$ is (1) a circle, (2) a point, or (3) the empty set.

*Theorem 15–1.* *The Perpendicular Bisector Concurrence Theorem.* The perpendicular bisectors of the sides of a triangle are concurrent. Their point of concurrency is equidistant from the vertices of the triangle.

*Theorem 15–2.* *The Altitude Concurrence Theorem.* The three altitudes of a triangle are always concurrent.

*Theorem 15–3.* The bisector of an angle, minus its end point, is the set of all points of the interior of the angle that are equidistant from the sides.

*Theorem 15–4.* *The Angle Bisector Concurrence Theorem.* The angle bisectors of a triangle are concurrent in a point which is equidistant from the three sides.

*Theorem 15–5.* *The Median Concurrence Theorem.* The medians of every triangle are concurrent. And their point of concurrency is two-thirds of the way along each median, from the vertex to the opposite side.

*Theorem 15–6.* *The Two-Circle Theorem.* Given two circles of radius $a$ and $b$, with $c$ as the distance between their centers. If each of the numbers $a$, $b$, and $c$ is less than the sum of the other two, then the circles intersect in two points, on opposite sides of the line through the centers.

*Theorem 16–1.* The ratio of the circumference to the diameter is the same for all circles.

*Theorem 16–2.* The area of a circle of radius $r$ is $\pi r^2$.

*Theorem 16–3.* If two arcs have equal radii, then their lengths are proportional to their measures.

*Theorem 16–4.* If an arc has measure $q$ and radius $r$, then its length is

$$L = \frac{q}{180} \cdot \pi r.$$

*Theorem 16–5.* The area of a sector is half the product of its radius and the length of its arc. That is, $A = \frac{1}{2}rL$.

*Theorem 16–6.* If a sector has radius $r$ and its arc has measure $q$, then its area is

$$A = \frac{q}{360} \cdot \pi r^2.$$

*Theorem 17–1.* For every $\angle A$, $(\sin \angle A)^2 + (\cos \angle A)^2 = 1$.

***Theorem 17–2.*** For every $\angle A$, $\tan \angle A = \dfrac{\sin \angle A}{\cos \angle A}$.

***Theorem 17–3.*** If $\angle A$ and $\angle B$ are complementary, then $\sin \angle B = \cos \angle A$ and $\cos \angle B = \sin \angle A$.

***Theorem 17–4.*** For every real number $\theta$, $\sin^2 \theta + \cos^2 \theta = 1$.

***Theorem 17–5.*** If $\cos \theta \neq 0$, then $\dfrac{\sin \theta}{\cos \theta} = \tan \theta$.

***Theorem 17–6.*** For every $\theta$ $\sin(-\theta) = -\sin \theta$, and $\cos(-\theta) = \cos \theta$. $\tan(-\theta) = -\tan \theta$, (if $\cos \theta \neq 0$).

***Theorem 17–7.*** *The Addition Formula—Cosine.* For all real numbers $a$ and $b$, $\cos(a + b) = \cos a \cos b - \sin a \sin b$.

***Theorem 17–8.*** For every real number $\theta$, $\cos(\theta + \pi) = -\cos \theta$.

***Theorem 17–9.*** For all real numbers $\theta$, $\cos(\theta + \frac{1}{2}\pi) = -\sin \theta$, and $\sin(\theta + \frac{1}{2}\pi) = \cos \theta$.

***Theorem 17–10.*** *The Addition Formula—Sine.* For all real numbers $a$ and $b$, $\sin(a + b) = \sin a \cos b + \cos a \sin b$.

***Theorem 17–11.*** For all real numbers $\theta$, $\sin(\theta + \pi) = -\sin \theta$.

***Theorem 17–12.*** *The Difference Formulas.* For all real numbers $a$ and $b$,
$$\cos(a - b) = \cos a \cos b + \sin a \sin b,$$
$$\sin(a - b) = \sin a \cos b - \cos a \sin b.$$

***Theorem 17–13.*** For all real numbers $a$ and $b$, $\tan(a + b) = \dfrac{\tan a + \tan b}{1 - \tan a \tan b}$ (whenever $\tan a \tan b \neq 1$).

***Theorem 17–14.*** For all real numbers $a$ and $b$, $\tan(a - b) = \dfrac{\tan a - \tan b}{1 + \tan a \tan b}$ (whenever $\tan a \tan b \neq -1$).

***Theorem 18–1.*** If a plane figure is symmetric about each of two perpendicular lines, then it is symmetric about the point where the lines intersect.

***Theorem 18–2.*** Distances are preserved under reflections across a line.

***Theorem 18–3.*** Every translation is a rigid motion.

***Theorem 18–4.*** Every rotation is a rigid motion.

***Theorem 18–5.*** Let $E$ be a coordinate plane, and let $P_o = (h, k)$ be a vector in $E$. Then the correspondence $P \leftrightarrow P' = P + P_o$ is the translation of $E$ by $P_o$.

***Theorem 18–6.*** *The Parallelogram Law of Addition.* Let $P_1 = (x_1, y_1)$ and $P_2 = (x_2, y_2)$, and suppose that $P_1$, $P_2$, and $O$ are not collinear. Then $P_1 + P_2$ is the fourth vertex of the parallelogram determined by $O$, $P_1$, and $P_2$.

***Theorem 18–7.*** If $P$ and $P'$ are any two points, then there is a line-reflection under which $P \leftrightarrow P'$.

***Theorem 18–8.*** Let $P$ and $P'$ be any two points, and let $A$ be a point such that $AP = AP'$. Then there is a line-reflection under which $A \leftrightarrow A'$ and $P \leftrightarrow P'$.

***Theorem 18–9.*** Let $\triangle ABC$ and $\triangle A'B'C'$ be triangles in a plane. If $\triangle ABC \cong \triangle A'B'C'$, then there is a rigid motion under which $A \leftrightarrow A'$, $B \leftrightarrow B'$, and $C \leftrightarrow C'$.

*Theorem 18–10.* Let $\triangle ABC$ and $\triangle A'B'C'$ be triangles in a plane. If $\triangle ABC \cong \triangle A'B'C'$, then there is a rigid motion under which $\triangle ABC$ is moved onto $\triangle A'B'C'$.

*Theorem 8–11.* Let $\triangle ABC$ and $\triangle A'B'C'$ be triangles in a plane. If $\triangle ABC \sim \triangle A'B'C'$, then $\triangle ABC$ can be moved onto $\triangle A'B'C'$ by a rigid motion, followed by a dilation.

*Theorem 19–1.* All cross sections of a triangular prism are congruent to the base.

*Theorem 19–2.* *The Prism Cross-Section Theorem.* All cross sections of a prism have the same area.

*Theorem 19–3.* The lateral faces of a prism are parallelogram regions.

*Theorem 19–4.* Every cross section of a triangular pyramid, between the base and the vertex, is a triangular region similar to the base. If $h$ is the altitude, and $k$ is the distance from the vertex to the cross section, then the area of the cross section is equal to $k^2/h^2$ times the area of the base.

*Theorem 19–5.* In any pyramid, the ratio of the area of a cross section to the area of the base is $k^2/h^2$, where $h$ is the altitude of the pyramid and $k$ is the distance from the vertex to the plane of the cross section.

*Theorem 19–6. The Pyramid Cross-Section Theorem.* If two pyramids have the same base area and the same altitude, then cross sections equidistant from the vertices have the same area.

*Theorem 19–7.* The volume of any prism is the product of the altitude and the area of the base.

*Theorem 19–8.* If two pyramids have the same altitude and the same base area, and their bases lie in the same plane, then they have the same volume.

*Theorem 19–9.* The volume of a triangular pyramid is one-third the product of its altitude and its base area.

*Theorem 19–10.* The volume of a pyramid is one-third the product of its altitude and its base area.

*Theorem 19–11.* Every cross section of a circular cylinder is a circular region congruent to the base.

*Theorem 19–12.* Every cross section of a circular cylinder has the same area as the base.

*Theorem 19–13.* Given a cone of altitude $h$, and a cross section made by a plane at a distance $k$ from the vertex. The area of the cross section is equal to $k^2/h^2$ times the area of the base.

*Theorem 19–14.* The volume of a circular cylinder is the product of its altitude and the area of its base.

*Theorem 19–15.* The volume of a circular cone is one-third the product of its altitude and the area of its base.

*Theorem 19–16.* The volume of a sphere of radius $r$ is $\frac{4}{3}\pi r^3$.

*Theorem 19–17.* The surface area of a sphere of radius $r$ is $A = 4\pi r^2$.

# LIST OF SYMBOLS

Following are short explanations of the symbols used in this book, with references to the pages where fuller explanations are given.

| Symbols | Meaning | For definition See Page |
|---|---|---|
| $\{a, b, c\}$ | The set whose elements are $a$, $b$, and $c$ | 15 |
| $A \subset B$ | Set $A$ is a subset of set $B$ | 16 |
| $x \in A$ | $x$ is an element of set $A$ | 16 |
| $=$ | Equals; is equal to; is the same as | 16 |
| $\neq$ | Is not equal to; is different from | 16 |
| $A \cap B$ | The intersection of sets $A$ and $B$ | 17 |
| $A \cup B$ | The union of sets $A$ and $B$ | 17 |
| $\emptyset$ | The empty set | 17 |
| $<$ | Is less than: | |
| | for numbers | 23 |
| | for segments | 213 |
| | for angle measure | 213 |
| $\leq$ | Is less than or equal to: | |
| | for numbers | 23 |
| $>$ | Is greater than: | |
| | for numbers | 23 |
| $\geq$ | Is greater than or equal to: | |
| | for numbers | 23 |
| $\sqrt{a}$ | The positive square root of $a$ | 24 |
| $|a|$ | The absolute value of $a$ | 27 |
| $AB$ | The distance between points $A$ and $B$ | 29 |
| $A$-$B$-$C$ | $B$ is between $A$ and $C$ | 37 |
| $\overleftrightarrow{AB}$ | The line containing points $A$ and $B$ | 39 |
| $\overline{AB}$ | The segment whose end points are $A$ and $B$ | 39 |
| $\overrightarrow{AB}$ | The ray having end point $A$ and containing $B$ | 39 |
| $\angle BAC$ | The angle whose sides are $\overrightarrow{AB}$ and $\overrightarrow{AC}$ | 77 |
| $\triangle ABC$ | The triangle whose vertices are $A$, $B$, and $C$ | 79 |

# INDEX

Ratio(s), cosine, 558
sine, 557
tangent, 558
Rational numbers, 21
Ray(s), 39–40
opposite, 40
perpendicular, 95
union of, 77
Real numbers, 21, 22
Rectangle(s), 167, 288
area of, 333
Rectangular parallelepiped, 628
Reflection(s), 596–597, 601–602
distance under, 602
product of, 601
Reflexive Property, 101
Rhombus, 288
Right angle, 94
Rigid motion, 595, 602
Rotation, 606–608
Ruler Placement Postulate, 34
Ruler Postulate, 33

SAA correspondence, 221
SAA Theorem, 222
SAS correspondence, 136
SAS Postulate, 137
SAS Similarity Theorem, 386
Scalar, 613
Scalene triangle, 155
Secant, of a circle, 450
of sphere, 450
ratio, 570
segment, 482
Second Minimum Theorem, 255
Sector(s), 551
arc of, 551
area of, 551
radius of, 551
Segment(s), 2, 39
of circle, 552
perpendicular bisector of, 188
Semicircle(s), 468
end points of, 468
Set(s), 15–18
auxiliary, 194–195
convex, 62
Side(s), of angle, 77
of dihedral angle, 314
included, of triangle, 132
of polygon, 535

of quadrilateral, 167
of triangle, 79
Similar, right triangles, 391–392
triangles, 138, 361–362, 368–369
triangles, areas of, 394–395
Similarity(ies), 361–362, 368–369
Sine function, Addition Formula for, 589
Sine ratio, 557
Skew, lines, 261
quadrilateral, 318
Slope, of line, 417
of segment, 413–416
Slope-intercept form, 443
Space, 49
Space Separation Postulate, 65
Sphere(s), 449
chord of, 450
concentric, 449
exterior of, 462
great circle of, 451
interior of, 462
radius of, 449
secant of, 450
surface area of, 651
tangent plane, 463
volume of, 649–651
Spherical shell, 651
Square(s), 168, 288
roots, existence of, 24
roots, positive, 24
Squaring the circle, 529
SSS correspondence, 137, 202
SSS Postulate, 137
SSS Similarity Theorem, 387
Subset(s), 15
Supplement Postulate, 87
Supplement Theorem, 102
Supplementary angles, 87
Surface area of sphere, 651
Symmetric Property, 98
Symmetry, 595–598
axis of, 597
center of, 598

Tangent, circles, 455
plane, 463
ratio, 558
segment, 481
to circle, 454
Tangent-Secant Power Theorem, 483

# SOLUTION SECTION

## Chapter 3  Lines, Planes, and Separation

### Problem Set 3-3

**19.** The planes $E$ and $F$ are identical. $L_1$ lies in $E$. Since the points $P$ and $R$ which are on $L_2$ both lie in $E$, $L_2$ lies in $E$ by Postulate 6. Similarly the two intersecting lines $L_1$ and $L_2$ are contained in plane $F$. But by Theorem 3-4, given two intersecting lines, there is exactly one plane containing them. Therefore $E$ and $F$ are identical.

## Chapter 4  Angles and Triangles

### Problem Set 4-1

**31.** To show that $G$ is in the interior of $\triangle ABC$ it will be sufficient to show that $G$ is in the interior of each of the angles of $\triangle ABC$.

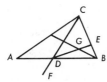

Part I: Proof that $G$ is in the interior of $\angle B$.

(a) Since $B$ is on $\overleftrightarrow{BC}$ and $D$ is on $\overrightarrow{BA}$, $D$ is on the same side of $\overleftrightarrow{BC}$ as $A$. Since $E$ is on $\overleftrightarrow{BC}$ and $G$ is on $\overrightarrow{ED}$, $G$ is on the same side of $\overleftrightarrow{BC}$ as $D$. Consequently, $G$ is on the same side of $\overleftrightarrow{BC}$ as $A$.

(b) It can be shown, in the same way, that $G$ is on the same side of $\overleftrightarrow{AB}$ as $E$.

(c) Hence, $G$ is, by definition, in the interior of $\angle B$.

Part II: Proof that $G$ is in the interior of $\angle A$.

(a) It can be shown as in part I(a) that $G$ is on the same side of $\overleftrightarrow{AB}$ as $C$.

(b) Since $A$ is on $\overleftrightarrow{AC}$ and $D$ is on $\overleftrightarrow{AB}$, $D$ is on the same side of $\overleftrightarrow{AC}$ as $B$. Similarly $E$ is on the same side of $\overleftrightarrow{AC}$ as $B$. Consequently $D$ and $E$ are on the same side of $\overleftrightarrow{AC}$. By the Plane Separation Postulate, the entire segment $\overline{DE}$ lies in the same side of $\overleftrightarrow{AC}$ as $B$. Since $G$ is on $\overline{DE}$, $G$ is on the same side of $\overleftrightarrow{AC}$ as $B$.

(c) Hence, $G$ is, by definition, in the interior of $\angle A$.

Part III: It can be shown, just as in Part II, that $G$ is in the interior of $\angle C$.

## Chapter 5  Congruence

### Problem Set 5-4

**14.**

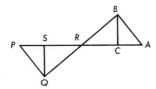

| Statements | Reasons |
|---|---|
| 1. $\overline{QS} \perp \overline{PA}$, $\overline{BC} \perp \overline{PA}$. | 1. Given |
| 2. $\angle QSR$ and $\angle BCR$ are right angles. | 2. Definition of perpendicular |
| 3. $\angle QSR \cong \angle BCR$. | 3. Theorem 4-4 |
| 4. $RS = RC$. | 4. Given |
| 5. $\angle QRS \cong \angle BRC$. | 5. Theorem 4-8 |
| 6. $\triangle QRS \cong \triangle BRC$. | 6. ASA Postulate. Steps 3, 4, 5 |
| 7. $QR = RB$. | 7. Definition of congruent triangles |
| 8. $\overline{PA}$ bisects $\overline{BQ}$. | 8. Definition of bisects |
| 9. $\overline{QS} \cong \overline{BC}$. | 9. Definition of congruent triangles. Step 6 |
| 10. $\angle QSP \cong \angle BCA$. | 10. Steps similar to 1, 2, 3 |
| 11. $\overline{BQ}$ bisects $\overline{PA}$ at $R$. | 11. Given |
| 12. $PR = RA$. | 12. Definition of bisects |
| 13. $RS = RC$. | 13. Given |
| 14. $PS = AC$. | 14. Subtraction. Steps 12, 13 |

**15.**

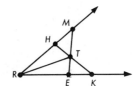

| Statements | Reasons |
|---|---|
| 1. $RH = RE$. | 1. Given |
| 2. $\angle HRT \cong \angle ERT$. | 2. Given |
| 3. $RT = RT$. | 3. Reflexive Property |
| 4. $\triangle HRT \cong \triangle ERT$. | 4. SAS Postulate |
| 5. $\angle RHT \cong \angle RET$. | 5. Definition of congruent triangles |
| 6. $\angle HRK \cong \angle ERM$. | 6. Identity |
| 7. $\triangle HRK \cong \triangle ERM$. | 7. ASA Postulate. Steps 1, 5, 6 |
| 8. $RM = RK$. | 8. Definition of congruent triangles |
| 9. $HM = EK$. | 9. Subtraction. Steps 1 and 8 |
| 10. $\angle RHT$ and $\angle THM$ are supplementary. $\angle RET$ and $\angle TEK$ are supplementary. | 10. If two angles form a linear pair, they are supplementary. |

**15. (continued)**

| Statements | Reasons |
|---|---|
| 11. $\angle THM \cong \angle TEK$. | 11. Supplements of congruent angles are congruent. Steps 5 and 10 |
| 12. $\overline{HT} \cong \overline{EK}$. | 12. Definition of congruent triangles. Step 5 |
| 13. $\triangle MTH \cong \triangle KTE$. | 13. SAS Postulate. Steps 9, 11, 12 |

## Problem Set 5–6

**9.**

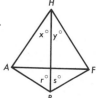

| Statements | Reasons |
|---|---|
| 1. $AB = AC$, $PB = PC$. | 1. Given |
| 2. $\overline{AB} \cong \overline{AC}$, $\overline{PB} \cong \overline{PC}$. | 2. Definition of congruent segments |
| 3. $\overrightarrow{AD}$ bisects $\angle BAC$. | 3. Given |
| 4. $\angle BAD \cong \angle CAD$. | 4. Definition of angle bisector |
| 5. $\overline{AD} \cong \overline{AD}$. | 5. Reflexive property of congruence |
| 6. $\triangle ABD \cong \triangle ACD$. | 6. SAS |
| 7. $\overline{BD} \cong \overline{CD}$. | 7. CPCTC |
| 8. $\overline{PD} \cong \overline{PD}$. | 8. Relexive property of congruence |
| 9. $\triangle DPB \cong \triangle DPC$. | 9. SSS |
| 10. $\angle BPD \cong \angle CPD$. | 10. CPCTC |
| 11. $\overrightarrow{PD}$ bisects $\angle BPC$. | 11. Definition of angle bisector |

## Problem Set 5–7

**15.** Since $\triangle ABD$ is equiangular, it is also equilateral by Corollary 5–5.1. Therefore $AB = AD = DB$. But since $\triangle ABC$ is equilateral, $AB = AC = BC$. This means that $AB = AB$, $AC = AD$, and $CB = DB$. Therefore the correspondence $\triangle ABC \leftrightarrow \triangle ABD$ is a congruence by the SSS Postulate, and so $\angle C \cong \angle D$ by the definition of congruent triangles.

**17.** (1) $\angle PMN \cong \angle PNM$, $PM = PN$ by Theorem 5–5.
(2) $\angle MPQ \cong \angle NPQ$.
(3) $PQ = PQ$. Therefore, $\triangle PMQ \cong \triangle PNQ$ by SAS, and so $\angle PMQ \cong \angle PNQ$.

# Chapter 6   A Closer Look at Proof

## Problem Set 6–4

**15.**

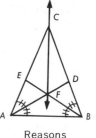

| Statements | Reasons |
|---|---|
| 1. $AC = BC$. | 1. Given |
| 2. $m\angle A = m\angle B$. | 2. Isosceles Triangle Theorem |
| 3. $\frac{1}{2}m\angle A = \frac{1}{2}m\angle B$. | 3. Multiplying in Step 2 |
| 4. $\angle DAB \cong \angle EBA$. | 4. Step 3 and definition of angle bisector |
| 5. $AF = BF$. | 5. If two angles of a triangle are congruent, the sides opposite them are congruent. |
| 6. $\overleftrightarrow{CF}$ is the perpendicular bisector of $\overline{AB}$. | 6. Corollary 6–2.1 |

**16.** Given: $\overrightarrow{HB}$ bisects $\angle AHF$ and $\angle ABF$.
Prove: $\overrightarrow{HB}$ bisects $\overline{AF}$.

| Statements | Reasons |
|---|---|
| 1. $x = y$, $r = s$. | 1. Definition of bisect |
| 2. $HB = HB$. | 2. Reflexive Property |
| 3. $\triangle ABH \cong \triangle FBH$. | 3. ASA |
| 4. $HA = HF$, $BA = BF$. | 4. Corresponding parts |
| 5. $\overrightarrow{HB}$ bisects $\overline{AF}$. | 5. Corollary 6–2.1 |

**17.**

| Statements | Reasons |
|---|---|
| 1. $PB = QB$; $\angle PBC \cong \angle QBC$. | 1. Given |
| 2. $BC = BC$. | 2. Reflexive Property |
| 3. $\triangle PBC \cong \triangle QBC$. | 3. SAS |
| 4. $PC = QC$. | 4. Corresponding parts |
| 5. $A$ is the midpoint of $\overline{PQ}$. | 5. Given |
| 6. $PA = AQ$. | 6. Definition of midpoint |
| 7. $\overline{PQ} \perp \overline{AC}$. | 7. Corollary 6–2.1 |

**6.**

| Statements | Reasons |
| --- | --- |
| 1. $AE = BC$, $DE = DC$ | 1. Given |
| 2. Introduce $F$, the midpoint of $AB$. | 2. Theorem 2–5 |
| 3. Introduce $\overline{DF}$. | 3. Two points determine a line. |
| 4. $\overline{DF}$ is the perpendicular bisector of $\overline{AB}$. | 4. Given and Theorems 6–1, 6–2 |
| 5. $DA = DB$. | 5. Theorem 6–2 |
| 6. $\triangle DAE \cong \triangle DBC$. | 6. SSS |
| 7. $\angle DAE \cong \angle DBC$. | 7. Corresponding parts |
| 8. $\angle DAB \cong \angle DBA$. | 8. Theorem 5–4 |
| 9. $\angle EAB \cong \angle CBA$. | 9. AAP |
| 10. $AB = AB$. | 10. Identity |
| 11. $\triangle EAB \cong \triangle CBA$. | 11. SAS |
| 12. $AC = BE$. | 12. Corresponding parts |

**11.**

| Statements | Reasons |
| --- | --- |
| 1. Introduce $\overline{RT}$. | 1. Two points determine a line. |
| 2. $QR = QT$. | 2. Given |
| 3. $m\angle QRT = m\angle QTR$. | 3. Base angles of an isosceles triangle are congruent. |
| 4. $m\angle R = m\angle T$. | 4. Given |
| 5. $m\angle R = m\angle QRT + m\angle TRS$ $m\angle T = m\angle QTR + m\angle RTS$. | 5. Angle Addition Postulate |
| 6. $m\angle QRT + m\angle TRS = m\angle QTR + m\angle RTS$. | 6. Steps 4, 5. Transitive and Symmetric Property of Equality |
| 7. $m\angle TRS = m\angle RTS$. | 7. Steps 3 and 6. Subtraction Property of Equality |
| 8. $SR = ST$. | 8. If two angles of a triangle are congruent, the sides opposite those angles are congruent. |

Step 5, and consequently the entire proof, depends on the fact that $Q$, $R$, $S$, and $T$ are coplanar.

**12.**

| Statements | Reasons |
| --- | --- |
| 1. Introduce $\overline{BQ}$. | 1. Two points determine a line. |
| 2. $BQ = BQ$. | 2. Identity |
| 3. $AB = PQ$ and $BP = AQ$. | 3. Given |

| | |
| --- | --- |
| 4. $\triangle BAQ \cong \triangle QPB$. | 4. SSS |
| 5. $\angle A \cong \angle P$. | 5. Corresponding parts |
| 6. $m\angle ABQ = m\angle PQB$. | 6. Corresponding parts |
| 7. $m\angle PBQ = m\angle AQB$. | 7. Corresponding parts. Step 4 |
| 8. $m\angle ABP = m\angle PQA$. | 8. The Angle Addition Postulate. Subtraction Property of Equality Steps 6 and 7 |
| 9. $\triangle ABM \cong \triangle PQM$. | 9. ASA. Steps 3, 5 and 8 |

**15.**

| Statements | Reasons |
| --- | --- |
| 1. Introduce $\overline{ES}$. | 1. Two points determine a line. |
| 2. $ES = ES$. | 2. Identity |
| 3. $EA = EY$; $SA = SY$. | 3. Given |
| 4. $\triangle EAS \cong \triangle EYS$. | 4. SSS |
| 5. $\angle EAS \cong \angle EYS$. | 5. Corresponding parts |

[Note that it is not possible to prove that $\angle EAS \cong \angle EYS$ by first showing that $m\angle EAY = m\angle EYA$ and $m\angle SAY = m\angle SYA$ and then applying the AAP. The AAP is *only* applicable if the $E$, $A$, $S$, and $Y$ are coplanar.]

**17.**

| Statements | Reasons |
| --- | --- |
| 1. Introduce $\overline{CF}$. | 1. Two points determine a line. |
| 2. $AF = EF$, $AC = EC$. | 2. Given |
| 3. $CF = CF$. | 3. Identity |
| 4. $\triangle ACF \cong \triangle ECF$. | 4. SSS |
| 5. $\angle A \cong \angle E$. | 5. Corresponding parts |
| 6. $\triangle AFB \cong \triangle EFD$. | 6. ASA |
| 7. $BF = DF$. | 7. Corresponding parts |
| 8. $\triangle BDF$ is isosceles. | 8. Definition of isosceles triangle |

**18.**

| Statements | Reasons |
| --- | --- |
| 1. Introduce $\overline{CF}$. | 1. Two points determine a line. |
| 2. $CF = CF$. | 2. Identity |
| 3. $AF = EF$, $AC = EC$. | 3. Given |
| 4. $\triangle ACF \cong \triangle ECF$. | 4. SSS |
| 5. $\angle A \cong \angle E$. | 5. Corresponding parts |
| 6. $m\angle EFD + m\angle DFB = m\angle EFB$. $m\angle AFB + m\angle DFB = m\angle AFD$. | 6. AAP |
| 7. $m\angle EFB = m\angle AFD$. | 7. Given and definition of congruent angles |

**18.** (continued)

| | |
|---|---|
| 8. $m\angle EFD = m\angle AFB$. | 8. Subtraction Postulate and Transitive Property of Equality |
| 9. $\angle EFD \cong \angle AFB$. | 9. Definition of congruent angles |
| 10. $\triangle AFB \cong \triangle EFD$. | 10. ASA |
| 11. $BF = DF$. | 11. Corresponding parts |
| 12. $\overline{CF} \perp \overline{BD}$. | 12. Theorem 6–2 |

**19.**

Proof I.

| Statements | Reasons |
|---|---|
| 1. $AB = AC$, $BD = CD$. | 1. Given |
| 2. $m\angle ABC = m\angle ACB$. $m\angle DBC = m\angle DCB$. | 2. Base angles of an isosceles triangle are congruent. |
| 3. $m\angle ABC$ $= m\angle ABD + m\angle DBC$. $m\angle ACB$ $= m\angle ACD + m\angle DCB$. | 3. Angle Addition Postulate |
| 4. $m\angle ABD + m\angle DBC$ $= m\angle ACD + m\angle DCB$. | 4. Substitution |
| 5. $m\angle ABD = m\angle ACD$. | 5. Subtraction Property of Equality |

This proof requires that $A$, $B$, $C$, and $D$ be coplanar. (Step 3)

Proof II.

| Statements | Reasons |
|---|---|
| 1. Introduce $\overline{AD}$. | 1. Two points determine a line. |
| 2. $AD = AD$. | 2. Identity |
| 3. $AB = AC$. $BD = CD$. | 3. Given |
| 4. $\triangle ABD \cong \triangle ACD$. | 4. SSS |
| 5. $\angle ABD \cong \angle ACD$. | 5. Definition of congruent triangles |

This proof does not require that $A$, $B$, $C$, and $D$ be coplanar.

**Problem Set 6–6**

**5.** Let $H_1$ and $H_2$ be the half-planes with edge $L$, $H_1$ being the half-plane which contains $C$. There are three ways in which $B$ could be located relative to line $L$: (1) $B$ is on $L$. (2) $B$ is in $H_1$. (3) $B$ is in $H_2$.

Case I. If $B$ is on $L$, $L$ intersects both sides $\overline{AB}$ and $\overleftrightarrow{CD}$.

Case II. $B$ is in $H_1$. Since $B$ and $C$ are on the same side of $L$, and $A$ and $C$ are on opposite sides of $L$, $A$ and $B$ are on opposite sides of $L$. Then, by the Plane Separation Postulate, $L$ intersects $\overline{AB}$.

Case III. $B$ is in $H_2$. In this case $B$ and $C$ are on opposite sides of $L$, since $C$ is in $H_1$, and $L$ intersects $\overline{BC}$.

**680**

**8.**

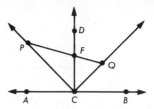

Suppose that $\overline{PQ} \perp \overleftrightarrow{CD}$ and that the point of intersection is $F$. Then $\angle CFP \cong \angle CFQ$, since they are right angles. $\angle ACD \cong \angle BCD$ by definition of perpendicular, and $\angle ACP \cong \angle BCQ$ (given). By the AAP and the subtraction property, $\angle PCD \cong \angle QCD$. Since $FC = FC$, by the Reflexive Property, $\triangle PFC \cong \triangle QFC$ by ASA; and $PC = QC$ by corresponding parts. But this contradicts the fact that $PC \neq QC$. Therefore $\overleftrightarrow{CD}$ is not perpendicular to $\overrightarrow{PQ}$.

**Honors Problem**

The argument (using the first drawing) depends on the assumption from the drawing that $E$ is inside $\angle XBC'$. In a careful drawing (see top of next column) $X$ and $E$ will be on opposite sides of $\overleftrightarrow{BC'}$.

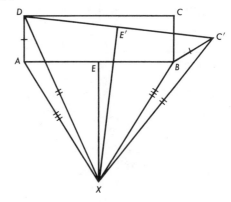

**Chapter Review**

**12.**

| Statements | Reasons |
|---|---|
| 1. Introduce $\overline{MP}$ and $\overline{MQ}$. | 1. Two points determine a line. |
| 2. $MP = MQ$. | 2. Theorem 6–2 |
| 3. $SM = MR$, $PN = NQ$. | 3. Definition of bisector |
| 4. $\angle SMN \cong \angle RMN$. $\angle MNP \cong \angle MNQ$. | 4. Definition of perpendicular and of right angle |
| 5. $MN = NM$. | 5. Identity |
| 6. $\triangle PMN \cong \triangle QMN$. | 6. SAS |
| 7. $\angle QMN \cong \angle PMN$. | 7. Corresponding parts |
| 8. $\angle SMP \cong \angle RMQ$. | 8. AAP and Subtraction Property |
| 9. $\triangle SPM \cong \triangle RQM$. | 9. SAS |
| 10. $PS = QR$. | 10. Corresponding parts |

**14.**

| Statements | Reasons |
|---|---|
| 1. Introduce $\overline{AM}$ and $\overline{CK}$. | 1. Two points determine a line. |
| 2. $AT = SC$, $SK = TM$, $\angle T \cong \angle S$. | 2. Given |
| 3. $\triangle ATM \cong \triangle CSK$. | 3. SAS |
| 4. $\angle AMT \cong \angle SKC$, $AM = CK$. | 4. Corresponding parts |
| 5. $\angle M \cong \angle K$. | 5. Given |
| 6. $\angle AMK \cong \angle CKM$. | 6. AAP, Subtraction, and Transitivity |
| 7. $MB = KB$. | 7. Theorem 5-5 (converse isosceles) |
| 8. $AM + AB = MB$. $CK + CB = KB$. | 8. $A$ is between $M$ and $B$. $C$ is between $K$ and $B$. |
| 9. $AB = BC$. | 9. Transitivity and Subtraction |

**15.** $\overline{AB}$ and $\overline{CD}$ must be placed so that the problem will be meaningful. (See the figure below.)

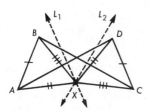

Let $L_1$ and $L_2$ be the perpendicular bisectors of $\overline{AD}$ and $\overline{BC}$ respectively. Then $AX = DX$ and $BX = CX$, by the Perpendicular Bisector Theorem. $AB = CD$ by hypothesis. Therefore $\triangle ABX \cong \triangle DCX$, by SSS.

## Chapter 7 Geometric Inequalities

### Problem Set 7-2

**15.**
1. $0 < x < y$. (Given)
2. $a < 0$. (Given)
3. $a + (-a) < 0 + (-a)$. (Step 2 and Addition Property)
4. $-a > 0$. (Step 3)
5. $(-a)x < (-a)y$. (Steps 1 and 4, and Multiplication Property)
6. $-ax < -ay$. (Step 5)
7. $-ax + ax + ay < -ay + ax + ay$. (Step 6 and Addition Property)
8. $ay < ax$. (Step 7)
9. $ax > ay$. (Step 8)
   Note that in this proof the hypothesis that $0 < x$ was not used. Next we shall show that $1/y < 1/x$.
10. $xy > 0$. (Multiplication Property)
    Now we know by the Trichotomy Property that

(a) $1/y < 1/x$, or (b) $1/y = 1/x$, or (c) $1/y > 1/x$.
If (b) holds, then $(1/y)(xy) = (1/x)(xy)$, and $x = y$, which is false, by Step 1.
If (c) holds, then $(1/y)(xy) > (1/x)(xy)$, by the Multiplication Property. Therefore $x > y$, which is false, by Step 1.
The only remaining possibility is (a), which was to be proved.

### Problem Set 7-4

**9.** Analysis: (I) First prove $\triangle ADT \cong \triangle BCR$ by SAA and then (II) prove $\triangle ADF \cong \triangle BCE$ by ASA.

| Statements | Reasons |
|---|---|
| 1. $\triangle APR \cong \triangle BQT$. | 1. Given |
| 2. $AR = TB$. | 2. Corresponding parts |
| 3. $RT = RT$. | 3. Reflexive Property |
| 4. $AT = RB$. | 4. Steps 2, 3. Addition Property of Equality. Definition of between |
| 5. $\angle ARP \cong \angle BTQ$. | 5. Corresponding parts. Step 1 |
| 6. $\angle GRT \cong \angle GTR$. | 6. Step 5. Vertical Angles. Substitution |
| 7. $\angle D \cong \angle C$. | 7. Given |
| 8. $\triangle ADT \cong \triangle BCR$. | 8. SAA. Steps 4, 6, and 7 |
| 9. $AD = BC$. | 9. Corresponding parts |
| 10. $m\angle DAT = m\angle CBR$. | 10. Corresponding parts. Step 8 |
| 11. $m\angle RAP = m\angle TBQ$. | 11. Corresponding parts. Step 1 |
| 12. $m\angle DAF = m\angle CBE$. | 12. Steps 10, 11. AAP and APE |
| 13. $\triangle ADF \cong \triangle BCE$. | 13. ASA. Steps 7, 9, and 12 |

**10.** (I) First prove $\triangle PAQ \cong \triangle PBQ$, as follows: Since $\angle PAB \cong \angle PBA$, $\overline{PA} \cong \overline{PB}$. $\overline{PQ} \cong \overline{PQ}$, and $\angle PQA \cong \angle PQB$ (Definition of perpendicular, right angle, congruent angles). Therefore $\triangle PAQ \cong \triangle PBQ$ (The Hypotenuse Leg Theorem), and consequently $m\angle PAQ = m\angle PBQ$. (II) $\triangle AQR \cong \triangle BQR$ (SAS), and therefore $m\angle QAR = m\angle QBR$. (III) Hence $m\angle PAQ + m\angle QAR = m\angle PBQ + m\angle QBR$, or, by the AAP, $m\angle PAR = m\angle PBR$.

### Problem Set 7-6

**12.** (a) If the points are noncollinear, the inequality follows from Theorem 7-8.
(b) If the points are collinear, then either (1) $B$ is on the segment $\overline{AC}$, in which case $AB + BC = AC$, or (2) $A$ is between $B$ and $C$, in which case $BC > AC$, so that $AB + BC > AC$, or (3) $C$ is between $A$ and $B$, in which case $AB > AC$, so that $AB + BC > AC$.

**13.** For each $n \geq 3$, let $P_n$ be the proposition that

$$A_1A_2 + A_2A_3 + \cdots + A_{n-1}A_n \geq A_1A_n.$$

Then $P_3$ says that $A_1A_2 + A_2A_3 \geq A_1A_3$, which is true, by the result of the preceding problem. Given that $P_3$ is true, it follows that $P_4$ is also true, because

$$\begin{aligned}
A_1A_2 + A_2A_3 + A_3A_4 &= (A_1A_2 + A_2A_3) + A_3A_4 \\
&\geq A_1A_3 + A_3A_4 \qquad \text{(By } P_3) \\
&\geq A_1A_4. \qquad \text{(By } P_3)
\end{aligned}$$

We shall show that given that $P_n$ is true, it follows that $P_{n+1}$ is true. Proof:

$$\begin{aligned}
A_1A_2 &+ A_2A_3 + \cdots + A_{n-1}A_n + A_nA_{n+1} \\
&= (A_1A_2 + A_2A_3 + \cdots + A_{n-1}A_n) + A_nA_{n+1} \\
&\geq A_1A_n + A_nA_{n+1} \qquad \text{(By } P_n) \\
&\geq A_1A_{n+1}. \qquad \text{(By } P_3).
\end{aligned}$$

Thus, in the sequence $P_3$, $P_4$, ... of statements, we start with the true statement $P_3$, and each statement in the sequence implies the next. It follows that *all* the statements in the sequence are true, which was to be proved.

**Problem Set 7–8**

**12.** Given: $\triangle ABC$ with altitude, angle bisector, and median $C$ intersecting $\overline{AB}$ at $D$, $E$, and $M$, respectively, such that $D$-$E$-$M$.
Prove: $\overline{CD} < \overline{CE} < \overline{CM}$.

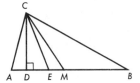

Proof: (1) $\overline{CD}$ is the altitude to $\overline{AB}$ and by Theorem 7–7, $CD$ is the minimum distance to $\overline{AB}$. Therefore $\overline{CD} < \overline{CE}$.

(2) Since $\angle CDE$ is a right triangle, it follows that $\angle CED$ and $\angle CMD$ are both acute. Since $\angle CED$ and $\angle CEM$ form a linear pair, $\angle CEM$ is obtuse, and $\angle CMD < \angle CEM$. Since $D$-$E$-$M$, $\angle CMD = \angle CME$, and $\angle CME < \angle CEM$. By Theorem 7–6, applied to $\triangle CEM$, it follows that $\overline{CE} < \overline{CM}$.

**13.** Suppose $A$-$B$-$G$ and $D$-$E$-$H$. $\triangle BCG \cong \triangle EFH$ by HL, and consequently $\angle CBG \cong \angle FEH$. Because supplements of congruent angles are congruent, $\angle ABC \cong \angle DEF$. Therefore, $\triangle ABC \cong \triangle DEF$ by SAS.

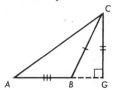 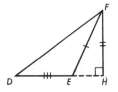

The proof for the case in which $G$-$A$-$B$ and $H$-$D$-$E$ is similar.

**Honors Problem**

The proof is indirect. Suppose that $P$ and $Q$ are on the same side of $\overleftrightarrow{AC}$, as in the figure. Then $m\angle 1 < 90$, by the Exterior Angle Theorem applied to $\triangle ABP$, and $m\angle 2 < 90$ by the Exterior Angle Theorem applied to $\triangle CBQ$. But this contradicts the Supplement Postulate, which asserts that $m\angle 1 + m\angle 2 = 180$. Therefore, $P$ and $Q$ are not on the same side of $\overleftrightarrow{AC}$.

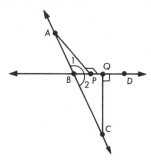

## Chapter 8  Perpendicular Lines and Planes in Space

**Problem Set 8–3**

**16.** The two portions of the statement are:
(1) *If:* If four points, each equidistant from two fixed points, are collinear, then they are coplanar with the two fixed points.
(2) *Only if:* If four points, each equidistant from two fixed points, are coplanar with the two fixed points, then the four points are collinear.

**18.** *Theorem.* Through a given point of a given plane there passes a line perpendicular to the given plane.

Proof. Let $E$ be the given plane, and let $P$ be the given point. Let $L_1$ and $L_2$ be two lines in $E$ through $P$. By Theorem 8–3 there is a plane $E_1$ which is perpendicular to $L_1$ at $P$, and there is a plane $E_2$ which is perpendicular to $L_2$ at $P$. Since $E_1$ and $E_2$ intersect at $P$, their intersection is a line $L$. $L \perp L_1$, because $L$ lies in $E_1$, and $L \perp L_2$, because $L$ lies in $E_2$. By Theorem 8–2 it follows that $L \perp E$.

## Chapter 13  Plane Coordinate Geometry

**Problem Set 13–10**

**Honors Problem**

Given $\triangle ABC$ with vertices $A(a, a')$, $B(b, b')$, and $C(c, c')$ such that $0 < a < c < b$ and $0 < a' < b' < c'$. Let the projections of $A$, $B$, and $C$ on the x-axis be $M$, $N$, and $P$ respectively, and note that their coordinates obviously are: $M(a, 0)$, $N(b, 0)$, $P(c, 0)$.

Since the given information implies that the points are located as in the figure, we can conclude by the Area Addition Postulate that $a\triangle ABC = a\square AMPC + a\square BNPC - a\square AMNB$.

Since the quadrilaterals are trapezoids their areas can be easily computed.

$$\begin{aligned}
a\square AMPC &= \tfrac{1}{2}(c - a)(a' + c'), \\
a\square BNPC &= \tfrac{1}{2}(b - c)(b' + c'), \\
a\square AMNB &= \tfrac{1}{2}(b - a)(a' + b').
\end{aligned}$$

Upon simplification we obtain

$$a\triangle ABC = \tfrac{1}{2}[a(b' - c') + b(c' - a') + c(a' - b')].$$

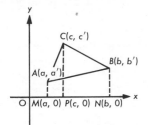

Figure 1

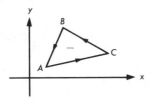

Figure 2

If $A$ and $B$ are interchanged, we should interchange $a$ and $b$ (and $a'$ and $b'$) in the formula. This gives

$$\tfrac{1}{2}[b(a' - c') + a(c' - b') + c(b' - a')]$$
$$= -\tfrac{1}{2}[a(b' - c') + b(c' - a') + c(a' - b')]$$

Similarly, the sign changes when we interchange $A$ and $C$ (or $B$ and $C$).

Thus the original formula is not really a formula for area, but rather a formula for *signed* area. It gives the area only if the vertices are named in the counterclockwise order (Figure 3):

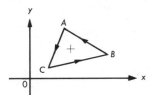

Figure 3

Figure 4

If the clockwise order is used, the formula gives the negative of the area (Figure 4).

Note 1. Observe that the given inequalities are used in deriving the formula, but also observe that they guarantee that the vertices are named in counterclockwise order.

Note 2. Observe that the area formula given can be written as a determinant:

$$a\triangle ABC = \begin{vmatrix} a & a' & 1 \\ b & b' & 1 \\ c & c' & 1 \end{vmatrix}.$$

Interchanging two vertices, such as $A$ and $B$, effects an interchange of two rows of the determinant; and recall that such a transformation changes the sign of the determinant.

## Chapter 15   Characterizations and Constructions

### Problem Set 15–1

9.

10.

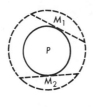

11.

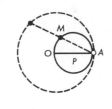

13.

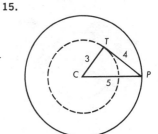

14.

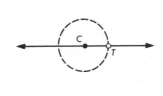

15.

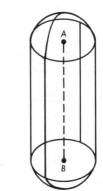

17.

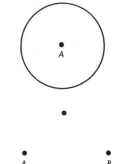

18.

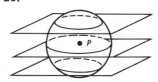

19.

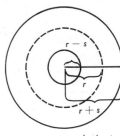

20.

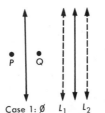

22.

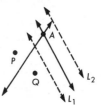

23.

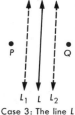

Case 1: $\emptyset$    $L_1$    $L_2$    Case 2: The point $A$    Case 3: The line $L$

**24.**

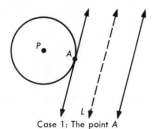

Case 1: The point A

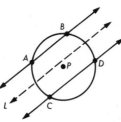

Case 2: The points A and B

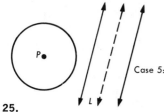

Case 3: The points A, B, and C

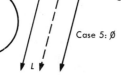

Case 4: The points A, B, C, and D

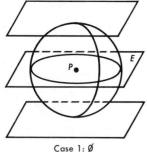

Case 5: Ø

**25.**

Points A and B are the desired set.

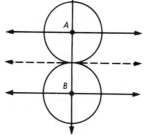

**26.**

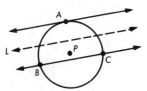

Case 1: Ø

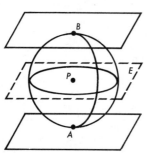

Case 2: The points A and B

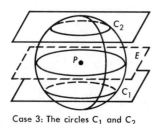

Case 3: The circles $C_1$ and $C_2$

**Problem Set 15–4**

**Honors Problem**

Take a coordinate system in which Queen's Road is the *x*-axis and King's Road is the *y*-axis.

The coordinates of the elm, spruce, and pine are as indicated. The maple is gone, but its assumed position is labeled $(0, m)$. The slope of $\overleftrightarrow{EP}$ is $\frac{3}{4}$, so its equation (in slope-intercept form) is

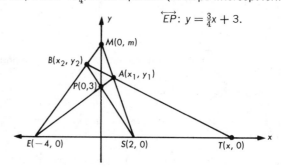

$$\overleftrightarrow{EP}: y = \tfrac{3}{4}x + 3.$$

The slope of $\overleftrightarrow{SM}$ is $-m/2$, so its equation (in point-slope form) is

$$\overleftrightarrow{SM}: y = -\frac{m}{2}(x - 2).$$

Solving these two equations simultaneously, we find the coordinates of $A$:

$$A: \begin{cases} x_1 = \dfrac{4(m - 3)}{2m + 3}, \\[2mm] y_1 = \dfrac{9m}{2m + 3}. \end{cases}$$

Similarly, we get the equations

$$\overleftrightarrow{SP}: y = -\tfrac{3}{2}x + 3,$$

$$\overleftrightarrow{EM}: y = \frac{m}{4}(x + 4),$$

and the point of intersection is

$$B: \begin{cases} x_2 = -\dfrac{4(m - 3)}{m + 6}, \\[2mm] y_2 = \dfrac{9m}{m + 6}. \end{cases}$$

The line $\overleftrightarrow{AB}$ has the equation,

$$\overleftrightarrow{AB}: y - y_1 = \left(\frac{y_2 - y_1}{x_2 - x_1}\right)(x - x_1).$$

The intersection $T$ of $\overleftrightarrow{AB}$ and the *x*-axis is found by letting $y = 0$ and solving for $x$:

$$x = x_1 - y_1\left(\frac{x_2 - x_1}{y_2 - y_1}\right), \quad x = \frac{x_1 y_2 - x_2 y_1}{y_2 - y_1}.$$

Now

$$x_1y_2 - x_2y_1 = \frac{4(m-3)}{2m+3} \cdot \frac{9m}{m+6} + \frac{4(m-3)}{m+6} \cdot \frac{9m}{2m+3}$$

$$= \frac{72m(m-3)}{(m+6)(2m+3)},$$

$$y_2 - y_1 = \frac{9m}{m+6} - \frac{9m}{2m+3} = \frac{9m(m-3)}{(m+6)(2m+3)}.$$

Dividing, we get $x = 8$. Therefore the treasure was buried 8 miles east of the crossing.

Suppose now that the pine were also missing. Assume coordinates $(0, p)$, for $P$ and carry through the calculation in terms of both $m$ and $p$. The algebra is a little more complicated, but if it is done correctly both $m$ and $p$ drop out in the final result, which is again $x = 8$.

### Problem Set 15-8

**3.** Construct an angle $\angle RAS$ of the given measure. On $\overrightarrow{AR}$ locate a point $B$ such that $AB = s$, the length of the shorter side. Through $B$ construct a line parallel to $\overrightarrow{AS}$. Construct an arc of the circle with center at $A$ and radius equal to $d$, the length of the given diagonal and let $C$ be the point of intersection of this arc with the line through $B$. Through $C$ construct a line parallel to $\overline{AB}$ and let $D$ be the point of intersection of this line with $\overrightarrow{AS}$. $\square ABCD$ is the required parallelogram.

**5.** Given: A segment of length $b$, the length of the base.
A segment of length $a$, the length of the altitude.

(1) Mark off a segment $\overline{AC}$ of length $b$ on a line.
(2) Construct the perpendicular bisector of this segment.
(3) Using the foot $M$ of the perpendicular as one end point mark off a segment $\overline{MB}$ of length $a$ along the perpendicular bisector.

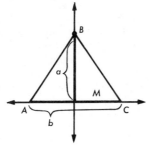

Then $\triangle ABC$ is the required triangle. It obviously has the given dimensions, and it is isosceles, since any point on the perpendicular bisector of a segment is equidistant from the end points of the segment.

**6.** Given: A segment of length $h$, the altitude of the equilateral triangle.

(1) At any point $F$ on a line $L$, construct a ray $\overrightarrow{FG}$ perpendicular to $L$.
(2) Locate a point $P$ on $\overrightarrow{FG}$ such that $FP = h$.
(3) On either side of $\overrightarrow{PF}$ construct $30°$ angles. Let $A$ and $B$ be the points of intersection of these rays with the line $L$. $\triangle APB$ is equilateral, and has an altitude of the given length $h$.

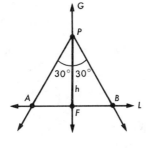

**8.** Given: (1) An acute angle, $\angle B$.
(2) A segment of length $h$, the altitude to the base.

(1) Copy the given angle on a side of ray $\overrightarrow{BX}$.
(2) Construct a line $L$ parallel to the line $\overleftrightarrow{BX}$ and $h$ units from $\overleftrightarrow{BX}$. Let $A$ be the point of intersection of this line $L$ with the other side of $\angle B$.
(3) Using $A$ as a vertex, copy the given angle so that one side of the angle is contained in $L$ and the other side of the angle is on the same side of $L$ as the point $B$. Let $C$ be the intersection of this side of the angle with $\overleftrightarrow{BX}$.

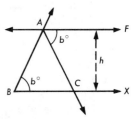

$\triangle ABC$ is the required isosceles triangle. Since $L \parallel \overline{BC}$, $\angle BCA \cong \angle CAF$ and thus $\angle BCA \cong \angle B$; hence $AB = AC$. The altitude from $A$ to $\overline{BC}$ is of length $h$.

**11.** Construct a segment $\overline{RT}$ such that $RT = a + b$, and let $S$ be the point on $\overline{RT}$ such that $RS = a$ and $ST = b$. Using the midpoint, $M$, of $\overline{RT}$ as a center, construct a semicircle having $\overline{RT}$ as a diameter. Construct a ray perpendicular to $\overline{RT}$ at $S$ and let $P$ be the point of intersection of this ray with the semicircle. Then $SP$ is the geometric mean of $a$ and $b$.

**13.** Given: (1) Segments of length $a$, $b$ (with $a > b$) the lengths of two sides.
(2) A segment of length $m_a$, the length of the median to the longer side.

(1) Construct a segment $\overline{BC}$ of length $a$ along a line $L$.
(2) Locate the midpoint $M$ of $\overline{BC}$.
(3) Using $M$ as a center and $m_a$ as a radius swing an arc.
(4) Using $C$ as a center and $b$ as a radius swing an arc. Let $A$ be the point of intersection of these arcs.
(5) Complete the figure by constructing $\overline{AB}$ and $\overline{AC}$.

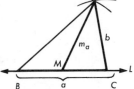

$\triangle ABC$ is obviously the required triangle.

**14.** Given: $\angle A$; A segment of length $b$, the length of a side of the parallelogram; a segment of length $h$, the altitude on that side.

(1) Copy $\angle A$ on a side of a ray $\overrightarrow{AX}$.
(2) Construct a line $L$ parallel to $\overleftrightarrow{AX}$ and $h$ units from $\overleftrightarrow{AX}$. Let $B$ be the point of intersection of $L$ with the side of $\angle A$.
(3) Locate the point $D$ on $\overrightarrow{AX}$ such that $AD = b$.
(4) Locate the point $C$ on $L$ and on the same side of $\overleftrightarrow{AB}$ as $D$ such that $BC = b$. Introduce $\overline{CD}$.

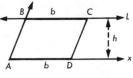

$\square ABCD$ is the required parallelogram by Theorem 9-20.

**15.** Given radii $r_1$ and $r_2$ with $r_1 > r_2$. Construct a segment $\overline{AB}$ such that $AB = r_1$. On $\overline{AB}$ locate the point $C$ such that $BC = r_2$. Using $A$ as center and $r_1$ as radius, construct a circle. Using

C as center and $r_2$ as radius construct a second circle. These two circles are internally tangent at $B$, since they are each tangent to the line perpendicular to $\overline{AB}$ at $B$.

**16.** Given $\angle ABC$ and a segment of length $r$, the radius of the circle. Construct a line $L$ parallel to one of the sides, $\overleftrightarrow{BC}$, of $\angle ABC$, $r$ units from $\overleftrightarrow{BC}$, and on the same side of $\overleftrightarrow{BC}$ as $A$. Construct a line $J$ parallel to $\overleftrightarrow{BA}$, $r$ units from $\overleftrightarrow{BA}$ and on the same side of $\overleftrightarrow{BA}$ as $C$. Let $E$ be the intersection of $L$ and $J$. Let $F$ be the foot of the perpendicular segment from $E$ to $\overleftrightarrow{BA}$, and $G$ be the foot of the perpendicular segment from $E$ to $\overleftrightarrow{BC}$. Construct the circle with center at $E$ and radius $r$. Observe that this circle is tangent to $\overleftrightarrow{BA}$ at $F$ and to $\overleftrightarrow{BC}$ at $G$.

**19.**

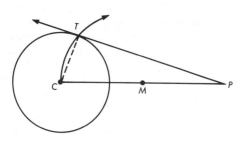

Let $M$ be the midpoint of $\overline{CP}$. With $M$ as a center and $MC$ as a radius, construct an arc and let $T$ be the point of intersection of this arc with the given circle. Since $\angle CTP$ is inscribed in a semicircle, it is a right angle, and $\overrightarrow{PT}$ is perpendicular to the radius $\overline{CT}$ at $T$; $\overleftrightarrow{PT}$, the required tangent, is tangent to the circle.

**20.** Given: Segments of length $b_1, b_2$ (with $b_1 > b_2$) the lengths of the bases of the trapezoid; a segment of length $d$, the length of a diagonal.

Start with $\overline{AB}$ of length $b_1$.

(1) On $\overline{AB}$ locate a point $E$
such that $AE = \dfrac{b_1 - b_2}{2}$.

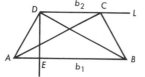

(2) At $E$ construct a perpendicular to $\overleftrightarrow{AB}$.

(3) Using $B$ as a center and $d$ as a radius swing an arc and let $D$ be the point of intersection of this arc and the perpendicular at $E$.

(4) Through $D$ construct a line $L$ parallel to $\overleftrightarrow{AB}$.

(5) Using $A$ as a center and $d$ as a radius swing an arc and let $C$ be the point of intersection of this arc with $L$. Construct $\overline{AD}$ and $\overline{BC}$.

$\square ABCD$ is obviously a trapezoid with one base $AB = b_1$, and diagonals of length $d$. It is easy to prove that $DC = b_2$ and that the trapezoid is isosceles.

**21.** At a point $D$ on a line $L$ construct a line $H$ perpendicular to $L$. On $H$ locate a point $C$ such that $DC = h$. Using $C$ as a center and $b$ as a radius swing an arc and let $A$ be the intersection of this arc with $L$. Then using $C$ as a vertex and $\overrightarrow{CA}$ as one side construct a ray $\overrightarrow{CX}$ on the same side of $\overleftrightarrow{CA}$ as $D$

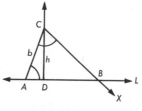

such that $m\angle ACX = m\angle CAD$. Let $B$ be the intersection of $\overrightarrow{CX}$ and $L$. Then $\triangle ABC$ is an isosceles triangle with $b$ as a base and $h$ as the altitude on one of the congruent sides.

**22.** Given: $\angle A$; and a segment of length $k$, the sum of the lengths of the legs.

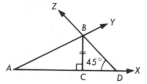

On one side of a ray $\overrightarrow{AX}$ copy the given acute angle and let its other side be $\overrightarrow{AY}$. Locate a point $D$ on $\overrightarrow{AX}$ such that $AD = k$, the sum of the lengths of the legs. On the same side of $\overleftrightarrow{DA}$ as $Y$ construct a ray $\overrightarrow{DZ}$ such that $m\angle ADZ = 45$, and let $B$ be the point of intersection of $\overrightarrow{AY}$ and $\overrightarrow{DZ}$. Through $B$ construct a perpendicular to $\overleftrightarrow{AD}$ and let $C$ be the foot of the perpendicular. Since $\triangle BCD$ is isosceles, $CB = CD$, and so $AC + CB = AC + CD = AD = k$. Therefore $\triangle ACB$ is a right triangle in which the sum of the legs is equal to the given number $k$.

**23.** Analysis: In order to construct the circle we must know its center and radius. The center $Q$ must lie on a ray $\overrightarrow{BH}$ per-

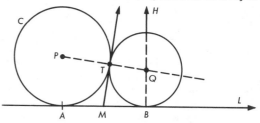

pendicular to $L$ and on the same side of $L$ as $P$. Secondly, let $T$ be the point of tangency, and let $M$ be the point at which the common internal tangent to the circles intersects $L$. Since $\overline{MA}$ and $\overline{MT}$ are tangent segments to the circle $C$, $MA = MT$. Similarly $MT = MB$. Therefore, $AM = MB$, that is $M$ is the midpoint of $\overline{AB}$. Hence, one step in our construction will be to construct a tangent to the circle $C$ from the midpoint of $\overline{AB}$.

(1) Construct a ray $\overrightarrow{BH}$ perpendicular to $L$ at $B$ and on the same side of $L$ as $P$.

(2) Locate the midpoint $M$ of $\overline{AB}$ and from $M$ construct a ray tangent to $C$. Let $T$ be the point of tangency.

(3) Introduce $\overrightarrow{PT}$ and let $Q$ be the intersection of $\overrightarrow{PT}$ and $\overrightarrow{BH}$. $Q$ is the center of the desired circle.

(4) Using $Q$ as the center and $QB$ as radius construct a circle. This circle is tangent to $L$ at $B$ and also tangent to $C$.

**25.** Given: Segment $\overline{AB}$ and $\angle C$.
Analysis: Let $m\angle C = x$. If $\angle APB$ is inscribed in a circle and intercepts an arc $\overarc{AB}$ such that $m\overarc{AB} = 2x$, then by Theorem 14–16, $m\angle APB = x$. Hence, what we have to do is find the center $O$ and radius of a circle in which the given segment $\overline{AB}$ determines a minor arc of measure $2x$. This is easy. If $O$ is the center of the desired circle, we know that the mea-

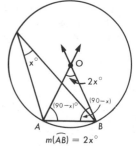

$m(\overarc{AB}) = 2x°$

sure of the central angle ∠AOB must be 2x. Since △AOB will be isosceles with AO = OB this means that m∠OAB = (180 − 2x)/2 = 90 − x. Therefore, the actual steps in the construction are as follows:

  (1) Using $\overrightarrow{AB}$ as one side construct an angle which is the complement of the given angle ∠C.

  (2) Using $\overrightarrow{BA}$ as one side construct again an angle which is the complement of the given angle. See the figure below. Let O be the point of intersection of these two rays.

  (3) Using O as center and OA as radius construct a circle. This circle passes through both points A and B and the measure of minor arc $\overset{\frown}{AB}$ is 2x.

Therefore, the major arc $\overset{\frown}{APB}$, minus the points A and B, is the set of all points on the same side of $\overleftrightarrow{AB}$ as O which can be the vertex of a triangle △APB having given side $\overline{AB}$ and vertex angle congruent to ∠C. Since there is an arc $\overset{\frown}{AP'B}$ congruent to $\overset{\frown}{APB}$ on the side of $\overleftrightarrow{AB}$ opposite to O, the required set of points is the union of $\overset{\frown}{APB}$ and $\overset{\frown}{AP'B}$ minus the points A and B.

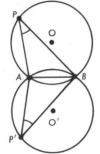

**Problem Set 15–9**

**9.** Given segments of lengths b and r, the length of the base of the triangle and the radius of the inscribed circle. First construct a segment $\overline{AB}$ such that AB = b.

  (1) Construct the perpendicular bisector $\overleftrightarrow{MN}$ of $\overline{AC}$, M being the midpoint of AC.

  (2) Locate a point P on $\overrightarrow{MN}$ such that MP = r.

  (3) Using P as a center and r as a radius construct a circle.

  (4) Construct a tangent to C(P, r) from point A, and construct a tangent to C(P, r) from point B. Let D be the point of intersection of these tangents.

Then △ABD is the required triangle. AB = b; the sides of △ABD are tangent to C(P, r), so that C(P, r) is inscribed in △ABD. Since △PAM ≅ △PBM by SAS, m∠PAM = m∠PBM. Since △PAT ≅ △PBR by the Hypotenuse-Leg Theorem, m∠PAT = m∠PBR, and hence by the AAP m∠DAB = m∠DBA. Therefore △ADB is isosceles. [Note that since D is equidistant from A and B, D lies on the perpendicular bisector $\overleftrightarrow{MN}$ of $\overline{AB}$. We have not, however, made use of this fact.]

**10.** Let P be the midpoint of a segment $\overline{AB}$ of length 2r. Using P as a center and r as a radius construct a circle C(P, r). Construct the perpendicular bisector $\overleftrightarrow{PM}$ of $\overline{AB}$ and let D be one of the points of intersection of $\overleftrightarrow{PM}$ with C(P, r). Introduce $\overline{AD}$ and $\overline{DB}$. Then △ABD is a right triangle, since ∠ADB is inscribed in a semicircle, and △ABD is isosceles, since D is on the perpendicular bisector of $\overline{AB}$.

**11.** (1) Construct a circle C(P, r) with P as a center and r as a radius.

  (2) Construct three radii $\overline{PR}$, $\overline{PS}$, and $\overline{PT}$ of C(P, r) in such a way that each segment forms a 120° angle with each of the other segments.

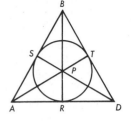

  (3) At points R, S, and T construct tangents to C(P, r) and let A, B and C be their points of intersection.

Then △ABD is obviously circumscribed about C(P, r). It remains to show that it is equilateral. You can easily convince yourself that △ABD is equilateral by introducing $\overline{PA}$, $\overline{PB}$, and $\overline{PD}$, and observing that there are six congruent 30-60-90 triangles formed. The actual proof that all six of these triangles are congruent is a bit of a nuisance: Each pair of triangles which have a common vertex at a vertex of △ABD, such as △APR and △APS, are congruent by any method you want. Since the m∠RPS = 120, this means that m∠APR = 60. Similarly, m∠DPR = 60, and you can use this fact to prove that any pair of triangles such as △APR and △DPR are congruent.

Therefore all six of the 30-60-90 triangles are congruent to one another, not just congruent in pairs. This makes △ABD equilateral.

**12.** Let a be the length of the given leg and r the radius of the inscribed circle.

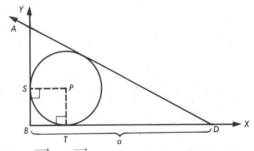

  (1) Let $\overrightarrow{BX}$ and $\overrightarrow{BY}$ be a pair of perpendicular rays.

  (2) Locate a point T on $\overrightarrow{BX}$ such that BT = r and let S be a point on $\overrightarrow{BY}$ such that BS = r. Then locate a point P such that □BTPS is a square, and construct C(P, r). Observe that $\overrightarrow{BX}$ and $\overrightarrow{BY}$ are each tangent to C(P, r).

  (3) Locate a point D on $\overrightarrow{BX}$ such that BD = a.

  (4) From D construct a tangent to C(P, r) and let A be the point of intersection of this tangent with $\overrightarrow{BX}$ as A.

Then △ABD is the required triangle.

**13.** Given: ∠A the vertex angle, and r the radius of the inscribed circle.

  (1) Bisect the given angle, and on one side of a ray $\overrightarrow{AX}$ copy this "half angle." Let $\overrightarrow{AY}$ be the other side of this angle.

  (2) Construct a line L parallel to $\overleftrightarrow{AX}$, r units from

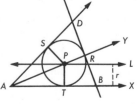

$\overleftrightarrow{AX}$ and on the same side of $\overleftrightarrow{AX}$ as $Y$. Let $L \cap \overrightarrow{AY} = \{P\}$.

(3) Construct $C(P, r)$. $\overrightarrow{AY}$ intersects $C(P, r)$ at two points. Let $R$ be the point of intersection which is farthest from $A$.

(4) Through $A$ construct the tangent to $C(P, r)$. Let $S$ be the point of tangency.

(5) Construct the tangent to $C(P, r)$ at $R$. Let $B$ and $D$ be the points of intersection of this tangent with the tangents $\overrightarrow{AT}$ and $\overrightarrow{AS}$ respectively.

Then $\triangle ABD$ is the required triangle. The radius of the inscribed circle is obviously $r$. Since $\overrightarrow{AT}$ and $\overrightarrow{AS}$ are tangent to $C(P, r)$ they form congruent angles with $AP$: $\angle PAT \cong \angle PAS$. Therefore $\triangle RAB \cong \triangle RAD$ by ASA and thus $\triangle ABD$ is isosceles with $\angle BAD$ the required acute angle.

**14.** Let the sides and hypotenuse of the right triangle $\triangle ABD$ be $a$, $b$, and $c$ respectively. Let the center and radius of the inscribed circle $C(Q, r_1)$ be $Q$ and $r_1$, and let the center and radius of the circumscribed circle $C(P, r_2)$ be $P$ and $r_2$. We want to show that $d_1 + 2d_2 = a + b + c$.

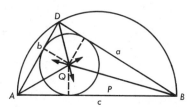

(1) First observe that since $C(Q, r_1)$ is inscribed in $\triangle ABD$, the radii to the points of tangency are perpendicular to the sides of the triangle, and so $a\triangle ABD = a\triangle BDQ + a\triangle ADQ + a\triangle ABQ$. Therefore,

$\frac{1}{2}ab = \frac{1}{2}ar_1 + \frac{1}{2}br_1 + \frac{1}{2}cr_1$, so that $r_1 = \dfrac{ab}{a + b + c}$.

(2) Since $C(P, r_2)$ is circumscribed about $\triangle ABD$, $2r_2 = c$.
(3) Since $\triangle ABD$ is a right triangle, $c^2 = a^2 + b^2$.

Therefore, $d_1 + 2d_2 = 2r_1 + 4r_2$

$$= \frac{2ab}{a + b + c} + 2c$$

$$= \frac{2ab + 2ac + 2bc + 2c^2}{a + b + c}$$

$$= \frac{2ab + 2ac + 2bc + a^2 + b^2 + c^2}{a + b + c}$$

$$= \frac{(a + b + c)^2}{a + b + c}$$

$$= a + b + c.$$

## Chapter Review

**9.** Prove that the orthocenter, the centroid, and the circumcenter of a triangle are all collinear and that the centroid is a point of trisection of the segment between the orthocenter and the circumcenter. To prove this, place the coordinate system so that the coordinates of the vertices of $\triangle ABC$ are as shown in the figure. Let $H$ be the orthocenter, $M$ the centroid, and $D$ the circumcenter of $\triangle ABC$.

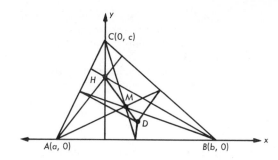

It is easy to prove that the coordinates of the orthocenter $H$ are $\left(0, \dfrac{-ab}{c}\right)$ and that the coordinates of the centroid $M$ are $\left(\dfrac{a + b}{3}, \dfrac{c}{3}\right)$.

To find the coordinates of the circumcenter $D$ proceed as follows: The equation of $L$, the perpendicular bisector of $\overline{AB}$, is $x = (a + b)/2$. The equation of $K$, the perpendicular bisector of $\overline{BC}$, is

$$y - \frac{c}{2} = \frac{b}{c}\left(x - \frac{b}{2}\right).$$

The coordinates of $D$ are therefore

$$\left(\frac{a + b}{2}, \frac{cl + ab}{2}\right).$$

By the distance formula,

$$(HM)^2 = \left(\frac{a + b}{3}\right)^2 + \left(\frac{c^2 + 3ab}{3c}\right)^2 = \frac{c^2(a + b)^2 + (c^2 + 3ab)^2}{(3c)^2},$$

$$(HD)^2 = \left(\frac{a + b}{2}\right)^2 + \left(\frac{c^2 + 3ab}{2c}\right)^2 = \frac{c^2(a + b)^2 + (c^2 + 3ab)^2}{(2c)^2},$$

$$(MD)^2 = \left(\frac{a + b}{6}\right)^2 + \left(\frac{c^2 + 3ab}{6c}\right)^2 = \frac{c^2(a + b)^2 + (c^2 + 3ab)^2}{(6c)^2}.$$

From the equations we conclude (1) $HM + MD = HD$, and thus that $H$, $M$, and $D$ are collinear, and (2) $MD = \frac{1}{3}HD$, which means that $M$ is a point of trisection of $\overline{HD}$.

**18.** Given $s$ the length of one side, $d$ the length of the longer diagonal, and $\angle A$ an acute angle of the parallelogram.

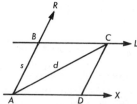

(1) Copy the given angle on a side of a ray $\overrightarrow{AX}$. Let $\overrightarrow{AR}$ be the other side of $\angle A$.
(2) On $\overrightarrow{AR}$ locate a point $B$ such that $AB = s$.
(3) Through $B$ construct a line $L$ parallel to $\overrightarrow{AX}$.
(4) Using $A$ as a center and $d$ as a radius, swing an arc. This arc will intersect $L$ at two points. Let $C$ be the point of intersection which lies on the same side of $\overleftrightarrow{AB}$ as $X$.

(5) Locate a point $D$ on $\overrightarrow{AX}$ such that $AD = BC$. Draw $\overline{CD}$. It follows from Theorem 9–20 that $\square ABCD$ is the required parallelogram.

**19.** Given an acute angle $\angle A$ and $r$, the radius of the inscribed circle.

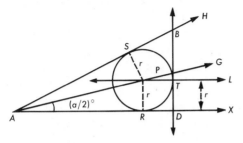

(1) Bisect the given angle, and copy the resulting "half angle" on one side of a ray $\overrightarrow{AX}$. Let $\overrightarrow{AG}$ be the other side of this angle.
(2) Construct a line $L$ parallel to $\overleftrightarrow{AX}$, $r$ units from $\overleftrightarrow{AX}$, and on the same side of $\overleftrightarrow{AX}$ as $G$. Let $P$ be the intersection of $\overrightarrow{AG}$ and $L$.
(3) Construct $C(P, r)$. Let $R$ be the point at which $C$ is tangent to $\overleftrightarrow{AX}$. The circle $C$ intersects $L$ at two points. Let $T$ be the point of intersection which is "farthest" from $A$.
(4) Construct $\overrightarrow{AH}$ tangent to $C(P, r)$. Call the point of tangency $S$.
(5) Construct the tangent to $C(P, r)$ at point $T$ and designate the points of intersection of this tangent with $\overrightarrow{AX}$ and $\overrightarrow{AH}$ as $D$ and $B$ respectively.

$\triangle ABD$ obviously has the property that the radius of the inscribed circle is equal to $r$. The fact that $\angle D$ is a right angle follows from Theorem 9–12, and the fact that $\angle BAD$ in $\triangle ABD$ is congruent to the given acute angle follows from Theorem 14–20.

**20.** This problem becomes easy if we think of it backwards, assuming that the square is given, and laying off a segment congruent to the diagonal, as in the figure below.

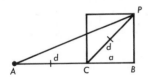

It is now easy to calculate that $m\angle PAB = 22\frac{1}{2}$. This tells us how to construct $\overline{BP}$ when $\overline{AB}$ is given, and also furnishes a proof that the construction is correct.

**21.** This is a variation on the preceding problem.

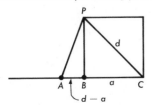

In the figure, $CA = CP = d$, so that $AB = d - a$. We can then calculate $m\angle PAC = 67\frac{1}{2}$. This tells us how to do the construction, and gives a proof that the construction works.

## Chapter 16   Areas of Circles and Sectors

### Problem Set 16–1

#### Honors Problem

First Solution:

This solution makes use of the concept of a polygon as defined in the text.

The pipe lines connecting $A$ and $B$ to both $G$ and $W$ do not intersect, and thus they form a simple polygon. We are not concerned with the number of sides. The figure is drawn with four.

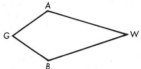

Now there are three possibilities: the points $C$ and $E$ must fall both without, both within, or one without and one within, this polygon. In the third case, since the polygon separates the plane, any polygonal path from $C$ to $E$ cuts the polygon. If both $C$ and $E$ are in the interior of the polygon, consider the pipe lines connecting $C$ to both $G$ and $W$.

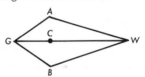

The polygon $AGBW$ is now split into two polygons, $AGCW$ and $CGBW$. The point $A$ is in the exterior of polygon $CGBW$, and $B$ is in the exterior of $AGCW$. (This requires proof but is not difficult.) The point $E$ is in the interior of one of these two polygons, and so cannot be connected both to $A$ and to $B$. The argument for the first case, when both $C$ and $E$ are exterior to polygon $AGBW$, is similar to that above and is omitted.

Second Solution:

The teacher and student realize that "lines" connecting $A$, $B$, and $C$ with $G$, $W$, $E$ can be "arcs" rather than segments. The problem is consequently a topology problem of a more general nature. Six "arcs" $AG$, $GB$, $BW$, $WC$, $CE$, and $EA$ form a closed "curve" (Figure 1).

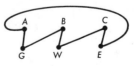
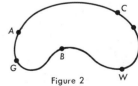

Figure 1      Figure 2

This curve is "topologically equivalent" to the more convenient curve in Figure 2.

Of the remaining three arcs *AW*, *BE*, and *CG* one will have to be placed inside this curve and one outside. (Figure 3).

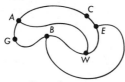

Figure 3

But no matter how this is done it is impossible to place the last arc in the plane of the figure without crossing one of the arcs in Figure 3.

This last assertion is dependent on a theorem which we state without proof:

*Theorem*. Suppose *X*, *Y*, *Z*, and *W* are points, in that order, on a closed curve.

Part I. If arc *XZ* lies in the interior of this closed curve, then it is impossible to join *W* and *Y* by an arc in the interior of the given closed curve without crossing arc *XZ*.

Part II. If arc *XZ* lies in the exterior of the given curve, then it is impossible to join *W* and *Y* by an arc in the exterior of the given closed curve without crossing arc *XZ*.

[Note: It would obviously be easy to connect the gas-electricity-water network if we drop the restriction that the arcs have to lie in a plane. The gas-electricity-water network is the simplest example of a nonplanar network, that is, a network which is not "topologically equivalent" to a network in a plane].